FAR
AIM

2002

U.S. Department of Transportation:
From Title 14 of the
Code of Federal Regulations
(14 CFR)

**Includes Federal Aviation
Regulations Parts 1, 43,
61, 67, 71, 73, 91, 97, 103,
105, 119, 135, 137, 141,
142, NTSB 830, and
the complete Aeronautical
Information Manual**

Updated and Published by

Aviation Supplies & Academics, Inc.
7005 132nd Place SE
Newcastle, WA 98059-3153

ASA-00-FR-AM-BK

FAR/AIM
(Federal Aviation Regulations and Aeronautical Information Manual)
2000 Edition

Aviation Supplies & Academics, Inc.
7005 132nd Place SE
Newcastle, WA 98059-3153

ASA-00-FAR-AM-BK
ISBN 1-56027-372-0

Printed in the United States of America

00   9   8   7   6   5   4   3   2

·ASA's 2000 FAR and AIM Series

FAR/AIM   *FAR Flight Crew*   *FAR AMT*

ASA has been supplying the standard reference of the industry, the FAR and AIM series, for nearly two decades. The 2000 series continues to provide unabridged information from the Federal Aviation Regulations and the *Aeronautical Information Manual*, along with these important features:

- Free Midyear Updates available through mail-in coupon, fax, telephone, or internet download

- All changes since last printing are clearly identified

- Suggested study list of AIM paragraphs and regulations pertinent to specific pilot certificates is included

- Indexes included for both FAR and AIM provide an alphabetized listing of subject matter with appropriate AIM paragraph numbers or regulation parts

- AIM produced with full-color graphics

Each FAR Part is preceded by a table of contents. Changes since last year's printing are identified on Page v and in the table of contents for each FAR part (in bold and marked with an asterisk), as well as within the text for quick reference (changed text is indicated with a bold line in the margin). In the AIM, changes are explained in a list at the beginning (there is a list for each quarterly change), and marked with a bold line in the margin throughout the chapters. It is recommended you familiarize yourself with all of the changes in order to identify those which affect your aviation activities.

Please complete the mail-in coupon located at the back of the book for your Free Midyear Update. Changes affecting the regulations take place daily, and this is a way to ensure you stay current. The update, which will be mailed to you in July, will include all changes that take place from the print date of this book through May 15, 2000. The coupon expires October 31, 2000. Please note there is a questionnaire on the coupon — we welcome your suggestions and comments, as they can help generate further improvements to future editions. You can also visit the FAA's website at http://www.fedworld.gov to review regulation changes.

Although ASA is not a government agency, and we are not responsible for the writing of the regulations, we do work closely with the FAA. Questions or concerns can be forwarded to my attention, and I will, in turn, pass the comments on to the FAA. They are interested in user-feedback and your comments could foster improvements in the regulations which affect us all.

Jackie Spanitz, Technical Editor
FAR/AIM Comments
ASA, Inc.
7005 132nd Place SE
Newcastle, WA 98059-3153

Internet: http://www.asa2fly.com
Fax: (425) 235-0128

What's Changed Since Last Year?

Changes since last year's printing of the book are noted in the table of contents of each Part with an asterisk and bold title:

Example:

*61.5   Certificates and rating issued
            under this part.

The updated text within the context of the regulation is indicated by a bold line in the margin:

> **(a)** The following certificates are issued under this part to an applicant who satisfactorily accomplishes the training and certification requirements for the certificate sought:
>   (1) Pilot certificates—
>   (i) Student pilot.
>   (ii) Recreational pilot.
>   (iii) Private pilot.
>   (iv) Commercial pilot.
>   (v) Airline transport pilot.
>   (2) Flight instructor certificates.
>   (3) Ground instructor certificates.

How to Identify the Currency of the Regulations

In each Part following the Table of Contents is a Source, with the date of origin for that regulation.

Example:

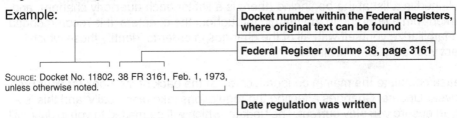

Docket number within the Federal Registers, where original text can be found

Federal Register volume 38, page 3161

SOURCE: Docket No. 11802, 38 FR 3161, Feb. 1, 1973, unless otherwise noted.

Date regulation was written

If a change has taken place since the original Regulation was written, it is noted at the end of the regulation.

Example:

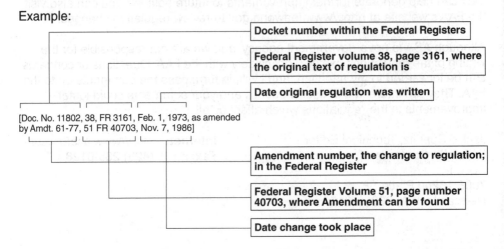

Docket number within the Federal Registers

Federal Register volume 38, page 3161, where the original text of regulation is

Date original regulation was written

[Doc. No. 11802, 38, FR 3161, Feb. 1, 1973, as amended by Amdt. 61-77, 51 FR 40703, Nov. 7, 1986]

Amendment number, the change to regulation; in the Federal Register

Federal Register Volume 51, page number 40703, where Amendment can be found

Date change took place

List of Changes Since October 1998

Part 61   *Exceptions to recent flight experience were added for pilots who operate more than one type of an airplane that is certified for more than one pilot crewmember.*

§ 61.57 Recent flight experience: Pilot in command.

Part 67   *§ 67.5 which governs certification of foreign airmen was removed.*

Part 71   *References to FAA Order 7400.9F changed to Order 7400.9G throughout.*

Part 91   *Special Federal Aviation Regulation affecting flight in the vicinity of the Grand Canyon was updated. A Special Federal Aviation Regulation was added affecting certain flights within the airspace of Serbia–Montenegro.*

The regulations affecting foreign aircraft operations and operations of U.S.-registered civil aircraft outside of the United States were edited.

SFAR 50–2 Special Flight Rules in the Vicinity of the Grand Canyon National Park, AZ

SFAR 84 Prohibition Against Certain Flights Within the Territory and Airspace of Serbia–Montenegro

SFAR 86 Airspace and Flight Operations Requirements for the 1999 and 2000 Kodak Albuquerque International Balloon Fiestas, Albuquerque, NM

§ 91.1 Applicability.

§ 91.11 Prohibition on interference with crewmembers.

§ 91.701 Applicability.

§ 91.702 Persons on board.

Part 135   *A regulation was added affecting portable electronic devices and the regulation affecting interference with crewmembers was edited.*

SFAR 36

SFAR 50–2 Special Flight Rules in the Vicinity of the Grand Canyon National Park, AZ

§ 135.120 Prohibition on interference with crewmembers.

§ 135.144 Portable electronic devices.

§ 135.243 Pilot in command qualifications.

Part 141   *§ 141.15 which affects location of facilities outside the United States was removed.*

Part 142   *The regulations affecting satellite training centers were changed to allow centers outside the United States.*

§ 142.15 Facilities.

§ 142.17 Satellite training centers.

AIM   *Changes made throughout the publication year are indicated by a bold line in the outside margin adjacent to changed text; also, the effective date of the change is printed at the top of the updated pages.*

FAR Parts Listed in Title 14

Location Key

ALL   Published in ASA's *FAR/AIM*, *FAR-FC*, and *FAR-AMT* books
FAR/AIM   *FAR/AIM* combination book
FAR-FC   *FAR for Flight Crew* book
FAR-AMT   *FAR for Aviation Maintenance Technicians* book
GPO   Available from the Government Printing Office

Subchapter E—Airspace

Subchapter F—Air Traffic and General Operating Rules

Subchapter G—Air Carriers and Operators for Compensation or Hire: Certification and Operations

Subchapter H—Schools and Other Certificated Agencies

Subchapter I—Airports

Subchapter J — Navigational Facilities

Subchapter K—Administrative Regulations

Subchapters L through M *[Reserved]*

Subchapter N — War Risk Insurance

Suggested Study List
FAR Parts and AIM Paragraphs Pertinent to Specific Pilot Certificates

Applicants preparing for the computerized FAA Knowledge Exams should have full understanding of the following applicable regulations and AIM paragraphs:

Recreational/Private

FAR

Part 1	91.103	91.215	Chapter 3	4-3-14
1.1	91.105	91.303	3-2-1	4-3-18
1.2	91.107	91.307	3-2-3	4-4-5
Part 21	91.111	91.309	3-2-4	4-4-14
21.181	91.113	91.313	3-2-5	Chapter 5
Part 43	91.115	91.319	3-2-6	5-1-4
ALL	91.117	91.403	3-4-3	5-1-12
Part 61	91.119	91.407	3-4-4	Chapter 6
61.3	91.121	91.409	3-4-5	6-2-5
61.23	91.123	91.413	3-4-6	Chapter 7
61.31	91.125	91.417	3-5-1	7-1-3
61.56	91.126	**NTSB**	3-5-2	7-1-4
61.57	91.127	830.5	3-5-5	7-1-8
61.60	91.129	830.10	Chapter 4	7-3-2
61.69	91.130	830.15	4-1-8	7-3-3
61.95	91.131		4-1-9	7-3-4
61.101	91.135	**AIM**	4-1-11	7-3-5
61.113	91.151	Chapter 1	4-1-13	7-3-6
Part 71	91.155	1-1-4	4-1-14	7-4-6
71.5	91.157	1-1-18	4-1-17	Chapter 8
Part 91	91.159	Chapter 2	4-1-19	8-1-4
91.3	91.203	2-1-2	4-2-3	8-1-5
91.7	91.205	2-1-7	4-2-9	8-1-6
91.9	91.207	2-1-8	4-2-13	8-1-8
91.15	91.209	2-3-3	4-3-3	Pilot/Controller
91.17	91.211		4-3-4	Glossary

Flight Engineer

FAR

Part 1	Part 91	121.365	121.549	Chapter 5
1.1	91.17	121.367	121.563	5-5-15
1.2	91.123	121.385	121.583	Chapter 6
Part 25	91.501	121.397	121.627	6-3-1
25.1001	Part 121	121.400	121.687	6-3-4
Part 61	121.243	121.425	121.695	Chapter 7
61.15	121.285	121.433	121.721	7-2-2
Part 63	121.289	121.434	121.723	7-2-3
63.3	121.305	121.453	Part 125 .... (all)	7-3-3
63.11	121.309	121.471		Chapter 8
63.12	121.310	121.483	**AIM**	8-1-2
63.13	121.329	121.485	Chapter 4	
63.15	121.331	121.493	4-1-13	
63.16	121.333	121.515	4-1-19	
63.19	121.337	121.519	4-3-13	
63.20	121.343	121.542	4-3-25	
63.31	121.359	121.543		
63.37	121.360	121.547		

Instrument/CFII

Commercial

Flight Instructor

Airline Transport Pilot

FAA Addresses and Phone Numbers

National Headquarters

FAA National Headquarters
800 Independence Avenue SW
Washington, DC 20591
(202) 366-4000

Aircraft Accident Information

National Transportation Safety Board
Public Inquiry Section, RE-51
490 L'Enfant Plaza East SW
Washington, DC 20594
(202) 314-6551

Aeronautical Charts

NOAA Distribution Branch, N/CG33
National Ocean Service
6501 Lafayette Avenue
Riverdale, MD 20737-1199
(301) 436-6990 or (800) 638-8972
Fax: (301) 436-6829

Aircraft Certificates

Flight Standards Service
Aircraft Registration Branch,
  AFS-750
FAA
PO Box 25082
Oklahoma City, OK 73125
(405) 954-3131

Airman Certificates

Flight Standards Service
Airman Certification Branch,
  AFS-760
FAA
PO Box 25082
Oklahoma City, OK 73125
(405) 954-3205

For Copies of Airworthiness Directives

Federal Aviation Administration
Engineering & Manufacturing
  Branch, AFS-610
PO Box 26460
Oklahoma City, OK 73125
(405) 954-4374

Flight Standards District Offices (FSDOs) by Region

Alaskan Region

FAA Alaska Regional Headquarters
222 West 7th Avenue #14
Anchorage, AK 99513
(907) 271-5645

Anchorage FSDO
4510 Int'l Airport Road, Suite 302
Anchorage, AK 99502
(907) 271-2000

Fairbanks FSDO
6450 Airport Way
Fairbanks, AK 99709
(907) 474-0276

Juneau FSDO
1873 Shell Simmons Drive
Juneau, AK 99801
(907) 586-7532

Central Region

FAA Central Region Headquarters
601 East 12th Street
Federal Building
Kansas City, MO 64106
(816) 426-5626

Des Moines FSDO 61
3021 Army Post Road
Des Moines, IA 50321
(515) 285-9895

Wichita FSDO 64
Mid Continent Airport
FAA Building
1801 Airport Road, Room 103
Wichita, KS 67209
(316) 941-1200

Saint Louis FSDO 62
FAA Building
10801 Pear Tree Lane, Suite 200
Saint Ann, MO 63074
(314) 429-1006

Lincoln FSDO 65
Lincoln Municipal Airport
General Aviation Building
Lincoln, NE 68524
(402) 437-5485

Eastern Region

Eastern Region Headquarters
Fitzgerald Federal Building
JFK International Airport
Jamaica, NY 11430
(718) 553-3000

Washington DC FSDO 27
GT Building, Suite 112
600 West Service Road
Washington, DC 20041-3025
(703) 661-8160

Glen Burnie FSDO 07
890 Airport Park Road, Suite 101
Cromwell Business Park
Glen Burnie, MD 21061-2559
(410) 787-0040

Teterboro FSDO 25
Teterboro Airport
225 Fred Wehran Drive Room 1
Teterboro, NJ 07608
(201) 393-6700

Albany FSDO 01
7 Airport Park
Albany, NY 12110
(518) 785-5660

New York FSDO 11
Administration Building, Suite 235
7150 Republic Airport
Farmingdale, NY 11735-1583
(516) 755-1300

New York FSDO 15
990 Stewart Avenue, Suite 630
Garden City, NY 11530-4858
(516) 228-8033

Rochester FSDO 23
1 Airport Way, Suite 110
Rochester, NY 14624
(716) 436-3880

Allentown FSDO 05
961 Marcon Boulevard, Suite 111
Allentown, PA 18103
(610) 264-2220

Harrisburg FSDO 13
Capital City Airport, Room 101
400 Airport Drive
Harrisburg, PA 17070-2489
(717) 774-8271

Philadelphia FSDO 17
International Plaza #2, Suite 210
Philadelphia, PA 19113
(610) 595-1500

Pittsburgh FSDO 03
Graham Building, Suite 300
3000 Lebanon Church Road
West Miffin, PA 15122-2630
(412) 466-5357

Pittsburgh FSDO 19
One Thorn Run Center
1187 Thorn Run Extension,
Suite 200
Coraopolis, PA 15108
(412) 262-9034

Richmond, FSDO 21
Richmond International Airport
5707 Hunstman Road, Suite 100
Richmond, VA 23250-2415
(804) 222-7498

Charleston FSDO 9
Yeager Airport
301 Eagle Mountain Rd, Room 144
Charleston, WV 25311

Great Lakes Region

Great Lakes Region Headquarters
O'Hare Lake Office Center
2300 East Devon Avenue
Des Plaines, IL 60018
(847) 294-7427

Chicago (DPA) FSDO
DuPage Airport
31W775 North Avenue
West Chicago, IL 60185
(630) 443-3100

Springfield FSDO
Capitol Airport
#3 North Airport Drive
Springfield, IL 62707-8417
(217) 744-1910

Gary FSDO
Indianapolis International Airport
8303 W Southern Avenue
Indianapolis, IN 46241
(371) 487-2400

South Bend FSDO
1843 Commerce Drive
South Bend, IN 46628
(219) 236-8480

Detroit FSDO
Willow-Run Airport-East Side
8800 Beck Road
Belleville, MI 48111
(313) 487-7222

Grand Rapids FSDO
Kent County International Airport
FSDO Building
5500 44th Street SE
Grand Rapids, MI 49588-8879
(616) 954-6657

Minneapolis FSDO
Minneapolis-St. Paul Int'l Airport
6020 28th Avenue South, Room 201
Minneapolis, MN 55450
(612) 713-4211

Fargo FSDO
Hector Airport
1801 N 23rd Avenue, Room 216
Fargo, ND 58102-1047
(701) 232-8949

Cincinnati FSDO
Cincinnati Branch
Lunken Airport Executive Building
4240 Airport Road
Cincinnati, OH 45266
(513) 533-8110

Cleveland FSDO
Cleveland Hopkins Int'l Airport
Federal Facilities Building, Suite 131
Cleveland, OH 44135
(216) 265-1345

Columbus FSDO
Port Columbus International Airport
3939 Int'l Gateway, 2nd Floor
Columbus, OH 43219
(614) 237-1039

Rapid City FSDO
4200 Airport Road, Suite 50
Rapid City, SD 57701-8703
(605) 393-1359

Milwaukee FSDO
4915 South Howell Avenue
Milwaukee, WI 53207
(414) 747-5531

New England Region

New England Region Headquarters
12 New England Executive Park
Burlington, MA 01803
(617) 238-7020

Windsor Locks FSDO 03
Building 85-214
Bradley International Airport
Windsor Locks, CT 06096
(860) 654-1000

Bangor FSDO 05
Portland International Jetport
21 Al McKay Avenue
Bangor, ME 04102
(207) 780-3263

Bedford FSDO 01
Civil Air Terminal Building, 2nd Floor
Hanscom Field
Bedford, MA 01730
(781) 274-7130

East Boston FSDO 02
Logan International Airport
1 Harborside Drive
Boston, MA 02128
(617) 561-5789

Northwest Mountain Region

Northwest Mountain Region
  Headquarters
1601 Lind Avenue SW
Renton, WA 98055-4056
(425) 227-2001

Denver FSDO
26805 E 68th Avenue, Suite 200
Denver, CO 80249-6361
(303) 342-1100

Boise FSDO
3295 Elder Street
Airport Plaza, Suite 350
Boise, ID 83705-4712
(208) 334-1238

Helena FSDO
2725 Skyway Drove, Suite 1
Helena Regional Airport
Helena, MT 59601
(406) 449-5270

Portland FSDO
Portland-Hillsboro Airport
1800 NE 25th Avenue, Suite 15
Hillsboro, OR 97124
(503) 681-5500

Salt Lake City FSDO
116 North 2400 West
Salt Lake City, UT 84116
(801) 524-4247

Seattle FSDO
1601 Lind Avenue SW
Renton, WA 98055-4056
(425) 227-2813

Spokane FSDO
6133 East Rutter Avenue
Spokane, WA 99212
(509) 353-2434

Casper FSDO
Natrona County International Airport
Terminal building, Second Floor
Casper, WY 82604
(307) 261-5425

Southern Region

Southern Region Headquarters
1701 Columbia Avenue
College Park, GA 30337
(404) 305-5000

Birmingham FSDO 09
Liberty Park, Building 1500
1500 Urban Center Drive
Birmingham, AL 35242
(205) 731-1640

Fort Lauderdale FSDO 17
1050 Lee Wagener, Suite 201
Fort Lauderdale, FL 33315
(954) 356-7526

Miami FSDO 19
5600 NW 36th Street, Suite 334
Miami, FL 33159
(305) 526-2572

Orlando FSDO 15
5950 Hazeltine National Dr,
 Suite 500
Orlando, FL 32822-5023
(407) 816-0000

Tampa FSDO 35
5402 Hoover Boulevard, Suite C
Tampa, FL 33634
(813) 243-5819

Atlanta FSDO 11
1701 Columbia Avenue
College Park, GA 30337-2747
(404) 305-7200

Louisville FSDO 01
Watterson Towers, 11th Floor
1930 Bishop Lane
Louisville, KY 40218
(502) 582-5491

Jackson FSDO 7
120 North Hangar Drive, Suite C
Jackson Municipal Airport
Jackson, MS 39208
(601) 965-4633

Charlotte FSDO 33
4700 Yorkmont Road, Room 203
Charlotte, NC 28208
(704) 344-6488

Winston-Salem FSDO 5
8025 North Point Blvd, Suite 250
Winston-Salem, NC 27106
(910) 631-5147

Puerto Rico FSDO 21
Plaza Los Americas
Roosevelt Avenue
Los Torre de Plaza, Suite 901
Hato Rey, PR 00918
(787) 764-2538

Columbia FSDO 13
Foreign Trade Zone
103 Trade Zone Drive, Suite 30-C
Columbia, SC 29170
(803) 765-5931

Memphis FSDO 25
3385 Airways Boulevard, Suite 115
Memphis, TN 38116
(901) 544-3820

Nashville FSDO 3
2 International Plaza Drive,
 Suite 700
Nashville, TN 37217
(615) 781-5437

Southwest Region

Southwest Region Headquarters
2601 Meacham Boulevard
Fort Worth, TX 76137
(817) 222-5001

Little Rock FSDO SW11
1701 Bond Street
Little Rock, AR 72202-5733
(501) 324-5565

Baton Rouge FSDO SW03
Local Coordinator
Ryan Field
9191 Plank Road
Baton Rouge, LA 70811
(504) 358-6800

Albuquerque FSDO SW01
1601 Randolph Road SE,
 Suite 200N
Albuquerque, NM 87106
(505) 764-1200

Oklahoma City FSDO SW15
The Parkway Building
1300 S Meridian, Suite 16
Oklahoma City, OK 73108
(405) 951-4200

Dallas FSDO SW05
Local Coordinator
7701 North Stemmons Freeway
 Suite 300
Dallas, TX 75247
(214) 767-5850

Dallas/Fort Worth FSDO SW07
DFW Business Center, Suite 400
2150 Northbound Access Road
Dallas/Ft Worth, TX 75261
(972) 574-2150

Fort Worth FSDO SW19
Alliance Airport
2260 Alliance Boulevard
Fort Worth, TX 76117-4300
(817) 491-5000

Houston FSDO SW09
13100 Space Center Blvd,
 Suite 5400
Houston, TX 77059-3398
(281) 212-9700

Lubbock FSDO SW13
Lubbock International Airport
South End, Old Terminal Building
Lubbock, TX 79401-9712
(806) 740-3800

San Antonio FSDO SW 17
10100 Reunion Place, Suite 200
San Antonio, TX 78216-4118
(210) 308-3300

Western-Pacific Region

Western-Pacific Region
 Headquarters
15000 Aviation Boulevard
Hawthorne, CA 90261
(310) 725-3550

Scottsdale FSDO
Scottsdale Municipal Airport
15041 North Airport Drive
Scottsdale, AZ 85260
(602) 640-2561

Fresno FSDO
4955E Anderson Avenue, Suite 110
Fresno, CA 93727
(209) 487-5306

Long Beach FSDO
Long Beach Airport
5001 Airport Plaza Drive, Suite 100
Long Beach, CA 90815
(562) 420-1755

Los Angeles FSDO
2250 E Imperial, Suite 140
El Segundo, CA 90245
(310) 215-2150

Oakland FSDO
8517 Earhart Road, Suite 100
Hangar 5
Oakland Airport
Oakland, CA 94614
(510) 273-7155

Riverside FSDO
Riverside Municipal Airport
6961 Flight Road
Riverside, CA 92504
(714) 276-6701

Sacramento FSDO
Sacramento Executive Airport
6650 Belleau Wood Lane
Sacramento, CA 95822
(916) 422-0272

San Diego FSDO
8525 Gibbs Drive, #210
San Diego, CA 92123
(619) 557-5281

San Jose FSDO
San Jose Airport/Jet Center
1250 Aviation Avenue, Suite 215
San Jose, CA 95110
(408) 291-7681

Van Nuys FSDO
Skylane Building
16501 Sherman Way, Suite 330
Van Nuys, CA 91406
(818) 904-6291

Honolulu FSDO
135 Nakolo Place, Room 215
Island of Oahu
Honolulu, HI 96819
(808) 837-8300

Las Vegas FSDO
6020 S Spencer Avenue, Suite 7-A
Las Vegas, NV 89119
(702) 388-6482

Reno FSDO
4900 Energy Way
Reno, NV 89502
(702) 858-7700

International Offices of the FAA

International Headquarters

Assistant Administrator for Policy,
  Planning & International Aviation
U.S. Federal Aviation Administration
USDOT FAA API-1
800 Independence Avenue SW
Washington, DC 20591
(202) 267-3033
Fax: (202) 267-5800

Director
Office of International Aviation
USDOT FAA AIA-1
800 Independence Avenue SW,
  Room 1027
Washington, DC 20591
(202) 267-3213
Fax: (202) 267-5306 or
  (202) 267-5032

Americas, AIA-200, (202) 267-9480
Asia Pacific, AIA-400,
  (202) 267-3231
Europe, Africa, and MidEast,
  AIA-300, (202) 267-8157
Global Issues, AIA-100,
  (202) 267-8124

FAA Centers

Mike Monroney Aeronautical Center
6500 South MacArthur
Oklahoma City, OK 73169
(405) 954-4521

FAA Technical Center
Atlantic City International Airport
Atlantic City, NJ 08504
(609) 485-6641

FAR/AIM Contents

Federal Aviation Regulations (Title 14 Code of Federal Regulations)

FAR INDEX
1
43
61
67
71
73
91
97
103
105
119
135
137
141
142
830
AIM
P/C
AIM INDEX
NASA FORM

Glide slope

Training centers

SUBCHAPTER A
DEFINITIONS

PART 1
DEFINITIONS AND ABBREVIATIONS

Sec.
1.1 General definitions.
1.2 Abbreviations and symbols.
1.3 Rules of construction.

Authority: 49 U.S.C. 106(g), 40113, 44701.

§ 1.1 General definitions.

As used in Subchapters A through K of this chapter, unless the context requires otherwise:

Administrator means the Federal Aviation Administrator or any person to whom he has delegated his authority in the matter concerned.

Aerodynamic coefficients means nondimensional coefficients for aerodynamic forces and moments.

Air carrier means a person who undertakes directly by lease, or other arrangement, to engage in air transportation.

Air commerce means interstate, overseas, or foreign air commerce or the transportation of mail by aircraft or any operation or navigation of aircraft within the limits of any Federal airway or any operation or navigation of aircraft which directly affects, or which may endanger safety in, interstate, overseas, or foreign air commerce.

Aircraft means a device that is used or intended to be used for flight in the air.

Aircraft engine means an engine that is used or intended to be used for propelling aircraft. It includes turbosuperchargers, appurtenances, and accessories necessary for its functioning, but does not include propellers.

Airframe means the fuselage, booms, nacelles, cowlings, fairings, airfoil surfaces (including rotors but excluding propellers and rotating airfoils of engines), and landing gear of an aircraft and their accessories and controls.

Airplane means an engine-driven fixed-wing aircraft heavier than air, that is supported in flight by the dynamic reaction of the air against its wings.

Airport means an area of land or water that is used or intended to be used for the landing and takeoff of aircraft, and includes its buildings and facilities, if any.

Airship means an engine-driven lighter-than-air aircraft that can be steered.

Air traffic means aircraft operating in the air or on an airport surface, exclusive of loading ramps and parking areas.

Air traffic clearance means an authorization by air traffic control, for the purpose of preventing collision between known aircraft, for an aircraft to proceed under specified traffic conditions within controlled airspace.

Air traffic control means a service operated by appropriate authority to promote the safe, orderly, and expeditious flow of air traffic.

Air transportation means interstate, overseas, or foreign air transportation or the transportation of mail by aircraft.

Alert Area. An alert area is established to inform pilots of a specific area wherein a high volume of pilot training or an unusual type of aeronautical activity is conducted.

Alternate airport means an airport at which an aircraft may land if a landing at the intended airport becomes inadvisable.

Altitude engine means a reciprocating aircraft engine having a rated takeoff power that is producible from sea level to an established higher altitude.

Appliance means any instrument, mechanism, equipment, part, apparatus, appurtenance, or accessory, including communications equipment, that is used or intended to be used in operating or controlling an aircraft in flight, is installed in or attached to the aircraft, and is not part of an airframe, engine, or propeller.

Approved, unless used with reference to another person, means approved by the Administrator.

Area navigation (RNAV) means a method of navigation that permits aircraft operations on any desired course within the coverage of station-referenced navigation signals or within the limits of self-contained system capability.

Area navigation low route means an area navigation route within the airspace extending upward from 1,200 feet above the surface of the earth to, but not including, 18,000 feet MSL.

Area navigation high route means an area navigation route within the airspace extending upward from, and including, 18,000 feet MSL to flight level 450.

Armed Forces means the Army, Navy, Air Force, Marine Corps, and Coast Guard, including their regular and reserve components and members serving without component status.

Autorotation means a rotorcraft flight condition in which the lifting rotor is driven entirely by action of the air when the rotorcraft is in motion.

Auxiliary rotor means a rotor that serves either to counteract the effect of the main rotor torque on a rotorcraft or to maneuver the rotorcraft about one or more of its three principal axes.

Balloon means a lighter-than-air aircraft that is not engine driven, and that sustains flight through the use of either gas buoyancy or an airborne heater.

Brake horsepower means the power delivered at the propeller shaft (main drive or main output) of an aircraft engine.

Calibrated airspeed means the indicated airspeed of an aircraft, corrected for position and instrument error. Calibrated airspeed is equal to true airspeed in standard atmosphere at sea level.

Canard means the forward wing of a canard configuration and may be a fixed, movable, or variable geometry surface, with or without control surfaces.

Canard configuration means a configuration in which the span of the forward wing is substantially less than that of the main wing.

Category:

(1) As used with respect to the certification, ratings, privileges, and limitations of airmen, means a broad classification of aircraft. Examples include: airplane; rotorcraft; glider; and lighter-than-air; and

(2) As used with respect to the certification of aircraft, means a grouping of aircraft based upon intended use or operating limitations. Examples include: transport, normal, utility, acrobatic, limited, restricted, and provisional.

Category A, with respect to transport category rotorcraft, means multiengine rotorcraft designed with engine and system isolation features specified in Part 29 and utilizing scheduled takeoff and landing operations under a critical engine failure concept which assures adequate designated surface area and adequate performance capability for continued safe flight in the event of engine failure.

Category B, with respect to transport category rotorcraft, means single-engine or multiengine rotorcraft which do not fully meet all Category A standards. Category B rotorcraft have no guaranteed stay-up ability in the event of engine failure and unscheduled landing is assumed.

Category II operations, with respect to the operation of aircraft, means a straight-in ILS approach to the runway of an airport under a Category II ILS instrument approach procedure issued by the Administrator or other appropriate authority.

Category III operations, with respect to the operation of aircraft, means an ILS approach to, and landing on, the runway of an airport using a Category III ILS instrument approach procedure issued by the Administrator or other appropriate authority.

Category IIIa operations, an ILS approach and landing with no decision height (DH), or a DH below 100 feet (30 meters), and controlling runway visual range not less than 700 feet (200 meters).

Category IIIb operations, an ILS approach and landing with no DH, or with a DH below 50 feet (15 meters), and controlling runway visual

range less than 700 feet (200 meters), but not less than 150 feet (50 meters).

Category IIIc operations, an ILS approach and landing with no DH and no runway visual range limitation.

Ceiling means the height above the earth's surface of the lowest layer of clouds or obscuring phenomena that is reported as "broken", "overcast", or "obscuration", and not classified as "thin" or "partial".

Civil aircraft means aircraft other than public aircraft.

Class:

(1) As used with respect to the certification, ratings, privileges, and limitations of airmen, means a classification of aircraft within a category having similar operating characteristics. Examples include: single engine; multiengine; land; water; gyroplane; helicopter; airship; and free balloon; and

(2) As used with respect to the certification of aircraft, means a broad grouping of aircraft having similar characteristics of propulsion, flight, or landing. Examples include: airplane; rotorcraft; glider; balloon; landplane; and seaplane.

Clearway means:

(1) For turbine engine powered airplanes certificated after August 29, 1959, an area beyond the runway, not less than 500 feet wide, centrally located about the extended centerline of the runway, and under the control of the airport authorities. The clearway is expressed in terms of a clearway plane, extending from the end of the runway with an upward slope not exceeding 1.25 percent, above which no object nor any terrain protrudes. However, threshold lights may protrude above the plane if their height above the end of the runway is 26 inches or less and if they are located to each side of the runway.

(2) For turbine engine powered airplanes certificated after September 30, 1958, but before August 30, 1959, an area beyond the takeoff runway extending no less than 300 feet on either side of the extended centerline of the runway, at an elevation no higher than the elevation of the end of the runway, clear of all fixed obstacles, and under the control of the airport authorities.

Climbout speed, with respect to rotorcraft, means a referenced airspeed which results in a flight path clear of the height-velocity envelope during initial climbout.

Commercial operator means a person who, for compensation or hire, engages in the carriage by aircraft in air commerce of persons or property, other than as an air carrier or foreign air carrier or under the authority of Part 375 of this title. Where it is doubtful that an operation is for "compensation or hire", the test applied is whether the carriage by air is merely incidental to the person's other business or is, in itself, a major enterprise for profit.

Controlled airspace means an airspace of defined dimensions within which air traffic control service is provided to IFR flights and to VFR flights in accordance with the airspace classification.

NOTE—Controlled airspace is a generic term that covers Class A, Class B, Class C, Class D, and Class E airspace.

Controlled Firing Area. A controlled firing area is established to contain activities, which if not conducted in a controlled environment, would be hazardous to nonparticipating aircraft.

Crewmember means a person assigned to perform duty in an aircraft during flight time.

Critical altitude means the maximum altitude at which, in standard atmosphere, it is possible to maintain, at a specified rotational speed, a specified power or a specified manifold pressure. Unless otherwise stated, the critical altitude is the maximum altitude at which it is possible to maintain, at the maximum continuous rotational speed, one of the following:

(1) The maximum continuous power, in the case of engines for which this power rating is the same at sea level and at the rated altitude.

(2) The maximum continuous rated manifold pressure, in the case of engines, the maximum continuous power of which is governed by a constant manifold pressure.

Critical engine means the engine whose failure would most adversely affect the performance or handling qualities of an aircraft.

Decision height, with respect to the operation of aircraft, means the height at which a decision must be made, during an ILS or PAR instrument approach, to either continue the approach or to execute a missed approach.

Equivalent airspeed means the calibrated airspeed of an aircraft corrected for adiabatic compressible flow for the particular altitude. Equivalent airspeed is equal to calibrated airspeed in standard atmosphere at sea level.

Extended over-water operation means—

(1) With respect to aircraft other than helicopters, an operation over water at a horizontal distance of more than 50 nautical miles from the nearest shoreline; and

(2) With respect to helicopters, an operation over water at a horizontal distance of more than 50 nautical miles from the nearest shoreline and more than 50 nautical miles from an off-shore heliport structure.

External load means a load that is carried, or extends, outside of the aircraft fuselage.

External-load attaching means the structural components used to attach an external load to an aircraft, including external-load containers, the backup structure at the attachment points, and any quick-release device used to jettison the external load.

Fireproof—

(1) With respect to materials and parts used to confine fire in a designated fire zone, means the capacity to withstand at least as well as steel in dimensions appropriate for the purpose for which they are used, the heat produced when there is a severe fire of extended duration in that zone; and

(2) With respect to other materials and parts, means the capacity to withstand the heat associated with fire at least as well as steel in dimensions appropriate for the purpose for which they are used.

Fire resistant—

(1) With respect to sheet or structural members means the capacity to withstand the heat associated with fire at least as well as aluminum alloy in dimensions appropriate for the purpose for which they are used; and

(2) With respect to fluid-carrying lines, fluid system parts, wiring, air ducts, fittings, and powerplant controls, means the capacity to perform the intended functions under the heat and other conditions likely to occur when there is a fire at the place concerned.

Flame resistant means not susceptible to combustion to the point of propagating a flame, beyond safe limits, after the ignition source is removed.

Flammable, with respect to a fluid or gas, means susceptible to igniting readily or to exploding.

Flap extended speed means the highest speed permissible with wing flaps in a prescribed extended position.

Flash resistant means not susceptible to burning violently when ignited.

Flight crewmember means a pilot, flight engineer, or flight navigator assigned to duty in an aircraft during flight time.

Flight level means a level of constant atmospheric pressure related to a reference datum of 29.92 inches of mercury. Each is stated in three digits that represent hundreds of feet. For example, flight level 250 represents a barometric altimeter indication of 25,000 feet; flight level 255, an indication of 25,500 feet.

Flight plan means specified information, relating to the intended flight of an aircraft, that is filed orally or in writing with air traffic control.

Flight time means:

(1) Pilot time that commences when an aircraft moves under its own power for the purpose of flight and ends when the aircraft comes to rest after landing; or

(2) For a glider without self-launch capability, pilot times that commences when the glider is towed for the purpose of flight and ends when the glider comes to rest after landing.

Flight visibility means the average forward horizontal distance, from the cockpit of an aircraft in flight, at which prominent unlighted objects may be seen and identified by day and prominent lighted objects may be seen and identified by night.

Foreign air carrier means any person other than a citizen of the United States, who undertakes directly, by lease or other arrangement, to engage in air transportation.

Foreign air commerce means the carriage by aircraft of persons or property for compensation or hire, or the carriage of mail by aircraft, or the operation or navigation of aircraft in the conduct or furtherance of a business or vocation, in commerce between a place in the United States and any place outside thereof; whether such commerce moves wholly by aircraft or partly by aircraft and partly by other forms of transportation.

Foreign air transportation means the carriage by aircraft of persons or property as a common carrier for compensation or hire, or the carriage of mail by aircraft, in commerce between a place in the United States and any place outside of the United States, whether that commerce moves wholly by aircraft or partly by aircraft and partly by other forms of transportation.

Forward wing means a forward lifting surface of a canard configuration or tandem-wing configuration airplane. The surface may be a fixed, movable, or variable geometry surface, with or without control surfaces.

Glider means a heavier-than-air aircraft, that is supported in flight by the dynamic reaction of the air against its lifting surfaces and whose free flight does not depend principally on an engine.

Go-around power or thrust setting means the maximum allowable in-flight power or thrust setting identified in the performance data.

Ground visibility means prevailing horizontal visibility near the earth's surface as reported by the United States National Weather Service or an accredited observer.

Gyrodyne means a rotorcraft whose rotors are normally engine-driven for takeoff, hovering, and landing, and for forward flight through part of its speed range, and whose means of propulsion, consisting usually of conventional propellers, is independent of the rotor system.

Gyroplane means a rotorcraft whose rotors are not engine-driven, except for initial starting, but are made to rotate by action of the air when the rotorcraft is moving; and whose means of propulsion, consisting usually of conventional propellers, is independent of the rotor system.

Helicopter means a rotorcraft that, for its horizontal motion, depends principally on its engine-driven rotors.

Heliport means an area of land, water, or structure used or intended to be used for the landing and takeoff of helicopters.

Idle thrust means the jet thrust obtained with the engine power control level set at the stop for the least thrust position at which it can be placed.

IFR conditions means weather conditions below the minimum for flight under visual flight rules.

IFR over-the-top, with respect to the operation of aircraft, means the operation of an aircraft over-the-top on an IFR flight plan when cleared by air traffic control to maintain "VFR conditions" or "VFR conditions on top".

Indicated airspeed means the speed of an aircraft as shown on its pitot static airspeed indicator calibrated to reflect standard atmosphere adiabatic compressible flow at sea level uncorrected for airspeed system errors.

Instrument means a device using an internal mechanism to show visually or aurally the attitude, altitude, or operation of an aircraft or aircraft part. It includes electronic devices for automatically controlling an aircraft in flight.

Interstate air commerce means the carriage by aircraft of persons or property for compensation or hire, or the carriage of mail by aircraft, or the operation or navigation of aircraft in the conduct or furtherance of a business or vocation, in commerce between a place in any State of the United States, or the District of Columbia, and a place in any other State of the United States, or the District of Columbia; or between places in the same State of the United States through the airspace over any place outside thereof; or between places in the same territory or possession of the United States, or the District of Columbia.

Interstate air transportation means the carriage by aircraft of persons or property as a common carrier for compensation or hire, or the carriage of mail by aircraft in commerce:

(1) Between a place in a State or the District of Columbia and another place in another State or the District of Columbia;

(2) Between places in the same State through the airspace over any place outside that State; or

(3) Between places in the same possession of the United States;

Whether that commerce moves wholly by aircraft of partly by aircraft and partly by other forms of transportation.

Intrastate air transportation means the carriage of persons or property as a common carrier for compensation or hire, by turbojet-powered aircraft capable of carrying thirty or more persons, wholly within the same State of the United States.

Kite means a framework, covered with paper, cloth, metal, or other material, intended to be flown at the end of a rope or cable, and having as its only support the force of the wind moving past its surfaces.

Landing gear extended speed means the maximum speed at which an aircraft can be safely flown with the landing gear extended.

Landing gear operating speed means the maximum speed at which the landing gear can be safely extended or retracted.

Large aircraft means aircraft of more than 12,500 pounds, maximum certificated takeoff weight.

Lighter-than-air aircraft means aircraft that can rise and remain suspended by using contained gas weighing less than the air that is displaced by the gas.

Load factor means the ratio of a specified load to the total weight of the aircraft. The specified load is expressed in terms of any of the following: aerodynamic forces, inertia forces, or ground or water reactions.

Long-range communication system (LRCS). A system that uses satellite relay, data link, high frequency, or another approved communication system which extends beyond line of sight.

Long-range navigation system (LRNS). An electronic navigation unit that is approved for use under instrument flight rules as a primary means of navigation, and has at least one source of navigational input, such as inertial navigation system, global positioning system, Omega/very low frequency, or Loran C.

Mach number means the ratio of true airspeed to the speed of sound.

Main rotor means the rotor that supplies the principal lift to a rotorcraft.

Maintenance means inspection, overhaul, repair, preservation, and the replacement of parts, but excludes preventive maintenance.

Major alteration means an alteration not listed in the aircraft, aircraft engine, or propeller specifications—

(1) That might appreciably affect weight, balance, structural strength, performance, powerplant operation, flight characteristics, or other qualities affecting airworthiness; or

(2) That is not done according to accepted practices or cannot be done by elementary operations.

Major repair means a repair:

(1) That, if improperly done, might appreciably affect weight, balance, structural strength, performance, powerplant operation, flight characteristics, or other qualities affecting airworthiness; or

(2) That is not done according to accepted practices or cannot be done by elementary operations.

Manifold pressure means absolute pressure as measured at the appropriate point in the induction system and usually expressed in inches of mercury.

Maximum speed for stability characteristics, V_{FC}/M_{FC} means a speed that may not be less than a speed midway between maximum operating limit speed (V_{MO}/M_{MO}) and demonstrated flight diving speed (V_{DF}/M_{DF}), except that, for altitudes where the Mach number is the limiting factor, M_{FC} need not exceed the Mach number at which effective speed warning occurs.

Medical certificate means acceptable evidence of physical fitness on a form prescribed by the Administrator.

Military operations area. A military operations area (MOA) is airspace established outside Class A airspace to separate or segregate certain non-hazardous military activities from IFR Traffic and to identify for VFR traffic where theses activities are conducted.

Minimum descent altitude means the lowest altitude, expressed in feet above mean sea level, to which descent is authorized on final approach or during circle-to-land maneuvering in execution of a standard instrument approach procedure, where no electronic glide slope is provided.

Minor alteration means an alteration other than a major alteration.

Minor repair means a repair other than a major repair.

Navigable airspace means airspace at and above the minimum flight altitudes prescribed by or under this chapter, including airspace needed for safe takeoff and landing.

Night means the time between the end of evening civil twilight and the beginning of morning civil twilight, as published in the American Air Almanac, converted to local time.

Nonprecision approach procedure means a standard instrument approach procedure in which no electronic glide slope is provided.

Operate, with respect to aircraft, means use, cause to use or authorize to use aircraft, for the purpose (except as provided in § 91.13 of this chapter) of air navigation including the piloting of aircraft, with or without the right of legal control (as owner, lessee, or otherwise).

Operational control, with respect to a flight, means the exercise of authority over initiating, conducting or terminating a flight.

Overseas air commerce means the carriage by aircraft of persons or property for compensation or hire, or the carriage of mail by aircraft, or the operation or navigation of aircraft in the conduct or furtherance of a business or vocation, in commerce between a place in any State of the United States, or the District of Columbia, and any place in a territory or possession of the United States; or between a place in a territory or possession of the United States, and a place in any other territory or possession of the United States.

Overseas air transportation means the carriage by aircraft of persons or property as a common carrier for compensation or hire, or the carriage of mail by aircraft, in commerce:

(1) Between a place in a State or the District of Columbia and a place in a possession of the United States; or

(2) Between a place in a possession of the United States and a place in another possession of the United States; whether that commerce moves wholly by aircraft or partly by aircraft and partly by other forms of transportation.

Over-the-top means above the layer of clouds or other obscuring phenomena forming the ceiling.

Parachute means a device used or intended to be used to retard the fall of a body or object through the air.

Person means an individual, firm, partnership, corporation, company, association, joint-stock association, or governmental entity. It includes a trustee, receiver, assignee, or similar representative of any of them.

Pilotage means navigation by visual reference to landmarks.

Pilot in command means the person who:

(1) Has final authority and responsibility for the operation and safety of the flight;

(2) Has been designated as pilot in command before or during the flight; and

(3) Holds the appropriate category, class, and type rating, if appropriate, for the conduct of the flight.

Pitch setting means the propeller blade setting as determined by the blade angle measured in a manner, and at a radius, specified by the instruction manual for the propeller.

Positive control means control of all air traffic, within designated airspace, by air traffic control.

Powered-lift means a heavier-than-air aircraft capable of vertical takeoff, vertical landing, and low speed flight that depends principally on engine-driven lift devices or engine thrust for lift during these flight regimes and on nonrotating airfoil(s) for lift during horizontal flight.

Precision approach procedure means a standard instrument approach procedure in which an electronic glide slope is provided, such as ILS and PAR.

Preventive maintenance means simple or minor preservation operations and the replacement of small standard parts not involving complex assembly operations.

Prohibited area. A prohibited area is airspace designated under part 73 within which no person may operate an aircraft without the permission of the using agency.

Propeller means a device for propelling an aircraft that has blades on an engine-driven shaft and that, when rotated, produces by its action on the air, a thrust approximately perpendicular to its plane of rotation. It includes control components normally supplied by its manufacturer, but does not include main and auxiliary rotors or rotating airfoils of engines.

Public aircraft means an aircraft used only for the United States Government, or owned and operated (except for commercial purposes), or exclusively leased for at least 90 continuous days, by a government (except the United States Government), including a State, the District of Columbia, or a territory or possession of the United States, or political subdivision of that government; but does not include a government-owned aircraft transporting property for commercial purposes, or transporting passengers other than transporting (for other than commercial purposes) crewmembers or other persons aboard the aircraft whose presence is required to perform, or is associated with the performance of, a governmental function such as firefighting, search and rescue, law enforcement, aeronautical research, or biological or geological resource management; or transporting (for other than commercial purposes) persons aboard the aircraft if the aircraft is operated by the Armed Forces or an intelligence agency of the United States. An aircraft described in the preceding sentence shall, notwithstanding any limitation relating to use of the aircraft for commercial purposes, be considered to be a public aircraft for the purposes of this Chapter without regard to whether the aircraft is operated by a unit of government on behalf of another unit of government, pursuant to a cost reimbursement agreement between such units of government, if the unit of government on whose behalf the operation is conducted certifies to the Administrator of the Federal Aviation Administration that the operation was necessary to respond to a significant and imminent threat to life or property (including natural resources) and that no service by a private operator was reasonably available to meet the threat.

Rated continuous OEI power, with respect to rotorcraft turbine engines, means the approved brake horsepower developed under static conditions at specified altitudes and temperatures within the operating limitations established for the engine under Part 33 of this chapter, and limited in use to the time required to complete the flight after the failure of one engine of a multiengine rotorcraft.

Rated maximum continuous augmented thrust, with respect to turbojet engine type certification, means the approved jet thrust that is developed statically or in flight, in standard atmosphere at a specified altitude, with fluid injection or with the burning of fuel in a separate combustion chamber, within the engine operating limitations established under Part 33 of this chapter, and approved for unrestricted periods of use.

Rated maximum continuous power, with respect to reciprocating, turbopropeller, and turboshaft engines, means the approved brake horsepower that is developed statically or in flight, in standard atmosphere at a specified altitude, within the engine operating limitations established under Part 33, and approved for unrestricted periods of use.

Rated maximum continuous thrust, with respect to turbojet engine type certification, means the approved jet thrust that is developed statically or in flight, in standard atmosphere at a specified altitude, without fluid injection and without the burning of fuel in a separate combustion chamber, within the engine operating limitations established under Part 33 of this chapter, and approved for unrestricted periods of use.

Rated takeoff augmented thrust, with respect to turbojet engine type certification, means the approved jet thrust that is developed statically under standard sea level conditions, with fluid injection or with the burning of fuel in a separate combustion chamber, within the engine operating limitations established under Part 33 of this chapter, and limited in use to periods of not over 5 minutes for takeoff operation.

Rated takeoff power, with respect to reciprocating, turbopropeller, and turboshaft engine type certification, means the approved brake horsepower that is developed statically under standard sea level conditions, within the engine operating limitations established under Part 33, and limited in use to periods of not over 5 minutes for takeoff operation.

Rated takeoff thrust, with respect to turbojet engine type certification, means the approved jet thrust that is developed statically under standard sea level conditions, without fluid injection and without the burning of fuel in a separate combustion chamber, within the engine operating limitations established under Part 33 of this chapter, and limited in use to periods of not over 5 minutes for takeoff operation.

Rated 30-minute OEI power, with respect to rotorcraft turbine engines, means the approved brake horsepower developed under static conditions at specified altitudes and temperatures within the operating limitations established for the engine under Part 33 of this chapter, and limited in use to a period of not more than 30 minutes after the failure of one engine of a multiengine rotorcraft.

Rated 30-second OEI power, with respect to rotorcraft turbine engines, means the approved brake horsepower developed under static conditions at specified altitudes and temperatures within the operating limitations established for the engine under Part 33 of this chapter, for continued one-flight operation after the failure of one engine in multiengine rotorcraft, limited to three periods

of use no longer than 30 seconds each in any one flight, and followed by mandatory inspection and prescribed maintenance action.

Rated 2-minute OEI power, with respect to rotorcraft turbine engines, means the approved brake horsepower developed under static conditions at specified altitudes and temperatures within the operating limitations established for the engine under Part 33 of this chapter, for continued one-flight operation after the failure of one engine in multiengine rotorcraft, limited to three periods of use no longer than 2 minutes each in any one flight, and followed by mandatory inspection and prescribed maintenance action.

Rated 2$\frac{1}{2}$-minute OEI power, with respect to rotorcraft turbine engines, means the approved brake horsepower developed under static conditions at specified altitudes and temperatures within the operating limitations established for the engine under Part 33 of this chapter, and limited in use to a period of not more than 2$\frac{1}{2}$ minutes after the failure of one engine of a multiengine rotorcraft.

Rating means a statement that, as a part of a certificate, sets forth special conditions, privileges, or limitations.

Reporting point means a geographical location in relation to which the position of an aircraft is reported.

Restricted area. A restricted area is airspace designated under Part 73 within which the flight of aircraft, while not wholly prohibited, is subject to restriction.

RNAV way point (W/P) means a predetermined geographical position used for route or instrument approach definition or progress reporting purposes that is defined relative to a VORTAC station position.

Rocket means an aircraft propelled by ejected expanding gases generated in the engine from self-contained propellants and not dependent on the intake of outside substances. It includes any part which becomes separated during the operation.

Rotorcraft means a heavier-than-air aircraft that depends principally for its support in flight on the lift generated by one or more rotors.

Rotorcraft-load combination means the combination of a rotorcraft and an external-load, including the external-load attaching means. Rotorcraft-load combinations are designated as Class A, Class B, Class C, and Class D, as follows:

(1) Class A rotorcraft-load combination means one in which the external load cannot move freely, cannot be jettisoned, and does not extend below the landing gear.

(2) Class B rotorcraft-load combination means one in which the external load is jettisonable and is lifted free of land or water during the rotorcraft operation.

(3) Class C rotorcraft-load combination means one in which the external load is jettisonable and remains in contact with land or water during the rotorcraft operation.

(4) Class D rotorcraft-load combination means one in which the external-load is other than a Class A, B, or C and has been specifically approved by the Administrator for that operation.

Route segment means a part of a route. Each end of that part is identified by:

(1) A continental or insular geographical location; or

(2) A point at which a definite radio fix can be established.

Sea level engine means a reciprocating aircraft engine having a rated takeoff power that is producible only at sea level.

Second in command means a pilot who is designated to be second in command of an aircraft during flight time.

Show, unless the context otherwise requires, means to show to the satisfaction of the Administrator.

Small aircraft means aircraft of 12,500 pounds or less, maximum certificated takeoff weight.

Special VFR conditions mean meteorological conditions that are less than those required for basic VFR flight in controlled airspace and in which some aircraft are permitted flight under visual flight rules.

Special VFR operations means aircraft operating in accordance with clearances within controlled airspace in meteorological conditions less than the basic VFR weather minima. Such operations must be requested by the pilot and approved by ATC.

Standard atmosphere means the atmosphere defined in U.S. Standard Atmosphere, 1962 (Geopotential altitude tables).

Stopway means an area beyond the takeoff runway, no less wide than the runway and centered upon the extended centerline of the runway, able to support the airplane during an aborted takeoff, without causing structural damage to the airplane, and designated by the airport authorities for use in decelerating the airplane during an aborted takeoff.

Takeoff power:

(1) With respect to reciprocating engines, means the brake horsepower that is developed under standard sea level conditions, and under the maximum conditions of crankshaft rotational speed and engine manifold pressure approved for the normal takeoff, and limited in continuous use to the period of time shown in the approved engine specification; and

(2) With respect to turbine engines, means the brake horsepower that is developed under static conditions at a specified altitude and atmospheric temperature, and under the maximum conditions of rotor shaft rotational speed and gas temperature approved for the normal takeoff, and limited in continuous use to the period of time shown in the approved engine specification.

Takeoff safety speed means a referenced airspeed obtained after lift-off at which the required one-engine-inoperative climb performance can be achieved.

Takeoff thrust, with respect to turbine engines, means the jet thrust that is developed under static conditions at a specific altitude and atmospheric temperature under the maximum conditions of rotorshaft rotational speed and gas temperature approved for the normal takeoff, and limited in continuous use to the period of time shown in the approved engine specification.

Tandem wing configuration means a configuration having two wings of similar span, mounted in tandem.

TCAS I means a TCAS that utilizes interrogations of, and replies from, airborne radar beacon transponders and provides traffic advisories to the pilot.

TCAS II means a TCAS that utilizes interrogations of, and replies from airborne radar beacon transponders and provides traffic advisories and resolution advisories in the vertical plane.

TCAS III means a TCAS that utilizes interrogation of, and replies from, airborne radar beacon transponders and provides traffic advisories and resolution advisories in the vertical and horizontal planes to the pilot.

Time in service, with respect to maintenance time records, means the time from the moment an aircraft leaves the surface of the earth until it touches it at the next point of landing.

True airspeed means the airspeed of an aircraft relative to undisturbed air. True airspeed is equal to equivalent airspeed multiplied by $(\rho 0/\rho)^{1/2}$.

Traffic pattern means the traffic flow that is prescribed for aircraft landing at, taxiing on, or taking off from, an airport.

Type:

(1) As used with respect to the certification, ratings, privileges, and limitations of airmen, means a specific make and basic model of aircraft, including modifications thereto that do not change its handling or flight characteristics. Examples include: DC-7, 1049, and F-27; and

(2) As used with respect to the certification of aircraft, means those aircraft which are similar in design. Examples include: DC-7 and DC-7C; 1049G and 1049H; and F-27 and F-27F.

(3) As used with respect to the certification of aircraft engines means those engines which are similar in design. For example, JT8D and JT8D-7 are engines of the same type, and JT9D-3A and JT9D-7 are engines of the same type.

United States, in a geographical sense, means (1) the States, the District of Columbia, Puerto Rico, and the possessions, including the territorial waters, and (2) the airspace of those areas.

United States air carrier means a citizen of the United States who undertakes directly by lease, or other arrangement, to engage in air transportation.

VFR over-the-top, with respect to the operation of aircraft, means the operation of an aircraft over-the-top under VFR when it is not being operated on an IFR flight plan.

Warning area. A warning area is airspace of defined dimensions, extending from 3 nautical miles outward from the coast of the United States, that contains activity that may be hazardous to nonparticipating aircraft. The purpose of such warning areas is to warn nonparticipating pilots of the potential danger. A warning area may be located over domestic or international waters or both.

Winglet or tip fin means an out-of-plane surface extending from a lifting surface. The surface may or may not have control surfaces.

[Docket No. 1150, 27 FR 4588, May 15, 1962; as amended by Amdt. 1–39, 60 FR 5075, Jan. 25, 1995; Amdt. 1–40, 60 FR 30749, June 9, 1995; Amdt. 1–42, 61 FR 2081, Jan. 24, 1996; Amdt. 1–43, 61 FR 5183, Feb. 9, 1996; Amdt. 1–44, 61 FR 7190, Feb. 26, 1996; Amdt. 1–46, 61 FR 31328, June 19, 1996; Amdt. 1–45, 61 FR 34547, July 2, 1996; Amdt. 1–47, 62 FR 16298, April 4, 1997]

§1.2 Abbreviations and symbols.

In Subchapters A through K of this chapter:

"AGL" means above ground level.

"ALS" means approach light system.

"ASR" means airport surveillance radar.

"ATC" means air traffic control.

"CAS" means calibrated airspeed.

"CAT II" means Category II.

"CONSOL or CONSOLAN" means a kind of low or medium frequency long range navigational aid.

"DH" means decision height.

"DME" means distance measuring equipment compatible with TACAN.

"EAS" means equivalent airspeed.

"FAA" means Federal Aviation Administration.

"FM" means fan marker.

"GS" means glide slope.

"HIRL" means high-intensity runway light system.

"IAS" means indicated airspeed.

"ICAO" means International Civil Aviation Organization.

"IFR" means instrument flight rules.

"ILS" means instrument landing system.

"IM" means ILS inner marker.

"INT" means intersection.

"LDA" means localizer-type directional aid.

"LFR" means low-frequency radio range.

"LMM" means compass locator at middle marker.

"LOC" means ILS localizer.

"LOM" means compass locator at outer marker.

"M" means mach number.

"MAA" means maximum authorized IFR altitude.

"MALS" means medium intensity approach light system.

"MALSR" means medium intensity approach light system with runway alignment indicator lights.

"MCA" means minimum crossing altitude.

"MDA" means minimum descent altitude.

"MEA" means minimum en route IFR altitude.

"MM" means ILS middle marker.

"MOCA" means minimum obstruction clearance altitude.

"MRA" means minimum reception altitude.

"MSL" means mean sea level.

"NDB (ADF)" means nondirectional beacon (automatic direction finder).

"NOPT" means no procedure turn required.

"OEI" means one engine inoperative.

"OM" means ILS outer marker.

"PAR" means precision approach radar.

"RAIL" means runway alignment indicator light system.

"RBN" means radio beacon.

"RCLM" means runway centerline marking.

"RCLS" means runway centerline light system.

"REIL" means runway end identification lights.

"RR" means low or medium frequency radio range station.

"RVR" means runway visual range as measured in the touchdown zone area.

"SALS" means short approach light system.

"SSALS" means simplified short approach light system.

"SSALSR" means simplified short approach light system with runway alignment indicator lights.

"TACAN" means ultra-high frequency tactical air navigational aid.

"TAS" means true airspeed.

"TCAS" means a traffic alert and collision avoidance system.

"TDZL" means touchdown zone lights.

"TVOR" means very high frequency terminal omnirange station.

V_A means design maneuvering speed.

V_B means design speed for maximum gust intensity.

V_C means design cruising speed.

V_D means design diving speed.

V_{DF}/M_{DF} means demonstrated flight diving speed.

V_{EF} means the speed at which the critical engine is assumed to fail during takeoff.

V_F means design flap speed.

V_{FC}/M_{FC} means maximum speed for stability characteristics.

V_{FE} means maximum flap extended speed.

V_H means maximum speed in level flight with maximum continuous power.

V_{LE} means maximum landing gear extended speed.

V_{LO} means maximum landing gear operating speed.

V_{LOF} means lift-off speed.

V_{MC} means minimum control speed with the critical engine inoperative.

V_{MO}/M_{MO} means maximum operating limit speed.

V_{MU} means minimum unstick speed.

V_{NE} means never-exceed speed.

V_{NO} means maximum structural cruising speed.

V_R means rotation speed.

V_S means the stalling speed or the minimum steady flight speed at which the airplane is controllable.

V_{S0} means the stalling speed or the minimum steady flight speed in the landing configuration.

V_{S1} means the stalling speed or the minimum steady flight speed obtained in a specific configuration.

V_{TOSS} means takeoff safety speed for Category A rotorcraft.

V_X means speed for best angle of climb.

V_Y means speed for best rate of climb.

V_1 means the maximum speed in the takeoff at which the pilot must take the first action (e.g., apply brakes, reduce thrust, deploy speed brakes) to stop the airplane within the accelerate-stop distance. V_1 also means the minimum speed in the takeoff, following a failure of the critical engine at V_{EF}, at which the pilot can continue the takeoff and achieve the required height above the takeoff surface within the takeoff distance.

V_2 means takeoff safety speed.

V_{2min} means minimum takeoff safety speed.

"VFR" means visual flight rules.

"VHF" means very high frequency.

"VOR" means very high frequency omnirange station.

"VORTAC" means collocated VOR and TACAN.

[Docket No. 1150, 27 FR 4590, May 15, 1962; as amended by Amdt. 1–48, 63 FR 8318, Feb. 18, 1998]

§ 1.3 Rules of construction.

(a) In Subchapters A through K of this chapter, unless the context requires otherwise:

(1) Words importing the singular include the plural;

(2) Words importing the plural include the singular; and

(3) Words importing the masculine gender include the feminine.

(b) In Subchapters A through K of this chapter, the word:

(1) "Shall" is used in an imperative sense;

(2) "May" is used in a permissive sense to state authority or permission to do the act prescribed, and the words "no person may * * *" or "a person may not * * *" mean that no person is required, authorized, or permitted to do the act prescribed; and

(3) "Includes" means "includes but is not limited to".

[Docket No. 1150, 27 FR 4590, May 15, 1962; as amended by Amdt. 1–10, 31 FR 5055, March 29, 1966]

PART 43

MAINTENANCE, PREVENTIVE MAINTENANCE, REBUILDING, AND ALTERATION

Authority: 49 U.S.C. 106(g), 40113, 44701, 44703, 44705, 44707, 44711, 44713, 44717.

Source: Docket No. 1993, 29 FR 5451, April 23, 1964, unless otherwise noted.

Editorial Note: For miscellaneous technical amendments to this Part 43, see Amdt. 43–3, 31 FR 3336, March 3, 1966, and Amdt. 43–6, 31 FR 9211, July 6, 1966.

§ 43.1 Applicability.

(a) Except as provided in paragraph (b) of this section, this part prescribes rules governing the maintenance, preventive maintenance, rebuilding, and alteration of any —

(1) Aircraft having a U.S. airworthiness certificate;

(2) Foreign-registered civil aircraft used in common carriage or carriage of mail under the provisions of Part 121, 127, or 135 of this chapter; and

(3) Airframe, aircraft engines, propellers, appliances, and component parts of such aircraft.

(b) This part does not apply to any aircraft for which an experimental airworthiness certificate has been issued, unless a different kind of airworthiness certificate had previously been issued for that aircraft.

[Docket No. 1993, 29 FR 5451, Apr. 23, 1964; as amended by Amdt. 43–23, 47 FR 41084, Sept. 16, 1982]

§ 43.2 Records of overhaul and rebuilding.

(a) No person may describe in any required maintenance entry or form an aircraft, airframe, aircraft engine, propeller, appliance, or component part as being overhauled unless —

(1) Using methods, techniques, and practices acceptable to the Administrator, it has been disassembled, cleaned, inspected, repaired as necessary, and reassembled; and

(2) It has been tested in accordance with approved standards and technical data, or in accordance with current standards and technical data acceptable to the Administrator, which have been developed and documented by the holder of the type certificate, supplemental type certificate, or a material, part, process, or applicance approval under § 21.305 of this chapter.

(b) No person may describe in any required maintenance entry or form an aircraft, airframe, aircraft engine, propeller, appliance, or component part as being rebuilt unless it has been disassembled, cleaned, inspected, repaired as necessary, reassembled, and tested to the same tolerances and limits as a new item, using either new parts or used parts that either conform to new part tolerances and limits or to approved oversized or undersized dimensions.

[Amdt. 43–23, 47 FR 41084, Sept. 16, 1982]

§ 43.3 Persons authorized to perform maintenance, preventive maintenance, rebuilding, and alterations.

(a) Except as provided in this section and § 43.17, no person may maintain, rebuild, alter, or perform preventive maintenance on an aircraft, airframe, aircraft engine, propeller, appliance, or component part to which this part applies. Those items, the performance of which is a major alteration, a major repair, or preventive maintenance, are listed in Appendix A.

(b) The holder of a mechanic certificate may perform maintenance, preventive maintenance, and alterations as provided in Part 65 of this chapter.

(c) The holder of a repairman certificate may perform maintenance and preventive maintenance as provided in Part 65 of this chapter.

(d) A person working under the supervision of a holder of a mechanic or repairman certificate may perform the maintenance, preventive maintenance, and alterations that his supervisor is authorized to perform, if the supervisor personally observes the work being done to the extent necessary to ensure that it is being done properly and if the supervisor is readily available, in person, for consultation. However, this paragraph does not authorize the performance of any inspection required by Part 91 or Part 125 of this chapter or any inspection performed after a major repair or alteration.

(e) The holder of a repair station certificate may perform maintenance, preventive maintenance, and alterations as provided in Part 145 of this chapter.

(f) The holder of an air carrier operating certificate or an operating certificate issued under Part 121, 127, or 135, may perform maintenance, preventive maintenance, and alterations as provided in Part 121, 127, or 135.

(g) The holder of a pilot certificate issued under Part 61 may perform preventive maintenance on any aircraft owned or operated by that pilot which is not used under Part 121, 127, 129, or 135.

(h) Notwithstanding the provisions of paragraph (g) of this section, the Administrator may approve a certificate holder under Part 135 of this chapter, operating rotorcraft in a remote area, to allow a pilot to perform specific preventive maintenance items provided—

(1) The items of preventive maintenance are a result of a known or suspected mechanical difficulty or malfunction that occurred en route to or in a remote area;

(2) The pilot has satisfactorily completed an approved training program and is authorized in writing by the certificate holder for each item of preventive maintenance that the pilot is authorized to perform;

(3) There is no certificated mechanic available to perform preventive maintenance;

(4) The certificate holder has procedures to evaluate the accomplishment of a preventive maintenance item that requires a decision concerning the airworthiness of the rotorcraft; and

(5) The items of preventive maintenance authorized by this section are those listed in paragraph (c) of Appendix A of this part.

(i) Notwithstanding the provisions of paragraph (g) of this section, in accordance with an approval issued to the holder of a certificate issued under part 135 of this chapter, a pilot of an aircraft type-certificated for 9 or fewer passenger seats, excluding any pilot seat, may perform the removal and reinstallation of approved aircraft cabin seats, approved cabin-mounted stretchers, and when no tools are required, approved cabin-mounted medical oxygen bottles, provided—

(1) The pilot has satisfactorily completed an approved training program and is authorized in writing by the certificate holder to perform each task; and

(2) The certificate holder has written procedures available to the pilot to evaluate the accomplishment of the task.

(j) A manufacturer may —

(1) Rebuild or alter any aircraft, aircraft engine, propeller, or appliance manufactured by him under a type or production certificate;

(2) Rebuild or alter any appliance or part of aircraft, aircraft engines, propellers, or appliances manufactured by him under a Technical Standard Order Authorization, an FAA-Parts Manufacturer Approval, or Product and Process Specification issued by the Administrator; and

(3) Perform any inspection required by Part 91 or Part 125 of this chapter on aircraft it manufacturers, while currently operating under a production certificate or under a currently approved production inspection system for such aircraft.

[Docket No. 1993, 29 FR 5451, Apr. 23, 1964; as amended by Amdt. 43–4, 31 FR 5249, April 1, 1966; Amdt. 43–23, 47 FR 41084, Sept. 16, 1982; Amdt. 43–25, 51 FR 40702, Nov. 7, 1986; Amdt. 43–36, 61 FR 19501, May 1, 1996]

§ 43.5 Approval for return to service after maintenance, preventive maintenance, rebuilding, or alteration.

No person may approve for return to service any aircraft, airframe, aircraft engine, propeller, or appliance, that has undergone maintenance, preventive maintenance, rebuilding, or alteration unless—

(a) The maintenance record entry required by § 43.9 or § 43.11, as appropriate, has been made;

(b) The repair or alteration form authorized by or furnished by the Administrator has been executed in a manner prescribed by the Administrator; and

(c) If a repair or an alteration results in any change in the aircraft operating limitations or flight data contained in the approved aircraft flight manual, those operating limitations or flight data are appropriately revised and set forth as prescribed in § 91.9 of this chapter.

[Docket No. 1993, 29 FR 5451, April 23, 1964; as amended by Amdt. 43–23, 47 FR 41084, Sept. 16, 1982; Amdt. 43–31, 54 FR 34330, Aug. 18, 1989]

§ 43.7 Persons authorized to approve aircraft, airframes, aircraft engines, propellers, appliances, or component parts for return to service after maintenance, preventive maintenance, rebuilding, or alteration.

(a) Except as provided in this section and § 43.17, no person, other than the Administrator, may approve an aircraft, airframe, aircraft engine, propeller, appliance, or component part for return to service after it has undergone maintenance, preventive maintenance, rebuilding, or alteration.

(b) The holder of a mechanic certificate or an inspection authorization may approve an aircraft, airframe, aircraft engine, propeller, appliance, or component part for return to service as provided in Part 65 of this chapter.

(c) The holder of a repair station certificate may approve an aircraft, airframe, aircraft engine, propeller, appliance, or component part for return to service as provided in Part 145 of this chapter.

(d) A manufacturer may approve for return to service any aircraft, airframe, aircraft engine, propeller, appliance, or component part which that manufacturer has worked on under § 43.3(j). However, except for minor alterations, the work must have been done in accordance with technical data approved by the Administrator.

(e) The holder of an air carrier operating certificate or an operating certificate issued under Part 121, 127, or 135, may approve an aircraft, airframe, aircraft engine, propeller, appliance, or component part for return to service as provided in Part 121, 127, or 135 of this chapter, as applicable.

(f) A person holding at least a private pilot certificate may approve an aircraft for return to service after performing preventive maintenance under the provisions of § 43.3(g).

[Amdt. 43–23, 47 FR 41084, Sept. 16, 1982; amended by Amdt. 43–36, 61 FR 19501, May 1, 1996]

§ 43.9 Content, form, and disposition of maintenance, preventive maintenance, rebuilding, and alteration records (except inspections performed in accordance with Part 91, Part 123, Part 125, § 135.411(a)(1), and § 135.419 of this chapter).

(a) *Maintenance record entries.* Except as provided in paragraphs (b) and (c) of this section, each person who maintains, performs preventive maintenance, rebuilds, or alters an aircraft, airframe, aircraft engine, propeller, appliance, or component part shall make an entry in the maintenance record of that equipment containing the following information:

(1) A description (or reference to data acceptable to the Administrator) of work performed.

(2) The date of completion of the work performed.

(3) The name of the person performing the work if other than the person specified in paragraph (a)(4) of this section.

(4) If the work performed on the aircraft, airframe, aircraft engine, propeller, appliance, or component part has been performed satisfactorily, the signature, certificate number, and kind of certificate held by the person approving the work. The signature constitutes the approval for return to service only for the work performed.

In addition to the entry required by this paragraph, major repairs and major alterations shall be entered on a form, and the form disposed of, in the manner prescribed in Appendix B, by the person performing the work.

(b) Each holder of an air carrier operating certificate or an operating certificate issued under Part 121, 127, or 135, that is required by its approved operations specifications to provide for a continuous airworthiness maintenance program, shall make a record of the maintenance, preventive maintenance, rebuilding, and alteration, on aircraft, airframes, aircraft engines, propellers, appliances, or component parts which it operates in accordance with the applicable provisions of Part 121, 127, or 135 of this chapter, as appropriate.

(c) This section does not apply to persons performing inspections in accordance with Part 91, 123, 125, § 135.411(a)(1), or § 135.419 of this chapter.

[Amdt. 43–23, 47 FR 41085, Sept. 16, 1982]

§ 43.11 Content, form, and disposition of records for inspections conducted under Parts 91 and 125 and §§ 135.411(a)(1) and 135.419 of this chapter.

(a) *Maintenance record entries.* The person approving or disapproving for return to service an aircraft, airframe, aircraft engine, propeller, appliance, or component part after any inspection performed in accordance with Part 91, 123, 125, §§ 135.411(a)(1), or 135.419 shall make an entry in the maintenance record of that equipment containing the following information:

(1) The type of inspection and a brief description of the extent of the inspection.

(2) The date of the inspection and aircraft total time in service.

(3) The signature, the certificate number, and kind of certificate held by the person approving or disapproving for return to service the aircraft, airframe, aircraft engine, propeller, appliance, component part, or portions thereof.

(4) Except for progressive inspections, if the aircraft is found to be airworthy and approved for return to service, the following or a similarly worded statement — "I certify that this aircraft has been inspected in accordance with (insert type) inspection and was determined to be in airworthy condition."

(5) Except for progressive inspections, if the aircraft is not approved for return to service because of needed maintenance, noncompliance with applicable specifications, airworthiness directives, or other approved data, the following or a similarly worded statement — "I certify that this aircraft has been inspected in accordance with (insert type) inspection and a list of discrepancies and unairworthy items dated (date) has been provided for the aircraft owner or operator."

(6) For progressive inspections, the following or a similarly worded statement — "I certify that in accordance with a progressive inspection program, a routine inspection of (identify whether aircraft or components) and a detailed inspection of (identify components) were performed and the (aircraft or components) are (approved or disapproved) for return to service." If disapproved, the entry will further state "and a list of discrepancies and unairworthy items dated (date) has been provided to the aircraft owner or operator."

(7) If an inspection is conducted under an inspection program provided for in Part 91, 123, 125, or § 135.411(a)(1), the entry must identify the inspection program, that part of the inspection program accomplished, and contain a statement that the inspection was performed in accordance with the inspections and procedures for that particular program.

(b) *Listing of discrepancies and placards.* If the person performing any inspection required by Part 91 or 125 or § 135.411(a)(1) of this chapter finds that the aircraft is unairworthy or does not meet the applicable type certificate data, airworthiness directives, or other approved data upon which its airworthiness depends, that persons must give the owner or lessee a signed and dated list of those discrepancies. For those items permitted to be inoperative under § 91.213(d)(2) of this chapter, that person shall place a placard, that meets the aircraft's airworthiness certification regulations, on each inoperative instrument and the cockpit control of each item of inoperative equipment, marking it "Inoperative," and shall add the items to the signed and dated list of discrepancies given to the owner or lessee.

[Amdt. 43–23, 47 FR 41085, Sept. 16, 1982; as amended by Amdt. 43–30, 53 FR 50195, Dec. 13, 1988; Amdt. 43–36, 61 FR 19501, May 1, 1996]

§ 43.12 Maintenance records: Falsification, reproduction, or alteration.

(a) No person may make or cause to be made:

(1) Any fraudulent or intentionally false entry in any record or report that is required to be made, kept, or used to show compliance with any requirement under this part;

(2) Any reproduction, for fraudulent purpose, of any record or report under this part; or

(3) Any alteration, for fraudulent purpose, of any record or report under this part.

(b) The commission by any person of an act prohibited under paragraph (a) of this section is a basis for suspending or revoking the applicable airman, operator, or production certificate, Technical Standard Order Authorization, FAA-Parts Manufacturer Approval, or Product and Process Specification issued by the Administrator and held by that person.

[Amdt. 43–19, 43 FR 22639, May 25, 1978; as amended by Amdt. 43–23, 47 FR 41085, Sept. 16, 1982]

§ 43.13 Performance rules (general).

(a) Each person performing maintenance, alteration, or preventive maintenance on an aircraft, engine, propeller, or appliance shall use the methods, techniques, and practices prescribed in the current manufacturer's maintenance manual or Instructions for Continued Airworthiness prepared by its manufacturer, or other methods, techniques, and practices acceptable to the Administrator, except as noted in § 43.16. He shall use the tools, equipment, and test apparatus necessary to assure completion of the work in accordance with accepted industry practices. If special equipment or test apparatus is recommended by the manufacturer involved, he must use that equipment or apparatus or its equivalent acceptable to the Administrator.

(b) Each person maintaining or altering, or performing preventive maintenance, shall do that work in such a manner and use materials of such a quality, that the condition of the aircraft, airframe, aircraft engine, propeller, or appliance worked on will be at least equal to its original or properly altered condition (with regard to aerodynamic function, structural strength, resistance to vibration and deterioration, and other qualities affecting airworthiness).

(c) *Special provisions for holders of air carrier operating certificates and operating certificates issued under the provisions of Part 121, 127, or 135 and Part 129 operators holding operations specifications.* Unless otherwise notified by the administrator, the methods, techniques, and practices contained in the maintenance manual or the maintenance part of the manual of the holder of an air carrier operating certificate or an operating certificate under Part 121, 127, or 135 and Part 129 operators holding operations specifications (that is required by its operating specifications to provide a continuous airworthiness maintenance and inspection program) constitute acceptable means of compliance with this section.

[Docket No. 1993, 29 FR 5451, April 23, 1964; as amended by Amdt. 43–20, 45 FR 60182, Sept. 11, 1980; Amdt. 43–23, 47 FR 41085, Sept. 16, 1982; Amdt. 43–28, 52 FR 20028, June 16, 1987]

§ 43.15 Additional performance rules for inspections.

(a) *General.* Each person performing an inspection required by Part 91, 123, 125, or 135 of this chapter, shall—

(1) Perform the inspection so as to determine whether the aircraft, or portion(s) thereof under inspection, meets all applicable airworthiness requirements; and

(2) If the inspection is one provided for in Part 123, 125, 135, or § 91.409(e) of this chapter, perform the inspection in accordance with the instructions and procedures set forth in the inspection program for the aircraft being inspected.

(b) *Rotorcraft.* Each person performing an inspection required by Part 91 on a rotorcraft shall inspect the following systems in accordance with the maintenance manual or Instructions for Continued Airworthiness of the manufacturer concerned:

(1) The drive shafts or similar systems.

(2) The main rotor transmission gear box for obvious defects.

(3) The main rotor and center section (or the equivalent area).

(4) The auxiliary rotor on helicopters.

(c) *Annual and 100-hour inspections.*

(1) Each person performing an annual or 100-hour inspection shall use a checklist while performing the inspection. The checklist may be of the person's own design, one provided by the manufacturer of the equipment being inspected or one obtained from another source. This checklist must include the scope and detail of the items contained in Appendix D to this part and paragraph (b) of this section.

(2) Each person approving a reciprocating-engine-powered aircraft for return to service after an annual or 100-hour inspection shall, before that approval, run the aircraft engine or engines to determine satisfactory performance in accordance with the manufacturer's recommendations of—

(i) Power output (static and idle r.p.m.);

(ii) Magnetos;

(iii) Fuel and oil pressure; and

(iv) Cylinder and oil temperature.

(3) Each person approving a turbine-engine-powered aircraft for return to service after an annual, 100-hour, or progressive inspection shall, before that approval, run the aircraft engine or engines to determine satisfactory performance in accordance with the manufacturer's recommendations.

(d) *Progressive inspection.*

(1) Each person performing a progressive inspection shall, at the start of a progressive inspection system, inspect the aircraft completely. After this initial inspection, routine and detailed inspections must be conducted as prescribed in the progressive inspection schedule. Routine inspections consist of visual examination or check of the appliances, the aircraft, and its components and systems, insofar as practicable without disassembly. Detailed inspections consist of a thorough examination of the appliances, the aircraft, and its components and systems, with such disassembly as is necessary. For the purposes of this subparagraph, the overhaul of a component or system is considered to be a detailed inspection.

(2) If the aircraft is away from the station where inspections are normally conducted, an appropriately rated mechanic, a certificated repair station, or the manufacturer of the aircraft may perform inspections in accordance with the procedures and using the forms of the person who would otherwise perform the inspection.

[Docket No. 1993, 29 FR 5451, April 23, 1964; as amended by Amdt. 43–23, 47 FR 41086, Sept. 16, 1982; Amdt. 43–25, 51 FR 40702, Nov. 7, 1986; Amdt. 43–31, 54 FR 34330, Aug. 18, 1989]

§ 43.16 Airworthiness Limitations.

Each person performing an inspection or other maintenance specified in an Airworthiness Limitations section of a manufacturer's maintenance manual or Instructions for Continued Airworthiness shall perform the inspection or other maintenance in accordance with that section, or in accordance with operations specifications approved by the Administrator under Parts 121, 123, 127, or 135, or an inspection program approved under § 91.409(e).

[Amdt. 43–20, 45 FR 60183, Sept. 11, 1980; as amended by Amdt. 43–23, 47 FR 41086, Sept. 16, 1982; Amdt. 43–31, 54 FR 34330, Aug. 18, 1989]

§ 43.17 Maintenance, preventive maintenance, and alterations performed on U.S. aeronautical products by certain Canadian persons.

(a) *Definitions.* For purposes of this section:

Aeronautical product means any civil aircraft or airframe, aircraft engine, propeller, appliance, component, or part to be installed thereon.

Canadian aeronautical product means any civil aircraft or airframe, aircraft engine, propeller, or appliance under airworthiness regulation by the Canadian Department of Transport, or component or part to be installed thereon.

U.S. aeronautical product means any civil aircraft or airframe, aircraft engine, propeller, or appliance under airworthiness regulation by the FAA, or component or part to be installed thereon.

(b) *Applicability.* This section does not apply to any U.S. aeronautical products maintained or altered under any bilateral agreement made between Canada and any country other than the United States.

(c) *Authorized persons.*

(1) A person holding a valid Canadian Department of Transport license (Aircraft Maintenance Engineer) and appropriate ratings may, with respect to a U.S.-registered aircraft located in Canada, perform maintenance, preventive maintenance, and alterations in accordance with the requirements of paragraph (d) of this section and approve the affected aircraft for return to service in accordance with the requirements of paragraph (e) of this section.

(2) A company (Approved Maintenance Organization) (AMO) whose system of quality control for the maintenance, alteration, and inspection of aeronautical products has been approved by the Canadian Department of Transport, or a person who is an authorized employee performing work for such a company may, with respect to a U.S.-registered aircraft located in Canada or other U.S. aeronautical products transported to Canada from the United States, perform maintenance, preventive maintenance, and alterations in accordance with the requirements of paragraph (d) of this section and approve the affected products for return to service in accordance with the requirements of paragraph (e) of this section.

(d) *Performance requirements.* A person authorized in paragraph (c) of this section may perform maintenance (including any inspection required by § 91.409 of this chapter, except an annual inspection), preventive maintenance, and alterations, provided:

(1) The person performing the work is authorized by the Canadian Department of Transport to perform the same type of work with respect to Canadian aeronautical products;

(2) The work is performed in accordance with §§ 43.13, 43.15, and 43.16 of this chapter, as applicable;

(3) The work is performed such that the affected product complies with the applicable requirements of Part 36 of this chapter; and

(4) The work is recorded in accordance with §§ 43.2(a), 43.9, and 43.11 of this chapter, as applicable.

(e) *Approval requirements.*

(1) To return an affected product to service, a person authorized in paragraph (c) of this section must approve (certify) maintenance, preventive maintenance, and alterations performed under this section, except that an Aircraft Maintenance Engineer may not approve a major repair or major alteration.

(2) An AMO whose system of quality control for the maintenance, preventive maintenance, alteration, and inspection of aeronautical products has been approved by the Canadian Department of Transport, or an authorized employee performing work for such an AMO, may approve (certify) a major repair or major alteration performed under this section if the work was performed in accordance with technical data approved by the Administrator.

(f) No person may operate in air commerce an aircraft, airframe, aircraft engine, propeller, or appliance on which maintenance, preventive maintenance, or alteration has been performed under this section unless it has been approved for return to service by a person authorized in this section.

[Amdt. 43–33, 56 FR 57571, Nov. 12, 1991]

APPENDIX A TO PART 43
MAJOR ALTERATIONS, MAJOR REPAIRS, AND PREVENTIVE MAINTENANCE

(a) *Major alterations —*
(1) *Airframe major alterations.* Alterations of the following parts and alterations of the following types, when not listed in the aircraft specifications issued by the FAA, are airframe major alterations:
(i) Wings.
(ii) Tail surfaces.
(iii) Fuselage.
(iv) Engine mounts.
(v) Control system.
(vi) Landing gear.
(vii) Hull or floats.
(viii) Elements of an airframe including spars, ribs, fittings, shock absorbers, bracing, cowling, fairings, and balance weights.
(ix) Hydraulic and electrical actuating system of components.
(x) Rotor blades.
(xi) Changes to the empty weight or empty balance which result in an increase in the maximum certificated weight or center of gravity limits of the aircraft.
(xii) Changes to the basic design of the fuel, oil, cooling, heating, cabin pressurization, electrical, hydraulic, de-icing, or exhaust systems.
(xiii) Changes to the wing or to fixed or movable control surfaces which affect flutter and vibration characteristics.
(2) *Powerplant major alterations.* The following alterations of a powerplant when not listed in the engine specifications issued by the FAA, are powerplant major alterations.
(i) Conversion of an aircraft engine from one approved model to another, involving any changes in compression ratio, propeller reduction gear, impeller gear ratios or the substitution of major engine parts which requires extensive rework and testing of the engine.
(ii) Changes to the engine by replacing aircraft engine structural parts with parts not supplied by the original manufacturer or parts not specifically approved by the Administrator.
(iii) Installation of an accessory which is not approved for the engine.
(iv) Removal of accessories that are listed as required equipment on the aircraft or engine specification.
(v) Installation of structural parts other than the type of parts approved for the installation.
(vi) Conversions of any sort for the purpose of using fuel of a rating or grade other than that listed in the engine specifications.
(3) *Propeller major alterations.* The following alterations of a propeller when not authorized in the propeller specifications issued by the FAA are propeller major alterations:
(i) Changes in blade design.
(ii) Changes in hub design.
(iii) Changes in the governor or control design.
(iv) Installation of a propeller governor or feathering system.
(v) Installation of propeller de-icing system.
(vi) Installation of parts not approved for the propeller.
(4) *Appliance major alterations.* Alterations of the basic design not made in accordance with recommendations of the appliance manufacturer or in accordance with an FAA Airworthiness Directive are appliance major alterations. In addition, changes in the basic design of radio communication and navigation equipment approved under type certification or a Technical Standard Order that have an effect on frequency stability, noise level, sensitivity, selectivity, distortion, spurious radiation, AVC characteristics, or ability to meet environmental test conditions and other changes that have an effect on the performance of the equipment are also major alterations.
(b) *Major repairs —*
(1) *Airframe major repairs.* Repairs to the following parts of an airframe and repairs of the following types, involving the strengthening, reinforcing, splicing, and manufacturing of primary structural members or their replacement, when replacement is by fabrication such as riveting or welding, are airframe major repairs.
(i) Box beams.
(ii) Monocoque or semimonocoque wings or control surfaces.
(iii) Wing stringers or chord members.
(iv) Spars.
(v) Spar flanges.
(vi) Members of truss-type beams.
(vii) Thin sheet webs of beams.
(viii) Keel and chine members of boat hulls or floats.
(ix) Corrugated sheet compression members which act as flange material of wings or tail surfaces.
(x) Wing main ribs and compression members.
(xi) Wing or tail surface brace struts.
(xii) Engine mounts.
(xiii) Fuselage longerons.
(xiv) Members of the side truss, horizontal truss, or bulkheads.
(xv) Main seat support braces and brackets.
(xvi) Landing gear brace struts.
(xvii) Axles.
(xviii) Wheels.
(xix) Skis, and ski pedestals.
(xx) Parts of the control system such as control columns, pedals, shafts, brackets, or horns.
(xxi) Repairs involving the substitution of material.

(xxii) The repair of damaged areas in metal or plywood stressed covering exceeding six inches in any direction.

(xxiii) The repair of portions of skin sheets by making additional seams.

(xxiv) The splicing of skin sheets.

(xxv) The repair of three or more adjacent wing or control surface ribs or the leading edge of wings and control surfaces, between such adjacent ribs.

(xxvi) Repair of fabric covering involving an area greater than that required to repair two adjacent ribs.

(xxvii) Replacement of fabric on fabric covered parts such as wings, fuselages, stabilizers, and control surfaces.

(xxviii) Repairing, including rebottoming, of removable or integral fuel tanks and oil tanks.

(2) *Powerplant major repairs.* Repairs of the following parts of an engine and repairs of the following types, are powerplant major repairs:

(i) Separation or disassembly of a crankcase or crankshaft of a reciprocating engine equipped with an integral supercharger.

(ii) Separation or disassembly of a crankcase or crankshaft of a reciprocating engine equipped with other than spur-type propeller reduction gearing.

(iii) Special repairs to structural engine parts by welding, plating, metalizing, or other methods.

(3) *Propeller major repairs.* Repairs of the following types to a propeller are propeller major repairs:

(i) Any repairs to, or straightening of steel blades.

(ii) Repairing or machining of steel hubs.

(iii) Shortening of blades.

(iv) Retipping of wood propellers.

(v) Replacement of outer laminations on fixed pitch wood propellers.

(vi) Repairing elongated bolt holes in the hub of fixed pitch wood propellers.

(vii) Inlay work on wood blades.

(viii) Repairs to composition blades.

(ix) Replacement of tip fabric.

(x) Replacement of plastic covering.

(xi) Repair of propeller governors.

(xii) Overhaul of controllable pitch propellers.

(xiii) Repairs to deep dents, cuts, scars, nicks, etc., and straightening of aluminum blades.

(xiv) The repair or replacement of internal elements of blades.

(4) *Appliance major repairs.* Repairs of the following types to appliances are appliance major repairs:

(i) Calibration and repair of instruments.

(ii) Calibration of radio equipment.

(iii) Rewinding the field coil of an electrical accessory.

(iv) Complete disassembly of complex hydraulic power valves.

(v) Overhaul of pressure type carburetors, and pressure type fuel, oil and hydraulic pumps.

(c) *Preventive maintenance.* Preventive maintenance is limited to the following work, provided it does not involve complex assembly operations:

(1) Removal, installation, and repair of landing gear tires.

(2) Replacing elastic shock absorber cords on landing gear.

(3) Servicing landing gear shock struts by adding oil, air, or both.

(4) Servicing landing gear wheel bearings, such as cleaning and greasing.

(5) Replacing defective safety wiring or cotter keys.

(6) Lubrication not requiring disassembly other than removal of nonstructural items such as cover plates, cowlings, and fairings.

(7) Making simple fabric patches not requiring rib stitching or the removal of structural parts or control surfaces. In the case of balloons, the making of small fabric repairs to envelopes (as defined in, and in accordance with, the balloon manufacturers' instructions) not requiring load tape repair or replacement.

(8) Replenishing hydraulic fluid in the hydraulic reservoir.

(9) Refinishing decorative coating of fuselage, balloon baskets, wings tail group surfaces (excluding balanced control surfaces), fairings, cowlings, landing gear, cabin, or cockpit interior when removal or disassembly of any primary structure or operating system is not required.

(10) Applying preservative or protective material to components where no disassembly of any primary structure or operating system is involved and where such coating is not prohibited or is not contrary to good practices.

(11) Repairing upholstery and decorative furnishings of the cabin, cockpit, or balloon basket interior when the repairing does not require disassembly of any primary structure or operating system or interfere with an operating system or affect the primary structure of the aircraft.

(12) Making small simple repairs to fairings, nonstructural cover plates, cowlings, and small patches and reinforcements not changing the contour so as to interfere with proper air flow.

(13) Replacing side windows where that work does not interfere with the structure or any operating system such as controls, electrical equipment, etc.

(14) Replacing safety belts.

(15) Replacing seats or seat parts with replacement parts approved for the aircraft, not involving disassembly of any primary structure or operating system.

(16) Trouble shooting and repairing broken circuits in landing light wiring circuits.

(17) Replacing bulbs, reflectors, and lenses of position and landing lights.

(18) Replacing wheels and skis where no weight and balance computation is involved.

(19) Replacing any cowling not requiring removal of the propeller or disconnection of flight controls.

(20) Replacing or cleaning spark plugs and setting of spark plug gap clearance.

(21) Replacing any hose connection except hydraulic connections.

(22) Replacing prefabricated fuel lines.

(23) Cleaning or replacing fuel and oil strainers or filter elements.

(24) Replacing and servicing batteries.

(25) Cleaning of balloon burner pilot and main nozzles in accordance with the balloon manufacturer's instructions.

(26) Replacement or adjustment of nonstructural standard fasteners incidental to operations.

(27) The interchange of balloon baskets and burners on envelopes when the basket or burner is designated as interchangeable in the balloon type certificate data and the baskets and burners are specifically designed for quick removal and installation.

(28) The installations of anti-misfueling devices to reduce the diameter of fuel tank filler openings provided the specific device has been made a part of the aircraft type certificate data by the aircraft manufacturer, the aircraft manufacturer has provided FAA-approved instructions for installation of the specific device, and installation does not involve the disassembly of the existing tank filler opening.

(29) Removing, checking, and replacing magnetic chip detectors.

(30) The inspection and maintenance tasks prescribed and specifically identified as preventive maintenance in a primary category aircraft type certificate or supplemental type certificate holder's approved special inspection and preventive maintenance program when accomplished on a primary category aircraft provided:

(i) They are performed by the holder of at least a private pilot certificate issued under part 61 who is the registered owner (including co-owners) of the affected aircraft and who holds a certificate of competency for the affected aircraft (1) issued by a school approved under § 147.21(e) of this chapter; (2) issued by the holder of the production certificate for that primary category aircraft that has a special training program approved under § 21.24 of this subchapter; or (3) issued by another entity that has a course approved by the Administrator; and

(ii) The inspections and maintenance tasks are performed in accordance with instructions contained by the special inspection and preventive maintenance program approved as part of the aircraft's type design or supplemental type design.

(31) Removing and replacing self-contained, front instrument panel-mounted navigation and communication devices that employ tray-mounted connectors that connect the unit when the unit is installed into the instrument panel, (excluding automatic flight control systems, transponders, and microwave frequency distance measuring equipment (DME)). The approved unit must be designed to be readily and repeatedly removed and replaced, and pertinent instructions must be provided. Prior to the unit's intended use, an operational check must be performed in accordance with the applicable sections of part 91 of this chapter.

(32) Updating self-contained, front instrument panel-mounted Air Traffic Control (ATC) navigational software data bases (excluding those of automatic flight control systems, transponders, and microwave frequency distance measuring equipment (DME)) provided no disassembly of the unit is required and pertinent instructions are provided. Prior to the unit's intended use, an operational check must be performed in accordance with applicable sections of part 91 of this chapter.

(Secs. 313, 601 through 610, and 1102, Federal Aviation Act of 1958 as amended (49 U.S.C. 1354, 1421 through 1430 and 1502); (49 U.S.C. 106(g) (Revised Pub. L. 97–449, Jan. 21, 1983); and 14 CFR 11.45)

[Docket No. 1993, 29 FR 5451, Apr. 23, 1964; as amended by Amdt. 43–14, 37 FR 14291, June 19, 1972; Amdt. 43–23, 47 FR 41086, Sept. 16, 1982; Amdt. 43–24, 49 FR 44602, Nov. 7, 1984; Amdt. 43–25, 51 FR 40703, Nov. 7, 1986; Amdt. 43–27, 52 FR 17277, May 6, 1987; Amdt. 43–34, 57 FR 41369, Sept. 9, 1992; Amdt. No. 43–36, 61 FR 19501, May 1, 1996]

APPENDIX B TO PART 43
RECORDING OF MAJOR REPAIRS AND
MAJOR ALTERATIONS

(a) Except as provided in paragraphs (b), (c), and (d) of this appendix, each person performing a major repair or major alteration shall—
(1) Execute FAA Form 337 at least in duplicate;
(2) Give a signed copy of that form to the aircraft owner; and
(3) Forward a copy of that form to the local Flight Standards District Office within 48 hours after the aircraft, airframe, aircraft engine, propeller, or appliance is approved for return to service.

(b) For major repairs made in accordance with a manual or specifications acceptable to the Administrator, a certificated repair station may, in place of the requirements of paragraph (a)—
(1) Use the customer's work order upon which the repair is recorded;
(2) Give the aircraft owner a signed copy of the work order and retain a duplicate copy for at least two years from the date of approval for return to service of the aircraft, airframe, aircraft engine, propeller, or appliance;
(3) Give the aircraft owner a maintenance release signed by an authorized representative of the repair station and incorporating the following information:
(i) Identity of the aircraft, airframe, aircraft engine, propeller or appliance.
(ii) If an aircraft, the make, model, serial number, nationality and registration marks, and location of the repaired area.
(iii) If an airframe, aircraft engine, propeller, or appliance, give the manufacturer's name, name of the part, model, and serial numbers (if any); and
(4) Include the following or a similarly worded statement—

"The aircraft, airframe, aircraft engine, propeller, or appliance identified above was repaired and inspected in accordance with current Regulations of the Federal Aviation Agency and is approved for return to service.

Pertinent details of the repair are on file at this repair station under Order No. _____
Date _____
Signed _____
(For signature of authorized representative)

(Repair station name)
(Certificate No.) _____."
(Address)

(c) For a major repair or major alteration made by a person authorized in § 43.17, the person who performs the major repair or major alteration and the person authorized by § 43.17 to approve that work shall execute a FAA Form 337 at least in duplicate. A completed copy of that form shall be—
(1) Given to the aircraft owner; and
(2) Forwarded to the Federal Aviation Administration, Aircraft Registration Branch, Post Office Box 25082, Oklahoma City, Okla. 73125, within 48 hours after the work is inspected.

(d) For extended-range fuel tanks installed within the passenger compartment or a baggage compartment, the person who performs the work and the person authorized to approve the work by § 43.7 of this part shall execute an FAA Form 337 in at least triplicate. One (1) copy of the FAA Form 337 shall be placed on board the aircraft as specified in § 91.417 of this chapter. The remaining forms shall be distributed as required by paragraph (a) (2) and (3) or (c) (1) and (2) of this paragraph as appropriate.

(Secs. 101, 610, 72 Stat. 737, 780, 49 U.S.C. 1301, 1430)

[Docket No. 1993, 29 FR 5451, April 23, 1964; as amended by Amdt. 43–10, 33 FR 15989, Oct. 31, 1968; Amdt. 43–29, 52 FR 34101, Sept. 9, 1987; Amdt. 43–31, 54 FR 34330, Aug. 18, 1989]

APPENDIX C TO PART 43 — [RESERVED]

APPENDIX D TO PART 43
SCOPE AND DETAIL OF ITEMS (AS APPLICABLE TO THE PARTICULAR AIRCRAFT) TO BE INCLUDED IN ANNUAL AND 100-HOUR INSPECTIONS

(a) Each person performing an annual or 100-hour inspection shall, before that inspection, remove or open all necessary inspection plates, access doors, fairing, and cowling. He shall thoroughly clean the aircraft and aircraft engine.

(b) Each person performing an annual or 100-hour inspection shall inspect (where applicable) the following components of the fuselage and hull group:
(1) Fabric and skin — for deterioration, distortion, other evidence of failure, and defective or insecure attachment of fittings.
(2) Systems and components — for improper installation, apparent defects, and unsatisfactory operation.
(3) Envelope, gas bags, ballast tanks, and related parts — for poor condition.

(c) Each person performing an annual or 100-hour inspection shall inspect (where applicable) the following components of the cabin and cockpit group:
(1) Generally — for uncleanliness and loose equipment that might foul the controls.

(2) Seats and safety belts — for poor condition and apparent defects.

(3) Windows and windshields — for deterioration and breakage.

(4) Instruments — for poor condition, mounting, marking, and (where practicable) improper operation.

(5) Flight and engine controls — for improper installation and improper operation.

(6) Batteries — for improper installation and improper charge.

(7) All systems — for improper installation, poor general condition, apparent and obvious defects, and insecurity of attachment.

(d) Each person performing an annual or 100-hour inspection shall inspect (where applicable) components of the engine and nacelle group as follows:

(1) Engine section — for visual evidence of excessive oil, fuel, or hydraulic leaks, and sources of such leaks.

(2) Studs and nuts — for improper torquing and obvious defects.

(3) Internal engine — for cylinder compression and for metal particles or foreign matter on screens and sump drain plugs. If there is weak cylinder compression, for improper internal condition and improper internal tolerances.

(4) Engine mount — for cracks, looseness of mounting, and looseness of engine to mount.

(5) Flexible vibration dampeners — for poor condition and deterioration.

(6) Engine controls — for defects, improper travel, and improper safetying.

(7) Lines, hoses, and clamps — for leaks, improper condition and looseness.

(8) Exhaust stacks — for cracks, defects, and improper attachment.

(9) Accessories — for apparent defects in security of mounting.

(10) All systems — for improper installation, poor general condition, defects, and insecure attachment.

(11) Cowling — for cracks, and defects.

(e) Each person performing an annual or 100-hour inspection shall inspect (where applicable) the following components of the landing gear group:

(1) All units — for poor condition and insecurity of attachment.

(2) Shock absorbing devices — for improper oleo fluid level.

(3) Linkages, trusses, and members — for undue or excessive wear fatigue, and distortion.

(4) Retracting and locking mechanism — for improper operation.

(5) Hydraulic lines — for leakage.

(6) Electrical system — for chafing and improper operation of switches.

(7) Wheels — for cracks, defects, and condition of bearings.

(8) Tires — for wear and cuts.

(9) Brakes — for improper adjustment.

(10) Floats and skis — for insecure attachment and obvious or apparent defects.

(f) Each person performing an annual or 100-hour inspection shall inspect (where applicable) all components of the wing and center section assembly for poor general condition, fabric or skin deterioration, distortion, evidence of failure, and insecurity of attachment.

(g) Each person performing an annual or 100-hour inspection shall inspect (where applicable) all components and systems that make up the complete empennage assembly for poor general condition, fabric or skin deterioration, distortion, evidence of failure, insecure attachment, improper component installation, and improper component operation.

(h) Each person performing an annual or 100-hour inspection shall inspect (where applicable) the following components of the propeller group:

(1) Propeller assembly — for cracks, nicks, binds, and oil leakage.

(2) Bolts — for improper torquing and lack of safetying.

(3) Anti-icing devices — for improper operations and obvious defects.

(4) Control mechanisms — for improper operation, insecure mounting, and restricted travel.

(i) Each person performing an annual or 100-hour inspection shall inspect (where applicable) the following components of the radio group:

(1) Radio and electronic equipment — for improper installation and insecure mounting.

(2) Wiring and conduits — for improper routing, insecure mounting, and obvious defects.

(3) Bonding and shielding — for improper installation and poor condition.

(4) Antenna including trailing antenna — for poor condition, insecure mounting, and improper operation.

(j) Each person performing an annual or 100-hour inspection shall inspect (where applicable) each installed miscellaneous item that is not otherwise covered by this listing for improper installation and improper operation.

APPENDIX E TO PART 43
ALTIMETER SYSTEM TEST AND INSPECTION

Each person performing the altimeter system tests and inspections required by § 91.411 shall comply with the following:

(a) *Static pressure system:*

(1) Ensure freedom from entrapped moisture and restrictions.

(2) Determine that leakage is within the tolerances established in § 23.1325 or § 25.1325, whichever is applicable.

(3) Determine that the static port heater, if installed, is operative.

(4) Ensure that no alterations or deformations of the airframe surface have been made that would affect the relationship between air pressure in the static pressure system and true ambient static air pressure for any flight condition.

(b) *Altimeter:*

(1) Test by an appropriately rated repair facility in accordance with the following subparagraphs. Unless otherwise specified, each test for performance may be conducted with the instrument subjected to vibration. When tests are conducted with the temperature substantially different from ambient temperature of approximately 25 degrees C., allowance shall be made for the variation from the specified condition.

(i) *Scale error.* With the barometric pressure scale at 29.92 inches of mercury, the altimeter shall be subjected successively to pressures corresponding to the altitude specified in Table I up to the maximum normally expected operating altitude of the airplane in which the altimeter is to be installed. The reduction in pressure shall be made at a rate not in excess of 20,000 feet per minute to within approximately 2,000 feet of the test point. The test point shall be approached at a rate compatible with the test equipment. The altimeter shall be kept at the pressure corresponding to each test point for at least 1 minute, but not more than 10 minutes, before a reading is taken. The error at all test points must not exceed the tolerances specified in Table I.

(ii) *Hysteresis.* The hysteresis test shall begin not more than 15 minutes after the altimeter's initial exposure to the pressure corresponding to the upper limit of the scale error test prescribed in subparagraph (i); and while the altimeter is at this pressure, the hysteresis test shall commence. Pressure shall be increased at a rate simulating a descent in altitude at the rate of 5,000 to 20,000 feet per minute until within 3,000 feet of the first test point (50 percent of maximum altitude). The test point shall then be approached at a rate of approximately 3,000 feet per minute. The altimeter shall be kept at this pressure for at least 5 minutes, but not more than 15 minutes, before the test reading is taken. After the reading has been taken, the pressure shall be increased further, in the same manner as before, until the pressure corresponding to the second test point (40 percent of maximum altitude) is reached. The altimeter shall be kept at this pressure for at least 1 minute, but not more than 10 minutes, before the test reading is taken. After the reading has been taken, the pressure shall be increased further, in the same manner as before, until atmospheric

pressure is reached. The reading of the altimeter at either of the two test points shall not differ by more than the tolerance specified in Table II from the reading of the altimeter for the corresponding altitude recorded during the scale error test prescribed in paragraph (b)(i).

(iii) *After effect.* Not more than 5 minutes after the completion of the hysteresis test prescribed in paragraph (b)(ii), the reading of the altimeter (corrected for any change in atmospheric pressure) shall not differ from the original atmospheric pressure reading by more than the tolerance specified in Table II.

(iv) *Friction.* The altimeter shall be subjected to a steady rate of decrease of pressure approximating 750 feet per minute. At each altitude listed in Table III, the change in reading of the pointers after vibration shall not exceed the corresponding tolerance listed in Table III.

(v) *Case leak.* The leakage of the altimeter case, when the pressure within it corresponds to an altitude of 18,000 feet, shall not change the altimeter reading by more than the tolerance shown in Table II during an interval of 1 minute.

(vi) *Barometric scale error.* At constant atmospheric pressure, the barometric pressure scale shall be set at each of the pressures (falling within its range of adjustment) that are listed in Table IV, and shall cause the pointer to indicate the equivalent altitude difference shown in Table IV with a tolerance of 25 feet.

(2) Altimeters which are the air data computer type with associated computing systems, or which incorporate air data correction internally, may be tested in a manner and to specifications developed by the manufacturer which are acceptable to the Administrator.

(c) Automatic Pressure Altitude Reporting Equipment and ATC Transponder System Integration Test. The test must be conducted by an appropriately rated person under the conditions specified in paragraph (a). Measure the automatic pressure altitude at the output of the installed ATC transponder when interrogated on Mode C at a sufficient number of test points to ensure that the altitude reporting equipment, altimeters, and ATC transponders perform their intended functions as installed in the aircraft. The difference between the automatic reporting output and the altitude displayed at the altimeter shall not exceed 125 feet.

(d) Records: Comply with the provisions of § 43.9 of this chapter as to content, form, and disposition of the records. The person performing the altimeter tests shall record on the altimeter the date and maximum altitude to which the altimeter has been tested and the persons approving the airplane for return to service shall enter that data in the airplane log or other permanent record.

Table I

Altitude	Equivalent pressure (inches of mercury)	Tolerance ± (feet)
-1,000	31.018	20
0	29.921	20
500	29.385	20
1,000	28.856	20
1,500	28.335	25
2,000	27.821	30
3,000	26.817	30
4,000	25.842	35
6,000	23.978	40
8,000	22.225	60
10,000	20.577	80
12,000	19.029	90
14,000	17.577	100
16,000	16.216	110
18,000	14.942	120
20,000	13.750	130
22,000	12.636	140
25,000	11.104	155
30,000	8.885	180
35,000	7.041	205
40,000	5.538	230
45,000	4.355	255
50,000	3.425	280

Table II — Test Tolerances

Test	Tolerance (feet)
Case Leak Test	±100
Hysteresis Test:	
First Test Point (50 percent of maximum altitude)	75
Second Test Point (40 percent of maximum altitude)	75
After Effect Test	30

Table III — Friction

Altitude (feet)	Tolerance (feet)
1,000	±70
2,000	70
3,000	70
5,000	70
10,000	80
15,000	90
20,000	100
25,000	120
30,000	140
35,000	160
40,000	180
50,000	250

Table IV — Pressure-Altitude Difference

Pressure (inches of Hg)	Altitude difference (feet)
28.10	-1,727
28.50	-1,340
29.00	-863
29.50	-392
29.92	0
30.50	+531
30.90	+893
30.99	+974

(Secs. 313, 314, and 601 through 610 of the Federal Aviation Act of 1958 (49 U.S.C. 1354, 1355, and 1421 through 1430) and sec. 6(c), Dept. of Transportation Act (49 U.S.C. 1655(c)))

[Amdt. 43–2, 30 FR 8262, June 29, 1965; as amended by Amdt. 43–7, 32 FR 7587, May 24, 1967; Amdt. 43–19, 43 FR 22639, May 25, 1978; Amdt. 43–23, 47 FR 41086, Sept. 16, 1982; Amdt. 43–31, 54 FR 34330, Aug. 18, 1989]

APPENDIX F TO PART 43

ATC TRANSPONDER TESTS AND INSPECTIONS

The ATC transponder tests required by § 91.413 of this chapter may be conducted using a bench check or portable test equipment and must meet the requirements prescribed in paragraphs (a) through (j) of this appendix. If portable test equipment with appropriate coupling to the aircraft antenna system is used, operate the test equipment for ATCRBS transponders at a nominal rate of 235 interrogations per second to avoid possible ATCRBS interference. Operate the test equipment at a nominal rate of 50 Mode S interrogations per second for Mode S. An additional 3 dB loss is allowed to compensate for antenna coupling errors during receiver sensitivity measurements conducted in accordance with paragraph (c)(1) when using portable test equipment.

(a) Radio Reply Frequency:

(1) For all classes of ATCRBS transponders, interrogate the transponder and verify that the reply frequency is 1090±3 Megahertz (MHz).

(2) For classes 1B, 2B, and 3B Mode S transponders, interrogate the transponder and verify that the reply frequency is 1090±3 MHz.

(3) For classes 1B, 2B, and 3B Mode S transponders that incorporate the optional 1090±1 MHz reply frequency, interrogate the transponder and verify that the reply frequency is correct.

(4) For classes 1A, 2A, 3A, and 4 Mode S transponders, interrogate the transponder and verify that the reply frequency is 1090±1 MHz.

(b) Suppression: When Classes 1B and 2B ATCRBS Transponders, or Classes 1B, 2B, and 3B Mode S transponders are interrogated Mode 3/A at an interrogation rate between 230 and 1,000 interrogations per second; or when Classes 1A and 2A ATCRBS Transponders, or Classes 1B, 2A, 3A, and 4 Mode S transponders are interrogated at a rate between 230 and 1,200 Mode 3/A interrogations per second:

(1) Verify that the transponder does not respond to more than 1 percent of ATCRBS interrogations when the amplitude of P_2 pulse is equal to the P_1 pulse.

(2) Verify that the transponder replies to at least 90 percent of ATCRBS interrogations when the amplitude of the P_2 pulse is 9 dB less than the P_1 pulse. If the test is conducted with a radiated test signal, the interrogation rate shall be 235±5 interrogations per second unless a higher rate has been approved for the test equipment used at that location.

(c) Receiver Sensitivity:

(1) Verify that for any class of ATCRBS Transponder, the receiver minimum triggering level (MTL) of the system is −73 ±4 dbm, or that for any class of Mode S transponder the receiver MTL for Mode S format (P6 type) interrogations is −74 ±3 dbm by use of a test set either:

(i) Connected to the antenna end of the transmission line;

(ii) Connected to the antenna terminal of the transponder with a correction for transmission line loss; or

(iii) Utilized radiated signal.

(2) Verify that the difference in Mode 3/A and Mode C receiver sensitivity does not exceed 1 db for either any class of ATCRBS transponder or any class of Mode S transponder.

(d) Radio Frequency (RF) Peak Output Power:

(1) Verify that the transponder RF output power is within specifications for the class of transponder. Use the same conditions as described in (c)(1) (i), (ii), and (iii) above.

(i) For Class 1A and 2A ATCRBS transponders, verify that the minimum RF peak output power is at least 21.0 dbw (125 watts).

(ii) For Class 1B and 2B ATCRBS Transponders, verify that the minimum RF peak output power is at least 18.5 dbw (70 watts).

(iii) For Class 1A, 2A, 3A, and 4 and those Class 1B, 2B, and 3B Mode S transponders that include the optional high RF peak output power, verify that the minimum RF peak output power is at least 21.0 dbw (125 watts).

(iv) For Classes 1B, 2B, and 3B Mode S transponders, verify that the minimum RF peak output power is at least 18.5 dbw (70 watts).

(v) For any class of ATCRBS or any class of Mode S transponders, verify that the maximum RF peak output power does not exceed 27.0 dbw (500 watts).

Note: The tests in (e) through (j) apply only to Mode S transponders.

(e) Mode S Diversity Transmission Channel Isolation: For any class of Mode S transponder that incorporates diversity operation, verify that the RF peak output power transmitted from the selected antenna exceeds the power transmitted from the nonselected antenna by at least 20 db.

(f) Mode S Address: Interrogate the Mode S transponder and verify that it replies only to its assigned address. Use the correct address and at least two incorrect addresses. The interrogations should be made at a nominal rate of 50 interrogations per second.

(g) Mode S Formats: Interrogate the Mode S transponder with uplink formats (UF) for which it is equipped and verify that the replies are made in the correct format. Use the surveillance formats UF=4 and 5. Verify that the altitude reported in the replies to UF=4 are the same as that reported in a valid ATCRBS Mode C reply. Verify that the identity reported in the replies to UF=5 are the same as that reported in a valid ATCRBS Mode 3/A reply. If the transponder is so equipped, use the communication formats UF=20, 21, and 24.

(h) Mode S All-Call Interrogations: Interrogate the Mode S transponder with the Mode S-only all-call format UF=11, and the ATCRBS/Mode S all-call formats (1.6 microsecond P_4 pulse) and verify that the correct address and capability are reported in the replies (downlink format DF=11).

(i) ATCRBS-Only All-Call Interrogation: Interrogate the Mode S transponder with the ATCRBS-only all-call interrogation (0.8 microsecond P_4 pulse) and verify that no reply is generated.

(j) Squitter: Verify that the Mode S transponder generates a correct squitter approximately once per second.

(k) Records: Comply with the provisions of § 43.9 of this chapter as to content, form, and disposition of the records.

[Amdt. 43–26, 52 FR 3390, Feb. 3, 1987; 52 FR 6651, March 4, 1987; Amdt. 43–31, 54 FR 34330, Aug. 18, 1989]

SUBCHAPTER D
AIRMEN

PART 61
CERTIFICATION:
PILOTS, FLIGHT INSTRUCTORS,
AND GROUND INSTRUCTORS

SPECIAL FEDERAL AVIATION REGULATIONS

SFAR No. 58 [Note]
SFAR No. 73

61

Authority: 49 U.S.C. 106(g), 40113, 44701–44703, 44707, 44709–44711, 45102–45103, 45301–45302.

Source: Docket No. 25910, 62 FR 16298, April 4, 1997, unless otherwise noted.

SPECIAL FEDERAL AVIATION REGULATIONS

SFAR No. 58 to Part 61

ADVANCED QUALIFICATION PROGRAM

Editorial Note: For the text of SFAR No. 58, see Part 121 of this chapter.

SFAR No. 73 to Part 61

ROBINSON R-22 / R-44 SPECIAL TRAINING AND EXPERIENCE REQUIREMENTS

Sections
  1. *Applicability.*
  2. *Required training, aeronautical experience, endorsements, and flight review.*
  3. *Expiration date.*

  1. *Applicability.* Under the procedures prescribed herein, this SFAR applies to all persons who seek to manipulate the controls or act as pilot in command of a Robinson model R-22 or R-44 helicopter. The requirements stated in this SFAR are in addition to the current requirements of part 61.
  2. *Required training, aeronautical experience, endorsements, and flight review.*
  (a) Awareness Training:
  (1) Except as provided in paragraph (a)(2) of this section, no person may manipulate the controls of a Robinson model R-22 or R-44 helicopter

after March 27, 1995, for the purpose of flight unless the awareness training specified in paragraph (a)(3) of this section is completed and the person's logbook has been endorsed by a certified flight instructor authorized under paragraph (b)(5) of this section.

(2) A person who holds a rotorcraft category and helicopter class rating on that person's pilot certificate and meets the experience requirements of paragraph (b)(1) or paragraph (b)(2) of this section may not manipulate the controls of a Robinson model R-22 or R-44 helicopter for the purpose of flight after April 26, 1995, unless the awareness training specified in paragraph (a)(3) of this section is completed and the person's logbook has been endorsed by a certified flight instructor authorized under paragraph (b)(5) of this section.

(3) Awareness training must be conducted by a certified flight instructor who has been endorsed under paragraph (b)(5) of this section and consists of instruction in the following general subject areas:

(i) Energy management;

(ii) Mast bumping;

(iii) Low rotor RPM (blade stall);

(iv) Low G hazards; and

(v) Rotor RPM decay.

(4) A person who can show satisfactory completion of the manufacturer's safety course after January 1, 1994, may obtain an endorsement from an FAA aviation safety inspector in lieu of completing the awareness training required in paragraphs (a)(1) and (a)(2) of this section.

(b) Aeronautical Experience:

(1) No person may act as pilot in command of a Robinson model R-22 unless that person:

(i) Has had at least 200 flight hours in helicopters, at least 50 flight hours of which were in the Robinson R-22; or

(ii) Has had at least 10 hours dual instruction in the Robinson R-22 and has received an endorsement from a certified flight instructor authorized under paragraph (b)(5) of this section that the individual has been given the training required by this paragraph and is proficient to act as pilot in command of an R-22. Beginning 12 calendar months after the date of the endorsement, the individual may not act as pilot in command unless the individual has completed a flight review in an R-22 within the preceding 12 calendar months and obtained an endorsement for that flight review. The dual instruction must include at least the following abnormal and emergency procedures flight training:

(A) Enhanced training in autorotation procedures,

(B) Engine rotor RPM control without the use of the governor,

(C) Low rotor RPM recognition and recovery, and

(D) Effects of low G maneuvers and proper recovery procedures.

(2) No person may act as pilot in command of a Robinson R-44 unless that person—

(i) Has had at least 200 flight hours in helicopters, at least 50 flight hours of which were in the Robinson R-44. The pilot in command may credit up to 25 flight hours in the Robinson R-22 toward the 50 hour requirement in the Robinson R-44; or

(ii) Has had at least 10 hours dual instruction in a Robinson helicopter, at least 5 hours of which must have been accomplished in the Robinson R-44 helicopter and has received an endorsement from a certified flight instructor authorized under paragraph (b)(5) of this section that the individual has been given the training required by this paragraph and is proficient to act as pilot in command of an R-44. Beginning 12 calendar months after the date of the endorsement, the individual may not act as pilot in command unless the individual has completed a flight review in a Robinson R-44 within the preceding 12 calendar months and obtained an endorsement for that flight review. The dual instruction must include at least the following abnormal and emergency procedures flight training—

(A) Enhanced training in autorotation procedures;

(B) Engine rotor RPM control without the use of the governor;

(C) Low rotor RPM recognition and recovery; and

(D) Effects of low G maneuvers and proper recovery procedures.

(3) A person who does not hold a rotorcraft category and helicopter class rating must have had at least 20 hours of dual instruction in a Robinson R-22 helicopter prior to operating it in solo flight. In addition, the person must obtain an endorsement from a certified flight instructor authorized under paragraph (b)(5) of this section that instruction has been given in those maneuvers and procedures, and the instructor has found the applicant proficient to solo a Robinson R-22. This endorsement is valid for a period of 90 days. The dual instruction must include at least the following abnormal and emergency procedures flight training:

(i) Enhanced training in autorotation procedures,

(ii) Engine rotor RPM control without the use of the governor,

(iii) Low rotor RPM recognition and recovery, and

(iv) Effects of low G maneuvers and proper recovery procedures.

(4) A person who does not hold a rotorcraft category and helicopter class rating must have had at least 20 hours of dual instruction in a Robinson

R-44 helicopter prior to operating it in solo flight. In addition, the person must obtain an endorsement from a certified flight instructor authorized under paragraph (b)(5) of this section that instruction has been given in those maneuvers and procedures, and the instructor has found the applicant proficient to solo a Robinson R-44. This endorsement is valid for a period of 90 days. The dual instruction must include at least the following abnormal and emergency procedures flight training:

(i) Enhanced training in autorotation procedures,

(ii) Engine rotor RPM control without the use of the governor,

(iii) Low rotor RPM recognition and recovery; and

(iv) Effects of low G maneuvers and proper recovery procedures.

(5) No certificated flight instructor may provide instruction or conduct a flight review in a Robinson R-22 or R-44 unless that instructor—

(i) Completes the awareness training in paragraph (2)(a) of this SFAR.

(ii) For the Robinson R-22, has had at least 200 flight hours in helicopters, at least 50 flight hours of which were in the Robinson R-22, or for the Robinson R-44, has had at least 200 flight hours in helicopters, 50 flight hours of which were in Robinson helicopters. Up to 25 flight hours of Robinson R-22 flight time may be credited toward the 50 hour requirement.

(iii) Has completed flight training in a Robinson R-22, R-44, or both, on the following abnormal and emergency procedures—

(A) Enhanced training in autorotation procedures;

(B) Engine rotor RPM control without the use of the governor;

(C) Low rotor RPM recognition and recovery; and

(D) Effects of low G maneuvers and proper recovery procedures.

(iv) Has been authorized by endorsement from an FAA aviation safety inspector or authorized designated examiner that the instructor has completed the appropriate training, meets the experience requirements and has satisfactorily demonstrated an ability to provide instruction on the general subject areas of paragraph 2(a)(3) of this SFAR, and the flight training identified in paragraph 2(b)(5)(iii) of this SFAR.

(c) Flight Review:

(1) No flight review completed to satisfy § 61.56 by an individual after becoming eligible to function as pilot in command in a Robinson R-22 helicopter shall be valid for the operation of R-22 helicopter unless that flight review was taken in an R-22.

(2) No flight review completed to satisfy § 61.56 by an individual after becoming eligible to function as pilot in command in a Robinson R-44 helicop-

ter shall be valid for the operation of R-44 helicopter unless that flight review was taken in the R-44.

(3) The flight review will include a review of the awareness training subject areas of paragraph 2(a)(3) of this SFAR and the flight training identified in paragraph 2(b) of this SFAR.

(d) Currency Requirements: No person may act as pilot in command of a Robinson model R-22 or R-44 helicopter carrying passengers unless the pilot in command has met the recency of flight experience requirements of § 61.57 in an R-22 or R-44, as appropriate.

3. *Expiration date.* This SFAR expires December 31, 2002, unless sooner superseded or rescinded.

[Docket No. 28095, 63 FR 666, Jan. 7, 1998]

Subpart A—General

§ 61.1 Applicability and definitions.

(a) This part prescribes:

(1) The requirements for issuing pilot, flight instructor, and ground instructor certificates and ratings; the conditions under which those certificates and ratings are necessary; and the privileges and limitations of those certificates and ratings.

(2) The requirements for issuing pilot, flight instructor, and ground instructor authorizations; the conditions under which those authorizations are necessary; and the privileges and limitations of those authorizations.

(3) The requirements for issuing pilot, flight instructor, and ground instructor certificates and ratings for persons who have taken courses approved by the Administrator under other parts of this chapter.

(b) For the purpose of this part:

(1) *Aeronautical experience* means pilot time obtained in an aircraft, flight simulator, or flight training device for meeting the appropriate training and flight time requirements for an airman certificate, rating, flight review, or recency of flight experience requirements of this part.

(2) *Authorized instructor* means—

(i) A person who holds a valid ground instructor certificate issued under part 61 or part 143 of this chapter when conducting ground training in accordance with the privileges and limitations of his or her ground instructor certificate;

(ii) A person who holds a current flight instructor certificate issued under part 61 of this chapter when conducting ground training or flight training in accordance with the privileges and limitations of his or her flight instructor certificate; or

(iii) A person authorized by the Administrator to provide ground training or flight training under SFAR No. 58, or part 61, 121, 135, or 142 of this chapter when conducting ground training or flight training in accordance with that authority.

(3) *Cross-country time* means—

(i) Except as provided in paragraphs (b)(3)(ii), (iii), (iv), and (v) of this section, time acquired during a flight—

(A) Conducted by a person who holds a pilot certificate;

(B) Conducted in an aircraft;

(C) That includes a landing at a point other than the point of departure; and

(D) That involves the use of dead reckoning, pilotage, electronic navigation aids, radio aids, or other navigation systems to navigate to the landing point.

(ii) For the purpose of meeting the aeronautical experience requirements (except for a rotorcraft category rating), for a private pilot certificate, a commercial pilot certificate, or an instrument rating, or for the purpose of exercising recreational pilot privileges (except in a rotorcraft) under § 61.101(c), time acquired during a flight—

(A) Conducted in an appropriate aircraft;

(B) That includes a point of landing that was at least a straight-line distance of more than 50 nautical miles from the original point of departure; and

(C) That involves the use of dead reckoning, pilotage, electronic navigation aids, radio aids, or other navigation systems to navigate to the landing point.

(iii) For the purpose of meeting the aeronautical experience requirements for any pilot certificate with a rotorcraft category rating or an instrument-helicopter rating, or for the purpose of exercising recreational pilot privileges, in a rotorcraft, under § 61.101(c), time acquired during a flight—

(A) Conducted in an appropriate aircraft;

(B) That includes a point of landing that was at least a straight-line distance of more than 25 nautical miles from the original point of departure; and

(C) That involves the use of dead reckoning, pilotage, electronic navigation aids, radio aids, or other navigation systems to navigate to the landing point.

(iv) For the purpose of meeting the aeronautical experience requirements for an airline transport pilot certificate (except with a rotorcraft category rating), time acquired during a flight—

(A) Conducted in an appropriate aircraft;

(B) That is at least a straight-line distance of more than 50 nautical miles from the original point of departure; and

(C) That involves the use of dead reckoning, pilotage, electronic navigation aids, radio aids, or other navigation systems.

(v) For a military pilot who qualifies for a commercial pilot certificate (except with a rotorcraft

category rating) under § 61.73 of this part, time acquired during a flight—

(A) Conducted in an appropriate aircraft;

(B) That is at least a straight-line distance of more than 50 nautical miles from the original point of departure; and

(C) That involves the use of dead reckoning, pilotage, electronic navigation aids, radio aids, or other navigation systems.

(4) *Examiner* means any person who is authorized by the Administrator to conduct a pilot proficiency test or a practical test for an airman certificate or rating issued under this part, or a person who is authorized to conduct a knowledge test under this part.

(5) *Flight simulator* means a device that—

(i) is a full-size aircraft cockpit replica of a specific type of aircraft, or make, model, and series of aircraft;

(ii) Includes the hardware and software necessary to represent the aircraft in ground operations and flight operations;

(iii) Uses a force cueing system that provides cues at least equivalent to those cues provided by a 3 degree freedom of motion system;

(iv) Uses a visual system that provides at least a 45 degree horizontal field of view and a 30 degree vertical field of view simultaneously for each pilot; and

(v) Has been evaluated, qualified, and approved by the Administrator.

(6) *Flight training* means that training, other than ground training, received from an authorized instructor in flight in an aircraft.

(7) *Flight training device* means a device that—

(i) Is a full-size replica of the instruments, equipment, panels, and controls of an aircraft, or set of aircraft, in an open flight deck area or in an enclosed cockpit, including the hardware and software for the systems installed, that is necessary to simulate the aircraft in ground and flight operations;

(ii) Need not have a force (motion) cueing or visual system; and

(iii) Has been evaluated, qualified, and approved by the Administrator.

(8) *Ground training* means that training, other than flight training, received from an authorized instructor.

(9) *Instrument approach* means an approach procedure defined in part 97 of this chapter.

(10) *Instrument training* means that time in which instrument training is received from an authorized instructor under actual or simulated instrument conditions.

(11) *Knowledge test* means a test on the aeronautical knowledge areas required for an airman certificate or rating that can be administered in written form or by a computer.

(12) *Pilot time* means that time in which a person—

(i) Serves as a required pilot flight crewmember;

(ii) Receives training from an authorized instructor in an aircraft, flight simulator, or flight training device; or

(iii) Gives training as an authorized instructor in an aircraft, flight simulator, or flight training device.

(13) *Practical test* means a test on the areas of operations for an airman certificate, rating, or authorization that is conducted by having the applicant respond to questions and demonstrate maneuvers in flight, in a flight simulator, or in a flight training device.

(14) *Set of aircraft* means aircraft that share similar performance characteristics, such as similar airspeed and altitude operating envelopes, similar handling characteristics, and the same number and type of propulsion systems.

(15) *Training time* means training received—

(i) In flight from an authorized instructor;

(ii) On the ground from an authorized instructor, or

(iii) In a flight simulator or flight training device from an authorized instructor.

[Docket No. 25910, 62 FR 16298, April 4, 1997; as amended by Amdt. 61–103, 62 FR 40893, July 30, 1997]

§ 61.3 Requirement for certificates, ratings, and authorizations.

(a) *Pilot certificate.* A person may not act as pilot in command or in any other capacity as a required pilot flight crewmember of a civil aircraft of U.S. registry, unless that person has a valid pilot certificate or special purpose pilot authorization issued under this part in that person's physical possession or readily accessible in the aircraft when exercising the privileges of that pilot certificate or authorization. However, when the aircraft is operated within a foreign country, a current pilot license issued by the country in which the aircraft is operated may be used.

(b) *Required pilot certificate for operating a foreign-registered aircraft.* A person may not act as pilot in command or in any other capacity as a required pilot flight crewmember of a civil aircraft of foreign registry within the United States, unless that person's pilot certificate:

(1) Is valid and in that person's physical possession, or readily accessible in the aircraft when exercising the privileges of that pilot certificate; and

(2) Has been issued under this part, or has been issued or validated by the country in which the aircraft is registered.

(c) *Medical certificate.*

(1) Except as provided for in paragraph (c)(2) of this section, a person may not act as pilot in command or in any other capacity as a required pilot

flight crewmember of an aircraft, under a certificate issued to that person under this part, unless that person has a current and appropriate medical certificate that has been issued under part 67 of this chapter, or other documentation acceptable to the Administrator, which is in that person's physical possession or readily accessible in the aircraft.

(2) A person is not required to meet the requirements of paragraph (c)(1) of this section if that person—

(i) Is exercising the privileges of a student pilot certificate while seeking a pilot certificate with a glider category rating or balloon class rating;

(ii) Is holding a pilot certificate with a balloon class rating and is piloting or providing training in a balloon as appropriate;

(iii) Is holding a pilot certificate or a flight instructor certificate with a glider category rating, and is piloting or providing training in a glider, as appropriate;

(iv) Except as provided in paragraph (c)(2)(iii) of this section, is exercising the privileges of a flight instructor certificate, provided the person is not acting as pilot in command or as a required pilot flight crewmember;

(v) Is exercising the privileges of a ground instructor certificate;

(vi) Is operating an aircraft within a foreign country using a pilot license issued by that country and possesses evidence of current medical qualification for that license; or

(vii) Is operating an aircraft within a U.S. pilot certificate, issued on the basis of a foreign pilot license, issued under § 61.75 of this part, and holds a current medical certificate issued by the foreign country that issued the foreign pilot license, which is in that person's physical possession or readily accessible in the aircraft when exercising the privileges of that airman certificate.

(d) *Flight instructor certificate.*

(1) A person who holds a flight instructor certificate issued under this part must have that certificate, or other documentation acceptable to the Administrator, in that person's physical possession or readily accessible in the aircraft when exercising the privileges of that flight instructor certificate.

(2) Except as provided in paragraph (d)(3) of this section, no person other than the holder of a flight instructor certificate issued under this part with the appropriate rating on that certificate may—

(i) Give training required to qualify a person for solo flight and solo cross-country flight;

(ii) Endorse an applicant for a—

(A) Pilot certificate or rating issued under this part;

(B) Flight instructor certificate or rating issued under this part; or

(C) Ground instructor certificate or rating issued under this part;

(iii) Endorse a pilot logbook to show training given; or

(iv) Endorse a student pilot certificate and logbook for solo operating privileges.

(3) A flight instructor certificate issued under this part is not necessary—

(i) Under paragraph (d)(2) of this section, if the training is given by the holder of a commercial pilot certificate with a lighter-than-air rating, provided the training is given in accordance with the privileges of the certificate in a lighter-than-air aircraft;

(ii) Under paragraph (d)(2) of this section, if the training is given by the holder of an airline transport pilot certificate with a rating appropriate to the aircraft in which the training is given, provided the training is given in accordance with the privileges of the certificate and conducted in accordance with an approved air carrier training program approved under part 121 or part 135 of this chapter;

(iii) Under paragraph (d)(2) of this section, if the training is given by a person who is qualified in accordance with subpart C of part 142 of this chapter, provided the training is conducted in accordance with an approved part 142 training program;

(iv) Under paragraphs (d)(2)(i), (d)(2)(ii)(C), and (d)(2)(iii) of this section, if the training is given by the holder of a ground instructor certificate in accordance with the privileges of the certificate; or

(v) Under paragraph (d)(2)(iii) of this section, if the training is given by an authorized flight instructor under § 61.41 of this part.

(e) *Instrument rating.* No person may act as pilot in command of a civil aircraft under IFR or in weather conditions less than the minimums prescribed for VFR flight unless that person holds:

(1) The appropriate aircraft category, class, type (if required), and instrument rating on that person's pilot certificate for any airplane, helicopter, or powered-lift being flown;

(2) An airline transport pilot certificate with the appropriate aircraft category, class, and type rating (if required) for the aircraft being flown;

(3) For a glider, a pilot certificate with a glider category rating and an airplane instrument rating; or

(4) For an airship, a commercial pilot certificate with a lighter-than-air category rating and airship class rating.

(f) *Category II pilot authorization.* Except for a pilot conducting Category II operations under part 121 or part 135, a person may not:

(1) Act as pilot in command of a civil aircraft during Category II operations unless that person—

(i) Holds a current Category II pilot authorization for that category or class of aircraft, and the type of aircraft, if applicable; or

(ii) In the case of a civil aircraft of foreign registry, is authorized by the country of registry to act as pilot in command of that aircraft in Category II operations.

(2) Act as second in command of a civil aircraft during Category II operations unless that person—

(i) Holds a valid pilot certificate with category and class ratings for that aircraft and a current instrument rating for that category aircraft;

(ii) Holds an airline transport pilot certificate with category and class ratings for that aircraft; or

(iii) In the case of a civil aircraft of foreign registry, is authorized by the country of registry to act as second in command of that aircraft during Category II operations.

(g) *Category III pilot authorization.* Except for a pilot conducting Category III operations under part 121 or part 135, a person may not:

(1) Act as pilot in command of a civil aircraft during Category III operations unless that person—

(i) Holds a current Category III pilot authorization for that category or class of aircraft, and the type of aircraft, if applicable; or

(ii) In the case of a civil aircraft of foreign registry, is authorized by the country of registry to act as pilot in command of that aircraft in Category III operations.

(2) Act as second in command of a civil aircraft during Category III operations unless that person—

(i) Holds a valid pilot certificate with category and class ratings for that aircraft and a current instrument rating for that category aircraft;

(ii) Holds an airline transport pilot certificate with category and class ratings for that aircraft; or

(iii) In the case of a civil aircraft of foreign registry, is authorized by the country of registry to act as second in command of that aircraft during Category III operations.

(h) *Category A aircraft pilot authorization.* The Administrator may issue a certificate of authorization for a Category II or Category III operation to the pilot of a small aircraft that is a Category A aircraft, as identified in § 97.3(b)(1) of this chapter if:

(1) The Administrator determines that the Category II or Category III operation can be performed safely by that pilot under the terms of the certificate of authorization; and

(2) The Category II or Category III operation does not involve the carriage of persons or property for compensation or hire.

(i) *Ground instructor certificate.*

(1) Each person who holds a ground instructor certificate issued under this part or part 143 must have that certificate in that person's physical pos-

session or immediately accessible when exercising the privileges of that certificate.

(2) Except as provided in paragraph (i)(3) of this section, no person other than the holder of a ground instructor certificate, issued under this part or part 143, with the appropriate rating on that certificate may—

(i) Give ground training required to qualify a person for solo flight and solo cross-country flight;

(ii) Endorse an applicant for a knowledge test required for a pilot, flight instructor, or ground instructor certificate or rating issued under this part; or

(iii) Endorse a pilot logbook to show ground training given.

(3) A ground instructor certificate issued under this part is not necessary—

(i) Under paragraph (i)(2) of this section, if the training is given by the holder of a flight instructor certificate issued under this part in accordance with the privileges of that certificate;

(ii) Under paragraph (i)(2) of this section, if the training is given by the holder of a commercial pilot certificate with a lighter-than-air rating, provided the training is given in accordance with the privileges of the certificate in a lighter-than-air aircraft;

(iii) Under paragraph (i)(2) of this section, if the training is given by the holder of an airline transport pilot certificate with a rating appropriate to the aircraft in which the training is given, provided the training is given in accordance with the privileges of the certificate and conducted in accordance with an approved air carrier training program approved under part 121 or part 135 of this chapter;

(iv) Under paragraph (i)(2) of this section, if the training is given by a person who is qualified in accordance with subpart C of part 142 of this chapter, provided the training is conducted in accordance with an approved part 142 training program; or

(v) Under paragraph (i)(2)(iii) of this section, if the training is given by an authorized flight instructor under § 61.41 of this part.

(j) *Age limitation for certain operations.*

(1) *Age limitation.* Except as provided in paragraph (j)(3) of this section, no person who holds a pilot certificate issued under this part shall serve as a pilot on a civil airplane of U.S. registry in the following operations if the person has reached his or her 60th birthday—

(i) Scheduled international air services carrying passengers in turbojet-powered airplanes;

(ii) Scheduled international air services carrying passengers in airplanes having a passenger-seat configuration of more than nine passenger seats, excluding each crewmember seat;

(iii) Nonscheduled international air transportation for compensation or hire in airplanes having a

passenger-seat configuration of more than 30 passenger seats, excluding each crewmember seat; or

(iv) Scheduled international air services, or nonscheduled international air transportation for compensation or hire, in airplanes having a payload capacity of more than 7,500 pounds.

(2) *Definitions.*

(i) "International air service," as used in paragraph (j) of this section, means scheduled air service performed in airplanes for the public transport of passengers, mail, or cargo, in which the service passes through the airspace over the territory of more than one country.

(ii) "International air transportation," as used in paragraph (j) of this section, means air transportation performed in airplanes for the public transport of passengers, mail, or cargo, in which the service passes through the airspace over the territory of more than one country.

(3) *Delayed pilot age limitation.* Until December 20, 1999, a person may serve as a pilot in operations covered by this paragraph after that person has reached his or her 60th birthday if, on March 20, 1997, that person was employed as a pilot in operations covered by this paragraph.

(k) *Special purpose pilot authorization.* Any person that is required to hold a special purpose pilot authorization, issued in accordance with § 61.77 of this part, must have that authorization and the person's foreign pilot license in that person's physical possession or have it readily accessible in the aircraft when exercising the privileges of that authorization.

(l) *Inspection of certificate.* Each person who holds an airman certificate, medical certificate, authorization, or license required by this part must present it for inspection upon a request from:

(1) The Administrator;

(2) An authorized representative of the National Transportation Safety Board; or

(3) Any Federal, State, or local law enforcement officer.

[Docket No. 25910, 62 FR 16298, April 4, 1997; as amended by Amdt. 61–103, 62 FR 40894, July 30, 1997]

§ 61.4 Qualification and approval of flight simulators and flight training devices.

(a) Except as specified in paragraph (b) or (c) of this section, each flight simulator and flight training device used for training, and for which an airman is to receive credit to satisfy any training, testing, or checking requirement under this chapter, must be qualified and approved by the Administrator for—

(1) The training, testing, and checking for which it is used;

(2) Each particular maneuver, procedure, or crewmember function performed; and

(3) The representation of the specific category and class of aircraft, type of aircraft, particular variation within the type of aircraft, or set of aircraft for certain flight training devices.

(b) Any device used for flight training, testing, or checking that has been determined to be acceptable to or approved by the Administrator prior to August 1, 1996, which can be shown to function as originally designed, is considered to be a flight training device, provided it is used for the same purposes for which it was originally accepted or approved and only to the extent of such acceptance or approval.

(c) The Administrator may approve a device other than a flight simulator or flight training device for specific purposes.

[Docket No. 25910, 62 FR 16298, April 4, 1997; as amended by Amdt. 61–103, 62 FR 40894, July 30, 1997]

§ 61.5 Certificates and ratings issued under this part.

(a) The following certificates are issued under this part to an applicant who satisfactorily accomplishes the training and certification requirements for the certificate sought:

(1) Pilot certificates—
(i) Student pilot.
(ii) Recreational pilot.
(iii) Private pilot.
(iv) Commercial pilot.
(v) Airline transport pilot.
(2) Flight instructor certificates.
(3) Ground instructor certificates.

(b) The following ratings are placed on a pilot certificate (other than student pilot) when an applicant satisfactorily accomplishes the training and certification requirements for the rating sought:

(1) Aircraft category ratings—
(i) Airplane.
(ii) Rotorcraft.
(iii) Glider.
(iv) Lighter-than-air.
(v) Powered-lift.

(2) Airplane class ratings—
(i) Single-engine land.
(ii) Multiengine land.
(iii) Single-engine sea.
(iv) Multiengine sea.

(3) Rotorcraft class ratings—
(i) Helicopter.
(ii) Gyroplane.

(4) Lighter-than-air class ratings—
(i) Airship.
(ii) Balloon.

(5) Aircraft type ratings—
(i) Large aircraft other than lighter-than-air.
(ii) Turbojet-powered airplanes.
(iii) Other aircraft type ratings specified by the Administrator through the aircraft type certification procedures.

(6) Instrument ratings (on private and commercial pilot certificates only)—
(i) Instrument—Airplane.
(ii) Instrument—Helicopter.
(iii) Instrument—Powered-lift.

(c) The following ratings are placed on a flight instructor certificate when an applicant satisfactorily accomplishes the training and certification requirements for the rating sought:

(1) Aircraft category ratings—
(i) Airplane.
(ii) Rotorcraft.
(iii) Glider.
(iv) Powered-lift.

(2) Airplane class ratings—
(i) Single-engine.
(ii) Multiengine.

(3) Rotorcraft class ratings—
(i) Helicopter.
(ii) Gyroplane.

(4) Instrument ratings—
(i) Instrument—Airplane.
(ii) Instrument—Helicopter.
(iii) Instrument—Powered-lift.

(d) The following ratings are placed on a ground instructor certificate when an applicant satisfactorily accomplishes the training and certification requirements for the rating sought:

(1) Basic.
(2) Advanced.
(3) Instrument.

§ 61.7 Obsolete certificates and ratings.

(a) The holder of a free-balloon pilot certificate issued before November 1, 1973, may not exercise the privileges of that certificate.

(b) The holder of a pilot certificate that bears any of the following category ratings without an associated class rating may not exercise the privileges of that category rating:

(1) Rotorcraft.
(2) Lighter-than-air.
(3) Helicopter.
(4) Autogyro.

§ 61.9 [Reserved]

§ 61.11 Expired pilot certificates and reissuance.

(a) No person who holds an expired pilot certificate or rating may:

(1) Exercise the privileges of that pilot certificate or rating; or

(2) Act as pilot in command or as a required pilot flight crewmember of an aircraft of the same category and class specified on the expired pilot certificate or rating.

(b) The following pilot certificates and ratings have expired and will not be issued:

(1) An airline transport pilot certificate issued before May 1, 1949, or an airline transport pilot certificate that contains a horsepower limitation;

(2) A private or commercial pilot certificate issued before July 1, 1945; and

(3) A pilot certificate with a lighter-than-air or free-balloon rating issued before July 1, 1945.

(c) A pilot certificate issued on the basis of a foreign pilot license will expire on the date the foreign license expires unless otherwise specified on the U.S. pilot certificate. A certificate without an expiration date is issued to the holder of the expired certificate only if that person meets the requirements of § 61.75 for the issuance of a pilot certificate based on a foreign pilot license.

(d) An airline transport pilot certificate issued after April 30, 1949, that bears an expiration date but does not contain a horsepower limitation may be reissued without an expiration date.

(e) A private or commercial pilot certificate issued after June 30, 1945, that bears an expiration date may be reissued without an expiration date.

(f) A pilot certificate with a lighter-than-air or free-balloon rating issued after June 30, 1945, that bears an expiration date may be reissued without an expiration date.

[Docket No. 25910, 62 FR 16298, April 4, 1997; as amended by Amdt. 61–103, 62 FR 40895, July 30, 1997]

§ 61.13 Issuance of airman certificates, ratings, and authorizations.

(a) *Application.*

(1) An applicant for an airman certificate, rating, or authorization under this part must make that application on a form and in a manner acceptable to the Administrator.

(2) An applicant who is neither a citizen of the United States nor a resident alien of the United States—

(i) Must show evidence that the appropriate fee prescribed in Appendix A to part 187 of this chapter has been paid when that person applies for a—

(A) Student pilot certificate that is issued outside the United States; or

(B) Knowledge test or practical test for an airman certificate or rating issued under this part, if the test is administered outside the United States.

(ii) May be refused issuance of any U.S. airman certificate, rating, or authorization by the Administrator.

(3) Except as provided in paragraph (a)(2)(ii) of this section, an applicant who satisfactorily accomplishes the training and certification requirements for the certificate, rating, or authorization sought is entitled to receive that airman certificate, rating, or authorization.

(b) *Limitations.*

(1) An applicant who cannot comply with certain areas of operation required on the practical test because of physical limitations may be issued an airman certificate, rating, or authorization with the appropriate limitation placed on the applicant's airman certificate provided the—

(i) Applicant is able to meet all other certification requirements for the airman certificate, rating, or authorization sought;

(ii) Physical limitation has been recorded with the FAA on the applicant's medical records; and

(iii) Administrator determines that the applicant's inability to perform the particular area of operation will not adversely affect safety.

(2) A limitation placed on a person's airman certificate may be removed, provided that person demonstrates for an examiner satisfactory proficiency in the area of operation appropriate to the airman certificate, rating, or authorization sought.

(c) *Additional requirements for Category II and Category III pilot authorizations.*

(1) A Category II or Category III pilot authorization is issued by a letter of authorization as part of an applicant's instrument rating or airline transport pilot certificate.

(2) Upon original issue, the authorization contains the following limitations:

(i) For Category II operations, the limitation is 1,600 feet RVR and a 150-foot decision height; and

(ii) For Category III operations, each initial limitation is specified in the authorization document.

(3) The limitations on a Category II or Category III pilot authorization may be removed as follows:

(i) In the case of Category II limitations, a limitation is removed when the holder shows that, since the beginning of the sixth preceding month, the holder has made three Category II ILS approaches with a 150-foot decision height to a landing under actual or simulated instrument conditions.

(ii) In the case of Category III limitations, a limitation is removed as specified in the authorization.

(4) To meet the experience requirements of paragraph (c)(3) of this section, and for the practical test required by this part for a Category II or a Category III pilot authorization, a flight simulator

or flight training device may be used if it is approved by the Administrator for such use.

(d) *Application during suspension or revocation.*

(1) Unless otherwise authorized by the Administrator, a person whose pilot, flight instructor, or ground instructor certificate has been suspended may not apply for any certificate, rating, or authorization during the period of suspension.

(2) Unless otherwise authorized by the Administrator, a person whose pilot, flight instructor, or ground instructor certificate has been revoked may not apply for any certificate, rating, or authorization for 1 year after the date of revocation.

[Docket No. 25910, 62 FR 40895, July 30, 1997]

§ 61.14 Refusal to submit to a drug or alcohol test.

(a) This section applies to an employee who performs a function listed in Appendix I to part 121 or Appendix J to part 121 of this chapter directly or by contract for a part 121 air carrier, a part 135 air carrier, or for a person conducting operations as specified in § 135.1(a)(5) of this chapter.

(b) Refusal by the holder of a certificate issued under this part to take a drug test required under the provisions of Appendix I to part 121 or an alcohol test required under the provisions of Appendix J to part 121 is grounds for:

(1) Denial of an application for any certificate, rating, or authorization issued under this part for a period of up to 1 year after the date of such refusal; and

(2) Suspension or revocation of any certificate, rating, authorization issued under this part.

§ 61.15 Offenses involving alcohol or drugs.

(a) A conviction for the violation of any Federal or State statute relating to the growing, processing, manufacture, sale, disposition, possession, transportation, or importation of narcotic drugs, marijuana, or depressant or stimulant drugs or substances is grounds for:

(1) Denial of an application for any certificate, rating, or authorization issued under this part for a period of up to 1 year after the date of final conviction; or

(2) Suspension or revocation of any certificate, rating, or authorization issued under this part.

(b) Committing an act prohibited by § 91.17(a) or § 91.19(a) of this chapter is grounds for:

(1) Denial of an application for a certificate, rating, or authorization issued under this part for a period of up to 1 year after the date of that act; or

(2) Suspension or revocation of any certificate, rating, or authorization issued under this part.

(c) For the purposes of paragraph (d), (e), and (f) of this section, a motor vehicle action means:

(1) A conviction after November 29, 1990, for the violation of any Federal or State statute relating to the operation of a motor vehicle while intoxicated by alcohol or a drug, while impaired by alcohol or a drug, or while under the influence of alcohol or a drug;

(2) The cancellation, suspension, or revocation of a license to operate a motor vehicle after November 29, 1990, for a cause related to the operation of a motor vehicle while intoxicated by alcohol or a drug, while impaired by alcohol or a drug, or while under the influence of alcohol or a drug; or

(3) The denial after November 29, 1990, of an application for a license to operate a motor vehicle for a cause related to the operation of a motor vehicle while intoxicated by alcohol or a drug, while impaired by alcohol or a drug, or while under the influence of alcohol or a drug.

(d) Except for a motor vehicle action that results from the same incident or arises out of the same factual circumstances, a motor vehicle action occurring within 3 years of a previous motor vehicle action is grounds for:

(1) Denial of an application for any certificate, rating, or authorization issued under this part for a period of up to 1 year after the date of the last motor vehicle action; or

(2) Suspension or revocation of any certificate, rating, or authorization issued under this part.

(e) Each person holding a certificate issued under this part shall provide a written report of each motor vehicle action to the FAA, Civil Aviation Security Division (AMC–700), P.O. Box 25810, Oklahoma City, OK 73125, not later than 60 days after the motor vehicle action. The report must include:

(1) The person's name, address, date of birth, and airman certificate number;

(2) The type of violation that resulted in the conviction or the administrative action;

(3) The date of the conviction or administrative action;

(4) The State that holds the record of conviction or administrative action; and

(5) A statement of whether the motor vehicle action resulted from the same incident or arose out of the same factual circumstances related to a previously reported motor vehicle action.

(f) Failure to comply with paragraph (e) of this section is grounds for:

(1) Denial of an application for any certificate, rating, or authorization issued under this part for a period of up to 1 year after the date of the motor vehicle action; or

(2) Suspension or revocation of any certificate, rating, or authorization issued under this part.

§ 61.16 Refusal to submit to an alcohol test or to furnish test results.

A refusal to submit to a test to indicate the percentage by weight of alcohol in the blood, when requested by a law enforcement officer in accordance with § 91.17(c) of this chapter, or a refusal to furnish or authorize the release of the test results requested by the Administrator in accordance with § 91.17(c) or (d) of this chapter, is grounds for:

(a) Denial of an application for any certificate, rating, or authorization issued under this part for a period of up to 1 year after the date of that refusal; or

(b) Suspension or revocation of any certificate, rating, or authorization issued under this part.

§61.17 Temporary certificate.

(a) A temporary pilot, flight instructor, or ground instructor certificate or rating is issued for up to 120 days, at which time a permanent certificate will be issued to a person whom the Administrator finds qualified under this part.

(b) A temporary pilot, flight instructor, or ground instructor certificate or rating expires:

(1) On the expiration date shown on the certificate;

(2) Upon receipt of the permanent certificate; or

(3) Upon receipt of a notice that the certificate or rating sought is denied or revoked.

§ 61.19 Duration of pilot and instructor certificates.

(a) *General.* The holder of a certificate with an expiration date may not, after that date, exercise the privileges of that certificate.

(b) *Student pilot certificate.* A student pilot certificate expires 24 calendar months from the month in which it is issued.

(c) *Other pilot certificates.* A pilot certificate (other than a student pilot certificate) issued under this part is issued without a specific expiration date. The holder of a pilot certificate issued on the basis of a foreign pilot license may exercise the privileges of that certificate only while that person's foreign pilot license is effective.

(d) *Flight instructor certificate.* A flight instructor certificate:

(1) Is effective only while the holder has a current pilot certificate; and

(2) Except as specified in § 61.197(b) of this part, expires 24 calendar months from the month in which it was issued or renewed.

(e) *Ground instructor certificate.* A ground instructor certificate issued under this part is issued without a specific expiration date.

(f) *Surrender, suspension, or revocation.* Any certificate issued under this part ceases to be effective if it is surrendered, suspended, or revoked.

(g) *Return of certificates.* The holder of any certificate issued under this part that has been suspended or revoked must return that certificate to the FAA when requested to do so by the Administrator.

§ 61.21 Duration of a Category II and a Category III pilot authorization (for other than Part 121 and Part 135 use).

(a) A Category II pilot authorization or a Category III pilot authorization expires at the end of the sixth calendar month after the month in which it was issued or renewed.

(b) Upon passing a practical test for a Category II or Category III pilot authorization, the authorization may be renewed for each type of aircraft for which the authorization is held.

(c) A Category II or Category III pilot authorization for a specific type aircraft for which an authorization is held will not be renewed beyond 12 calendar months from the month the practical test was accomplished in that type aircraft.

(d) If the holder of a Category II or Category III pilot authorization passes the practical test for a renewal in the month before the authorization expires, the holder is considered to have passed it during the month the authorization expired.

§ 61.23 Medical certificates: Requirement and duration.

(a) *Operations requiring a medical certificate.* Except as provided in paragraph (b) of this section, a person:

(1) Must hold a first-class medical certificate when exercising the privileges of an airline transport pilot certificate;

(2) Must hold at least a second-class medical certificate when exercising the privileges of a commercial pilot certificate; or

(3) Must hold at least a third-class medical certificate—

(i) When exercising the privileges of a private pilot certificate;

(ii) When exercising the privileges of a recreational pilot certificate;

(iii) Except as specified in paragraph (b)(3) of this section, when exercising the privileges of a student pilot certificate;

(iv) When exercising the privileges of a flight instructor certificate, except for a flight instructor certificate with a glider category rating, if the person is acting as the pilot in command or is serving as a required pilot flight crewmember; or

(v) Except for a glider category rating or a balloon class rating, prior to taking a practical test that is performed in an aircraft for a certificate or rating at the recreational, private, commercial, or airline transport pilot certificate level.

(b) *Operations not requiring a medical certificate.* A person is not required to hold a medical certificate:

(1) When exercising the privileges of a pilot certificate with a glider category rating;

(2) When exercising the privileges of a pilot certificate with a balloon class rating;

(3) When exercising the privileges of a student pilot certificate while seeking a pilot certificate with a glider category rating or balloon class rating;

(4) When exercising the privileges of a flight instructor certificate with a glider category rating;

(5) When exercising the privileges of a flight instructor certificate if the person is not acting as pilot in command or serving as a required pilot flight crewmember;

(6) When exercising the privileges of a ground instructor certificate;

(7) When serving as an examiner or check airman during the administration of a test or check for a certificate, rating, or authorization conducted in a flight simulator or flight training device; or

(8) When taking a test or check for a certificate, rating, or authorization conducted in a flight simulator or flight training device.

(c) *Duration of a medical certificate.*

(1) A first-class medical certificate expires at the end of the last day of—

(i) The sixth month after the month of the date of examination shown on the certificate for operations requiring an airline transport pilot certificate;

(ii) The 12th month after the month of the date of examination shown on the certificate for operations requiring a commercial pilot certificate or an air traffic control tower operator certificate; and

(iii) The period specified in paragraph (c)(3) of this section for operations requiring a recreational pilot certificate, a private pilot certificate, a flight instructor certificate (when acting as pilot in command or a required pilot flight crewmember in operations other than glider or balloon), or a student pilot certificate.

(2) A second-class medical certificate expires at the end of the last day of—

(i) The 12th month after the month of the date of examination shown on the certificate for operations requiring a commercial pilot certificate or an air traffic control tower operator certificate; and

(ii) The period specified in paragraph (c)(3) of this section for operations requiring a recreational pilot certificate, a private pilot certificate, a flight instructor certificate (when acting as pilot in command or a required pilot flight crewmember in operations other than glider or balloon), or a student pilot certificate.

(3) A third-class medical certificate for operations requiring a recreational pilot certificate, a

private pilot certificate, a flight instructor certificate (when acting as pilot in command or a required pilot flight crewmember in operations other than glider or balloon), or a student pilot certificate issued—

(i) Before September 16, 1996, expires at the end of the 24th month after the month of the date of examination shown on the certificate; or

(ii) On or after September 16, 1996, expires at the end of:

(A) The 36th month after the month of the date of the examination shown on the certificate if the person has not reached his or her 40th birthday on or before the date of examination; or

(B) The 24th month after the month of the date of the examination shown on the certificate if the person has reached his or her 40th birthday on or before the date of the examination.

[Docket No. 25910, 62 FR 16298, April 4, 1997; as amended by Amdt. 61–103, 62 FR 40895, July 30, 1997]

§61.25 Change of name.

(a) An application to change the name on a certificate issued under this part must be accompanied by the applicant's:

(1) Current airman certificate; and

(2) A copy of the marriage license, court order, or other document verifying the name change.

(b) The documents in paragraph (a) of this section will be returned to the applicant after inspection.

§61.27 Voluntary surrender or exchange of certificate.

(a) The holder of a certificate issued under this part may voluntarily surrender it for:

(1) Cancellation;

(2) Issuance of a lower grade certificate; or

(3) Another certificate with specific ratings deleted.

(b) Any request made under paragraph (a) of this section must include the following signed statement or its equivalent: "This request is made for my own reasons, with full knowledge that my (insert name of certificate or rating, as appropriate) may not be reissued to me unless I again pass the tests prescribed for its issuance."

§61.29 Replacement of a lost or destroyed airman or medical certificate or knowledge test report.

(a) A request for the replacement of a lost or destroyed airman certificate issued under this part must be made by letter to the Department of Transportation, FAA, Airman Certification Branch, P.O. Box 25082, Oklahoma City, OK 73125, and must be accompanied by a check or money order for the appropriate fee payable to the FAA.

(b) A request for the replacement of a lost or destroyed medical certificate must be made by letter to the Department of Transportation, FAA, Aeromedical Certification Branch, P.O. Box 25082, Oklahoma City, OK 73125, and must be accompanied by a check or money order for the appropriate fee payable to the FAA.

(c) A request for the replacement of a lost or destroyed knowledge test report must be made by letter to the Department of Transportation, FAA, Airman Certification Branch, P.O. Box 25082, Oklahoma City, OK 73125, and must be accompanied by a check or money order for the appropriate fee payable to the FAA.

(d) The letter requesting replacement of a lost or destroyed airman certificate, medical certificate, or knowledge test report must state:

(1) The name of the person;

(2) The permanent mailing address (including ZIP code), or if the permanent mailing address includes a post office box number, then the person's current residential address;

(3) The social security number;

(4) The date and place of birth of the certificate holder; and

(5) Any available information regarding the—

(i) Grade, number, and date of issuance of the certificate, and the ratings, if applicable;

(ii) Date of the medical examination, if applicable; and

(iii) Date the knowledge test was taken, if applicable.

(e) A person who has lost an airman certificate, medical certificate, or knowledge test report may obtain a facsimile from the FAA Aeromedical Certification Branch or the Airman Certification Branch, as appropriate, confirming that it was issued and the:

(1) Facsimile may be carried as an airman certificate, medical certificate, or knowledge test report, as appropriate, for up to 60 days pending the person's receipt of a duplicate under paragraph (a), (b), or (c) of this section, unless the person has been notified that the certificate has been suspended or revoked.

(2) Request for such a facsimile must include the date on which a duplicate certificate or knowledge test report was previously requested.

[Docket No. 25910, 62 FR 16298, April 4, 1997; as amended by Amdt. 61–103, 62 FR 40896, July 30, 1997]

§ 61.31 Type rating requirements, additional training, and authorization requirements.

(a) *Type ratings required.* A person who acts as a pilot in command of any of the following aircraft must hold a type rating for that aircraft:

(1) Large aircraft (except lighter-than-air).

(2) Turbojet-powered airplanes.

(3) Other aircraft specified by the Administrator through aircraft type certificate procedures.

(b) *Authorization in lieu of a type rating.* A person may be authorized to operate without a type rating for up to 60 days an aircraft requiring a type rating, provided—

(1) The Administrator has authorized the flight or series of flights;

(2) The Administrator has determined that an equivalent level of safety can be achieved through the operating limitations on the authorization;

(3) The person shows that compliance with paragraph (a) of this section is impracticable for the flight or series of flights; and

(4) The flight—

(i) Involves only a ferry flight, training flight, test flight, or practical test for a pilot certificate or rating;

(ii) Is within the United States;

(iii) Does not involve operations for compensation or hire unless the compensation or hire involves payment for the use of the aircraft for training or taking a practical test; and

(iv) Involves only the carriage of flight crewmembers considered essential for the flight.

(5) If the flight or series of flights cannot be accomplished within the time limit of the authorization, the Administrator may authorize an additional period of up to 60 days to accomplish the flight or series of flights.

(c) *Aircraft category, class, and type ratings*: Limitations on the carriage of persons, or operating for compensation or hire. Unless a person holds a category, class, and type rating (if a class and type rating is required) that applies to the aircraft, that person may not act as pilot in command of an aircraft that is carrying another person, or is operated for compensation or hire. That person also may not act as pilot in command of that aircraft for compensation or hire.

(d) *Aircraft category, class, and type ratings*: Limitations on operating an aircraft as the pilot in command. To serve as the pilot in command of an aircraft, a person must—

(1) Hold the appropriate category, class, and type rating (if a class rating and type rating are required) for the aircraft to be flown;

(2) Be receiving training for the purpose of obtaining an additional pilot certificate and rating that are appropriate to that aircraft, and be under the supervision of an authorized instructor; or

(3) Have received training required by this part that is appropriate to the aircraft category, class, and type rating (if a class or type rating is required) for the aircraft to be flown, and have received the required endorsements from an instructor who is authorized to provide the required endorsements for solo flight in that aircraft.

(e) *Additional training required for operating complex airplanes.*

(1) Except as provided in paragraph (e)(2) of this section, no person may act as pilot in command of a complex airplane (an airplane that has a retractable landing gear, flaps, and a controllable pitch propeller; or, in the case of a seaplane, flaps and a controllable pitch propeller), unless the person has—

(i) Received and logged ground and flight training from an authorized instructor in a complex airplane, or in a flight simulator or flight training device that is representative of a complex airplane, and has been found proficient in the operation and systems of the airplane; and

(ii) Received a one-time endorsement in the pilot's logbook from an authorized instructor who certifies the person is proficient to operate a complex airplane.

(2) The training and endorsement required by paragraph (e)(1) of this section is not required if the person has logged flight time as pilot in command of a complex airplane, or in a flight simulator or flight training device that is representative of a complex airplane prior to August 4, 1997.

(f) *Additional training required for operating high-performance airplanes.*

(1) Except as provided in paragraph (f)(2) of this section, no person may act as pilot in command of a high-performance airplane (an airplane with an engine of more than 200 horsepower), unless the person has—

(i) Received and logged ground and flight training from an authorized instructor in a high-performance airplane, or in a flight simulator or flight training device that is representative of a high-performance airplane, and has been found proficient in the operation and systems of the airplane; and

(ii) Received a one-time endorsement in the pilot's logbook from an authorized instructor who certifies the person is proficient to operate a high-performance airplane.

(2) The training and endorsement required by paragraph (f)(1) of this section is not required if the person has logged flight time as pilot in command of a high-performance airplane, or in a flight simulator or flight training device that is representative of a high-performance airplane prior to August 4, 1997.

(g) *Additional training required for operating pressurized aircraft capable of operating at high altitudes.*

(1) Except as provided in paragraph (g)(3) of this section, no person may act as pilot in command of a pressurized aircraft (an aircraft that has a service ceiling or maximum operating altitude, whichever is lower, above 25,000 feet MSL), unless that person has received and logged ground training from an authorized instructor and obtained an endorsement in the person's logbook or training record from an authorized instructor who certifies the person has satisfactorily accomplished the ground training. The ground training must include at least the following subjects:

(i) High-altitude aerodynamics and meteorology;

(ii) Respiration;

(iii) Effects, symptoms, and causes of hypoxia and any other high-altitude sickness;

(iv) Duration of consciousness without supplemental oxygen;

(v) Effects of prolonged usage of supplemental oxygen;

(vi) Causes and effects of gas expansion and gas bubble formation;

(vii) Preventive measures for eliminating gas expansion, gas bubble formation, and high-altitude sickness;

(viii) Physical phenomena and incidents of decompression; and

(ix) Any other physiological aspects of high-altitude flight.

(2) Except as provided in paragraph (g)(3) of this section, no person may act as pilot in command of a pressurized aircraft unless that person has received and logged training from an authorized instructor in a pressurized aircraft, or in a flight simulator or flight training device that is representative of a pressurized aircraft, and obtained an endorsement in the person's logbook or training record from an authorized instructor who found the person proficient in the operation of a pressurized aircraft. The flight training must include at least the following subjects:

(i) Normal cruise flight operations while operating above 25,000 feet MSL;

(ii) Proper emergency procedures for simulated rapid decompression without actually depressurizing the aircraft; and

(iii) Emergency descent procedures.

(3) The training and endorsement required by paragraphs (g)(1) and (g)(2) of this section are not required if that person can document satisfactory accomplishment of any of the following in a pressurized aircraft, or in a flight simulator or flight training device that is representative of a pressurized aircraft:

(i) Serving as pilot in command before April 15, 1991;

(ii) Completing a pilot proficiency check for a pilot certificate or rating before April 15, 1991;

(iii) Completing an official pilot-in-command check conducted by the military services of the United States; or

(iv) Completing a pilot-in-command proficiency check under part 121, 125, or 135 of this chapter conducted by the Administrator or by an approved pilot check airman.

(h) *Additional aircraft type-specific training.* No person may serve as pilot in command of an aircraft that the Administrator has determined requires aircraft type-specific training unless that person has—

(1) Received and logged type-specific training in the aircraft, or in a flight simulator or flight training device that is representative of that type of aircraft; and

(2) Received a logbook endorsement from an authorized instructor who has found the person proficient in the operation of the aircraft and its systems.

(i) *Additional training required for operating tail-wheel airplanes.*

(1) Except as provided in paragraph (i)(2) of this section, no person may act as pilot in command of a tailwheel airplane unless that person has received and logged flight training from an authorized instructor in a tailwheel airplane and received an endorsement in the person's logbook from an authorized instructor who found the person proficient in the operation of a tailwheel airplane. The flight training must include at least the following maneuvers and procedures:

(i) Normal and crosswind takeoffs and landings;

(ii) Wheel landings (unless the manufacturer has recommended against such landings); and

(iii) Go-around procedures.

(2) The training and endorsement required by paragraph (i)(1) of this section is not required if the person logged pilot-in-command time in a tailwheel airplane before April 15, 1991.

(j) *Additional training required for operating a glider.*

(1) No person may act as pilot in command of a glider—

(i) Using ground-tow procedures, unless that person has satisfactorily accomplished ground and flight training on ground-tow procedures and operations, and has received an endorsement from an authorized instructor who certifies in that pilot's logbook that the pilot has been found proficient in ground-tow procedures and operations;

(ii) Using aerotow procedures, unless that person has satisfactorily accomplished ground and flight training on aerotow procedures and operations, and has received an endorsement from an authorized instructor who certifies in that pilot's logbook that the pilot has been found proficient in aerotow procedures and operations; or

(iii) Using self-launch procedures, unless that person has satisfactorily accomplished ground

and flight training on self-launch procedures and operations, and has received an endorsement from an authorized instructor who certifies in that pilot's logbook that the pilot has been found proficient in self-launch procedures and operations.

(2) The holder of a glider rating issued prior to August 4, 1997, is considered to be in compliance with the training and logbook endorsement requirements of this paragraph for the specific operating privilege for which the holder is already qualified.

(k) *Exceptions.*

(1) This section does not require a category and class rating for aircraft not type certificated as airplanes, rotorcraft, or lighter-than-air aircraft, or a class rating for gliders or powered-lifts.

(2) The rating limitations of this section do not apply to—

(i) An applicant when taking a practical test given by an examiner;

(ii) The holder of a student pilot certificate;

(iii) The holder of a pilot certificate when operating an aircraft under the authority of an experimental or provisional aircraft type certificate;

(iv) The holder of a pilot certificate with a lighter-than-air category rating when operating a balloon; or

(v) The holder of a recreational pilot certificate operating under the provisions of § 61.101(h).

[Docket No. 25910, 62 FR 40896, July 30, 1997; as amended by Amdt. 61–104, 63 FR 20286, April 23, 1998]

§ 61.33 Tests: General procedure.

Tests prescribed by or under this part are given at times and places, and by persons designated by the Administrator.

§ 61.35 Knowledge test: Prerequisites and passing grades.

(a) An applicant for a knowledge test must have:

(1) Received an endorsement, if required by this part, from an authorized instructor certifying that the applicant accomplished the appropriate ground-training or a home-study course required by this part for the certificate or rating sought and is prepared for the knowledge test; and

(2) Proper identification at the time of application that contains the applicant's—

(i) Photograph;

(ii) Signature;

(iii) Date of birth, which shows the applicant meets or will meet the age requirements of this part for the certificate sought before the expiration date of the airman knowledge test report; and

(iv) Actual residential address, if different from the applicant's mailing address.

(b) The Administrator shall specify the minimum passing grade for the knowledge test.

[Docket No. 25910, 62 FR 40896, July 30, 1997; as amended by Amdt. 61–104, 63 FR 20286, April 23, 1998]

§ 61.37 Knowledge tests: Cheating or other unauthorized conduct.

(a) An applicant for a knowledge test may not:

(1) Copy or intentionally remove any knowledge test;

(2) Give to another applicant or receive from another applicant any part or copy of a knowledge test;

(3) Give assistance on, or receive assistance on, a knowledge test during the period that test is being given;

(4) Take any part of a knowledge test on behalf of another person;

(5) Be represented by, or represent, another person for a knowledge test;

(6) Use any material or aid during the period that the test is being given, unless specifically authorized to do so by the Administrator; and

(7) Intentionally cause, assist, or participate in any act prohibited by this paragraph.

(b) An applicant who the Administrator finds has committed an act prohibited by paragraph (a) of this section is prohibited, for 1 year after the date of committing that act, from:

(1) Applying for any certificate, rating, or authorization issued under this chapter; and

(2) Applying for and taking any test under this chapter.

(c) Any certificate or rating held by an applicant may be suspended or revoked if the Administrator finds that person has committed an act prohibited by paragraph (a) of this section.

§ 61.39 Prerequisites for practical tests.

(a) Except as provided in paragraphs (b) and (c) of this section, to be eligible for a practical test for a certificate or rating issued under this part, an applicant must:

(1) Pass the required knowledge test within the 24-calendar-month period preceding the month the applicant completes the practical test, if a knowledge test is required;

(2) Present the knowledge test report at the time of application for the practical test, if a knowledge test is required;

(3) Have satisfactorily accomplished the required training and obtained the aeronautical experience prescribed by this part for the certificate or rating sought;

(4) Hold at least a current third-class medical certificate, if a medical certificate is required;

(5) Meet the prescribed age requirement of this part for the issuance of the certificate or rating sought;

(6) Have an endorsement, if required by this part, in the applicant's logbook or training record that has been signed by an authorized instructor who certifies that the applicant—

(i) Has received and logged training time within 60 days preceding the date of application in preparation for the practical test;

(ii) Is prepared for the required practical test; and

(iii) Has demonstrated satisfactory knowledge of the subject areas in which the applicant was deficient on the airman knowledge test; and

(7) Have a completed and signed application form.

(b) Notwithstanding the provisions of paragraphs (a)(1) and (2) of this section, an applicant for an airline transport pilot certificate or an additional rating to an airline transport certificate may take the practical test for that certificate or rating with an expired knowledge test report, provided that the applicant:

(1) Is employed as a flight crewmember by a certificate holder under part 121, 125, or 135 of this chapter at the time of the practical test and has satisfactorily accomplished that operator's approved—

(i) Pilot in command aircraft qualification training program that is appropriate to the certificate and rating sought; and

(ii) Qualification training requirements appropriate to the certificate and rating sought; or

(2) Is employed as a flight crewmember in scheduled U.S. military air transport operations at the time of the practical test, and has accomplished the pilot in command aircraft qualification training program that is appropriate to the certificate and rating sought.

(c) A person is not required to comply with the provisions of paragraph (a)(6) of this section if that person:

(1) Holds a foreign-pilot license issued by a contracting State to the Convention on International Civil Aviation that authorizes at least the pilot privileges of the airman certificate sought;

(2) Is applying for a type rating only, or a class rating with an associated type rating; or

(3) Is applying for an airline transport pilot certificate or an additional rating to an airline transport pilot certificate in an aircraft that does not require an aircraft type rating practical test.

(d) If all increments of the practical test for a certificate or rating are not completed on one date, all remaining increments of the test must be satisfactorily completed not more than 60 calendar days after the date on which the applicant began the test.

(e) If all increments of the practical test for a certificate or a rating are not satisfactorily completed within 60 calendar days after the date on which the applicant began the test, the applicant must retake the entire practical test, including those increments satisfactorily completed.

[Docket No. 25910, 62 FR 16298, April 4, 1997; as amended by Amdt. 61–103, 62 FR 40897, July 30, 1997; Amdt. 61–104, 63 FR 20286, April 23, 1998]

§ 61.41 Flight training received from flight instructors not certificated by the FAA.

(a) A person may credit flight training toward the requirements of a pilot certificate or rating issued under this part, if that person received the training from:

(1) A flight instructor of an Armed Force in a program for training military pilots of either—

(i) The United States; or

(ii) A foreign contracting State to the Convention on International Civil Aviation.

(2) A flight instructor who is authorized to give such training by the licensing authority of a foreign contracting State to the Convention on International Civil Aviation, and the flight training is given outside the United States.

(b) A flight instructor described in paragraph (a) of this section is only authorized to give endorsements to show training given.

§ 61.43 Practical tests: General procedures.

(a) Except as provided in paragraph (b) of this section, the ability of an applicant for a certificate or rating issued under this part to perform the required tasks on the practical test is based on that applicant's ability to safely:

(1) Perform the tasks specified in the areas of operation for the certificate or rating sought within the approved standards;

(2) Demonstrate mastery of the aircraft with the successful outcome of each task performed never seriously in doubt;

(3) Demonstrate satisfactory proficiency and competency within the approved standards;

(4) Demonstrate sound judgment; and

(5) Demonstrate single-pilot competence if the aircraft is type certificated for single-pilot operations.

(b) If an applicant does not demonstrate single pilot proficiency, as required in paragraph (a)(5) of this section, a limitation of "Second in Command Required" will be placed on the applicant's airman certificate. The limitation may be removed if the applicant passes the appropriate practical test by demonstrating single-pilot competency in the aircraft in which single-pilot privileges are sought.

(c) If an applicant fails any area of operation, that applicant fails the practical test.

(d) An applicant is not eligible for a certificate or rating sought until all the areas of operation are passed.

(e) The examiner or the applicant may discontinue a practical test at any time:

(1) When the applicant fails one or more of the areas of operation; or

(2) Due to inclement weather conditions, aircraft airworthiness, or any other safety-of-flight concern.

(f) If a practical test is discontinued, the applicant is entitled credit for those areas of operation that were passed, but only if the applicant:

(1) Passes the remainder of the practical test within the 60-day period after the date the practical test was discontinued;

(2) Presents to the examiner for the retest the original notice of disapproval form or the letter of discontinuance form, as appropriate;

(3) Satisfactorily accomplishes any additional training needed and obtains the appropriate instructor endorsements, if additional training is required; and

(4) Presents to the examiner for the retest a properly completed and signed application.

§ 61.45 Practical tests: Required aircraft and equipment.

(a) *General.* Except as provided in paragraph (a)(2) of this section or when permitted to accomplish the entire flight increment of the practical test in a flight simulator or a flight training device, an applicant for a certificate or rating issued under this part must furnish:

(1) An aircraft of U.S. registry for each required test that—

(i) Is of the category, class, and type, if applicable, for which the applicant is applying for a certificate or rating; and

(ii) Has a current standard, limited, or primary airworthiness certificate.

(2) At the discretion of the examiner who administers the practical test, the applicant may furnish—

(i) An aircraft that has a current airworthiness certificate other than standard, limited, or primary, but that otherwise meets the requirement of paragraph (a)(1) of this section;

(ii) An aircraft of the same category, class, and type, if applicable, of foreign registry that is properly certificated by the country of registry; or

(iii) A military aircraft of the same category, class, and type, if applicable, for which the applicant is applying for a certificate or rating.

(b) *Required equipment (other than controls).*
(1) Except as provided in paragraph (b)(2) of this section, an aircraft used for a practical test must have —

(i) The equipment for each area of operation required for the practical test;

(ii) No prescribed operating limitations that prohibit its use in any of the areas of operation required for the practical test;

(iii) Except as provided in paragraph (e) of this section, at least two pilot stations with adequate visibility for each person to operate the aircraft safely; and

(iv) Cockpit and outside visibility adequate to evaluate the performance of the applicant when an additional jump seat is provided for the examiner.

(2) An applicant for a certificate or rating may use an aircraft with operating characteristics that preclude the applicant from performing all of the tasks required for the practical test. However, the applicant's certificate or rating, as appropriate, will be issued with an appropriate limitation.

(c) *Required controls.* An aircraft (other than a lighter-than-air aircraft) used for a practical test must have engine power controls and flight controls that are easily reached and operable in a conventional manner by both pilots, unless the examiner determines that the practical test can be conducted safely in the aircraft without the controls being easily reached.

(d) *Simulated instrument flight equipment.* An applicant for a practical test that involves maneuvering an aircraft solely by reference to instruments must furnish:

(1) Equipment on board the aircraft that permits the applicant to pass the areas of operation that apply to the rating sought; and

(2) A device that prevents the applicant from having visual reference outside the aircraft, but does not prevent the examiner from having visual reference outside the aircraft, and is otherwise acceptable to the Administrator.

(e) *Aircraft with single controls.* A practical test may be conducted in an aircraft having a single set of controls, provided the:

(1) Examiner agrees to conduct the test;

(2) Test does not involve a demonstration of instrument skills; and

(3) Proficiency of the applicant can be observed by an examiner who is in a position to observe the applicant.

[Docket No. 25910, 62 FR 16298, April 4, 1997; as amended by Amdt. 61–103, 62 FR 40897, July 30, 1997; Amdt. 61–104, 63 FR 20286, April 23, 1998]

§ 61.47 Status of an examiner who is authorized by the Administrator to conduct practical tests.

(a) An examiner represents the Administrator for the purpose of conducting practical tests for certificates and ratings issued under this part and to observe an applicant's ability to perform the areas of operation on the practical test.

(b) The examiner is not the pilot in command of the aircraft during the practical test unless the examiner agrees to act in that capacity for the flight or for a portion of the flight by prior arrangement with:

(1) The applicant; or

(2) A person who would otherwise act as pilot in command of the flight or for a portion of the flight.

(c) Notwithstanding the type of aircraft used during the practical test, the applicant and the examiner (and any other occupants authorized to be on board by the examiner) are not subject to the requirements or limitations for the carriage of passengers that are specified in this chapter.

[Docket No. 25910, 62 FR 16298, April 4, 1997; as amended by Amdt. 61–103, 62 FR 40897, July 30, 1997]

§ 61.49 Retesting after failure.

(a) An applicant for a knowledge or practical test who fails that test may reapply for the test only after the applicant has received:

(1) The necessary training from an authorized instructor who has determined that the applicant is proficient to pass the test; and

(2) An endorsement from an authorized instructor who gave the applicant the additional training.

(b) An applicant for a flight instructor certificate with an airplane category rating or, for a flight instructor certificate with a glider category rating, who has failed the practical test due to deficiencies in instructional proficiency on stall awareness, spin entry, spins, or spin recovery must:

(1) Comply with the requirements of paragraph (a) of this section before being retested;

(2) Bring an aircraft to the retest that is of the appropriate aircraft category for the rating sought and is certificated for spins; and

(3) Demonstrate satisfactory instructional proficiency on stall awareness, spin entry, spins, and spin recovery to an examiner during the retest.

§ 61.51 Pilot logbooks.

(a) *Training time and aeronautical experience.* Each person must document and record the following time in a manner acceptable to the Administrator:

(1) Training and aeronautical experience used to meet the requirements for a certificate, rating, or flight review of this part.

(2) The aeronautical experience required for meeting the recent flight experience requirements of this part.

(b) *Logbook entries.* For the purposes of meeting the requirements of paragraph (a) of this section, each person must enter the following information for each flight or lesson logged:

(1) General—

(i) Date.

(ii) Total flight time or lesson time.

(iii) Location where the aircraft departed and arrived, or for lessons in a flight simulator or a flight training device, the location where the lesson occurred.

(iv) Type and identification of aircraft, flight simulator, or flight training device, as appropriate.

(v) The name of a safety pilot, if required by § 91.109(b) of this chapter.

(2) Type of pilot experience or training—

(i) Solo.

(ii) Pilot in command.

(iii) Second in command.

(iv) Flight and ground training received from an authorized instructor.

(v) Training received in a flight simulator or flight training device from an authorized instructor.

(3) Conditions of flight—

(i) Day or night.

(ii) Actual instrument.

(iii) Simulated instrument conditions in flight, a flight simulator, or a flight training device.

(c) *Logging of pilot time.* The pilot time described in this section may be used to:

(1) Apply for a certificate or rating issued under this part; or

(2) Satisfy the recent flight experience requirements of this part.

(d) *Logging of solo flight time.* Except for a student pilot performing the duties of pilot in command of an airship requiring more than one pilot flight crewmember, a pilot may log as solo flight time only that flight time when the pilot is the sole occupant of the aircraft.

(e) *Logging pilot-in-command flight time.*

(1) A recreational, private, or commercial pilot may log pilot-in-command time only for that flight time during which that person—

(i) Is the sole manipulator of the controls of an aircraft for which the pilot is rated;

(ii) Is the sole occupant of the aircraft; or

(iii) Except for a recreational pilot, is acting as pilot in command of an aircraft on which more than one pilot is required under the type certification of the aircraft or the regulations under which the flight is conducted.

(2) An airline transport pilot may log as pilot-in-command time all of the flight time while acting as pilot-in-command of an operation requiring an airline transport pilot certificate.

(3) An authorized instructor may log as pilot-in-command time all flight time while acting as an authorized instructor.

(4) A student pilot may log pilot-in-command time only when the student pilot—

(i) Is the sole occupant of the aircraft or is performing the duties of pilot in command of an airship requiring more than one pilot flight crewmember;

(ii) Has a current solo flight endorsement as required under § 61.87 of this part; and

(iii) Is undergoing training for a pilot certificate or rating.

(f) *Logging second-in-command flight time.* A person may log second-in-command time only for that flight time during which that person:

(1) Is qualified in accordance with the second-in-command requirements of § 61.55 of this part, and occupies a crewmember station in an aircraft that requires more than one pilot by the aircraft's type certificate; or

(2) Holds the appropriate category, class, and instrument rating (if an instrument rating is required for the flight) for the aircraft being flown, and more than one pilot is required under the type certification of the aircraft or the regulations under which the flight is being conducted.

(g) *Logging instrument flight time.*

(1) A person may log instrument time only for that flight time when the person operates the aircraft solely by reference to instruments under actual or simulated instrument flight conditions.

(2) An authorized instructor may log instrument time when conducting instrument flight instruction in actual instrument flight conditions.

(3) For the purposes of logging instrument time to meet the recent instrument experience requirements of § 61.57(c) of this part, the following information must be recorded in the person's logbook—

(i) The location and type of each instrument approach accomplished; and

(ii) The name of the safety pilot, if required.

(4) A flight simulator or flight training device may be used by a person to log instrument time, provided an authorized instructor is present during the simulated flight.

(h) *Logging training time.*

(1) A person may log training time when that person receives training from an authorized in-

structor in an aircraft, flight simulator, or flight training device.

(2) The training time must be logged in a logbook and must:

(i) Be endorsed in a legible manner by the authorized instructor; and

(ii) Include a description of the training given, the length of the training lesson, and the authorized instructor's signature, certificate number, and certificate expiration date.

(i) *Presentation of required documents.*

(1) Persons must present their pilot certificate, medical certificate, logbook, or any other record required by this part for inspection upon a reasonable request by—

(i) The Administrator;

(ii) An authorized representative from the National Transportation Safety Board; or

(iii) Any Federal, State, or local law enforcement officer.

(2) A student pilot must carry the following items in the aircraft on all solo cross-country flights as evidence of the required authorized instructor clearances and endorsements—

(i) Pilot logbook;

(ii) Student pilot certificate; and

(iii) Any other record required by this section.

(3) A recreational pilot must carry his or her logbook with the required authorized instructor endorsements on all solo flights—

(i) That exceed 50 nautical miles from the airport at which training was received;

(ii) Within airspace that requires communication with air traffic control;

(iii) Conducted between sunset and sunrise; or

(iv) In an aircraft for which the pilot does not hold an appropriate category or class rating.

[Docket No. 25910, 62 FR 16298, April 4, 1997; as amended by Amdt. 61–103, 62 FR 40897, July 30, 1997; Amdt. 61–104, 63 FR 20286, April 23, 1998]

§ 61.53 Prohibition on operations during medical deficiency.

(a) *Operations that require a medical certificate.* Except as provided for in paragraph (b) of this section, a person who holds a current medical certificate issued under part 67 of this chapter shall not act as pilot in command, or in any other capacity as a required pilot flight crewmember, while that person:

(1) Knows or has reason to know of any medical condition that would make the person unable to meet the requirements for the medical certificate necessary for the pilot operation; or

(2) Is taking medication or receiving other treatment for a medical condition that results in the person being unable to meet the requirements for the medical certificate necessary for the pilot operation.

(b) *Operations that do not require a medical certificate.* For operations provided for in § 61.23(b) of this part, a person shall not act as pilot in command, or in any other capacity as a required pilot flight crewmember, while that person knows or has reason to know of any medical condition that would make the person unable to operate the aircraft in a safe manner.

§ 61.55 Second-in-command qualifications.

(a) Except as provided in paragraph (d) of this section, no person may serve as a second in command of an aircraft type certificated for more than one required pilot flight crewmember or in operations requiring a second in command unless that person holds:

(1) At least a current private pilot certificate with the appropriate category and class rating; and

(2) An instrument rating that applies to the aircraft being flown if the flight is under IFR.

(b) Except as provided in paragraph (d) of this section, no person may serve as a second in command of an aircraft type certificated for more than one required pilot flight crewmember or in operations requiring a second in command unless that person has within the previous 12 calendar months:

(1) Become familiar with the following information for the specific type aircraft for which second-in-command privileges are requested—

(i) Operational procedures applicable to the powerplant, equipment, and systems.

(ii) Performance specifications and limitations.

(iii) Normal, abnormal, and emergency operating procedures.

(iv) Flight manual.

(v) Placards and markings.

(2) Except as provided in paragraph (e) of this section, performed and logged pilot time in the type of aircraft or in a flight simulator that represents the type of aircraft for which second-in-command privileges are requested, which includes—

(i) Three takeoffs and three landings to a full stop as the sole manipulator of the flight controls;

(ii) Engine-out procedures and maneuvering with an engine out while executing the duties of pilot in command; and

(iii) Crew resource management training.

(c) If a person complies with the requirements in paragraph (b) of this section in the calendar month before or the calendar month after the month in which compliance with this section is required, then that person is considered to have accomplished the training and practice in the month it is due.

(d) This section does not apply to a person who is:

(1) Designated and qualified as a pilot in command under part 121, 125, or 135 of this chapter in that specific type of aircraft;

(2) Designated as the second in command under part 121, 125, or 135 of this chapter, in that specific type of aircraft;

(3) Designated as the second in command in that specific type of aircraft for the purpose of receiving flight training required by this section, and no passengers or cargo are carried on the aircraft; or

(4) Designated as a safety pilot for purposes required by § 91.109(b) of this chapter.

(e) The holder of a commercial or airline transport pilot certificate with the appropriate category and class rating is not required to meet the requirements of paragraph (b)(2) of this section, provided the pilot:

(1) Is conducting a ferry flight, aircraft flight test, or evaluation flight of an aircraft's equipment; and

(2) Is not carrying any person or property on board the aircraft, other than necessary for conduct of the flight.

(f) For the purpose of meeting the requirements of paragraph (b) of this section, a person may serve as second in command in that specific type aircraft, provided:

(1) The flight is conducted under day VFR or day IFR; and

(2) No person or property is carried on board the aircraft, other than necessary for conduct of the flight.

(g) Except as provided in paragraph (h) of this section, the requirements of paragraph (b) of this section may be accomplished in a flight simulator that is used in accordance with an approved course conducted by a training center certificated under part 142 of this chapter.

(h) An applicant for an initial second-in-command qualification for a particular type of aircraft who is qualifying under the terms of paragraph (g) of this section must satisfactorily complete a minimum of one takeoff and one landing in an aircraft of the same type for which the qualification is sought.

[Docket No. 25910, 62 FR 16298, April 4, 1997; as amended by Amdt. 61–103, 62 FR 40898, July 30, 1997]

§ 61.56 Flight review.

(a) Except as provided in paragraphs (b) and (f) of this section, a flight review consists of a minimum of 1 hour of flight training and 1 hour of ground training. The review must include:

(1) A review of the current general operating and flight rules of part 91 of this chapter; and

(2) A review of those maneuvers and procedures that, at the discretion of the person giving the review, are necessary for the pilot to demonstrate the safe exercise of the privileges of the pilot certificate.

(b) Glider pilots may substitute a minimum of three instructional flights in a glider, each of which includes a flight to traffic pattern altitude, in lieu of the 1 hour of flight training required in paragraph (a) of this section.

(c) Except as provided in paragraphs (d), (e), and (g) of this section, no person may act as pilot in command of an aircraft unless, since the beginning of the 24th calendar month before the month in which that pilot acts as pilot in command, that person has—

(1) Accomplished a flight review given in an aircraft for which that pilot is rated by an authorized instructor; and

(2) A logbook endorsed from an authorized instructor who gave the review certifying that the person has satisfactorily completed the review.

(d) A person who has, within the period specified in paragraph (c) of this section, passed a pilot proficiency check conducted by an examiner, an approved pilot check airman, or a U.S. Armed Force, for a pilot certificate, rating, or operating privilege need not accomplish the flight review required by this section.

(e) A person who has, within the period specified in paragraph (c) of this section, satisfactorily accomplished one or more phases of an FAA-sponsored pilot proficiency award program need not accomplish the flight review required by this section.

(f) A person who holds a current flight instructor certificate who has, within the period specified in paragraph (c) of this section, satisfactorily completed a renewal of a flight instructor certificate under the provisions in § 61.197 need not accomplish the 1 hour of ground training specified in paragraph (a) of this section.

(g) A student pilot need not accomplish the flight review required by this section provided the student pilot is undergoing training for a certificate and has a current solo flight endorsement as required under § 61.87 of this part.

(h) The requirements of this section may be accomplished in combination with the requirements of § 61.57 and other applicable recent experience requirements at the discretion of the authorized instructor conducting the flight review.

(i) A flight simulator or flight training device may be used to meet the flight review requirements of this section subject to the following conditions:

(1) The flight simulator or flight training device must be used in accordance with an approved course conducted by a training center certificated under part 142 of this chapter.

(2) Unless the flight review is undertaken in a flight simulator that is approved for landings, the applicant must meet the takeoff and landing requirements of § 61.57(a) or § 61.57(b) of this part.

(3) The flight simulator or flight training device used must represent an aircraft or set of aircraft for which the pilot is rated.

[Docket No. 25910, 62 FR 16298, April 4, 1997; as amended by Amdt. 61–103, 62 FR 40898, July 30, 1997; Amdt. 61–104, 63 FR 20287, April 23, 1998]

§ 61.57 Recent flight experience: Pilot in command.

(a) *General experience.*

(1) Except as provided in paragraph (e) of this section, no person may act as a pilot in command of an aircraft carrying passengers or of an aircraft certificated for more than one pilot flight crew-member unless that person has made at least three takeoffs and three landings within the preceding 90 days, and—

(i) The person acted as the sole manipulator of the flight controls; and

(ii) The required takeoffs and landings were performed in an aircraft of the same category, class, and type (if a type rating is required), and, if the aircraft to be flown is an airplane with a tail-wheel, the takeoffs and landings must have been made to a full stop in an airplane with a tailwheel.

(2) For the purpose of meeting the requirements of paragraph (a)(1) of this section, a person may act as a pilot in command of an aircraft under day VFR or day IFR, provided no persons or property are carried on board the aircraft, other than those necessary for the conduct of the flight.

(3) The takeoffs and landings required by paragraph (a)(1) of this section may be accomplished in a flight simulator or flight training device that is—

(i) Approved by the Administrator for landings; and

(ii) Used in accordance with an approved course conducted by a training center certificated under part 142 of this chapter.

(b) *Night takeoff and landing experience.*

(1) Except as provided in paragraph (e) of this section, no person may act as pilot in command of an aircraft carrying passengers during the period beginning 1 hour after sunset and ending 1 hour before sunrise, unless within the preceding 90 days that person has made at least three takeoffs and three landings to a full stop during the period beginning 1 hour after sunset and ending 1 hour before sunrise, and—

(i) That person acted as sole manipulator of the flight controls; and

(ii) The required takeoffs and landings were performed in an aircraft of the same category, class, and type (if a type rating is required).

(2) The takeoffs and landings required by paragraph (b)(1) of this section may be accomplished in a flight simulator that is—

(i) Approved by the Administrator for takeoffs and landings, if the visual system is adjusted to represent the period described in paragraph (b)(1) of this section; and

(ii) Used in accordance with an approved course conducted by a training center certificated under part 142 of this chapter.

(c) *Instrument experience.* Except as provided in paragraph (e) of this section, no person may act as pilot in command under IFR or in weather conditions less than the minimums prescribed for VFR, unless within the preceding 6 calendar months, that person has:

(1) For the purpose of obtaining instrument experience in an aircraft (other than a glider), performed and logged under actual or simulated instrument conditions, either in flight in the appropriate category of aircraft for the instrument privileges sought or in a flight simulator or flight training device that is representative of the aircraft category for the instrument privileges sought—

(i) At least six instrument approaches;

(ii) Holding procedures; and

(iii) Intercepting and tracking courses through the use of navigation systems.

(2) For the purpose of obtaining instrument experience in a glider, performed and logged under actual or simulated instrument conditions—

(i) At least 3 hours of instrument time in flight, of which 1-1/2 hours may be acquired in an airplane or a glider if no passengers are to be carried; or

(ii) 3 hours of instrument time in flight in a glider if a passenger is to be carried.

(d) *Instrument proficiency check.* Except as provided in paragraph (e) of this section, a person who does not meet the instrument experience requirements of paragraph (c) of this section within the prescribed time, or within 6 calendar months after the prescribed time, may not serve as pilot in command under IFR or in weather conditions less than the minimums prescribed for VFR until that person passes an instrument proficiency check consisting of a representative number of tasks required by the instrument rating practical test.

(1) The instrument proficiency check must be—

(i) In an aircraft that is appropriate to the aircraft category;

(ii) For other than a glider, in a flight simulator or flight training device that is representative of the aircraft category; or

(iii) For a glider, in a single-engine airplane or a glider.

(2) The instrument proficiency check must be given by—

(i) An examiner;

(ii) A person authorized by the U.S. Armed Forces to conduct instrument flight tests, provided the person being tested is a member of the U.S. Armed Forces;

(iii) A company check pilot who is authorized to conduct instrument flight tests under part 121, 125, or 135 of this chapter, and provided that both the check pilot and the pilot being tested are employees of that operator;

(iv) An authorized instructor; or

(v) A person approved by the Administrator to conduct instrument practical tests.

(e) *Exceptions.*

(1) Paragraphs (a) and (b) of this section do not apply to a pilot in command who is employed by a certificate holder under part 125 and engaged in a flight operation for that certificate holder if the pilot is in compliance with §§ 125.281 and 125.285 of this chapter.

(2) This section does not apply to a pilot in command who is employed by an air carrier certificated under part 121 or 135 and is engaged in a flight operation under part 91, 121, or 135 for that air carrier if the pilot is in compliance with §§ 121.437 and 121.439, or §§ 135.243 and 135.247 of this chapter, as appropriate.

(3) Paragraph (b) of this section does not apply to a pilot in command who operates more than one type of an airplane that is type certificated for more than one pilot flight crewmember, provided the pilot—

(i) Holds at least a valid commercial pilot certificate with the appropriate type rating for each airplane that the pilot seeks to operate under this alternative;

(ii) Has logged at least 1500 hours total time as a pilot;

(iii) Has accomplished at least 15 hours of flight time in the type of airplane that the pilot seeks to operate under this alternative within the preceding 90 days prior to the operation of that airplane; and

(iv) Has accomplished—

(A) At least three takeoffs and three landings to a full stop, during the period beginning 1 hour after sunset and ending 1 hour before sunrise as the sole manipulator of the flight controls in at least one of the types of airplanes that the pilot seeks to operate under this alternative, within the preceding 90 days prior to the operation of any of the types of airplanes that the pilot seeks to operate under this alternative; or

(B) Completion of an approved training program under part 142 of this chapter within the preceding 12 calendar months prior to the month of the flight, which requires the performance of at least 6 takeoffs and 6 landings to a full stop as the sole manipulator of the controls in a flight simulator that is representative of at least one of the types of airplanes that the pilot seeks to operate under this alternative, and the flight simulator's visual system was adjusted to represent the period

beginning 1 hour after sunset and ending 1 hour before sunrise.

[Docket No. 25910, 62 FR 16298, April 4, 1997; as amended by Amdt. 61–103, 62 FR 40898, July 30, 1997; Amdt. 61–106, 64 FR 23529, April 30, 1999]

§ 61.58 Pilot-in-command proficiency check: Operation of aircraft requiring more than one pilot flight crewmember.

(a) Except as otherwise provided in this section, to serve as pilot in command of an aircraft that is type certificated for more than one required pilot flight crewmember, a person must—

(1) Within the preceding 12 calendar months, complete a pilot-in-command proficiency check in an aircraft that is type certificated for more than one required pilot flight crewmember; and

(2) Within the preceding 24 calendar months, complete a pilot-in-command proficiency check in the particular type of aircraft in which that person will serve as pilot in command.

(b) This section does not apply to persons conducting operations under part 121, 125, 133, 135, or 137 of this chapter, or persons maintaining continuing qualification under an Advanced Qualification Program approved under SFAR 58.

(c) The pilot-in-command proficiency check given in accordance with the provisions of part 121, 125, or 135 of this chapter may be used to satisfy the requirements of this section.

(d) The pilot-in-command proficiency check required by paragraph (a) of this section may be accomplished by satisfactory completion of one of the following:

(1) A pilot-in-command proficiency check conducted by a person authorized by the Administrator, consisting of the maneuvers and procedures required for a type rating, in an aircraft type certificated for more than one required pilot flight crewmember;

(2) The practical test required for a type rating, in an aircraft type certificated for more than one required pilot flight crewmember;

(3) The initial or periodic practical test required for the issuance of a pilot examiner or check airman designation, in an aircraft type certificated for more than one required pilot flight crewmember; or

(4) A military flight check required for a pilot in command with instrument privileges, in an aircraft that the military requires to be operated by more than one pilot flight crewmember.

(e) A check or test described in paragraphs (d)(1) through (d)(4) of this section may be accomplished in a flight simulator under part 142 of this chapter, subject to the following:

(1) Except as provided for in paragraphs (e)(2) and (e)(3) of this section, if an otherwise qualified

and approved flight simulator used for a pilot-in-command proficiency check is not qualified and approved for a specific required maneuver—

(i) The training center must annotate, in the applicant's training record, the maneuver or maneuvers omitted; and

(ii) Prior to acting as pilot in command, the pilot must demonstrate proficiency in each omitted maneuver in an aircraft or flight simulator qualified and approved for each omitted maneuver.

(2) If the flight simulator used pursuant to paragraph (e) of this section is not qualified and approved for circling approaches—

(i) The applicant's record must include the statement, "Proficiency in circling approaches not demonstrated"; and

(ii) The applicant may not perform circling approaches as pilot in command when weather conditions are less than the basic VFR conditions described in § 91.155 of this chapter, until proficiency in circling approaches has been successfully demonstrated in a flight simulator qualified and approved for circling approaches or in an aircraft to a person authorized by the Administrator to conduct the check required by this section.

(3) If the flight simulator used pursuant to paragraph (e) of this section is not qualified and approved for landings, the applicant must—

(i) Hold a type rating in the airplane represented by the simulator; and

(ii) Have completed within the preceding 90 days at least three takeoffs and three landings (one to a full stop) as the sole manipulator of the flight controls in the type airplane for which the pilot-in-command proficiency check is sought.

(f) For the purpose of meeting the pilot-in-command proficiency check requirements of paragraph (a) of this section, a person may act as pilot in command of a flight under day VFR conditions or day IFR conditions if no person or property is carried, other than as necessary to demonstrate compliance with this part.

(g) If a pilot takes the pilot-in-command proficiency check required by this section in the calendar month before or the calendar month after the month in which it is due, the pilot is considered to have taken it in the month in which it was due for the purpose of computing when the next pilot-in-command proficiency check is due.

[Docket No. 25910, 62 FR 40898, July 30, 1997]

§ 61.59 Falsification, reproduction, or alteration of applications, certificates, logbooks, reports, or records.

(a) No person may make or cause to be made:

(1) Any fraudulent or intentionally false statement on any application for a certificate, rating, authorization, or duplicate thereof, issued under this part;

(2) Any fraudulent or intentionally false entry in any logbook, record, or report that is required to be kept, made, or used to show compliance with any requirement for the issuance or exercise of the privileges of any certificate, rating, or authorization under this part;

(3) Any reproduction for fraudulent purpose of any certificate, rating, or authorization, under this part; or

(4) Any alteration of any certificate, rating, or authorization under this part.

(b) The commission of an act prohibited under paragraph (a) of this section is a basis for suspending or revoking any airman certificate, rating, or authorization held by that person.

§ 61.60 Change of address.

The holder of a pilot, flight instructor, or ground instructor certificate who has made a change in permanent mailing address may not, after 30 days from that date, exercise the privileges of the certificate unless the holder has notified in writing the FAA, Airman Certification Branch, P.O. Box 25082, Oklahoma City, OK 73125, of the new permanent mailing address, or if the permanent mailing address includes a post office box number, then the holder's current residential address.

Subpart B— Aircraft Ratings and Pilot Authorizations

§ 61.61 Applicability.

This subpart prescribes the requirements for the issuance of additional aircraft ratings after a pilot certificate is issued, and the requirements for and limitations of pilot authorizations issued by the Administrator.

§ 61.63 Additional aircraft ratings (other than on an airline transport pilot certificate).

(a) *General.* To be eligible for an additional aircraft rating to a pilot certificate, for other than an airline transport pilot certificate, an applicant must meet the appropriate requirements of this section for the additional aircraft rating sought.

(b) *Additional category rating.* An applicant who holds a pilot certificate and applies to add a category rating to that pilot certificate:

(1) Must have received the required training and possess the aeronautical experience prescribed by this part that applies to the pilot certificate for the aircraft category and, if applicable, class rating sought;

(2) Must have an endorsement in his or her logbook or training record from an authorized instructor, and that endorsement must attest that the applicant has been found competent in the aeronautical knowledge areas appropriate to the pilot certificate for the aircraft category and, if applicable, class rating sought;

(3) Must have an endorsement in his or her logbook or training record from an authorized instructor, and that endorsement must attest that the applicant has been found proficient on the areas of operation that are appropriate to the pilot certificate for the aircraft category and, if applicable, class rating sought;

(4) Must pass the required practical test that is appropriate to the pilot certificate for the aircraft category and, if applicable, class rating sought; and

(5) Need not take an additional knowledge test, provided the applicant holds an airplane, rotorcraft, powered-lift, or airship rating at that pilot certificate level.

(c) *Additional class rating.* Any person who applies for an additional class rating to be added on a pilot certificate:

(1) Must have an endorsement in his or her logbook or training record from an authorized instructor and that endorsement must attest that the applicant has been found competent in the aeronautical knowledge areas appropriate to the pilot certificate for the aircraft class rating sought;

(2) Must have an endorsement in his or her logbook or training record from an authorized instructor, and that endorsement must attest that the applicant has been found proficient in the areas of operation appropriate to the pilot certificate for the aircraft class rating sought;

(3) Must pass the required practical test that is appropriate to the pilot certificate for the aircraft class rating sought;

(4) Need not meet the specified training time requirements prescribed by this part that apply to the pilot certificate for the aircraft class rating sought unless the person holds a lighter-than-air category rating with a balloon class rating and is seeking an airship class rating; and

(5) Need not take an additional knowledge test, provided the applicant holds an airplane, rotorcraft, powered-lift, or airship rating at that pilot certificate level.

(d) *Additional type rating.* Except as specified in paragraph (d)(7) of this section, a person who applies for an additional aircraft type rating to be added on a pilot certificate, or the addition of an aircraft type rating that is accomplished concurrently with an additional aircraft category or class rating:

(1) Must hold or concurrently obtain an instrument rating that is appropriate to the aircraft category, class, or type rating sought;

(2) Must have an endorsement in his or her logbook or training record from an authorized instructor, and that endorsement must attest that the applicant has been found competent in the aeronautical knowledge areas appropriate to the pilot certificate for the aircraft category, class, or type rating sought;

(3) Must have an endorsement in his or her logbook, or training record from an authorized instructor, and that endorsement must attest that the applicant has been found proficient in the areas of operation required for the issuance of an airline transport pilot certificate for the aircraft category, class, and type rating sought;

(4) Must pass the required practical test appropriate to the airline transport pilot certificate for the aircraft category, class, and type rating sought;

(5) Must perform the practical test in actual or simulated instrument conditions, unless the aircraft's type certificate makes the aircraft incapable of operating under instrument flight rules. If the practical test cannot be accomplished for this reason, the person may obtain a type rating limited to "VFR only." The "VFR only" limitation may be removed for that aircraft type when the person passes the practical test in actual or simulated instrument conditions. When an instrument rating is issued to a person who holds one or more type ratings, the type ratings on the amended pilot certificate shall bear the "VFR only" limitation for each aircraft type rating for which the person has not demonstrated instrument competency;

(6) Need not take an additional knowledge test, provided the applicant holds an airplane, rotorcraft, powered-lift, or airship rating on their pilot certificate; and

(7) In the case of a pilot employee of a part 121 or a part 135 certificate holder, must have—

(i) Met the appropriate requirements of paragraphs (d)(1), (d)(4), and (d)(5) of this section for the aircraft type rating sought; and

(ii) Received an endorsement in his or her flight training record from the certificate holder attesting that the applicant has completed the certificate holder's approved ground and flight training program appropriate to the aircraft type rating sought.

(e) *Use of a flight simulator or flight training device for an additional rating in an airplane.* The areas of operation required to be performed by paragraphs (b), (c), and (d) of this section shall be performed as follows:

(1) Except as provided in paragraph (e)(2) of this section, the areas of operation must be performed in an airplane of the same category, class, and type, if applicable, as the airplane for which the additional rating is sought.

(2) Subject to the limitations of paragraph (e)(3) through (e)(12) of this section, the areas of operation may be performed in a flight simulator or flight

training device that represents the airplane for which the additional rating is sought.

(3) The use of a flight simulator or flight training device permitted by paragraph (e)(2) of this section shall be conducted in accordance with an approved course at a training center certificated under part 142 of this chapter.

(4) To complete all training and testing (except preflight inspection) for an additional airplane rating without limitations when using a flight simulator—

(i) The flight simulator must be qualified and approved as Level C or Level D; and

(ii) The applicant must meet at least one of the following:

(A) Hold a type rating for a turbojet airplane of the same class of airplane for which the type rating is sought, or have been appointed by a military service as a pilot in command of an airplane of the same class of airplane for which the type rating is sought, if a type rating in a turbojet airplane is sought.

(B) Hold a type rating for a turbopropeller airplane of the same class of airplane for which the type rating is sought, or have been designated by a military service as a pilot in command of an airplane of the same class of airplane for which the type rating is sought, if a type rating in a turbopropeller airplane is sought.

(C) Have at least 2,000 hours of flight time, of which 500 hours is in turbine-powered airplanes of the same class of airplane for which the type rating is sought.

(D) Have at least 500 hours of flight time in the same type airplane as the airplane for which the rating is sought.

(E) Have at least 1,000 hours of flight time in at least two different airplanes requiring a type rating.

(5) Subject to the limitation of paragraph (e)(6) of this section, an applicant who does not meet the requirements of paragraph (e)(4) of this section may complete all training and testing (except for preflight inspection) for an additional rating when using a flight simulator if—

(i) The flight simulator is qualified and approved as a Level C or Level D; and

(ii) The applicant meets at least one of the following:

(A) Holds a type rating in a propeller-driven airplane if a type rating in a turbojet airplane is sought, or holds a type rating in a turbojet airplane if a type rating in a propeller-driven airplane is sought; or

(B) Since the beginning of the 12th calendar month before the month in which the applicant completes the practical test for an additional airplane rating, has logged:

(1) At least 100 hours of flight time in airplanes of the same class for which the type rating is sought and which requires a type rating; and

(2) At least 25 hours of flight time in airplanes of the same type for which the rating is sought.

(6) An applicant meeting only the requirements of paragraph (e)(5) of this section will be issued an additional rating with a limitation.

(7) The limitation on a certificate issued under the provisions of paragraph (e)(6) of this section shall state, "This certificate is subject to pilot-in-command limitations for the additional rating."

(8) An applicant who has been issued a pilot certificate with the limitation specified in paragraph (e)(7) of this section—

(i) May not act as pilot in command of that airplane for which the additional rating was obtained under the provisions of this section until the limitation is removed from the pilot certificate; and

(ii) May have the limitation removed by accomplishing 15 hours of supervised operating experience as pilot in command under the supervision of a qualified and current pilot in command, in the seat normally occupied by the pilot in command, in the same type of airplane to which the limitation applies.

(9) An applicant who does not meet the requirements of paragraph (e)(4) or paragraph (e)(5) of this section may be issued an additional rating after successful completion of one of the following requirements:

(i) Compliance with paragraphs (e)(2) and (e)(3) of this section and the following tasks, which must be successfully completed on a static airplane or in flight, as appropriate:

(A) Preflight inspection;

(B) Normal takeoff;

(C) Normal ILS approach;

(D) Missed approach; and

(E) Normal landing.

(ii) Compliance with paragraphs (e)(2), (e)(3), and (e)(10) through (e)(12) of this section.

(10) An applicant meeting only the requirements of paragraph (e)(9)(ii) of this section will be issued an additional rating with a limitation.

(11) The limitation on a certificate issued under the provisions of paragraph (e)(10) of this section shall state, "This certificate is subject to pilot-in-command limitations for the additional rating."

(12) An applicant who has been issued a pilot certificate with the limitation specified in paragraph (e)(11) of this section—

(i) May not act as pilot in command of that airplane for which the additional rating was obtained under the provisions of this section until the limitation is removed from the pilot certificate; and

(ii) May have the limitation removed by accomplishing 25 hours of supervised operating experience as pilot in command under the supervision of a qualified and current pilot in command, in the seat normally occupied by the pilot in command, in that airplane of the same type to which the limitation applies.

(f) *Use of a flight simulator or flight training device for an additional rating in a helicopter.* The areas of operation required to be performed by paragraphs (b), (c), and (d) of this section shall be performed as follows:

(1) Except as provided in paragraph (f)(2) of this section, the areas of operation must be performed in a helicopter of the same type for the additional rating sought.

(2) Subject to the limitations of paragraph (f)(3) through (f)(12) of this section, the areas of operation may be performed in a flight simulator or flight training device that represents that helicopter for the additional rating sought.

(3) The use of a flight simulator or flight training device permitted by paragraph (f)(2) of this section shall be conducted in accordance with an approved course at a training center certificated under part 142 of this chapter.

(4) To complete all training and testing (except preflight inspection) for an additional helicopter rating without limitations when using a flight simulator—

(i) The flight simulator must be qualified and approved as Level C or Level D; and

(ii) The applicant must meet at least one of the following if a type rating is sought in a turbine-powered helicopter:

(A) Hold a type rating in a turbine-powered helicopter or have been appointed by a military service as a pilot in command of a turbine-powered helicopter.

(B) Have at least 2,000 hours of flight time that includes at least 500 hours in turbine-powered helicopters.

(C) Have at least 500 hours of flight time in turbine-powered helicopters.

(D) Have at least 1,000 hours of flight time in at least two different turbine-powered helicopters.

(5) Subject to the limitation of paragraph (f)(6) of this section, an applicant who does not meet the requirements of paragraph (f)(4) of this section may complete all training and testing (except for preflight inspection) for an additional rating when using a flight simulator if—

(i) The flight simulator is qualified and approved as Level C or Level D; and

(ii) The applicant meets at least one of the following:

(A) Holds a type rating in a turbine-powered helicopter if a type rating in a turbine-powered helicopter is sought; or

(B) Since the beginning of the 12th calendar month before the month in which the applicant completes the practical test for an additional helicopter rating, has logged at least 25 hours of flight time in helicopters of the same type for which the rating is sought.

(6) An applicant meeting only the requirements of paragraph (f)(5) of this section will be issued an additional rating with a limitation.

(7) The limitation on a certificate issued under the provisions of paragraph (f)(6) of this section shall state, "This certificate is subject to pilot-in-command limitations for the additional rating."

(8) An applicant who is issued a pilot certificate with the limitation specified in paragraph (f)(7) of this section—

(i) May not act as pilot in command of that helicopter for which the additional rating was obtained under the provisions of this section until the limitation is removed from the pilot certificate; and

(ii) May have the limitation removed by accomplishing 15 hours of supervised operating experience as pilot in command under the supervision of a qualified and current pilot in command, in the seat normally occupied by the pilot in command, in the same type of helicopter to which the limitation applies.

(9) An applicant who does not meet the requirements of paragraph (f)(4) or paragraph (f)(5) of this section may be issued an additional rating after successful completion of one of the following requirements:

(i) Compliance with paragraphs (f)(2) and (f)(3) of this section and the following tasks, which must be successfully completed on a static helicopter or in flight, as appropriate:

(A) Preflight inspection;

(B) Normal takeoff;

(C) Normal ILS approach;

(D) Missed approach; and

(E) Normal landing.

(ii) Compliance with paragraphs (f)(2), (f)(3), and (f)(10) through (f)(12) of this section.

(10) An applicant meeting only the requirements of paragraph (f)(9)(ii) of this section will be issued an additional rating with a limitation.

(11) The limitation on a certificate issued under the provisions of paragraph (f)(10) of this section shall state, "This certificate is subject to pilot-in-command limitations for the additional rating."

(12) An applicant who has been issued a pilot certificate with the limitation specified in paragraph (f)(11) of this section—

(i) May not act as pilot in command of that helicopter for which the additional rating was obtained under the provisions of this section until the limitation is removed from the pilot certificate; and

(ii) May have the limitation removed by accomplishing 25 hours of supervised operating experience as pilot in command under the supervision of a qualified and current pilot in command, in the seat normally occupied by the pilot in command, in that helicopter of the same type as to which the limitation applies.

(g) *Use of a flight simulator or flight training device for an additional rating in a powered-lift.* The areas of operation required to be performed by paragraphs (b), (c), and (d) of this section shall be performed as follows:

(1) Except as provided in paragraph (g)(2) of this section, the areas of operation must be performed in a powered-lift of the same type for the additional rating sought.

(2) Subject to the limitations of paragraphs (g)(3) through (g)(12) of this section, the areas of operation may be performed in a flight simulator or flight training device that represents that powered-lift for the additional rating sought.

(3) The use of a flight simulator or flight training device permitted by paragraph (g)(2) of this section shall be conducted in accordance with an approved course at a training center certificated under part 142 of this chapter.

(4) To complete all training and testing (except preflight inspection) for an additional powered-lift rating without limitations when using a flight simulator—

(i) The flight simulator must be qualified and approved as Level C or Level D; and

(ii) The applicant must meet at least one of the following if a type rating is sought in a turbine powered-lift:

(A) Hold a type rating in a turbine powered-lift or have been appointed by a military service as a pilot in command of a turbine powered-lift.

(B) Have at least 2,000 hours of flight time that includes at least 500 hours in turbine powered-lifts.

(C) Have at least 500 hours of flight time in turbine powered-lifts.

(D) Have at least 1,000 hours of flight time in at least two different turbine powered-lifts.

(5) Subject to the limitation of paragraph (g)(6) of this section, an applicant who does not meet the requirements of paragraph (g)(4) of this section may complete all training and testing (except for preflight inspection) for an additional rating when using a flight simulator if—

(i) The flight simulator is qualified and approved as Level C or Level D; and

(ii) The applicant meets at least one of the following:

(A) Holds a type rating in a turbine powered-lift if a type rating in a turbine powered-lift is sought; or

(B) Since the beginning of the 12th calendar month before the month in which the applicant completes the practical test for an additional powered-lift rating, has logged at least 25 hours of flight time in powered-lifts of the same type for which the rating is sought.

(6) An applicant meeting only the requirements of paragraph (g)(5) of this section will be issued an additional rating with a limitation.

(7) The limitation on a certificate issued under the provisions of paragraph (g)(6) of this section shall state, "This certificate is subject to pilot-in-command limitations for the additional rating."

(8) An applicant who is issued a pilot certificate with the limitation specified in paragraph (g)(7) of this section—

(i) May not act as pilot in command of that powered-lift for which the additional rating was obtained under the provisions of this section until the limitation is removed from the pilot certificate; and

(ii) May have the limitation removed by accomplishing 15 hours of supervised operating experience as pilot in command under the supervision of a qualified and current pilot in command, in the seat normally occupied by the pilot in command, in the same type of powered-lift to which the limitation applies.

(9) An applicant who does not meet the requirements of paragraph (g)(4) or paragraph (g)(5) of this section may be issued an additional rating after successful completion of one of the following requirements:

(i) Compliance with paragraphs (g)(2) and (g)(3) of this section and the following tasks, which must be successfully completed on a static powered-lift or in flight, as appropriate:

(A) Preflight inspection;

(B) Normal takeoff;

(C) Normal ILS approach;

(D) Missed approach; and

(E) Normal landing.

(ii) Compliance with paragraphs (g)(2), (g)(3), and (g)(10) through (g)(12) of this section.

(10) An applicant meeting only the requirements of paragraph (g)(9)(ii) of this section will be issued an additional rating with a limitation.

(11) The limitation on a certificate issued under the provisions of paragraph (g)(10) of this section shall state, "This certificate is subject to pilot-in-command limitations for the additional rating."

(12) An applicant who has been issued a pilot certificate with the limitation specified in paragraph (g)(11) of this section—

(i) May not act as pilot in command of that powered-lift for which the additional rating was obtained under the provisions of this section until the limitation is removed from the pilot certificate; and

(ii) May have the limitation removed by accomplishing 25 hours of supervised operating experience as pilot in command under the supervision of a qualified and current pilot in command, in the seat normally occupied by the pilot in command, in that powered-lift of the same type as to which the limitation applies.

(h) *Aircraft not capable of instrument maneuvers and procedures.* An applicant for a type rating who provides an aircraft not capable of the instrument maneuvers and procedures required by the appropriate requirements contained in § 61.157 of this part for the practical test may—

(1) Obtain a type rating limited to "VFR only"; and

(2) Remove the "VFR only" limitation for each aircraft type in which the applicant demonstrates compliance with the appropriate instrument requirements contained in § 61.157 or § 61.73 of this part.

(i) *Multiengine, single-pilot station airplane.* An applicant for a type rating in a multiengine, single-pilot station airplane may meet the requirements of this part in a multiseat version of that multiengine airplane.

(j) *Single-engine, single-pilot station airplane.* An applicant for a type rating in a single-engine, single-pilot station airplane may meet the requirements of this part in a multiseat version of that single-engine airplane.

(k) *Waivers.* Unless the Administrator requires certain or all tasks to be performed, the examiner who conducts the practical test may waive any of the tasks for which the Administrator approves waiver authority.

[Docket No. 25910, 62 FR 16298, April 4, 1997; as amended by Amdt. 61–103, 62 FR 40899, July 30, 1997; Amdt. 61–104, 63 FR 20287, April 23, 1998]

§ 61.64 [Reserved]

§ 61.65 Instrument rating requirements.

(a) *General.* A person who applies for an instrument rating must:

(1) Hold at least a current private pilot certificate with an airplane, helicopter, or powered-lift rating appropriate to the instrument rating sought;

(2) Be able to read, speak, write, and understand the English language. If the applicant is unable to meet any of these requirements due to a medical condition, the Administrator may place such operating limitations on the applicant's pilot certificate as are necessary for the safe operation of the aircraft;

(3) Receive and log ground training from an authorized instructor or accomplish a home-study course of training on the aeronautical knowledge areas of paragraph (b) of this section that apply to the instrument rating sought;

(4) Receive a logbook or training record endorsement from an authorized instructor certifying that the person is prepared to take the required knowledge test;

(5) Receive and log training on the areas of operation of paragraph (c) of this section from an authorized instructor in an aircraft, flight simulator, or flight training device that represents an airplane, helicopter, or powered-lift appropriate to the instrument rating sought;

(6) Receive a logbook or training record endorsement from an authorized instructor certifying

that the person is prepared to take the required practical test;

(7) Pass the required knowledge test on the aeronautical knowledge areas of paragraph (b) of this section; however, an applicant is not required to take another knowledge test when that person already holds an instrument rating; and

(8) Pass the required practical test on the areas of operation in paragraph (c) of this section in—

(i) An airplane, helicopter, or powered-lift appropriate to the rating sought; or

(ii) A flight simulator or a flight training device appropriate to the rating sought and approved for the specific maneuver or procedure performed. If a flight training device is used for the practical test, the instrument approach procedures conducted in that flight training device are limited to one precision and one nonprecision approach, provided the flight training device is approved for the procedure performed.

(b) *Aeronautical knowledge.* A person who applies for an instrument rating must have received and logged ground training from an authorized instructor or accomplished a home-study course on the following aeronautical knowledge areas that apply to the instrument rating sought:

(1) Federal Aviation Regulations of this chapter that apply to flight operations under IFR;

(2) Appropriate information that applies to flight operations under IFR in the "Aeronautical Information Manual;"

(3) Air traffic control system and procedures for instrument flight operations;

(4) IFR navigation and approaches by use of navigation systems;

(5) Use of IFR en route and instrument approach procedure charts;

(6) Procurement and use of aviation weather reports and forecasts and the elements of forecasting weather trends based on that information and personal observation of weather conditions;

(7) Safe and efficient operation of aircraft under instrument flight rules and conditions;

(8) Recognition of critical weather situations and windshear avoidance;

(9) Aeronautical decision making and judgment; and

(10) Crew resource management, including crew communication and coordination.

(c) *Flight proficiency.* A person who applies for an instrument rating must receive and log training from an authorized instructor in an aircraft, or in a flight simulator or flight training device, in accordance with paragraph (e) of this section, that includes the following areas of operation:

(1) Preflight preparation;

(2) Preflight procedures;

(3) Air traffic control clearances and procedures;

(4) Flight by reference to instruments;

(5) Navigation systems;

(6) Instrument approach procedures;

(7) Emergency operations; and

(8) Postflight procedures.

(d) *Aeronautical experience.* A person who applies for an instrument rating must have logged the following:

(1) At least 50 hours of cross-country flight time as pilot in command, of which at least 10 hours must be in airplanes for an instrument-airplane rating; and

(2) A total of 40 hours of actual or simulated instrument time on the areas of operation of this section, to include—

(i) At least 15 hours of instrument flight training from an authorized instructor in the aircraft category for which the instrument rating is sought;

(ii) At least 3 hours of instrument training that is appropriate to the instrument rating sought from an authorized instructor in preparation for the practical test within the 60 days preceding the date of the test;

(iii) For an instrument-airplane rating, instrument training on cross-country flight procedures specific to airplanes that includes at least one cross-country flight in an airplane that is performed under IFR, and consists of—

(A) A distance of at least 250 nautical miles along airways or ATC-directed routing;

(B) An instrument approach at each airport; and

(C) Three different kinds of approaches with the use of navigation systems;

(iv) For an instrument-helicopter rating, instrument training specific to helicopters on cross-country flight procedures that includes at least one cross-country flight in a helicopter that is performed under IFR, and consists of—

(A) A distance of at least 100 nautical miles along airways or ATC-directed routing;

(B) An instrument approach at each airport; and

(C) Three different kinds of approaches with the use of navigation systems; and

(v) For an instrument-powered-lift rating, instrument training specific to a powered-lift on cross-country flight procedures that includes at least one cross-country flight in a powered-lift that is performed under IFR and consists of—

(A) A distance of at least 250 nautical miles along airways or ATC-directed routing;

(B) An instrument approach at each airport; and

(C) Three different kinds of approaches with the use of navigation systems.

(e) *Use of flight simulators or flight training devices.* If the instrument training was provided by an authorized instructor in a flight simulator or flight training device—

(1) A maximum of 30 hours may be performed in that flight simulator or flight training device if the training was accomplished in accordance with part 142 of this chapter; or

(2) A maximum of 20 hours may be performed in that flight simulator or flight training device if the training was not accomplished in accordance with part 142 of this chapter.

§ 61.67 Category II pilot authorization requirements.

(a) *General.* A person who applies for a Category II pilot authorization must hold:

(1) At least a private or commercial pilot certificate with an instrument rating or an airline transport pilot certificate;

(2) A type rating for the aircraft for which the authorization is sought if that aircraft requires a type rating; and

(3) A category and class rating for the aircraft for which the authorization is sought.

(b) *Experience requirements.* An applicant for a Category II pilot authorization must have at least—

(1) 50 hours of night flight time as pilot in command.

(2) 75 hours of instrument time under actual or simulated instrument conditions that may include not more than—

(i) A combination of 25 hours of simulated instrument flight time in a flight simulator or flight training device; or

(ii) 40 hours of simulated instrument flight time if accomplished in an approved course conducted by an appropriately rated training center certificated under part 142 of this chapter.

(3) 250 hours of cross-country flight time as pilot in command.

(c) *Practical test requirements.*

(1) A practical test must be passed by a person who applies for—

(i) Issuance or renewal of a Category II pilot authorization; and

(ii) The addition of another type aircraft to the applicant's Category II pilot authorization.

(2) To be eligible for the practical test for an authorization under this section, an applicant must—

(i) Meet the requirements of paragraphs (a) and (b) of this section; and

(ii) If the applicant has not passed a practical test for this authorization during the 12 calendar months preceding the month of the test, then that person must—

(A) Meet the requirements of § 61.57(c); and

(B) Have performed at least six ILS approaches during the 6 calendar months preceding the month of the test, of which at least three of the approaches must have been conducted without the use of an approach coupler.

(3) The approaches specified in paragraph (c)(2)(ii)(B) of this section—

(i) Must be conducted under actual or simulated instrument flight conditions;

(ii) Must be conducted to the decision height for the ILS approach in the type aircraft in which the practical test is to be conducted;

(iii) Need not be conducted to the decision height authorized for Category II operations;

(iv) Must be conducted to the decision height authorized for Category II operations only if conducted in a flight simulator or flight training device; and

(v) Must be accomplished in an aircraft of the same category and class, and type, as applicable, as the aircraft in which the practical test is to be conducted or in a flight simulator that—

(A) Represents an aircraft of the same category and class, and type, as applicable, as the aircraft in which the authorization is sought; and

(B) Is used in accordance with an approved course conducted by a training center certificated under part 142 of this chapter.

(4) The flight time acquired in meeting the requirements of paragraph (c)(2)(ii)(B) of this section may be used to meet the requirements of paragraph (c)(2)(ii)(A) of this section.

(d) *Practical test procedures.* The practical test consists of an oral increment and a flight increment.

(1) *Oral increment.* In the oral increment of the practical test an applicant must demonstrate knowledge of the following:

(i) Required landing distance;

(ii) Recognition of the decision height;

(iii) Missed approach procedures and techniques using computed or fixed attitude guidance displays;

(iv) Use and limitations of RVR;

(v) Use of visual clues, their availability or limitations, and altitude at which they are normally discernible at reduced RVR readings;

(vi) Procedures and techniques related to transition from nonvisual to visual flight during a final approach under reduced RVR;

(vii) Effects of vertical and horizontal windshear;

(viii) Characteristics and limitations of the ILS and runway lighting system;

(ix) Characteristics and limitations of the flight director system, auto approach coupler (including split axis type if equipped), auto throttle system (if equipped), and other required Category II equipment;

(x) Assigned duties of the second in command during Category II approaches, unless the aircraft for which authorization is sought does not require a second in command; and

(xi) Instrument and equipment failure warning systems.

(2) *Flight increment.* The following requirements apply to the flight increment of the practical test:

(i) The flight increment must be conducted in an aircraft of the same category, class, and type, as applicable, as the aircraft in which the authorization is sought or in a flight simulator that—

(A) Represents an aircraft of the same category and class, and type, as applicable, as the aircraft in which the authorization is sought; and

(B) Is used in accordance with an approved course conducted by a training center certificated under part 142 of this chapter.

(ii) The flight increment must consist of at least two ILS approaches to 100 feet AGL including at least one landing and one missed approach.

(iii) All approaches performed during the flight increment must be made with the use of an approved flight control guidance system, except if an approved auto approach coupler is installed, at least one approach must be hand flown using flight director commands.

(iv) If a multiengine airplane with the performance capability to execute a missed approach with one engine inoperative is used for the practical test, the flight increment must include the performance of one missed approach with an engine, which shall be the most critical engine, if applicable, set at idle or zero thrust before reaching the middle marker.

(v) If a multiengine flight simulator or multiengine flight training device is used for the practical test, the applicant must execute a missed approach with the most critical engine, if applicable, failed.

(vi) For an authorization for an aircraft that requires a type rating, the practical test must be performed in coordination with a second in command who holds a type rating in the aircraft in which the authorization is sought.

(vii) Oral questioning may be conducted at any time during a practical test.

[Docket No. 25910, 62 FR 16298, April 4, 1997; as amended by Amdt. 61–103, 62 FR 40900, July 30, 1997]

§ 61.68 Category III pilot authorization requirements.

(a) *General.* A person who applies for a Category III pilot authorization must hold:

(1) At least a private pilot certificate or commercial pilot certificate with an instrument rating or an airline transport pilot certificate;

(2) A type rating for the aircraft for which the authorization is sought if that aircraft requires a type rating; and

(3) A category and class rating for the aircraft for which the authorization is sought.

(b) *Experience requirements.* An applicant for a Category III pilot authorization must have at least—

(1) 50 hours of night flight time as pilot in command.

(2) 75 hours of instrument flight time during actual or simulated instrument conditions that may include not more than—

(i) A combination of 25 hours of simulated instrument flight time in a flight simulator or flight training device; or

(ii) 40 hours of simulated instrument flight time if accomplished in an approved course conducted by an appropriately rated training center certificated under part 142 of this chapter.

(3) 250 hours of cross-country flight time as pilot in command.

(c) *Practical test requirements.*

(1) A practical test must be passed by a person who applies for—

(i) Issuance or renewal of a Category III pilot authorization; and

(ii) The addition of another type of aircraft to the applicant's Category III pilot authorization.

(2) To be eligible for the practical test for an authorization under this section, an applicant must—

(i) Meet the requirements of paragraphs (a) and (b) of this section; and

(ii) If the applicant has not passed a practical test for this authorization during the 12 calendar months preceding the month of the test, then that person must—

(A) Meet the requirements of § 61.57(c); and

(B) Have performed at least six ILS approaches during the 6 calendar months preceding the month of the test, of which at least three of the approaches must have been conducted without the use of an approach coupler.

(3) The approaches specified in paragraph (c)(2)(ii)(B) of this section—

(i) Must be conducted under actual or simulated instrument flight conditions;

(ii) Must be conducted to the alert height or decision height for the ILS approach in the type aircraft in which the practical test is to be conducted;

(iii) Need not be conducted to the decision height authorized for Category III operations;

(iv) Must be conducted to the alert height or decision height, as applicable, authorized for Category III operations only if conducted in a flight simulator or flight training device; and

(v) Must be accomplished in an aircraft of the same category and class, and type, as applicable, as the aircraft in which the practical test is to be conducted or in a flight simulator that—

(A) Represents an aircraft of the same category and class, and type, as applicable, as the aircraft for which the authorization is sought; and

(B) Is used in accordance with an approved course conducted by a training center certificated under part 142 of this chapter.

(4) The flight time acquired in meeting the requirements of paragraph (c)(2)(ii)(B) of this section may be used to meet the requirements of paragraph (c)(2)(ii)(A) of this section.

(d) *Practical test procedures.* The practical test consists of an oral increment and a flight increment.

(1) *Oral increment.* In the oral increment of the practical test an applicant must demonstrate knowledge of the following:

(i) Required landing distance;

(ii) Determination and recognition of the alert height or decision height, as applicable, including use of a radar altimeter;

(iii) Recognition of and proper reaction to significant failures encountered prior to and after reaching the alert height or decision height, as applicable;

(iv) Missed approach procedures and techniques using computed or fixed attitude guidance displays and expected height loss as they relate to manual go-around or automatic go-around, and initiation altitude, as applicable;

(v) Use and limitations of RVR, including determination of controlling RVR and required transmissometers;

(vi) Use, availability, or limitations of visual cues and the altitude at which they are normally discernible at reduced RVR readings including—

(A) Unexpected deterioration of conditions to less than minimum RVR during approach, flare, and rollout;

(B) Demonstration of expected visual references with weather at minimum conditions;

(C) The expected sequence of visual cues during an approach in which visibility is at or above landing minima; and

(D) Procedures and techniques for making a transition from instrument reference flight to visual flight during a final approach under reduced RVR.

(vii) Effects of vertical and horizontal windshear;

(viii) Characteristics and limitations of the ILS and runway lighting system;

(ix) Characteristics and limitations of the flight director system auto approach coupler (including split axis type if equipped), auto throttle system (if equipped), and other Category III equipment;

(x) Assigned duties of the second in command during Category III operations, unless the aircraft for which authorization is sought does not require a second in command;

(xi) Recognition of the limits of acceptable aircraft position and flight path tracking during approach, flare, and, if applicable, rollout; and

(xii) Recognition of, and reaction to, airborne or ground system faults or abnormalities, particularly after passing alert height or decision height, as applicable.

(2) *Flight increment.* The following requirements apply to the flight increment of the practical test—

(i) The flight increment may be conducted in an aircraft of the same category and class, and type, as applicable, as the aircraft for which the authorization is sought, or in a flight simulator that—

(A) Represents an aircraft of the same category and class, and type, as applicable, as the aircraft in which the authorization is sought; and

(B) Is used in accordance with an approved course conducted by a training center certificated under part 142 of this chapter.

(ii) The flight increment must consist of at least two ILS approaches to 100 feet AGL, including one landing and one missed approach initiated from a very low altitude that may result in a touchdown during the go-around maneuver;

(iii) All approaches performed during the flight increment must be made with the approved automatic landing system or an equivalent landing system approved by the Administrator;

(iv) If a multiengine aircraft with the performance capability to execute a missed approach with one engine inoperative is used for the practical test, the flight increment must include the performance of one missed approach with the most critical engine, if applicable, set at idle or zero thrust before reaching the middle or outer marker;

(v) If a multiengine flight simulator or multiengine flight training device is used, a missed approach must be executed with an engine, which shall be the most critical engine, if applicable, failed;

(vi) For an authorization for an aircraft that requires a type rating, the practical test must be performed in coordination with a second in command who holds a type rating in the aircraft in which the authorization is sought;

(vii) Oral questioning may be conducted at any time during the practical test;

(viii) Subject to the limitations of this paragraph, for Category IIIb operations predicated on the use of a fail-passive rollout control system, at least one manual rollout using visual reference or a combination of visual and instrument references must be executed. The maneuver required by this paragraph shall be initiated by a fail-passive disconnect of the rollout control system—

(A) After main gear touchdown;

(B) Prior to nose gear touchdown;

(C) In conditions representative of the most adverse lateral touchdown displacement allowing a safe landing on the runway; and

(D) In weather conditions anticipated in Category IIIb operations.

[Docket No. 25910, 62 FR 16298, April 4, 1997; as amended by Amdt. 61–103, 62 FR 40900, July 30, 1997]

§ 61.69 Glider towing: Experience and training requirements.

(a) No person may act as pilot in command for towing a glider unless that person:

(1) Holds at least a private pilot certificate with a category rating for powered aircraft;

(2) Has logged at least 100 hours of pilot-in-command time in the aircraft category, class, and type, if required, that the pilot is using to tow a glider;

(3) Has a logbook endorsement from an authorized instructor who certifies that the person has received ground and flight training in gliders and is proficient in—

(i) The techniques and procedures essential to the safe towing of gliders, including airspeed limitations;

(ii) Emergency procedures;

(iii) Signals used; and

(iv) Maximum angles of bank.

(4) Except as provided in paragraph (b) of this section, has logged at least three flights as the sole manipulator of the controls of an aircraft towing a glider or simulating glider-towing flight procedures while accompanied by a pilot who meets the requirements of paragraphs (c) and (d) of this section;

(5) Except as provided in paragraph (b) of this section, has received a logbook endorsement from the pilot, described in paragraph (a)(4) of this section, certifying that the person has accomplished at least 3 flights in an aircraft while towing a glider, or while simulating glider-towing flight procedures; and

(6) Within the preceding 12 months has—

(i) Made at least three actual or simulated glider tows while accompanied by a qualified pilot who meets the requirements of this section; or

(ii) Made at least three flights as pilot in command of a glider towed by an aircraft.

(b) Any person who before May 17, 1967, has made and logged 10 or more flights as pilot in command of an aircraft towing a glider in accordance with a certificate of waiver need not comply with paragraphs (a)(4) and (a)(5) of this section.

(c) The pilot, described in paragraph (a)(4) of this section, who endorses the logbook of a person seeking glider-towing privileges must have:

(1) Met the requirements of this section prior to endorsing the logbook of the person seeking glider-towing privileges; and

(2) Logged at least 10 flights as pilot in command of an aircraft while towing a glider.

(d) If the pilot described in paragraph (a)(4) of this section holds only a private pilot certificate, then that pilot must have:

(1) Logged at least 100 hours of pilot-in-command time in airplanes, or 200 hours of pilot-in-

command time in a combination of powered and other-than-powered aircraft; and

(2) Performed and logged at least three flights within the 12 calendar months preceding the month that pilot accompanies or endorses the logbook of a person seeking glider-towing privileges—

(i) In an aircraft while towing a glider accompanied by another pilot who meets the requirements of this section; or

(ii) As pilot in command of a glider being towed by an aircraft.

[Docket No. 25910, 62 FR 16298, April 4, 1997; as amended by Amdt. 61–103, 62 FR 40901, July 30, 1997]

§ 61.71 Graduates of an approved training program other than under this part: Special rules.

(a) A person who graduates from an approved training program under part 141 or part 142 of this chapter is considered to have met the applicable aeronautical experience, aeronautical knowledge, and areas of operation requirements of this part if that person presents the graduation certificate and passes the required practical test within the 60-day period after the date of graduation.

(b) A person may apply for an airline transport pilot certificate, type rating, or both under this part, and will be considered to have met the applicable requirements under § 61.157 of this part for that certificate and rating, if that person has:

(1) Satisfactorily accomplished an approved training program and the pilot-in-command proficiency check for that airplane type, in accordance with the pilot-in-command requirements under subparts N and O of part 121 of this chapter; and

(2) Applied for the airline transport pilot certificate, type rating, or both within the 60-day period from the date the person satisfactorily accomplished the approved training program and pilot-in-command proficiency check for that airplane type.

[Docket No. 25910, 62 FR 16298, April 4, 1997; as amended by Amdt. 61–103, 62 FR 40901, July 30, 1997]

§ 61.73 Military pilots or former military pilots: Special rules.

(a) *General.* Except for a rated military pilot or former rated military pilot who has been removed from flying status for lack of proficiency, or because of disciplinary action involving aircraft operations, a rated military pilot or former rated military pilot who meets the applicable requirements of this section may apply, on the basis of his or her military training, for:

(1) A commercial pilot certificate;

(2) An aircraft rating in the category and class of aircraft for which that military pilot is qualified;

(3) An instrument rating with the appropriate aircraft rating for which that military pilot is qualified; or

(4) A type rating, if appropriate.

(b) *Military pilots on active flying status within the past 12 months.* A rated military pilot or former rated military pilot who has been on active flying status within the 12 months before applying must:

(1) Pass a knowledge test on the appropriate parts of this chapter that apply to pilot privileges and limitations, air traffic and general operating rules, and accident reporting rules;

(2) Present documentation showing compliance with the requirements of paragraph (d) of this section for at least one aircraft category rating; and

(3) Present documentation showing that the applicant is or was, at any time during the 12 calendar months before the month of application—

(i) A rated military pilot on active flying status in an armed force of the United States; or

(ii) A rated military pilot of an armed force of a foreign contracting State to the Convention on International Civil Aviation, assigned to pilot duties (other than flight training) with an armed force of the United States and holds, at the time of application, a current civil pilot license issued by that contracting State authorizing at least the privileges of the pilot certificate sought.

(c) *Military pilots not on active flying status during the 12 calendar months before the month of application.* A rated military pilot or former rated military pilot who has not been on active flying status within the 12 calendar months before the month of application must:

(1) Pass the appropriate knowledge and practical tests prescribed in this part for the certificate or rating sought; and

(2) Present documentation showing that the applicant was, before the beginning of the 12th calendar month before the month of application, a rated military pilot as prescribed by paragraph (b)(3)(i) or paragraph (b)(3)(ii) of this section.

(d) *Aircraft category, class, and type ratings.* A rated military pilot or former rated military pilot who applies for an aircraft category, class, or type rating, if applicable, is issued that rating at the commercial pilot certificate level if the pilot presents documentary evidence that shows satisfactory accomplishment of:

(1) An official U.S. military pilot check and instrument proficiency check in that aircraft category, class, or type, if applicable, as pilot in command during the 12 calendar months before the month of application;

(2) At least 10 hours of pilot-in-command time in that aircraft category, class, or type, if applicable, during the 12 calendar months before the month of application; or

(3) An FAA practical test in that aircraft after—

(i) Meeting the requirements of paragraphs (b)(1) and (b)(2) of this section; and

(ii) Having received an endorsement from an authorized instructor who certifies that the pilot is proficient to take the required practical test, and that endorsement is made within the 60-day period preceding the date of the practical test.

(e) *Instrument rating.* A rated military pilot or former rated military pilot who applies for an airplane instrument rating, a helicopter instrument rating, or a powered-lift instrument rating to be added to his or her commercial pilot certificate may apply for an instrument rating if the pilot has, within the 12 calendar months preceding the month of application:

(1) Passed an instrument proficiency check by a U.S. Armed Force in the aircraft category for the instrument rating sought; and

(2) Received authorization from a U.S. Armed Force to conduct IFR flights on Federal airways in that aircraft category and class for the instrument rating sought.

(f) *Aircraft type rating.* An aircraft type rating is issued only for aircraft types that the Administrator has certificated for civil operations.

(g) *Aircraft type rating placed on an airline transport pilot certificate.* A rated military pilot or former rated military pilot who holds an airline transport pilot certificate and who requests an aircraft type rating to be placed on that person's airline transport pilot certificate may be issued that aircraft type rating at the airline transport pilot certificate level, provided that person:

(1) Holds a category and class rating for that type of aircraft at the airline transport pilot certificate level; and

(2) Passed an official U.S. military pilot check and instrument proficiency check in that type of aircraft as pilot in command during the 12 calendar months before the month of application.

(h) *Evidentiary documents.* The following documents are satisfactory evidence for the purposes indicated:

(1) An official identification card issued to the pilot by an armed force may be used to demonstrate membership in the armed forces.

(2) An original or a copy of a certificate of discharge or release may be used to demonstrate discharge or release from an armed force or former membership in an armed force.

(3) Current or previous status as a rated military pilot with a U.S. Armed Force may be demonstrated by—

(i) An official U.S. Armed Force order to flight status as a military pilot;

(ii) An official U.S. Armed Force form or logbook showing military pilot status; or

(iii) An official order showing that the rated military pilot graduated from a U.S. military pilot school and received a rating as a military pilot.

(4) A certified U.S. Armed Force logbook or an appropriate official U.S. Armed Force form or summary may be used to demonstrate flight time in military aircraft as a member of a U.S. Armed Force.

(5) An official U.S. Armed Force record of a military checkout as pilot in command may be used to demonstrate pilot in command status.

(6) A current instrument grade slip that is issued by a U.S. Armed Force, or an official record of satisfactory accomplishment of an instrument proficiency check during the 12 calendar months preceding the month of the application may be used to demonstrate instrument pilot qualification.

[Docket No. 25910, 62 FR 16298, April 4, 1997; as amended by Amdt. 61–103, 62 FR 40901, July 30, 1997]

§ 61.75 Private pilot certificate issued on the basis of a foreign pilot license.

(a) *General.* A person who holds a current foreign pilot license issued by a contracting State to the Convention on International Civil Aviation may apply for and be issued a private pilot certificate with the appropriate ratings when the application is based on the foreign pilot license that meets the requirements of this section.

(b) *Certificate issued.* A U.S. private pilot certificate that is issued under this section shall specify the person's foreign license number and country of issuance. A person who holds a current foreign pilot license issued by a contracting State to the Convention on International Civil Aviation may be issued a private pilot certificate based on the foreign pilot license without any further showing of proficiency, provided the applicant:

(1) Meets the requirements of this section;

(2) Holds a foreign pilot license that—

(i) Is not under an order of revocation or suspension by the foreign country that issued the foreign pilot license; and

(ii) Does not contain an endorsement stating that the applicant has not met all of the standards of ICAO for that license;

(3) Does not currently hold a U.S. pilot certificate;

(4) Holds a current medical certificate issued under part 67 of this chapter or a current medical certificate issued by the country that issued the person's foreign pilot license; and

(5) Is able to read, speak, write, and understand the English language. If the applicant is unable to meet one of these requirements due to medical reasons, then the Administrator may place such operating limitations on that applicant's pilot certificate as are necessary for the safe operation of the aircraft.

(c) *Aircraft ratings issued.* Aircraft ratings listed on a person's foreign pilot license, in addition to any issued after testing under the provisions of this part, may be placed on that person's U.S. pilot certificate.

(d) *Instrument ratings issued.* A person who holds an instrument rating on the foreign pilot license issued by a contracting State to the Convention on International Civil Aviation may be issued an instrument rating on a U.S. private pilot certificate provided:

(1) The person's foreign pilot license authorizes instrument privileges;

(2) Within 24 months preceding the month in which the person applies for the instrument rating, the person passes the appropriate knowledge test; and

(3) The person is able to read, speak, write, and understand the English language. If the applicant is unable to meet one of these requirements due to medical reasons, then the Administrator may place such operating limitations on that applicant's pilot certificate as are necessary for the safe operation of the aircraft.

(e) *Operating privileges and limitations.* A person who receives a U.S. private pilot certificate that has been issued under the provisions of this section:

(1) May act as a pilot of a civil aircraft of U.S. registry in accordance with the private pilot privileges authorized by this part;

(2) Is limited to the privileges placed on the certificate by the Administrator;

(3) Is subject to the limitations and restrictions on the person's U.S. certificate and foreign pilot license when exercising the privileges of that U.S. pilot certificate in an aircraft of U.S. registry operating within or outside the United States; and

(4) Shall not exercise the privileges of that U.S. private pilot certificate when the person's foreign pilot license has been revoked or suspended.

(f) *Limitation on licenses used as the basis for a U.S. certificate.* Only one foreign pilot license may be used as a basis for issuing a U.S. private pilot certificate. The foreign pilot license and medical certification used as a basis for issuing a U.S. private pilot certificate under this section must be in the English language or accompanied by an English language transcription that has been signed by an official or representative of the foreign aviation authority that issued the foreign pilot license.

(g) *Limitation placed on a U.S. private pilot certificate.* A U.S. private pilot certificate issued under this section is valid only when the holder has the foreign pilot license upon which the issuance of the U.S. private pilot certificate was based in the holder's personal possession or readily accessible in the aircraft.

§ 61.77 Special purpose pilot authorization: Operation of U.S.-registered civil aircraft leased by a person who is not a U.S. citizen.

(a) *General.* The holder of a foreign pilot license issued by a contracting State to the Convention on International Civil Aviation who meets the requirements of this section may be issued a special purpose pilot authorization by the Administrator for the purpose of performing pilot duties.

(1) On a civil aircraft of U.S. registry that is leased to a person who is not a citizen of the United States, and

(2) For carrying persons or property for compensation or hire on that aircraft.

(b) *Eligibility.* To be eligible for the issuance or renewal of a special purpose pilot authorization, an applicant must present the following to an FAA Flight Standards District Office:

(1) A current foreign pilot license that has been issued by the aeronautical authority of a contracting State to the Convention on International Civil Aviation from which the person holds citizenship or resident status and that contains the appropriate aircraft category, class, instrument rating, and type rating, if appropriate, for the aircraft to be flown;

(2) A current certification by the lessee of the aircraft—

(i) Stating that the applicant is employed by the lessee;

(ii) Specifying the aircraft type on which the applicant will perform pilot duties; and

(iii) Stating that the applicant has received ground and flight instruction that qualifies the applicant to perform the duties to be assigned on the aircraft.

(3) Documentation showing when the applicant will reach the age of 60 years (an official copy of the applicant's birth certificate or other official documentation);

(4) Documentation that the applicant meets the medical standards for the issuance of the foreign pilot license from the aeronautical authority of the contracting State to the Convention on International Civil Aviation where the applicant holds citizenship or resident status;

(5) Documentation that the applicant meets the recent flight experience requirements of this part (a logbook or flight record); and

(6) A statement that the applicant does not already hold a special purpose pilot authorization; however, if the applicant already holds a special purpose pilot authorization, then that special purpose pilot authorization must be surrendered to either the FAA Flight Standards District Office that issued it, or the FAA Flight Standards District Office processing the application for the authoriza-

tion, prior to being issued another special purpose pilot authorization.

(c) *Privileges.* A person issued a special purpose pilot authorization under this section—

(1) May exercise the privileges prescribed on the special purpose pilot authorization; and

(2) Must comply with the limitations specified in this section and any additional limitations specified on the special purpose pilot authorization.

(d) *General limitations.* A special purpose pilot authorization is valid only—

(1) For flights between foreign countries or for flights in foreign air commerce within the time period allotted on the authorization;

(2) If the foreign pilot license required by paragraph (b)(1) of this section, the medical documentation required by paragraph (b)(4) of this section, and the special purpose pilot authorization issued under this section are in the holder's physical possession or immediately accessible in the aircraft;

(3) While the holder is employed by the person to whom the aircraft described in the certification required by paragraph (b)(2) of this section is leased;

(4) While the holder is performing pilot duties on the U.S.-registered aircraft described in the certification required by paragraph (b)(2) of this section; and

(5) If the holder has only one special purpose pilot authorization as provided in paragraph (b)(6) of this section.

(e) *Age limitation.* Except as provided in paragraph (g) of this section, no person who holds a special purpose pilot authorization issued under this part, and no person who holds a special purpose pilot certificate issued under this part before August 4, 1997, shall serve as a pilot on a civil airplane of U.S. registry if the person has reached his or her 60th birthday, in the following operations:

(1) Scheduled international air services carrying passengers in turbojet-powered airplanes;

(2) Scheduled international air services carrying passengers in airplanes having a passenger-seat configuration of more than nine passenger seats, excluding each crewmember seat;

(3) Nonscheduled international air transportation for compensation or hire in airplanes having a passenger-seat configuration of more than 30 passenger seats, excluding each crewmember seat; or

(4) Scheduled international air services, or nonscheduled international air transportation for compensation or hire, in airplanes having a payload capacity of more than 7,500 pounds.

(f) *Definitions.*

(1) *International air service,* as used in paragraph (e) of this section, means scheduled air service performed in airplanes for the public transport of passengers, mail, or cargo, in which

the service passes through the air space over the territory of more than one country.

(2) *International air transportation,* as used in paragraph (e) of this section, means air transportation performed in airplanes for the public transport of passengers, mail, or cargo, in which service passes through the air space over the territory of more than one country.

(g) *Delayed pilot age limitations for certain operations.* Until December 20, 1999, a person may serve as a pilot in the operations specified in paragraph (e) of this section after that person has reached his or her 60th birthday, if, on March 20, 1997, that person was employed as a pilot in any of the following operations:

(1) Scheduled international air services carrying passengers in nontransport category turbo-propeller-powered airplanes type certificated after December 31, 1964, that have a passenger-seat configuration of 10 to 19 seats;

(2) Scheduled international air services carrying passengers in transport category turbopropeller-powered airplanes that have a passenger-seat configuration of 20 to 30 seats; or

(3) Scheduled international air services carrying passengers in turbojet-powered airplanes having a passenger-seat configuration of 1 to 30 seats.

(h) *Expiration date.* Each special purpose pilot authorization issued under this section expires—

(1) 60 calendar months from the month it was issued, unless sooner suspended or revoked;

(2) When the lease agreement for the aircraft expires or the lessee terminates the employment of the person who holds the special purpose pilot authorization;

(3) Whenever the person's foreign pilot license has been suspended, revoked, or is no longer valid; or

(4) When the person no longer meets the medical standards for the issuance of the foreign pilot license.

(i) *Renewal.* A person exercising the privileges of a special purpose pilot authorization may apply for a 60-calendar-month extension of that authorization, provided the person—

(1) Continues to meet the requirements of this section; and

(2) Surrenders the expired special purpose pilot authorization upon receipt of the new authorization.

(j) *Surrender.* The holder of a special purpose pilot authorization must surrender the authorization to the Administrator within 7 days after the date the authorization terminates.

[Docket No. 25910, 62 FR 40901, July 30, 1997]

Subpart C—Student Pilots

§ 61.81 Applicability.

This subpart prescribes the requirements for the issuance of student pilot certificates, the conditions under which those certificates are necessary, and the general operating rules and limitations for the holders of those certificates.

§ 61.83 Eligibility requirements for student pilots.

To be eligible for a student pilot certificate, an applicant must:

(a) Be at least 16 years of age for other than the operation of a glider or balloon.

(b) Be at least 14 years of age for the operation of a glider or balloon.

(c) Be able to read, speak, write, and understand the English language. If the applicant is unable to meet one of these requirements due to medical reasons, then the Administrator may place such operating limitations on that applicant's pilot certificate as are necessary for the safe operation of the aircraft.

§ 61.85 Application.

An application for a student pilot certificate is made on a form and in a manner provided by the Administrator and is submitted to:

(a) A designated aviation medical examiner if applying for an FAA medical certificate under part 67 of this chapter;

(b) An examiner; or

(c) A Flight Standards District Office.

§ 61.87 Solo requirements for student pilots.

(a) *General.* A student pilot may not operate an aircraft in solo flight unless that student has met the requirements of this section. The term "solo flight" as used in this subpart means that flight time during which a student pilot is the sole occupant of the aircraft or that flight time during which the student performs the duties of a pilot in command of a gas balloon or an airship requiring more than one pilot flight crewmember.

(b) *Aeronautical knowledge.* A student pilot must demonstrate satisfactory aeronautical knowledge on a knowledge test that meets the requirements of this paragraph:

(1) The test must address the student pilot's knowledge of—

(i) Applicable sections of parts 61 and 91 of this chapter;

(ii) Airspace rules and procedures for the airport where the solo flight will be performed; and

(iii) Flight characteristics and operational limitations for the make and model of aircraft to be flown.

(2) The student's authorized instructor must—

(i) Administer the test; and

(ii) At the conclusion of the test, review all incorrect answers with the student before authorizing that student to conduct a solo flight.

(c) *Pre-solo flight training.* Prior to conducting a solo flight, a student pilot must have:

(1) Received and logged flight training for the maneuvers and procedures of this section that are appropriate to the make and model of aircraft to be flown; and

(2) Demonstrated satisfactory proficiency and safety, as judged by an authorized instructor, on the maneuvers and procedures required by this section in the make and model of aircraft or similar make and model of aircraft to be flown.

(d) *Maneuvers and procedures for pre-solo flight training in a single-engine airplane.* A student pilot who is receiving training for a single-engine airplane rating must receive and log flight training for the following maneuvers and procedures:

(1) Proper flight preparation procedures, including preflight planning and preparation, power-plant operation, and aircraft systems;

(2) Taxiing or surface operations, including run-ups;

(3) Takeoffs and landings, including normal and crosswind;

(4) Straight and level flight, and turns in both directions;

(5) Climbs and climbing turns;

(6) Airport traffic patterns, including entry and departure procedures;

(7) Collision avoidance, windshear avoidance, and wake turbulence avoidance;

(8) Descents, with and without turns, using high and low drag configurations;

(9) Flight at various airspeeds from cruise to slow flight;

(10) Stall entries from various flight attitudes and power combinations with recovery initiated at the first indication of a stall, and recovery from a full stall;

(11) Emergency procedures and equipment malfunctions;

(12) Ground reference maneuvers;

(13) Approaches to a landing area with simulated engine malfunctions;

(14) Slips to a landing; and

(15) Go-arounds.

(e) *Maneuvers and procedures for pre-solo flight training in a multiengine airplane.* A student pilot who is receiving training for a multiengine airplane rating must receive and log flight training for the following maneuvers and procedures:

(1) Proper flight preparation procedures, including preflight planning and preparation, powerplant operation, and aircraft systems;

(2) Taxiing or surface operations, including run-ups;

(3) Takeoffs and landings, including normal and crosswind;

(4) Straight and level flight, and turns in both directions;

(5) Climbs and climbing turns;

(6) Airport traffic patterns, including entry and departure procedures;

(7) Collision avoidance, windshear avoidance, and wake turbulence avoidance;

(8) Descents, with and without turns, using high and low drag configurations;

(9) Flight at various airspeeds from cruise to slow flight;

(10) Stall entries from various flight attitudes and power combinations with recovery initiated at the first indication of a stall, and recovery from a full stall;

(11) Emergency procedures and equipment malfunctions;

(12) Ground reference maneuvers;

(13) Approaches to a landing area with simulated engine malfunctions; and

(14) Go-arounds.

(f) *Maneuvers and procedures for pre-solo flight training in a helicopter.* A student pilot who is receiving training for a helicopter rating must receive and log flight training for the following maneuvers and procedures:

(1) Proper flight preparation procedures, including preflight planning and preparation, powerplant operation, and aircraft systems;

(2) Taxiing or surface operations, including run-ups;

(3) Takeoffs and landings, including normal and crosswind;

(4) Straight and level flight, and turns in both directions;

(5) Climbs and climbing turns;

(6) Airport traffic patterns, including entry and departure procedures;

(7) Collision avoidance, windshear avoidance, and wake turbulence avoidance;

(8) Descents with and without turns;

(9) Flight at various airspeeds;

(10) Emergency procedures and equipment malfunctions;

(11) Ground reference maneuvers;

(12) Approaches to the landing area;

(13) Hovering and hovering turns;

(14) Go-arounds;

(15) Simulated emergency procedures, including autorotational descents with a power recovery and power recovery to a hover;

(16) Rapid decelerations; and

(17) Simulated one-engine-inoperative approaches and landings for multiengine helicopters.

(g) *Maneuvers and procedures for pre-solo flight training in a gyroplane.* A student pilot who is receiving training for a gyroplane rating must receive and log flight training for the following maneuvers and procedures:

(1) Proper flight preparation procedures, including preflight planning and preparation, powerplant operation, and aircraft systems;

(2) Taxiing or surface operations, including run-ups;

(3) Takeoffs and landings, including normal and crosswind;

(4) Straight and level flight, and turns in both directions;

(5) Climbs and climbing turns;

(6) Airport traffic patterns, including entry and departure procedures;

(7) Collision avoidance, windshear avoidance, and wake turbulence avoidance;

(8) Descents with and without turns;

(9) Flight at various airspeeds;

(10) Emergency procedures and equipment malfunctions;

(11) Ground reference maneuvers;

(12) Approaches to the landing area;

(13) High rates of descent with power on and with simulated power off, and recovery from those flight configurations;

(14) Go-arounds; and

(15) Simulated emergency procedures, including simulated power-off landings and simulated power failure during departures.

(h) *Maneuvers and procedures for pre-solo flight training in a powered-lift.* A student pilot who is receiving training for a powered-lift rating must receive and log flight training in the following maneuvers and procedures:

(1) Proper flight preparation procedures, including preflight planning and preparation, powerplant operation, and aircraft systems;

(2) Taxiing or surface operations, including run-ups;

(3) Takeoffs and landings, including normal and crosswind;

(4) Straight and level flight, and turns in both directions;

(5) Climbs and climbing turns;

(6) Airport traffic patterns, including entry and departure procedures;

(7) Collision avoidance, windshear avoidance, and wake turbulence avoidance;

(8) Descents with and without turns;

(9) Flight at various airspeeds from cruise to slow flight;

(10) Stall entries from various flight attitudes and power combinations with recovery initiated at the first indication of a stall, and recovery from a full stall;

(11) Emergency procedures and equipment malfunctions;

(12) Ground reference maneuvers;

(13) Approaches to a landing with simulated engine malfunctions;

(14) Go-arounds;

(15) Approaches to the landing area;

(16) Hovering and hovering turns; and

(17) For multiengine powered-lifts, simulated one-engine-inoperative approaches and landings.

(i) *Maneuvers and procedures for pre-solo flight training in a glider.* A student pilot who is receiving training for a glider rating must receive and log flight training for the following maneuvers and procedures:

(1) Proper flight preparation procedures, including preflight planning, preparation, aircraft systems, and, if appropriate, powerplant operations;

(2) Taxiing or surface operations, including run-ups, if applicable;

(3) Launches, including normal and crosswind;

(4) Straight and level flight, and turns in both directions, if applicable;

(5) Airport traffic patterns, including entry procedures;

(6) Collision avoidance, windshear avoidance, and wake turbulence avoidance;

(7) Descents with and without turns using high and low drag configurations;

(8) Flight at various airspeeds;

(9) Emergency procedures and equipment malfunctions;

(10) Ground reference maneuvers, if applicable;

(11) Inspection of towline rigging and review of signals and release procedures, if applicable;

(12) Aerotow, ground tow, or self-launch procedures;

(13) Procedures for disassembly and assembly of the glider;

(14) Stall entry, stall, and stall recovery;

(15) Straight glides, turns, and spirals;

(16) Landings, including normal and crosswind;

(17) Slips to a landing;

(18) Procedures and techniques for thermalling; and

(19) Emergency operations, including towline break procedures.

(j) *Maneuvers and procedures for pre-solo flight training in an airship.* A student pilot who is receiving training for an airship rating must receive and log flight training for the following maneuvers and procedures:

(1) Proper flight preparation procedures, including preflight planning and preparation, powerplant operation, and aircraft systems;

(2) Taxiing or surface operations, including run-ups;

(3) Takeoffs and landings, including normal and crosswind;

(4) Straight and level flight, and turns in both directions;

(5) Climbs and climbing turns;

(6) Airport traffic patterns, including entry and departure procedures;

(7) Collision avoidance, windshear avoidance, and wake turbulence avoidance;

(8) Descents with and without turns;

(9) Flight at various airspeeds from cruise to slow flight;

(10) Emergency procedures and equipment malfunctions;

(11) Ground reference maneuvers;

(12) Rigging, ballasting, and controlling pressure in the ballonets, and superheating; and

(13) Landings with positive and with negative static trim.

(k) *Maneuvers and procedures for pre-solo flight training in a balloon.* A student pilot who is receiving training in a balloon must receive and log flight training for the following maneuvers and procedures:

(1) Layout and assembly procedures;

(2) Proper flight preparation procedures, including preflight planning and preparation, and aircraft systems;

(3) Ascents and descents;

(4) Landing and recovery procedures;

(5) Emergency procedures and equipment malfunctions;

(6) Operation of hot air or gas source, ballast, valves, vents, and rip panels, as appropriate;

(7) Use of deflation valves or rip panels for simulating an emergency;

(8) The effects of wind on climb and approach angles; and

(9) Obstruction detection and avoidance techniques.

(l) *Limitations on student pilots operating an aircraft in solo flight.* A student pilot may not operate an aircraft in solo flight unless that student pilot has received:

(1) An endorsement from an authorized instructor on his or her student pilot certificate for the specific make and model aircraft to be flown; and

(2) An endorsement in the student's logbook for the specific make and model aircraft to be flown by an authorized instructor, who gave the training within the 90 days preceding the date of the flight.

(m) *Limitations on student pilots operating an aircraft in solo flight at night.* A student pilot may not operate an aircraft in solo flight at night unless that student pilot has received:

(1) Flight training at night on night flying procedures that includes takeoffs, approaches, landings, and go-arounds at night at the airport where the solo flight will be conducted;

(2) Navigation training at night in the vicinity of the airport where the solo flight will be conducted; and

(3) An endorsement in the student's logbook for the specific make and model aircraft to be flown for night solo flight by an authorized instructor who gave the training within the 90-day period preceding the date of the flight.

(n) *Limitations on flight instructors authorizing solo flight.*

(1) No instructor may authorize a student pilot to perform a solo flight unless that instructor has—

(i) Given that student pilot training in the make and model of aircraft or a similar make and model of aircraft in which the solo flight is to be flown;

(ii) Determined the student pilot is proficient in the maneuvers and procedures prescribed in this section;

(iii) Determined the student pilot is proficient in the make and model of aircraft to be flown;

(iv) Ensured that the student pilot's certificate has been endorsed by an instructor authorized to provide flight training for the specific make and model aircraft to be flown; and

(v) Endorsed the student pilot's logbook for the specific make and model aircraft to be flown, and that endorsement remains current for solo flight privileges, provided an authorized instructor updates the student's logbook every 90 days thereafter.

(2) The flight training required by this section must be given by an instructor authorized to provide flight training who is appropriately rated and current.

[Docket No. 25910, 62 FR 16298, April 4, 1997; as amended by Amdt. 61–103, 62 FR 40902, July 30, 1997; Amdt. 61–104, 63 FR 20287, April 23, 1998]

§ 61.89 General limitations.

(a) A student pilot may not act as pilot in command of an aircraft:

(1) That is carrying a passenger;

(2) That is carrying property for compensation or hire;

(3) For compensation or hire;

(4) In furtherance of a business;

(5) On an international flight, except that a student pilot may make solo training flights from Haines, Gustavus, or Juneau, Alaska, to White Horse, Yukon, Canada, and return over the province of British Columbia;

(6) With a flight or surface visibility of less than 3 statute miles during daylight hours or 5 statute miles at night;

(7) When the flight cannot be made with visual reference to the surface; or

(8) In a manner contrary to any limitations placed in the pilot's logbook by an authorized instructor.

(b) A student pilot may not act as a required pilot flight crewmember on any aircraft for which more than one pilot is required by the type certificate of the aircraft or regulations under which the flight is conducted, except when receiving flight training from an authorized instructor on board an airship, and no person other than a required flight crewmember is carried on the aircraft.

§ 61.91 [Reserved]

§ 61.93 Solo cross-country flight requirements.

(a) *General.*

(1) Except as provided in paragraph (b) of this section, a student pilot must meet the requirements of this section before—

(i) Conducting a solo cross-country flight, or any flight greater than 25 nautical miles from the airport from where the flight originated.

(ii) Making a solo flight and landing at any location other than the airport of origination.

(2) Except as provided in paragraph (b) of this section, a student pilot who seeks solo cross-country flight privileges must:

(i) Have received flight training from an instructor authorized to provide flight training on the maneuvers and procedures of this section that are appropriate to the make and model of aircraft for which solo cross-country privileges are sought;

(ii) Have demonstrated cross-country proficiency on the appropriate maneuvers and procedures of this section to an authorized instructor;

(iii) Have satisfactorily accomplished the pre-solo flight maneuvers and procedures required by § 61.87 of this part in the make and model of aircraft or similar make and model of aircraft for which solo cross-country privileges are sought; and

(iv) Comply with any limitations included in the authorized instructor's endorsement that are required by paragraph (c) of this section.

(3) A student pilot who seeks solo cross-country flight privileges must have received ground and flight training from an authorized instructor on the cross-country maneuvers and procedures listed in this section that are appropriate to the aircraft to be flown.

(b) *Authorization to perform certain solo flights and cross-country flights.* A student pilot must obtain an endorsement from an authorized instructor to make solo flights from the airport where the student pilot normally receives training to another location. A student pilot who receives this endorsement must comply with the requirements of this paragraph.

(1) Solo flights may be made to another airport that is within 25 nautical miles from the airport where the student pilot normally receives training, provided—

(i) An authorized instructor has given the student pilot flight training at the other airport, and that training includes flight in both directions over the route, entering and exiting the traffic pattern, and takeoffs and landings at the other airport;

(ii) The authorized instructor who gave the training endorses the student pilot's logbook authorizing the flight;

(iii) The student pilot has current solo flight endorsements in accordance with § 61.87 of this part;

(iv) The authorized instructor has determined that the student pilot is proficient to make the flight; and

(v) The purpose of the flight is to practice takeoffs and landings at that other airport.

(2) Repeated specific solo cross-country flights may be made to another airport that is within 50 nautical miles of the airport from which the flight originated, provided—

(i) The authorized instructor has given the student flight training in both directions over the route, including entering and exiting the traffic patterns, takeoffs, and landings at the airports to be used;

(ii) The authorized instructor who gave the training has endorsed the student's logbook certifying that the student is proficient to make such flights;

(iii) The student has current solo flight endorsements in accordance with § 61.87 of this part; and

(iv) The student has current solo cross-country flight endorsements in accordance with paragraph (c) of this section; however, for repeated solo cross-country flights to another airport within 50 nautical miles from which the flight originated, separate endorsements are not required to be made for each flight.

(c) *Endorsements for solo cross-country flights.* Except as specified in paragraph (b)(2) of this section, a student pilot must have the endorsements prescribed in this paragraph for each cross-country flight:

(1) *Student pilot certificate endorsement.* A student pilot must have a solo cross-country endorsement from the authorized instructor who conducted the training, and that endorsement must be placed on that person's student pilot certificate for the specific category of aircraft to be flown.

(2) *Logbook endorsement.*

(i) A student pilot must have a solo cross-country endorsement from an authorized instructor that is placed in the student pilot's logbook for the specific make and model of aircraft to be flown.

(ii) For each cross-country flight, the authorized instructor who reviews the cross-country planning must make an endorsement in the person's logbook after reviewing that person's cross-country planning, as specified in paragraph (d) of this section. The endorsement must—

(A) Specify the make and model of aircraft to be flown;

(B) State that the student's preflight planning and preparation is correct and that the student is prepared to make the flight safely under the known conditions; and

(C) State that any limitations required by the student's authorized instructor are met.

(d) *Limitations on authorized instructors to permit solo cross-country flights.* An authorized instructor may not permit a student pilot to conduct a solo cross-country flight unless that instructor has:

(1) Determined that the student's cross-country planning is correct for the flight;

(2) Reviewed the current and forecast weather conditions and has determined that the flight can be completed under VFR;

(3) Determined that the student is proficient to conduct the flight safely;

(4) Determined that the student has the appropriate solo cross-country endorsement for the make and model of aircraft to be flown; and

(5) Determined that the student's solo flight endorsement is current for the make and model aircraft to be flown.

(e) *Maneuvers and procedures for cross-country flight training in a single-engine airplane.* A student pilot who is receiving training for cross-country flight in a single-engine airplane must receive and log flight training in the following maneuvers and procedures:

(1) Use of aeronautical charts for VFR navigation using pilotage and dead reckoning with the aid of a magnetic compass;

(2) Use of aircraft performance charts pertaining to cross-country flight;

(3) Procurement and analysis of aeronautical weather reports and forecasts, including recognition of critical weather situations and estimating visibility while in flight;

(4) Emergency procedures;

(5) Traffic pattern procedures that include area departure, area arrival, entry into the traffic pattern, and approach;

(6) Procedures and operating practices for collision avoidance, wake turbulence precautions, and windshear avoidance;

(7) Recognition, avoidance, and operational restrictions of hazardous terrain features in the geographical area where the cross-country flight will be flown;

(8) Procedures for operating the instruments and equipment installed in the aircraft to be flown,

including recognition and use of the proper operational procedures and indications;

(9) Use of radios for VFR navigation and two-way communications;

(10) Takeoff, approach, and landing procedures, including short-field, soft-field, and cross-wind takeoffs, approaches, and landings;

(11) Climbs at best angle and best rate; and

(12) Control and maneuvering solely by reference to flight instruments, including straight and level flight, turns, descents, climbs, use of radio aids, and ATC directives.

(f) *Maneuvers and procedures for cross-country flight training in a multiengine airplane.* A student pilot who is receiving training for cross-country flight in a multiengine airplane must receive and log flight training in the following maneuvers and procedures:

(1) Use of aeronautical charts for VFR navigation using pilotage and dead reckoning with the aid of a magnetic compass;

(2) Use of aircraft performance charts pertaining to cross-country flight;

(3) Procurement and analysis of aeronautical weather reports and forecasts, including recognition of critical weather situations and estimating visibility while in flight;

(4) Emergency procedures;

(5) Traffic pattern procedures that include area departure, area arrival, entry into the traffic pattern, and approach;

(6) Procedures and operating practices for collision avoidance, wake turbulence precautions, and windshear avoidance;

(7) Recognition, avoidance, and operational restrictions of hazardous terrain features in the geographical area where the cross-country flight will be flown;

(8) Procedures for operating the instruments and equipment installed in the aircraft to be flown, including recognition and use of the proper operational procedures and indications;

(9) Use of radios for VFR navigation and two-way communications;

(10) Takeoff, approach, and landing procedures, including short-field, soft-field, and cross-wind takeoffs, approaches, and landings;

(11) Climbs at best angle and best rate; and

(12) Control and maneuvering solely by reference to flight instruments, including straight and level flight, turns, descents, climbs, use of radio aids, and ATC directives.

(g) *Maneuvers and procedures for cross-country flight training in a helicopter.* A student pilot who is receiving training for cross-country flight in a helicopter must receive and log flight training for the following maneuvers and procedures:

(1) Use of aeronautical charts for VFR navigation using pilotage and dead reckoning with the aid of a magnetic compass;

(2) Use of aircraft performance charts pertaining to cross-country flight;

(3) Procurement and analysis of aeronautical weather reports and forecasts, including recognition of critical weather situations and estimating visibility while in flight;

(4) Emergency procedures;

(5) Traffic pattern procedures that include area departure, area arrival, entry into the traffic pattern, and approach;

(6) Procedures and operating practices for collision avoidance, wake turbulence precautions, and windshear avoidance;

(7) Recognition, avoidance, and operational restrictions of hazardous terrain features in the geographical area where the cross-country flight will be flown;

(8) Procedures for operating the instruments and equipment installed in the aircraft to be flown, including recognition and use of the proper operational procedures and indications;

(9) Use of radios for VFR navigation and two-way communications; and

(10) Takeoff, approach, and landing procedures.

(h) *Maneuvers and procedures for cross-country flight training in a gyroplane.* A student pilot who is receiving training for cross-country flight in a gyroplane must receive and log flight training in the following maneuvers and procedures:

(1) Use of aeronautical charts for VFR navigation using pilotage and dead reckoning with the aid of a magnetic compass;

(2) Use of aircraft performance charts pertaining to cross-country flight;

(3) Procurement and analysis of aeronautical weather reports and forecasts, including recognition of critical weather situations and estimating visibility while in flight;

(4) Emergency procedures;

(5) Traffic pattern procedures that include area departure, area arrival, entry into the traffic pattern, and approach;

(6) Procedures and operating practices for collision avoidance, wake turbulence precautions, and windshear avoidance;

(7) Recognition, avoidance, and operational restrictions of hazardous terrain features in the geographical area where the cross-country flight will be flown;

(8) Procedures for operating the instruments and equipment installed in the aircraft to be flown, including recognition and use of the proper operational procedures and indications;

(9) Use of radios for VFR navigation and two-way communications; and

(10) Takeoff, approach, and landing procedures, including short-field and soft-field takeoffs, approaches, and landings.

(i) *Maneuvers and procedures for cross-country flight training in a powered-lift.* A student pilot who is receiving training for cross-country flight training in a powered-lift must receive and log flight training in the following maneuvers and procedures:

(1) Use of aeronautical charts for VFR navigation using pilotage and dead reckoning with the aid of a magnetic compass;

(2) Use of aircraft performance charts pertaining to cross-country flight;

(3) Procurement and analysis of aeronautical weather reports and forecasts, including recognition of critical weather situations and estimating visibility while in flight;

(4) Emergency procedures;

(5) Traffic pattern procedures that include area departure, area arrival, entry into the traffic pattern, and approach;

(6) Procedures and operating practices for collision avoidance, wake turbulence precautions, and windshear avoidance;

(7) Recognition, avoidance, and operational restrictions of hazardous terrain features in the geographical area where the cross-country flight will be flown;

(8) Procedures for operating the instruments and equipment installed in the aircraft to be flown, including recognition and use of the proper operational procedures and indications;

(9) Use of radios for VFR navigation and two-way communications;

(10) Takeoff, approach, and landing procedures that include high-altitude, steep, and shallow takeoffs, approaches, and landings; and

(11) Control and maneuvering solely by reference to flight instruments, including straight and level flight, turns, descents, climbs, use of radio aids, and ATC directives.

(j) *Maneuvers and procedures for cross-country flight training in a glider.* A student pilot who is receiving training for cross-country flight in a glider must receive and log flight training in the following maneuvers and procedures:

(1) Use of aeronautical charts for VFR navigation using pilotage and dead reckoning with the aid of a magnetic compass;

(2) Use of aircraft performance charts pertaining to cross-country flight;

(3) Procurement and analysis of aeronautical weather reports and forecasts, including recognition of critical weather situations and estimating visibility while in flight;

(4) Emergency procedures;

(5) Traffic pattern procedures that include area departure, area arrival, entry into the traffic pattern, and approach;

(6) Procedures and operating practices for collision avoidance, wake turbulence precautions, and windshear avoidance;

(7) Recognition, avoidance, and operational restrictions of hazardous terrain features in the geographical area where the cross-country flight will be flown;

(8) Procedures for operating the instruments and equipment installed in the aircraft to be flown, including recognition and use of the proper operational procedures and indications;

(9) Landings accomplished without the use of the altimeter from at least 2,000 feet above the surface; and

(10) Recognition of weather and upper air conditions favorable for cross-country soaring, ascending and descending flight, and altitude control.

(k) *Maneuvers and procedures for cross-country flight training in an airship.* A student pilot who is receiving training for cross-country flight in an airship must receive and log flight training for the following maneuvers and procedures:

(1) Use of aeronautical charts for VFR navigation using pilotage and dead reckoning with the aid of a magnetic compass;

(2) Use of aircraft performance charts pertaining to cross-country flight;

(3) Procurement and analysis of aeronautical weather reports and forecasts, including recognition of critical weather situations and estimating visibility while in flight;

(4) Emergency procedures;

(5) Traffic pattern procedures that include area departure, area arrival, entry into the traffic pattern, and approach;

(6) Procedures and operating practices for collision avoidance, wake turbulence precautions, and windshear avoidance;

(7) Recognition, avoidance, and operational restrictions of hazardous terrain features in the geographical area where the cross-country flight will be flown;

(8) Procedures for operating the instruments and equipment installed in the aircraft to be flown, including recognition and use of the proper operational procedures and indications;

(9) Use of radios for VFR navigation and two-way communications;

(10) Control of air pressure with regard to ascending and descending flight and altitude control;

(11) Control of the airship solely by reference to flight instruments; and

(12) Recognition of weather and upper air conditions conducive for the direction of cross-country flight.

[Docket No. 25910, 62 FR 16298, April 4, 1997; as amended by Amdt. 61–103, 62 FR 40902, July 30, 1997]

§ 61.95 Operations in Class B airspace and at airports located within Class B airspace.

(a) A student pilot may not operate an aircraft on a solo flight in Class B airspace unless:

(1) The student pilot has received both ground and flight training from an authorized instructor on that Class B airspace area, and the flight training was received in the specific Class B airspace area for which solo flight is authorized;

(2) The logbook of that student pilot has been endorsed by the authorized instructor who gave the student pilot flight training, and the endorsement is dated within the 90-day period preceding the date of the flight in that Class B airspace area; and

(3) The logbook endorsement specifies that the student pilot has received the required ground and flight training, and has been found proficient to conduct solo flight in that specific Class B airspace area.

(b) A student pilot may not operate an aircraft on a solo flight to, from, or at an airport located within Class B airspace pursuant to § 91.131(b) of this chapter unless:

(1) The student pilot has received both ground and flight training from an instructor authorized to provide training to operate at that airport, and the flight and ground training has been received at the specific airport for which the solo flight is authorized;

(2) The logbook of that student pilot has been endorsed by an authorized instructor who gave the student pilot flight training, and the endorsement is dated within the 90-day period preceding the date of the flight at that airport; and

(3) The logbook endorsement specifies that the student pilot has received the required ground and flight training, and has been found proficient to conduct solo flight operations at that specific airport.

[Docket No. 25910, 62 FR 16298, April 4, 1997; as amended by Amdt. 61–103, 62 FR 40902, July 30, 1997]

Subpart D— Recreational Pilots

§ 61.96 Applicability and eligibility requirements: General.

(a) This subpart prescribes the requirement for the issuance of recreational pilot certificates and ratings, the conditions under which those certificates and ratings are necessary, and the general operating rules for persons who hold those certificates and ratings.

(b) To be eligible for a recreational pilot certificate, a person who applies for that certificate must:

(1) Be at least 17 years of age;

(2) Be able to read, speak, write, and understand the English language. If the applicant is unable to meet one of these requirements due to medical reasons, then the Administrator may place such operating limitations on that applicant's pilot certificate as are necessary for the safe operation of the aircraft;

(3) Receive a logbook endorsement from an authorized instructor who—

(i) Conducted the training or reviewed the applicant's home study on the aeronautical knowledge areas listed in § 61.97(b) of this part that apply to the aircraft category and class rating sought; and

(ii) Certified that the applicant is prepared for the required knowledge test.

(4) Pass the required knowledge test on the aeronautical knowledge areas listed in § 61.97(b) of this part;

(5) Receive flight training and a logbook endorsement from an authorized instructor who—

(i) Conducted the training on the areas of operation listed in § 61.98(b) of this part that apply to the aircraft category and class rating sought; and

(ii) Certified that the applicant is prepared for the required practical test.

(6) Meet the aeronautical experience requirements of § 61.99 of this part that apply to the aircraft category and class rating sought before applying for the practical test;

(7) Pass the required practical test on the areas of operation listed in § 61.98(b) of this part that apply to the aircraft category and class rating sought; and

(8) Comply with the sections of this part that apply to the aircraft category and class rating sought.

[Docket No. 25910, 62 FR 16298, April 4, 1997; as amended by Amdt. 61–103, 62 FR 40902, July 30, 1997]

§ 61.97 Aeronautical knowledge.

(a) *General.* A person who applies for a recreational pilot certificate must receive and log ground training from an authorized instructor or complete a home-study course on the aeronautical knowledge areas of paragraph (b) of this section that apply to the aircraft category and class rating sought.

(b) *Aeronautical knowledge areas.*

(1) Applicable Federal Aviation Regulations of this chapter that relate to recreational pilot privileges, limitations, and flight operations;

(2) Accident reporting requirements of the National Transportation Safety Board;

(3) Use of the applicable portions of the "Aeronautical Information Manual" and FAA advisory circulars;

(4) Use of aeronautical charts for VFR navigation using pilotage with the aid of a magnetic compass;

(5) Recognition of critical weather situations from the ground and in flight, windshear avoidance, and the procurement and use of aeronautical weather reports and forecasts;

(6) Safe and efficient operation of aircraft, including collision avoidance, and recognition and avoidance of wake turbulence;

(7) Effects of density altitude on takeoff and climb performance;

(8) Weight and balance computations;

(9) Principles of aerodynamics, powerplants, and aircraft systems;

(10) Stall awareness, spin entry, spins, and spin recovery techniques, if applying for an airplane single-engine rating;

(11) Aeronautical decision making and judgment; and

(12) Preflight action that includes—

(i) How to obtain information on runway lengths at airports of intended use, data on takeoff and landing distances, weather reports and forecasts, and fuel requirements; and

(ii) How to plan for alternatives if the planned flight cannot be completed or delays are encountered.

[Docket No. 25910, 62 FR 16298, April 4, 1997; as amended by Amdt. 61–103, 62 FR 40902, July 30, 1997]

§ 61.98 Flight proficiency.

(a) *General.* A person who applies for a recreational pilot certificate must receive and log ground and flight training from an authorized instructor on the areas of operation of this section that apply to the aircraft category and class rating sought.

(b) *Areas of operation.*
(1) For a single-engine airplane rating:
(i) Preflight preparation;
(ii) Preflight procedures;
(iii) Airport operations;
(iv) Takeoffs, landings, and go-arounds;
(v) Performance maneuvers;
(vi) Ground reference maneuvers;
(vii) Navigation;
(viii) Slow flight and stalls;
(ix) Emergency operations; and
(x) Postflight procedures.

(2) For a helicopter rating:
(i) Preflight preparation;
(ii) Preflight procedures;
(iii) Airport and heliport operations;
(iv) Hovering maneuvers;
(v) Takeoffs, landings, and go-arounds;
(vi) Performance maneuvers;
(vii) Ground reference maneuvers;

(viii) Navigation;
(ix) Emergency operations; and
(x) Postflight procedures.

(3) For a gyroplane rating:
(i) Preflight preparation;
(ii) Preflight procedures;
(iii) Airport operations;
(iv) Takeoffs, landings, and go-arounds;
(v) Performance maneuvers;
(vi) Ground reference maneuvers;
(vii) Navigation;
(viii) Flight at slow airspeeds;
(ix) Emergency operations; and
(x) Postflight procedures.

[Docket No. 25910, 62 FR 16298, April 4, 1997; as amended by Amdt. 61–103, 62 FR 40902, July 30, 1997]

§ 61.99 Aeronautical experience.

A person who applies for a recreational pilot certificate must receive and log at least 30 hours of flight training time that includes at least:

(a) 15 hours of flight training from an authorized instructor on the areas of operation listed in § 61.98 of this part that consists of at least:

(1) Except as provided in § 61.100 of this part, 2 hours of flight training en route to an airport that is located more than 25 nautical miles from the airport where the applicant normally trains, which includes at least three takeoffs and three landings at the airport located more than 25 nautical miles from the airport where the applicant normally trains; and

(2) 3 hours of flight training in the aircraft for the rating sought in preparation for the practical test within the 60 days preceding the date of the practical test.

(b) 3 hours of solo flying in the aircraft for the rating sought, on the areas of operation listed in § 61.98 of this part that apply to the aircraft category and class rating sought.

§ 61.100 Pilots based on small islands.

(a) An applicant located on an island from which the flight training required in § 61.99(a)(1) of this part cannot be accomplished without flying over water for more than 10 nautical miles from the nearest shoreline need not comply with the requirements of that section. However, if other airports that permit civil operations are available to which a flight may be made without flying over water for more than 10 nautical miles from the nearest shoreline, the applicant must show completion of a dual flight between two airports, which must include three landings at the other airport.

(b) An applicant who complies with paragraph (a) of this section and meets all requirements for the issuance of a recreational pilot certificate, except the requirements of § 61.99(a)(1) of this part, will be issued a pilot certificate with an endorsement containing the following limitation, "Passenger carrying prohibited on flights more than 10 nautical miles from (the appropriate island)." The limitation may be subsequently amended to include another island if the applicant complies with the requirements of paragraph (a) of this section for another island.

(c) Upon meeting the requirements of § 61.99(a)(1) of this part, the applicant may have the limitation(s) in paragraph (b) of this section removed.

§ 61.101 Recreational pilot privileges and limitations.

(a) A person who holds a recreational pilot certificate may:

(1) Carry no more than one passenger; and

(2) Not pay less than the pro rata share of the operating expenses of a flight with a passenger, provided the expenses involve only fuel, oil, airport expenses, or aircraft rental fees.

(b) A person who holds a recreational pilot certificate may act as pilot in command of an aircraft on a flight that is within 50 nautical miles from the departure airport, provided that person has:

(1) Received ground and flight training for takeoff, departure, arrival, and landing procedures at the departure airport;

(2) Received ground and flight training for the area, terrain, and aids to navigation that are in the vicinity of the departure airport;

(3) Been found proficient to operate the aircraft at the departure airport and the area within 50 nautical miles from that airport; and

(4) Received from an authorized instructor a logbook endorsement, which is carried in the person's possession in the aircraft, that permits flight within 50 nautical miles from the departure airport.

(c) A person who holds a recreational pilot certificate may act as pilot in command of an aircraft on a flight that exceeds 50 nautical miles from the departure airport, provided that person has:

(1) Received ground and flight training from an authorized instructor on the cross-country training requirements of subpart E of this part that apply to the aircraft rating held;

(2) Been found proficient in cross-country flying; and

(3) Received from an authorized instructor a logbook endorsement, which is carried on the person's possession in the aircraft, that certifies the person has received and been found proficient in the cross-country training requirements of subpart E of this part that apply to the aircraft rating held.

(d) Except as provided in paragraph (h) of this section, a recreational pilot may not act as pilot in command of an aircraft:

(1) That is certificated for more than four occupants, with more than one powerplant, with a powerplant of more than 180 horsepower, or with retractable landing gear.

(2) That is classified as a multiengine airplane, powered-lift, glider, airship, or balloon;

(3) That is carrying a passenger or property for compensation or hire;

(4) For compensation or hire;

(5) In furtherance of a business;

(6) Between sunset and sunrise;

(7) In airspace in which communication with air traffic control is required;

(8) At an altitude of more than 10,000 feet MSL or 2,000 feet AGL, whichever is higher;

(9) When the flight or surface visibility is less than 3 statute miles;

(10) Without visual reference to the surface;

(11) On a flight outside the United States;

(12) To demonstrate that aircraft in flight to a prospective buyer;

(13) That is used in a passenger-carrying airlift and sponsored by a charitable organization; and

(14) That is towing any object.

(e) A recreational pilot may not act as a pilot flight crewmember on any aircraft for which more than one pilot is required by the type certificate of the aircraft or the regulations under which the flight is conducted, except when:

(1) Receiving flight training from a person authorized to provide flight training on board an airship; and

(2) No person other than a required flight crewmember is carried on the aircraft.

(f) A person who holds a recreational pilot certificate, has logged fewer than 400 flight hours, and has not logged pilot-in-command time in an aircraft within the 180 days preceding the flight shall not act as pilot in command of an aircraft until the pilot receives flight training and a logbook endorsement from an authorized instructor, and the instructor certifies that the person is proficient to act as pilot in command of the aircraft. This requirement can be met in combination with the requirements of §§ 61.56 and 61.57 of this part, at the discretion of the authorized instructor.

(g) A recreational pilot certificate issued under this subpart carries the notation, "Holder does not meet ICAO requirements."

(h) For the purpose of obtaining additional certificates or ratings while under the supervision of an authorized instructor, a recreational pilot may fly as the sole occupant of an aircraft:

(1) For which the pilot does not hold an appropriate category or class rating;

(2) Within airspace that requires communication with air traffic control; or

(3) Between sunset and sunrise, provided the flight or surface visibility is at least 5 statute miles.

(i) In order to fly solo as provided in paragraph (h) of this section, the recreational pilot must meet the appropriate aeronautical knowledge and flight training requirements of § 61.87 for that aircraft. When operating an aircraft under the conditions specified in paragraph (h) of this section, the recreational pilot shall carry the logbook that has been endorsed for each flight by an authorized instructor who:

(1) Has given the recreational pilot training in the make and model of aircraft in which the solo flight is to be made;

(2) Has found that the recreational pilot has met the applicable requirements of § 61.87; and

(3) Has found that the recreational pilot is competent to make solo flights in accordance with the logbook endorsement.

Subpart E—Private Pilots

§ 61.102 Applicability.

This subpart prescribes the requirements for the issuance of private pilot certificates and ratings, the conditions under which those certificates and ratings are necessary, and the general operating rules for persons who hold those certificates and ratings.

§ 61.103 Eligibility requirements: General.

To be eligible for a private pilot certificate, a person must:

(a) Be at least 17 years of age for a rating in other than a glider or balloon.

(b) Be at least 16 years of age for a rating in a glider or balloon.

(c) Be able to read, speak, write, and understand the English language. If the applicant is unable to meet one of these requirements due to medical reasons, then the Administrator may place such operating limitations on that applicant's pilot certificate as are necessary for the safe operation of the aircraft.

(d) Receive a logbook endorsement from an authorized instructor who:

(1) Conducted the training or reviewed the person's home study on the aeronautical knowledge areas listed in § 61.105(b) of this part that apply to the aircraft rating sought; and

(2) Certified that the person is prepared for the required knowledge test.

(e) Pass the required knowledge test on the aeronautical knowledge areas listed in § 61.105(b) of this part.

(f) Receive flight training and a logbook endorsement from an authorized instructor who:

(1) Conducted the training in the areas of operation listed in § 61.107(b) of this part that apply to the aircraft rating sought; and

(2) Certified that the person is prepared for the required practical test.

(g) Meet the aeronautical experience requirements of this part that apply to the aircraft rating sought before applying for the practical test.

(h) Pass a practical test on the areas of operation listed in § 61.107(b) of this part that apply to the aircraft rating sought.

(i) Comply with the appropriate sections of this part that apply to the aircraft category and class rating sought.

§ 61.105 Aeronautical knowledge.

(a) *General.* A person who is applying for a private pilot certificate must receive and log ground training from an authorized instructor or complete a home-study course on the aeronautical knowledge areas of paragraph (b) of this section that apply to the aircraft category and class rating sought.

(b) *Aeronautical knowledge areas.*

(1) Applicable Federal Aviation Regulations of this chapter that relate to private pilot privileges, limitations, and flight operations;

(2) Accident reporting requirements of the National Transportation Safety Board;

(3) Use of the applicable portions of the "Aeronautical Information Manual" and FAA advisory circulars;

(4) Use of aeronautical charts for VFR navigation using pilotage, dead reckoning, and navigation systems;

(5) Radio communication procedures;

(6) Recognition of critical weather situations from the ground and in flight, windshear avoidance, and the procurement and use of aeronautical weather reports and forecasts;

(7) Safe and efficient operation of aircraft, including collision avoidance, and recognition and avoidance of wake turbulence;

(8) Effects of density altitude on takeoff and climb performance;

(9) Weight and balance computations;

(10) Principles of aerodynamics, powerplants, and aircraft systems;

(11) Stall awareness, spin entry, spins, and spin recovery techniques for the airplane and glider category ratings;

(12) Aeronautical decision making and judgment; and

(13) Preflight action that includes—

(i) How to obtain information on runway lengths at airports of intended use, data on takeoff and landing distances, weather reports and forecasts, and fuel requirements; and

(ii) How to plan for alternatives if the planned flight cannot be completed or delays are encountered.

[Docket No. 25910, 62 FR 16298, April 4, 1997; as amended by Amdt. 61–103, 62 FR 40902, July 30, 1997]

§ 61.107 Flight proficiency.

(a) *General.* A person who applies for a private pilot certificate must receive and log ground and flight training from an authorized instructor on the areas of operation of this section that apply to the aircraft category and class rating sought.

(b) *Areas of operation.*

(1) For an airplane category rating with a single-engine class rating:
(i) Preflight preparation;
(ii) Preflight procedures;
(iii) Airport and seaplane base operations;
(iv) Takeoffs, landings, and go-arounds;
(v) Performance maneuvers;
(vi) Ground reference maneuvers;
(vii) Navigation;
(viii) Slow flight and stalls;
(ix) Basic instrument maneuvers;
(x) Emergency operations;
(xi) Night operations, except as provided in § 61.110 of this part; and
(xii) Postflight procedures.

(2) For an airplane category rating with a multiengine class rating:
(i) Preflight preparation;
(ii) Preflight procedures;
(iii) Airport and seaplane base operations;
(iv) Takeoffs, landings, and go-arounds;
(v) Performance maneuvers;
(vi) Ground reference maneuvers;
(vii) Navigation;
(viii) Slow flight and stalls;
(ix) Basic instrument maneuvers;
(x) Emergency operations;
(xi) Multiengine operations;
(xii) Night operations, except as provided in § 61.110 of this part; and
(xiii) Postflight procedures.

(3) For a rotorcraft category rating with a helicopter class rating:
(i) Preflight preparation;
(ii) Preflight procedures;
(iii) Airport and heliport operations;
(iv) Hovering maneuvers;
(v) Takeoffs, landings, and go-arounds;
(vi) Performance maneuvers;
(vii) Navigation;
(viii) Emergency operations;
(ix) Night operations, except as provided in § 61.110 of this part; and

(x) Postflight procedures.

(4) For a rotorcraft category rating with a gyroplane class rating:
(i) Preflight preparation;
(ii) Preflight procedures;
(iii) Airport operations;
(iv) Takeoffs, landings, and go-arounds;
(v) Performance maneuvers;
(vi) Ground reference maneuvers;
(vii) Navigation;
(viii) Flight at slow airspeeds;
(ix) Emergency operations;
(x) Night operations, except as provided in § 61.110 of this part; and
(xi) Postflight procedures.

(5) For a powered-lift category rating:
(i) Preflight preparation;
(ii) Preflight procedures;
(iii) Airport and heliport operations;
(iv) Hovering maneuvers;
(v) Takeoffs, landings, and go-arounds;
(vi) Performance maneuvers;
(vii) Ground reference maneuvers;
(viii) Navigation;
(ix) Slow flight and stalls;
(x) Basic instrument maneuvers;
(xi) Emergency operations;
(xii) Night operations, except as provided in § 61.110 of this part; and
(xiii) Postflight procedures.

(6) For a glider category rating:
(i) Preflight preparation;
(ii) Preflight procedures;
(iii) Airport and gliderport operations;
(iv) Launches and landings;
(v) Performance speeds;
(vi) Soaring techniques;
(vii) Performance maneuvers;
(viii) Navigation;
(ix) Slow flight and stalls;
(x) Emergency operations; and
(xi) Postflight procedures.

(7) For a lighter-than-air category rating with an airship class rating:
(i) Preflight preparation;
(ii) Preflight procedures;
(iii) Airport operations;
(iv) Takeoffs, landings, and go-arounds;
(v) Performance maneuvers;
(vi) Ground reference maneuvers;
(vii) Navigation;
(viii) Emergency operations; and
(ix) Postflight procedures.

(8) For a lighter-than-air category rating with a balloon class rating:
(i) Preflight preparation;
(ii) Preflight procedures;
(iii) Airport operations;

(iv) Launches and landings;
(v) Performance maneuvers;
(vi) Navigation;
(vii) Emergency operations; and
(viii) Postflight procedures.

§ 61.109 Aeronautical experience.

(a) *For an airplane single-engine rating.* Except as provided in paragraph (i) of this section, a person who applies for a private pilot certificate with an airplane category and single-engine class rating must log at least 40 hours of flight time that includes at least 20 hours of flight training from an authorized instructor and 10 hours of solo flight training in the areas of operation listed in § 61.107(b)(1) of this part, and the training must include at least—

(1) 3 hours of cross-country flight training in a single-engine airplane;

(2) Except as provided in § 61.110 of this part, 3 hours of night flight training in a single-engine airplane that includes—

(i) One cross-country flight of over 100 nautical miles total distance; and

(ii) 10 takeoffs and 10 landings to a full stop (with each landing involving a flight in the traffic pattern) at an airport.

(3) 3 hours of flight training in a single-engine airplane on the control and maneuvering of an airplane solely by reference to instruments, including straight and level flight, constant airspeed climbs and descents, turns to a heading, recovery from unusual flight attitudes, radio communications, and the use of navigation systems/facilities and radar services appropriate to instrument flight;

(4) 3 hours of flight training in preparation for the practical test in a single-engine airplane, which must have been performed within 60 days preceding the date of the test; and

(5) 10 hours of solo flight time in a single-engine airplane, consisting of at least—

(i) 5 hours of solo cross-country time;

(ii) One solo cross-country flight of at least 150 nautical miles total distance with full-stop landings at a minimum of three points, and one segment of the flight consisting of a straight-line distance of at least 50 nautical miles between the takeoff and landing locations; and

(iii) Three takeoffs and three landings to a full stop (with each landing involving a flight in the traffic pattern) at an airport with an operating control tower.

(b) *For an airplane multiengine rating.* Except as provided in paragraph (i) of this section, a person who applies for a private pilot certificate with an airplane category and multiengine class rating must log at least 40 hours of flight time that includes at least 20 hours of flight training from an authorized instructor and 10 hours of solo flight training in the areas of operation listed in § 61.107(b)(2) of this part, and the training must include at least—

(1) 3 hours of cross-country flight training in a multiengine airplane;

(2) Except as provided in § 61.110 of this part, 3 hours of night flight training in a multiengine airplane that includes—

(i) One cross-country flight of over 100 nautical miles total distance; and

(ii) 10 takeoffs and 10 landings to a full stop (with each landing involving a flight in the traffic pattern) at an airport.

(3) 3 hours of flight training in a multiengine airplane on the control and maneuvering of an airplane solely by reference to instruments, including straight and level flight, constant airspeed climbs and descents, turns to a heading, recovery from unusual flight attitudes, radio communications, and the use of navigation systems/facilities and radar services appropriate to instrument flight;

(4) 3 hours of flight training in preparation for the practical test in a multiengine airplane, which must have been performed within the 60-day period preceding the date of the test; and

(5) 10 hours of solo flight time in an airplane consisting of at least—

(i) 5 hours of solo cross-country time;

(ii) One solo cross-country flight of at least 150 nautical miles total distance, with full-stop landings at a minimum of three points, and one segment of the flight consisting of a straight-line distance of at least 50 nautical miles between the takeoff and landing locations; and

(iii) Three takeoffs and three landings to a full stop (with each landing involving a flight in the traffic pattern) at an airport with an operating control tower.

(c) *For a helicopter rating.* Except as provided in paragraph (i) of this section, a person who applies for a private pilot certificate with rotorcraft category and helicopter class rating must log at least 40 hours of flight time that includes at least 20 hours of flight training from an authorized instructor and 10 hours of solo flight training in the areas of operation listed in § 61.107(b)(3) of this part, and the training must include at least—

(1) 3 hours of cross-country flight training in a helicopter;

(2) Except as provided in § 61.110 of this part, 3 hours of night flight training in a helicopter that includes—

(i) One cross-country flight of over 50 nautical miles total distance; and

(ii) 10 takeoffs and 10 landings to a full stop (with each landing involving a flight in the traffic pattern) at an airport.

(3) 3 hours of flight training in preparation for the practical test in a helicopter, which must have been performed within 60 days preceding the date of the test; and

(4) 10 hours of solo flight time in a helicopter, consisting of at least—

(i) 3 hours cross-country time;

(ii) One solo cross-country flight of at least 75 nautical miles total distance, with landings at a minimum of three points, and one segment of the flight being a straight-line distance of at least 25 nautical miles between the takeoff and landing locations; and

(iii) Three takeoffs and three landings to a full stop (with each landing involving a flight in the traffic pattern) at an airport with an operating control tower.

(d) *For a gyroplane rating.* Except as provided in paragraph (i) of this section, a person who applies for a private pilot certificate with rotorcraft category and gyroplane class rating must log at least 40 hours of flight time that includes at least 20 hours of flight training from an authorized instructor and 10 hours of solo flight training in the areas of operation listed in § 61.107(b)(4) of this part, and the training must include at least—

(1) 3 hours of cross-country flight training in a gyroplane;

(2) Except as provided in § 61.110 of this part, 3 hours of night flight training in a gyroplane that includes—

(i) One cross-country flight of over 50 nautical miles total distance; and

(ii) 10 takeoffs and 10 landings to a full stop (with each landing involving a flight in the traffic pattern) at an airport.

(3) 3 hours of flight training in preparation for the practical test in a gyroplane, which must have been performed within the 60-day period preceding the date of the test; and

(4) 10 hours of solo flight time in a gyroplane, consisting of at least—

(i) 3 hours of cross-country time;

(ii) One solo cross-country flight of over 75 nautical miles total distance, with landings at a minimum of three points, and one segment of the flight being a straight-line distance of at least 25 nautical miles between the takeoff and landing locations; and

(iii) Three takeoffs and three landings to a full stop (with each landing involving a flight in the traffic pattern) at an airport with an operating control tower.

(e) *For a powered-lift rating.* Except as provided in paragraph (i) of this section, a person who applies for a private pilot certificate with a powered-lift category rating must log at least 40 hours of flight time that includes at least 20 hours of flight training from an authorized instructor and 10 hours of solo flight training in the areas of op-

eration listed in § 61.107(b)(5) of this part, and the training must include at least—

(1) 3 hours of cross-country flight training in a powered-lift;

(2) Except as provided in § 61.110 of this part, 3 hours of night flight training in a powered-lift that includes—

(i) One cross-country flight of over 100 nautical miles total distance; and

(ii) 10 takeoffs and 10 landings to a full stop (with each landing involving a flight in the traffic pattern) at an airport.

(3) 3 hours of flight training in a powered-lift on the control and maneuvering of a powered-lift solely by reference to instruments, including straight and level flight, constant airspeed climbs and descents, turns to a heading, recovery from unusual flight attitudes, radio communications, and the use of navigation systems/facilities and radar services appropriate to instrument flight;

(4) 3 hours of flight training in preparation for the practical test in a powered-lift, which must have been performed within the 60-day period preceding the date of the test; and

(5) 10 hours of solo flight time in an airplane or powered-lift consisting of at least—

(i) 5 hours cross-country time;

(ii) One cross-country flight of at least 150 nautical miles total distance, with landings at a minimum of three points, and one segment of the flight being a straight-line distance of at least 50 nautical miles between the takeoff and landing locations; and

(iii) Three takeoffs and three landings to a full stop (with each landing involving a flight in the traffic pattern) at an airport with an operating control tower.

(f) *For a glider category rating.*

(1) If the applicant for a private pilot certificate with a glider category rating has not logged at least 40 hours of flight time as a pilot in a heavier-than-air aircraft, the applicant must log at least 10 hours of flight time in a glider in the areas of operation listed in § 61.107(b)(6) of this part, and that flight time must include at least—

(i) 20 flights in a glider in the areas of operations listed in § 61.107(b)(6) of this part, including at least 3 training flights in a glider with an authorized instructor in preparation for the practical test that must have been performed within the 60-day period preceding the date of the test; and

(ii) 2 hours of solo flight time in a glider in the areas of operation listed in § 61.107(b)(6) of this part, with not less than 10 launches and landings being performed.

(2) If the applicant has logged at least 40 hours of flight time in a heavier-than-air aircraft, the applicant must log at least 3 hours of flight time in a glider in the areas of operation listed in

§ 61.107(b)(6) of this part, and that flight time must include at least—

(i) 10 solo flights in a glider in the areas of operation listed in § 61.107(b)(6) of this part; and

(ii) 3 training flights in a glider with an authorized instructor in preparation for the practical test that must have been performed within the 60-day period preceding the date of the test.

(g) *For an airship rating.* A person who applies for a private pilot certificate with a lighter-than-air category and airship class rating must log at least:

(1) 25 hours of flight training in airships on the areas of operation listed in § 61.107(b)(7) of this part, which consists of at least:

(i) 3 hours of cross-country flight training in an airship;

(ii) Except as provided in § 61.110 of this part, 3 hours of night flight training in an airship that includes:

(A) A cross-country flight of over 25 nautical miles total distance; and

(B) Five takeoffs and five landings to a full stop (with each landing involving a flight in the traffic pattern) at an airport.

(2) 3 hours of flight training in an airship on the control and maneuvering of an airship solely by reference to instruments, including straight and level flight, constant airspeed climbs and descents, turns to a heading, recovery from unusual flight attitudes, radio communications, and the use of navigation systems/facilities and radar services appropriate to instrument flight;

(3) 3 hours of flight training in an airship in preparation for the practical test within the 60 days preceding the date of the test; and

(4) 5 hours performing the duties of pilot in command in an airship with an authorized instructor.

(h) *For a balloon rating.* A person who applies for a private pilot certificate with a lighter-than-air category and balloon class rating must log at least 10 hours of flight training that includes at least six training flights with an authorized instructor in the areas of operation listed in § 61.107(b)(8) of this part, that includes—

(1) *Gas balloon.* If the training is being performed in a gas balloon, at least two flights of 2 hours each that consists of—

(i) At least one training flight with an authorized instructor within 60 days prior to application for the rating on the areas of operation for a gas balloon;

(ii) At least one flight performing the duties of pilot in command in a gas balloon with an authorized instructor; and

(iii) At least one flight involving a controlled ascent to 3,000 feet above the launch site.

(2) *Balloon with an airborne heater.* If the training is being performed in a balloon with an airborne heater, at least—

(i) Two flights of 1 hour each within 60 days prior to application for the rating on the areas of operation appropriate to a balloon with an airborne heater;

(ii) One solo flight in a balloon with an airborne heater; and

(iii) At least one flight involving a controlled ascent to 2,000 feet above the launch site.

(i) *Permitted credit for use of a flight simulator or flight training device.*

(1) Except as provided in paragraphs (i)(2) of this section, a maximum of 2.5 hours of training in a flight simulator or flight training device representing the category, class, and type, if applicable, of aircraft appropriate to the rating sought, may be credited toward the flight training time required by this section, if received from an authorized instructor.

(2) A maximum of 5 hours of training in a flight simulator or flight training device representing the category, class, and type, if applicable, of aircraft appropriate to the rating sought, may be credited toward the flight training time required by this section if the training is accomplished in a course conducted by a training center certificated under part 142 of this chapter.

(3) Except when fewer hours are approved by the Administrator, an applicant for a private pilot certificate with an airplane, rotorcraft, or powered-lift rating, who has satisfactorily completed an approved private pilot course conducted by a training center certificated under part 142 of this chapter, need only have a total of 35 hours of aeronautical experience to meet the requirements of this section.

[Docket No. 25910, 62 FR 40902, July 30, 1997; as amended by Amdt. 61–104, 63 FR 20287, April 23, 1998]

§ 61.110 Night flying exceptions.

(a) Subject to the limitations of paragraph (b) of this section, a person is not required to comply with the night flight training requirements of this subpart if the person receives flight training in and resides in the State of Alaska.

(b) A person who receives flight training in and resides in the State of Alaska but does not meet the night flight training requirements of this section:

(1) May be issued a pilot certificate with a limitation "Night flying prohibited"; and

(2) Must comply with the appropriate night flight training requirements of this subpart within the 12-calendar-month period after the issuance of the pilot certificate. At the end of that period, the certificate will become invalid for use until the person complies with the appropriate night training requirements of this subpart. The person may have the "Night flying prohibited" limitation removed if the person—

(i) Accomplishes the appropriate night flight training requirements of this subpart; and

(ii) Presents to an examiner a logbook or training record endorsement from an authorized instructor that verifies accomplishment of the appropriate night flight training requirements of this subpart.

[Docket No. 25910, 62 FR 16298, April 4, 1997; as amended by Amdt. 61–103, 62 FR 40904, July 30, 1997]

§ 61.111 Cross-country flights: Pilots based on small islands.

(a) Except as provided in paragraph (b) of this section, an applicant located on an island from which the cross-country flight training required in § 61.109 of this part cannot be accomplished without flying over water for more than 10 nautical miles from the nearest shoreline need not comply with the requirements of that section.

(b) If other airports that permit civil operations are available to which a flight may be made without flying over water for more than 10 nautical miles from the nearest shoreline, the applicant must show completion of two round-trip solo flights between those two airports that are farthest apart, including a landing at each airport on both flights.

(c) An applicant who complies with paragraph (a) or paragraph (b) of this section, and meets all requirements for the issuance of a private pilot certificate, except the cross-country training requirements of § 61.109 of this part, will be issued a pilot certificate with an endorsement containing the following limitation, "Passenger carrying prohibited on flights more than 10 nautical miles from (the appropriate island)." The limitation may be subsequently amended to include another island if the applicant complies with the requirements of paragraph (b) of this section for another island.

(d) Upon meeting the cross-country training requirements of § 61.109 of this part, the applicant may have the limitation in paragraph (c) of this section removed.

[Docket No. 25910, 62 FR 16298, April 4, 1997; as amended by Amdt. 61–103, 62 FR 40904, July 30, 1997]

§ 61.113 Private pilot privileges and limitations: Pilot in command.

(a) Except as provided in paragraphs (b) through (g) of this section, no person who holds a private pilot certificate may act as pilot in command of an aircraft that is carrying passengers or property for compensation or hire; nor may that person, for compensation or hire, act as pilot in command of an aircraft.

(b) A private pilot may, for compensation or hire, act as pilot in command of an aircraft in connection with any business or employment if:

(1) The flight is only incidental to that business or employment; and

(2) The aircraft does not carry passengers or property for compensation or hire.

(c) A private pilot may not pay less than the pro rata share of the operating expenses of a flight with passengers, provided the expenses involve only fuel, oil, airport expenditures, or rental fees.

(d) A private pilot may act as pilot in command of an aircraft used in a passenger-carrying airlift sponsored by a charitable organization described in paragraph (d)(7) of this section, and for which the passengers make a donation to the organization, when the following requirements are met:

(1) The sponsor of the airlift notifies the FAA Flight Standards District Office with jurisdiction over the area concerned at least 7 days before the event and furnishes—

(i) A signed letter from the sponsor that shows the name of the sponsor, the purpose of the charitable event, the date and time of the event, and the location of the event; and

(ii) A photocopy of each pilot in command's pilot certificate, medical certificate, and logbook entries that show the pilot is current in accordance with §§ 61.56 and 61.57 of this part and has logged at least 200 hours of flight time.

(2) The flight is conducted from a public airport that is adequate for the aircraft to be used, or from another airport that has been approved by the FAA for the operation.

(3) No aerobatic or formation flights are conducted.

(4) Each aircraft used for the charitable event holds a standard airworthiness certificate.

(5) Each aircraft used for the charitable event is airworthy and complies with the applicable requirements of subpart E of part 91 of this chapter.

(6) Each flight for the charitable event is made during day VFR conditions.

(7) The charitable organization is an organization identified as such by the U.S. Department of Treasury.

(e) A private pilot may be reimbursed for aircraft operating expenses that are directly related to search and location operations, provided the expenses involve only fuel, oil, airport expenditures, or rental fees, and the operation is sanctioned and under the direction and control of:

(1) A local, State, or Federal agency; or

(2) An organization that conducts search and location operations.

(f) A private pilot who is an aircraft salesman and who has at least 200 hours of logged flight time may demonstrate an aircraft in flight to a prospective buyer.

(g) A private pilot who meets the requirements of § 61.69 of this part may act as pilot in command of an aircraft towing a glider.

§ 61.115 Balloon rating: Limitations.

(a) If a person who applies for a private pilot certificate with a balloon rating takes a practical test in a balloon with an airborne heater:

(1) The pilot certificate will contain a limitation restricting the exercise of the privileges of that certificate to a balloon with an airborne heater; and

(2) The limitation may be removed when the person obtains the required aeronautical experience in a gas balloon and receives a logbook endorsement from an authorized instructor who attests to the person's accomplishment of the required aeronautical experience and ability to satisfactorily operate a gas balloon.

(b) If a person who applies for a private pilot certificate with a balloon rating takes a practical test in a gas balloon:

(1) The pilot certificate will contain a limitation restricting the exercise of the privilege of that certificate to a gas balloon; and

(2) The limitation may be removed when the person obtains the required aeronautical experience in a balloon with an airborne heater and receives a logbook endorsement from an authorized instructor who attests to the person's accomplishment of the required aeronautical experience and ability to satisfactorily operate a balloon with an airborne heater.

§ 61.117 Private pilot privileges and limitations: Second in command of aircraft requiring more than one pilot.

Except as provided in § 61.113 of this part, no private pilot may, for compensation or hire, act as second in command of an aircraft that is type certificated for more than one pilot, nor may that pilot act as second in command of such an aircraft that is carrying passengers or property for compensation or hire.

[Docket No. 25910, 62 FR 16298, April 4, 1997; as amended by Amdt. 61–103, 62 FR 40904, July 30, 1997]

§ 61.118 – 61.120 [Reserved]

Subpart F—
Commercial Pilots

§ 61.121 Applicability.

This subpart prescribes the requirements for the issuance of commercial pilot certificates and ratings, the conditions under which those certificates and ratings are necessary, and the general operating rules for persons who hold those certificates and ratings.

§ 61.123 Eligibility requirements: General.

To be eligible for a commercial pilot certificate, a person must:

(a) Be at least 18 years of age;

(b) Be able to read, speak, write, and understand the English language. If the applicant is unable to meet one of these requirements due to medical reasons, then the Administrator may place such operating limitations on that applicant's pilot certificate as are necessary for the safe operation of the aircraft.

(c) Receive a logbook endorsement from an authorized instructor who:

(1) Conducted the required ground training or reviewed the person's home study on the aeronautical knowledge areas listed in § 61.125 of this part that apply to the aircraft category and class rating sought; and

(2) Certified that the person is prepared for the required knowledge test that applies to the aircraft category and class rating sought.

(d) Pass the required knowledge test on the aeronautical knowledge areas listed in § 61.125 of this part;

(e) Receive the required training and a logbook endorsement from an authorized instructor who:

(1) Conducted the training on the areas of operation listed in § 61.127(b) of this part that apply to the aircraft category and class rating sought; and

(2) Certified that the person is prepared for the required practical test.

(f) Meet the aeronautical experience requirements of this subpart that apply to the aircraft category and class rating sought before applying for the practical test;

(g) Pass the required practical test on the areas of operation listed in § 61.127(b) of this part that apply to the aircraft category and class rating sought;

(h) Hold at least a private pilot certificate issued under this part or meet the requirements of § 61.73; and

(i) Comply with the sections of this part that apply to the aircraft category and class rating sought.

§ 61.125 Aeronautical knowledge.

(a) *General.* A person who applies for a commercial pilot certificate must receive and log ground training from an authorized instructor, or complete a home-study course, on the aeronautical knowledge areas of paragraph (b) of this section that apply to the aircraft category and class rating sought.

(b) *Aeronautical knowledge areas.*

(1) Applicable Federal Aviation Regulations of this chapter that relate to commercial pilot privileges, limitations, and flight operations;

(2) Accident reporting requirements of the National Transportation Safety Board;

(3) Basic aerodynamics and the principles of flight;

(4) Meteorology to include recognition of critical weather situations, windshear recognition and avoidance, and the use of aeronautical weather reports and forecasts;

(5) Safe and efficient operation of aircraft;

(6) Weight and balance computations;

(7) Use of performance charts;

(8) Significance and effects of exceeding aircraft performance limitations;

(9) Use of aeronautical charts and a magnetic compass for pilotage and dead reckoning;

(10) Use of air navigation facilities;

(11) Aeronautical decision making and judgment;

(12) Principles and functions of aircraft systems;

(13) Maneuvers, procedures, and emergency operations appropriate to the aircraft;

(14) Night and high-altitude operations;

(15) Procedures for operating within the National Airspace System; and

(16) Procedures for flight and ground training for lighter-than-air ratings.

§ 61.127 Flight proficiency.

(a) *General.* A person who applies for a commercial pilot certificate must receive and log ground and flight training from an authorized instructor on the areas of operation of this section that apply to the aircraft category and class rating sought.

(b) *Areas of operation.*

(1) For an airplane category rating with a single-engine class rating:
(i) Preflight preparation;
(ii) Preflight procedures;
(iii) Airport and seaplane base operations;
(iv) Takeoffs, landings, and go-arounds;
(v) Performance maneuvers;
(vi) Ground reference maneuvers;
(vii) Navigation;
(viii) Slow flight and stalls;
(ix) Emergency operations;
(x) High-altitude operations; and
(xi) Postflight procedures.

(2) For an airplane category rating with a multiengine class rating:
(i) Preflight preparation;
(ii) Preflight procedures;
(iii) Airport and seaplane base operations;

(iv) Takeoffs, landings, and go-arounds;
(v) Performance maneuvers;
(vi) Navigation;
(vii) Slow flight and stalls;
(viii) Emergency operations;
(ix) Multiengine operations;
(x) High-altitude operations; and
(xi) Postflight procedures.

(3) For a rotorcraft category rating with a helicopter class rating:
(i) Preflight preparation;
(ii) Preflight procedures;
(iii) Airport and heliport operations;
(iv) Hovering maneuvers;
(v) Takeoffs, landings, and go-arounds;
(vi) Performance maneuvers;
(vii) Navigation;
(viii) Emergency operations;
(ix) Special operations; and
(x) Postflight procedures.

(4) For a rotorcraft category rating with a gyroplane class rating:
(i) Preflight preparation;
(ii) Preflight procedures;
(iii) Airport operations;
(iv) Takeoffs, landings, and go-arounds;
(v) Performance maneuvers;
(vi) Navigation;
(vii) Flight at slow airspeeds;
(viii) Emergency operations; and
(ix) Postflight procedures.

(5) For a powered-lift category rating:
(i) Preflight preparation;
(ii) Preflight procedures;
(iii) Airport and heliport operations;
(iv) Hovering maneuvers;
(v) Takeoffs, landings, and go-arounds;
(vi) Performance maneuvers;
(vii) Ground reference maneuvers;
(viii) Navigation;
(ix) Slow flight and stalls;
(x) Emergency operations;
(xi) High-altitude operations;
(xii) Special operations; and
(xiii) Postflight procedures.

(6) For a glider category rating:
(i) Preflight preparation;
(ii) Preflight procedures;
(iii) Airport and gliderport operations;
(iv) Launches and landings;
(v) Performance speeds;
(vi) Soaring techniques;
(vii) Performance maneuvers;
(viii) Navigation;
(ix) Slow flight and stalls;
(x) Emergency operations; and
(xi) Postflight procedures.

(7) For a lighter-than-air category rating with an airship class rating:
(i) Fundamentals of instructing;
(ii) Technical subjects;
(iii) Preflight preparation;
(iv) Preflight lesson on a maneuver to be performed in flight;
(v) Preflight procedures;
(vi) Airport operations;
(vii) Takeoffs, landings, and go-arounds;
(viii) Performance maneuvers;
(ix) Navigation;
(x) Emergency operations; and
(xi) Postflight procedures.

(8) For a lighter-than-air category rating with a balloon class rating:
(i) Fundamentals of instructing;
(ii) Technical subjects;
(iii) Preflight preparation;
(iv) Preflight lesson on a maneuver to be performed in flight;
(v) Preflight procedures;
(vi) Airport operations;
(vii) Launches and landings;
(viii) Performance maneuvers;
(ix) Navigation;
(x) Emergency operations; and
(xi) Postflight procedures.

§ 61.129 Aeronautical experience.

(a) *For an airplane single-engine rating.* Except as provided in paragraph (i) of this section, a person who applies for a commercial pilot certificate with an airplane category and single-engine class rating must log at least 250 hours of flight time as a pilot that consists of at least:
(1) 100 hours in powered aircraft, of which 50 hours must be in airplanes.
(2) 100 hours of pilot-in-command flight time, which includes at least—
(i) 50 hours in airplanes; and
(ii) 50 hours in cross-country flight of which at least 10 hours must be in airplanes.
(3) 20 hours of training on the areas of operation listed in § 61.127(b)(1) of this part that includes at least—
(i) 10 hours of instrument training of which at least 5 hours must be in a single-engine airplane;
(ii) 10 hours of training in an airplane that has a retractable landing gear, flaps, and a controllable pitch propeller, or is turbine-powered, or for an applicant seeking a single-engine seaplane rating, 10 hours of training in a seaplane that has flaps and a controllable pitch propeller;
(iii) One cross-country flight of at least 2 hours in a single-engine airplane in day VFR conditions, consisting of a total straight-line distance of more than 100 nautical miles from the original point of departure;

(iv) One cross-country flight of at least 2 hours in a single-engine airplane in night VFR conditions, consisting of a total straight-line distance of more than 100 nautical miles from the original point of departure; and
(v) 3 hours in a single-engine airplane in preparation for the practical test within the 60-day period preceding the date of the test.
(4) 10 hours of solo flight in a single-engine airplane on the areas of operation listed in § 61.127(b)(1) of this part, which includes at least—
(i) One cross-country flight of not less than 300 nautical miles total distance, with landings at a minimum of three points, one of which is a straight-line distance of at least 250 nautical miles from the original departure point. However, if this requirement is being met in Hawaii, the longest segment need only have a straight-line distance of at least 150 nautical miles; and
(ii) 5 hours in night VFR conditions with 10 takeoffs and 10 landings (with each landing involving a flight in the traffic pattern) at an airport with an operating control tower.

(b) *For an airplane multiengine rating.* Except as provided in paragraph (i) of this section, a person who applies for a commercial pilot certificate with an airplane category and multiengine class rating must log at least 250 hours of flight time as a pilot that consists of at least:
(1) 100 hours in powered aircraft, of which 50 hours must be in airplanes.
(2) 100 hours of pilot-in-command flight time, which includes at least—
(i) 50 hours in airplanes; and
(ii) 50 hours in cross-country flight of which at least 10 hours must be in airplanes.
(3) 20 hours of training on the areas of operation listed in § 61.127(b)(2) of this part that includes at least—
(i) 10 hours of instrument training of which at least 5 hours must be in a multiengine airplane;
(ii) 10 hours of training in a multiengine airplane that has a retractable landing gear, flaps, and controllable pitch propellers, or is turbine-powered, or for an applicant seeking a multiengine seaplane rating, 10 hours of training in a multiengine seaplane that has flaps and a controllable pitch propeller;
(iii) One cross-country flight of at least 2 hours in a multiengine airplane in day VFR conditions, consisting of a total straight-line distance of more than 100 nautical miles from the original point of departure;
(iv) One cross-country flight of at least 2 hours in a multiengine airplane in night VFR conditions, consisting of a total straight-line distance of more than 100 nautical miles from the original point of departure; and

(v) 3 hours in a multiengine airplane in preparation for the practical test within the 60-day period preceding the date of the test.

(4) 10 hours of solo flight time in a multiengine airplane or 10 hours of flight time performing the duties of pilot in command in a multiengine airplane with an authorized instructor (either of which may be credited towards the flight time requirement in paragraph (b)(2) of this section), on the areas of operation listed in § 61.127(b)(2) of this part that includes at least—

(i) One cross-country flight of not less than 300 nautical miles total distance with landings at a minimum of three points, one of which is a straight-line distance of at least 250 nautical miles from the original departure point. However, if this requirement is being met in Hawaii, the longest segment need only have a straight-line distance of at least 150 nautical miles; and

(ii) 5 hours in night VFR conditions with 10 takeoffs and 10 landings (with each landing involving a flight with a traffic pattern) at an airport with an operating control tower.

(c) *For a helicopter rating.* Except as provided in paragraph (i) of this section, a person who applies for a commercial pilot certificate with a rotorcraft category and helicopter class rating must log at least 150 hours of flight time as a pilot that consists of at least:

(1) 100 hours in powered aircraft, of which 50 hours must be in helicopters.

(2) 100 hours of pilot-in-command flight time, which includes at least—

(i) 35 hours in helicopters; and

(ii) 10 hours in cross-country flight in helicopters.

(3) 20 hours of training on the areas of operation listed in § 61.127(b)(3) of this part that includes at least—

(i) 10 hours of instrument training in an aircraft;

(ii) One cross-country flight of at least 2 hours in a helicopter in day VFR conditions, consisting of a total straight-line distance of more than 50 nautical miles from the original point of departure;

(iii) One cross-country flight of at least 2 hours in a helicopter in night VFR conditions, consisting of a total straight-line distance of more than 50 nautical miles from the original point of departure; and

(iv) 3 hours in a helicopter in preparation for the practical test within the 60-day period preceding the date of the test.

(4) 10 hours of solo flight in a helicopter on the areas of operation listed in § 61.127(b)(3) of this part, which includes at least—

(i) One cross-country flight with landings at a minimum of three points, with one segment consisting of a straight-line distance of at least 50 nautical miles from the original point of departure; and

(ii) 5 hours in night VFR conditions with 10 takeoffs and 10 landings (with each landing involving a flight in the traffic pattern).

(d) *For a gyroplane rating.* A person who applies for a commercial pilot certificate with a rotorcraft category and gyroplane class rating must log at least 150 hours of flight time as a pilot (of which 5 hours may have been accomplished in a flight simulator or flight training device that is representative of a gyroplane) that consists of at least:

(1) 100 hours in powered aircraft, of which 25 hours must be in gyroplanes.

(2) 100 hours of pilot-in-command flight time, which includes at least—

(i) 10 hours in gyroplanes; and

(ii) 3 hours in cross-country flight in gyroplanes.

(3) 20 hours of training on the areas of operation listed in § 61.127(b)(4) of this part that includes at least—

(i) 5 hours of instrument training in an aircraft;

(ii) One cross-country flight of at least 2 hours in a gyroplane in day VFR conditions, consisting of a total straight-line distance of more than 50 nautical miles from the original point of departure;

(iii) One cross-country flight of at least 2 hours in a gyroplane in night VFR conditions, consisting of a total straight-line distance of more than 50 nautical miles from the original point of departure; and

(iv) 3 hours in a gyroplane in preparation for the practical test within the 60-day period preceding the date of the test.

(4) 10 hours of solo flight in a gyroplane on the areas of operation listed in § 61.127(b)(4) of this part, which includes at least—

(i) One cross-country flight with landings at a minimum of three points, with one segment consisting of a straight-line distance of at least 50 nautical miles from the original point of departure; and

(ii) 5 hours in night VFR conditions with 10 takeoffs and 10 landings (with each landing involving a flight in the traffic pattern).

(e) *For a powered-lift rating.* Except as provided in paragraph (i) of this section, a person who applies for a commercial pilot certificate with a powered-lift category rating must log at least 250 hours of flight time as a pilot that consists of at least:

(1) 100 hours in powered aircraft, of which 50 hours must be in a powered-lift.

(2) 100 hours of pilot-in-command flight time, which includes at least—

(i) 50 hours in a powered-lift; and

(ii) 50 hours in cross-country flight of which 10 hours must be in a powered-lift.

(3) 20 hours of training on the areas of operation listed in § 61.127(b)(5) of this part that includes at least—

(i) 10 hours of instrument training, of which at least 5 hours must be in a powered-lift;

(ii) One cross-country flight of at least 2 hours in a powered-lift in day VFR conditions, consisting of a total straight-line distance of more than 100 nautical miles from the original point of departure;

(iii) One cross-country flight of at least 2 hours in a powered-lift in night VFR conditions, consisting of a total straight-line distance of more than 100 nautical miles from the original point of departure; and

(iv) 3 hours in a powered-lift in preparation for the practical test within the 60-day period preceding the date of the test.

(4) 10 hours of solo flight in a powered-lift on the areas of operation listed in § 61.127(b)(5) of this part, which includes at least—

(i) One cross-country flight of not less than 300 nautical miles total distance with landings at a minimum of three points, one of which is a straight-line distance of at least 250 nautical miles from the original departure point. However, if this requirement is being met in Hawaii the longest segment need only have a straight-line distance of at least 150 nautical miles; and

(ii) 5 hours in night VFR conditions with 10 takeoffs and 10 landings (with each landing involving a flight in the traffic pattern) at an airport with an operating control tower.

(f) *For a glider rating.* A person who applies for a commercial pilot certificate with a glider category rating must log at least—

(1) 25 hours of flight time as a pilot in a glider and that flight time must include at least 100 flights in a glider as pilot in command, including at least—

(i) 3 hours of flight training in a glider or 10 training flights in a glider with an authorized instructor on the areas of operation listed in § 61.127(b)(6) of this part, including at least 3 training flights in a glider with an authorized instructor in preparation for the practical test within the 60-day period preceding the date of the test; and

(ii) 2 hours of solo flight that include not less than 10 solo flights in a glider on the areas of operation listed in § 61.127(b)(6) of this part; or

(2) 200 hours of flight time as a pilot in heavier-than-air aircraft and at least 20 flights in a glider as pilot in command, including at least—

(i) 3 hours of flight training in a glider or 10 training flights in a glider with an authorized instructor on the areas of operation listed in § 61.127(b)(6) of this part including at least 3 training flights in a glider with an authorized instructor in preparation for the practical test within the 60-day period preceding the date of the test; and

(ii) 5 solo flights in a glider on the areas of operation listed in § 61.127(b)(6) of this part.

(g) *For an airship rating.* A person who applies for a commercial pilot certificate with a lighter-than-air category and airship class rating must log at least 200 hours of flight time as a pilot, which includes at least the following hours:

(1) 50 hours in airships.

(2) 30 hours of pilot-in-command time in airships, which consists of at least—

(i) 10 hours of cross-country flight time in airships; and

(ii) 10 hours of night flight time in airships.

(3) 40 hours of instrument time, which consists of at least 20 hours in flight, of which 10 hours must be in flight in airships.

(4) 20 hours of flight training in airships on the areas of operation listed in § 61.127(b)(7) of this part, which includes at least—

(i) 3 hours in an airship in preparation for the practical test within the 60-day period preceding the date of the test;

(ii) One cross-country flight of at least 1 hour in duration in an airship in day VFR conditions, consisting of a total straight-line distance of more than 25 nautical miles from the original point of departure; and

(iii) One cross-country flight of at least 1 hour in duration in an airship in night VFR conditions, consisting of a total straight-line distance of more than 25 nautical miles from the original point of departure.

(5) 10 hours of flight training performing the duties of pilot in command with an authorized instructor on the areas of operation listed in § 61.127(b)(7) of this part, which includes at least—

(i) One cross-country flight with landings at a minimum of three points, with one segment consisting of a straight-line distance of at least 25 nautical miles from the original point of departure; and

(ii) 5 hours in night VFR conditions with 10 takeoffs and 10 landings (with each landing involving a flight in the traffic pattern).

(h) *For a balloon rating.* A person who applies for a commercial pilot certificate with a lighter-than-air category and a balloon class rating must log at least 35 hours of flight time as a pilot, which includes at least the following requirements:

(1) 20 hours in balloons;

(2) 10 flights in balloons;

(3) Two flights in balloons as the pilot in command; and

(4) 10 hours of flight training that includes at least 10 training flights with an authorized instructor in balloons on the areas of operation listed in § 61.127(b)(8) of this part, which consists of at least—

(i) For a gas balloon—

(A) 2 training flights of 2 hours each with an authorized instructor in a gas balloon on the areas of operation appropriate to a gas balloon within 60 days prior to application for the rating;

(B) 2 flights performing the duties of pilot in command in a gas balloon with an authorized instructor on the appropriate areas of operation; and

(C) One flight involving a controlled ascent to 5,000 feet above the launch site.

(ii) For a balloon with an airborne heater—

(A) 2 training flights of 1 hour each with an authorized instructor in a balloon with an airborne heater on the areas of operation appropriate to a balloon with an airborne heater within 60 days prior to application for the rating;

(B) Two solo flights in a balloon with an airborne heater on the appropriate areas of operation; and

(C) One flight involving a controlled ascent to 3,000 feet above the launch site.

(i) *Permitted credit for use of a flight simulator or flight training device.*

(1) Except as provided in paragraph (i)(2) of this section, an applicant who has not accomplished the training required by this section in a course conducted by a training center certificated under part 142 of this chapter may:

(i) Credit a maximum of 50 hours toward the total aeronautical experience requirements for an airplane or powered-lift rating, provided the aeronautical experience was obtained from an authorized instructor in a flight simulator or flight training device that represents that class of airplane or powered-lift category and type, if applicable, appropriate to the rating sought; and

(ii) Credit a maximum of 25 hours toward the total aeronautical experience requirements of this section for a helicopter rating, provided the aeronautical experience was obtained from an authorized instructor in a flight simulator or flight training device that represents a helicopter and type, if applicable, appropriate to the rating sought.

(2) An applicant who has accomplished the training required by this section in a course conducted by a training center certificated under part 142 of this chapter may:

(i) Credit a maximum of 100 hours toward the total aeronautical experience requirements of this section for an airplane and powered-lift rating, provided the aeronautical experience was obtained from an authorized instructor in a flight simulator or flight training device that represents that class of airplane or powered-lift category and type, if applicable, appropriate to the rating sought; and

(ii) Credit a maximum of 50 hours toward the total aeronautical experience requirements of this section for a helicopter rating, provided the aeronautical experience was obtained from an authorized instructor in a flight simulator or flight train-

ing device that represents a helicopter and type, if applicable, appropriate to the rating sought.

(3) Except when fewer hours are approved by the Administrator, an applicant for a commercial pilot certificate with an airplane or a powered-lift rating who has satisfactorily completed an approved commercial pilot course conducted by a training center certificated under part 142 of this chapter need only have 190 hours of total aeronautical experience to meet the requirements of this section.

[Docket No. 25910, 62 FR 16298, April 4, 1997; as amended by Amdt. 61–101, 62 FR 16892, April 8, 1997; Amdt. 61–1034, 62 FR 40904, July 30, 1997; Amdt. 61–104, 63 FR 20288, April 23, 1998]

§ 61.131 Exceptions to the night flying requirements.

(a) Subject to the limitations of paragraph (b) of this section, a person is not required to comply with the night flight training requirements of this subpart if the person receives flight training in and resides in the State of Alaska.

(b) A person who receives flight training in and resides in the State of Alaska but does not meet the night flight training requirements of this section:

(1) May be issued a pilot certificate with the limitation "night flying prohibited."

(2) Must comply with the appropriate night flight training requirements of this subpart within the 12-calendar-month period after the issuance of the pilot certificate. At the end of that period, the certificate will become invalid for use until the person complies with the appropriate night flight training requirements of this subpart. The person may have the "night flying prohibited" limitation removed if the person—

(i) Accomplishes the appropriate night flight training requirements of this subpart; and

(ii) Presents to an examiner a logbook or training record endorsement from an authorized instructor that verifies accomplishment of the appropriate night flight training requirements of this subpart.

[Docket No. 25910, 62 FR 16298, April 4, 1997; as amended by Amdt. 61–103, 62 FR 40905, July 30, 1997]

§ 61.133 Commercial pilot privileges and limitations.

(a) *Privileges.*

(1) General. A person who holds a commercial pilot certificate may act as pilot in command of an aircraft—

(i) Carrying persons or property for compensation or hire, provided the person is qualified in accordance with this part and with the applicable parts of this chapter that apply to the operation; and

(ii) For compensation or hire, provided the person is qualified in accordance with this part and with the applicable parts of this chapter that apply to the operation.

(2) *Commercial pilots with lighter-than-air category ratings.* A person with a commercial pilot certificate with a lighter-than-air category rating may—

(i) *For an airship—*

(A) Give flight and ground training in an airship for the issuance of a certificate or rating;

(B) Give an endorsement for a pilot certificate with an airship rating;

(C) Endorse a student pilot certificate or logbook for solo operating privileges in an airship;

(D) Act as pilot in command of an airship under IFR or in weather conditions less than the minimum prescribed for VFR flight; and

(E) Give flight and ground training and endorsements that are required for a flight review, an operating privilege, or recency-of-experience requirements of this part.

(ii) *For a balloon—*

(A) Give flight and ground training in a balloon for the issuance of a certificate or rating;

(B) Give an endorsement for a pilot certificate with a balloon rating;

(C) Endorse a student pilot certificate or logbook for solo operating privileges in a balloon; and

(D) Give ground and flight training and endorsements that are required for a flight review, an operating privilege, or recency-of-experience requirements of this part.

(b) *Limitations.*

(1) A person who applies for a commercial pilot certificate with an airplane category or powered-lift category rating and does not hold an instrument rating in the same category and class will be issued a commercial pilot certificate that contains the limitation, "The carriage of passengers for hire in (airplanes) (powered-lifts) on cross-country flights in excess of 50 nautical miles or at night is prohibited." The limitation may be removed when the person satisfactorily accomplishes the requirements listed in § 61.65 of this part for an instrument rating in the same category and class of aircraft listed on the person's commercial pilot certificate.

(2) If a person who applies for a commercial pilot certificate with a balloon rating takes a practical test in a balloon with an airborne heater—

(i) The pilot certificate will contain a limitation restricting the exercise of the privileges of that certificate to a balloon with an airborne heater.

(ii) The limitation specified in paragraph (b)(2)(i) of this section may be removed when the person obtains the required aeronautical experience in a gas balloon and receives a logbook endorsement from an authorized instructor who attests to the person's accomplishment of the required aero-

nautical experience and ability to satisfactorily operate a gas balloon.

(3) If a person who applies for a commercial pilot certificate with a balloon rating takes a practical test in a gas balloon—

(i) The pilot certificate will contain a limitation restricting the exercise of the privileges of that certificate to a gas balloon.

(ii) The limitation specified in paragraph (b)(3)(i) of this section may be removed when the person obtains the required aeronautical experience in a balloon with an airborne heater and receives a logbook endorsement from an authorized instructor who attests to the person's accomplishment of the required aeronautical experience and ability to satisfactorily operate a balloon with an airborne heater.

[Docket No. 25910, 62 FR 16298, April 4, 1997; as amended by Amdt. 61–103, 62 FR 40905, July 30, 1997]

§ 61.135 – 61.141 [Reserved]

Subpart G— Airline Transport Pilots

§ 61.151 Applicability.

This subpart prescribes the requirements for the issuance of airline transport pilot certificates and ratings, the conditions under which those certificates and ratings are necessary, and the general operating rules for persons who hold those certificates and ratings.

§ 61.153 Eligibility requirements: General.

To be eligible for an airline transport pilot certificate, a person must:

(a) Be at least 23 years of age;

(b) Be able to read, speak, write, and understand the English language. If the applicant is unable to meet one of these requirements due to medical reasons, then the Administrator may place such operating limitations on that applicant's pilot certificate as are necessary for the safe operation of the aircraft;

(c) Be of good moral character;

(d) Meet at least one of the following requirements:

(1) Hold at least a commercial pilot certificate and an instrument rating;

(2) Meet the military experience requirements under § 61.73 of this part to qualify for a commercial pilot certificate, and an instrument rating if the person is a rated military pilot or former rated military pilot of an Armed Force of the United States; or

(3) Hold either a foreign airline transport pilot or foreign commercial pilot license and an instrument rating, without limitations, issued by a contracting State to the Convention on International Civil Aviation.

(e) Meet the aeronautical experience requirements of this subpart that apply to the aircraft category and class rating sought before applying for the practical test;

(f) Pass a knowledge test on the aeronautical knowledge areas of § 61.155(c) of this part that apply to the aircraft category and class rating sought;

(g) Pass the practical test on the areas of operation listed in § 61.157(e) of this part that apply to the aircraft category and class rating sought; and

(h) Comply with the sections of this part that apply to the aircraft category and class rating sought.

[Docket No. 25910, 62 FR 16298, April 4, 1997; as amended by Amdt. 61–103, 62 FR 40905, July 30, 1997]

§ 61.155 Aeronautical knowledge.

(a) *General.* The knowledge test for an airline transport pilot certificate is based on the aeronautical knowledge areas listed in paragraph (c) of this section that are appropriate to the aircraft category and class rating sought.

(b) *Aircraft type rating.* A person who is applying for an additional aircraft type rating to be added to an airline transport pilot certificate is not required to pass a knowledge test if that person's airline transport pilot certificate lists the aircraft category and class rating that is appropriate to the type rating sought.

(c) *Aeronautical knowledge areas.*

(1) Applicable Federal Aviation Regulations of this chapter that relate to airline transport pilot privileges, limitations, and flight operations;

(2) Meteorology, including knowledge of and effects of fronts, frontal characteristics, cloud formations, icing, and upper-air data;

(3) General system of weather and NOTAM collection, dissemination, interpretation, and use;

(4) Interpretation and use of weather charts, maps, forecasts, sequence reports, abbreviations, and symbols;

(5) National Weather Service functions as they pertain to operations in the National Airspace System;

(6) Windshear and microburst awareness, identification, and avoidance;

(7) Principles of air navigation under instrument meteorological conditions in the National Airspace System;

(8) Air traffic control procedures and pilot responsibilities as they relate to en route operations, terminal area and radar operations, and instrument departure and approach procedures;

(9) Aircraft loading, weight and balance, use of charts, graphs, tables, formulas, and computations, and their effect on aircraft performance;

(10) Aerodynamics relating to an aircraft's flight characteristics and performance in normal and abnormal flight regimes;

(11) Human factors;

(12) Aeronautical decision making and judgment; and

(13) Crew resource management to include crew communication and coordination.

§ 61.157 Flight proficiency.

(a) *General.*

(1) The practical test for an airline transport pilot certificate is given for—

(i) An airplane category and single-engine class rating;

(ii) An airplane category and multiengine class rating;

(iii) A rotorcraft category and helicopter class rating;

(iv) A powered-lift category rating; and

(v) An aircraft type rating for the category and class ratings listed in paragraphs (a)(1)(i) through (a)(1)(iv) of this section.

(2) A person who is applying for an airline transport pilot practical test must meet—

(i) The eligibility requirements of § 61.153 of this part; and

(ii) The aeronautical knowledge and aeronautical experience requirements of this subpart that apply to the aircraft category and class rating sought.

(b) *Aircraft type rating.* Except as provided in paragraph (c) of this section, a person who is applying for an aircraft type rating to be added to an airline transport pilot certificate:

(1) Must receive and log ground and flight training from an authorized instructor on the areas of operation in this section that apply to the aircraft type rating sought;

(2) Must receive a logbook endorsement from an authorized instructor certifying that the applicant completed the training on the areas of operation listed in paragraph (e) of this section that apply to the aircraft type rating sought; and

(3) Must perform the practical test in actual or simulated instrument conditions, unless the aircraft's type certificate makes the aircraft incapable of operating under instrument flight rules. If the practical test cannot be accomplished for this reason, the person may obtain a type rating limited to "VFR only." The "VFR only" limitation may be removed for that aircraft type when the person passes the practical test in actual or simulated instrument conditions.

(c) *Exceptions.* A person who is applying for an aircraft type rating to be added to an airline transport pilot certificate or an aircraft type rating concurrently with an airline transport pilot certificate, and who is an employee of a certificate holder operating under part 121 or part 135 of this chapter, need not comply with the requirements of paragraph (b) of this section if the applicant presents a training record that shows satisfactory completion of that certificate holder's approved pilot-in-command training program for the aircraft type rating sought.

(d) *Upgrading type ratings.* Any type rating(s) on the pilot certificate of an applicant who successfully completes an airline transport pilot practical test shall be included on the airline transport pilot certificate with the privileges and limitations of the airline transport pilot certificate, provided the applicant passes the practical test in the same category and class of aircraft for which the applicant holds the type rating(s). However, if a type rating for that category and class of aircraft on the superseded pilot certificate is limited to VFR, that limitation shall be carried forward to the person's airline transport pilot certificate level.

(e) *Areas of operation.*

(1) For an airplane category—single-engine class rating:
(i) Preflight preparation;
(ii) Preflight procedures;
(iii) Takeoff and departure phase;
(iv) In-flight maneuvers;
(v) Instrument procedures;
(vi) Landings and approaches to landings;
(vii) Normal and abnormal procedures;
(viii) Emergency procedures; and
(ix) Postflight procedures.

(2) For an airplane category—multiengine class rating:
(i) Preflight preparation;
(ii) Preflight procedures;
(iii) Takeoff and departure phase;
(iv) In-flight maneuvers;
(v) Instrument procedures;
(vi) Landings and approaches to landings;
(vii) Normal and abnormal procedures;
(viii) Emergency procedures; and
(ix) Postflight procedures.

(3) For a powered-lift category rating:
(i) Preflight preparation;
(ii) Preflight procedures;
(iii) Takeoff and departure phase;
(iv) In-flight maneuvers;
(v) Instrument procedures;
(vi) Landings and approaches to landings;
(vii) Normal and abnormal procedures;
(viii) Emergency procedures; and
(ix) Postflight procedures.

(4) For a rotorcraft category—helicopter class rating:
(i) Preflight preparation;
(ii) Preflight procedures;
(iii) Takeoff and departure phase;
(iv) In-flight maneuvers;
(v) Instrument procedures;
(vi) Landings and approaches to landings;
(vii) Normal and abnormal procedures;
(viii) Emergency procedures; and
(ix) Postflight procedures.

(f) *Proficiency and competency checks conducted under part 121 or part 135.*

(1) Successful completion of a pilot-in-command proficiency check under § 121.441 of this chapter or successful completion of both a competency check, under § 135.293 of this chapter, and a pilot-in-command instrument proficiency check, under § 135.297 of this chapter, satisfies the requirements of this section for the appropriate aircraft rating.

(2) The checks specified in paragraph (f)(1) of this section must be conducted by an authorized designated pilot examiner or FAA aviation safety inspector.

(g) *Use of a flight simulator or flight training device for an airplane rating.* If a flight simulator or flight training device is used for accomplishing all of the training and the required practical test for an airplane transport pilot certificate with an airplane category, class, and type rating, if applicable, the applicant, flight simulator, and flight training device are subject to the following requirements:

(1) The flight simulator and flight training device must represent that airplane type if the rating involves a type rating in an airplane, or is representative of an airplane if the applicant is only seeking an airplane class rating and does not require a type rating.

(2) The flight simulator and flight training device must be used in accordance with an approved course at a training center certificated under part 142 of this chapter.

(3) All training and testing (except preflight inspection) must be accomplished by the applicant to receive an airplane class rating and type rating, if applicable, without limitations and—

(i) The flight simulator must be qualified and approved as Level C or Level D; and

(ii) The applicant must meet the aeronautical experience requirements of § 61.159 of this part and at least one of the following—

(A) Hold a type rating for a turbojet airplane of the same class of airplane for which the type rating is sought, or have been designated by a military service as a pilot in command of an airplane of the same class of airplane for which the type rating is sought, if a turbojet type rating is sought;

(B) Hold a type rating for a turbopropeller airplane of the same class as the airplane for which the type rating is sought, or have been appointed by a military service as a pilot in command of an airplane of the same class of airplane for which the type rating is sought, if a turbopropeller airplane type rating is sought;

(C) Have at least 2,000 hours of flight time, of which 500 hours must be in turbine-powered airplanes of the same class as the airplane for which the type rating is sought;

(D) Have at least 500 hours of flight time in the same type of airplane as the airplane for which the type rating is sought; or

(E) Have at least 1,000 hours of flight time in at least two different airplanes requiring a type rating.

(4) Subject to the limitation of paragraph (g)(5) of this section, an applicant who does not meet the requirements of paragraph (g)(3) of this section may complete all training and testing (except for preflight inspection) for an additional rating if—

(i) The flight simulator is qualified and approved as Level C or Level D; and

(ii) The applicant meets the aeronautical experience requirements of § 61.159 of this part and at least one of the following—

(A) Holds a type rating in a propeller-driven airplane if a type rating in a turbojet airplane is sought, or holds a type rating in a turbojet airplane if a type rating in a propeller-driven airplane is sought;

(B) Since the beginning of the 12th calendar month before the month in which the applicant completes the practical test for the additional rating, has logged—

(1) At least 100 hours of flight time in airplanes in the same class as the airplane for which the type rating is sought and which requires a type rating; and

(2) At least 25 hours of flight time in airplanes of the same type for which the type rating is sought.

(5) An applicant meeting only the requirements of paragraph (g)(4)(ii)(A) and (B) of this section will be issued an additional rating, or an airline transport pilot certificate with an added rating, as applicable, with a limitation. The limitation shall state: "This certificate is subject to pilot-in-command limitations for the additional rating."

(6) An applicant who has been issued a certificate with the limitation specified in paragraph (g)(5) of this section—

(i) May not act as pilot in command of the aircraft for which an additional rating was obtained under the provisions of this section until the limitation is removed from the certificate; and

(ii) May have the limitation removed by accomplishing 15 hours of supervised operating experience as pilot in command under the supervision of a qualified and current pilot in command, in the seat normally occupied by the pilot in command, in an airplane of the same type for which the limitation applies.

(7) An applicant who does not meet the requirements of paragraph (g)(3)(ii)(A) through (E) or (g)(4)(ii)(A) and (B) of this section may be issued an airline transport pilot certificate or an additional rating to that pilot certificate after successful completion of one of the following requirements—

(i) An approved course at a part 142 training center that includes all training and testing for that certificate or rating, followed by training and testing on the following tasks, which must be successfully completed on a static airplane or in flight, as appropriate—

(A) Preflight inspection;

(B) Normal takeoff;

(C) Normal ILS approach;

(D) Missed approach; and

(E) Normal landing.

(ii) An approved course at a part 142 training center that complies with paragraphs (g)(8) and (g)(9) of this section and includes all training and testing for a certificate or rating.

(8) An applicant meeting only the requirements of paragraph (g)(7)(ii) of this section will be issued an additional rating or an airline transport pilot certificate with an additional rating, as applicable, with a limitation. The limitation shall state: "This certificate is subject to the pilot-in-command limitations for the additional rating."

(9) An applicant issued a pilot certificate with the limitation specified in paragraph (g)(8) of this section—

(i) May not act as pilot in command of the aircraft for which an additional rating was obtained under the provisions of this section until the limitation is removed from the certificate; and

(ii) May have the limitation removed by accomplishing 25 hours of supervised operating experience as pilot in command under the supervision of a qualified and current pilot in command, in the seat normally occupied by the pilot in command, in an airplane of the same type for which the limitation applies.

(h) *Use of a flight simulator or flight training device for a helicopter rating.* If a flight simulator or flight training device is used for accomplishing all of the training and the required practical test for an airline transport pilot certificate with a helicopter class rating and type rating, if applicable, the applicant, flight simulator, and flight training device are subject to the following requirements:

(1) The flight simulator and flight training device must represent that helicopter type if the rating involves a type rating in a helicopter, or is representative of a helicopter if the applicant is only seeking a helicopter class rating and does not require a type rating.

(2) The flight simulator and flight training device must be used in accordance with an approved course at a training center certificated under part 142 of this chapter.

(3) All training and testing requirements (except preflight inspection) must be accomplished by the applicant to receive a helicopter class rating and type rating, if applicable, without limitations and—

(i) The flight simulator must be qualified and approved as a Level C or Level D; and

(ii) The applicant must meet the aeronautical experience requirements of § 61.161 of this part and at least one of the following—

(A) Hold a type rating for a turbine-powered helicopter, or have been designated by a military service as a pilot in command of a turbine-powered helicopter, if a turbine-powered helicopter type rating is sought;

(B) Have at least 1,200 hours of flight time, of which 500 hours must be in turbine-powered helicopters;

(C) Have at least 500 hours of flight time in the same type helicopter as the helicopter for which the type rating is sought; or

(D) Have at least 1,000 hours of flight time in at least two different helicopters requiring a type rating.

(4) Subject to the limitation of paragraph (h)(5) of this section, an applicant who does not meet the requirements of paragraph (h)(3) of this section may complete all training and testing (except for preflight inspection) for an additional rating if—

(i) The flight simulator is qualified and approved as Level C or Level D; and

(ii) The applicant meets the aeronautical experience requirements of § 61.161 of this part and, since the beginning of the 12th calendar month before the month in which the applicant completes the practical test for the additional rating, has logged—

(A) At least 100 hours of flight time in helicopters; and

(B) At least 15 hours of flight time in helicopters of the same type of helicopter for which the type rating is sought.

(5) An applicant meeting only the requirements of paragraph (h)(4)(ii) (A) and (B) of this section will be issued an additional rating or an airline transport pilot certificate with a limitation. The limitation shall state: "This certificate is subject to pilot-in-command limitations for the additional rating."

(6) An applicant who has been issued a certificate with the limitation specified in paragraph (h)(5) of this section—

(i) May not act as pilot in command of the helicopter for which an additional rating was obtained under the provisions of this section until the limitation is removed from the certificate; and

(ii) May have the limitation removed by accomplishing 15 hours of supervised operating experience as pilot in command under the supervision of a qualified and current pilot in command, in the seat normally occupied by the pilot in command, in a helicopter of the same type for which the limitation applies.

(7) An applicant who does not meet the requirements of paragraph (h)(3)(ii) (A) through (D), or (h)(4)(ii) (A) and (B) of this section may be issued an airline transport pilot certificate or an additional rating to that pilot certificate after successful completion of one of the following requirements—

(i) An approved course at a part 142 training center that includes all training and testing for that certificate or rating, followed by training and testing on the following tasks, which must be successfully completed on a static aircraft or in flight, as appropriate—

(A) Preflight inspection;

(B) Normal takeoff from a hover;

(C) Manually flown precision approach; and

(D) Steep approach and landing to an off-airport heliport; or

(ii) An approved course at a training center that includes all training and testing for that certificate or rating and compliance with paragraphs (h)(8) and (h)(9) of this section.

(8) An applicant meeting only the requirements of paragraph (h)(7) of this section will be issued an additional rating or an airline transport pilot certificate with an additional rating, as applicable, with a limitation. The limitation shall state: "This certificate is subject to pilot-in-command limitations for the additional rating."

(9) An applicant issued a certificate with the limitation specified in paragraph (h)(8) of this section—

(i) May not act as pilot in command of the aircraft for which an additional rating was obtained under the provisions of this section until the limitation is removed from the certificate; and

(ii) May have the limitation removed by accomplishing 25 hours of supervised operating experience as pilot in command under the supervision of a qualified and current pilot in command, in the seat normally occupied by the pilot in command, in an aircraft of the same type for which the limitation applies.

(i) *Use of a flight simulator or flight training device for a powered-lift rating.* If a flight simulator or flight training device is used for accomplishing all of the training and the required practical test for an airline transport pilot certificate with a powered-lift category rating and type rating, if applicable, the applicant, flight simulator, and flight training device are subject to the following requirements:

(1) The flight simulator and flight training device must represent that powered-lift type, if the rating

involves a type rating in a powered-lift, or is representative of a powered-lift if the applicant is only seeking a powered-lift category rating and does not require a type rating.

(2) The flight simulator and flight training device must be used in accordance with an approved course at a training center certificated under part 142 of this chapter.

(3) All training and testing requirements (except preflight inspection) must be accomplished by the applicant to receive a powered-lift category rating and type rating, if applicable, without limitations; and—

(i) The flight simulator must be qualified and approved as Level C or Level D; and

(ii) The applicant must meet the aeronautical experience requirements of § 61.163 of this part and at least one of the following—

(A) Hold a type rating for a turbine-powered powered-lift, or have been designated by a military service as a pilot in command of a turbine-powered powered-lift, if a turbine-powered powered-lift type rating is sought;

(B) Have at least 1,200 hours of flight time, of which 500 hours must be in turbine-powered powered-lifts;

(C) Have at least 500 hours of flight time in the same type of powered-lift for which the type rating is sought; or

(D) Have at least 1,000 hours of flight time in at least two different powered-lifts requiring a type rating.

(4) Subject to the limitation of paragraph (i)(5) of this section, an applicant who does not meet the requirements of paragraph (i)(3) of this section may complete all training and testing (except for preflight inspection) for an additional rating if—

(i) The flight simulator is qualified and approved as Level C or Level D; and

(ii) The applicant meets the aeronautical experience requirements of § 61.163 of this part and, since the beginning of the 12th calendar month before the month in which the applicant completes the practical test for the additional rating, has logged—

(A) At least 100 hours of flight time in powered-lifts; and

(B) At least 15 hours of flight time in powered-lifts of the same type of powered-lift for the type rating sought.

(5) An applicant meeting only the requirements of paragraph (i)(4)(ii) (A) and (B) of this section will be issued an additional rating or an airline transport pilot certificate with a limitation. The limitation shall state: "This certificate is subject to pilot-in-command limitations for the additional rating."

(6) An applicant who has been issued a certificate with the limitation specified in paragraph (i)(5) of this section—

(i) May not act as pilot in command of the powered-lift for which an additional rating was obtained under the provisions of this section until the limitation is removed from the certificate; and

(ii) May have the limitation removed by accomplishing 15 hours of supervised operating experience as pilot in command under the supervision of a qualified and current pilot in command, in the seat normally occupied by the pilot in command, in a powered-lift of the same type for which the limitation applies.

(7) An applicant who does not meet the requirements of paragraph (i)(3)(ii) (A) through (D) or (i)(4)(ii) (A) and (B) of this section may be issued an airline transport pilot certificate or an additional rating to that pilot certificate after successful completion of one of the following requirements—

(i) An approved course at a part 142 training center that includes all training and testing for that certificate or rating, followed by training and testing on the following tasks, which must be successfully completed on a static aircraft or in flight, as appropriate—

(A) Preflight inspection;

(B) Normal takeoff from a hover;

(C) Manually flown precision approach; and

(D) Steep approach and landing to an off-airport site; or

(ii) An approved course at a training center that includes all training and testing for that certificate or rating and is in compliance with paragraphs (i)(8) and (i)(9) of this section.

(8) An applicant meeting only the requirements of paragraph (i)(7)(ii) of this section will be issued an additional rating or an airline transport pilot certificate with an additional rating, as applicable, with a limitation. The limitation shall state: "This certificate is subject to pilot-in-command limitations for the additional rating."

(9) An applicant issued a pilot certificate with the limitation specified in paragraph (i)(8) of this section—

(i) May not act as pilot in command of the aircraft for which an additional rating was obtained under the provisions of this section until the limitation is removed from the certificate; and

(ii) May have the limitation removed by accomplishing 25 hours of supervised operating experience as pilot in command under the supervision of a qualified and current pilot in command, in the seat normally occupied by the pilot in command, in a powered-lift of the same type for which the limitation applies.

(j) *Waiver authority.* Unless the Administrator requires certain or all tasks to be performed, the examiner who conducts the practical test for an airline transport pilot certificate may waive any of the tasks for which the Administrator approves waiver authority.

[Docket No. 25910, 62 FR 16298, April 4, 1997; as amended by Amdt. 61–103, 62 FR 40905, July 30, 1997; Amdt. 61–104, 63 FR 20288, April 23, 1998]

§ 61.158 [Reserved]

§ 61.159 Aeronautical experience: Airplane category rating.

(a) Except as provided in paragraphs (b), (c), and (d) of this section, a person who is applying for an airline transport pilot certificate with an airplane category and class rating must have at least 1,500 hours of total time as a pilot that includes at least:

(1) 500 hours of cross-country flight time.

(2) 100 hours of night flight time.

(3) 75 hours of instrument flight time, in actual or simulated instrument conditions, subject to the following:

(i) Except as provided in paragraph (a)(3)(ii) of this section, an applicant may not receive credit for more than a total of 25 hours of simulated instrument time in a flight simulator or flight training device.

(ii) A maximum of 50 hours of training in a flight simulator or flight training device may be credited toward the instrument flight time requirements of paragraph (a)(3) of this section if the training was accomplished in a course conducted by a training center certificated under part 142 of this chapter.

(iii) Training in a flight simulator or flight training device must be accomplished in a flight simulator or flight training device, representing an airplane.

(4) 250 hours of flight time in an airplane as a pilot in command, or as second in command performing the duties of pilot in command while under the supervision of a pilot in command, or any combination thereof, which includes at least—

(i) 100 hours of cross-country flight time; and

(ii) 25 hours of night flight time.

(5) Not more than 100 hours of the total aeronautical experience requirements of paragraph (a) of this section may be obtained in a flight simulator or flight training device that represents an airplane, provided the aeronautical experience was obtained in an approved course conducted by a training center certificated under part 142 of this chapter.

(b) A person who has performed at least 20 night takeoffs and landings to a full stop may substitute each additional night takeoff and landing to a full stop for 1 hour of night flight time to satisfy the requirements of paragraph (a)(2) of this section; however, not more than 25 hours of night flight time may be credited in this manner.

(c) A commercial pilot may credit the following second-in-command flight time or flight-engineer flight time toward the 1,500 hours of total time as a pilot required by paragraph (a) of this section:

(1) Second-in-command time, provided the time is acquired in an airplane—

(i) Required to have more than one pilot flight crewmember by the airplane's flight manual, type certificate, or the regulations under which the flight is being conducted;

(ii) Engaged in operations under part 121 or part 135 of this chapter for which a second in command is required; or

(iii) That is required by the operating rules of this chapter to have more than one pilot flight crewmember.

(2) Flight-engineer time, provided the time—

(i) Is acquired in an airplane required to have a flight engineer by the airplane's flight manual or type certificate;

(ii) Is acquired while engaged in operations under part 121 of this chapter for which a flight engineer is required;

(iii) Is acquired while the person is participating in a pilot training program approved under part 121 of this chapter; and

(iv) Does not exceed more than 1 hour for each 3 hours of flight engineer flight time for a total credited time of no more than 500 hours.

(d) An applicant may be issued an airline transport pilot certificate with the endorsement, "Holder does not meet the pilot in command aeronautical experience requirements of ICAO," as prescribed by Article 39 of the Convention on International Civil Aviation, if the applicant:

(1) Credits second-in-command or flight-engineer time under paragraph (c) of this section toward the 1,500 hours total flight time requirement of paragraph (a) of this section;

(2) Does not have at least 1,200 hours of flight time as a pilot, including no more than 50 percent of his or her second-in-command time and none of his or her flight-engineer time; and

(3) Otherwise meets the requirements of paragraph (a) of this section.

(e) When the applicant specified in paragraph (d) of this section presents satisfactory evidence of the accumulation of 1,200 hours of flight time as a pilot including no more than 50 percent of his or her second-in-command flight time and none of his or her flight-engineer time, the applicant is entitled to an airline transport pilot certificate without the endorsement prescribed in that paragraph.

[Docket No. 25910, 62 FR 16298, April 4, 1997; as amended by Amdt. 61–103, 62 FR 40906, July 30, 1997; Amdt. 61–104, 63 FR 20288, April 23, 1998]

§ 61.161 Aeronautical experience: Rotorcraft category and helicopter class rating.

(a) A person who is applying for an airline transport pilot certificate with a rotorcraft category and helicopter class rating, must have at least 1,200 hours of total time as a pilot that includes at least:

(1) 500 hours of cross-country flight time;

(2) 100 hours of night flight time, of which 15 hours are in helicopters;

(3) 200 hours of flight time in helicopters, which includes at least 75 hours as a pilot in command, or as second in command performing the duties of a pilot in command under the supervision of a pilot in command, or any combination thereof; and

(4) 75 hours of instrument flight time in actual or simulated instrument meteorological conditions, of which at least 50 hours are obtained in flight with at least 25 hours in helicopters as a pilot in command, or as second in command performing the duties of a pilot in command under the supervision of a pilot in command, or any combination thereof.

(b) Training in a flight simulator or flight training device may be credited toward the instrument flight time requirements of paragraph (a)(4) of this section, subject to the following:

(1) Training in a flight simulator or a flight training device must be accomplished in a flight simulator or flight training device that represents a rotorcraft.

(2) Except as provided in paragraph (b)(3) of this section, an applicant may receive credit for not more than a total of 25 hours of simulated instrument time in a flight simulator and flight training device.

(3) A maximum of 50 hours of training in a flight simulator or flight training device may be credited toward the instrument flight time requirements of paragraph (a)(4) of this section if the aeronautical experience is accomplished in an approved course conducted by a training center certificated under part 142 of this chapter.

[Docket No. 25910, 62 FR 16298, April 4, 1997; as amended by Amdt. 61–103, 62 FR 40906, July 30, 1997; Amdt. 61–104, 63 FR 20289, April 23, 1998]

§ 61.163 Aeronautical experience: Powered-lift category rating.

(a) A person who is applying for an airline transport pilot certificate with a powered-lift category rating must have at least 1,500 hours of total time as a pilot that includes at least:

(1) 500 hours of cross-country flight time;

(2) 100 hours of night flight time;

(3) 250 hours in a powered-lift as a pilot in command, or as a second in command performing the duties of a pilot in command under the supervision of a pilot in command, or any combination thereof, which includes at least—

(i) 100 hours of cross-country flight time; and

(ii) 25 hours of night flight time.

(4) 75 hours of instrument flight time in actual or simulated instrument conditions, subject to the following:

(i) Except as provided in paragraph (a)(4)(ii) of this section, an applicant may not receive credit for more than a total of 25 hours of simulated instrument time in a flight simulator or flight training device.

(ii) A maximum of 50 hours of training in a flight simulator or flight training device may be credited toward the instrument flight time requirements of paragraph (a)(4) of this section if the training was accomplished in a course conducted by a training center certificated under part 142 of this chapter.

(iii) Training in a flight simulator or flight training device must be accomplished in a flight simulator or flight training device that represents a powered-lift.

(b) Not more than 100 hours of the total aeronautical experience requirements of paragraph (a) of this section may be obtained in a flight simulator or flight training device that represents a powered-lift, provided the aeronautical experience was obtained in an approved course conducted by a training center certificated under part 142 of this chapter.

[Docket No. 25910, 62 FR 16298, April 4, 1997; as amended by Amdt. 61–103, 62 FR 40906, July 30, 1997; Amdt. 61–104, 63 FR 20289, April 23, 1998]

§ 61.165 Additional aircraft category and class ratings.

(a) *Rotorcraft category and helicopter class rating.* A person applying for an airline transport certificate with a rotorcraft category and helicopter class rating who holds an airline transport pilot certificate with another aircraft category rating must:

(1) Meet the eligibility requirements of § 61.153 of this part;

(2) Pass a knowledge test on the aeronautical knowledge areas of § 61.155(c) of this part;

(3) Comply with the requirements in § 61.157(b) of this part, if appropriate;

(4) Meet the applicable aeronautical experience requirements of § 61.161 of this part; and

(5) Pass the practical test on the areas of operation of § 61.157(e)(4) of this part.

(b) *Airplane category rating with a single-engine class rating.* A person applying for an airline transport certificate with an airplane category and single-engine class rating who holds an airline transport pilot certificate with another aircraft category rating must:

(1) Meet the eligibility requirements of § 61.153 of this part;

(2) Pass a knowledge test on the aeronautical knowledge areas of § 61.155(c) of this part;

(3) Comply with the requirements in § 61.157(b) of this part, if appropriate;

(4) Meet the applicable aeronautical experience requirements of § 61.159 of this part; and

(5) Pass the practical test on the areas of operation of § 61.157(e)(1) of this part.

(c) *Airplane category rating with a multiengine class rating.* A person applying for an airline transport certificate with an airplane category and multiengine class rating who holds an airline transport certificate with another aircraft category rating must:

(1) Meet the eligibility requirements of § 61.153 of this part;

(2) Pass a knowledge test on the aeronautical knowledge areas of § 61.155(c) of this part;

(3) Comply with the requirements in § 61.157(b) of this part, if appropriate;

(4) Meet the applicable aeronautical experience requirements of § 61.159 of this part; and

(5) Pass the practical test on the areas of operation of § 61.157(e)(2) of this part.

(d) *Powered-lift category.* A person applying for an airline transport pilot certificate with a powered-lift category rating who holds an airline transport certificate with another aircraft category rating must:

(1) Meet the eligibility requirements of § 61.153 of this part;

(2) Pass a required knowledge test on the aeronautical knowledge areas of § 61.155(c) of this part;

(3) Comply with the requirements in § 61.157(b) of this part, if appropriate;

(4) Meet the applicable aeronautical experience requirements of § 61.163 of this part; and

(5) Pass the required practical test on the areas of operation of § 61.157(e)(3) of this part.

(e) *Additional class rating within the same aircraft category.* A person applying for an airline transport certificate with an additional class rating who holds an airline transport certificate in the same aircraft category must—

(1) Meet the eligibility requirements of § 61.153, except paragraph (f) of that section;

(2) Comply with the requirements in § 61.157(b) of this part, if applicable;

(3) Meet the applicable aeronautical experience requirements of subpart G of this part; and

(4) Pass a practical test on the areas of operation of § 61.157(e) appropriate to the aircraft rating sought.

[Docket No. 25910, 62 FR 16298, April 4, 1997; as amended by Amdt. 61–103, 62 FR 40906, July 30, 1997]

§ 61.167 Privileges.

(a) A person who holds an airline transport pilot certificate is entitled to the same privileges as those afforded a person who holds a commercial pilot certificate with an instrument rating.

(b) An airline transport pilot may instruct—

(1) Other pilots in air transportation service in aircraft of the category, class, and type, as applicable, for which the airline transport pilot is rated and endorse the logbook or other training record of the person to whom training has been given;

(2) In flight simulators, and flight training devices representing the aircraft referenced in paragraph (b)(1) of this section, when instructing under the provisions of this section and endorse the logbook or other training record of the person to whom training has been given;

(3) Only as provided in this section, unless the airline transport pilot also holds a flight instructor certificate, in which case the holder may exercise the instructor privileges of subpart H of part 61 for which he or she is rated; and

(4) In an aircraft, only if the aircraft has functioning dual controls, when instructing under the provisions of this section.

(c) Excluding briefings and debriefings, an airline transport pilot may not instruct in aircraft, flight simulators, and flight training devices under this section—

(1) For more than 8 hours in any 24-consecutive-hour period; or

(2) For more than 36 hours in any 7-consecutive-day period.

(d) An airline transport pilot may not instruct in Category II or Category III operations unless he or she has been trained and successfully tested under Category II or Category III operations, as applicable.

[Docket No. 25910, 62 FR 16298, April 4, 1997; as amended by Amdt. 61–103, 62 FR 40907, July 30, 1997]

§ 61.169 – § 61.171 [Reserved]

Subpart H—
Flight Instructors

§ 61.181 Applicability.

This subpart prescribes the requirements for the issuance of flight instructor certificates and ratings, the conditions under which those certificates and ratings are necessary, and the limitations on those certificates and ratings.

§ 61.183 Eligibility requirements.

To be eligible for a flight instructor certificate or rating a person must:

(a) Be at least 18 years of age;

(b) Be able to read, speak, write, and understand the English language. If the applicant is unable to meet one of these requirements due to medical reasons, then the Administrator may place such operating limitations on that applicant's flight instructor certificate as are necessary;

(c) Hold either a commercial pilot certificate or airline transport pilot certificate with:

(1) An aircraft category and class rating that is appropriate to the flight instructor rating sought; and

(2) An instrument rating or privileges on that person's pilot certificate that are appropriate to the flight instructor rating sought, if applying for—

(i) A flight instructor certificate with an airplane category and single-engine class rating;

(ii) A flight instructor certificate with an airplane category and multiengine class rating;

(iii) A flight instructor certificate with a powered-lift rating; or

(iv) A flight instructor certificate with an instrument rating.

(d) Receive a logbook endorsement from an authorized instructor on the fundamentals of instructing listed in § 61.185 of this part appropriate to the required knowledge test;

(e) Pass a knowledge test on the areas listed in § 61.185(a)(1) of this part, unless the applicant:

(1) Holds a flight instructor certificate or ground instructor certificate issued under this part;

(2) Holds a current teacher's certificate issued by a State, county, city, or municipality that authorizes the person to teach at an educational level of the 7th grade or higher; or

(3) Is employed as a teacher at an accredited college or university.

(f) Pass a knowledge test on the aeronautical knowledge areas listed in § 61.185(a)(2) and (a)(3) of this part that are appropriate to the flight instructor rating sought;

(g) Receive a logbook endorsement from an authorized instructor on the areas of operation listed in § 61.187(b) of this part, appropriate to the flight instructor rating sought;

(h) Pass the required practical test that is appropriate to the flight instructor rating sought in an:

(1) Aircraft that is representative of the category and class of aircraft for the aircraft rating sought; or

(2) Flight simulator or flight training device that is representative of the category and class of aircraft for the rating sought, and used in accordance with an approved course at a training center certificated under part 142 of this chapter.

(i) Accomplish the following for a flight instructor certificate with an airplane or a glider rating:

(1) Receive a logbook endorsement from an authorized instructor indicating that the applicant is competent and possesses instructional proficiency in stall awareness, spin entry, spins, and spin recovery procedures after providing the applicant with flight training in those training areas in an airplane or glider, as appropriate, that is certificated for spins; and

(2) Demonstrate instructional proficiency in stall awareness, spin entry, spins, and spin recovery procedures. However, upon presentation of the endorsement specified in paragraph (i)(1) of this section an examiner may accept that endorsement as satisfactory evidence of instructional proficiency in stall awareness, spin entry, spins, and spin recovery procedures for the practical test, provided that the practical test is not a retest as a result of the applicant failing the previous test for deficiencies in the knowledge or skill of stall awareness, spin entry, spins, or spin recovery instructional procedures. If the retest is a result of deficiencies in the ability of an applicant to demonstrate knowledge or skill of stall awareness, spin entry, spins, or spin recovery instructional procedures, the examiner must test the person on stall awareness, spin entry, spins, and spin recovery instructional procedures in an airplane or glider, as appropriate, that is certificated for spins;

(j) Log at least 15 hours as pilot in command in the category and class of aircraft that is appropriate to the flight instructor rating sought; and

(k) Comply with the appropriate sections of this part that apply to the flight instructor rating sought.

[Docket No. 25910, 62 FR 16298, April 4, 1997; as amended by Amdt. 61–103, 62 FR 40907, July 30, 1997]

§ 61.185 Aeronautical knowledge.

(a) A person who is applying for a flight instructor certificate must receive and log ground training from an authorized instructor on:

(1) Except as provided in paragraph (b) of this section, the fundamentals of instructing, including:

(i) The learning process;

(ii) Elements of effective teaching;

(iii) Student evaluation and testing;

(iv) Course development;

(v) Lesson planning; and
(vi) Classroom training techniques.
(2) The aeronautical knowledge areas for a recreational, private, and commercial pilot certificate applicable to the aircraft category for which flight instructor privileges are sought; and
(3) The aeronautical knowledge areas for the instrument rating applicable to the category for which instrument flight instructor privileges are sought.
(b) The following applicants do not need to comply with paragraph (a)(1) of this section:
(1) The holder of a flight instructor certificate or ground instructor certificate issued under this part;
(2) The holder of a current teacher's certificate issued by a State, county, city, or municipality that authorizes the person to teach at an educational level of the 7th grade or higher; or
(3) A person employed as a teacher at an accredited college or university.

[Docket No. 25910, 62 FR 16298, April 4, 1997; as amended by Amdt. 61–103, 62 FR 40907, July 30, 1997]

§ 61.187 Flight proficiency.

(a) *General.* A person who is applying for a flight instructor certificate must receive and log flight and ground training from an authorized instructor on the areas of operation listed in this section that apply to the flight instructor rating sought. The applicant's logbook must contain an endorsement from an authorized instructor certifying that the person is proficient to pass a practical test on those areas of operation.
(b) *Areas of operation.*

(1) For an airplane category rating with a single-engine class rating:
(i) Fundamentals of instructing;
(ii) Technical subject areas;
(iii) Preflight preparation;
(iv) Preflight lesson on a maneuver to be performed in flight;
(v) Preflight procedures;
(vi) Airport and seaplane base operations;
(vii) Takeoffs, landings, and go-arounds;
(viii) Fundamentals of flight;
(ix) Performance maneuvers;
(x) Ground reference maneuvers;
(xi) Slow flight, stalls, and spins;
(xii) Basic instrument maneuvers;
(xiii) Emergency operations; and
(xiv) Postflight procedures.

(2) For an airplane category rating with a multiengine class rating:
(i) Fundamentals of instructing;
(ii) Technical subject areas;
(iii) Preflight preparation;
(iv) Preflight lesson on a maneuver to be performed in flight;

(v) Preflight procedures;
(vi) Airport and seaplane base operations;
(vii) Takeoffs, landings, and go-arounds;
(viii) Fundamentals of flight;
(ix) Performance maneuvers;
(x) Ground reference maneuvers;
(xi) Slow flight and stalls;
(xii) Basic instrument maneuvers;
(xiii) Emergency operations;
(xiv) Multiengine operations; and
(xv) Postflight procedures.

(3) For a rotorcraft category rating with a helicopter class rating:
(i) Fundamentals of instructing;
(ii) Technical subject areas;
(iii) Preflight preparation;
(iv) Preflight lesson on a maneuver to be performed in flight;
(v) Preflight procedures;
(vi) Airport and heliport operations;
(vii) Hovering maneuvers;
(viii) Takeoffs, landings, and go-arounds;
(ix) Fundamentals of flight;
(x) Performance maneuvers;
(xi) Emergency operations;
(xii) Special operations; and
(xiii) Postflight procedures.

(4) For a rotorcraft category rating with a gyroplane class rating:
(i) Fundamentals of instructing;
(ii) Technical subject areas;
(iii) Preflight preparation;
(iv) Preflight lesson on a maneuver to be performed in flight;
(v) Preflight procedures;
(vi) Airport operations;
(vii) Takeoffs, landings, and go-arounds;
(viii) Fundamentals of flight;
(ix) Performance maneuvers;
(x) Flight at slow airspeeds;
(xi) Ground reference maneuvers;
(xii) Emergency operations; and
(xiii) Postflight procedures.

(5) For a powered-lift category rating:
(i) Fundamentals of instructing;
(ii) Technical subject areas;
(iii) Preflight preparation;
(iv) Preflight lesson on a maneuver to be performed in flight;
(v) Preflight procedures;
(vi) Airport and heliport operations;
(vii) Hovering maneuvers;
(viii) Takeoffs, landings, and go-arounds;
(ix) Fundamentals of flight;
(x) Performance maneuvers;
(xi) Ground reference maneuvers;
(xii) Slow flight and stalls;
(xiii) Basic instrument maneuvers;
(xiv) Emergency operations;

(xv) Special operations; and
(xvi) Postflight procedures.

(6) For a glider category rating:
(i) Fundamentals of instructing;
(ii) Technical subject areas;
(iii) Preflight preparation;
(iv) Preflight lesson on a maneuver to be performed in flight;
(v) Preflight procedures;
(vi) Airport and gliderport operations;
(vii) Launches, landings, and go-arounds;
(viii) Fundamentals of flight;
(ix) Performance speeds;
(x) Soaring techniques;
(xi) Performance maneuvers;
(xii) Slow flight, stalls, and spins;
(xiii) Emergency operations; and
(xiv) Postflight procedures.

(7) For an instrument rating with the appropriate aircraft category and class rating:
(i) Fundamentals of instructing;
(ii) Technical subject areas;
(iii) Preflight preparation;
(iv) Preflight lesson on a maneuver to be performed in flight;
(v) Air traffic control clearances and procedures;
(vi) Flight by reference to instruments;
(vii) Navigation aids;
(viii) Instrument approach procedures;
(ix) Emergency operations; and
(x) Postflight procedures.
(c) The flight training required by this section may be accomplished:
(1) In an aircraft that is representative of the category and class of aircraft for the rating sought; or
(2) In a flight simulator or flight training device representative of the category and class of aircraft for the rating sought, and used in accordance with an approved course at a training center certificated under part 142 of this chapter.

[Docket No. 25910, 62 FR 16298, April 4, 1997; as amended by Amdt. 61–103, 62 FR 40907, July 30, 1997]

§ 61.189 Flight instructor records.

(a) A flight instructor must sign the logbook of each person to whom that instructor has given flight training or ground training.
(b) A flight instructor must maintain a record in a logbook or a separate document that contains the following:
(1) The name of each person whose logbook or student pilot certificate that instructor has endorsed for solo flight privileges, and the date of the endorsement; and
(2) The name of each person that instructor has endorsed for a knowledge test or practical test, and the record shall also indicate the kind of test, the date, and the results.
(c) Each flight instructor must retain the records required by this section for at least 3 years.

§ 61.191 Additional flight instructor ratings.

(a) A person who applies for an additional flight instructor rating on a flight instructor certificate must meet the eligibility requirements listed in § 61.183 of this part that apply to the flight instructor rating sought.
(b) A person who applies for an additional rating on a flight instructor certificate is not required to pass the knowledge test on the areas listed in § 61.185(a)(1) of this part.

[Docket No. 25910, 62 FR 16298, April 4, 1997; as amended by Amdt. 61–103, 62 FR 40907, July 30, 1997]

§ 61.193 Flight instructor privileges.

A person who holds a flight instructor certificate is authorized within the limitations of that person's flight instructor certificate and ratings to give training and endorsements that are required for, and relate to:
(a) A student pilot certificate;
(b) A pilot certificate;
(c) A flight instructor certificate;
(d) A ground instructor certificate;
(e) An aircraft rating;
(f) An instrument rating;
(g) A flight review, operating privilege, or recency of experience requirement of this part;
(h) A practical test; and
(i) A knowledge test.

[Docket No. 25910, 62 FR 16298, April 4, 1997; as amended by Amdt. 61–103, 62 FR 40907, July 30, 1997]

§ 61.195 Flight instructor limitations and qualifications.

(a) *Hours of training.* In any 24-consecutive-hour period, a flight instructor may not conduct more than 8 hours of flight training.
(b) *Aircraft ratings.* A flight instructor may not conduct flight training in any aircraft for which the flight instructor does not hold:
(1) A pilot certificate and flight instructor certificate with the applicable category and class rating; and
(2) If appropriate, a type rating.
(c) *Instrument Rating.* A flight instructor who provides instrument flight training for the issuance of an instrument rating or a type rating not limited to VFR must hold an instrument rating on his or her flight instructor certificate and pilot certificate that is appropriate to the category and class of

aircraft in which instrument training is being provided.

(d) *Limitations on endorsements.* A flight instructor may not endorse a:

(1) Student pilot's certificate or logbook for solo flight privileges, unless that flight instructor has—

(i) Given that student the flight training required for solo flight privileges required by this part; and

(ii) Determined that the student is prepared to conduct the flight safely under known circumstances, subject to any limitations listed in the student's logbook that the instructor considers necessary for the safety of the flight.

(2) Student pilot's certificate and logbook for a solo cross-country flight, unless that flight instructor has determined the student's flight preparation, planning, equipment, and proposed procedures are adequate for the proposed flight under the existing conditions and within any limitations listed in the logbook that the instructor considers necessary for the safety of the flight;

(3) Student pilot's certificate and logbook for solo flight in a Class B airspace area or at an airport within Class B airspace unless that flight instructor has—

(i) Given that student ground and flight training in that Class B airspace or at that airport; and

(ii) Determined that the student is proficient to operate the aircraft safely.

(4) Logbook of a recreational pilot, unless that flight instructor has—

(i) Given that pilot the ground and flight training required by this part; and

(ii) Determined that the recreational pilot is proficient to operate the aircraft safely.

(5) Logbook of a pilot for a flight review, unless that instructor has conducted a review of that pilot in accordance with the requirements of § 61.56(a) of this part; or

(6) Logbook of a pilot for an instrument proficiency check, unless that instructor has tested that pilot in accordance with the requirements of § 61.57(d) of this part.

(e) *Training in an aircraft that requires a type rating.* A flight instructor may not give flight training in an aircraft that requires the pilot in command to hold a type rating unless the flight instructor holds a type rating for that aircraft on his or her pilot certificate.

(f) *Training received in a multiengine airplane, a helicopter, or a powered-lift.* A flight instructor may not give training required for the issuance of a certificate or rating in a multiengine airplane, a helicopter, or a powered-lift unless that flight instructor has at least 5 flight hours of pilot-in-command time in the specific make and model of multiengine airplane, helicopter, or powered-lift, as appropriate.

(g) *Position in aircraft and required pilot stations for providing flight training.*

(1) A flight instructor must perform all training from in an aircraft that complies with the requirements of § 91.109 of this chapter.

(2) A flight instructor who provides flight training for a pilot certificate or rating issued under this part must provide that flight training in an aircraft that meets the following requirements—

(i) The aircraft must have at least two pilot stations and be of the same category, class, and type, if appropriate, that applies to the pilot certificate or rating sought.

(ii) For single-place aircraft, the pre-solo flight training must have been provided in an aircraft that has two pilot stations and is of the same category, class, and type, if appropriate.

(h) *Qualifications of the flight instructor for training first-time flight instructor applicants.*

(1) The ground training provided to an initial applicant for a flight instructor certificate must be given by an authorized instructor who—

(i) Holds a current ground or flight instructor certificate with the appropriate rating, has held that certificate for at least 24 months, and has given at least 40 hours of ground training; or

(ii) Holds a current ground or flight instructor certificate with the appropriate rating, and has given at least 100 hours of ground training in an FAA-approved course.

(2) Except for an instructor who meets the requirements of paragraph (h)(3)(ii) of this section, a flight instructor who provides training to an initial applicant for a flight instructor certificate must—

(i) Meet the eligibility requirements prescribed in § 61.183 of this part;

(ii) Hold the appropriate flight instructor certificate and rating;

(iii) Have held a flight instructor certificate for at least 24 months;

(iv) For training in preparation for an airplane, rotorcraft, or powered-lift rating, have given at least 200 hours of flight training as a flight instructor; and

(v) For training in preparation for a glider rating, have given at least 80 hours of flight training as a flight instructor.

(3) A flight instructor who serves as a flight instructor in an FAA-approved course for the issuance of a flight instructor rating must hold a current flight instructor certificate with the appropriate rating and pass the required initial and recurrent flight instructor proficiency tests, in accordance with the requirements of the part under which the FAA-approved course is conducted, and must—

(i) Meet the requirements of paragraph (h)(2) of this section; or

(ii) Have trained and endorsed at least five applicants for a practical test for a pilot certificate, flight instructor certificate, ground instructor certificate, or an additional rating, and at least 80 percent of those applicants passed that test on their first attempt; and

(A) Given at least 400 hours of flight training as a flight instructor for training in an airplane, a rotorcraft, or for a powered-lift rating; or

(B) Given at least 100 hours of flight training as a flight instructor, for training in a glider rating.

(i) *Prohibition against self-endorsements.* A flight instructor shall not make any self-endorsement for a certificate, rating, flight review, authorization, operating privilege, practical test, or knowledge test that is required by this part.

(j) Additional qualifications required to give training in Category II or Category III operations. A flight instructor may not give training in Category II or Category III operations unless the flight instructor has been trained and tested in Category II or Category III operations, pursuant to § 61.67 or § 61.68 of this part, as applicable.

[Docket No. 25910, 62 FR 16298, April 4, 1997; as amended by Amdt. 61–103, 62 FR 40907, July 30, 1997]

§ 61.197 Renewal of flight instructor certificates.

(a) A person who hold s a flight instructor certificate that has not expired may renew that certificate by—

(1) Passing a practical test for—

(i) One of the ratings listed on the current flight instructor certificate; or

(ii) An additional flight instructor rating; or

(2) Presenting to an authorized FAA Flight Standards Inspector—

(i) A record of training students showing that, during the preceding 24 calendar months, the flight instructor has endorsed at least five students for a practical test for a certificate or rating and at least 80 percent of those students passed that test on the first attempt;

(ii) A record showing that, within the preceding 24 calendar months, the flight instructor has served as a company check pilot, chief flight instructor, company check airman, or flight instructor in a part 121 or part 135 operation, or in a position involving the regular evaluation of pilots; or

(iii) A graduation certificate showing that, within the preceding 3 calendar months, the person has successfully completed an approved flight instructor refresher course consisting of ground training or flight training, or a combination of both.

(b) The expiration month of a renewed flight instructor certificate shall be 24 calendar months from—

(1) The month the renewal requirements of paragraph (a) of this section are accomplished; or

(2) The month of expiration of the current flight instructor certificate provided—

(i) The renewal requirements of paragraph (a) of this section are accomplished within the 3 calendar months preceding the expiration month of the current flight instructor certificate, and

(ii) If the renewal is accomplished under paragraph (a)(2)(iii) of this section, the approved flight instructor refresher course must be completed within the 3 calendar months preceding the expiration month of the current flight instructor certificate.

(c) The practical test required by paragraph (a)(1) of this section may be accomplished in a flight simulator or flight training device if the test is accomplished pursuant to an approved course conducted by a training center certificated under part 142 of this chapter.

[Docket No. 25910, 62 FR 16298, April 4, 1997; as amended by Amdt. 61–103, 62 FR 40907, July 30, 1997; Amdt. 61–104, 63 FR 20289, April 23, 1998]

§ 61.199 Expired flight instructor certificates and ratings.

(a) *Flight instructor certificates.* The holder of an expired flight instructor certificate may exchange that certificate for a new certificate with the same ratings by passing a practical test as prescribed in § 61.183(h) of this part for one of the ratings listed on the expired flight instructor certificate.

(b) *Flight instructor ratings.*

(1) A flight instructor rating or a limited flight instructor rating on a pilot certificate is no longer valid and may not be exchanged for a similar rating or a flight instructor certificate.

(2) The holder of a flight instructor rating or a limited flight instructor rating on a pilot certificate may be issued a flight instructor certificate with the current ratings, but only if the person passes the required knowledge and practical test prescribed in this subpart for the issuance of the current flight instructor certificate and rating.

[Docket No. 25910, 62 FR 16298, April 4, 1997; as amended by Amdt. 61–104, 63 FR 20289, April 23, 1998]

§ 61.201 [Reserved]

Subpart I—
Ground Instructors

§ 61.211 Applicability.

This subpart prescribes the requirements for the issuance of ground instructor certificates and ratings, the conditions under which those certificates and ratings are necessary, and the limitations upon those certificates and ratings.

§ 61.213 Eligibility requirements.

(a) To be eligible for a ground instructor certificate or rating a person must:

(1) Be at least 18 years of age;

(2) Be able to read, write, speak, and understand the English language. If the applicant is unable to meet one of these requirements due to medical reasons, then the Administrator may place such operating limitations on that applicant's ground instructor certificate as are necessary;

(3) Except as provided in paragraph (b) of this section, pass a knowledge test on the fundamentals of instructing to include—

(i) The learning process;

(ii) Elements of effective teaching;

(iii) Student evaluation and testing;

(iv) Course development;

(v) Lesson planning; and

(vi) Classroom training techniques.

(4) Pass a knowledge test on the aeronautical knowledge areas in—

(i) For a basic ground instructor rating, §§ 61.97 and 61.105;

(ii) For an advanced ground instructor rating, §§ 61.97, 61.105, 61.125, and 61.155; and

(iii) For an instrument ground instructor rating, § 61.65.

(b) The knowledge test specified in paragraph (a)(3) of this section is not required if the applicant:

(1) Holds a ground instructor certificate or flight instructor certificate issued under this part;

(2) Holds a current teacher's certificate issued by a State, county, city, or municipality that authorizes the person to teach at an educational level of the 7th grade or higher; or

(3) Is employed as a teacher at an accredited college or university.

§ 61.215 Ground instructor privileges.

(a) A person who holds a basic ground instructor rating is authorized to provide:

(1) Ground training in the aeronautical knowledge areas required for the issuance of a recreational pilot certificate, private pilot certificate, or associated ratings under this part;

(2) Ground training required for a recreational pilot and private pilot flight review; and

(3) A recommendation for a knowledge test required for the issuance of a recreational pilot certificate or private pilot certificate under this part.

(b) A person who holds an advanced ground instructor rating is authorized to provide:

(1) Ground training in the aeronautical knowledge areas required for the issuance of any certificate or rating under this part;

(2) Ground training required for any flight review; and

(3) A recommendation for a knowledge test required for the issuance of any certificate under this part.

(c) A person who holds an instrument ground instructor rating is authorized to provide:

(1) Ground training in the aeronautical knowledge areas required for the issuance of an instrument rating under this part;

(2) Ground training required for an instrument proficiency check; and

(3) A recommendation for a knowledge test required for the issuance of an instrument rating under this part.

(d) A person who holds a ground instructor certificate is authorized, within the limitations of the ratings on the ground instructor certificate, to endorse the logbook or other training record of a person to whom the holder has provided the training or recommendation specified in paragraphs (a) through (c) of this section.

§ 61.217 Recent experience requirements.

The holder of a ground instructor certificate may not perform the duties of a ground instructor unless, within the preceding 12 months:

(a) The person has served for at least 3 months as a ground instructor; or

(b) The person has received an endorsement from an authorized ground or flight instructor certifying that the person has demonstrated satisfactory proficiency in the subject areas prescribed in § 61.213(a)(3) and (a)(4), as applicable.

[Docket No. 25910, 62 FR 16298, April 4, 1997; as amended by Amdt. 61–103, 62 FR 40907, July 30, 1997]

PART 67
MEDICAL STANDARDS AND CERTIFICATION

Authority: 49 U.S.C. 106(g), 40113, 44701–44703, 44707, 44709–44711, 45102–45103, 45301–45303.

Source: Docket No. 27940, 61 FR 11256, March 19, 1996, unless otherwise noted.

Subpart A—General

§ 67.1 Applicability.

This part prescribes the medical standards and certification procedures for issuing medical certificates for airmen and for remaining eligible for a medical certificate.

§ 67.3 Issue.

Except as provided in § 67.5, a person who meets the medical standards prescribed in this part, based on medical examination and evaluation of the person's history and condition, is entitled to an appropriate medical certificate.

§ 67.7 Access to the National Driver Register.

At the time of application for a certificate issued under this part, each person who applies for a medical certificate shall execute an express consent form authorizing the Administrator to request the chief driver licensing official of any state designated by the Administrator to transmit information contained in the National Driver Register about the person to the Administrator. The Administrator shall make information received from the National Driver Register, if any, available on request to the person for review and written comment.

Subpart B—First-Class Airman Medical Certificate

§ 67.101 Eligibility.

To be eligible for a first-class airman medical certificate, and to remain eligible for a first-class airman medical certificate, a person must meet the requirements of this subpart.

§ 67.103 Eye.

Eye standards for a first-class airman medical certificate are:

(a) Distant visual acuity of 20/20 or better in each eye separately, with or without corrective lenses. If corrective lenses (spectacles or contact lenses) are necessary for 20/20 vision, the person may be eligible only on the condition that corrective lenses are worn while exercising the privileges of an airman certificate.

(b) Near vision of 20/40 or better, Snellen equivalent, at 16 inches in each eye separately, with or without corrective lenses. If age 50 or older, near vision of 20/40 or better, Snellen equivalent, at both 16 inches and 32 inches in each eye separately, with or without corrective lenses.

(c) Ability to perceive those colors necessary for the safe performance of airman duties.

(d) Normal fields of vision.

(e) No acute or chronic pathological condition of either eye or adnexa that interferes with the proper function of an eye, that may reasonably be expected to progress to that degree, or that may reasonably be expected to be aggravated by flying.

(f) Bifoveal fixation and vergence-phoria relationship sufficient to prevent a break in fusion under conditions that may reasonably be expected to occur in performing airman duties. Tests for the factors named in this paragraph are not required except for persons found to have more than 1 prism diopter of hyperphoria, 6 prism diopters of esophoria, or 6 prism diopters of exophoria. If any of these values are exceeded, the Federal Air Surgeon may require the person to be examined by a qualified eye specialist to determine if there is bifoveal fixation and an adequate vergence-phoria relationship. However, if otherwise eligible, the person is issued a medical certificate pending the results of the examination.

§ 67.105 Ear, nose, throat, and equilibrium.

Ear, nose, throat, and equilibrium standards for a first-class airman medical certificate are:

(a) The person shall demonstrate acceptable hearing by at least one of the following tests:

(1) Demonstrate an ability to hear an average conversational voice in a quiet room, using both ears, at a distance of 6 feet from the examiner, with the back turned to the examiner.

(2) Demonstrate an acceptable understanding of speech as determined by audiometric speech discrimination testing to a score of at least 70 percent obtained in one ear or in a sound field environment.

(3) Provide acceptable results of pure tone audiometric testing of unaided hearing acuity according to the following table of worst acceptable thresholds, using the calibration standards of the American National Standards Institute, 1969 (11 West 42d Street, New York, NY 10036):

Frequency (Hz)	500 Hz	1000 Hz	2000 Hz	3000 Hz
Better ear (Db)	35	30	30	40
Poorer ear (Db)	35	50	50	60

(b) No disease or condition of the middle or internal ear, nose, oral cavity, pharynx, or larynx that—

(1) Interferes with, or is aggravated by, flying or may reasonably be expected to do so; or

(2) Interferes with, or may reasonably be expected to interfere with, clear and effective speech communication.

(c) No disease or condition manifested by, or that may reasonably be expected to be manifested by, vertigo or a disturbance of equilibrium.

§ 67.107 Mental.

Mental standards for a first-class airman medical certificate are:

(a) No established medical history or clinical diagnosis of any of the following:

(1) A personality disorder that is severe enough to have repeatedly manifested itself by overt acts.

(2) A psychosis. As used in this section, "psychosis" refers to a mental disorder in which:

(i) The individual has manifested delusions, hallucinations, grossly bizarre or disorganized behavior, or other commonly accepted symptoms of this condition; or

(ii) The individual may reasonably be expected to manifest delusions, hallucinations, grossly bizarre or disorganized behavior, or other commonly accepted symptoms of this condition.

(3) A bipolar disorder.

(4) Substance dependence, except where there is established clinical evidence, satisfactory to the Federal Air Surgeon, of recovery, including sustained total abstinence from the substance(s) for not less than the preceding 2 years. As used in this section—

(i) "Substance" includes: Alcohol; other sedatives and hypnotics; anxiolytics; opioids; central nervous system stimulants such as cocaine, amphetamines, and similarly acting sympathomimetics; hallucinogens; phencyclidine or similarly acting arylcyclohexylamines; cannabis; inhalants; and other psychoactive drugs and chemicals; and

(ii) "Substance dependence" means a condition in which a person is dependent on a substance, other than tobacco or ordinary xanthine-containing (e.g., caffeine) beverages, as evidenced by—

(A) Increased tolerance;

(B) Manifestation of withdrawal symptoms;

(C) Impaired control of use; or

(D) Continued use despite damage to physical health or impairment of social, personal, or occupational functioning.

(b) No substance abuse within the preceding 2 years defined as:

(1) Use of a substance in a situation in which that use was physically hazardous, if there has been at any other time an instance of the use of a substance also in a situation in which that use was physically hazardous;

(2) A verified positive drug test result acquired under an anti-drug program or internal program of the U.S. Department of Transportation or any other Administration within the U.S. Department of Transportation; or

(3) Misuse of a substance that the Federal Air Surgeon, based on case history and appropriate, qualified medical judgment relating to the substance involved—

(i) Makes the person unable to safely perform the duties or exercise the privileges of the airman certificate applied for or held; or

(ii) May reasonably be expected, for the maximum duration of the airman medical certificate applied for or held, to make the person unable to perform those duties or exercise those privileges.

(c) No other personality disorder, neurosis, or other mental condition that the Federal Air Surgeon, based on the case history and appropriate, qualified medical judgment relating to the condition involved, finds—

(1) Makes the person unable to safely perform the duties or exercise the privileges of the airman certificate applied for or held; or

(2) May reasonably be expected, for the maximum duration of the airman medical certificate applied for or held, to make the person unable to perform those duties or exercise those privileges.

§ 67.109 Neurologic.

Neurologic standards for a first-class airman medical certificate are:

(a) No established medical history or clinical diagnosis of any of the following:

(1) Epilepsy;

(2) A disturbance of consciousness without satisfactory medical explanation of the cause; or

(3) A transient loss of control of nervous system function(s) without satisfactory medical explanation of the cause.

(b) No other seizure disorder, disturbance of consciousness, or neurologic condition that the Federal Air Surgeon, based on the case history and appropriate, qualified medical judgment relating to the condition involved, finds—

(1) Makes the person unable to safely perform the duties or exercise the privileges of the airman certificate applied for or held; or

(2) May reasonably be expected, for the maximum duration of the airman medical certificate applied for or held, to make the person unable to perform those duties or exercise those privileges.

§ 67.111 Cardiovascular.

Cardiovascular standards for a first-class airman medical certificate are:

(a) No established medical history or clinical diagnosis of any of the following:

(1) Myocardial infarction;

(2) Angina pectoris;

(3) Coronary heart disease that has required treatment or, if untreated, that has been symptomatic or clinically significant;

(4) Cardiac valve replacement;

(5) Permanent cardiac pacemaker implantation; or

(6) Heart replacement;

(b) A person applying for first-class medical certification must demonstrate an absence of myocardial infarction and other clinically significant abnormality on electrocardiographic examination:

(1) At the first application after reaching the 35th birthday; and

(2) On an annual basis after reaching the 40th birthday.

(c) An electrocardiogram will satisfy a requirement of paragraph (b) of this section if it is dated no earlier than 60 days before the date of the application it is to accompany and was performed and transmitted according to acceptable standards and techniques.

§ 67.113 General medical condition.

The general medical standards for a first-class airman medical certificate are:

(a) No established medical history or clinical diagnosis of diabetes mellitus that requires insulin or any other hypoglycemic drug for control.

(b) No other organic, functional, or structural disease, defect, or limitation that the Federal Air Surgeon, based on the case history and appropriate, qualified medical judgment relating to the condition involved, finds—

(1) Makes the person unable to safely perform the duties or exercise the privileges of the airman certificate applied for or held; or

(2) May reasonably be expected, for the maximum duration of the airman medical certificate applied for or held, to make the person unable to perform those duties or exercise those privileges.

(c) No medication or other treatment that the Federal Air Surgeon, based on the case history and appropriate, qualified medical judgment relating to the medication or other treatment involved, finds—

(1) Makes the person unable to safely perform the duties or exercise the privileges of the airman certificate applied for or held; or

(2) May reasonably be expected, for the maximum duration of the airman medical certificate applied for or held, to make the person unable to perform those duties or exercise those privileges.

§ 67.115 Discretionary issuance.

A person who does not meet the provisions of §§ 67.103 through 67.113 may apply for the discretionary issuance of a certificate under § 67.401.

Subpart C—Second-Class Airman Medical Certificate

§ 67.201 Eligibility.

To be eligible for a second-class airman medical certificate, and to remain eligible for a second-class airman medical certificate, a person must meet the requirements of this subpart.

§ 67.203 Eye.

Eye standards for a second-class airman medical certificate are:

(a) Distant visual acuity of 20/20 or better in each eye separately, with or without corrective lenses. If corrective lenses (spectacles or contact lenses) are necessary for 20/20 vision, the person may be eligible only on the condition that corrective lenses are worn while exercising the privileges of an airman certificate.

(b) Near vision of 20/40 or better, Snellen equivalent, at 16 inches in each eye separately, with or without corrective lenses. If age 50 or older, near vision of 20/40 or better, Snellen equivalent, at both 16 inches and 32 inches in each eye separately, with or without corrective lenses.

(c) Ability to perceive those colors necessary for the safe performance of airman duties.

(d) Normal fields of vision.

(e) No acute or chronic pathological condition of either eye or adnexa that interferes with the proper function of an eye, that may reasonably be expected to progress to that degree, or that may reasonably be expected to be aggravated by flying.

(f) Bifoveal fixation and vergence-phoria relationship sufficient to prevent a break in fusion under conditions that may reasonably be expected to occur in performing airman duties. Tests for the factors named in this paragraph are not required except for persons found to have more than 1 prism diopter of hyperphoria, 6 prism diopters of esophoria, or 6 prism diopters of exophoria. If any of these values are exceeded, the Federal Air Surgeon may require the person to be examined by a qualified eye specialist to determine if there is bifoveal fixation and an adequate vergence-phoria relationship. However, if otherwise eligible, the person is issued a medical certificate pending the results of the examination.

§ 67.205 Ear, nose, throat, and equilibrium.

Ear, nose, throat, and equilibrium standards for a second-class airman medical certificate are:

(a) The person shall demonstrate acceptable hearing by at least one of the following tests:

(1) Demonstrate an ability to hear an average conversational voice in a quiet room, using both ears, at a distance of 6 feet from the examiner, with the back turned to the examiner.

(2) Demonstrate an acceptable understanding of speech as determined by audiometric speech discrimination testing to a score of at least 70 percent obtained in one ear or in a sound field environment.

(3) Provide acceptable results of pure tone audiometric testing of unaided hearing acuity according to the following table of worst acceptable thresholds, using the calibration standards of the American National Standards Institute, 1969:

Frequency (Hz)	500 Hz	1000 Hz	2000 Hz	3000 Hz
Better ear (Db)	35	30	30	40
Poorer ear (Db)	35	50	50	60

(b) No disease or condition of the middle or internal ear, nose, oral cavity, pharynx, or larynx that—

(1) Interferes with, or is aggravated by, flying or may reasonably be expected to do so; or

(2) Interferes with, or may reasonably be expected to interfere with, clear and effective speech communication.

(c) No disease or condition manifested by, or that may reasonably be expected to be manifested by, vertigo or a disturbance of equilibrium.

§ 67.207 Mental.

Mental standards for a second-class airman medical certificate are:

(a) No established medical history or clinical diagnosis of any of the following:

(1) A personality disorder that is severe enough to have repeatedly manifested itself by overt acts.

(2) A psychosis. As used in this section, "psychosis" refers to a mental disorder in which:

(i) The individual has manifested delusions, hallucinations, grossly bizarre or disorganized behavior, or other commonly accepted symptoms of this condition; or

(ii) The individual may reasonably be expected to manifest delusions, hallucinations, grossly bizarre or disorganized behavior, or other commonly accepted symptoms of this condition.

(3) A bipolar disorder.

(4) Substance dependence, except where there is established clinical evidence, satisfactory to the Federal Air Surgeon, of recovery, including sustained total abstinence from the substance(s) for not less than the preceding 2 years. As used in this section—

(i) "Substance" includes: Alcohol; other sedatives and hypnotics; anxiolytics; opioids; central nervous system stimulants such as cocaine, amphetamines, and similarly acting sympathomimetics; hallucinogens; phencyclidine or similarly acting arylcyclohexylamines; cannabis; inhalants; and other psychoactive drugs and chemicals; and

(ii) "Substance dependence" means a condition in which a person is dependent on a substance, other than tobacco or ordinary xanthine-containing (e.g., caffeine) beverages, as evidenced by—

(A) Increased tolerance;

(B) Manifestation of withdrawal symptoms;

(C) Impaired control of use; or

(D) Continued use despite damage to physical health or impairment of social, personal, or occupational functioning.

(b) No substance abuse within the preceding 2 years defined as:

(1) Use of a substance in a situation in which that use was physically hazardous, if there has been at any other time an instance of the use of a substance also in a situation in which that use was physically hazardous;

(2) A verified positive drug test result acquired under an anti-drug program or internal program of the U.S. Department of Transportation or any other Administration within the U.S. Department of Transportation; or

(3) Misuse of a substance that the Federal Air Surgeon, based on case history and appropriate, qualified medical judgment relating to the substance involved, finds—

(i) Makes the person unable to safely perform the duties or exercise the privileges of the airman certificate applied for or held; or

(ii) May reasonably be expected, for the maximum duration of the airman medical certificate applied for or held, to make the person unable to perform those duties or exercise those privileges.

(c) No other personality disorder, neurosis, or other mental condition that the Federal Air Surgeon, based on the case history and appropriate, qualified medical judgment relating to the condition involved, finds—

(1) Makes the person unable to safely perform the duties or exercise the privileges of the airman certificate applied for or held; or

(2) May reasonably be expected, for the maximum duration of the airman medical certificate applied for or held, to make the person unable to perform those duties or exercise those privileges.

§ 67.209 Neurologic.

Neurologic standards for a second-class airman medical certificate are:

(a) No established medical history or clinical diagnosis of any of the following:

(1) Epilepsy;

(2) A disturbance of consciousness without satisfactory medical explanation of the cause; or

(3) A transient loss of control of nervous system function(s) without satisfactory medical explanation of the cause;

(b) No other seizure disorder, disturbance of consciousness, or neurologic condition that the Federal Air Surgeon, based on the case history and appropriate, qualified medical judgment relating to the condition involved, finds—

(1) Makes the person unable to safely perform the duties or exercise the privileges of the airman certificate applied for or held; or

(2) May reasonably be expected, for the maximum duration of the airman medical certificate applied for or held, to make the person unable to perform those duties or exercise those privileges.

§ 67.211 Cardiovascular.

Cardiovascular standards for a second-class medical certificate are no established medical history or clinical diagnosis of any of the following:

(a) Myocardial infarction;

(b) Angina pectoris;

(c) Coronary heart disease that has required treatment or, if untreated, that has been symptomatic or clinically significant;

(d) Cardiac valve replacement;

(e) Permanent cardiac pacemaker implantation; or

(f) Heart replacement.

§ 67.213 General medical condition.

The general medical standards for a second-class airman medical certificate are:

(a) No established medical history or clinical diagnosis of diabetes mellitus that requires insulin or any other hypoglycemic drug for control.

(b) No other organic, functional, or structural disease, defect, or limitation that the Federal Air Surgeon, based on the case history and appropriate, qualified medical judgment relating to the condition involved, finds—

(1) Makes the person unable to safely perform the duties or exercise the privileges of the airman certificate applied for or held; or

(2) May reasonably be expected, for the maximum duration of the airman medical certificate applied for or held, to make the person unable to perform those duties or exercise those privileges.

(c) No medication or other treatment that the Federal Air Surgeon, based on the case history and appropriate, qualified medical judgment relating to the medication or other treatment involved, finds—

(1) Makes the person unable to safely perform the duties or exercise the privileges of the airman certificate applied for or held; or

(2) May reasonably be expected, for the maximum duration of the airman medical certificate applied for or held, to make the person unable to perform those duties or exercise those privileges.

§ 67.215 Discretionary issuance.

A person who does not meet the provisions of §§ 67.203 through 67.213 may apply for the discretionary issuance of a certificate under § 67.401.

Subpart D—Third-Class Airman Medical Certificate

§ 67.301 Eligibility.

To be eligible for a third-class airman medical certificate, or to remain eligible for a third-class airman medical certificate, a person must meet the requirements of this subpart.

§ 67.303 Eye.

Eye standards for a third-class airman medical certificate are:

(a) Distant visual acuity of 20/40 or better in each eye separately, with or without corrective lenses. If corrective lenses (spectacles or contact lenses) are necessary for 20/40 vision, the person may be eligible only on the condition that corrective lenses are worn while exercising the privileges of an airman certificate.

(b) Near vision of 20/40 or better, Snellen equivalent, at 16 inches in each eye separately, with or without corrective lenses.

(c) Ability to perceive those colors necessary for the safe performance of airman duties.

(d) No acute or chronic pathological condition of either eye or adnexa that interferes with the proper function of an eye, that may reasonably be expected to progress to that degree, or that may reasonably be expected to be aggravated by flying.

§ 67.305 Ear, nose, throat, and equilibrium.

Ear, nose, throat, and equilibrium standards for a third-class airman medical certificate are:

(a) The person shall demonstrate acceptable hearing by at least one of the following tests:

(1) Demonstrate an ability to hear an average conversational voice in a quiet room, using both ears, at a distance of 6 feet from the examiner, with the back turned to the examiner.

(2) Demonstrate an acceptable understanding of speech as determined by audiometric speech discrimination testing to a score of at least 70 percent obtained in one ear or in a sound field environment.

(3) Provide acceptable results of pure tone audiometric testing of unaided hearing acuity according to the following table of worst acceptable thresholds, using the calibration standards of the American National Standards Institute, 1969:

Frequency (Hz)	500 Hz	1000 Hz	2000 Hz	3000 Hz
Better ear (Db)	35	30	30	40
Poorer ear (Db)	35	50	50	60

(b) No disease or condition of the middle or internal ear, nose, oral cavity, pharynx, or larynx that—

(1) Interferes with, or is aggravated by, flying or may reasonably be expected to do so; or

(2) Interferes with clear and effective speech communication.

(c) No disease or condition manifested by, or that may reasonably be expected to be manifested by, vertigo or a disturbance of equilibrium.

§ 67.307 Mental.

Mental standards for a third-class airman medical certificate are:

(a) No established medical history or clinical diagnosis of any of the following:

(1) A personality disorder that is severe enough to have repeatedly manifested itself by overt acts.

(2) A psychosis. As used in this section, "psychosis" refers to a mental disorder in which—

(i) The individual has manifested delusions, hallucinations, grossly bizarre or disorganized behavior, or other commonly accepted symptoms of this condition; or

(ii) The individual may reasonably be expected to manifest delusions, hallucinations, grossly bizarre or disorganized behavior, or other commonly accepted symptoms of this condition.

(3) A bipolar disorder.

(4) Substance dependence, except where there is established clinical evidence, satisfactory to the Federal Air Surgeon, of recovery, including sustained total abstinence from the substance(s) for not less than the preceding 2 years. As used in this section—

(i) "Substance" includes: alcohol; other sedatives and hypnotics; anxiolytics; opioids; central nervous system stimulants such as cocaine, amphetamines, and similarly acting sympathomimetics; hallucinogens; phencyclidine or similarly acting arylcyclohexylamines; cannabis; inhalants; and other psychoactive drugs and chemicals; and

(ii) "Substance dependence" means a condition in which a person is dependent on a substance, other than tobacco or ordinary xanthine-containing (e.g., caffeine) beverages, as evidenced by—

(A) Increased tolerance;

(B) Manifestation of withdrawal symptoms;

(C) Impaired control of use; or

(D) Continued use despite damage to physical health or impairment of social, personal, or occupational functioning.

(b) No substance abuse within the preceding 2 years defined as:

(1) Use of a substance in a situation in which that use was physically hazardous, if there has been at any other time an instance of the use of a substance also in a situation in which that use was physically hazardous;

(2) A verified positive drug test result conducted under an anti-drug rule or internal program of the U.S. Department of Transportation or any other Administration within the U.S. Department of Transportation; or

(3) Misuse of a substance that the Federal Air Surgeon, based on case history and appropriate, qualified medical judgment relating to the substance involved, finds—

(i) Makes the person unable to safely perform the duties or exercise the privileges of the airman certificate applied for or held; or

(ii) May reasonably be expected, for the maximum duration of the airman medical certificate applied for or held, to make the person unable to perform those duties or exercise those privileges.

(c) No other personality disorder, neurosis, or other mental condition that the Federal Air Surgeon, based on the case history and appropriate, qualified medical judgment relating to the condition involved, finds—

(1) Makes the person unable to safely perform the duties or exercise the privileges of the airman certificate applied for or held; or

(2) May reasonably be expected, for the maximum duration of the airman medical certificate applied for or held, to make the person unable to perform those duties or exercise those privileges.

§ 67.309 Neurologic.

Neurologic standards for a third-class airman medical certificate are:

(a) No established medical history or clinical diagnosis of any of the following:

(1) Epilepsy;

(2) A disturbance of consciousness without satisfactory medical explanation of the cause; or

(3) A transient loss of control of nervous system function(s) without satisfactory medical explanation of the cause.

(b) No other seizure disorder, disturbance of consciousness, or neurologic condition that the Federal Air Surgeon, based on the case history and appropriate, qualified medical judgment relating to the condition involved, finds—

(1) Makes the person unable to safely perform the duties or exercise the privileges of the airman certificate applied for or held; or

(2) May reasonably be expected, for the maximum duration of the airman medical certificate applied for or held, to make the person unable to perform those duties or exercise those privileges.

§ 67.311 Cardiovascular.

Cardiovascular standards for a third-class airman medical certificate are no established medical history or clinical diagnosis of any of the following:

(a) Myocardial infarction;

(b) Angina pectoris;

(c) Coronary heart disease that has required treatment or, if untreated, that has been symptomatic or clinically significant;

(d) Cardiac valve replacement;

(e) Permanent cardiac pacemaker implantation; or

(f) Heart replacement.

§ 67.313 General medical condition.

The general medical standards for a third-class airman medical certificate are:

(a) No established medical history or clinical diagnosis of diabetes mellitus that requires insulin or any other hypoglycemic drug for control.

(b) No other organic, functional, or structural disease, defect, or limitation that the Federal Air Surgeon, based on the case history and appropriate, qualified medical judgment relating to the condition involved, finds—

(1) Makes the person unable to safely perform the duties or exercise the privileges of the airman certificate applied for or held; or

(2) May reasonably be expected, for the maximum duration of the airman medical certificate applied for or held, to make the person unable to perform those duties or exercise those privileges.

(c) No medication or other treatment that the Federal Air Surgeon, based on the case history and appropriate, qualified medical judgment relating to the medication or other treatment involved, finds—

(1) Makes the person unable to safely perform the duties or exercise the privileges of the airman certificate applied for or held; or

(2) May reasonably be expected, for the maximum duration of the airman medical certificate applied for or held, to make the person unable to perform those duties or exercise those privileges.

§ 67.315 Discretionary issuance.

A person who does not meet the provisions of §§ 67.303 through 67.313 may apply for the discretionary issuance of a certificate under § 67.401.

Subpart E— Certification Procedures

§ 67.401 Special issuance of medical certificates.

(a) At the discretion of the Federal Air Surgeon, an Authorization for Special Issuance of a Medical Certificate (Authorization), valid for a specified period, may be granted to a person who does not meet the provisions of subparts B, C, or D of this part if the person shows to the satisfaction of the Federal Air Surgeon that the duties authorized by the class of medical certificate applied for can be performed without endangering public safety during the period in which the Authorization would be in force. The Federal Air Surgeon may authorize a special medical flight test, practical test, or medical evaluation for this purpose. A medical certificate of the appropriate class may be issued to a person who does not meet the provisions of subparts B, C, or D of this part if that person possesses a valid Authorization and is otherwise eligible. An airman medical certificate issued in accordance with this section shall expire no later than the end of the validity period or upon the withdrawal of the Authorization upon which it is based. At the end of its specified validity period, for grant of a new Authorization, the person must again show to the satisfaction of the Federal Air Surgeon that the duties authorized by the class of medical certificate applied for can be performed without endangering public safety during the period in which the Authorization would be in force.

(b) At the discretion of the Federal Air Surgeon, a Statement of Demonstrated Ability (SODA) may be granted, instead of an Authorization, to a person whose disqualifying condition is static or nonprogressive and who has been found capable of performing airman duties without endangering public safety. A SODA does not expire and authorizes a designated aviation medical examiner to issue a medical certificate of a specified class if the examiner finds that the condition described on its face has not adversely changed.

(c) In granting an Authorization or SODA, the Federal Air Surgeon may consider the person's operational experience and any medical facts that may affect the ability of the person to perform airman duties including—

(1) The combined effect on the person of failure to meet more than one requirement of this part; and

(2) The prognosis derived from professional consideration of all available information regarding the person.

(d) In granting an Authorization or SODA under this section, the Federal Air Surgeon specifies the class of medical certificate authorized to be issued and may do any or all of the following:

(1) Limit the duration of an Authorization;

(2) Condition the granting of a new Authorization on the results of subsequent medical tests, examinations, or evaluations;

(3) State on the Authorization or SODA, and any medical certificate based upon it, any operational limitation needed for safety; or

(4) Condition the continued effect of an Authorization or SODA, and any second- or third-class medical certificate based upon it, on compliance with a statement of functional limitations issued to the person in coordination with the Director of Flight Standards or the Director's designee.

(e) In determining whether an Authorization or SODA should be granted to an applicant for a third-class medical certificate, the Federal Air Surgeon considers the freedom of an airman, exercising the privileges of a private pilot certificate, to accept reasonable risks to his or her person and property that are not acceptable in the exercise of commercial or airline transport pilot privileges, and, at the same time, considers the need to protect the safety of persons and property in other aircraft and on the ground.

(f) An Authorization or SODA granted under the provisions of this section to a person who does not meet the applicable provisions of subparts B, C, or D of this part may be withdrawn, at the discretion of the Federal Air Surgeon, at any time if—

(1) There is adverse change in the holder's medical condition;

(2) The holder fails to comply with a statement of functional limitations or operational limitations issued as a condition of certification under this section;

(3) Public safety would be endangered by the holder's exercise of airman privileges;

(4) The holder fails to provide medical information reasonably needed by the Federal Air Surgeon for certification under this section; or

(5) The holder makes or causes to be made a statement or entry that is the basis for withdrawal of an Authorization or SODA under § 67.403.

(g) A person who has been granted an Authorization or SODA under this section based on a special medical flight or practical test need not take the test again during later physical examinations unless the Federal Air Surgeon determines or has reason to believe that the physical deficiency has or may have degraded to a degree to require another special medical flight test or practical test.

(h) The authority of the Federal Air Surgeon under this section is also exercised by the Manager, Aeromedical Certification Division, and each Regional Flight Surgeon.

(i) If an Authorization or SODA is withdrawn under paragraph (f) of this section the following procedures apply:

(1) The holder of the Authorization or SODA will be served a letter of withdrawal, stating the reason for the action;

(2) By not later than 60 days after the service of the letter of withdrawal, the holder of the Authorization or SODA may request, in writing, that the Federal Air Surgeon provide for review of the decision to withdraw. The request for review may be accompanied by supporting medical evidence;

(3) Within 60 days of receipt of a request for review, a written final decision either affirming or reversing the decision to withdraw will be issued; and

(4) A medical certificate rendered invalid pursuant to a withdrawal, in accordance with paragraph (a) of this section, shall be surrendered to the Administrator upon request.

(j) No grant of a special issuance made prior to September 16, 1996, may be used to obtain a medical certificate after the earlier of the following dates:

(1) September 16, 1997; or

(2) The date on which the holder of such special issuance is required to provide additional information to the FAA as a condition for continued medical certification.

§ 67.403 Applications, certificates, logbooks, reports, and records: Falsification, reproduction, or alteration; incorrect statements.

(a) No person may make or cause to be made—

(1) A fraudulent or intentionally false statement on any application for a medical certificate or on a request for any Authorization for Special Issuance of a Medical Certificate (Authorization) or Statement of Demonstrated Ability (SODA) under this part;

(2) A fraudulent or intentionally false entry in any logbook, record, or report that is kept, made, or used, to show compliance with any requirement for any medical certificate or for any Authorization or SODA under this part;

(3) A reproduction, for fraudulent purposes, of any medical certificate under this part; or

(4) An alteration of any medical certificate under this part.

(b) The commission by any person of an act prohibited under paragraph (a) of this section is a basis for—

(1) Suspending or revoking all airman, ground instructor, and medical certificates and ratings held by that person;

(2) Withdrawing all Authorizations or SODA's held by that person; and

(3) Denying all applications for medical certification and requests for Authorizations or SODA's.

(c) The following may serve as a basis for suspending or revoking a medical certificate; withdrawing an Authorization or SODA; or denying an application for a medical certificate or request for an authorization or SODA:

(1) An incorrect statement, upon which the FAA relied, made in support of an application for a medical certificate or request for an Authorization or SODA.

(2) An incorrect entry, upon which the FAA relied, made in any logbook, record, or report that is kept, made, or used to show compliance with any requirement for a medical certificate or an Authorization or SODA.

§ 67.405 Medical examinations: Who may give.

(a) *First-class.* Any aviation medical examiner who is specifically designated for the purpose may give the examination for the first-class medical certificate. Any interested person may obtain a list of these aviation medical examiners, in any area, from the FAA Regional Flight Surgeon of the region in which the area is located.

(b) *Second- and third-class.* Any aviation medical examiner may give the examination for the second- or third-class medical certificate. Any interested person may obtain a list of aviation medical examiners, in any area, from the FAA Regional Flight Surgeon of the region in which the area is located.

§ 67.407 Delegation of authority.

(a) The authority of the Administrator under 49 U.S.C. 44703 to issue or deny medical certificates is delegated to the Federal Air Surgeon to the extent necessary to—

(1) Examine applicants for and holders of medical certificates to determine whether they meet applicable medical standards; and

(2) Issue, renew, and deny medical certificates, and issue, renew, deny, and withdraw Authorizations for Special Issuance of a Medical Certificate and Statements of Demonstrated Ability to a person based upon meeting or failing to meet applicable medical standards.

(b) Subject to limitations in this chapter, the delegated functions of the Federal Air Surgeon to examine applicants for and holders of medical certificates for compliance with applicable medical standards and to issue, renew, and deny medical certificates are also delegated to aviation medical examiners and to authorized representatives of the Federal Air Surgeon within the FAA.

(c) The authority of the Administrator under 49 U.S.C. 44702, to reconsider the action of an aviation medical examiner is delegated to the Federal Air Surgeon; the Manager, Aeromedical Certification Division; and each Regional Flight Surgeon. Where the person does not meet the standards of §§ 67.107(b)(3) and (c), 67.109(b), 67.113(b) and (c), 67.207(b)(3) and (c), 67.209(b), 67.213(b) and (c), 67.307(b)(3) and (c), 67.309(b), or 67.313(b) and (c), any action taken under this paragraph other than by the Federal Air Surgeon is subject to reconsideration by the Federal Air Surgeon. A certificate issued by an aviation medical examiner is considered to be affirmed as issued unless an FAA official named in this paragraph (authorized official) reverses that issuance within 60 days after the date of issuance. However, if within 60 days after the date of issuance an authorized official requests the certificate holder to submit additional medical information, an authorized official may reverse the issuance within 60 days after receipt of the requested information.

(d) The authority of the Administrator under 49 U.S.C. 44709 to re-examine any civil airman to the extent necessary to determine an airman's qualification to continue to hold an airman medical certificate, is delegated to the Federal Air Surgeon and his or her authorized representatives within the FAA.

§ 67.409 Denial of medical certificate.

(a) Any person who is denied a medical certificate by an aviation medical examiner may, within 30 days after the date of the denial, apply in writing and in duplicate to the Federal Air Surgeon, Attention: Manager, Aeromedical Certification Division, AAM-300, Federal Aviation Administration, P.O. Box 26080, Oklahoma City, Oklahoma 73126, for reconsideration of that denial. If the person does not ask for reconsideration during the 30-day period after the date of the denial, he or she is considered to have withdrawn the application for a medical certificate.

(b) The denial of a medical certificate—

(1) By an aviation medical examiner is not a denial by the Administrator under 49 U.S.C. 44703.

(2) By the Federal Air Surgeon is considered to be a denial by the Administrator under 49 U.S.C. 44703.

(3) By the Manager, Aeromedical Certification Division, or a Regional Flight Surgeon is considered to be a denial by the Administrator under 49 U.S.C. 44703 except where the person does not meet the standards of §§ 67.107(b)(3) and (c), 67.109(b), or 67.113(b) and (c); 67.207(b)(3) and (c), 67.209(b), or 67.213(b) and (c); or 67.307(b)(3) and (c), 67.309(b), or 67.313(b) and (c).

(c) Any action taken under § 67.407(c) that wholly or partly reverses the issue of a medical certificate by an aviation medical examiner is the denial of a medical certificate under paragraph (b) of this section.

(d) If the issue of a medical certificate is wholly or partly reversed by the Federal Air Surgeon; the Manager, Aeromedical Certification Division; or a Regional Flight Surgeon, the person holding that certificate shall surrender it, upon request of the FAA.

§ 67.411 Medical certificates by flight surgeons of Armed Forces.

(a) The FAA has designated flight surgeons of the Armed Forces on specified military posts, stations, and facilities, as aviation medical examiners.

(b) An aviation medical examiner described in paragraph (a) of this section may give physical examinations for the FAA medical certificates to persons who are on active duty or who are, under Department of Defense medical programs, eligible for FAA medical certification as civil airmen. In addition, such an examiner may issue or deny an appropriate FAA medical certificate in accordance with the regulations of this chapter and the policies of the FAA.

(c) Any interested person may obtain a list of the military posts, stations, and facilities at which a flight surgeon has been designated as an aviation medical examiner from the Surgeon General of the Armed Force concerned or from the Manager, Aeromedical Education Division, AAM-400, Federal Aviation Administration, P.O. Box 26082, Oklahoma City, Oklahoma 73125.

§ 67.413 Medical records.

(a) Whenever the Administrator finds that additional medical information or history is necessary to determine whether an applicant for or the holder of a medical certificate meets the medical standards for it, the Administrator requests that person to furnish that information or to authorize any clinic, hospital, physician, or other person to release to the Administrator all available information or records concerning that history. If the applicant or holder fails to provide the requested medical information or history or to authorize the release so requested, the Administrator may suspend, modify, or revoke all medical certificates the airman holds or may, in the case of an applicant, deny the application for an airman medical certificate.

(b) If an airman medical certificate is suspended or modified under paragraph (a) of this section, that suspension or modification remains in effect until the requested information, history, or authorization is provided to the FAA and until the Federal Air Surgeon determines whether the person meets the medical standards under this part.

§ 67.415 Return of medical certificate after suspension or revocation.

The holder of any medical certificate issued under this part that is suspended or revoked shall, upon the Administrator's request, return it to the Administrator.

67

SUBCHAPTER E
AIRSPACE

PART 71

DESIGNATION OF CLASS A, CLASS B, CLASS C, CLASS D, AND CLASS E AIRSPACE AREAS; AIRWAYS; ROUTES; AND REPORTING POINTS

Authority: 49 U.S.C. 106(g), 40103, 40113, 40120; E.O. 10854, 24 FR 9565, 3 CFR, 1959–1963 Comp., p. 389.

Source: Amdt. 71–14, 56 FR 65654, Dec. 17, 1991, unless otherwise noted.

Subpart A— General; Class A Airspace

§ 71.1 Applicability.

The complete listing for all Class A, Class B, Class C, Class D, and Class E airspace areas and for all reporting points can be found in FAA Order 7400.9G, Airspace Designations and Reporting Points, dated September 1, 1999. This incorporation by reference was approved by the Director of the Federal Register in accordance with 5 U.S.C. 552(a) and 1 CFR part 51. The approval to incorporate by reference FAA Order 7400.9G is effective September 16, 1999, through September 15, 2000. During the incorporation by reference period, proposed changes to the listings of Class A, Class B, Class C, Class D, and Class E airspace areas and to reporting points will be published in full text as proposed rule documents in the **Federal Register**. Amendments to the listings of Class A, Class B, Class C, Class D, and Class E airspace areas and to reporting points will be published in full text as final rules in the **Federal Register**. Periodically, the final rule amendments will be integrated into a revised edition of the Order and submitted to the Director of the Federal Register for approval for incorporation by reference in this section. Copies of FAA Order 7400.9G may be obtained from the Airspace and Rules Division, ATA–400, Federal Aviation Administration, 800 Independence Avenue SW, Washington, DC 20591, (202) 267-8783. Copies of FAA Order 7400.9G may be inspected in Docket No. 29334 at the Federal Aviation Administration, Office of the Chief Counsel, AGC–200, Room 915G, 800 Independence Avenue SW, Washington, DC, weekdays between 8:30 a.m. and 5:00 p.m., or at the Office of the Federal Register, 800 North Capitol Street NW, Suite 700, Washington, DC. This section is effective September 16, 1999, through September 15, 2000.

[Docket No. 29334, 63 FR 50140, Sept. 21, 1998; as amended by Amdt. 71–31, 64 FR 50444, Sept. 17, 1999]

§ 71.3 [Reserved]

§ 71.5 Reporting points.

The reporting points listed in subpart H of FAA Order 7400.9G (incorporated by reference, see § 71.1) consist of geographic locations at which the position of an aircraft must be reported in accordance with part 91 of this chapter.

[Amdt. 71–14, 56 FR 65654, Dec. 17, 1991; as amended by Amdt. 71–20, 58 FR 36299, July 6, 1993; Amdt. 71–23, 59 FR 43035, Aug. 22, 1994; Amdt. 71–26, 60 FR 47267, Sept. 12, 1995; 71–28, 61 FR 48404, Sept. 13, 1996; Amdt. 71–29, 62 FR 52492, Oct. 8, 1997; Amdt.

71–30, 63 FR 50140, Sept. 21, 1998; Amdt. 71–31, 64 FR 50444, Sept. 17, 1999]

§ 71.7 Bearings, radials, and mileages.

All bearings and radials in this part are true and are applied from point of origin and all mileages in this part are stated as nautical miles.

§ 71.9 Overlapping airspace designations.

(a) When overlapping airspace designations apply to the same airspace, the operating rules associated with the more restrictive airspace designation apply.

(b) For the purpose of this section—

(1) Class A airspace is more restrictive than Class B, Class C, Class D, Class E, or Class G airspace;

(2) Class B airspace is more restrictive than Class C, Class D, Class E, or Class G airspace;

(3) Class C airspace is more restrictive than Class D, Class E, or Class G airspace;

(4) Class D airspace is more restrictive than Class E or Class G airspace; and

(5) Class E is more restrictive than Class G airspace.

§ 71.31 Class A airspace.

The airspace descriptions contained in § 71.33 and the routes contained in subpart A of FAA Order 7400.9G (incorporated by reference, see § 71.1) are designated as Class A airspace within which all pilots and aircraft are subject to the rating requirements, operating rules, and equipment requirements of part 91 of this chapter.

[Amdt. 71–14, 56 FR 65654, Dec. 17, 1991; as amended by Amdt. 71–20, 58 FR 36299, July 6, 1993; Amdt. 71–23, 59 FR 43035, Aug. 22, 1994; Amdt. 71–26, 60 FR 47267, Sept. 12, 1995; 71–28, 61 FR 48404, Sept. 13, 1996; Amdt. No. 71–29, 62 FR 52492, Oct. 8, 1997; Amdt. 71–30, 63 FR 50140, Sept. 21, 1998; Amdt. 71–31, 64 FR 50444, Sept. 17, 1999]

§ 71.33 Class A airspace areas.

(a) That airspace of the United States, including that airspace overlying the waters within 12 nautical miles of the coast of the 48 contiguous States, from 18,000 feet MSL to and including FL600 excluding the states of Alaska and Hawaii, Santa Barbara Island, Farallon Island, and the airspace south of latitude 25°04'00" North.

(b) That airspace of the State of Alaska, including that airspace overlying the waters within 12 nautical miles of the coast, from 18,000 feet MSL to and including FL600 but not including the airspace less than 1,500 feet above the surface of the earth and the Alaska Peninsula west of longitude 160°00'00" West.

(c) The airspace areas listed as offshore airspace areas in subpart A of FAA Order 7400.9G (incorporated by reference, see § 71.1) that are designated in international airspace within areas of domestic radio navigational signal or ATC radar coverage, and within which domestic ATC procedures are applied.

[Amdt. 71–14, 56 FR 65654, Dec. 17, 1991; as amended by Amdt. 71–19, 58 FR 12137, March 2, 1993; Amdt. 71–23, 59 FR 43035, Aug. 22, 1994; Amdt. 71–26, 60 FR 47267, Sept. 12, 1995; 71–28, 61 FR 48404, Sept. 13, 1996; Amdt. No. 71–29, 62 FR 52492, Oct. 8, 1997; Amdt. 71–30, 63 FR 50140, Sept. 21, 1998; Amdt. 71–31, 64 FR 50444, Sept. 17, 1999]

Subpart B— Class B Airspace

§ 71.41 Class B airspace.

The Class B airspace areas listed in subpart B of FAA Order 7400.9G (incorporated by reference, see § 71.1) consist of specified airspace within which all aircraft operators are subject to the minimum pilot qualification requirements, operating rules, and aircraft equipment requirements of part 91 of this chapter. Each Class B airspace area designated for an airport in subpart B of FAA Order 7400.9G (incorporated by reference, see § 71.1) contains at least one primary airport around which the airspace is designated.

[Amdt. 71–14, 56 FR 65654, Dec. 17, 1991; as amended by Amdt. 71–20, 58 FR 36299, July 6, 1993; Amdt. 71–23, 59 FR 43035, Aug. 22, 1994; Amdt. 71–26, 60 FR 47267, Sept. 12, 1995; 71–28, 61 FR 48404, Sept. 13, 1996; Amdt. No. 71–29, 62 FR 52492, Oct. 8, 1997; Amdt. 71–30, 63 FR 50140, Sept. 21, 1998; Amdt. 71–31, 64 FR 50444, Sept. 17, 1999]

Subpart C— Class C Airspace

§ 71.51 Class C airspace.

The Class C airspace areas listed in subpart C of FAA Order 7400.9G (incorporated by reference, see § 71.1) consist of specified airspace within which all aircraft operators are subject to operating rules and equipment requirements specified in part 91 of this chapter. Each Class C airspace area designated for an airport in subpart C of FAA Order 7400.9G (incorporated by reference, see § 71.1) contains at least one primary airport around which the airspace is designated.

[Amdt. 71–14, 56 FR 65654, Dec. 17, 1991; as amended by Amdt. 71–20, 58 FR 36299, July 6, 1993; Amdt. 71–23, 59 FR 43035, Aug. 22, 1994; Amdt. 71–26, 60 FR 47267, Sept. 12, 1995; 71–28, 61 FR 48404, Sept. 13,

[1996; Amdt. No. 71–29, 62 FR 52492, Oct. 8, 1997; Amdt. 71–30, 63 FR 50140, Sept. 21, 1998; Amdt. 71–31, 64 FR 50444, Sept. 17, 1999]

Subpart D— Class D Airspace

§ 71.61 Class D airspace.

The Class D airspace areas listed in subpart D of FAA Order 7400.9G (incorporated by reference, see § 71.1) consist of specified airspace within which all aircraft operators are subject to operating rules and equipment requirements specified in part 91 of this chapter. Each Class D airspace area designated for an airport in subpart D of FAA Order 7400.9G (incorporated by reference, see § 71.1) contains at least one primary airport around which the airspace is designated.

[Amdt. 71–14, 56 FR 65654, Dec. 17, 1991; as amended by Amdt. 71–20, 58 FR 36299, July 6, 1993; Amdt. 71–23, 59 FR 43035, Aug. 22, 1994; Amdt. 71–26, 60 FR 47267, Sept. 12, 1995; 71–28, 61 FR 48404, Sept. 13, 1996; Amdt. No. 71–29, 62 FR 52492, Oct. 8, 1997; Amdt. 71–30, 63 FR 50140, Sept. 21, 1998; Amdt. 71–31, 64 FR 50444, Sept. 17, 1999]

Subpart E— Class E Airspace

§ 71.71 Class E airspace.

Class E Airspace consists of:

(a) The airspace of the United States, including that airspace overlying the waters within 12 nautical miles of the coast of the 48 contiguous states and Alaska, extending upward from 14,500 feet MSL up to, but not including, 18,000 feet MSL, and the airspace above FL600, excluding—

(1) The Alaska peninsula west of longitude 160°00'00"W.; and

(2) The airspace below 1,500 feet above the surface of the earth.

(b) The airspace areas designated for an airport in subpart E of FAA Order 7400.9G (incorporated by reference, see § 71.1) within which all aircraft operators are subject to the operating rules specified in part 91 of this chapter.

(c) The airspace areas listed as domestic airspace areas in subpart E of FAA Order 7400.9G (incorporated by reference, see § 71.1) which extend upward from 700 feet or more above the surface of the earth when designated in conjunction with an airport for which an approved instrument approach procedure has been prescribed, or from 1,200 feet or more above the surface of the earth for the purpose of transitioning to or from the terminal or en route environment. When such areas are designated in conjunction with airways or routes, the extent of such designation has the lateral extent identical to that of a Federal airway and extends upward from 1,200 feet or higher. Unless otherwise specified, the airspace areas in the paragraph extend upward from 1,200 feet or higher above the surface to, but not including, 14,500 feet MSL.

(d) The Federal airways described in subpart E of FAA Order 7400.9G (incorporated by reference, see § 71.1).

(e) The airspace areas listed as en route domestic airspace areas in subpart E of FAA Order 7400.9G (incorporated by reference, see § 71.1). Unless otherwise specified, each airspace area has a lateral extent identical to that of a Federal airway and extends upward from 1,200 feet above the surface of the earth to the overlying or adjacent controlled airspace.

(f) The airspace areas listed as offshore airspace areas in subpart E of FAA Order 7400.9G (incorporated by reference, see § 71.1) that are designated in international airspace within areas of domestic radio navigational signal or ATC radar coverage, and within which domestic ATC procedures are applied. Unless otherwise specified, each airspace area extends upward from a specified altitude up to, but not including, 18,000 feet MSL.

[Amdt. 71–14, 56 FR 65654, Dec. 17, 1991; as amended by Amdt. 71–19, 58 FR 12137, March 2, 1993; Amdt. 71–16, 58 FR 15259, March 19, 1993; Amdt. 71–20, 58 FR 36299, July 6, 1993; Amdt. 71–21, 58 FR 44127, Aug. 19, 1993; Amdt. 71–23, 59 FR 43035, Aug. 22, 1994; Amdt. 71–26, 60 FR 47267, Sept. 12, 1995; 71–28, 61 FR 48404, Sept. 13, 1996; Amdt. No. 71–29, 62 FR 52492, Oct. 8, 1997; Amdt. 71–30, 63 FR 50140, Sept. 21, 1998; Amdt. 71–31, 64 FR 50444, Sept. 17, 1999]

§ 71.73 Classification of Federal airways.

Federal airways are classified as follows:

(a) Colored Federal airways:

(1) Green Federal airways.

(2) Amber Federal airways.

(3) Red Federal airways.

(4) Blue Federal airways.

(b) VOR Federal airways.

§ 71.75 Extent of Federal airways.

(a) Each Federal airway is based on a center line that extends from one navigational aid or intersection to another navigational aid (or through several navigational aids or intersections) specified for that airway.

(b) Unless otherwise specified:

(1) Each Federal airway includes the airspace within parallel boundary lines 4 miles each side of

the center line. Where an airway changes direction, it includes that airspace enclosed by extending the boundary lines of the airway segments until they meet.

(2) Where the changeover point for an airway segment is more than 51 miles from either of the navigational aids defining that segment, and—

(i) The changeover point is midway between the navigational aids, the airway includes the airspace between lines diverging at angles of 4.5° from the center line at each navigational aid and extending until they intersect opposite the changeover point; or

(ii) The changeover point is not midway between the navigational aids, the airway includes the airspace between lines diverging at angles of 4.5° from the center line at the navigational aid more distant from the changeover point, and extending until they intersect with the bisector of the angle of the center lines at the changeover point; and between lines connecting these points of intersection and the navigational aid nearer to the changeover point.

(3) Where an airway terminates at a point or intersection more than 51 miles from the closest associated navigational aid, it includes the additional airspace within lines diverging at angles of 4.5° from the center line extending from the associated navigational aid to a line perpendicular to the center line at the termination point.

(4) Where an airway terminates, it includes the airspace within a circle centered at the specified navigational aid or intersection having a diameter equal to the airway width at that point. However, an airway does not extend into an oceanic control area.

(c) Unless otherwise specified—

(1) Each Federal airway includes that airspace extending upward from 1,200 feet above the surface of the earth to, but not including, 18,000 feet MSL, except that Federal airways for Hawaii have no upper limits. Variations of the lower limits of an airway are expressed in digits representing hundreds of feet above the surface or MSL and, unless otherwise specified, apply to the segment of an airway between adjoining navigational aids or intersections; and

(2) The airspace of a Federal airway, within the lateral limits of a Class E airspace area with a lower floor, has a floor coincident with the floor of that area.

(d) A Federal airway does not include the airspace of a prohibited area.

§ 71.77 [Reserved]

§ 71.79 Designation of VOR Federal airways.

Unless otherwise specified the place names appearing in the descriptions of airspace areas in subpart E of FAA Order 7400.9G (incorporated by reference, see § 71.1) designated as VOR Federal airways indicate VOR or VORTAC navigational facilities identified by those names.

[Amdt. 71–14, 56 FR 65654, Dec. 17, 1991; as amended by Amdt. 71–20, 58 FR 36299, July 6, 1993; Amdt. 71–23, 59 FR 43035, Aug. 22, 1994; Amdt. 71–26, 60 FR 47267, Sept. 12, 1995; 71–28, 61 FR 48404, Sept. 13, 1996; Amdt. No. 71–29, 62 FR 52492, Oct. 8, 1997; Amdt. 71–30, 63 FR 50140, Sept. 21, 1998; Amdt. 71–31, 64 FR 50445, Sept. 17, 1999]

Subpart F–G—[Reserved]

Subpart H— Reporting Points

§ 71.901 Applicability.

Unless otherwise designated:

(a) Each reporting point listed in subpart H of FAA Order 7400.9G (incorporated by reference, see § 71.1) applies to all directions of flight. In any case where a geographic location is designated as a reporting point for less than all airways passing through that point, or for a particular direction of flight along an airway only, it is so indicated by including the airways or direction of flight in the designation of geographical location.

(b) Place names appearing in the reporting point descriptions indicate VOR or VORTAC facilities identified by those names.

[Amdt. 71–14, 56 FR 65654, Dec. 17, 1991; as amended by Amdt. 71–20, 58 FR 36299, July 6, 1993; Amdt. 71–23, 59 FR 43035, Aug. 22, 1994; Amdt. 71–26, 60 FR 47267, Sept. 12, 1995; 71–28, 61 FR 48404, Sept. 13, 1996; Amdt. No. 71–29, 62 FR 52492, Oct. 8, 1997; Amdt. 71–30, 63 FR 50140, Sept. 21, 1998; Amdt. 71–31, 64 FR 50445, Sept. 17, 1999]

PART 73
SPECIAL USE AIRSPACE

SPECIAL FEDERAL AVIATION REGULATION
SFAR No. 53

Authority: 49 U.S.C. 106(g), 40103, 40113, 40120; E.O. 10854, 24 FR 9565, 3 CFR, 1959–1963 Comp., p. 389.

Source: 46 FR 779, Jan. 2, 1981, unless otherwise noted.

SPECIAL FEDERAL AVIATION REGULATION

SFAR No. 53 TO PART 73

ESTABLISHMENT OF WARNING AREAS IN THE AIRSPACE OVERLYING THE WATERS BETWEEN 3 AND 12 NAUTICAL MILES FROM THE UNITED STATES COAST

1. *Applicability.* This rule establishes warning areas in the same location as nonregulatory warning areas previously designated over international waters. This special regulation does not affect the validity of any nonregulatory warning area which is designated over international waters beyond 12 nautical miles from the coast of the United States. This special regulation expires on January 15, 1996.

2. *Definition — Warning area.* A warning area established under this special rule is airspace of defined dimensions, extending from 3 to 12 nautical miles from the coast of the United States, that contains activity which may be hazardous to nonparticipating aircraft. The purpose of such warning areas is to warn nonparticipating pilots of the potential danger. Part 91 is applicable within the airspace designated under this special rule.

Non-regulatory warning area. A non-regulatory warning area is airspace of defined dimensions designated over international waters that contains activity which may be hazardous to nonparticipating aircraft. The purpose of such warning areas is to warn nonparticipating pilots of the potential danger.

3. *Participating aircraft.* Each person conducting an aircraft operation within a warning area designated under this special rule and operating with the approval of the using agency may deviate from the rules of part 91, subpart B, to the extent that the rules are not compatible with approved operations.

4. *Nonparticipating aircraft.* Nonparticipating pilots, while not excluded from the warning areas established by this SFAR, are on notice that military activity, which may be hazardous to nonparticipating aircraft, is conducted in these areas.

[Docket No. 25767, 54 FR 261, Jan. 4, 1989; as amended by SFAR 53–1, 54 FR 51287, Dec. 13, 1989; SFAR 53–2, 55 FR 53267, Dec. 27, 1990; SFAR 53–3, 58 FR 69130, Dec. 29, 1993]

Subpart A—General

§ 73.1 Applicability.

The airspace that is described in subpart B and subpart C of this part is designated as special use airspace. These parts prescribe the requirements for the use of that airspace.

§ 73.3 Special use airspace.

(a) Special use airspace consists of airspace of defined dimensions identified by an area on the surface of the earth wherein activities must be confined because of their nature, or wherein limitations are imposed upon aircraft operations that are not a part of those activities, or both.

(b) The vertical limits of special use airspace are measured by designated altitude floors and ceilings expressed as flight levels or as feet above mean sea level. Unless otherwise specified, the word "to" (an altitude or flight level) means "to and including" (that altitude or flight level).

(c) The horizontal limits of special use airspace are measured by boundaries described by geographic coordinates or other appropriate references that clearly define their perimeter.

(d) The period of time during which a designation of special use airspace is in effect is stated in the designation.

§ 73.5 Bearings; radials; miles.

(a) All bearings and radials in this part are true from point of origin.

(b) Unless otherwise specified, all mileages in this part are stated as statute miles.

Subpart B—
Restricted Areas

§ 73.11 Applicability.

This subpart designates restricted areas and prescribes limitations on the operation of aircraft within them.

§ 73.13 Restrictions.

No person may operate an aircraft within a restricted area between the designated altitudes and during the time of designation, unless he has the advance permission of

(a) The using agency described in § 73.15; or

(b) The controlling agency described in § 73.17.

§ 73.15 Using agency.

(a) For the purposes of this subpart, the following are using agencies;

(1) The agency, organization, or military command whose activity within a restricted area necessitated the area being so designated.

(b) Upon the request of the FAA, the using agency shall execute a letter establishing procedures for joint use of a restricted area by the using agency and the controlling agency, under which the using agency would notify the controlling agency whenever the controlling agency may grant permission for transit through the restricted area in accordance with the terms of the letter.

(c) The using agency shall—

(1) Schedule activities within the restricted area;

(2) Authorize transit through, or flight within, the restricted area as feasible; and

(3) Contain within the restricted area all activities conducted therein in accordance with the purpose for which it was designated.

§ 73.17 Controlling agency.

For the purposes of this part, the controlling agency is the FAA facility that may authorize transit through or flight within a restricted area in accordance with a joint-use letter issued under § 73.15.

§ 73.19 Reports by using agency.

(a) Each using agency shall prepare a report on the use of each restricted area assigned thereto during any part of the preceding 12-month period ended September 30, and transmit it by the following January 31 of each year to the Manager, Air Traffic Division in the regional office of the Federal Aviation Administration having jurisdiction over the area in which the restricted area is located, with a copy to the Program Director for Air Traffic Operations, Federal Aviation Administration, Washington, DC 20591.

(b) In the report under this section the using agency shall:

(1) State the name and number of the restricted area as published in this part, and the period covered by the report.

(2) State the activities (including average daily number of operations if appropriate) conducted in the area, and any other pertinent information concerning current and future electronic monitoring devices.

(3) State the number of hours daily, the days of the week, and the number of weeks during the year that the area was used.

(4) For restricted areas having a joint-use designation, also state the number of hours daily, the days of the week, and the number of weeks during the year that the restricted area was released to the controlling agency for public use.

(5) State the mean sea level altitudes or flight levels (whichever is appropriate) used in aircraft operations and the maximum and average ordinate of surface firing (expressed in feet, mean sea level altitude) used on a daily, weekly, and yearly basis.

(6) Include a chart of the area (of optional scale and design) depicting, if used, aircraft operating areas, flight patterns, ordnance delivery areas, surface firing points and target, fan, and impact areas. After once submitting an appropriate chart, subsequent annual charts are not required unless there is a change in the area, activity or altitude (or flight levels) used, which might alter the depiction of the activities originally reported. If no change is to be submitted, a statement indicating "no change" shall be included in the report.

(7) Include any other information not otherwise required under this part which is considered pertinent to activities carried on in the restricted area.

(c) If it is determined that the information submitted under paragraph (b) of this section is not sufficient to evaluate the nature and extent of the use of a restricted area, the FAA may request the using agency to submit supplementary reports. Within 60 days after receiving a request for additional information, the using agency shall submit such information as the Program Director for Air Traffic Operations considers appropriate. Supplementary reports must be sent to the FAA officials designated in paragraph (a) of this section.

(Secs. 307 and 313(a), Federal Aviation Act of 1958 (49 U.S.C. 1348 and 1354(a)))

[Docket No. 15379, 42 FR 54798, Oct. 11, 1977; as amended by Amdt. 73–5, 54 FR 39292, Sept. 25, 1989; Amdt. 73–6, 58 FR 42001, Aug. 6, 1993; Amdt. 73–8, 61 FR 26435, May 28, 1996]

Editorial Note: The restricted areas formerly carried as §§ 608.21 to 608.72 of this title were transferred to Part 73 as §§ 73.21 to 73.72 under Subpart B but are not carried in the Code of Federal Regulations. For Federal Register citations affecting these restricted areas, see the List of CFR Sections Affected in the Finding Aids section of this volume.

Subpart C— Prohibited Areas

§ 73.81 Applicability.

This subpart designates prohibited areas and prescribes limitations on the operation of aircraft therein.

§ 73.83 Restrictions.

No person may operate an aircraft within a prohibited area unless authorization has been granted by the using agency.

§ 73.85 Using agency.

For the purpose of this subpart, the using agency is the agency, organization or military command that established the requirements for the prohibited area.

Editorial Note: Sections 73.87 through 73.99 are reserved for descriptions of designated prohibited areas. For Federal Register citations affecting these prohibited areas, see the List of CFR Sections Affected in the Finding Aids section of this volume.

73

SUBCHAPTER F
AIR TRAFFIC AND GENERAL OPERATING RULES

PART 91
GENERAL OPERATING AND FLIGHT RULES

SPECIAL FEDERAL AVIATION REGULATIONS

Subpart A—General

Subpart B—Flight Rules

GENERAL

VISUAL FLIGHT RULES

INSTRUMENT FLIGHT RULES

91

Authority: 49 U.S.C. 106(g), 1155, 40103, 40113, 40120, 44101, 44111, 44701, 44709, 44711, 44712, 44715, 44716, 44717, 44722, 46306, 46315, 46316, 46504, 46506–46507, 47122, 47508, 47528–47531, Articles 12 and 29 of the Convention on International Civil Aviation (61 Stat. 1180). 902; 49 U.S.C. 106(g).

91

SPECIAL FEDERAL AVIATION REGULATIONS

SFAR No. 29–4 to Part 91

LIMITED IFR OPERATIONS OF ROTORCRAFT

Section 1. Contrary provisions of Parts 21, 27, and 29 of the Federal Aviation Regulations notwithstanding, an operator of a rotorcraft that is not otherwise certificated for IFR operations may conduct an approved limited IFR operation in the rotorcraft when—

(a) FAA approval for the operation has been issued under paragraph 2 of this SFAR;

(b) The operator complies with all conditions and limitations established by this SFAR and the approval; and

(c) A copy of the approval and this SFAR are set forth as a supplement to the Rotorcraft Flight Manual.

Section 2. FAA approval for the operation of a rotorcraft in limited IFR operations may be issued when the following conditions are met:

(a) The operation is approved as part of the FAA study of limited rotorcraft IFR operations.

(b) Specific FAA approval has been obtained for the following:

(i) The rotorcraft (make, model, and serial number).

(ii) The flightcrew.

(iii) The procedures to be followed in the operation of the rotorcraft under IFR and the equipment that must be operable during such operations.

(c) The conditions and limitations necessary for the safe operation of the rotorcraft in limited IFR operations have been established, approved, and incorporated into the operating limitations section of the Rotorcraft Flight Manual.

Section 3. An approval issued under paragraph 2 of this Special Federal Aviation Regulation and the change to the Rotorcraft Flight Manual specified in paragraph 2(c) of this Special Federal Aviation Regulation constitute a supplemental type certificate for each rotorcraft approved under paragraph 2 of this SFAR. The supplemental type certificate will remain in effect until the approval to operate issued under the Special Federal Aviation Regulation is surrendered, revoked, or otherwise terminated.

Section 4. Notwithstanding § 91.167(a)(3) of the Federal Aviation Regulations, a person may operate a rotorcraft in a limited IFR operation approved under paragraph 2(a) of the Special Federal Aviation Regulation with enough fuel to fly, after reaching the alternate airport, for not less than 30 minutes, when that period of time has been approved.

Section 5. *Expiration.*

(a) New applications for limited IFR rotorcraft operations under SFAR No. 29 may be submitted for approval until, but not including, the effective date of Amendment No. 1 of the Rotorcraft Regulatory Review Program. On and after the effective date of Amendment No. 1 of the Rotorcraft Regulatory Review Program, all applicants for certification of IFR rotorcraft operations must comply with the applicable provisions of the Federal Aviation Regulations.

(b) This Special Federal Aviation Regulation will terminate when all approvals issued under Special Federal Aviation Regulation No. 29 are surrendered, revoked, or otherwise terminated.

(Secs. 313(a), 601(a), and 603, Federal Aviation Act of 1958 (49 U.S.C. 1354(a), 1421(a), and 1423) and section 6(c), Department of Transportation Act (49 U.S.C. 1655(c)))

[Docket No. 14237, 48 FR 632, Jan. 6, 1983; as amended by Amdt. 91–211, 54 FR 34331, Aug. 18, 1989]

SFAR No. 50–2 to Part 91

SPECIAL FLIGHT RULES IN THE VICINITY OF THE GRAND CANYON NATIONAL PARK, AZ

Section 1. *Applicability.* This rule prescribes special operating rules for all persons operating aircraft in the following airspace, designated as the Grand Canyon National Park Special Flight Rules Area:

That airspace extending upward from the surface up to but not including 14,500 feet MSL within an area bounded by a line beginning at lat. 36°09'30" N., long. 114°03'00" W.; northeast to lat. 36°14'00" N., long. 113°09'50" W.; thence northeast along the boundary of the Grand Canyon National Park to lat. 36°24'47" N., long. 112°52'00" W.; to lat. 36°30'30" N., long. 112°36'15" W.; to lat. 36°21'30" N., long. 112°00'00" W.; to lat. 36°35'30" N., long. 111°53'10" W.; to lat. 36°53'00" N., long. 111°36'45" W.; to lat. 36°53'00" N., long. 111°33'00" W.; to lat. 36°19'00" N., long. 111°50'50" W.; to lat. 36°17'00" N., long. 111°42'00" W.; to lat. 35°59'30" N., long. 111°42'00" W.; to lat. 35°57'30" N., long. 112°03'55" W.; thence counterclockwise via the 5-statute mile radius of the Grand Canyon Airport reference point (lat. 35°57'09" N., long. 112°08'47" W.) to lat. 35°57'30" N., long. 112°14'00" W.; to lat. 35°57'30" N., long. 113°11'00" W.; to lat. 35°42'30" N., long. 113°11'00" W.; to lat. 35°38'30" N., long. 113°27'30" W.; thence counterclockwise via the 5-statute mile radius of the Peach Springs VORTAC to lat. 35°41'20" N., long. 113°36'00" W.; to lat. 35°55'25" N., long. 113°49'10" W.; to lat. 35°57'45" N., long. 113°45'20" W.; thence northwest along the park boundary to lat. 36°02'20" N., long. 113°50'15" W.; to lat. 36°00'10" N., long. 113°53'45" W.; thence to the point of beginning.

Section 3. *Aircraft operations: general.* Except in an emergency, no person may operate an aircraft in the Special Flight Rules Area under VFR on or after September 22, 1988, or under IFR on or after April 6, 1989, unless the operation—

(a) Is conducted in accordance with the following procedures:

Note: THE FOLLOWING PROCEDURES DO NOT RELIEVE THE PILOT FROM SEE-AND-AVOID RESPONSIBILITY OR COMPLIANCE WITH FAR 91.119.

(1) Unless necessary to maintain a safe distance from other aircraft or terrain—

(i) Remain clear of the areas described in Section 4; and

(ii) Remain at or above the following altitudes in each sector of the canyon:

Eastern section from Lees Ferry to North Canyon and North Canyon to Boundary Ridge: as prescribed in Section 5.

Boundary Ridge to Supai Point (Yumtheska Point): 10,000 feet MSL.

Western section from Diamond Creek to the Grant Wash Cliffs: 8,000 feet MSL.

(2) Proceed through the four flight corridors described in Section 4 at the following altitudes unless otherwise authorized in writing by the Flight Standards District Office:

Northbound
11,500 or
13,500 feet MSL

Southbound
10,500 or
12,500 feet MSL

(b) Is authorized in writing by the Flight Standards District Office and is conducted in compliance with the conditions contained in that authorization. Normally authorization will be granted for operation in the areas described in Section 4 or below altitudes listed in Section 5 only for operations of aircraft necessary for law enforcement, firefighting, emergency medical treatment/evacuation of persons in the vicinity of the Park; for support of Park maintenance or activities; or for aerial access to and maintenance of other property located within the Special Flight Rules Area. Authorization may be issued on a continuing basis.

(c)(1) Prior to November 1, 1988, is conducted in accordance with a specific authorization to operate in that airspace incorporated in the operator's part 135 operations specifications in accordance with the provisions of SFAR 50–1, notwithstanding the provisions of Sections 4 and 5; and

(2) On or after November 1, 1988, is conducted in accordance with a specific authorization to operate in that airspace incorporated in the opera-

tor's operations specifications and approved by the Flight Standards District Office in accordance with the provisions of SFAR 50–2.

(d) Is a search and rescue mission directed by the U.S. Air Force Rescue Coordination Center.

(e) Is conducted within 3 nautical miles of Whitmore Airstrip, Pearce Ferry Airstrip, North Rim Airstrip, Cliff Dwellers Airstrip, or Marble Canyon Airstrip at an altitude less than 3,000 feet above airport elevation, for the purpose of landing at or taking off from that facility. Or

(f) Is conducted under an IFR clearance and the pilot is acting in accordance with ATC instructions. An IFR flight plan may not be filed on a route or at an altitude that would require operation in an area described in Section 4.

Section 4. *Flight-free zones.* Except in an emergency or if otherwise necessary for safety of flight, or unless otherwise authorized by the Flight Standards District Office for a purpose listed in Section 3(b), no person may operate an aircraft in the Special Flight Rules Area within the following areas:

(a) *Desert View Flight-Free Zone.* Within an area bounded by a line beginning at Lat. 35°59'30" N., Long. 111°46'20" W. to 35°59'30" N., Long. 111°52'45" W.; to Lat. 36°04'50" N., Long. 111°52'00" W.; to Lat. 36°06'00" N., Long. 111°46'20" W.; to the point of origin; but not including the airspace at and above 10,500 feet MSL within 1 mile of the western boundary of the zone. The area between the Desert View and Bright Angel Flight-Free Zones is designated the "Zuni Point Corridor."

(b) *Bright Angel Flight-Free Zone.* Within an area bounded by a line beginning at Lat. 35°59'30" N., Long. 111°55'30" W.; to Lat. 35°59'30" N., Long. 112°04'00" W.; thence counterclockwise via the 5-statute-mile radius of the Grand Canyon Airport point (Lat. 35°57'09" N., Long. 112°08'47" W.) to Lat. 36°01'30" N., Long. 112°11'00" W.; to Lat. 36°06'15" N., Long. 112°12'50" W.; to Lat. 36°14'40" N., Long. 112°08'50" W.; to Lat. 36°14'40" N., Long. 111°57'30" W.; to Lat. 36°12'30" N., Long. 111°53'50" W.; to the point of origin; but not including the airspace at and above 10,500 feet MSL within 1 mile of the eastern boundary between the southern boundary and Lat. 36°04'50" N. or the airspace at and above 10,500 feet MSL within 2 miles of the northwest boundary. The area bounded by the Bright Angel and Shinumo Flight-Free zones is designated the "Dragon Corridor."

(c) *Shinumo Flight-Free Zone.* Within an area bounded by a line beginning at lat. 36°04'00" N., long. 112°16'40" W.; northwest along the park boundary to a point at lat. 36°12'47" N., long. 112°30'53" W.; to lat. 36°21'15" N., long. 112°20'20" W.; east along the park boundary to

91

lat. 36°21'15" N., long. 112°13'55" W.; to lat. 36°14'40" N., long. 112°11'25" W.; to the point of origin. The area between the Thunder River/Toroweap and Shinumo Flight-Free Zones is designated the "Fossil Canyon Corridor."

(d) *Toroweap/Thunder River Flight-Free Zone.* Within an area bounded by a line beginning at lat. 36°22'45" N., long. 112°20'35" W.; thence northwest along the boundary of the Grand Canyon National Park to lat. 36°17'48" N., long. 113°03'15" W.; to lat. 36°15'00" N., long. 113°07'10" W.; to lat. 36°10'30" N., long. 113°07'10" W.; thence east along the Colorado River to the confluence of Havasu Canyon (lat. 36°18'40" N., long. 112°45'45" W.;) including that area within a 1.5-nautical-mile radius of Toroweap Overlook (lat. 36°12'45" N., long. 113°03'30" W.) to the point of origin; but not including the following airspace designated as the "Tuckup Corridor": at or above 10,500 feet MSL within 2 nautical miles either side of a line extending between lat. 36°24'47" N., long. 112°48'50" W.; and lat. 36°17'10" N., long. 112°48'50" W.; to the point of origin.

Section 5. *Minimum flight altitudes.* Except in an emergency or if otherwise necessary for safety of flight, or unless otherwise authorized by the Flight Standards District Office for a purpose listed in Section 3(b), no person may operate an aircraft in the Special Flight Rules Area at an altitude lower than the following:

(a) Eastern section from Lees Ferry to North Canyon: 5,000 feet MSL.

(b) Eastern section from North Canyon to Boundary Ridge: 6,000 feet MSL.

(c) Boundary Ridge to Supai (Yumtheska) Point: 7,500 feet MSL.

(d) Supai Point to Diamond Creek: 6,500 feet MSL.

(e) Western section from Diamond Creek to the Grand Wash Cliffs: 5,000 feet MSL.

Section 9. *Termination date.* Sections 1. Applicability, Section 4, Flight-free zones, and Section 5. Minimum flight altitudes, expire on 0901 UTC, January 31, 2000.

[SFAR 50–2, 53 FR 20273, June 2, 1988; 53 FR 21988, June 13, 1988; 53 FR 32603, Aug. 26, 1988, as amended by 53 FR 36947, Sept. 22, 1988; 54 FR 11927, March 22, 1989; 54 FR 34331, Aug. 18, 1989; 55 FR 13445, April 10, 1990; 55 FR 15320, April 23, 1990; 57 FR 26766, June 15, 1992; 60 FR 31610, June 15, 1995; 60 FR 65913, Dec. 20, 1995; 61 FR 69330, Dec. 31, 1996; 62 FR 8864, Feb. 26, 1997; 62 FR 66249, Dec. 17, 1997; 63 FR 23604, April 29, 1998; Docket No. 28537, SFAR 50–2, 64 FR 5154, Feb. 3, 1999]

SFAR 50-2:
Special Flight Rules in the Vicinity of
Grand Canyon National Park

SFAR No. 51–1 to Part 91
Special Flight Rules in the Vicinity of Los Angeles International Airport

Section 1. *Applicability:* This rule establishes a special operating area for persons operating aircraft under visual flight rules (VFR) in the following airspace of the Los Angeles Class B airspace area designated as the Los Angeles Special Flight Rules Area***:

That part of Area A of the Los Angeles TCA between 3,500 feet above mean sea level (MSL) and 4,500 feet MSL, inclusive, bounded on the north by Ballona Creek, on the east by the San Diego Freeway, on the south by Imperial Highway, and on the west by the Pacific Ocean shoreline.

Section 2. *Aircraft operations, general.* Unless otherwise authorized by the Administrator, no person may operate an aircraft in the airspace described in Section 1 unless the operation is conducted under the following rules.

a. The flight must be conducted under VFR and only when operation may be conducted in compliance with § 91.155(a).

b. The aircraft must be equipped as specified in FAR 91.215(b) replying on Code 1201 prior to entering and while operating in this area.

c. The pilot shall have a current Los Angeles Terminal Area Chart in the aircraft.

d. The pilot shall operate on the Santa Monica very high frequency omni-directional radio range (VOR) 132° radial.

e. Operations in a southeasterly direction shall be in level flight at 3,500 feet MSL.

f. Operations in a northwesterly direction shall be in level flight at 4,500 feet MSL.

g. Indicated airspeed shall not exceed 140 knots.

h. Anticollision lights and aircraft position/navigation lights shall be on. Use of landing lights is recommended.

i. Turbojet aircraft are prohibited from VFR operations in this area

Section 3. Notwithstanding the provisions of § 91.131(a), an air traffic control authorization is not required in the Los Angeles Special Flight Rules Area for operations in compliance with section 2 of this SFAR. All other provisions of § 91.131 apply to operate in the Special Flight Rules Area.

Authority: 49 U.S.C. app. 1303, 1348, 1354(a), 1421, and 1422; 49 U.S.C. 106(g).

[Docket No. 87–AWA–31, SFAR 51–1, 53 FR 3812, Feb. 9, 1988; as amended by Amdt. 91–227, 56 FR 65652, Dec. 17, 1991]

SFAR No. 60 to Part 91
Air Traffic Control System Emergency Operation

Section 1. Each person shall, before conducting any operation under the Federal Aviation Regulations (14 CFR chapter I), be familiar with all available information concerning that operation, including Notices to Airmen issued under § 91.139 and, when activated, the provisions of the National Air Traffic Reduced Complement Operations Plan available for inspection at operating air traffic facilities and Regional air traffic division offices, and the General Aviation Reservation Program. No operator may change the designated airport of intended operation for any flight contained in the October 1, 1990, OAG.

Section 2. Notwithstanding any provision of the Federal Aviation Regulations to the contrary, no person may operate an aircraft in the Air Traffic Control System:

a. Contrary to any restriction, prohibition, procedure or other action taken by the Director of the Office of Air Traffic Systems Management (Director) pursuant to paragraph 3 of this regulation and announced in a Notice to Airmen pursuant to § 91.139 of the Federal Aviation Regulations.

b. When the National Air Traffic Reduced Complement Operations Plan is activated pursuant to paragraph 4 of this regulation, except in accordance with the pertinent provisions of the National Air Traffic Reduced Complement Operations Plan.

Section 3. Prior to or in connection with the implementation of the RCOP, and as conditions warrant, the Director is authorized to:

a. Restrict, prohibit, or permit VFR and/or IFR operations at any airport, Class B airspace area, Class C airspace area, or other class of controlled airspace.

b. Give priority at any airport to flights that are of military necessity, or are medical emergency flights, Presidential flights, and flights transporting critical Government employees.

c. Implement, at any airport, traffic management procedures, that may include reduction of flight operations. Reduction of flight operations will be accomplished, to the extent practical, on a pro rata basis among and between air carrier, commercial operator, and general aviation operations. Flights canceled under this SFAR at a high density traffic airport will be considered to have been operated for purposes of part 93 of the Federal Aviation Regulations.

Section 4. The Director may activate the National Air Traffic Reduced Complement Operations Plan at any time he finds that it is necessary for the safety and efficiency of the National Airspace System. Upon activation of the RCOP and notwithstanding any provision of the FAR to the contrary, the Director is authorized to suspend or modify any airspace designation.

Section 5. Notice of restrictions, prohibitions, procedures and other actions taken by the Director under this regulation with respect to the operation of the Air Traffic Control system will be announced in Notices to Airmen issued pursuant to § 91.139 of the Federal Aviation Regulations.

Section 6. The Director may delegate his authority under this regulation to the extent he considers necessary for the safe and efficient operation of the National Air Traffic Control System.

Authority: 49 U.S.C. app. 1301(7), 1303, 1344, 1348, 1352 through 1355, 1401, 1421 through 1431, 1471, 1472, 1502, 1510, 1522, and 2121 through 2125; articles 12, 29, 31, and 32(a) of the Convention on International Civil Aviation (61 stat. 1180); 42 U.S.C. 4321 et seq.; E.O. 11514, 35 FR 4247, 3 CFR, 1966–1970 Comp., p. 902; 49 U.S.C. 106(g).

[Docket No. 26351, 55 FR 40760, Oct. 4, 1990; as amended by Amdt. 91–227, 56 FR 65652, Dec. 17, 1991]

SFAR No. 61–2 to Part 91

Prohibition Against Certain Flights Between the United States and Iraq

Section 1. *Applicability.* This Special Federal Aviation Regulation (SFAR) No. 61–2 applies to all aircraft operations originating from, landing in, or overflying the territory of the United States.

Section 2. *Special flight restrictions.* Except as provided in paragraphs 3 and 4 of this SFAR No. 61–2—

(a) No person shall operate an aircraft on a flight to any point in Iraq, or to any intermediate point on a flight where the ultimate destination is any point in Iraq or that includes a landing at any point in Iraq in its intended itinerary, from any point in the United States;

(b) No person shall operate an aircraft on a flight to any point in the United States from any point in Iraq, or from any intermediate point on a flight where the origin is in Iraq, or from any point on a flight which includes a departure from any point in Iraq in its intended itinerary; or

(c) No person shall operate an aircraft over the territory of the United States if that aircraft's flight itinerary includes any landing at or departure from any point in Iraq.

Section 3. *Permitted operations.* This SFAR shall not prohibit the flight operations between the United States and Iraq described in section 2 of this SFAR by an aircraft authorized to conduct such operations by the United States Government in consultation with the committee established by UN Security Council Resolution 661 (1990), and in accordance with UN Security Council Resolution 666 (1990).

Section 4. *Emergency situations.* In an emergency that requires immediate decision and action for the safety of the flight, the pilot in command of an aircraft may deviate from this SFAR to the extent required by that emergency. Except for U.S. air carriers and commercial operators that are subject to the requirements of 14 CFR 121.557, 121.559, or 135.19, each person who deviates from this rule shall, within ten (10) days of the deviation, excluding Saturdays, Sundays, and Federal holidays, submit to the nearest FAA Flight Standards District Office a complete report of the operations or the aircraft involved in the deviation, including a description of the deviation and the reasons therefore.

Section 5. *Duration.* This SFAR No. 61–2 shall remain in effect until further notice.

[Docket No. 26380, 60 FR 49139, Sept. 21, 1995]

SFAR No. 62 to Part 91

Suspension of Certain Aircraft Operations from the Transponder with Automatic Pressure Altitude Reporting Capability Requirement

Section 1. For purposes of this SFAR:

(a) The airspace within 30 nautical miles of Class B airspace area primary airport, from the surface upward to 10,000 feet MSL, excluding the airspace designated as a Class B airspace is referred to as the Mode C veil.

(b) Effective until December 30, 1993, the transponder with automatic altitude reporting capability requirements of FAR § 91.215(b)(2) do not apply to the operation of an aircraft:

(1) In the airspace at or below the specified altitude and within a 2-nautical-mile radius, or, if directed by ATC, within a 5-nautical mile radius, of an airport listed in section 2 of this SFAR; and

(2) In the airspace at or below the specified altitude along the most direct and expeditious routing, or on a routing directed by ATC, between an airport listed in section 2 of this SFAR and the outer boundary of the Mode C veil airspace overlying that airport, consistent with established traffic patterns, noise abatement procedures, and safety.

Section 2. Effective until December 30, 1993. Airports at which the provisions of § 91.215(b)(2) do not apply.

(1) Airports within a 30-nautical-mile radius of The William B. Hartsfield Atlanta International Airport.

Airport name	Arpt ID	Alt. (AGL)
Air Acres Airport, Woodstock, GA	5GA4	1,500
B & L Strip Airport, Hollonville, GA	GA29	1,500
Camfield Airport, McDonough, GA	GA36	1,500
Cobb County-McCollum Field Airport, Marietta, GA	RYY	1,500
Covington Municipal Airport, Covington, GA	9A1	1,500
Diamond R Ranch Airport, Villa Rica, GA	3GA5	1,500
Dresden Airport, Newnan, GA	GA79	1,500
Eagles Landing Airport, Williamson, GA	5GA3	1,500
Fagundes Field Airport, Haralson, GA	6GA1	1,500
Gable Branch Airport, Haralson, GA	5GA0	1,500
Georgia Lite Flite Ultralight Airport, Acworth, GA	31GA	1,500
Griffin-Spalding County Airport, Griffin, GA	6A2	1,500
Howard Private Airport, Jackson, GA	GA02	1,500
Newnan Coweta County Airport, Newnan, GA	CCO	1,500
Peach State Airport, Williamson, GA	3GA7	1,500
Poole Farm Airport, Oxford, GA	2GA1	1,500
Powers Airport, Hollonville, GA	GA31	1,500
S & S Landing Strip Airport, Griffin, GA	8GA6	1,500
Shade Tree Airport, Hollonville, GA	GA73	1,500

(2) Airports within a 30-nautical-mile radius of the General Edward Lawrence Logan International Airport.

Airport name	Arpt ID	Alt. (AGL)
Berlin Landing Area Airport, Berlin, MA	MA19	2,500
Hopedale Industrial Park Airport, Hopedale, MA	1B6	2,500
Larson's SPB, Tyngsboro, MA	MA74	2,500
Moore AAF, Ayer/Ft Devens, MA	AYE	2,500
New England Gliderport, Salem, NH	NH29	2,500
Plum Island Airport, Newburyport, MA	2B2	2,500
Plymouth Municipal Airport, Plymouth, MA	PYM	2,500
Taunton Municipal Airport, Taunton, MA	TAN	2,500
Unknown Field Airport, Southborough, MA	1MA5	2,500

(3) Airports within a 30-nautical-mile radius of the Charlotte/Douglas International Airport.

Airport name	Arpt ID	Alt. (AGL)
Arant Airport, Wingate, NC	1NC6	2,500
Bradley Outernational Airport, China Grove, NC	NC29	2,500
Chester Municipal Airport, Chester, SC	9A6	2,500
China Grove Airport, China Grove, NC	76A	2,500
Goodnight's Airport, Kannapolis, NC	2NC8	2,500
Knapp Airport, Marshville, NC	3NC4	2,500
Lake Norman Airport, Mooresville, NC	14A	2,500
Lancaster County Airport, Lancaster, SC	LKR	2,500
Little Mountain Airport, Denver, NC	66A	2,500
Long Island Airport, Long Island, NC	NC26	2,500
Miller Airport, Mooresville, NC	8A2	2,500
U S Heliport, Wingate, NC	NC56	2,500
Unity Aerodrome Airport, Lancaster, SC	SC76	2,500
Wilhelm Airport, Kannapolis, NC	6NC2	2,500

(4) Airports within a 30-nautical-mile radius of the Chicago-O'Hare International Airport.

Airport name	Arpt ID	Alt. (AGL)
Aurora Municipal Airport, Chicago/Aurora, IL	ARR	1,200
Donald Alfred Gade Airport, Antioch, IL	IL11	1,200
Dr. Joseph W. Esser Airport, Hampshire, IL	7IL6	1,200
Flying M. Farm Airport, Aurora, IL	IL20	1,200
Fox Lake SPB, Fox Lake, IL	IS03	1,200
Graham SPB, Crystal Lake, IL	IS79	1,200
Herbert C. Mass Airport, Zion, IL	IL02	1,200
Landings Condominium Airport, Romeoville, IL	C49	1,200
Lewis University Airport, Romeoville, IL	LOT	1,200
McHenry Farms Airport, McHenry, IL	44IL	1,200
Olson Airport, Plato Center, IL	LL53	1,200
Redeker Airport, Milford, IL	IL85	1,200
Reid RLA Airport, Gilberts, IL	6IL6	1,200
Shamrock Beef Cattle Farm Airport, McHenry, IL	49LL	1,200
Sky Soaring Airport, Union, IL	55LL	1,200
Waukegan Regional Airport, Waukegan, IL	UGN	1,200
Wormley Airport, Oswego, IL	85LL	1,200

(5) Airports within a 30-nautical-mile radius of the Cleveland-Hopkins International Airport.

Airport name	Arpt ID	Alt. (AGL)
Akron Fulton International Airport, Akron, OH	AKR	1,300
Bucks Airport, Newbury, OH	40OH	1,300
Derecsky Airport, Auburn Center, OH	6OI0	1,300
Hannum Airport, Streetsboro, OH	69OH	1,300
Kent State University Airport, Kent, OH	1G3	1,300
Lost Nation Airport, Willoughby, OH	LNN	1,300
Mills Airport, Mantua, OH	OH06	1,300
Portage County Airport, Ravenna, OH	29G	1,300
Stoney's Airport, Ravenna, OH	OI32	1,300
Wadsworth Municipal Airport, Wadsworth, OH	3G3	1,300

(6) Airports within a 30-nautical-mile radius of the Dallas/Fort Worth International Airport.

Airport name	Arpt ID	Alt. (AGL)
Beggs Ranch/Aledo Airport, Aledo, TX	TX15	1,800
Belcher Airport, Sanger, TX	TA25	1,800
Bird Dog Field Airport, Krum, TX	TA48	1,800
Boe-Wrinkle Airport, Azle, TX	28TS	1,800
Flying V Airport, Sanger, TX	71XS	1,800
Graham Ranch Airport, Celina, TX	TX44	1,800
Haire Airport, Bolivar, TX	TX33	1,800
Hartlee Field Airport, Denton, TX	1F3	1,800
Hawkin's Ranch Strip Airport, Rhome, TX	TA02	1,800
Horseshoe Lake Airport, Sanger, TX	TE24	1,800
Ironhead Airport, Sanger, TX	T58	1,800
Kezer Air Ranch Airport, Springtown, TX	61F	1,800
Lane Field Airport, Sanger, TX	58F	1,800
Log Cabin Airport, Aledo, TX	TX16	1,800
Lone Star Airpark Airport, Denton, TX	T32	1,800
Rhome Meadows Airport, Rhome, TX	TS72	1,800
Richards Airport, Krum, TX	TA47	1,800
Tallows Field Airport, Celina, TX	79TS	1,800
Triple S Airport, Aledo, TX	42XS	1,800
Warshun Ranch Airport, Denton, TX	4TA1	1,800
Windy Hill Airport, Denton, TX	46XS	1,800
Aero Country Airport, McKinney, TX	TX05	1,400
Bailey Airport, Midlothian, TX	7TX8	1,400
Bransom Farm Airport, Burleson, TX	TX42	1,400
Carroll Air Park Airport, De Soto, TX	F66	1,400
Carroll Lake-View Airport, Venus, TX	70TS	1,400
Eagle's Nest Estates Airport, Ovilla, TX	2T36	1,400
Flying B Ranch Airport, Ovilla, TX	TS71	1,400
Lancaster Airport, Lancaster, TX	LNC	1,400
Lewis Farm Airport, Lucas, TX	6TX1	1,400
Markum Ranch Airport, Fort Worth, TX	TX79	1,400
McKinney Municipal Airport, McKinney, TX	TKI	1,400

91

O'Brien Airpark Airport, Waxahachie, TX	F25	1,400
Phil L. Hudson Municipal Airport, Mesquite, TX	HQZ	1,400
Plover Heliport, Crowley, TX	82Q	1,400
Venus Airport, Venus, TX	75TS	1,400

(7) Airports within a 30-nautical-mile radius of the Denver International Airport.

Airport name	Arpt ID	Alt. (AGL)
Air Dusters Inc. Airport, Roggen, CO	49CO	1,200
Bijou Basin Airport, Byers, CO	CD17	1,200
Boulder Municipal Airport, Boulder, CO	1V5	1,200
Bowen Farms No. 1 Airport, Littleton, CO	CO98	1,200
Bowen Farms No. 2 Airport, Strasburg, CO	3CO5	1,200
Carrera Airpark Airport, Mead, CO	93CO	1,200
Cartwheel Airport, Mead, CO	0CO8	1,200
Chaparral Airport, Byers, CO	CO18	1,200
Colorado Antique Field Airport, Niwot, CO	8CO7	1,200
Comanche Livestock Airport, Strasburg, CO	59CO	1,200
Dead Stick Ranch Airport, Kiowa, CO	18CO	1,200
Frederick-Firestone Air Strip Airport, Frederick, CO	CO58	1,200
Frontier Airstrip Airport, Mead, CO	84CO	1,200
Horseshoe Landings Airport, Keenesburg, CO	CO60	1,200
Hoy Airstrip Airport, Bennett, CO	76CO	1,200
J & S Airport, Bennett, CO	CD14	1,200
Kostroski Airport, Franktown, CO	43CO	1,200
Kugel-Strong Airport, Platteville, CO	27V	1,200
Land Airport, Keenesburg, CO	CO82	1,200
Lemons Private Strip Airport, Boulder, CO	CO10	1,200
Lindys Airpark Airport, Hudson, CO	7CO3	1,200
Parkland Airport, Erie, CO	7CO0	1,200
Pine View Airport, Elizabeth, CO	02V	1,200
Platte Valley Airport, Hudson, CO	18V	1,200
Rancho De Aereo Airport, Mead, CO	05CO	1,200

Reid Ranches Airport, Roggen, CO	7CO6	1,200
Singleton Ranch Airport, Byers, CO	68CO	1,200
Sky Haven Airport, Byers, CO	CO17	1,200
Spickard Farm Airport, Byers, CO	5CO4	1,200
Tri-County Airport, Erie, CO	48V	1,200
Westberg-Rosling Farms Airport, Roggen, CO	74CO	1,200
Yoder Airstrip Airport, Bennett, CO	CD09	1,200

(8) Airports within a 30-nautical-mile radius of the Detroit Metropolitan Wayne County Airport.

Airport name	Arpt ID	Alt. (AGL)
Al Meyers Airport, Tecumseh, MI	3TE	1,400
Brighton Airport, Brighton, MI	45G	1,400
Cackleberry Airport, Dexter, MI	2MI9	1,400
Erie Aerodome Airport, Erie, MI	05MI	1,400
Ham-A-Lot Field Airport, Petersburg, MI	MI48	1,400
Merillat Airport, Tecumseh, MI	34G	1,400
Rossettie Airport, Manchester, MI	75G	1,400
Tecumseh Products Airport, Tecumseh, MI	0D2	1,400

(9) Airport within a 30-nautical-mile radius of the Honolulu International Airport.

Airport name	Arpt ID	Alt. (AGL)
Dillingham Airfield Airport, Mokuleia, HI	HDH	2,500

(10) Airports within a 30-nautical-mile radius of the Houston Intercontinental Airport and the William P. Hobby Airport.

Airport name	Arpt ID	Alt. (AGL)
Ainsworth Airport, Cleveland, TX	OT6	1,200
Ausinia Ranch Airport, Texas City, TX	TS50	1,200
Bailes Airport, Angleton, TX	7R9	1,200
Biggin Hill Airport, Hockley, TX	TX49	1,200
Cleveland Municipal Airport, Cleveland, TX	6R3	1,200
Covey Trails Airport, Fulshear, TX	80XS	1,200
Creasy Airport, Santa Fe, TX	5TA5	1,200
Custom Aire Service Airport, Angleton, TX	81D	1,200
Fay Ranch Airport, Cedar Lane, TX	OT2	1,200

Airport name		
Flying C Ranch Airport, Needville, TX	XS25	1,200
Freeman Property Airport, Katy, TX	61T	1,200
Garrett Ranch Airport, Danbury, TX	77XS	1,200
Gum Island Airport, Dayton, TX	3T6	1,200
H&S Airfield Airport, Damon, TX	XS21	1,200
Harbican Airpark Airport, Katy, TX	9XS9	1,200
Harold Freeman Farm Airport, Katy, TX	8XS1	1,200
HHI Hitchcock Heliport, Hitchcock, TX	6TA5	1,200
Hoffpauir Airport, Katy, TX	59T	1,200
Horn-Katy Hawk International Airport, Katy, TX	57T	1,200
Johnnie Volk Field Airport, Hitchcock, TX	37R	1,200
King Air Airport, Katy, TX	55T	1,200
Lake Bay Gall Airport, Cleveland, TX	OT5	1,200
Lake Bonanza Airport, Montgomery, TX	33TA	1,200
Lane Airpark Airport, Rosenberg, TX	T54	1,200
Meyer Field Airport, Rosharon, TX	TA33	1,200
Prairie Aire Field Airport, Damon, TX	4TA0	1,200
R W J Airpark Airport, Baytown, TX	54TX	1,200
Westheimer Air Park Airport, Houston, TX	5TA4	1,200

(11) Airports within a 30-nautical-mile radius of the Kansas City International Airport.

Airport name	Arpt ID	Alt. (AGL)
Amelia Earhart Airport, Atchison, KS	K59	1,000
Booze Island Airport, St. Joseph, MO	64MO	1,000
Cedar Air Park Airport, Olathe, KS	51K	1,000
D'Field Airport, McLouth, KS	KS90	1,000
Dorei Airport, McLouth, KS	K69	1,000
East Kansas City Airport, Grain Valley, MO	3GV	1,000
Excelsior Springs Memorial Airport, Excelsior Springs, MO	3EX	1,000
Flying T Airport, Oskaloosa, KS	7KS0	1,000
Hermon Farm Airport, Gardner, KS	KS59	1,000

Airport name		
Hillside Airport, Stilwell, KS	63K	1,000
Independence Memorial Airport, Independence, MO	3IP	1,000
Johnson County Executive Airport, Olathe, KS	OJC	1,000
Johnson County Industrial Airport, Olathe, KS	IXD	1,000
Kimray Airport, Plattsburg, MO	7MO7	1,000
Lawrence Municipal Airport, Lawrence, KS	LWC	1,000
Martins Airport, Lawson, MO	21MO	1,000
Mayes Homestead Airport, Polo, MO	37MO	1,000
McComas-Lee's Summit Municipal Airport, Lee's Summit, MO	K84	1,000
Mission Road Airport, Stilwell, KS	64K	1,000
Northwood Airport, Holt, MO	2MO2	1,000
Plattsburg Airpark, Airport, Plattsburg, MO	MO28	1,000
Richards-Gebaur Airport, Kansas City, MO	GVW	1,000
Rosecrans Memorial Airport, St. Jospeh, MO	STJ	1,000
Runway Ranch Airport, Kansas City, MO	2MO9	1,000
Sheller's Airport, Tonganoxide, KS	11KS	1,000
Shomin Airport, Oskaloosa, KS	0KS1	1,000
Stonehenge Airport, Williams-town, KS	71KS	1,000
Threshing Bee Airport, McLouth, KS	41K	1,000

(12) Airport within a 30-nautical-mile radius of the McCarran International Airport.

Airport name	Arpt ID	Alt. (AGL)
Sky Ranch Estates Airport, Sandy Valley, NV	3L2	2,500

(13) Airports within a 30-nautical-mile radius of the Memphis International Airport.

Airport name	Arpt ID	Alt. (AGL)
Bernard Manor Airport, Earle, AR	M65	2,500
Holly Springs-Marshall County Airport, Holly Springs, MS	M41	2,500
McNeely Airport, Earle, AR	M63	2,500
Price Field Airport, Joiner, AR	80M	2,500
Tucker Field Airport, Hughes, AR	78M	2,500
Tunica Airport, Tunica, MS	30M	2,500
Tunica Municipal Airport, Tunica, MS	M97	2,500

(14) Airports within a 30-nautical-mile radius of the Minneapolis–St. Paul International Wold-Chamberlain Airport.

Airport name	Arpt ID	Alt. (AGL)
Belle Plaine Airport, Belle Plaine, MN	7Y7	1,200
Carleton Airport, Stanton, MN	SYN	1,200
Empire Farm Strip Airport, Bongards, MN	MN15	1,200
Flying M Ranch Airport, Roberts, WI	78WI	1,200
Johnson Airport, Rockford, MN	MY86	1,200
River Falls Airport, River Falls, WI	Y53	1,200
Rusmar Farms Airport, Roberts, WI	WS41	1,200
Waldref SPB, Forest Lake, MN	9Y6	1,200
Ziermann Airport, Mayer, MN	MN71	1,200

(15) Airports within a 30-nautical-mile radius of the New Orleans International/Moisant Field Airport.

Airport name	Arpt ID	Alt. (AGL)
Bollinger SPB, Larose, LA	L38	1,500
Clovelly Airport, Cut Off, LA	LA09	1,500

(16) Airports within a 30-nautical-mile radius of the John F. Kennedy International Airport, the La Guardia Airport, and the Newark International Airport.

Airport name	Arpt ID	Alt. (AGL)
Allaire Airport, Belmar/Farmingdale, NJ	BLM	2,000
Cuddihy Landing Strip Airport, Freehold, NJ	NJ60	2,000
Ekdahl Airport, Freehold, NJ	NJ59	2,000
Fla-Net Airport, Netcong, NJ	ONJ5	2,000
Forrestal Airport, Princeton, NJ	N21	2,000
Greenwood Lake Airport, West Milford, NJ	4N1	2,000
Greenwood Lake SPB, West Milford, NJ	6NJ7	2,000
Lance Airport, Whitehouse Station, NJ	6NJ8	2,000
Mar Bar L Farms, Englishtown, NJ	NJ46	2,000
Peekskill SPB, Peekskill, NY	7N2	2,000
Peters Airport, Somerville, NJ	4NJ8	2,000
Princeton Airport, Princeton/Rocky Hill, NJ	39N	2,000
Solberg-Hunterdon Airport, Readington, NJ	N51	2,000

(17) Airports within a 30-nautical-mile radius of the Orlando International Airport.

Airport name	Arpt ID	Alt. (AGL)
Arthur Dunn Air Park Airport, Titusville, FL	X21	1,400
Space Center Executive Airport, Titusville, FL	TIX	1,400

(18) Airports within a 30-nautical-mile radius of the Philadelphia International Airport.

Airport name	Arpt ID	Alt. (AGL)
Ginns Airport, West Grove, PA	78N	1,000
Hammonton Municipal Airport, Hammonton, NJ	N81	1,000
Li Calzi Airport, Bridgeton, NJ	N50	1,000
New London Airport, New London, PA	N01	1,000
Wide Sky Airpark Airport, Bridgeton, NJ	N39	1,000

(19) Airports within a 30-nautical-mile radius of the Phoenix Sky Harbor International Airport.

Airport name	Arpt ID	Alt. (AGL)
Ak Chin Community Airfield Airport, Maricopa, AZ	E31	2,500
Boulais Ranch Airport, Maricopa, AZ	9E7	2,500
Estrella Sailport, Maricopa, AZ	E68	2,500
Hidden Valley Ranch Airport, Maricopa, AZ	AZ17	2,500
Millar Airport, Maricopa, AZ	2AZ4	2,500
Pleasant Valley Airport, New River, AZ	AZ05	2,500
Serene Field Airport, Maricopa, AZ	AZ31	2,500b
Sky Ranch Carefree Airport, Carefree, AZ	E18	2,500
Sycamore Creek Airport, Fountain Hills, AZ	0AS0	2,500
University of Arizona, Maricopa Agricultural Center Airport, Maricopa, AZ	3AZ2	2,500

(20) Airports within a 30-nautical-mile radius of the Lambert/St. Louis International Airport.

Airport name	Arpt ID	Alt. (AGL)
Blackhawk Airport, Old Monroe, MO	6MO0	1,000
Lebert Flying L Airport, Lebanon, MO	3H5	1,000
Shafer Metro East Airport, St. Jacob, IL	3K6	1,000
Sloan's Airport, Elsberry, MO	0MO8	1,000
Wentzville Airport, Wentzville, MO	MO50	1,000
Woodliff Airpark Airport, Foristell, MO	98MO	1,000

(21) Airports within a 30-nautical-mile radius of the Salt Lake City International Airport.

Airport name	Arpt ID	Alt. (AGL)
Bolinder Field-Tooele Valley Airport, Tooele, UT	TVY	2,500
Cedar Valley Airport, Cedar Fort, UT	UT10	2,500
Morgan County Airport, Morgan, UT	42U	2,500
Tooele Municipal Airport, Tooele, UT	U26	2,500

(22) Airports within a 30-nautical-mile radius of the Seattle-Tacoma International Airport.

Airport name	Arpt ID	Alt. (AGL)
Firstair Field Airport, Monroe, WA	WA38	1,500
Gower Field Airport, Olympia, WA	6WAZ	1,500
Harvey Field Airport, Snohomish, WA	S43	1,500

(23) Airports within a 30-nautical-mile radius of the Tampa International Airport.

Airport name	Arpt ID	Alt. (AGL)
Hernando County Airport, Brooksville, FL	BKV	1,500
Lakeland Municipal Airport, Lakeland, FL	LAL	1,500
Zephyrhills Municipal Airport, Zephyrhills, FL	ZPH	1,500

(24) Effective until the establishment of the Washington Tri-Area Class B airspace area or December 30, 1993, whichever occurs first: Airports within a 30-nautical-mile radius of the Washington National Airport and Andrews Air Force Base Airport.

Airport name	Arpt ID	Alt. (AGL)
Barnes Airport, Lisbon, MD	MD47	2,000
Bay Bridge Airport, Stevensville, MD	W29	2,000
Castle Marina Airport, Chester, MD	0W6	2,000
Davis Airport, Laytonsville, MD	W50	2,000
Fremont Airport, Kemptown, MD	MD41	2,000
Kentmorr Airpark Airport, Stevensville, MD	3W3	2,000
Montgomery County Airpark Airport, Gaithersburg, MD	GAI	2,000
Waredaca Farm Airport, Brookeville, MD	MD16	2,000
Aqua-Land/Cliffton Skypark Airport, Newburg, MD	2W8	1,000
Buds Ferry Airport, Indian Head, MD	MD39	1,000
Burgess Field Airport, Riverside, MD	3W1	1,000
Chimney View Airport, Fredericksburg, VA	5VA5	1,000
Holly Springs Farm Airport, Nanjemoy, MD	MD55	1,000
Lanseair Farms Airport, La Plata, MD	MD97	1,000
Nyce Airport, Mount Victoria, MD	MD84	1,000

Parks Airpark Airport, Nanjemoy, MD	MD54	1,000
Pilots Cove Airport, Tompkinsville, MD	MD06	1,000
Quantico MCAF, Quantico, VA	NYG	1,000
Stewart Airport, St. Michaels, MD	MD64	1,000
U.S. Naval Weapons Center, Dahlgren Lab Airport, Dahlgren, VA	NDY	1,000

(25) Effective upon the establishment of the Washington Tri-Area Class B airspace area: Airports within a 30-nautical-mile radius of the Washington National Airport, Andrews Air Force Base Airport, Baltimore-Washington International Airport, and Dulles International Airport.

Airport name	Arpt ID	Alt. (AGL)
Albrecht Airstrip Airport, Long Green, MD	MD48	2,000
Armacost Farms Airport, Hampstead, MD	MD38	2,000
Barnes Airport, Lisbon, MD	MD47	2,000
Bay Bridge Airport, Stevensville, MD	W29	2,000
Carroll County Airport, Westminster, MD	W54	2,000
Castle Marina Airport, Chester, MD	OW6	2,000
Clearview Airpark Airport, Westminster, MD	2W2	2,000
Davis Airport, Laytonsville, MD	W50	2,000
Fallston Airport, Fallston, MD	W42	2,000
Faux-Burhans Airport, Frederick, MD	3MD0	2,000
Forest Hill Airport, Forest Hill, MD	MD31	2,000
Fort Detrick Helipad Heliport, Fort Detrick (Frederick), MD	MD32	2,000
Frederick Municipal Airport, Frederick, MD	FDK	2,000
Fremont Airport, Kemptown, MD	MD41	2,000
Good Neighbor Farm Airport, Unionville, MD	MD74	2,000
Happy Landings Farm Airport, Unionville, MD	MD73	2,000
Harris Airport, Still Pond, MD	MD69	2,000
Hybarc Farm Airport, Chestertown, MD	MD19	2,000
Kennersley Airport, Church Hill, MD	MD23	2,000
Kentmorr Airpark Airport, Stevensville, MD	3W3	2,000
Montgomery County Airpark Airport, Gaithersburg, MD	GAI	2,000
Phillips AAF, Aberdeen, MD	APG	2,000

Pond View Private Airport, Chestertown, MD	OMD4	2,000
Reservoir Airport, Finksburg, MD	1W8	2,000
Scheeler Field Airport, Chestertown, MD	OW7	2,000
Stolcrest STOL, Urbana, MD	MD75	2,000
Tinsely Airstrip Airport, Butler, MD	MD17	2,000
Walters Airport, Mount Airy, MD	OMD6	2,000
Waredaca Farm Airport, Brookeville, MD	MD16	2,000
Weide AAF, Edgewood Arsenal, MD	EDG	2,000
Woodbine Gliderport, Woodbine, MD	MD78	2,000
Wright Field Airport, Chestertown, MD	MD11	2,000
Aviacres Airport, Warrenton, VA	3VA2	1,500
Birch Hollow Airport, Hillsboro, VA	W60	1,500
Flying Circus Aerodrome Airport, Warrenton, VA	3VA3	1,500
Fox Acres Airport, Warrenton, VA	15VA	1,500
Hartwood Airport, Somerville, VA	8W8	1,500
Horse Feathers Airport, Midland, VA	53VA	1,500
Krens Farm Airport, Hillsboro, VA	14VA	1,500
Scott Airpark Airport, Lovettsville, VA	VA61	1,500
The Grass Patch Airport, Lovettsville, VA	VA62	1,500
Walnut Hill Airport, Calverton, VA	58VA	1,500
Warrenton Air Park Airport, Warrenton, VA	9W0	1,500
Warrenton-Fauquier Airport, Warrenton, VA	W66	1,500
Whitman Strip Airport, Manassas, VA	OV5	1,500
Aqua-Land/Cliffton Skypark Airport, Newburg, MD	2W8	1,000
Buds Ferry Airport, Indian Head, MD	MD39	1,000
Burgess Field Airport, Riverside, MD	3WI	1,000
Chimney View Airport, Fredericksburg, VA	5VA5	1,000
Holly Springs Farm Airport, Nanjemoy, MD	MD55	1,000
Lanseair Farms Airport, La Plata, MD	MD97	1,000
Nyce Airport, Mount Victoria, MD	MD84	1,000
Parks Airpark Airport, Nanjemoy, MD	MD54	1,000

Pilots Cove Airport, Tompkinsville, MD	MD06	1,000
Quantico MCAF, Quantico, VA	NYG	1,000
Stewart Airport, St. Michaels, MD	MD64	1,000
U.S. Naval Weapons Center, Dahlgren Lab Airport, Dahlgren, VA	NDY	1,000

Authority: 49 U.S.C. app. 1301(7), 1303, 1344, 1348, 1352 through 1355, 1401, 1421 through 1431, 1471, 1472, 1502, 1510, 1522, and 2121 through 2125; articles 12, 29, 31, and 32(a) of the Convention on International Civil Aviation (61 stat. 1180); 42 U.S.C. 4321 *et seq.*; E.O. 11514, 35 FR 4247, 3 CFR, 1966–1970 Comp., p. 902; 49 U.S.C. 106(g).

[Docket No. 26242, 55 FR 50307, Dec. 5, 1990; as amended by Amdt. 91–227, 56 FR 65652, Dec. 17, 1991; 57 FR 30822, July 10, 1992; Amdt. 91–227, 56 FR 65652, Dec. 17, 1991; 58 FR 48728, Sept. 17, 1993; 58 FR 60552, Nov. 17, 1993]

SFAR No. 64 to Part 91
SPECIAL FLIGHT AUTHORIZATIONS FOR NOISE RESTRICTED AIRCRAFT

Section 1. Contrary provisions of part 91, subpart I notwithstanding, an operator of a civil subsonic turbojet airplane with maximum weight of more than 75,000 pounds may conduct an approved limited nonrevenue operation of that airplane to or from a U.S. airport when such operation has been authorized by the FAA under paragraph 2 of this SFAR; and

(a) The operator complies with all conditions and limitations established by this SFAR and the authorization;

(b) A copy of the authorization is carried aboard the airplane during all operations to or from a U.S. airport;

(c) The airplane carries an appropriate airworthiness certificate issued by the country of registration and meets the registration and identification requirements of that country; and

(d) Whenever the application is for operation to a location at which FAA-approved noise abatement retrofit equipment is to be installed to make the aircraft comply with Stage 2 or Stage 3 noise levels as defined in part 36 of this chapter, the applicant must have a valid contract for such equipment.

Section 2. Authorization for the operation of a Stage 1 or Stage 2 civil turbojet airplane to or from a U.S. airport may be issued by the FAA for the following purposes:

STAGE 1 AIRPLANES

(a) For a Stage 1 airplane owned by a U.S. owner/applicant on and since November 4, 1990:

(i) Obtaining modifications necessary to meet Stage 2 noise levels as defined in part 36 of this chapter;

(ii) Obtaining modifications necessary to meet Stage 3 noise levels as defined in part 36 of this chapter; or

(iii) Scrapping the airplane, as deemed necessary by the FAA, to obtain spare parts to support U.S. programs for the national defense or safety.

(b) For a Stage 1 airplane owned by a non-U.S. owner/applicant:

(i) Obtaining modifications necessary to meet Stage 2 noise levels as defined in part 36 of this chapter;

(ii) Obtaining modifications necessary to meet Stage 3 noise levels as defined in part 36 of this chapter; or

(iii) Scrapping the airplane, as deemed necessary by the FAA, to obtain spare parts to support U.S. programs for the national defense or safety.

(c) For a Stage 1 airplane purchased by a U.S. owner/applicant on or after November 5, 1990;

(i) Obtaining modifications necessary to meet Stage 2 noise levels as defined in part 36 of this chapter, provided that the airplane does not subsequently operate in the contiguous United States;

(ii) Obtaining modifications necessary to meet Stage 3 noise levels as defined in part 36 of this chapter; or

(iii) Scrapping the airplane, as deemed necessary by the FAA, to obtain spare parts to support U.S. programs for the national defense or safety.

STAGE 2 AIRPLANES

(d) For a Stage 2 airplane purchased by a U.S. owner/applicant on or after November 5, 1990, obtaining modification to meet Stage 3 noise levels as defined in part 36 of this chapter.

(e) For Stage 2 airplanes that were U.S.-owned on and since November 4, 1990, and that have been removed from service to achieve compliance with § 91.865 or § 91.867 of this part:

(i) Obtaining modifications to meet Stage 3 noise levels as defined in part 36 of this chapter;

(ii) Prior to January 1, 2000, exporting an airplane, including flying the airplane to or from any airport in the contiguous United States necessary for the exportation of that airplane; or

(iii) Prior to January 1, 2000, operating the airplane as deemed necessary by the FAA for the sale, lease, storage, or scrapping of the airplane.

Section 3. An application for a special flight authorization under this Special Federal Aviation Regulation shall be submitted to the FAA, Director of the Office of Environment and Energy, received no less than five days prior to the requested flight, and include the following:

(a) The applicant's name and telephone number;

(b) The name of the airplane operator;

(c) The make, model, registration number, and serial number of the airplane;

(d) The reason why such authorization is necessary;

(e) The purpose of the flight;

(f) Each U.S. airport at which the flight will be operated and the number of takeoffs and landings at each;

(g) The approximate dates of the flights;

(h) The number of people on board the airplane and the function of each person;

(i) Whether a special flight permit under FAR part 21.199 or a special flight authorization under FAR part 91.715 is required for the flight;

(j) A copy of the contract for noise abatement retrofit equipment, if appropriate; and

(k) Any other information or documentation requested by the Director, Office of Environment and Energy, as necessary to determine whether the application should be approved.

Section 4. The Special Federal Aviation Regulation terminates on December 31, 1999, unless sooner rescinded or superseded.

[58 FR 31641, June 3, 1993; as amended by Amdt. 91–232, 58 FR 62035, Nov. 24, 1993]

SFAR No. 65–1 to Part 91
PROHIBITION AGAINST CERTAIN FLIGHTS BETWEEN THE UNITED STATES AND LIBYA

Section 1. *Applicability.* This Special Federal Aviation Regulation (SFAR) No. 65–1 applies to all aircraft operations originating from, landing in, or overflying the territory of the United States.

Section 2. *Special flight restrictions.* Except as provided in paragraphs 3 and 4 of this SFAR No. 65–1—

(a) No person shall operate an aircraft on a flight to any point in Libya, or to any intermediate point on a flight where the ultimate destination is any point in Libya or that includes a landing at any point in Libya in its intended itinerary, from any point in the United States;

(b) No person shall operate an aircraft on a flight to any point in the United States from any point in Libya, or from any intermediate point on a flight where the origin is in Libya, or from any point on a flight which includes a departure from any point in Libya in its intended itinerary; or

(c) No person shall operate an aircraft over the territory of the United States if that aircraft's flight itinerary includes any landing at or departure from any point in Libya.

Section 3. *Permitted operations.* This SFAR shall not prohibit the flight operations between the United States and Libya described in section 2 of this SFAR by an aircraft authorized to conduct such operations by the United States Government in consultation with the committee established by

the UN Security Council Resolution 748 (1992), as affirmed by UN Security Council Resolution 883 (1993).

Section 4. *Emergency situations.* In an emergency that requires immediate decision and action for the safety of the flight, the pilot in command of an aircraft may deviate from this SFAR to the extent required by that emergency. Except for U.S. air carriers and commercial operators that are subject to the requirements of 14 CFR 121.557, 121.559, or 135.19, each person who deviates from this rule shall, within ten (10) days of the deviation, excluding Saturdays, Sundays, and Federal holidays, submit to the nearest FAA Flight Standards District Office a complete report of the operations or the aircraft involved in the deviation, including a description of the deviation and the reasons therefor.

Section 5. *Duration.* This SFAR No. 65–1 shall remain in effect until further notice.

[SFAR 65–1, 60 FR 48644, Sept. 20, 1995]

SFAR No. 66–2 to Part 91
PROHIBITION AGAINST CERTAIN FLIGHTS BETWEEN THE UNITED STATES AND THE FEDERAL REPUBLIC OF YUGOSLAVIA (SERBIA AND MONTENEGRO)

Effective on January 2, 1996. Special Federal Aviation Regulation No. 66–2 in 14 CFR Part 91 is suspended indefinitely.

Section 1. *Applicability.* This Special Federal Aviation Regulation (SFAR) applies to all aircraft operations originating from, destined to land in, or overflying the territory of the United States.

Section 2. *Special flight restrictions.* Except as provided in paragraphs 3 and 4 of this SFAR No. 66–2—

(a) No person shall operate an aircraft from any point in the United States to any point in the Federal Republic of Yugoslavia (Serbia and Montenegro) (hereinafter "Serbia and Montenegro"), a flight having any intermediate or ultimate destination in Serbia and Montenegro, or a flight that includes a landing at any point in Serbia and Montenegro in its intended itinerary;

(b) No person shall operate an aircraft to any point in the United States from any point in Serbia and Montenegro, or a flight from any intermediate point of departure where the origin of the flight is in Serbia and Montenegro, or a flight that includes a departure from any point in Serbia and Montenegro in its intended itinerary; or

(c) No person shall operate an aircraft over the territory of the United States if that aircraft's flight itinerary includes any landing at or departure from any point in Serbia and Montenegro.

Section 3. *Permitted operations.* This SFAR shall not prohibit the flight operations between the

United States, Serbia and Montenegro described in section 2 of this SFAR by an aircraft authorized to conduct such operations by the United States Government.

Section 4. *Emergency situations.* In an emergency that requires immediate decision and action for the safety of the flight, the pilot in command of an aircraft may deviate from this SFAR to the extent required by that emergency. Any deviation required by an emergency shall be reported as soon as possible to the air traffic control facility having jurisdiction.

Section 5. *Expiration.* This Special Federal Aviation Regulation expires June 2, 1997.

[SFAR 66–2, 60 FR 28477, May 31, 1995; as amended by SFAR 66–2, 61 FR 629, Jan. 9, 1996]

SFAR No. 67 to Part 91

Prohibition Against Certain Flights Within the Territory and Airspace of Afghanistan

Section 1. *Applicability.* This rule applies to all U.S. air carriers and commercial operators, all persons exercising the privileges of an airman certificate issued by the FAA, and all operators using aircraft registered in the United States except where the operator of such aircraft is a foreign air carrier.

Section 2. *Flight prohibition.* Except as provided in paragraph 3 and 4 of this SFAR, no person described in paragraph 1 may conduct flight operations within the territory and airspace of Afghanistan.

Section 3. *Permitted Operations.* This SFAR does not prohibit persons described in paragraph 1 from conducting flight operations within the territory and airspace of Afghanistan where such operations are authorized either by exemption issued by the Administrator or by another agency of the United States Government with the approval of the FAA.

Section 4. *Emergency situations.* In an emergency that requires immediate decision and action for the safety of the flight, the pilot in command of an aircraft may deviate from this SFAR to the extent required by that emergency. Except for U.S. air carriers and commercial operators that are subject to the requirements of 14 CFR 121.557, 121.559, or 135.19, each person who deviates from this rule shall, within ten (10) days of the deviation, excluding Saturdays, Sundays, and Federal holidays, submit to the nearest FAA Flight Standards District Office a complete report of the operations of the aircraft involved in the deviation, including a description of the deviation and the reasons therefor.

Section 5. *Expiration.* This Special Federal Aviation Regulation remains in effect until May 10, 2000.

[SFAR 67, 59 FR 25283, May 13, 1994; as amended by 60 FR 25981, May 15, 1995; 61 FR 24431, May 14, 1996; 62 FR 26892, May 15, 1997; 63 FR 26687, May 13, 1998; 63 FR 45659, Aug. 26, 1998]

SFAR No. 71 to Part 91

Special Operating Rules for Air Tour Operators in the State of Hawaii

Section 1. *Applicability.* This Special Federal Aviation Regulation prescribes operating rules for airplane and helicopter visual flight rules air tour flights conducted in the State of Hawaii under 14 CFR parts 91, 121, and 135. This rule does not apply to:

(a) Operations conducted under 14 CFR part 121 in airplanes with a passenger seating configuration of more than 30 seats or a payload capacity of more than 7,500 pounds.

(b) Flights conducted in gliders or hot air balloons.

Section 2. *Definitions.* For the purposes of this SFAR:

"Air tour" means any sightseeing flight conducted under visual flight rules in an airplane or helicopter for compensation or hire.

"Air tour operator" means any person who conducts an air tour.

Section 3. *Helicopter flotation equipment.* No person may conduct an air tour in Hawaii in a single-engine helicopter beyond the shore of any island, regardless of whether the helicopter is within gliding distance of the shore, unless:

(a) The helicopter is amphibious or is equipped with floats adequate to accomplish a safe emergency ditching and approved flotation gear is easily accessible for each occupant; or

(b) Each person on board the helicopter is wearing approved flotation gear.

Section 4. *Helicopter performance plan.* Each operator must complete a performance plan before each helicopter air tour flight. The performance plan must be based on the information in the Rotorcraft Flight Manual (RFM), considering the maximum density altitude for which the operation is planned for the flight to determine the following:

(a) Maximum gross weight and center of gravity (CG) limitations for hovering in ground effect;

(b) Maximum gross weight and CG limitations for hovering out of ground effect; and,

(c) Maximum combination of weight, altitude, and temperature for which height velocity information in the RFM, is valid.

The pilot in command (PIC) must comply with the performance plan.

91

Section 5. *Helicopter operating limitations.* Except for approach to and transition from a hover, the PIC shall operate the helicopter at a combination of height and forward speed (including hover) that would permit a safe landing in event of engine power loss, in accordance with the height-speed envelope for that helicopter under current weight and aircraft altitude.

Section 6. *Minimum flight altitudes.* Except when necessary for takeoff and landing, or operating in compliance with an air traffic control clearance, or as otherwise authorized by the Administrator, no person may conduct an air tour in Hawaii:

(a) Below an altitude of 1,500 feet above the surface over all areas of the State of Hawaii, and,

(b) Closer than 1,500 feet to any person or property; or

(c) Below any altitude prescribed by federal statute or regulation.

Section 7. *Passenger briefing.* Before takeoff, each PIC of an air tour flight of Hawaii with a flight segment beyond the ocean shore of any island shall ensure that each passenger has been briefed on the following, in addition to requirements set forth in 14 CFR 91.107, 121.571, or 135.117:

(a) Water ditching procedures;

(b) Use of required flotation equipment; and

(c) Emergency egress from the aircraft in event of a water landing.

Section 8. *Termination date.* This Special Federal Aviation Regulation expires on October 26, 2000.

[SFAR 71, 59 FR 49145, Sept. 26, 1994; as amended by 60 FR 65913, Dec. 20, 1995; 62 FR 58859, Oct. 30, 1997]

SFAR No. 77 to Part 91
Prohibition Against Certain Flights Within the Territory and Airspace of Iraq

Section 1. *Applicability.* This rule applies to the following persons:

(a) All U.S. air carriers or commercial operators;

(b) All persons exercising the privileges of an airman certificate issued by the FAA except such persons operating U.S.-registered aircraft for a foreign air carrier; or

(c) All operators of aircraft registered in the United States except where the operator of such aircraft is a foreign air carrier.

Section 2. *Flight prohibition.* Except as provided in paragraphs 3 and 4 of this SFAR, no person described in paragraph 1 may conduct flight operations over or within the territory and airspace of Iraq.

Section 3. *Permitted operations.* This SFAR does not prohibit persons described in paragraph 1 from conducting flight operations over or within the territory and airspace of Iraq where such operations are authorized either by exemption issued by the Administrator or by another agency of the United States Government.

Section 4. *Emergency situations.* In an emergency that requires immediate decision and action for the safety of the flight, the pilot in command of an aircraft may deviate from this SFAR to the extent required by that emergency. Except for U.S. air carriers or commercial operators that are subject to the requirements of 14 CFR parts 119, 121, or 135, each person who deviates from this rule shall, within ten (10) days of the deviation, excluding Saturdays, Sundays, and Federal holidays, submit to the nearest FAA Flight Standards District Office a complete report of the operations of the aircraft involved in the deviation including a description of the deviation and the reasons therefore.

Section 5. *Expiration.* This Special Federal Aviation Regulation will remain in effect until further notice.

[Docket No. 28691, 61 FR 54021, Oct. 16, 1996]

SFAR No. 78 to Part 91
Special Operating Rules for Commercial Air Tour Operators in the Vicinity of the Rocky Mountain National Park

Section 1. *Applicability.* This Special Federal Aviation Regulation prescribes operating rules for commercial air tour flight operations within the lateral boundaries of the Rocky Mountain National Park, CO.

Section 2. *Definition.* For the purpose of this SFAR: "commercial air tour" means: the operation of an aircraft carrying passengers for compensation or hire for aerial sightseeing.

Section 3. *Restriction.* No person may conduct a commercial air tour operation in the airspace over Rocky Mountain National Park, CO.

Expiration: This SFAR will expire on the adoption of a final rule in Docket No. 27643.

[Docket No. 28577, 62 FR 1205, Jan. 8, 1997]

SFAR No. 79 to Part 91

PROHIBITION AGAINST CERTAIN FLIGHTS
WITHIN THE FLIGHT INFORMATION REGION
(FIR) OF THE DEMOCRATIC PEOPLE'S
REPUBLIC OF KOREA (DPRK)

Section 1. *Applicability.* This rule applied to the following persons:
(a) All U.S. air carriers or commercial operators.
(b) All persons exercising the privileges of an airman certificate issued by the FAA, except such persons operating U.S.-registered aircraft for a foreign air carrier.
(c) All operators of aircraft registered in the United States except where the operator of such aircraft is a foreign air carrier.

Section 2. *Flight Prohibition.* Except as provided in paragraphs 3 and 4 of this SFAR, no person described in paragraph 1 may conduct flight operations through the Pyongyang FIR west of 132 degrees east longitude.

Section 3. *Permitted Operations.* This SFAR does not prohibit persons described in paragraph 1 from conducting flight operations within the Pyongyang FIR west of 132 degrees east longitude where such operations are authorized either by exemption issued by the Administrator or by another agency of the United States Government with FAA approval.

Section 4. *Emergency situations.* In an emergency that requires immediate decision and action for the safety of the flight, the pilot in command on an aircraft may deviate from this SFAR to the extend required by that emergency. Except for U.S. air carriers and commercial operators that are subject to the requirements of 14 CFR parts 121, 125, or 135, each person who deviates from this rule shall, within ten (10) days of the deviation, excluding Saturdays, Sundays, and Federal holidays, submit to the nearest FAA Flight Standards District Office a complete report of the operations of the aircraft involved in the deviation, including a description of the deviation and the reasons therefore.

Section 5. *Expiration.* This Special Federal Aviation Regulation No. 79 will remain in effect until further notice.

[Docket No. 28831, 62 FR 20077, April 24, 1997; as amended by 63 FR 8017, Feb. 17, 1998; 63 FR 19286, April 17, 1998]

•

SFAR No. 82 to Part 91

PROHIBITION AGAINST CERTAIN FLIGHTS
WITHIN THE TERRITORY AND
AIRSPACE OF SUDAN

Section 1. *Applicability.* This rule applies to all U.S. air carriers and commercial operators, all persons exercising the privileges of an airman certificate issued by the FAA, and all operators using aircraft registered in the United States except where the operator of such aircraft is a foreign air carrier.

Section 2. *Flight prohibition.* Except as provided in paragraphs 3 and 4 of this SFAR, no person described in paragraph 1 may conduct flight operations within the territory and airspace of Sudan.

Section 3. *Permitted operations.* This SFAR does not prohibit persons described in paragraph 1 from conducting flight operations within the territory and airspace of Sudan where such operations are authorized either by exemption issued by the Administrator or by another agency of the United States Government with the approval of the FAA.

Section 4. *Emergency situations.* In an emergency that requires immediate decision and action for the safety of the flight, the pilot in command of an aircraft may deviate from this SFAR to the extent required by that emergency. Except for U.S. air carriers and commercial operators that are subject to the requirements of 14 CFR 121.557, 121.559, or 135.19, each person who deviates from this rule shall, within ten (10) days of the deviation, excluding Saturdays, Sundays, and Federal holidays, submit to the nearest FAA Flight Standards District Office a complete report of the operations of the aircraft involved in the deviation, including a description of the deviation and the reasons therefor.

Section 5. *Expiration.* This Special Federal Aviation Regulation shall remain in effect until further notice.

[Docket No. 29317, 63 FR 45653, Aug. 26, 1998]

91

SFAR No. 84 to Part 91

PROHIBITION AGAINST CERTAIN FLIGHTS WITHIN THE TERRITORY AND AIRSPACE OF SERBIA–MONTENEGRO

1. *Applicability.* This rule applies to all U.S. air carriers and commercial operators, all persons exercising the privileges of an airman certificate issued by the FAA unless that person is engaged in the operation of a U.S.-registered aircraft for a foreign air carrier, and all operators using aircraft registered in the United States except where the operator of such aircraft is a foreign air carrier.

2. *Flight prohibition.* Except as provided in paragraph 3 and 4 of this SFAR, no person described in paragraph 1 may conduct flight operations within the territory and airspace of Serbia–Montenegro.

3. *Permitted operations.* This SFAR does not prohibit persons described in paragraph 1 from conducting flight operations within the territory and airspace of Serbia–Montenegro where such operations are authorized either by exemption issued by the Administrator or by another agency of the United States Government with the approval of the FAA.

4. *Emergency situations.* In an emergency that requires immediate decision and action for the safety of the flight, the pilot in command of an aircraft may deviate from this SFAR to the extent required by that emergency. Except for U.S. air carriers and commercial operators that are subject to the requirements of 14 CFR 121.557, 121.559, or 135.19, each person who deviates from this rule shall, within ten (10) days of the deviation, excluding Saturdays, Sundays, and Federal holidays, submit to the nearest FAA Flight Standards District Office a complete report of the operations of the aircraft involved in the deviation, including a description of the deviation and the reasons therefore.

5. *Expiration.* This Special Federal Aviation Regulation shall remain in effect until further notice.

[Docket No. 29508, 64 FR 15121, March 29, 1999]

SFAR No. 86 to Part 91

AIRSPACE AND FLIGHT OPERATIONS REQUIREMENTS FOR THE 1999 AND 2000 KODAK ALBUQUERQUE INTERNATIONAL BALLOON FIESTAS; ALBUQUERQUE, NM

Section 1. *General.*

(a) Each person shall be familiar with all NOTAMs issued pursuant to this SFAR and all other available information concerning that operation before conducting any operation into or out of an airport or area specified in this SFAR or in NOTAMs pursuant to this SFAR. In addition, each person operating an international flight that will enter the U.S. shall be familiar with any international NOTAMs issued pursuant to this SFAR. NOTAMs are available for inspection at operating FAA air traffic facilities and regional air traffic division offices.

(b) Notwithstanding any provision of the Title 14, Code of Federal Regulations, no person may operate an aircraft contrary to any restriction procedure specified in this SFAR or by the Administrator, or through a NOTAM issued pursuant to this SFAR.

(c) As conditions warrant, the Administrator is authorized to—

(1) Restrict, prohibit, or permit IFR/VFR operations in the temporary flight restricted area designated in this SFAR or in a NOTAM issued pursuant to this SFAR;

(2) Give priority to or exclude the following flights from provisions of this SFAR and NOTAMs issued pursuant to this SFAR:

(i) Essential military.

(ii) Medical and rescue.

(iii) Presidential and Vice Presidential.

(iv) Flights carrying visiting heads of state.

(v) Law enforcement and security.

(vi) Flights authorized by the Director, Air Traffic Service.

(d) For security purposes, the Administrator may issue NOTAMs during the effective period of this SFAR to cancel or modify provisions of this SFAR and NOTAMs issued pursuant to this SFAR if such action is consistent with the safe and efficient use of airspace and the safety and security of persons and property on the ground as affected by air traffic.

Section 2. *Temporary Flight Restrictions.* At the following location, flight is restricted during the indicated dates and times: That airspace within a 4 NM radius centered on the Albuquerque VORTAC 038° radial 14 DME fix from the surface up to but not including 8,000 feet MSL unless otherwise authorized by Albuquerque ATCT.

Section 3. *Dates and Times of Designation.*

(a) October 2 through October 10, 1999, and October 7 through October 15, 2000, from 0530 MDT until 1200 MDT.

(b) October 2 through October 10, 1999, and October 7 through October 15, 2000, from 1600 MDT until 2200 MDT.

Section 4. *Expiration.* This Special Federal Aviation Regulation expires on October 16, 2000.

[Docket No. 29279, SFAR No. 86, 64 FR 44816, Aug. 17, 1999]

Subpart A—General

Source: Docket No. 18334, 54 FR 34292, Aug. 18, 1989, unless otherwise noted.

§ 91.1 Applicability.

(a) Except as provided in paragraphs (b) and (c) of this section and §§ 91.701 and 91.703, this part prescribes rules governing the operation of aircraft (other than moored balloons, kites, unmanned rockets, and unmanned free balloons, which are governed by part 101 of this chapter, and ultralight vehicles operated in accordance with part 103 of this chapter) within the United States, including the waters within 3 nautical miles of the U.S. coast.

(b) Each person operating an aircraft in the airspace overlying the waters between 3 and 12 nautical miles from the coast of the United States shall comply with §§ 91.1 through 91.21; §§ 91.101 through 91.143; §§ 91.151 through 91.159; §§ 91.167 through 91.193; § 91.203; § 91.205; §§ 91.209 through 91.217; § 91.221; §§ 91.303 through 91.319; § 91.323; § 91.605; § 91.609; §§ 91.703 through 91.715; and 91.903.

(c) This part applies to each person on board an aircraft being operated under this part, unless otherwise specified.

[Docket No. 18334, 54 FR 34292, Aug. 18, 1989; as amended by Amdt. 91–257, 64 FR 1079, Jan. 7, 1999]

§ 91.3 Responsibility and authority of the pilot in command.

(a) The pilot in command of an aircraft is directly responsible for, and is the final authority as to, the operation of that aircraft.

(b) In an in-flight emergency requiring immediate action, the pilot in command may deviate from any rule of this part to the extent required to meet that emergency.

(c) Each pilot in command who deviates from a rule under paragraph (b) of this section shall, upon the request of the Administrator, send a written report of that deviation to the Administrator.

(Approved by the Office of Management and Budget under control number 2120–0005)

§ 91.5 Pilot in command of aircraft requiring more than one required pilot.

No person may operate an aircraft that is type certificated for more than one required pilot flight crewmember unless the pilot in command meets the requirements of § 61.58 of this chapter.

§ 91.7 Civil aircraft airworthiness.

(a) No person may operate a civil aircraft unless it is in an airworthy condition.

(b) The pilot in command of a civil aircraft is responsible for determining whether that aircraft is in condition for safe flight. The pilot in command shall discontinue the flight when unairworthy mechanical, electrical, or structural conditions occur.

§ 91.9 Civil aircraft flight manual, marking, and placard requirements.

(a) Except as provided in paragraph (d) of this section, no person may operate a civil aircraft without complying with the operating limitations specified in the approved Airplane or Rotorcraft Flight Manual, markings, and placards, or as otherwise prescribed by the certificating authority of the country of registry.

(b) No person may operate a U.S.-registered civil aircraft—

(1) For which an Airplane or Rotorcraft Flight Manual is required by § 21.5 of this chapter unless there is available in the aircraft a current, approved Airplane or Rotorcraft Flight Manual or the manual provided for in § 121.141(b); and

(2) For which an Airplane or Rotorcraft Flight Manual is not required by § 21.5 of this chapter, unless there is available in the aircraft a current approved Airplane or Rotorcraft Flight Manual, approved manual material, markings, and placards, or any combination thereof.

(c) No person may operate a U.S.-registered civil aircraft unless that aircraft is identified in accordance with part 45 of this chapter.

(d) Any person taking off or landing a helicopter certificated under part 29 of this chapter at a heliport constructed over water may make such momentary flight as is necessary for takeoff or landing through the prohibited range of the limiting height-speed envelope established for the helicopter if that flight through the prohibited range takes place over water on which a safe ditching can be accomplished and if the helicopter is amphibious or is equipped with floats or other emergency flotation gear adequate to accomplish a safe emergency ditching on open water.

§ 91.11 Prohibition on interference with crewmembers.

No person may assault, threaten, intimidate, or interfere with a crewmember in the performance of the crewmember's duties aboard an aircraft being operated.

[Docket No. 18334, 54 FR 34292, Aug. 18, 1989; as amended by Amdt. 91–257, 64 FR 1079, Jan. 7, 1999]

§ 91.13 Careless or reckless operation.

(a) *Aircraft operations for the purpose of air navigation.* No person may operate an aircraft in a careless or reckless manner so as to endanger the life or property of another.

(b) *Aircraft operations other than for the purpose of air navigation.* No person may operate an aircraft, other than for the purpose of air navigation, on any part of the surface of an airport used by aircraft for air commerce (including areas used by those aircraft for receiving or discharging persons or cargo), in a careless or reckless manner so as to endanger the life or property of another.

§ 91.15 Dropping objects.

No pilot in command of a civil aircraft may allow any object to be dropped from that aircraft in flight that creates a hazard to persons or property. However, this section does not prohibit the dropping of any object if reasonable precautions are taken to avoid injury or damage to persons or property.

§ 91.17 Alcohol or drugs.

(a) No person may act or attempt to act as a crewmember of a civil aircraft—

(1) Within 8 hours after the consumption of any alcoholic beverage;

(2) While under the influence of alcohol;

(3) While using any drug that affects the person's faculties in any way contrary to safety; or

(4) While having .04 percent by weight or more alcohol in the blood.

(b) Except in an emergency, no pilot of a civil aircraft may allow a person who appears to be intoxicated or who demonstrates by manner or physical indications that the individual is under the influence of drugs (except a medical patient under proper care) to be carried in that aircraft.

(c) A crewmember shall do the following:

(1) On request of a law enforcement officer, submit to a test to indicate the percentage by weight of alcohol in the blood, when—

(i) The law enforcement officer is authorized under State or local law to conduct the test or to have the test conducted; and

(ii) The law enforcement officer is requesting submission to the test to investigate a suspected violation of State or local law governing the same or substantially similar conduct prohibited by paragraph (a)(1), (a)(2), or (a)(4) of this section.

(2) Whenever the Administrator has a reasonable basis to believe that a person may have violated paragraph (a)(1), (a)(2), or (a)(4) of this section, that person shall, upon request by the Administrator, furnish the Administrator, or authorize any clinic, hospital, doctor, or other person to release to the Administrator, the results of each test taken within 4 hours after acting or attempting to act as a crewmember that indicates percentage by weight of alcohol in the blood.

(d) Whenever the Administrator has a reasonable basis to believe that a person may have violated paragraph (a)(3) of this section, that person shall, upon request by the Administrator, furnish the Administrator, or authorize any clinic, hospital, doctor, or other person to release to the Administrator, the results of each test taken within 4 hours after acting or attempting to act as a crewmember that indicates the presence of any drugs in the body.

(e) Any test information obtained by the Administrator under paragraph (c) or (d) of this section may be evaluated in determining a person's qualifications for any airman certificate or possible violations of this chapter and may be used as evidence in any legal proceeding under section 602, 609, or 901 of the Federal Aviation Act of 1958.

§ 91.19 Carriage of narcotic drugs, marihuana, and depressant or stimulant drugs or substances.

(a) Except as provided in paragraph (b) of this section, no person may operate a civil aircraft within the United States with knowledge that narcotic drugs, marihuana, and depressant or stimulant drugs or substances as defined in Federal or State statutes are carried in the aircraft.

(b) Paragraph (a) of this section does not apply to any carriage of narcotic drugs, marihuana, and depressant or stimulant drugs or substances authorized by or under any Federal or State statute or by any Federal or State agency.

§ 91.21 Portable electronic devices.

(a) Except as provided in paragraph (b) of this section, no person may operate, nor may any operator or pilot in command of an aircraft allow the operation of, any portable electronic device on any of the following U.S.-registered civil aircraft:

(1) Aircraft operated by a holder of an air carrier operating certificate or an operating certificate; or

(2) Any other aircraft while it is operated under IFR.

(b) Paragraph (a) of this section does not apply to—

(1) Portable voice recorders;

(2) Hearing aids;

(3) Heart pacemakers;

(4) Electric shavers; or

(5) Any other portable electronic device that the operator of the aircraft has determined will not cause interference with the navigation or communication system of the aircraft on which it is to be used.

(c) In the case of an aircraft operated by a holder of an air carrier operating certificate or an operating certificate, the determination required by paragraph (b)(5) of this section shall be made by that operator of the aircraft on which the particular device is to be used. In the case of other aircraft, the determination may be made by the pilot in command or other operator of the aircraft.

§**91.23 Truth-in-leasing clause requirement in leases and conditional sales contracts.**

(a) Except as provided in paragraph (b) of this section, the parties to a lease or contract of conditional sale involving a U.S.-registered large civil aircraft and entered into after January 2, 1973, shall execute a written lease or contract and include therein a written truth-in-leasing clause as a concluding paragraph in large print, immediately preceding the space for the signature of the parties, which contains the following with respect to each such aircraft:

(1) Identification of the Federal Aviation Regulations under which the aircraft has been maintained and inspected during the 12 months preceding the execution of the lease or contract of conditional sale, and certification by the parties thereto regarding the aircraft's status of compliance with applicable maintenance and inspection requirements in this part for the operation to be conducted under the lease or contract of conditional sale.

(2) The name and address (printed or typed) and the signature of the person responsible for operational control of the aircraft under the lease or contract of conditional sale, and certification that each person understands that person's responsibilities for compliance with applicable Federal Aviation Regulations.

(3) A statement that an explanation of factors bearing on operational control and pertinent Federal Aviation Regulations can be obtained from the nearest FAA Flight Standards district office.

(b) The requirements of paragraph (a) of this section do not apply—

(1) To a lease or contract of conditional sale when—

(i) The party to whom the aircraft is furnished is a foreign air carrier or certificate holder under part 121, 125, 127, 135, or 141 of this chapter, or

(ii) The party furnishing the aircraft is a foreign air carrier or a person operating under part 121, 125, and 141 of this chapter, or a person operating under part 135 of this chapter having authority to engage in on-demand operations with large aircraft.

(2) To a contract of conditional sale, when the aircraft involved has not been registered anywhere prior to the execution of the contract, except as a new aircraft under a dealer's aircraft registration certificate issued in accordance with § 47.61 of this chapter.

(c) No person may operate a large civil aircraft of U.S. registry that is subject to a lease or contract of conditional sale to which paragraph (a) of this section applies, unless—

(1) The lessee or conditional buyer, or the registered owner if the lessee is not a citizen of the United States, has mailed a copy of the lease or contract that complies with the requirements of paragraph (a) of this section, within 24 hours of its execution, to the Aircraft Registration Branch, Attn: Technical Section, P.O. Box 25724, Oklahoma City, OK 73125;

(2) A copy of the lease or contract that complies with the requirements of paragraph (a) of this section is carried in the aircraft. The copy of the lease or contract shall be made available for review upon request by the Administrator, and

(3) The lessee or conditional buyer, or the registered owner if the lessee is not a citizen of the United States, has notified by telephone or in person the FAA Flight Standards district office nearest the airport where the flight will originate. Unless otherwise authorized by that office, the notification shall be given at least 48 hours before takeoff in the case of the first flight of that aircraft under that lease or contract and inform the FAA of—

(i) The location of the airport of departure;

(ii) The departure time; and

(iii) The registration number of the aircraft involved.

(d) The copy of the lease or contract furnished to the FAA under paragraph (c) of this section is commercial or financial information obtained from a person. It is, therefore, privileged and confidential and will not be made available by the FAA for public inspection or copying under 5 U.S.C. 552(b)(4) unless recorded with the FAA under part 49 of this chapter.

(e) For the purpose of this section, a lease means any agreement by a person to furnish an aircraft to another person for compensation or hire, whether with or without flight crewmembers, other than an agreement for the sale of an aircraft and a contract of conditional sale under section 101 of the Federal Aviation Act of 1958. The person furnishing the aircraft is referred to as the lessor, and the person to whom it is furnished the lessee.

(Approved by the Office of Management and Budget under control number 2120–0005)

[Docket No. 18334, 54 FR 34292, Aug. 18, 1989; as amended by Amdt. 91–212, 54 FR 39293, Sept. 25, 1989; Amdt. 91–253, 62 FR 13253, March 19, 1997]

§ 91.25 Aviation Safety Reporting Program: Prohibition against use of reports for enforcement purposes.

The Administrator of the FAA will not use reports submitted to the National Aeronautics and Space Administration under the Aviation Safety Reporting Program (or information derived therefrom) in any enforcement action except information concerning accidents or criminal offenses which are wholly excluded from the Program.

§ 91.27 – 91.99 [Reserved]

Subpart B—Flight Rules

Source: Docket No. 18334, 54 FR 34294, Aug. 18, 1989, unless otherwise noted.

GENERAL

§ 91.101 Applicability.

This subpart prescribes flight rules governing the operation of aircraft within the United States and within 12 nautical miles from the coast of the United States.

§ 91.103 Preflight action.

Each pilot in command shall, before beginning a flight, become familiar with all available information concerning that flight. This information must include—

(a) For a flight under IFR or a flight not in the vicinity of an airport, weather reports and forecasts, fuel requirements, alternatives available if the planned flight cannot be completed, and any known traffic delays of which the pilot in command has been advised by ATC;

(b) For any flight, runway lengths at airports of intended use, and the following takeoff and landing distance information:

(1) For civil aircraft for which an approved Airplane or Rotorcraft Flight Manual containing takeoff and landing distance data is required, the takeoff and landing distance data contained therein; and

(2) For civil aircraft other than those specified in paragraph (b)(1) of this section, other reliable information appropriate to the aircraft, relating to aircraft performance under expected values of airport elevation and runway slope, aircraft gross weight, and wind and temperature.

§ 91.105 Flight crewmembers at stations.

(a) During takeoff and landing, and while en route, each required flight crewmember shall—

(1) Be at the crewmember station unless the absence is necessary to perform duties in connection with the operation of the aircraft or in connection with physiological needs; and

(2) Keep the safety belt fastened while at the crewmember station.

(b) Each required flight crewmember of a U.S.-registered civil aircraft shall, during takeoff and landing, keep the shoulder harness fastened while at his or her assigned duty station. This paragraph does not apply if—

(1) The seat at the crewmember's station is not equipped with a shoulder harness; or

(2) The crewmember would be unable to perform required duties with the shoulder harness fastened.

[Docket No. 18334, 54 FR 34294, Aug. 18, 1989; as amended by Amdt. 91–231, 57 FR 42671, Sept. 15, 1992]

§ 91.107 Use of safety belts, shoulder harnesses, and child restraint systems.

(a) Unless otherwise authorized by the Administrator—

(1) No pilot may take off a U.S.-registered civil aircraft (except a free balloon that incorporates a basket or gondola, or an airship type certificated before November 2, 1987) unless the pilot in command of that aircraft ensures that each person on board is briefed on how to fasten and unfasten that person's safety belt and, if installed, shoulder harness.

(2) No pilot may cause to be moved on the surface, take off, or land a U.S.-registered civil aircraft (except a free balloon that incorporates a basket or gondola, or an airship certificated before November 2, 1987) unless the pilot in command of that aircraft ensures that each person on board has been notified to fasten his or her safety belt and, if installed, his or her shoulder harness.

(3) Except as provided in this paragraph, each person on board a U.S.-registered civil aircraft (except a free balloon that incorporates a basket or gondola or an airship certificated before November 2, 1987) must occupy an approved seat or berth with a safety belt and, if installed, shoul-

der harness, properly secured about him or her during movement on the surface, takeoff and landing. For seaplane and float equipped rotorcraft operations during movement on the surface, the person pushing off the seaplane or rotorcraft from the dock and the person mooring the seaplane or rotor craft at the dock are excepted from the preceding seating and safety belt requirements. Notwithstanding the preceding requirements of this paragraph, a person may:

(i) Be held by an adult who is occupying an approved seat or berth, provided that the person being held has not reached his or her second birthday and does not occupy or use any restraining device;

(ii) Use the floor of the aircraft as a seat, provided that the person is on board for the purpose of engaging in sport parachuting; or

(iii) Notwithstanding any other requirement of this chapter, occupy an approved child restraint system furnished by the operator or one of the persons described in paragraph (a)(3)(iii)(A) of this section provided that:

(A) The child is accompanied by a parent, guardian, or attendant designated by the child's parent or guardian to attend to the safety of the child during flight;

(B) Except as provided in paragraph (a)(3)(iii)(B)(4) of this action, the approved child restraint system bears one or more labels as follows:

(1) Seats manufactured to U.S. standards between January 1, 1981, and February 25, 1985, must bear the label: "This child restraint system conforms to all applicable Federal motor vehicle safety standards.";

(2) Seats manufactured to U.S. standards on or after February 26, 1985, must bear two labels:

(i) "This child restraint system conforms to all applicable Federal motor vehicle safety standards;" and

(ii) "THIS RESTRAINT IS CERTIFIED FOR USE IN MOTOR VEHICLES AND AIRCRAFT" in red lettering;

(3) Seats that do not qualify under paragraphs (a)(3)(iii)(B)(1) and (a)(3)(iii)(B)(2) of this section must bear either a label showing approval of a foreign government or a label showing that the seat was manufactured under the standards of the United Nations;

(4) Notwithstanding any other provision of this section, booster-type child restraint systems (as defined in Federal Motor Vehicle Safety Standard No. 213 (49 CFR 571.213)), vest- and harness-type child restraint systems, and lap held child restraints are not approved for use in aircraft; and

(C) The operator complies with the following requirements:

(1) The restraint system must be properly secured to an approved forward-facing seat or berth:

(2) The child must be properly secured in the restraint system and must not exceed the specified weight limit for the restraint system; and

(3) The restraint system must bear the appropriate label(s).

(b) Unless otherwise stated, this section does not apply to operations conducted under part 121, 125, or 135 of this chapter. Paragraph (a)(3) of this section does not apply to person subject to § 91.105.

[Docket No. 26142, 57 FR 42671, Sept. 15, 1992; as amended by Amdt. 91–250, 61 FR 28421, June 4, 1996]

§ 91.109 Flight instruction; Simulated instrument flight and certain flight tests.

(a) No person may operate a civil aircraft (except a manned free balloon) that is being used for flight instruction unless that aircraft has fully functioning dual controls. However, instrument flight instruction may be given in a single-engine airplane equipped with a single, functioning throwover control wheel in place of fixed, dual controls of the elevator and ailerons when—

(1) The instructor has determined that the flight can be conducted safely; and

(2) The person manipulating the controls has at least a private pilot certificate with appropriate category and class ratings.

(b) No person may operate a civil aircraft in simulated instrument flight unless—

(1) The other control seat is occupied by a safety pilot who possesses at least a private pilot certificate with category and class ratings appropriate to the aircraft being flown.

(2) The safety pilot has adequate vision forward and to each side of the aircraft, or a competent observer in the aircraft adequately supplements the vision of the safety pilot; and

(3) Except in the case of lighter-than-air aircraft, that aircraft is equipped with fully functioning dual controls. However, simulated instrument flight may be conducted in a single-engine airplane, equipped with a single, functioning, throwover control wheel, in place of fixed, dual controls of the elevator and ailerons, when—

(i) The safety pilot has determined that the flight can be conducted safely; and

(ii) The person manipulating the controls has at least a private pilot certificate with appropriate category and class ratings.

(c) No person may operate a civil aircraft that is being used for a flight test for an airline transport pilot certificate or a class or type rating on that certificate, or for a part 121 proficiency flight test, unless the pilot seated at the controls, other than the pilot being checked, is fully qualified to act as pilot in command of the aircraft.

§ 91.111   Operating near other aircraft.

(a) No person may operate an aircraft so close to another aircraft as to create a collision hazard.

(b) No person may operate an aircraft in formation flight except by arrangement with the pilot in command of each aircraft in the formation.

(c) No person may operate an aircraft, carrying passengers for hire, in formation flight.

§ 91.113   Right-of-way rules: Except water operations.

(a) *Inapplicability.* This section does not apply to the operation of an aircraft on water.

(b) *General.* When weather conditions permit, regardless of whether an operation is conducted under instrument flight rules or visual flight rules, vigilance shall be maintained by each person operating an aircraft so as to see and avoid other aircraft. When a rule of this section gives another aircraft the right-of-way, the pilot shall give way to that aircraft and may not pass over, under, or ahead of it unless well clear.

(c) *In distress.* An aircraft in distress has the right-of-way over all other air traffic.

(d) *Converging.* When aircraft of the same category are converging at approximately the same altitude (except head-on, or nearly so), the aircraft to the other's right has the right-of-way. If the aircraft are of different categories—

(1) A balloon has the right-of-way over any other category of aircraft;

(2) A glider has the right-of-way over an airship, airplane, or rotorcraft; and

(3) An airship has the right-of-way over an airplane or rotorcraft.

However, an aircraft towing or refueling other aircraft has the right-of-way over all other engine-driven aircraft.

(e) *Approaching head-on.* When aircraft are approaching each other head-on, or nearly so, each pilot of each aircraft shall alter course to the right.

(f) *Overtaking.* Each aircraft that is being overtaken has the right-of-way and each pilot of an overtaking aircraft shall alter course to the right to pass well clear.

(g) *Landing.* Aircraft, while on final approach to land or while landing, have the right-of-way over other aircraft in flight or operating on the surface, except that they shall not take advantage of this rule to force an aircraft off the runway surface which has already landed and is attempting to make way for an aircraft on final approach. When two or more aircraft are approaching an airport for the purpose of landing, the aircraft at the lower altitude has the right-of-way, but it shall not take advantage of this rule to cut in front of another which is on final approach to land or to overtake that aircraft.

§ 91.115   Right-of-way rules: Water operations.

(a) *General.* Each person operating an aircraft on the water shall, insofar as possible, keep clear of all vessels and avoid impeding their navigation, and shall give way to any vessel or other aircraft that is given the right-of-way by any rule of this section.

(b) *Crossing.* When aircraft, or an aircraft and a vessel, are on crossing courses, the aircraft or vessel to the other's right has the right-of-way.

(c) *Approaching head-on.* When aircraft, or an aircraft and a vessel, are approaching head-on, or nearly so, each shall alter its course to the right to keep well clear.

(d) *Overtaking.* Each aircraft or vessel that is being overtaken has the right-of-way, and the one overtaking shall alter course to keep well clear.

(e) *Special circumstances.* When aircraft, or an aircraft and a vessel, approach so as to involve risk of collision, each aircraft or vessel shall proceed with careful regard to existing circumstances, including the limitations of the respective craft.

§ 91.117   Aircraft speed.

(a) Unless otherwise authorized by the Administrator, no person may operate an aircraft below 10,000 feet MSL at an indicated airspeed of more than 250 knots (288 m.p.h.).

(b) Unless otherwise authorized or required by ATC, no person may operate an aircraft at or below 2,500 feet above the surface within 4 nautical miles of the primary airport of a Class C or Class D airspace area at an indicated airspeed of more than 200 knots (230 m.p.h.). This paragraph (b) does not apply to any operations within a Class B airspace area. Such operations shall comply with paragraph (a) of this section.

(c) No person may operate an aircraft in the airspace underlying a Class B airspace area designated for an airport or in a VFR corridor designated through such a Class B airspace area, at an indicated airspeed of more than 200 knots (230 mph).

(d) If the minimum safe airspeed for any particular operation is greater than the maximum speed prescribed in this section, the aircraft may be operated at that minimum speed.

[Docket No. 18334, 54 FR 34292, Aug. 18, 1989; as amended by Amdt. 91–219, 55 FR 34708, Aug. 24, 1990; Amdt. 91–227, 56 FR 65657, Dec. 17, 1991; Amdt. 91–233, 58 FR 43554, Aug. 17, 1993]

§ 91.119 Minimum safe altitudes: General.

Except when necessary for takeoff or landing, no person may operate an aircraft below the following altitudes:

(a) *Anywhere.* An altitude allowing, if a power unit fails, an emergency landing without undue hazard to persons or property on the surface.

(b) *Over congested areas.* Over any congested area of a city, town, or settlement, or over any open air assembly of persons, an altitude of 1,000 feet above the highest obstacle within a horizontal radius of 2,000 feet of the aircraft.

(c) *Over other than congested areas.* An altitude of 500 feet above the surface, except over open water or sparsely populated areas. In those cases, the aircraft may not be operated closer than 500 feet to any person, vessel, vehicle, or structure.

(d) *Helicopters.* Helicopters may be operated at less than the minimums prescribed in paragraph (b) or (c) of this section if the operation is conducted without hazard to persons or property on the surface. In addition, each person operating a helicopter shall comply with any routes or altitudes specifically prescribed for helicopters by the Administrator.

§ 91.121 Altimeter settings.

(a) Each person operating an aircraft shall maintain the cruising altitude or flight level of that aircraft, as the case may be, by reference to an altimeter that is set, when operating—

(1) Below 18,000 feet MSL, to—

(i) The current reported altimeter setting of a station along the route and within 100 nautical miles of the aircraft;

(ii) If there is no station within the area prescribed in paragraph (a)(1)(i) of this section, the current reported altimeter setting of an appropriate available station; or

(iii) In the case of an aircraft not equipped with a radio, the elevation of the departure airport or an appropriate altimeter setting available before departure; or

(2) At or above 18,000 feet MSL, to 29.92" Hg.

(b) The lowest usable flight level is determined by the atmospheric pressure in the area of operation as shown in the following table:

Current altimeter setting	Lowest usable flight level
29.92 (or higher)	180
29.91 through 29.42	185
29.41 through 28.92	190
28.91 through 28.42	195
28.41 through 27.92	200
27.91 through 27.42	205
27.41 through 26.92	210

(c) To convert minimum altitude prescribed under §§ 91.119 and 91.177 to the minimum flight level, the pilot shall take the flight level equivalent of the minimum altitude in feet and add the appropriate number of feet specified below, according to the current reported altimeter setting:

Current altimeter setting	Adjustment factor
29.92 (or higher)	None
29.91 through 29.42	500
29.41 through 28.92	1,000
28.91 through 28.42	1,500
28.41 through 27.92	2,000
27.91 through 27.42	2,500
27.41 through 26.92	3,000

§ 91.123 Compliance with ATC clearances and instructions.

(a) When an ATC clearance has been obtained, no pilot in command may deviate from that clearance unless an amended clearance is obtained, an emergency exists, or the deviation is in response to a traffic alert and collision avoidance system resolution advisory. However, except in Class A airspace, a pilot may cancel an IFR flight plan if the operation is being conducted in VFR weather conditions. When a pilot is uncertain of an ATC clearance, that pilot shall immediately request clarification from ATC.

(b) Except in an emergency, no person may operate an aircraft contrary to an ATC instruction in an area in which air traffic control is exercised.

(c) Each pilot in command who, in an emergency, or in response to a traffic alert and collision avoidance system resolution advisory, deviates from an ATC clearance or instruction shall notify ATC of that deviation as soon as possible.

(d) Each pilot in command who (though not deviating from a rule of this subpart) is given priority by ATC in an emergency, shall submit a detailed report of that emergency within 48 hours to the manager of that ATC facility, if requested by ATC.

(e) Unless otherwise authorized by ATC, no person operating an aircraft may operate that aircraft according to any clearance or instruction that has been issued to the pilot of another aircraft for radar air traffic control purposes.

(Approved by the Office of Management and Budget under control number 2120–0005)

[Docket No. 18834, 54 FR 34294, Aug. 18, 1989; as amended by Amdt. 91–227, 56 FR 65658, Dec. 17, 1991; Amdt. 91–244, 60 FR 50679, Sept. 29, 1995]

§ 91.125 ATC light signals.

ATC light signals have the meaning shown in the following table:

Color and type of signal	Meaning with respect to aircraft on the surface	Meaning with respect to aircraft in flight
Steady green	Cleared for takeoff	Cleared to land
Flashing green	Cleared to taxi	Return for landing (to be followed by steady green at proper time)
Steady red	Stop	Give way to other aircraft and continue circling
Flashing red	Taxi clear of runway in use	Airport unsafe — do not land
Flashing white	Return to starting point on airport	Not applicable
Alternating red and green	Exercise extreme caution	Exercise extreme caution

§ 91.126 Operating on or in the vicinity of an airport in Class G airspace.

(a) *General.* Unless otherwise authorized or required, each person operating an aircraft on or in the vicinity of an airport in a Class G airspace area must comply with the requirements of this section.

(b) *Direction of turns.* When approaching to land at an airport without an operating control tower in Class G airspace—

(1) Each pilot of an airplane must make all turns of that airplane to the left unless the airport displays approved light signals or visual markings indicating that turns should be made to the right, in which case the pilot must make all turns to the right; and

(2) Each pilot of a helicopter must avoid the flow of fixed-wing aircraft.

(c) *Flap settings.* Except when necessary for training or certification, the pilot in command of a civil turbojet-powered aircraft must use, as a final flap setting, the minimum certificated landing flap setting set forth in the approved performance information in the Airplane Flight Manual for the applicable conditions. However, each pilot in command has the final authority and responsibility for the safe operation of the pilot's airplane, and may use a different flap setting for that airplane if the pilot determines that it is necessary in the interest of safety.

(d) *Communications with control towers.* Unless otherwise authorized or required by ATC, no person may operate an aircraft to, from, through, or on an airport having an operational control tower unless two-way radio communications are maintained between that aircraft and the control tower. Communications must be established prior to 4 nautical miles from the airport, up to and including 2,500 feet AGL. However, if the aircraft radio fails in flight, the pilot in command may operate that aircraft and land if weather conditions are at or above basic VFR weather minimums, visual contact with the tower is maintained, and a clearance to land is received. If the aircraft radio fails while in flight under IFR, the pilot must comply with § 91.185.

[Docket No. 24458, 56 FR 65658, Dec. 17, 1991; as amended by Amdt. 91–239, 59 FR 11693, March 11, 1994]

§ 91.127 Operating on or in the vicinity of an airport in Class E airspace.

(a) Unless otherwise required by part 93 of this chapter or unless otherwise authorized or required by the ATC facility having jurisdiction over the Class E airspace area, each person operating an aircraft on or in the vicinity of an airport in a Class E airspace area must comply with the requirements of § 91.126.

(b) *Departures.* Each pilot of an aircraft must comply with any traffic patterns established for that airport in part 93 of this chapter.

(c) *Communications with control towers.* Unless otherwise authorized or required by ATC, no person may operate an aircraft to, from, through, or on an airport having an operational control tower unless two-way radio communications are maintained between that aircraft and the control tower. Communications must be established prior to 4 nautical miles from the airport, up to and including 2,500 feet AGL. However, if the aircraft radio fails in flight, the pilot in command may operate that aircraft and land if weather conditions are at or above basic VFR weather minimums, visual contact with the tower is maintained, and a clearance to land is received. If the aircraft radio fails while in flight under IFR, the pilot must comply with § 91.185.

[Docket No. 24458, 56 FR 65658, Dec. 17, 1991; as amended by Amdt. 91–239, 59 FR 11693, March 11, 1994]

§ 91.129 Operations in Class D airspace.

(a) *General.* Unless otherwise authorized or required by the ATC facility having jurisdiction over the Class D airspace area, each person operating an aircraft in Class D airspace must comply with the applicable provisions of this section. In addition, each person must comply with §§ 91.126 and 91.127. For the purpose of this section, the primary airport is the airport for which the Class D airspace area is designated. A satellite airport is any other airport within the Class D airspace area.

(b) *Deviations.* An operator may deviate from any provision of this section under the provisions of an ATC authorization issued by the ATC facility having jurisdiction over the airspace concerned. ATC may authorize a deviation on a continuing basis or for an individual flight, as appropriate.

(c) *Communications.* Each person operating an aircraft in Class D airspace must meet the following two-way radio communications requirements:

(1) *Arrival or through flight.* Each person must establish two-way radio communications with the ATC facility (including foreign ATC in the case of foreign airspace designated in the United States) providing air traffic services prior to entering that airspace and thereafter maintain those communications while within that airspace.

(2) *Departing flight.* Each person—

(i) From the primary airport or satellite airport with an operating control tower must establish and maintain two-way radio communications with the control tower, and thereafter as instructed by ATC while operating in the Class D airspace area; or

(ii) From a satellite airport without an operating control tower, must establish and maintain two-way radio communications with the ATC facility having jurisdiction over the Class D airspace area as soon as practicable after departing.

(d) *Communications failure.* Each person who operates an aircraft in a Class D airspace area must maintain two-way radio communications with the ATC facility having jurisdiction over that area.

(1) If the aircraft radio fails in flight under IFR, the pilot must comply with § 91.185 of the part.

(2) If the aircraft radio fails in flight under VFR, the pilot in command may operate that aircraft and land if—

(i) Weather conditions are at or above basic VFR weather minimums;

(ii) Visual contact with the tower is maintained; and

(iii) A clearance to land is received.

(e) *Minimum altitudes.* When operating to an airport in Class D airspace, each pilot of—

(1) A large or turbine-powered airplane shall, unless otherwise required by the applicable distance from cloud criteria, enter the traffic pattern at an altitude of at least 1,500 feet above the elevation of the airport and maintain at least 1,500 feet until further descent is required for a safe landing.

(2) A large or turbine-powered airplane approaching to land on a runway served by an instrument landing system (ILS), if the airplane is ILS equipped, shall fly that airplane at an altitude at or above the glide slope between the outer marker (or point of interception of glide slope, if compliance with the applicable distance from cloud criteria requires interception closer in) and the middle marker; and

(3) An airplane approaching to land on a runway served by a visual approach slope indicator shall maintain an altitude at or above the glide slope until a lower altitude is necessary for a safe landing.

Paragraphs (e)(2) and (e)(3) of this section do not prohibit normal bracketing maneuvers above or below the glide slope that are conducted for the purpose of remaining on the glide slope.

(f) *Approaches.* Except when conducting a circling approach under Part 97 of this chapter or unless otherwise required by ATC, each pilot must—

(1) Circle the airport to the left, if operating an airplane; or

(2) Avoid the flow of fixed-wing aircraft, if operating a helicopter.

(g) *Departures.* No person may operate an aircraft departing from an airport except in compliance with the following:

(1) Each pilot must comply with any departure procedures established for that airport by the FAA.

(2) Unless otherwise required by the prescribed departure procedure for that airport or the applicable distance from clouds criteria, each pilot of a turbine-powered airplane and each pilot of a large airplane must climb to an altitude of 1,500 feet above the surface as rapidly as practicable.

(h) *Noise abatement.* Where a formal runway use program has been established by the FAA, each pilot of a large or turbine-powered airplane assigned a noise abatement runway by ATC must use that runway. However, consistent with the final authority of the pilot in command concerning the safe operation of the aircraft as prescribed in § 91.3(a), ATC may assign a different runway if requested by the pilot in the interest of safety.

(i) *Takeoff, landing, taxi clearance.* No person may, at any airport with an operating control tower, operate an aircraft on a runway or taxiway, or take off or land an aircraft, unless an appropriate clearance is received from ATC. A clearance to "taxi to" the takeoff runway assigned to the aircraft is not a clearance to cross that assigned takeoff runway, or to taxi on that runway at any point, but is a clearance to cross other runways that intersect the taxi route to that assigned takeoff runway. A clearance to "taxi to" any point other than an assigned takeoff runway is clearance to cross all runways that intersect the taxi route to that point.

[Docket No. 24458, 56 FR 65658, Dec. 17, 1991; as amended by Amdt. 91–234, 58 FR 48793, Sept. 20, 1993]

§ 91.130 Operations in Class C airspace.

(a) *General.* Unless otherwise authorized by ATC each aircraft operation in Class C airspace must be conducted in compliance with this section and § 91.129. For the purpose of this section, the primary airport is the airport for which the Class C airspace area is designated. A satellite airport is any other airport within the Class C airspace area.

(b) *Traffic patterns.* No person may take off or land an aircraft at a satellite airport within a Class C airspace area except in compliance with FAA arrival and departure traffic patterns.

(c) *Communications.* Each person operating an aircraft in Class C airspace must meet the following two-way radio communications requirements:

(1) *Arrival or through flight.* Each person must establish two-way radio communications with the ATC facility (including foreign ATC in the case of foreign airspace designated in the United States) providing air traffic services prior to entering that airspace and thereafter maintain those communications while within that airspace.

(2) *Departing flight.* Each person—

(i) From the primary airport or satellite airport with an operating control tower must establish and maintain two-way radio communications with the control tower, and thereafter as instructed by ATC while operating in the Class C airspace area; or

(ii) From a satellite airport without an operating control tower, must establish and maintain two-way radio communications with the ATC facility having jurisdiction over the Class C airspace area as soon as practicable after departing.

(d) *Equipment requirements.* Unless otherwise authorized by the ATC having jurisdiction over the Class C airspace area, no person may operate an aircraft within a Class C airspace area designated for an airport unless that aircraft is equipped with the applicable equipment specified in § 91.215.

(e) *Deviations.* An operator may deviate from any provision of this section under the provisions of an ATC authorization issued by the ATC facility having jurisdiction over the airspace concerned. ATC may authorize a deviation on a continuing basis or for an individual flight, as appropriate.

[Docket No. 24458, 56 FR 65659, Dec. 17, 1991; as amended by Amdt. 91–232, 58 FR 40736, July 30, 1993; Amdt. 91–239, 59 FR 11693, March 11, 1994]

§ 91.131 Operations in Class B airspace.

(a) *Operating rules.* No person may operate an aircraft within a Class B airspace area except in compliance with § 91.129 and the following rules:

(1) The operator must receive an ATC clearance from the ATC facility having jurisdiction for that area before operating an aircraft in that area.

(2) Unless otherwise authorized by ATC, each person operating a large turbine engine-powered airplane to or from a primary airport for which a Class B airspace area is designated must operate at or above the designated floors of the Class B airspace area while within the lateral limits of that area.

(3) Any person conducting pilot training operations at an airport within a Class B airspace area must comply with any procedures established by ATC for such operations in that area.

(b) *Pilot requirements.*

(1) No person may take off or land a civil aircraft at an airport within a Class B airspace area or operate a civil aircraft within a Class B airspace area unless—

(i) The pilot in command holds at least a private pilot certificate; or

(ii) The aircraft is operated by a student pilot or recreational pilot who seeks private pilot certification and has met the requirements of § 61.95 of this chapter.

(2) Notwithstanding the provisions of paragraph (b)(1)(ii) of this section, no person may take off or land a civil aircraft at those airports listed in section 4 of Appendix D of this part unless the pilot in command holds at least a private pilot certificate.

(c) *Communications and navigation equipment requirements.* Unless otherwise authorized by ATC, no person may operate an aircraft within a Class B airspace area unless that aircraft is equipped with—

(1) For IFR operation. An operable VOR or TACAN receiver; and

(2) For all operations. An operable two-way radio capable of communications with ATC on appropriate frequencies for that Class B airspace area.

(d) *Transponder requirements.* No person may operate an aircraft in a Class B airspace area unless the aircraft is equipped with the applicable operating transponder and automatic altitude reporting equipment specified in paragraph (a) of § 91.215, except as provided in paragraph (d) of that section.

[Docket No. 24458, 56 FR 65658, Dec. 17, 1991]

§ 91.133 Restricted and prohibited areas.

(a) No person may operate an aircraft within a restricted area (designated in part 73) contrary to the restrictions imposed, or within a prohibited area, unless that person has the permission of the using or controlling agency, as appropriate.

(b) Each person conducting, within a restricted area, an aircraft operation (approved by the using agency) that creates the same hazards as the operations for which the restricted area was designated may deviate from the rules of this subpart that are not compatible with the operation of the aircraft.

§ 91.135 Operations in Class A airspace.

Except as provided in paragraph (d) of this section, each person operating an aircraft in Class A airspace must conduct that operation under instrument flight rules (IFR) and in compliance with the following:

(a) *Clearance.* Operations may be conducted only under an ATC clearance received prior to entering the airspace.

(b) *Communications.* Unless otherwise authorized by ATC, each aircraft operating in Class A airspace must be equipped with a two-way radio capable of communicating with ATC on a frequency assigned by ATC. Each pilot must maintain two-way radio communications with ATC while operating in Class A airspace.

(c) *Transponder requirement.* Unless otherwise authorized by ATC, no person may operate an aircraft within Class A airspace unless that aircraft is equipped with the applicable equipment specified in § 91.215.

(d) *ATC authorizations.* An operator may deviate from any provision of this section under the provisions of an ATC authorization issued by the ATC facility having jurisdiction of the airspace concerned. In the case of an inoperative transponder, ATC may immediately approve an operation within a Class A airspace area allowing flight to continue, if desired, to the airport of ultimate destination, including any intermediate stops, or to proceed to a place where suitable repairs can be made, or both. Requests for deviation from any provision of this section must be submitted in writing, at least 4 days before the proposed operation. ATC may authorize a deviation on a continuing basis or for an individual flight.

[Docket No. 24458, 56 FR 65659, Dec. 17, 1991]

§ 91.137 Temporary flight restrictions.

(a) The Administrator will issue a Notice to Airmen (NOTAM) designating an area within which temporary flight restrictions apply and specifying the hazard or condition requiring their imposition, whenever he determines it is necessary in order to—

(1) Protect persons and property on the surface or in the air from a hazard associated with an incident on the surface;

(2) Provide a safe environment for the operation of disaster relief aircraft; or

(3) Prevent an unsafe congestion of sightseeing and other aircraft above an incident or event which may generate a high degree of public interest.

The Notice to Airmen will specify the hazard or condition that requires the imposition of temporary flight restrictions.

(b) When a NOTAM has been issued under paragraph (a)(1) of this section, no person may operate an aircraft within the designated area unless that aircraft is participating in the hazard relief activities and is being operated under the direction of the official in charge of on scene emergency response activities.

(c) When a NOTAM has been issued under paragraph (a)(2) of this section, no person may operate an aircraft within the designated area unless at least one of the following conditions are met:

(1) The aircraft is participating in hazard relief activities and is being operated under the direction of the official in charge of on scene emergency response activities.

(2) The aircraft is carrying law enforcement officials.

(3) The aircraft is operating under the ATC approved IFR flight plan.

(4) The operation is conducted directly to or from an airport within the area, or is necessitated by the impracticability of VFR flight above or around the area due to weather, or terrain; notification is given to the Flight Service Station (FSS) or ATC facility specified in the NOTAM to receive advisories concerning disaster relief aircraft operations; and the operation does not hamper or endanger relief activities and is not conducted for the purpose of observing the disaster.

(5) The aircraft is carrying properly accredited news representatives, and, prior to entering the area, a flight plan is filed with the appropriate FAA or ATC facility specified in the Notice to Airmen and the operation is conducted above the altitude used by the disaster relief aircraft, unless otherwise authorized by the official in charge of on scene emergency response activities.

(d) When a NOTAM has been issued under paragraph (a)(3) of this section, no person may operate an aircraft within the designated area unless at least one of the following conditions is met:

(1) The operation is conducted directly to or from an airport within the area, or is necessitated by the impracticability of VFR flight above or around the area due to weather or terrain, and the operation is not conducted for the purpose of observing the incident or event.

(2) The aircraft is operating under an ATC approved IFR flight plan.

(3) The aircraft is carrying incident or event personnel, or law enforcement officials.

(4) The aircraft is carrying properly accredited news representatives and, prior to entering that area, a flight plan is filed with the appropriate FSS or ATC facility specified in the NOTAM.

(e) Flight plans filed and notifications made with an FSS or ATC facility under this section shall include the following information:

(1) Aircraft identification, type and color.

(2) Radio communications frequencies to be used.

(3) Proposed times of entry of, and exit from, the designated area.

(4) Name of news media or organization and purpose of flight.

(5) Any other information requested by ATC.

§ 91.138 Temporary flight restrictions in national disaster areas in the State of Hawaii.

(a) When the Administrator has determined, pursuant to a request and justification provided by the Governor of the State of Hawaii, or the Governor's designee, that an inhabited area within a declared national disaster area in the State of Hawaii is in need of protection for humanitarian reasons, the Administrator will issue a Notice to Airmen (NOTAM) designating an area within which temporary flight restrictions apply. The Administrator will designate the extent and duration of the temporary flight restrictions necessary to provide for the protection of persons and property on the surface.

(b) When a NOTAM has been issued in accordance with this section, no person may operate an aircraft within the designated airspace unless:

(1) That person has obtained authorization from the official in charge of associated emergency or disaster relief response activities, and is operating the aircraft under the conditions of that authorization;

(2) The aircraft is carrying law enforcement officials;

(3) The aircraft is carrying persons involved in an emergency or a legitimate scientific purpose;

(4) The aircraft is carrying properly accredited newspersons, and that prior to entering the area, a flight plan is filed with the appropriate FAA or ATC facility specified in the NOTAM and the operation is conducted in compliance with the conditions and restrictions established by the official in charge of on-scene emergency response activities; or,

(5) The aircraft is operating in accordance with an ATC clearance or instruction.

(c) A NOTAM issued under this section is effective for 90 days or until the national disaster area designation is terminated, whichever comes first, unless terminated by notice or extended by the Administrator at the request of the Governor of the State of Hawaii or the Governor's designee.

[Docket No. 26476, 56 FR 23178, May 20, 1991]

§ 91.139 Emergency air traffic rules.

(a) This section prescribes a process for utilizing Notices to Airmen (NOTAMs) to advise of the issuance and operations under emergency air traffic rules and regulations and designates the official who is authorized to issue NOTAMs on behalf of the Administrator in certain matters under this section.

(b) Whenever the Administrator determines that an emergency condition exists, or will exist, relating to the FAA's ability to operate the air traffic control system and during which normal flight operations under this chapter cannot be conducted consistent with the required levels of safety and efficiency—

(1) The Administrator issues an immediately effective air traffic rule or regulation in response to that emergency condition; and

(2) The Administrator or the Associate Administrator for Air Traffic may utilize the NOTAM system to provide notification of the issuance of the rule or regulation.

Those NOTAMs communicate information concerning the rules and regulations that govern flight operations, the use of navigation facilities, and designation of that airspace in which the rules and regulations apply.

(c) When a NOTAM has been issued under this section, no person may operate an aircraft, or other device governed by the regulation concerned, within the designated airspace except in accordance with the authorizations, terms, and conditions prescribed in the regulation covered by the NOTAM.

§ 91.141 Flight restrictions in the proximity of the Presidential and other parties.

No person may operate an aircraft over or in the vicinity of any area to be visited or traveled by the President, the Vice President, or other public figures contrary to the restrictions established by the Administrator and published in a Notice to Airmen (NOTAM).

§ 91.143 Flight limitation in the proximity of space flight operations.

No person may operate any aircraft of U.S. registry, or pilot any aircraft under the authority of an airman certificate issued by the Federal Aviation Administration within areas designated in a Notice to Airmen (NOTAM) for space flight operations except when authorized by ATC, or operated under the control of the Department of Defense Manager for Space Transportation System Contingency Support Operations.

§ 91.144 Temporary restriction on flight operations during abnormally high barometric pressure conditions.

(a) *Special flight restrictions.* When any information indicates that barometric pressure on the route of flight currently exceeds or will exceed 31 inches of mercury, no person may operate an aircraft or initiate a flight contrary to the requirements established by the Administrator and published in a Notice to Airmen issued under this section.

(b) *Waivers.* The administrator is authorized to waive any restriction issued under paragraph (a) of this section to permit emergency supply, transport, or medical services to be delivered to isolated communities, where the operation can be conducted with an acceptable level of safety.

[Docket No. 26806, 59 FR 17452, April 12, 1994; as amended by Amdt. 91–240, 59 FR 37669, July 25, 1994]

§ 91.145 – 91.149 [Reserved]

§ 91.151 Fuel requirements for flight in VFR conditions.

(a) No person may begin a flight in an airplane under VFR conditions unless (considering wind and forecast weather conditions) there is enough fuel to fly to the first point of intended landing and, assuming normal cruising speed—

(1) During the day, to fly after that for at least 30 minutes; or

(2) At night, to fly after that for at least 45 minutes.

(b) No person may begin a flight in a rotorcraft under VFR conditions unless (considering wind and forecast weather conditions) there is enough fuel to fly to the first point of intended landing and, assuming normal cruising speed, to fly after that for at least 20 minutes.

§ 91.153 VFR flight plan: Information required.

(a) *Information required.* Unless otherwise authorized by ATC, each person filing a VFR flight plan shall include in it the following information:

(1) The aircraft identification number and, if necessary, its radio call sign.

(2) The type of the aircraft or, in the case of a formation flight, the type of each aircraft and the number of aircraft in the formation.

(3) The full name and address of the pilot in command or, in the case of a formation flight, the formation commander.

(4) The point and proposed time of departure.

(5) The proposed route, cruising altitude (or flight level), and true airspeed at that altitude.

(6) The point of first intended landing and the estimated elapsed time until over that point.

(7) The amount of fuel on board (in hours).

(8) The number of persons in the aircraft, except where that information is otherwise readily available to the FAA.

(9) Any other information the pilot in command or ATC believes is necessary for ATC purposes.

(b) *Cancellation.* When a flight plan has been activated, the pilot in command, upon canceling or completing the flight under the flight plan, shall notify an FAA Flight Service Station or ATC facility.

§ 91.155 Basic VFR weather minimums.

(a) Except as provided in paragraph (b) of this section and § 91.157, no person may operate an aircraft under VFR when the flight visibility is less, or at a distance from clouds that is less, than that prescribed for the corresponding altitude and class of airspace in the following table:

Airspace	Flight visibility	Distance from clouds
Class A	Not applicable	Not applicable.
Class B	3 statute miles	Clear of clouds.
Class C	3 statute miles	500 feet below. 1,000 feet above. 2,000 feet horizontal.
Class D	3 statute miles	500 feet below. 1,000 feet above. 2,000 feet horizontal.
Class E: Less than 10,000 feet MSL	3 statute miles	500 feet below. 1,000 feet above. 2,000 feet horizontal.
At or above 10,000 feet MSL	5 statute miles	1,000 feet below. 1,000 feet above. 1 statute mile horizontal.
Class G: 1,200 feet or less above the surface (regardless of MSL altitude)		
Day, except as provided in § 91.155(b)	1 statute mile	Clear of clouds.
Night, except as provided in § 91.155(b)	3 statute miles	500 feet below. 1,000 feet above. 2,000 feet horizontal.
More than 1,200 feet above the surface but less than 10,000 feet MSL		
Day	1 statute mile	500 feet below. 1,000 feet above. 2,000 feet horizontal.
Night	3 statute miles	500 feet below. 1,000 feet above. 2,000 feet horizontal.
More than 1,200 feet above the surface and at or above 10,000 feet MSL	5 statute miles	1,000 feet below. 1,000 feet above. 1 statute mile horizontal.

(b) *Class G Airspace.* Notwithstanding the provisions of paragraph (a) of this section, the following operations may be conducted in Class G airspace below 1,200 feet above the surface:

(1) *Helicopter.* A helicopter may be operated clear of clouds if operated at a speed that allows the pilot adequate opportunity to see any air traffic or obstruction in time to avoid a collision.

(2) *Airplane.* When the visibility is less than 3 statute miles but not less than 1 statute mile during night hours, an airplane may be operated clear of clouds if operated in an airport traffic pattern within one-half mile of the runway.

(c) Except as provided in § 91.157, no person may operate an aircraft beneath the ceiling under VFR within the lateral boundaries of controlled airspace designated to the surface for an airport when the ceiling is less than 1,000 feet.

(d) Except as provided in § 91.157 of this part, no person may take off or land an aircraft, or enter the traffic pattern of an airport, under VFR, within the lateral boundaries of the surface areas of Class B, Class C, Class D, or Class E airspace designated for an airport—

(1) Unless ground visibility at that airport is at least 3 statute miles; or

(2) If ground visibility is not reported at that airport, unless flight visibility during landing or take-off, or while operating in the traffic pattern is at least 3 statute miles.

(e) For the purpose of this section, an aircraft operating at the base altitude of a Class E airspace area is considered to be within the airspace directly below that area.

[Docket No. 24458, 56 FR 65660, Dec. 17, 1991; as amended by Amdt. 91–235, 58 FR 51968, Oct. 5, 1993]

§ 91.157 Special VFR weather minimums.

(a) Except as provided in Appendix D, section 3, of this part, special VFR operations may be conducted under the weather minimums and requirements of this section, instead of those contained in § 91.155, below 10,000 feet MSL within the airspace contained by the upward extension of the lateral boundaries of the controlled airspace designated to the surface for an airport.

(b) Special VFR operations may only be conducted—

(1) With an ATC clearance;

(2) Clear of clouds;

(3) Except for helicopters, when flight visibility is at least 1 statute mile; and

(4) Except for helicopters, between sunrise and sunset (or in Alaska, when the sun is 6 degrees or more below the horizon) unless—

(i) The person being granted the ATC clearance meets the applicable requirements for instrument flight under part 61 of this chapter;

(ii) The aircraft is equipped as required in Part 91.205(d).

(c) No person may take off or land an aircraft (other than a helicopter) under special VFR—

(1) Unless ground visibility is at least 1 statute mile; or

(2) If ground visibility is not reported, unless flight visibility is at least 1 statute mile.

[Docket No. 18334, 54 FR 34294, Aug. 18, 1989, as amended by Amdt. 91–235, 58 FR 51968, Oct. 5, 1993; Amdt. 91–247, 60 FR 66875, Dec. 27, 1995]

§ 91.159 VFR cruising altitude or flight level.

Except while holding in a holding pattern of 2 minutes or less, or while turning, each person operating an aircraft under VFR in level cruising flight more than 3,000 feet above the surface shall maintain the appropriate altitude or flight level prescribed below, unless otherwise authorized by ATC:

(a) When operating below 18,000 feet MSL and—

(1) On a magnetic course of zero degrees through 179 degrees, any odd thousand foot MSL altitude +500 feet (such as 3,500, 5,500, or 7,500); or

(2) On a magnetic course of 180 degrees through 359 degrees, any even thousand foot MSL altitude +500 feet (such as 4,500, 6,500, or 8,500).

(b) When operating above 18,000 feet MSL to flight level 290 (inclusive) and—

(1) On a magnetic course of zero degrees through 179 degrees, any odd flight level +500 feet (such as 195, 215, or 235); or

(2) On a magnetic course of 180 degrees through 359 degrees, any even flight level +500 feet (such as 185, 205, or 225).

(c) When operating above flight level 290 and—

(1) On a magnetic course of zero degrees through 179 degrees, any flight level, at 4,000-foot intervals, beginning at and including flight level 300 (such as flight level 300, 340, or 380); or

(2) On a magnetic course of 180 degrees through 359 degrees, any flight level, at 4,000-foot intervals, beginning at and including flight level 320 (such as flight level 320, 360, or 400).

§ 91.161 – 91.165 [Reserved]

Instrument Flight Rules

§ 91.167 Fuel requirements for flight in IFR conditions.

(a) Except as provided in paragraph (b) of this section, no person may operate a civil aircraft in IFR conditions unless it carries enough fuel (considering weather reports and forecasts and weather conditions) to—

(1) Complete the flight to the first airport of intended landing;

(2) Fly from that airport to the alternate airport; and

(3) Fly after that for 45 minutes at normal cruising speed or, for helicopters, fly after that for 30 minutes at normal cruising speed.

(b) Paragraph (a)(2) of this section does not apply if—

(1) Part 97 of this chapter prescribes a standard instrument approach procedure for the first airport of intended landing; and

(2) For at least 1 hour before and 1 hour after the estimated time of arrival at the airport, the weather reports or forecasts or any combination of them indicate—

(i) The ceiling will be at least 2,000 feet above the airport elevation; and

(ii) Visibility will be at least 3 statute miles.

§ 91.169 IFR flight plan: Information required.

(a) *Information required.* Unless otherwise authorized by ATC, each person filing an IFR flight plan shall include in it the following information:

(1) Information required under § 91.153(a).

(2) An alternate airport, except as provided in paragraph (b) of this section.

(b) *Exceptions to applicability of paragraph (a)(2) of this section.* Paragraph (a)(2) of this section does not apply if part 97 of this chapter prescribes a standard instrument approach procedure for the first airport of intended landing and, for at least 1 hour before and 1 hour after the estimated time of arrival, the weather reports or forecasts, or any combination of them, indicate—

(1) The ceiling will be at least 2,000 feet above the airport elevation; and

(2) The visibility will be at least 3 statute miles.

(c) *IFR alternate airport weather minimums.* Unless otherwise authorized by the Administrator, no person may include an alternate airport in an IFR flight plan unless current weather forecasts indicate that, at the estimated time of arrival at the alternate airport, the ceiling and visibility at that airport will be at or above the following alternate airport weather minimums:

(1) If an instrument approach procedure has been published in part 97 of this chapter for that airport, the alternate airport minimums specified

in that procedure or, if none are so specified, the following minimums:

(i) Precision approach procedure: Ceiling 600 feet and visibility 2 statute miles.

(ii) Nonprecision approach procedure: Ceiling 800 feet and visibility 2 statute miles.

(2) If no instrument approach procedure has been published in part 97 of this chapter for that airport, the ceiling and visibility minimums are those allowing descent from the MEA, approach, and landing under basic VFR.

(d) *Cancellation.* When a flight plan has been activated, the pilot in command, upon canceling or completing the flight under the flight plan, shall notify an FAA Flight Service Station or ATC facility.

§ 91.171 VOR equipment check for IFR operations.

(a) No person may operate a civil aircraft under IFR using the VOR system of radio navigation unless the VOR equipment of that aircraft—

(1) Is maintained, checked, and inspected under an approved procedure; or

(2) Has been operationally checked within the preceding 30 days, and was found to be within the limits of the permissible indicated bearing error set forth in paragraph (b) or (c) of this section.

(b) Except as provided in paragraph (c) of this section, each person conducting a VOR check under paragraph (a)(2) of this section shall—

(1) Use, at the airport of intended departure, an FAA-operated or approved test signal or a test signal radiated by a certificated and appropriately rated radio repair station or, outside the United States, a test signal operated or approved by an appropriate authority to check the VOR equipment (the maximum permissible indicated bearing error is plus or minus 4 degrees); or

(2) Use, at the airport of intended departure, a point on the airport surface designated as a VOR system checkpoint by the Administrator, or, outside the United States, by an appropriate authority (the maximum permissible bearing error is plus or minus 4 degrees);

(3) If neither a test signal nor a designated checkpoint on the surface is available, use an airborne checkpoint designated by the Administrator or, outside the United States, by an appropriate authority (the maximum permissible bearing error is plus or minus 6 degrees); or

(4) If no check signal or point is available, while in flight—

(i) Select a VOR radial that lies along the centerline of an established VOR airway;

(ii) Select a prominent ground point along the selected radial preferably more than 20 nautical miles from the VOR ground facility and maneuver the aircraft directly over the point at a reasonably low altitude; and

(iii) Note the VOR bearing indicated by the receiver when over the ground point (the maximum permissible variation between the published radial and the indicated bearing is 6 degrees).

(c) If dual system VOR (units independent of each other except for the antenna) is installed in the aircraft, the person checking the equipment may check one system against the other in place of the check procedures specified in paragraph (b) of this section. Both systems shall be tuned to the same VOR ground facility and note the indicated bearings to that station. The maximum permissible variation between the two indicated bearings is 4 degrees.

(d) Each person making the VOR operational check, as specified in paragraph (b) or (c) of this section, shall enter the date, place, bearing error, and sign the aircraft log or other record. In addition, if a test signal radiated by a repair station, as specified in paragraph (b)(1) of this section, is used, an entry must be made in the aircraft log or other record by the repair station certificate holder or the certificate holder's representative certifying to the bearing transmitted by the repair station for the check and the date of transmission.

(Approved by the Office of Management and Budget under control number 2120–0005)

§ 91.173 ATC clearance and flight plan required.

No person may operate an aircraft in controlled airspace under IFR unless that person has—

(a) Filed an IFR flight plan; and

(b) Received an appropriate ATC clearance.

§ 91.175 Takeoff and landing under IFR.

(a) *Instrument approaches to civil airports.*

Unless otherwise authorized by the Administrator, when an instrument letdown to a civil airport is necessary, each person operating an aircraft, except a military aircraft of the United States, shall use a standard instrument approach procedure prescribed for the airport in part 97 of this chapter.

(b) *Authorized DH or MDA.* For the purpose of this section, when the approach procedure being used provides for and requires the use of a DH or MDA, the authorized DH or MDA is the highest of the following:

(1) The DH or MDA prescribed by the approach procedure.

(2) The DH or MDA prescribed for the pilot in command.

(3) The DH or MDA for which the aircraft is equipped.

(c) *Operation below DH or MDA.* Where a DH or MDA is applicable, no pilot may operate an aircraft, except a military aircraft of the United States, at any airport below the authorized MDA or continue an approach below the authorized DH unless—

(1) The aircraft is continuously in a position from which a descent to a landing on the intended runway can be made at a normal rate of descent using normal maneuvers, and for operations conducted under part 121 or part 135 unless that descent rate will allow touchdown to occur within the touchdown zone of the runway of intended landing;

(2) The flight visibility is not less than the visibility prescribed in the standard instrument approach being used; and

(3) Except for a Category II or Category III approach where any necessary visual reference requirements are specified by the Administrator, at least one of the following visual references for the intended runway is distinctly visible and identifiable to the pilot:

(i) The approach light system, except that the pilot may not descend below 100 feet above the touchdown zone elevation using the approach lights as a reference unless the red terminating bars or the red side row bars are also distinctly visible and identifiable.

(ii) The threshold.

(iii) The threshold markings.

(iv) The threshold lights.

(v) The runway end identifier lights.

(vi) The visual approach slope indicator.

(vii) The touchdown zone or touchdown zone markings.

(viii) The touchdown zone lights.

(ix) The runway or runway markings.

(x) The runway lights.

(d) *Landing.* No pilot operating an aircraft, except a military aircraft of the United States, may land that aircraft when the flight visibility is less than the visibility prescribed in the standard instrument approach procedure being used.

(e) *Missed approach procedures.* Each pilot operating an aircraft, except a military aircraft of the United States, shall immediately execute an appropriate missed approach procedure when either of the following conditions exist:

(1) Whenever the requirements of paragraph (c) of this section are not met at either of the following times:

(i) When the aircraft is being operated below MDA; or

(ii) Upon arrival at the missed approach point, including a DH where a DH is specified and its use is required, and at any time after that until touchdown.

(2) Whenever an identifiable part of the airport is not distinctly visible to the pilot during a circling maneuver at or above MDA, unless the inability to see an identifiable part of the airport results only from a normal bank of the aircraft during the circling approach.

(f) *Civil airport takeoff minimums.* Unless otherwise authorized by the Administrator, no pilot operating an aircraft under parts 121, 125, 127, 129, or 135 of this chapter may take off from a civil airport under IFR unless weather conditions are at or above the weather minimum for IFR takeoff prescribed for that airport under part 97 of this chapter. If takeoff minimums are not prescribed under part 97 of this chapter for a particular airport, the following minimums apply to takeoffs under IFR for aircraft operating under those parts:

(1) For aircraft, other than helicopters, having two engines or less—1 statute mile visibility.

(2) For aircraft having more than two engines—$\frac{1}{2}$-statute mile visibility.

(3) For helicopters—$\frac{1}{2}$-statute mile visibility.

(g) *Military airports.* Unless otherwise prescribed by the Administrator, each person operating a civil aircraft under IFR into or out of a military airport shall comply with the instrument approach procedures and the takeoff and landing minimum prescribed by the military authority having jurisdiction of that airport.

(h) *Comparable values of RVR and ground visibility.*

(1) Except for Category II or Category III minimums, if RVR minimums for takeoff or landing are prescribed in an instrument approach procedure, but RVR is not reported for the runway of intended operation, the RVR minimum shall be converted to ground visibility in accordance with the table in paragraph (h)(2) of this section and shall be the visibility minimum for takeoff or landing on that runway.

(2)

RVR (feet)	Visibility (statute miles)
1,600	1/4
2,400	1/2
3,200	5/8
4,000	3/4
4,500	7/8
5,000	1
6,000	1-1/4

(i) *Operations on unpublished routes and use of radar in instrument approach procedures.* When radar is approved at certain locations for ATC purposes, it may be used not only for surveillance and precision radar approaches, as applicable, but also may be used in conjunction with instrument approach procedures predicated on other types of radio navigational aids. Radar vectors may be authorized to provide course guidance through the segments of an approach to the final course or fix. When operating on an unpublished route or while being radar vectored, the pilot, when an approach clearance is received, shall, in addition to complying with § 91.177, maintain the last altitude assigned to that pilot until the aircraft is established on a segment of a published route or instrument approach procedure unless a different altitude is assigned by ATC. After the aircraft is so established, published altitudes apply to descent within each succeeding route or approach segment unless a different altitude is assigned by ATC. Upon reaching the final approach course or fix, the pilot may either complete the instrument approach in accordance with a procedure approved for the facility or continue a surveillance or precision radar approach to a landing.

(j) *Limitation on procedure turns.* In the case of a radar vector to a final approach course or fix, a timed approach from a holding fix, or an approach for which the procedure specifies "No PT," no pilot may make a procedure turn unless cleared to do so by ATC.

(k) *ILS components.* The basic ground components of an ILS are the localizer, glide slope, outer marker, middle marker, and, when installed for use with Category II or Category III instrument approach procedures, an inner marker. A compass locator or precision radar may be substituted for the outer or middle marker. DME, VOR, or nondirectional beacon fixes authorized in the standard instrument approach procedure or surveillance radar may be substituted for the outer marker. Applicability of, and substitution for, the inner marker for Category II or III approaches is determined by the appropriate part 97 approach procedure, letter of authorization, or operations specification pertinent to the operations.

§ 91.177 Minimum altitudes for IFR operations.

(a) *Operation of aircraft at minimum altitudes.* Except when necessary for takeoff or landing, no person may operate an aircraft under IFR below—

(1) The applicable minimum altitudes prescribed in parts 95 and 97 of this chapter; or

(2) If no applicable minimum altitude is prescribed in those parts—

(i) In the case of operations over an area designated as a mountainous area in part 95, an altitude of 2,000 feet above the highest obstacle within a horizontal distance of 4 nautical miles from the course to be flown; or

(ii) In any other case, an altitude of 1,000 feet above the highest obstacle within a horizontal distance of 4 nautical miles from the course to be flown.

However, if both a MEA and a MOCA are prescribed for a particular route or route segment, a person may operate an aircraft below the MEA down to, but not below, the MOCA, when within 22 nautical miles of the VOR concerned (based on the pilot's reasonable estimate of that distance).

(b) *Climb.* Climb to a higher minimum IFR altitude shall begin immediately after passing the point beyond which that minimum altitude applies, except that when ground obstructions intervene, the point beyond which that higher minimum altitude applies shall be crossed at or above the applicable MCA.

§ 91.179 IFR cruising altitude or flight level.

(a) *In controlled airspace.* Each person operating an aircraft under IFR in level cruising flight in controlled airspace shall maintain the altitude or flight level assigned that aircraft by ATC. However, if the ATC clearance assigns "VFR conditions on-top," that person shall maintain an altitude or flight level as prescribed by § 91.159.

(b) *In uncontrolled airspace.* Except while in a holding pattern of 2 minutes or less or while turning, each person operating an aircraft under IFR in level cruising flight in uncontrolled airspace shall maintain an appropriate altitude as follows:

(1) When operating below 18,000 feet MSL and—

(i) On a magnetic course of zero degrees through 179 degrees, any odd thousand foot MSL altitude (such as 3,000, 5,000, or 7,000); or

(ii) On a magnetic course of 180 degrees through 359 degrees, any even thousand foot MSL altitude (such as 2,000, 4,000, or 6,000).

(2) When operating at or above 18,000 feet MSL but below flight level 290, and—

(i) On a magnetic course of zero degrees through 179 degrees, any odd flight level (such as 190, 210, or 230); or

(ii) On a magnetic course of 180 degrees through 359 degrees, any even flight level (such as 180, 200, or 220).

(3) When operating at flight level 290 and above, and—

(i) On a magnetic course of zero degrees through 179 degrees, any flight level, at 4,000-foot intervals, beginning at and including flight level 290 (such as flight level 290, 330, or 370); or

(ii) On a magnetic course of 180 degrees through 359 degrees, any flight level, at 4,000-foot intervals, beginning at and including flight level 310 (such as flight level 310, 350, or 390).

§ 91.181 Course to be flown.

Unless otherwise authorized by ATC, no person may operate an aircraft within controlled airspace under IFR except as follows:

(a) On a Federal airway, along the centerline of that airway.

(b) On any other route, along the direct course between the navigational aids or fixes defining that route. However, this section does not prohibit maneuvering the aircraft to pass well clear of other air traffic or the maneuvering of the aircraft in VFR conditions to clear the intended flight path both before and during climb or descent.

§ 91.183 IFR radio communications.

The pilot in command of each aircraft operated under IFR in controlled airspace shall have a continuous watch maintained on the appropriate frequency and shall report by radio as soon as possible—

(a) The time and altitude of passing each designated reporting point, or the reporting points specified by ATC, except that while the aircraft is under radar control, only the passing of those reporting points specifically requested by ATC need be reported;

(b) Any unforecast weather conditions encountered; and

(c) Any other information relating to the safety of flight.

§ 91.185 IFR operations: Two-way radio communications failure.

(a) *General.* Unless otherwise authorized by ATC, each pilot who has two-way radio communications failure when operating under IFR shall comply with the rules of this section.

(b) *VFR conditions.* If the failure occurs in VFR conditions, or if VFR conditions are encountered after the failure, each pilot shall continue the flight under VFR and land as soon as practicable.

(c) *IFR conditions.* If the failure occurs in IFR conditions, or if paragraph (b) of this section cannot be complied with, each pilot shall continue the flight according to the following:

(1) *Route.*

(i) By the route assigned in the last ATC clearance received;

(ii) If being radar vectored, by the direct route from the point of radio failure to the fix, route, or airway specified in the vector clearance;

(iii) In the absence of an assigned route, by the route that ATC has advised may be expected in a further clearance; or

(iv) In the absence of an assigned route or a route that ATC has advised may be expected in a further clearance, by the route filed in the flight plan.

(2) *Altitude.* At the highest of the following altitudes or flight levels for the route segment being flown:

(i) The altitude or flight level assigned in the last ATC clearance received;

(ii) The minimum altitude (converted, if appropriate, to minimum flight level as prescribed in § 91.121(c)) for IFR operations; or

(iii) The altitude or flight level ATC has advised may be expected in a further clearance.

(3) *Leave clearance limit.*

(i) When the clearance limit is a fix from which an approach begins, commence descent or descent and approach as close as possible to the expect-further-clearance time if one has been received, or if one has not been received, as close as possible to the estimated time of arrival as calculated from the filed or amended (with ATC) estimated time en route.

(ii) If the clearance limit is not a fix from which an approach begins, leave the clearance limit at the expect-further-clearance time if one has been received, or if none has been received, upon arrival over the clearance limit, and proceed to a fix from which an approach begins and commence descent or descent and approach as close as possible to the estimated time of arrival as calculated from the filed or amended (with ATC) estimated time en route.

[Docket No. 18334, 54 FR 34294, Aug. 18, 1989; as amended by Amdt. 91–211, 54 FR 41211, Oct. 5, 1989]

§ 91.187 Operation under IFR in controlled airspace: Malfunction reports.

(a) The pilot in command of each aircraft operated in controlled airspace under IFR shall report as soon as practical to ATC any malfunctions of navigational, approach, or communication equipment occurring in flight.

(b) In each report required by paragraph (a) of this section, the pilot in command shall include the—

(1) Aircraft identification;

(2) Equipment affected;

(3) Degree to which the capability of the pilot to operate under IFR in the ATC system is impaired; and

(4) Nature and extent of assistance desired from ATC.

§ 91.189 Category II and III operations: General operating rules.

(a) No person may operate a civil aircraft in a Category II or III operation unless—

(1) The flight crew of the aircraft consists of a pilot in command and a second in command who

hold the appropriate authorizations and ratings prescribed in § 61.3 of this chapter;

(2) Each flight crewmember has adequate knowledge of, and familiarity with, the aircraft and the procedures to be used; and

(3) The instrument panel in front of the pilot who is controlling the aircraft has appropriate instrumentation for the type of flight control guidance system that is being used.

(b) Unless otherwise authorized by the Administrator, no person may operate a civil aircraft in a Category II or Category III operation unless each ground component required for that operation and the related airborne equipment is installed and operating.

(c) *Authorized DH.* For the purpose of this section, when the approach procedure being used provides for and requires the use of a DH, the authorized DH is the highest of the following:

(1) The DH prescribed by the approach procedure.

(2) The DH prescribed for the pilot in command.

(3) The DH for which the aircraft is equipped.

(d) Unless otherwise authorized by the Administrator, no pilot operating an aircraft in a Category II or Category III approach that provides and requires use of a DH may continue the approach below the authorized decision height unless the following conditions are met:

(1) The aircraft is in a position from which a descent to a landing on the intended runway can be made at a normal rate of descent using normal maneuvers, and where that descent rate will allow touchdown to occur within the touchdown zone of the runway of intended landing.

(2) At least one of the following visual references for the intended runway is distinctly visible and identifiable to the pilot:

(i) The approach light system, except that the pilot may not descend below 100 feet above the touchdown zone elevation using the approach lights as a reference unless the red terminating bars or the red side row bars are also distinctly visible and identifiable.

(ii) The threshold.

(iii) The threshold markings.

(iv) The threshold lights.

(v) The touchdown zone or touchdown zone markings.

(vi) The touchdown zone lights.

(e) Unless otherwise authorized by the Administrator, each pilot operating an aircraft shall immediately execute an appropriate missed approach whenever, prior to touchdown, the requirements of paragraph (d) of this section are not met.

(f) No person operating an aircraft using a Category III approach without decision height may land that aircraft except in accordance with the

provisions of the letter of authorization issued by the Administrator.

(g) Paragraphs (a) through (f) of this section do not apply to operations conducted by the holders of certificates issued under part 121, 125, 129, or 135 of this chapter. No person may operate a civil aircraft in a Category II or Category III operation conducted by the holders of certificates issued under part 121, 125, 129, or 135 of this chapter unless the operation is conducted in accordance with that certificate holder's operations specifications.

§ 91.191 Category II and Category III manual.

(a) Except as provided in paragraph (c) of this section, after August 4, 1997, no person may operate a U.S.-registered civil aircraft in a Category II or a Category III operation unless—

(1) There is available in the aircraft a current and approved Category II or Category III manual, as appropriate, for that aircraft;

(2) The operation is conducted in accordance with the procedures, instructions, and limitations in the appropriate manual; and

(3) The instruments and equipment listed in the manual that are required for a particular Category II or Category III operation have been inspected and maintained in accordance with the maintenance program contained in the manual.

(b) Each operator must keep a current copy of each approved manual at its principal base of operations and must make each manual available for inspection upon request by the Administrator.

(c) This section does not apply to operations conducted by a holder of a certificate issued under part 121 or part 135 of this chapter.

[Docket No. 18334, 54 FR 34294, Aug. 18, 1989; as amended by Amdt. 91–251, 61 FR 34560, July 2, 1996]

§ 91.193 Certificate of authorization for certain Category II operations.

The Administrator may issue a certificate of authorization authorizing deviations from the requirements of §§ 91.189, 91.191, and 91.205(f) for the operation of small aircraft identified as Category A aircraft in § 97.3 of this chapter in Category II operations if the Administrator finds that the proposed operation can be safely conducted under the terms of the certificate. Such authorization does not permit operation of the aircraft carrying persons or property for compensation or hire.

§ 91.195 – 91.199 [Reserved]

Subpart C—Equipment, Instrument, and Certificate Requirements

Source: Docket No. 18334, 54 FR 34304, Aug. 18, 1989, unless otherwise noted.

§ 91.201 [Reserved]

§ 91.203 Civil aircraft: Certifications required.

(a) Except as provided in § 91.715, no person may operate a civil aircraft unless it has within it the following:

(1) An appropriate and current airworthiness certificate. Each U.S. airworthiness certificate used to comply with this subparagraph (except a special flight permit, a copy of the applicable operations specifications issued under § 21.197(c) of this chapter, appropriate sections of the air carrier manual required by parts 121 and 135 of this chapter containing that portion of the operations specifications issued under § 21.197(c), or an authorization under § 91.611) must have on it the registration number assigned to the aircraft under part 47 of this chapter. However, the airworthiness certificate need not have on it an assigned special identification number before 10 days after that number is first affixed to the aircraft. A revised airworthiness certificate having on it an assigned special identification number, that has been affixed to an aircraft, may only be obtained upon application to an FAA Flight Standards district office.

(2) An effective U.S. registration certificate issued to its owner or, for operation within the United States, the second duplicate copy (pink) of the Aircraft Registration Application as provided for in § 47.31(b), or a registration certificate issued under the laws of a foreign country.

(b) No person may operate a civil aircraft unless the airworthiness certificate required by paragraph (a) of this section or a special flight authorization issued under § 91.715 is displayed at the cabin or cockpit entrance so that it is legible to passengers or crew.

(c) No person may operate an aircraft with a fuel tank installed within the passenger compartment or a baggage compartment unless the installation was accomplished pursuant to part 43 of this chapter, and a copy of FAA Form 337 authorizing that installation is on board the aircraft.

(d) No person may operate a civil airplane (domestic or foreign) into or out of an airport in the United States unless it complies with the fuel venting and exhaust emissions requirements of part 34 of this chapter.

[Docket No. 18334, 54 FR 34292, Aug. 18, 1989; as amended by Amdt. 91–218, 55 FR 32861, Aug. 10, 1990]

§ 91.205 Powered civil aircraft with standard category U.S. airworthiness certificates: Instrument and equipment requirements.

(a) *General.* Except as provided in paragraphs (c)(3) and (e) of this section, no person may operate a powered civil aircraft with a standard category U.S. airworthiness certificate in any operation described in paragraphs (b) through (f) of this section unless that aircraft contains the instruments and equipment specified in those paragraphs (or FAA-approved equivalents) for that type of operation, and those instruments and items of equipment are in operable condition.

(b) *Visual-flight rules (day).* For VFR flight during the day, the following instruments and equipment are required:

(1) Airspeed indicator.

(2) Altimeter.

(3) Magnetic direction indicator.

(4) Tachometer for each engine.

(5) Oil pressure gauge for each engine using pressure system.

(6) Temperature gauge for each liquid-cooled engine.

(7) Oil temperature gauge for each air-cooled engine.

(8) Manifold pressure gauge for each altitude engine.

(9) Fuel gauge indicating the quantity of fuel in each tank.

(10) Landing gear position indicator, if the aircraft has a retractable landing gear.

(11) For small civil airplanes certificated after March 11, 1996, in accordance with part 23 of this chapter, an approved aviation red or aviation white anticollision light system. In the event of failure of any light of the anticollision light system, operation of the aircraft may continue to a location where repairs or replacement can be made.

(12) If the aircraft is operated for hire over water and beyond power-off gliding distance from shore, approved flotation gear readily available to each occupant and at least one pyrotechnic signaling device. As used in this section, "shore" means that area of the land adjacent to the water which is above the high water mark and excludes land areas which are intermittently under water.

(13) An approved safety belt with an approved metal-to-metal latching device for each occupant 2 years of age or older.

(14) For small civil airplanes manufactured after July 18, 1978, an approved shoulder harness for each front seat. The shoulder harness must be designed to protect the occupant from serious

head injury when the occupant experiences the ultimate inertia forces specified in § 23.561(b)(2) of this chapter. Each shoulder harness installed at a flight crewmember station must permit the crewmember, when seated and with the safety belt and shoulder harness fastened, to perform all functions necessary for flight operations. For purposes of this paragraph—

(i) The date of manufacture of an airplane is the date the inspection acceptance records reflect that the airplane is complete and meets the FAA-approved type design data; and

(ii) A front seat is a seat located at a flight crewmember station or any seat located alongside such a seat.

(15) An emergency locator transmitter, if required by § 91.207.

(16) For normal, utility, and acrobatic category airplanes with a seating configuration, excluding pilot seats, of 9 or less, manufactured after December 12, 1986, a shoulder harness for—

(i) Each front seat that meets the requirements of § 23.785 (g) and (h) of this chapter in effect on December 12, 1985;

(ii) Each additional seat that meets the requirements of § 23.785(g) of this chapter in effect on December 12, 1985.

(17) For rotorcraft manufactured after September 16, 1992, a shoulder harness for each seat that meets the requirements of § 27.2 or § 29.2 of this chapter in effect on September 16, 1991.

(c) *Visual flight rules (night).* For VFR flight at night, the following instruments and equipment are required:

(1) Instruments and equipment specified in paragraph (b) of this section.

(2) Approved position lights.

(3) An approved aviation red or aviation white anticollision light system on all U.S.-registered civil aircraft. Anticollision light systems initially installed after August 11, 1971, on aircraft for which a type certificate was issued or applied for before August 11, 1971, must at least meet the anticollision light standards of part 23, 25, 27, or 29 of this chapter, as applicable, that were in effect on August 10, 1971, except that the color may be either aviation red or aviation white. In the event of failure of any light of the anticollision light system, operations with the aircraft may be continued to a stop where repairs or replacement can be made.

(4) If the aircraft is operated for hire, one electric landing light.

(5) An adequate source of electrical energy for all installed electrical and radio equipment.

(6) One spare set of fuses, or three spare fuses of each kind required, that are accessible to the pilot in flight.

(d) *Instrument flight rules.* For IFR flight, the following instruments and equipment are required:

(1) Instruments and equipment specified in paragraph (b) of this section, and, for night flight, instruments and equipment specified in paragraph (c) of this section.

(2) Two-way radio communications system and navigational equipment appropriate to the ground facilities to be used.

(3) Gyroscopic rate-of-turn indicator, except on the following aircraft:

(i) Airplanes with a third attitude instrument system usable through flight attitudes of 360 degrees of pitch and roll and installed in accordance with the instrument requirements prescribed in § 121.305(j) of this chapter; and

(ii) Rotorcraft with a third attitude instrument system usable through flight attitudes of ±80 degrees of pitch and ±120 degrees of roll and installed in accordance with § 29.1303(g) of this chapter.

(4) Slip-skid indicator.

(5) Sensitive altimeter adjustable for barometric pressure.

(6) A clock displaying hours, minutes, and seconds with a sweep-second pointer or digital presentation.

(7) Generator or alternator of adequate capacity.

(8) Gyroscopic pitch and bank indicator (artificial horizon).

(9) Gyroscopic direction indicator (directional gyro or equivalent).

(e) *Flight at and above 24,000 ft. MSL (FL 240).* If VOR navigational equipment is required under paragraph (d)(2) of this section, no person may operate a U.S.-registered civil aircraft within the 50 states and the District of Columbia at or above FL 240 unless that aircraft is equipped with approved distance measuring equipment (DME). When DME required by this paragraph fails at and above FL 240, the pilot in command of the aircraft shall notify ATC immediately, and then may continue operations at and above FL 240 to the next airport of intended landing at which repairs or replacement of the equipment can be made.

(f) *Category II operations.* The requirements for Category II operations are the instruments and equipment specified in—

(1) Paragraph (d) of this section; and

(2) Appendix A to this part.

(g) *Category III operations.* The instruments and equipment required for Category III operations are specified in paragraph (d) of this section.

(h) *Exclusions.* Paragraphs (f) and (g) of this section do not apply to operations conducted by a holder of a certificate issued under part 121 or part 135 of this chapter.

[Docket No. 18334, 54 FR 34292, Aug. 18, 1989; as amended by Amdt. 91–220, 55 FR 43310, Oct. 26, 1990; Amdt. 91–223, 56 FR 41052, Aug. 16, 1991; Amdt. 91–231, 57 FR 42672, Sept. 15, 1992; Amdt. 91–247, 61 FR 5171, Feb. 9, 1996; Amdt. 91–251, 61 FR 34560, July 2, 1996]

§ 91.207 Emergency locator transmitters.

(a) Except as provided in paragraphs (e) and (f) of this section, no person may operate a U.S. registered civil airplane unless—

(1) There is attached to the airplane an approved automatic type emergency locator transmitter that is in operable condition for the following operations, except that after June 21, 1995, an emergency locator transmitter that meets the requirements of TSO-C91 may not be used for new installations:

(i) Those operations governed by the supplemental air carrier and commercial operator rules of parts 121 and 125;

(ii) Charter flights governed by the domestic and flag air carrier rules of part 121 of this chapter; and

(iii) Operations governed by part 135 of this chapter; or

(2) For operations other than those specified in paragraph (a)(1) of this section, there must be attached to the airplane an approved personal type or an approved automatic type emergency locator transmitter that is in operable condition, except that after June 21, 1995, an emergency locator transmitter that meets the requirements of TSO-C91 may not be used for new installations.

(b) Each emergency locator transmitter required by paragraph (a) of this section must be attached to the airplane in such a manner that the probability of damage to the transmitter in the event of crash impact is minimized. Fixed and deployable automatic type transmitters must be attached to the airplane as far aft as practicable.

(c) Batteries used in the emergency locator transmitters required by paragraphs (a) and (b) of this section must be replaced (or recharged, if the batteries are rechargeable)—

(1) When the transmitter has been in use for more than 1 cumulative hour; or

(2) When 50 percent of their useful life (or, for rechargeable batteries, 50 percent of their useful life of charge) has expired, as established by the transmitter manufacturer under its approval. The new expiration date for replacing (or recharging) the battery must be legibly marked on the outside of the transmitter and entered in the aircraft maintenance record. Paragraph (c)(2) of this section does not apply to batteries (such as water-acti-

vated batteries) that are essentially unaffected during probable storage intervals.

(d) Each emergency locator transmitter required by paragraph (a) of this section must be inspected within 12 calendar months after the last inspection for—

(1) Proper installation;

(2) Battery corrosion;

(3) Operation of the controls and crash sensor; and

(4) The presence of a sufficient signal radiated from its antenna.

(e) Notwithstanding paragraph (a) of this section, a person may—

(1) Ferry a newly acquired airplane from the place where possession of it was taken to a place where the emergency locator transmitter is to be installed; and

(2) Ferry an airplane with an inoperative emergency locator transmitter from a place where repairs or replacements cannot be made to a place where they can be made.

No person other than required crewmembers may be carried aboard an airplane being ferried under paragraph (e) of this section.

(f) Paragraph (a) of this section does not apply to—

(1) Turbojet-powered aircraft;

(2) Aircraft while engaged in scheduled flights by scheduled air carriers;

(3) Aircraft while engaged in training operations conducted entirely within a 50-nautical mile radius of the airport from which such local flight operations began;

(4) Aircraft while engaged in flight operations incident to design and testing;

(5) New aircraft while engaged in flight operations incident to their manufacture, preparation, and delivery;

(6) Aircraft while engaged in flight operations incident to the aerial application of chemicals and other substances for agricultural purposes;

(7) Aircraft certificated by the Administrator for research and development purposes;

(8) Aircraft while used for showing compliance with regulations, crew training, exhibition, air racing, or market surveys;

(9) Aircraft equipped to carry not more than one person; and

(10) An aircraft during any period for which the transmitter has been temporarily removed for inspection, repair, modification, or replacement, subject to the following:

(i) No person may operate the aircraft unless the aircraft records contain an entry which includes the date of initial removal, the make, model, serial number, and reason for removing the transmitter, and a placard located in view of the pilot to show "ELT not installed."

(ii) No person may operate the aircraft more than 90 days after the ELT is initially removed from the aircraft.

[Docket No. 18334, 54 FR 34304, Aug. 18, 1989; as amended by Amdt. 91–242, 59 FR 32057, June 21, 1994; Amdt. 91–242, 59 FR 34578, July 6, 1994]

§ 91.209 Aircraft lights.

No person may:

(a) During the period from sunset to sunrise (or, in Alaska, during the period a prominent unlighted object cannot be seen from a distance of 3 statute miles or the sun is more than 6 degrees below the horizon)—

(1) Operate an aircraft unless it has lighted position lights;

(2) Park or move an aircraft in, or in dangerous proximity to, a night flight operations area of an airport unless the aircraft—

(i) Is clearly illuminated;

(ii) Has lighted position lights; or

(iii) is in an area that is marked by obstruction lights;

(3) Anchor an aircraft unless the aircraft—

(i) Has lighted anchor lights; or

(ii) Is in an area where anchor lights are not required on vessels; or

(b) Operate an aircraft that is equipped with an anticollision light system, unless it has lighted anticollision lights. However, the anticollision lights need not be lighted when the pilot-in-command determines that, because of operating conditions, it would be in the interest of safety to turn the lights off.

[Docket No. 27806, 61 FR 5171, Feb. 9, 1996]

§ 91.211 Supplemental oxygen.

(a) *General.* No person may operate a civil aircraft of U.S. registry—

(1) At cabin pressure altitudes above 12,500 feet (MSL) up to and including 14,000 feet (MSL) unless the required minimum flight crew is provided with and uses supplemental oxygen for that part of the flight at those altitudes that is of more than 30 minutes duration;

(2) At cabin pressure altitudes above 14,000 feet (MSL) unless the required minimum flight crew is provided with and uses supplemental oxygen during the entire flight time at those altitudes; and

(3) At cabin pressure altitudes above 15,000 feet (MSL) unless each occupant of the aircraft is provided with supplemental oxygen.

(b) *Pressurized cabin aircraft.*

(1) No person may operate a civil aircraft of U.S. registry with a pressurized cabin—

(i) At flight altitudes above flight level 250 unless at least a 10-minute supply of supplemental oxygen, in addition to any oxygen required to satisfy paragraph (a) of this section, is available for each occupant of the aircraft for use in the event that a descent is necessitated by loss of cabin pressurization; and

(ii) At flight altitudes above flight level 350 unless one pilot at the controls of the airplane is wearing and using an oxygen mask that is secured and sealed and that either supplies oxygen at all times or automatically supplies oxygen whenever the cabin pressure altitude of the airplane exceeds 14,000 feet (MSL), except that the one pilot need not wear and use an oxygen mask while at or below flight level 410 if there are two pilots at the controls and each pilot has a quick-donning type of oxygen mask that can be placed on the face with one hand from the ready position within 5 seconds, supplying oxygen and properly secured and sealed.

(2) Notwithstanding paragraph (b)(1)(ii) of this section, if for any reason at any time it is necessary for one pilot to leave the controls of the aircraft when operating at flight altitudes above flight level 350, the remaining pilot at the controls shall put on and use an oxygen mask until the other pilot has returned to that crewmember's station.

§ 91.213 Inoperative instruments and equipment.

(a) Except as provided in paragraph (d) of this section, no person may take off an aircraft with inoperative instruments or equipment installed unless the following conditions are met:

(1) An approved Minimum Equipment List exists for that aircraft.

(2) The aircraft has within it a letter of authorization, issued by the FAA Flight Standards district office having jurisdiction over the area in which the operator is located, authorizing operation of the aircraft under the Minimum Equipment List. The letter of authorization may be obtained by written request of the airworthiness certificate holder. The Minimum Equipment List and the letter of authorization constitute a supplemental type certificate for the aircraft.

(3) The approved Minimum Equipment List must—

(i) Be prepared in accordance with the limitations specified in paragraph (b) of this section; and

(ii) Provide for the operation of the aircraft with the instruments and equipment in an inoperable condition.

(4) The aircraft records available to the pilot must include an entry describing the inoperable instruments and equipment.

(5) The aircraft is operated under all applicable conditions and limitations contained in the Minimum Equipment List and the letter authorizing the use of the list.

(b) The following instruments and equipment may not be included in a Minimum Equipment List:

(1) Instruments and equipment that are either specifically or otherwise required by the airworthiness requirements under which the aircraft is type certificated and which are essential for safe operations under all operating conditions.

(2) Instruments and equipment required by an airworthiness directive to be in operable condition unless the airworthiness directive provides otherwise.

(3) Instruments and equipment required for specific operations by this part.

(c) A person authorized to use an approved Minimum Equipment List issued for a specific aircraft under part 121, 125, or 135 of this chapter shall use that Minimum Equipment List in connection with operations conducted with that aircraft under this part without additional approval requirements.

(d) Except for operations conducted in accordance with paragraph (a) or (c) of this section, a person may takeoff an aircraft in operations conducted under this part with inoperative instruments and equipment without an approved Minimum Equipment List provided—

(1) The flight operation is conducted in a—

(i) Rotorcraft, nonturbine-powered airplane, glider, or lighter-than-air aircraft for which a master Minimum Equipment List has not been developed; or

(ii) Small rotorcraft, nonturbine-powered small airplane, glider, or lighter-than-air aircraft for which a Master Minimum Equipment List has been developed; and

(2) The inoperative instruments and equipment are not—

(i) Part of the VFR-day type certification instruments and equipment prescribed in the applicable airworthiness regulations under which the aircraft was type certificated;

(ii) Indicated as required on the aircraft's equipment list, or on the Kinds of Operations Equipment List for the kind of flight operation being conducted;

(iii) Required by §91.205 or any other rule of this part for the specific kind of flight operation being conducted; or

(iv) Required to be operational by an airworthiness directive; and

(3) The inoperative instruments and equipment are—

(i) Removed from the aircraft, the cockpit control placarded, and the maintenance recorded in accordance with §43.9 of this chapter; or

(ii) Deactivated and placarded "Inoperative." If deactivation of the inoperative instrument or equipment involves maintenance, it must be ac-

complished and recorded in accordance with part 43 of this chapter; and

(4) A determination is made by a pilot, who is certificated and appropriately rated under part 61 of this chapter, or by a person, who is certificated and appropriately rated to perform maintenance on the aircraft, that the inoperative instrument or equipment does not constitute a hazard to the aircraft.

An aircraft with inoperative instruments or equipment as provided in paragraph (d) of this section is considered to be in a properly altered condition acceptable to the Administrator.

(e) Notwithstanding any other provision of this section, an aircraft with inoperable instruments or equipment may be operated under a special flight permit issued in accordance with §§21.197 and 21.199 of this chapter.

§91.215 ATC transponder and altitude reporting equipment and use.

(a) *All airspace: U.S.-registered civil aircraft.* For operations not conducted under part 121, 127 or 135 of this chapter, ATC transponder equipment installed must meet the performance and environmental requirements of any class of TSO-C74b (Mode A) or any class of TSO-C74c (Mode A with altitude reporting capability) as appropriate, or the appropriate class of TSO-C112 (Mode S).

(b) *All airspace.* Unless otherwise authorized or directed by ATC, no person may operate an aircraft in the airspace described in paragraphs (b)(1) through (b)(5) of this section, unless that aircraft is equipped with an operable coded radar beacon transponder having either Mode 3/A 4096 code capability, replying to Mode 3/A interrogations with the code specified by ATC, or a Mode S capability, replying to Mode 3/A interrogations with the code specified by ATC and intermode and Mode S interrogations in accordance with the applicable provisions specified in TSO-C112, and that aircraft is equipped with automatic pressure altitude reporting equipment having a Mode C capability that automatically replies to Mode C interrogations by transmitting pressure altitude information in 100-foot increments. This requirement applies—

(1) *All aircraft.* In Class A, Class B, and Class C airspace areas;

(2) *All aircraft.* In all airspace within 30 nautical miles of an airport listed in Appendix D, section 1 of this part from the surface upward to 10,000 feet MSL;

(3) Notwithstanding paragraph (b)(2) of this section, any aircraft which was not originally certificated with an engine-driven electrical system or which has not subsequently been certified with such a system installed, balloon or glider may

conduct operations in the airspace within 30 nautical miles of an airport listed in Appendix D, section 1 of this part provided such operations are conducted—

(i) Outside any Class A, Class B, or Class C airspace area; and

(ii) Below the altitude of the ceiling of a Class B or Class C airspace area designated for an airport or 10,000 feet MSL, whichever is lower; and

(4) All aircraft in all airspace above the ceiling and within the lateral boundaries of a Class B or Class C airspace area designated for an airport upward to 10,000 feet MSL; and

(5) All aircraft except any aircraft which was not originally certificated with an engine-driven electrical system or which has not subsequently been certified with such a system installed, balloon, or glider—

(i) In all airspace of the 48 contiguous states and the District of Columbia at and above 10,000 feet MSL, excluding the airspace at and below 2,500 feet above the surface; and

(ii) In the airspace from the surface to 10,000 feet MSL within a 10-nautical-mile radius of any airport listed in Appendix D, section 2 of this part, excluding the airspace below 1,200 feet outside of the lateral boundaries of the surface area of the airspace designated for that airport.

(c) *Transponder-on operation.* While in the airspace as specified in paragraph (b) of this section or in all controlled airspace, each person operating an aircraft equipped with an operable ATC transponder maintained in accordance with § 91.413 of this part shall operate the transponder, including Mode C equipment if installed, and shall reply on the appropriate code or as assigned by ATC.

(d) *ATC authorized deviations.* Requests for ATC authorized deviations must be made to the ATC facility having jurisdiction over the concerned airspace within the time periods specified as follows:

(1) For operation of an aircraft with an operating transponder but without operating automatic pressure altitude reporting equipment having a Mode C capability, the request may be made at any time.

(2) For operation of an aircraft with an inoperative transponder to the airport of ultimate destination, including any intermediate stops, or to proceed to a place where suitable repairs can be made or both, the request may be made at any time.

(3) For operation of an aircraft that is not equipped with a transponder, the request must be made at least one hour before the proposed operation.

(Approved by the Office of Management and Budget under control number 2120–0005)

[Docket No. 18334, 54 FR 34304, Aug. 18, 1989; as amended by Amdt. 91–221, 56 FR 469, Jan. 4, 1991; Amdt. 91–227, 56 FR 65660, Dec. 17, 1991; Amdt. 91–227, 7 FR 328, Jan. 3, 1992; Amdt. 91–229, 57 FR 34618, Aug. 5, 1992]

§ 91.217 Data correspondence between automatically reported pressure altitude data and the pilot's altitude reference.

No person may operate any automatic pressure altitude reporting equipment associated with a radar beacon transponder—

(a) When deactivation of that equipment is directed by ATC;

(b) Unless, as installed, that equipment was tested and calibrated to transmit altitude data corresponding within 125 feet (on a 95 percent probability basis) of the indicated or calibrated datum of the altimeter normally used to maintain flight altitude, with that altimeter referenced to 29.92 inches of mercury for altitudes from sea level to the maximum operating altitude of the aircraft; or

(c) Unless the altimeters and digitizers in that equipment meet the standards of TSO-C10b and TSO-C88, respectively.

§ 91.219 Altitude alerting system or device: Turbojet-powered civil airplanes.

(a) Except as provided in paragraph (d) of this section, no person may operate a turbojet-powered U.S.-registered civil airplane unless that airplane is equipped with an approved altitude alerting system or device that is in operable condition and meets the requirements of paragraph (b) of this section.

(b) Each altitude alerting system or device required by paragraph (a) of this section must be able to—

(1) Alert the pilot—

(i) Upon approaching a preselected altitude in either ascent or descent, by a sequence of both aural and visual signals in sufficient time to establish level flight at that preselected altitude; or

(ii) Upon approaching a preselected altitude in either ascent or descent, by a sequence of visual signals in sufficient time to establish level flight at that preselected altitude, and when deviating above and below that preselected altitude, by an aural signal;

(2) Provide the required signals from sea level to the highest operating altitude approved for the airplane in which it is installed;

(3) Preselect altitudes in increments that are commensurate with the altitudes at which the aircraft is operated;

(4) Be tested without special equipment to determine proper operation of the alerting signals; and

(5) Accept necessary barometric pressure settings if the system or device operates on barometric pressure. However, for operation below 3,000 feet AGL, the system or device need only provide one signal, either visual or aural, to comply with this paragraph. A radio altimeter may be included to provide the signal if the operator has an approved procedure for its use to determine DH or MDA, as appropriate.

(c) Each operator to which this section applies must establish and assign procedures for the use of the altitude alerting system or device and each flight crewmember must comply with those procedures assigned to him.

(d) Paragraph (a) of this section does not apply to any operation of an airplane that has an experimental certificate or to the operation of any airplane for the following purposes:

(1) Ferrying a newly acquired airplane from the place where possession of it was taken to a place where the altitude alerting system or device is to be installed.

(2) Continuing a flight as originally planned, if the altitude alerting system or device becomes inoperative after the airplane has taken off; however, the flight may not depart from a place where repair or replacement can be made.

(3) Ferrying an airplane with any inoperative altitude alerting system or device from a place where repairs or replacements cannot be made to a place where it can be made.

(4) Conducting an airworthiness flight test of the airplane.

(5) Ferrying an airplane to a place outside the United States for the purpose of registering it in a foreign country.

(6) Conducting a sales demonstration of the operation of the airplane.

(7) Training foreign flight crews in the operation of the airplane before ferrying it to a place outside the United States for the purpose of registering it in a foreign country.

§ 91.221 Traffic alert and collision avoidance system equipment and use.

(a) *All airspace: U.S.-registered civil aircraft.* Any traffic alert and collision avoidance system installed in a U.S.-registered civil aircraft must be approved by the Administrator.

(b) *Traffic alert and collision avoidance system, operation required.* Each person operating an aircraft equipped with an operable traffic alert and collision avoidance system shall have that system on and operating.

§ 91.223 – 91.299 [Reserved]

Subpart D— Special Flight Operations

Source: Docket No. 18334, 54 FR 34308, Aug. 18, 1989, unless otherwise noted.

§ 91.301 [Reserved]

§ 91.303 Aerobatic flight.

No person may operate an aircraft in aerobatic flight—

(a) Over any congested area of a city, town, or settlement;

(b) Over an open air assembly of persons;

(c) Within the lateral boundaries of the surface areas of Class B, Class C, Class D, or Class E airspace designated for an airport;

(d) Within 4 nautical miles of the center line of any Federal airway;

(e) Below an altitude of 1,500 feet above the surface; or

(f) When flight visibility is less than 3 statute miles.

For the purposes of this section, aerobatic flight means an intentional maneuver involving an abrupt change in an aircraft's attitude, an abnormal attitude, or abnormal acceleration, not necessary for normal flight.

[Docket No. 18334, 54 FR 34308, Aug. 18, 1989; as amended by Amdt. 91–227, 56 FR 65661, Dec. 17, 1991]

§ 91.305 Flight test areas.

No person may flight test an aircraft except over open water, or sparsely populated areas, having light air traffic.

§ 91.307 Parachutes and parachuting.

(a) No pilot of a civil aircraft may allow a parachute that is available for emergency use to be carried in that aircraft unless it is an approved type and—

(1) If a chair type (canopy in back), it has been packed by a certificated and appropriately rated parachute rigger within the preceding 120 days; or

(2) If any other type, it has been packed by a certificated and appropriately rated parachute rigger—

(i) Within the preceding 120 days, if its canopy, shrouds, and harness are composed exclusively of nylon, rayon, or other similar synthetic fiber or materials that are substantially resistant to damage from mold, mildew, or other fungi and other rotting agents propagated in a moist environment; or

(ii) Within the preceding 60 days, if any part of the parachute is composed of silk, pongee, or other natural fiber, or materials not specified in paragraph (a)(2)(i) of this section.

(b) Except in an emergency, no pilot in command may allow, and no person may make, a parachute jump from an aircraft within the United States except in accordance with part 105.

(c) Unless each occupant of the aircraft is wearing an approved parachute, no pilot of a civil aircraft carrying any person (other than a crewmember) may execute any intentional maneuver that exceeds—

(1) A bank of 60 degrees relative to the horizon; or

(2) A nose-up or nose-down attitude of 30 degrees relative to the horizon.

(d) Paragraph (c) of this section does not apply to—

(1) Flight tests for pilot certification or rating; or

(2) Spins and other flight maneuvers required by the regulations for any certificate or rating when given by—

(i) A certificated flight instructor; or

(ii) An airline transport pilot instructing in accordance with § 61.67 of this chapter.

(e) For the purposes of this section, *approved parachute* means—

(1) A parachute manufactured under a type certificate or a technical standard order (C-23 series); or

(2) A personnel-carrying military parachute identified by an NAF, AAF, or AN drawing number, an AAF order number, or any other military designation or specification number.

[Docket No. 18334, 54 FR 34308, Aug. 18, 1989; as amended by Amdt. 91–255, 62 FR 68137, Dec. 30, 1997]

§ 91.309 Towing: Gliders.

(a) No person may operate a civil aircraft towing a glider unless—

(1) The pilot in command of the towing aircraft is qualified under § 61.69 of this chapter;

(2) The towing aircraft is equipped with a tow-hitch of a kind, and installed in a manner, that is approved by the Administrator;

(3) The towline used has breaking strength not less than 80 percent of the maximum certificated operating weight of the glider and not more than twice this operating weight. However, the towline used may have a breaking strength more than twice the maximum certificated operating weight of the glider if—

(i) A safety link is installed at the point of attachment of the towline to the glider with a breaking strength not less than 80 percent of the maximum certificated operating weight of the glider and not greater than twice this operating weight.

(ii) A safety link is installed at the point of attachment of the towline to the towing aircraft with a breaking strength greater, but not more than 25 percent greater, than that of the safety link at the towed glider end of the towline and not greater than twice the maximum certificated operating weight of the glider;

(4) Before conducting any towing operation within the lateral boundaries of the surface areas of Class B, Class C, Class D, or Class E airspace designated for an airport, or before making each towing flight within such controlled airspace if required by ATC, the pilot in command notifies the control tower. If a control tower does not exist or is not in operation, the pilot in command must notify the FAA flight service station serving that controlled airspace before conducting any towing operations in that airspace; and

(5) The pilots of the towing aircraft and the glider have agreed upon a general course of action, including takeoff and release signals, airspeeds, and emergency procedures for each pilot.

(b) No pilot of a civil aircraft may intentionally release a towline, after release of a glider, in a manner that endangers the life or property of another.

[Docket No. 18834, 54 FR 34308, Aug. 18, 1989; as amended by Amdt. 91–227, 56 FR 65661, Dec. 17, 1991]

§ 91.311 Towing:
Other than under § 91.309.

No pilot of a civil aircraft may tow anything with that aircraft (other than under § 91.309) except in accordance with the terms of a certificate of waiver issued by the Administrator.

§ 91.313 Restricted category civil aircraft: Operating limitations.

(a) No person may operate a restricted category civil aircraft—

(1) For other than the special purpose for which it is certificated; or

(2) In an operation other than one necessary to accomplish the work activity directly associated with that special purpose.

(b) For the purpose of paragraph (a) of this section, operating a restricted category civil aircraft to provide flight crewmember training in a special purpose operation for which the aircraft is certificated is considered to be an operation for that special purpose.

(c) No person may operate a restricted category civil aircraft carrying persons or property for compensation or hire. For the purposes of this paragraph, a special purpose operation involving the carriage of persons or material necessary to accomplish that operation, such as crop dusting, seeding, spraying, and banner towing (including the carrying of required persons or material to the location of that operation), and operation for the purpose of providing flight crewmember training in a special purpose operation, are not considered to be the carriage of persons or property for compensation or hire.

(d) No person may be carried on a restricted category civil aircraft unless that person—

(1) Is a flight crewmember;

(2) Is a flight crewmember trainee;

(3) Performs an essential function in connection with a special purpose operation for which the aircraft is certificated; or

(4) Is necessary to accomplish the work activity directly associated with that special purpose.

(e) Except when operating in accordance with the terms and conditions of a certificate of waiver or special operating limitations issued by the Administrator, no person may operate a restricted category civil aircraft within the United States—

(1) Over a densely populated area;

(2) In a congested airway; or

(3) Near a busy airport where passenger transport operations are conducted.

(f) This section does not apply to nonpassenger-carrying civil rotorcraft external-load operations conducted under part 133 of this chapter.

(g) No person may operate a small restricted-category civil airplane manufactured after July 18, 1978, unless an approved shoulder harness is installed for each front seat. The shoulder harness must be designed to protect each occupant from serious head injury when the occupant experiences the ultimate inertia forces specified in § 23.561(b)(2) of this chapter. The shoulder harness installation at each flight crewmember station must permit the crewmember, when seated and with the safety belt and shoulder harness fastened, to perform all functions necessary for flight operation. For purposes of this paragraph—

(1) The date of manufacture of an airplane is the date the inspection acceptance records reflect that the airplane is complete and meets the FAA-approved type design data; and

(2) A front seat is a seat located at a flight crewmember station or any seat located alongside such a seat.

§ 91.315 Limited category civil aircraft: Operating limitations.

No person may operate a limited category civil aircraft carrying persons or property for compensation or hire.

§ 91.317 Provisionally certificated civil aircraft: Operating limitations.

(a) No person may operate a provisionally certificated civil aircraft unless that person is eligible for a provisional airworthiness certificate under § 21.213 of this chapter.

(b) No person may operate a provisionally certificated civil aircraft outside the United States unless that person has specific authority to do so from the Administrator and each foreign country involved.

(c) Unless otherwise authorized by the Director, Flight Standards Service, no person may operate a provisionally certificated civil aircraft in air transportation.

(d) Unless otherwise authorized by the Administrator, no person may operate a provisionally certificated civil aircraft except—

(1) In direct conjunction with the type or supplemental type certification of that aircraft;

(2) For training flight crews, including simulated air carrier operations;

(3) Demonstration flight by the manufacturer for prospective purchasers;

(4) Market surveys by the manufacturer;

(5) Flight checking of instruments, accessories, and equipment that do not affect the basic airworthiness of the aircraft; or

(6) Service testing of the aircraft.

(e) Each person operating a provisionally certificated civil aircraft shall operate within the prescribed limitations displayed in the aircraft or set forth in the provisional aircraft flight manual or other appropriate document. However, when operating in direct conjunction with the type or supplemental type certification of the aircraft, that person shall operate under the experimental aircraft limitations of § 21.191 of this chapter and when flight testing, shall operate under the requirements of § 91.305 of this part.

(f) Each person operating a provisionally certificated civil aircraft shall establish approved procedures for—

(1) The use and guidance of flight and ground personnel in operating under this section; and

(2) Operating in and out of airports where take-offs or approaches over populated areas are necessary. No person may operate that aircraft except in compliance with the approved procedures.

(g) Each person operating a provisionally certificated civil aircraft shall ensure that each flight crewmember is properly certificated and has adequate knowledge of, and familiarity with, the aircraft and procedures to be used by that crewmember.

(h) Each person operating a provisionally certificated civil aircraft shall maintain it as required by applicable regulations and as may be specially prescribed by the Administrator.

(i) Whenever the manufacturer, or the Administrator, determines that a change in design, construction, or operation is necessary to ensure safe operation, no person may operate a provisionally certificated civil aircraft until that change has been made and approved. Section 21.99 of this chapter applies to operations under this section.

(j) Each person operating a provisionally certificated civil aircraft—

(1) May carry in that aircraft only persons who have a proper interest in the operations allowed by this section or who are specifically authorized by both the manufacturer and the Administrator; and

(2) Shall advise each person carried that the aircraft is provisionally certificated.

(k) The Administrator may prescribe additional limitations or procedures that the Administrator considers necessary, including limitations on the number of persons who may be carried in the aircraft.

(Approved by the Office of Management and Budget under control number 2120–0005)

[Docket No. 18334, 54 FR 34308, Aug. 18, 1989; as amended by Amdt. 91–212, 54 FR 39293, Sept. 25, 1989]

§ 91.319 Aircraft having experimental certificates: Operating limitations.

(a) No person may operate an aircraft that has an experimental certificate—

(1) For other than the purpose for which the certificate was issued; or

(2) Carrying persons or property for compensation or hire.

(b) No person may operate an aircraft that has an experimental certificate outside of an area assigned by the Administrator until it is shown that—

(1) The aircraft is controllable throughout its normal range of speeds and throughout all the maneuvers to be executed; and

(2) The aircraft has no hazardous operating characteristics or design features.

(c) Unless otherwise authorized by the Administrator in special operating limitations, no person may operate an aircraft that has an experimental certificate over a densely populated area or in a congested airway. The Administrator may issue special operating limitations for particular aircraft to permit takeoffs and landings to be conducted over a densely populated area or in a congested airway, in accordance with terms and conditions specified in the authorization in the interest of safety in air commerce.

(d) Each person operating an aircraft that has an experimental certificate shall—

(1) Advise each person carried of the experimental nature of the aircraft;

(2) Operate under VFR, day only, unless otherwise specifically authorized by the Administrator; and

(3) Notify the control tower of the experimental nature of the aircraft when operating the aircraft into or out of airports with operating control towers.

(e) The Administrator may prescribe additional limitations that the Administrator considers necessary, including limitations on the persons that may be carried in the aircraft.

(Approved by the Office of Management and Budget under control number 2120–0005)

§ 91.321 Carriage of candidates in Federal elections.

(a) An aircraft operator, other than one operating an aircraft under the rules of part 121, 125, or 135 of this chapter, may receive payment for the carriage of a candidate in a Federal election, an agent of the candidate, or a person traveling on behalf of the candidate, if—

(1) That operator's primary business is not as an air carrier or commercial operator;

(2) The carriage is conducted under the rules of this part 91; and

(3) The payment for the carriage is required, and does not exceed the amount required to be paid, by regulations of the Federal Election Commission (11 CFR *et seq.*).

(b) For the purposes of this section, the terms *candidate* and *election* have the same meaning as that set forth in the regulations of the Federal Election Commission.

§ 91.323 Increased maximum certificated weights for certain airplanes operated in Alaska.

(a) Notwithstanding any other provision of the Federal Aviation Regulations, the Administrator will approve, as provided in this section, an increase in the maximum certificated weight of an airplane type certificated under Aeronautics Bulletin No. 7–A of the U.S. Department of Commerce dated January 1, 1931, as amended, or under the normal category of part 4a of the former Civil Air Regulations (14 CFR part 4a, 1964 ed.) if that airplane is operated in the State of Alaska by—

(1) A certificate holder conducting operations under part 121 or part 135 of this chapter; or

(2) The U.S. Department of Interior in conducting its game and fish law enforcement activities or its management, fire detection, and fire suppression activities concerning public lands.

(b) The maximum certificated weight approved under this section may not exceed—

(1) 12,500 pounds;

(2) 115 percent of the maximum weight listed in the FAA aircraft specifications;

(3) The weight at which the airplane meets the positive maneuvering load factor requirement for the normal category specified in § 23.337 of this chapter; or

(4) The weight at which the airplane meets the climb performance requirements under which it was type certificated.

(c) In determining the maximum certificated weight, the Administrator considers the structural soundness of the airplane and the terrain to be traversed.

(d) The maximum certificated weight determined under this section is added to the airplane's operation limitations and is identified as the maximum weight authorized for operations within the State of Alaska.

[Docket No. 18334, 54 FR 34308, Aug. 18, 1989; as amended by Amdt. 91–211, 54 FR 41211, Oct. 5, 1989; Amdt. 91–253, 62 FR 13253, March 19, 1997]

§ 91.325 Primary category aircraft: Operating limitations.

(a) No person may operate a primary category aircraft carrying passengers or property for compensation or hire.

(b) No person may operate a primary category aircraft that is maintained by the pilot-owner under an approved special inspection and maintenance program except—

(1) The pilot-owner; or

(2) A designee of the pilot-owner, provided that the pilot-owner does not receive compensation for the use of the aircraft.

[Docket No. 23345, 57 FR 41370, Sept. 9, 1992]

§ 91.326 – 91.399 [Reserved]

Subpart E— Maintenance, Preventive Maintenance, and Alterations

Source: Docket No. 18334, 54 FR 34311, Aug. 18, 1989, unless otherwise noted.

§ 91.401 Applicability.

(a) This subpart prescribes rules governing the maintenance, preventive maintenance, and alterations of U.S.-registered civil aircraft operating within or outside of the United States.

(b) Sections 91.405, 91.409, 91.411, 91.417, and 91.419 of this subpart do not apply to an aircraft maintained in accordance with a continuous

airworthiness maintenance program as provided in part 121, 127, 129, or § 135.411(a)(2) of this chapter.

(c) Sections 91.405 and 91.409 of this part do not apply to an airplane inspected in accordance with part 125 of this chapter.

§ 91.403 General.

(a) The owner or operator of an aircraft is primarily responsible for maintaining that aircraft in an airworthy condition, including compliance with part 39 of this chapter.

(b) No person may perform maintenance, preventive maintenance, or alterations on an aircraft other than as prescribed in this subpart and other applicable regulations, including part 43 of this chapter.

(c) No person may operate an aircraft for which a manufacturer's maintenance manual or instructions for continued airworthiness has been issued that contains an airworthiness limitations section unless the mandatory replacement times, inspection intervals, and related procedures specified in that section or alternative inspection intervals and related procedures set forth in an operations specification approved by the Administrator under part 121, 127 or 135 of this chapter or in accordance with an inspection program approved under § 91.409(e) have been complied with.

§ 91.405 Maintenance required.

Each owner or operator of an aircraft—

(a) Shall have that aircraft inspected as prescribed in subpart E of this part and shall between required inspections, except as provided in paragraph (c) of this section, have discrepancies repaired as prescribed in part 43 of this chapter;

(b) Shall ensure that maintenance personnel make appropriate entries in the aircraft maintenance records indicating the aircraft has been approved for return to service;

(c) Shall have any inoperative instrument or item of equipment, permitted to be inoperative by § 91.213(d)(2) of this part, repaired, replaced, removed, or inspected at the next required inspection; and

(d) When listed discrepancies include inoperative instruments or equipment, shall ensure that a placard has been installed as required by § 43.11 of this chapter.

§ 91.407 Operation after maintenance, preventive maintenance, rebuilding, or alteration.

(a) No person may operate any aircraft that has undergone maintenance, preventive maintenance, rebuilding, or alteration unless—

(1) It has been approved for return to service by a person authorized under § 43.7 of this chapter; and

(2) The maintenance record entry required by § 43.9 or § 43.11, as applicable, of this chapter has been made.

(b) No person may carry any person (other than crewmembers) in an aircraft that has been maintained, rebuilt, or altered in a manner that may have appreciably changed its flight characteristics or substantially affected its operation in flight until an appropriately rated pilot with at least a private pilot certificate flies the aircraft, makes an operational check of the maintenance performed or alteration made, and logs the flight in the aircraft records.

(c) The aircraft does not have to be flown as required by paragraph (b) of this section if, prior to flight, ground tests, inspection, or both show conclusively that the maintenance, preventive maintenance, rebuilding, or alteration has not appreciably changed the flight characteristics or substantially affected the flight operation of the aircraft.

(Approved by the Office of Management and Budget under control number 2120–0005)

§ 91.409 Inspections.

(a) Except as provided in paragraph (c) of this section, no person may operate an aircraft unless, within the preceding 12 calendar months, it has had—

(1) An annual inspection in accordance with part 43 of this chapter and has been approved for return to service by a person authorized by § 43.7 of this chapter; or

(2) An inspection for the issuance of an airworthiness certificate in accordance with part 21 of this chapter.

No inspection performed under paragraph (b) of this section may be substituted for any inspection required by this paragraph unless it is performed by a person authorized to perform annual inspections and is entered as an "annual" inspection in the required maintenance records.

(b) Except as provided in paragraph (c) of this section, no person may operate an aircraft carrying any person (other than a crewmember) for hire, and no person may give flight instruction for hire in an aircraft which that person provides, unless within the preceding 100 hours of time in service the aircraft has received an annual or 100-hour inspection and been approved for return to service in accordance with part 43 of this chapter or has received an inspection for the issuance of an airworthiness certificate in accordance with part 21 of this chapter. The 100-hour limitation may be exceeded by not more than 10 hours while en route to reach a place where the inspection can be done. The excess time used to reach a place where the inspection can be done must be included in computing the next 100 hours of time in service.

(c) Paragraphs (a) and (b) of this section do not apply to—

(1) An aircraft that carries a special flight permit, a current experimental certificate, or a provisional airworthiness certificate;

(2) An aircraft inspected in accordance with an approved aircraft inspection program under part 125, 127, or 135 of this chapter and so identified by the registration number in the operations specifications of the certificate holder having the approved inspection program;

(3) An aircraft subject to the requirements of paragraph (d) or (e) of this section; or

(4) Turbine-powered rotorcraft when the operator elects to inspect that rotorcraft in accordance with paragraph (e) of this section.

(d) *Progressive inspection.* Each registered owner or operator of an aircraft desiring to use a progressive inspection program must submit a written request to the FAA Flight Standards district office having jurisdiction over the area in which the applicant is located, and shall provide—

(1) A certificated mechanic holding an inspection authorization, a certificated airframe repair station, or the manufacturer of the aircraft to supervise or conduct the progressive inspection;

(2) A current inspection procedures manual available and readily understandable to pilot and maintenance personnel containing, in detail—

(i) An explanation of the progressive inspection, including the continuity of inspection responsibility, the making of reports, and the keeping of records and technical reference material;

(ii) An inspection schedule, specifying the intervals in hours or days when routine and detailed inspections will be performed and including instructions for exceeding an inspection interval by not more than 10 hours while en route and for changing an inspection interval because of service experience;

(iii) Sample routine and detailed inspection forms and instructions for their use; and

(iv) Sample reports and records and instructions for their use;

(3) Enough housing and equipment for necessary disassembly and proper inspection of the aircraft; and

(4) Appropriate current technical information for the aircraft.

The frequency and detail of the progressive inspection shall provide for the complete inspection of the aircraft within each 12 calendar months and be consistent with the manufacturer's recommendations, field service experience, and the kind of operation in which the aircraft is engaged. The progressive inspection schedule must ensure that the aircraft, at all times, will be airworthy and will conform to all applicable FAA aircraft specifications, type certificate data sheets, airworthiness directives, and other approved data. If the progressive inspection is discontinued, the owner or operator shall immediately notify the local FAA Flight Standards district office, in writing, of the discontinuance. After the discontinuance, the first annual inspection under § 91.409(a)(1) is due within 12 calendar months after the last complete inspection of the aircraft under the progressive inspection. The 100-hour inspection under § 91.409(b) is due within 100 hours after that complete inspection. A complete inspection of the aircraft, for the purpose of determining when the annual and 100-hour inspections are due, requires a detailed inspection of the aircraft and all its components in accordance with the progressive inspection. A routine inspection of the aircraft and a detailed inspection of several components is not considered to be a complete inspection.

(e) *Large airplanes (to which part 125 is not applicable), turbojet multiengine airplanes, turbopropeller-powered multiengine airplanes, and turbine-powered rotorcraft.* No person may operate a large airplane, turbojet multiengine airplane, turbopropeller-powered multiengine airplane, or turbine-powered rotorcraft unless the replacement times for life-limited parts specified in the aircraft specifications, type data sheets, or other documents approved by the Administrator are complied with and the airplane or turbine-powered rotorcraft, including the airframe, engines, propellers, rotors, appliances, survival equipment, and emergency equipment, is inspected in accordance with an inspection program selected under the provisions of paragraph (f) of this section, except that, the owner or operator of a turbine-powered rotorcraft may elect to use the inspection provisions of § 91.409(a), (b), (c), or (d) in lieu of an inspection option of § 91.409(f).

(f) *Selection of inspection program under paragraph (e) of this section.* The registered owner or operator of each airplane or turbine-powered rotorcraft described in paragraph (e) of this section must select, identify in the aircraft maintenance records, and use one of the following programs for the inspection of the aircraft:

(1) A continuous airworthiness inspection program that is part of a continuous airworthiness

maintenance program currently in use by a person holding an air carrier operating certificate or an operating certificate issued under part 121, 127, or 135 of this chapter and operating that make and model aircraft under part 121 of this chapter or operating that make and model under part 135 of this chapter and maintaining it under § 135.411(a)(2) of this chapter.

(2) An approved aircraft inspection program approved under § 135.419 of this chapter and currently in use by a person holding an operating certificate issued under part 135 of this chapter.

(3) A current inspection program recommended by the manufacturer.

(4) Any other inspection program established by the registered owner or operator of that airplane or turbine-powered rotorcraft and approved by the Administrator under paragraph (g) of this section. However, the Administrator may require revision of this inspection program in accordance with the provisions of § 91.415.

Each operator shall include in the selected program the name and address of the person responsible for scheduling the inspections required by the program and make a copy of that program available to the person performing inspections on the aircraft and, upon request, to the Administrator.

(g) *Inspection program approved under paragraph (e) of this section.* Each operator of an airplane or turbine-powered rotorcraft desiring to establish or change an approved inspection program under paragraph (f)(4) of this section must submit the program for approval to the local FAA Flight Standards district office having jurisdiction over the area in which the aircraft is based. The program must be in writing and include at least the following information:

(1) Instructions and procedures for the conduct of inspections for the particular make and model airplane or turbine-powered rotorcraft, including necessary tests and checks. The instructions and procedures must set forth in detail the parts and areas of the airframe, engines, propellers, rotors, and appliances, including survival and emergency equipment required to be inspected.

(2) A schedule for performing the inspections that must be performed under the program expressed in terms of the time in service, calendar time, number of system operations, or any combination of these.

(h) *Changes from one inspection program to another.* When an operator changes from one inspection program under paragraph (f) of this section to another, the time in service, calendar times, or cycles of operation accumulated under the previous program must be applied in determining inspection due times under the new program.

91

(Approved by the Office of Management and Budget under control number 2120–0005)

[Docket No. 18334, 54 FR 34311, Aug. 18, 1989; as amended by Amdt. 91–211, 54 FR 41211, Oct. 5, 1989]

§ 91.411 Altimeter system and altitude reporting equipment tests and inspections.

(a) No person may operate an airplane, or helicopter, in controlled airspace under IFR unless—

(1) Within the preceding 24 calendar months, each static pressure system, each altimeter instrument, and each automatic pressure altitude reporting system has been tested and inspected and found to comply with Appendix E of part 43 of this chapter;

(2) Except for the use of system drain and alternate static pressure valves, following any opening and closing of the static pressure system, that system has been tested and inspected and found to comply with paragraph (a), Appendices E and F, of part 43 of this chapter; and

(3) Following installation or maintenance on the automatic pressure altitude reporting system of the ATC transponder where data correspondence error could be introduced, the integrated system has been tested, inspected, and found to comply with paragraph (c), Appendix E, of part 43 of this chapter.

(b) The tests required by paragraph (a) of this section must be conducted by—

(1) The manufacturer of the airplane, or helicopter, on which the tests and inspections are to be performed;

(2) A certificated repair station properly equipped to perform those functions and holding—

(i) An instrument rating, Class I;

(ii) A limited instrument rating appropriate to the make and model of appliance to be tested;

(iii) A limited rating appropriate to the test to be performed;

(iv) An airframe rating appropriate to the airplane, or helicopter, to be tested; or

(v) A limited rating for a manufacturer issued for the appliance in accordance with § 145.101(b)(4) of this chapter; or

(3) A certificated mechanic with an airframe rating (static pressure system tests and inspections only).

(c) Altimeter and altitude reporting equipment approved under Technical Standard Orders are considered to be tested and inspected as of the date of their manufacture.

(d) No person may operate an airplane, or helicopter, in controlled airspace under IFR at an altitude above the maximum altitude at which all altimeters and the automatic altitude reporting system of that airplane, or helicopter, have been tested.

§ 91.413 ATC transponder tests and inspections.

(a) No persons may use an ATC transponder that is specified in § 91.215(a), § 121.345(c), § 127.123(b), or § 135.143(c) of this chapter unless, within the preceding 24 calendar months, the ATC transponder has been tested and inspected and found to comply with Appendix F of part 43 of this chapter; and

(b) Following any installation or maintenance on an ATC transponder where data correspondence error could be introduced, the integrated system has been tested, inspected, and found to comply with paragraph (c), Appendix E, of part 43 of this chapter.

(c) The tests and inspections specified in this section must be conducted by—

(1) A certificated repair station properly equipped to perform those functions and holding—

(i) A radio rating, Class III;

(ii) A limited radio rating appropriate to the make and model transponder to be tested;

(iii) A limited rating appropriate to the test to be performed;

(iv) A limited rating for a manufacturer issued for the transponder in accordance with § 145.101(b)(4) of this chapter; or

(2) A holder of a continuous airworthiness maintenance program as provided in part 121, 127 or § 135.411(a)(2) of this chapter; or

(3) The manufacturer of the aircraft on which the transponder to be tested is installed, if the transponder was installed by that manufacturer.

§ 91.415 Changes to aircraft inspection programs.

(a) Whenever the Administrator finds that revisions to an approved aircraft inspection program under § 91.409(f)(4) are necessary for the continued adequacy of the program, the owner or operator shall, after notification by the Administrator, make any changes in the program found to be necessary by the Administrator.

(b) The owner or operator may petition the Administrator to reconsider the notice to make any changes in a program in accordance with paragraph (a) of this section.

(c) The petition must be filed with the FAA Flight Standards district office which requested the change to the program within 30 days after the certificate holder receives the notice.

(d) Except in the case of an emergency requiring immediate action in the interest of safety, the filing of the petition stays the notice pending a decision by the Administrator.

§ 91.417 Maintenance records.

(a) Except for work performed in accordance with § 91.411 and 91.413, each registered owner or operator shall keep the following records for the periods specified in paragraph (b) of this section:

(1) Records of the maintenance, preventive maintenance, and alteration and records of the 100-hour, annual, progressive, and other required or approved inspections, as appropriate, for each aircraft (including the airframe) and each engine, propeller, rotor, and appliance of an aircraft. The records must include—

(i) A description (or reference to data acceptable to the Administrator) of the work performed; and

(ii) The date of completion of the work performed; and

(iii) The signature, and certificate number of the person approving the aircraft for return to service.

(2) Records containing the following information:

(i) The total time in service of the airframe, each engine, each propeller, and each rotor.

(ii) The current status of life-limited parts of each airframe, engine, propeller, rotor, and appliance.

(iii) The time since last overhaul of all items installed on the aircraft which are required to be overhauled on a specified time basis.

(iv) The current inspection status of the aircraft, including the time since the last inspection required by the inspection program under which the aircraft and its appliances are maintained.

(v) The current status of applicable airworthiness directives (AD) including, for each, the method of compliance, the AD number, and revision date. If the AD involves recurring action, the time and date when the next action is required.

(vi) Copies of the forms prescribed by § 43.9(a) of this chapter for each major alteration to the airframe and currently installed engines, rotors, propellers, and appliances.

(b) The owner or operator shall retain the following records for the periods prescribed:

(1) The records specified in paragraph (a)(1) of this section shall be retained until the work is repeated or superseded by other work or for 1 year after the work is performed.

(2) The records specified in paragraph (a)(2) of this section shall be retained and transferred with the aircraft at the time the aircraft is sold.

(3) A list of defects furnished to a registered owner or operator under § 43.11 of this chapter shall be retained until the defects are repaired and the aircraft is approved for return to service.

(c) The owner or operator shall make all maintenance records required to be kept by this section available for inspection by the Administrator or any authorized representative of the National Transportation Safety Board (NTSB). In addition, the owner or operator shall present Form 337 described in paragraph (d) of this section for inspection upon request of any law enforcement officer.

(d) When a fuel tank is installed within the passenger compartment or a baggage compartment pursuant to part 43 of this chapter, a copy of FAA Form 337 shall be kept on board the modified aircraft by the owner or operator.

(Approved by the Office of Management and Budget under control number 2120–0005)

§ 91.419 Transfer of maintenance records.

Any owner or operator who sells a U.S.-registered aircraft shall transfer to the purchaser, at the time of sale, the following records of that aircraft, in plain language form or in coded form at the election of the purchaser, if the coded form provides for the preservation and retrieval of information in a manner acceptable to the Administrator:

(a) The records specified in § 91.417(a)(2).

(b) The records specified in § 91.417(a)(1) which are not included in the records covered by paragraph (a) of this section, except that the purchaser may permit the seller to keep physical custody of such records. However, custody of records by the seller does not relieve the purchaser of the responsibility under § 91.417(c) to make the records available for inspection by the Administrator or any authorized representative of the National Transportation Safety Board (NTSB).

§ 91.421 Rebuilt engine maintenance records.

(a) The owner or operator may use a new maintenance record, without previous operating history, for an aircraft engine rebuilt by the manufacturer or by an agency approved by the manufacturer.

(b) Each manufacturer or agency that grants zero time to an engine rebuilt by it shall enter in the new record—

(1) A signed statement of the date the engine was rebuilt;

(2) Each change made as required by airworthiness directives; and

(3) Each change made in compliance with manufacturer's service bulletins, if the entry is specifically requested in that bulletin.

(c) For the purposes of this section, a rebuilt engine is a used engine that has been completely disassembled, inspected, repaired as necessary, reassembled, tested, and approved in the same manner and to the same tolerances and limits as a new engine with either new or used parts. However, all parts used in it must conform to the production drawing tolerances and limits for new parts or be of approved oversized or undersized dimensions for a new engine.

§ 91.423 – 91.499 [Reserved]

Subpart F— Large and Turbine-Powered Multiengine Airplanes

Source: Docket No. 18334, 54 FR 34314, Aug. 18, 1989, unless otherwise noted.

§ 91.501 Applicability.

(a) This subpart prescribes operating rules, in addition to those prescribed in other subparts of this part, governing the operation of large and of turbojet-powered multiengine civil airplanes of U.S. registry. The operating rules in this subpart do not apply to those airplanes when they are required to be operated under parts 121, 125, 129, 135, and 137 of this chapter. (Section 91.409 prescribes an inspection program for large and for turbine-powered (turbojet and turboprop) multiengine airplanes of U.S. registry when they are operated under this part or part 129 or 137.)

(b) Operations that may be conducted under the rules in this subpart instead of those in parts 121, 129, 135, and 137 of this chapter when common carriage is not involved, include—

(1) Ferry or training flights;

(2) Aerial work operations such as aerial photography or survey, or pipeline patrol, but not including fire fighting operations;

(3) Flights for the demonstration of an airplane to prospective customers when no charge is made except for those specified in paragraph (d) of this section;

(4) Flights conducted by the operator of an airplane for his personal transportation, or the transportation of his guests when no charge, assessment, or fee is made for the transportation;

(5) Carriage of officials, employees, guests, and property of a company on an airplane operated by that company, or the parent or a subsidiary of the company or a subsidiary of the parent, when the carriage is within the scope of, and incidental to, the business of the company (other than transportation by air) and no charge, assessment or fee is made for the carriage in excess of the cost of owning, operating, and maintaining the airplane, except that no charge of any kind may be made for the carriage of a guest of a company, when the carriage is not within the scope of, and incidental to, the business of that company;

(6) The carriage of company officials, employees, and guests of the company on an airplane operated under a time sharing, interchange, or joint ownership agreement as defined in paragraph (c) of this section;

(7) The carriage of property (other than mail) on an airplane operated by a person in the furtherance of a business or employment (other than transportation by air) when the carriage is within the scope of, and incidental to, that business or employment and no charge, assessment, or fee is made for the carriage other than those specified in paragraph (d) of this section;

(8) The carriage on an airplane of an athletic team, sports group, choral group, or similar group having a common purpose or objective when there is no charge, assessment, or fee of any kind made by any person for that carriage; and

(9) The carriage of persons on an airplane operated by a person in the furtherance of a business other than transportation by air for the purpose of selling them land, goods, or property, including franchises or distributorships, when the carriage is within the scope of, and incidental to, that business and no charge, assessment, or fee is made for that carriage.

(c) As used in this section—

(1) *A time sharing agreement* means an arrangement whereby a person leases his airplane with flight crew to another person, and no charge is made for the flights conducted under that arrangement other than those specified in paragraph (d) of this section;

(2) *An interchange agreement* means an arrangement whereby a person leases his airplane to another person in exchange for equal time, when needed, on the other person's airplane, and no charge, assessment, or fee is made, except that a charge may be made not to exceed the difference between the cost of owning, operating, and maintaining the two airplanes;

(3) *A joint ownership agreement* means an arrangement whereby one of the registered joint owners of an airplane employs and furnishes the flight crew for that airplane and each of the registered joint owners pays a share of the charge specified in the agreement.

(d) The following may be charged, as expenses of a specific flight, for transportation as authorized by paragraphs (b)(3) and (7) and (c)(1) of this section:

(1) Fuel, oil, lubricants, and other additives.

(2) Travel expenses of the crew, including food, lodging, and ground transportation.

(3) Hangar and tie-down costs away from the aircraft's base of operation.

(4) Insurance obtained for the specific flight.

(5) Landing fees, airport taxes, and similar assessments.

　　　　　　　　　　　　　　　　　　　　　　　　ASA 2000

(6) Customs, foreign permit, and similar fees directly related to the flight.

(7) In flight food and beverages.

(8) Passenger ground transportation.

(9) Flight planning and weather contract services.

(10) An additional charge equal to 100 percent of the expenses listed in paragraph (d)(1) of this section.

§91.503 Flying equipment and operating information.

(a) The pilot in command of an airplane shall ensure that the following flying equipment and aeronautical charts and data, in current and appropriate form, are accessible for each flight at the pilot station of the airplane:

(1) A flashlight having at least two size "D" cells, or the equivalent, that is in good working order.

(2) A cockpit checklist containing the procedures required by paragraph (b) of this section.

(3) Pertinent aeronautical charts.

(4) For IFR, VFR over-the-top, or night operations, each pertinent navigational en route, terminal area, and approach and letdown chart.

(5) In the case of multiengine airplanes, one-engine inoperative climb performance data.

(b) Each cockpit checklist must contain the following procedures and shall be used by the flight crewmembers when operating the airplane:

(1) Before starting engines.

(2) Before takeoff.

(3) Cruise.

(4) Before landing.

(5) After landing.

(6) Stopping engines.

(7) Emergencies.

(c) Each emergency cockpit checklist procedure required by paragraph (b)(7) of this section must contain the following procedures, as appropriate:

(1) Emergency operation of fuel, hydraulic, electrical, and mechanical systems.

(2) Emergency operation of instruments and controls.

(3) Engine inoperative procedures.

(4) Any other procedures necessary for safety.

(d) The equipment, charts, and data prescribed in this section shall be used by the pilot in command and other members of the flight crew, when pertinent.

§91.505 Familiarity with operating limitations and emergency equipment.

(a) Each pilot in command of an airplane shall, before beginning a flight, become familiar with the Airplane Flight Manual for that airplane, if one is required, and with any placards, listings, instru-

ment markings, or any combination thereof, containing each operating limitation prescribed for that airplane by the Administrator, including those specified in §91.9(b).

(b) Each required member of the crew shall, before beginning a flight, become familiar with the emergency equipment installed on the airplane to which that crewmember is assigned and with the procedures to be followed for the use of that equipment in an emergency situation.

§91.507 Equipment requirements: Over-the-top or night VFR operations.

No person may operate an airplane over-the-top or at night under VFR unless that airplane is equipped with the instruments and equipment required for IFR operations under §91.205(d) and one electric landing light for night operations. Each required instrument and item of equipment must be in operable condition.

§91.509 Survival equipment for overwater operations.

(a) No person may take off an airplane for a flight over water more than 50 nautical miles from the nearest shore unless that airplane is equipped with a life preserver or an approved flotation means for each occupant of the airplane.

(b) No person may take off an airplane for a flight over water more than 30 minutes flying time or 100 nautical miles from the nearest shore unless it has on board the following survival equipment:

(1) A life preserver, equipped with an approved survivor locator light, for each occupant of the airplane.

(2) Enough liferafts (each equipped with an approved survival locator light) of a rated capacity and buoyancy to accommodate the occupants of the airplane.

(3) At least one pyrotechnic signaling device for each liferaft.

(4) One self-buoyant, water-resistant, portable emergency radio signaling device that is capable of transmission on the appropriate emergency frequency or frequencies and not dependent upon the airplane power supply.

(5) A lifeline stored in accordance with §25.1411(g) of this chapter.

(c) The required liferafts, life preservers, and signaling devices must be installed in conspicuously marked locations and easily accessible in the event of a ditching without appreciable time for preparatory procedures.

(d) A survival kit, appropriately equipped for the route to be flown, must be attached to each required liferaft.

(e) As used in this section, the term shore means that area of the land adjacent to the water which is above the high water mark and excludes land areas which are intermittently under water.

§ 91.511 Radio equipment for overwater operations.

(a) Except as provided in paragraphs (c), (d), and (f) of this section, no person may take off an airplane for a flight over water more than 30 minutes flying time or 100 nautical miles from the nearest shore unless it has at least the following operable equipment:

(1) Radio communication equipment appropriate to the facilities to be used and able to transmit to, and receive from, any place on the route, at least one surface facility:

(i) Two transmitters.

(ii) Two microphones.

(iii) Two headsets or one headset and one speaker.

(iv) Two independent receivers.

(2) Appropriate electronic navigational equipment consisting of at least two independent electronic navigation units capable of providing the pilot with the information necessary to navigate the airplane within the airspace assigned by air traffic control. However, a receiver that can receive both communications and required navigational signals may be used in place of a separate communications receiver and a separate navigational signal receiver or unit.

(b) For the purposes of paragraphs (a)(1)(iv) and (a)(2) of this section, a receiver or electronic navigation unit is independent if the function of any part of it does not depend on the functioning of any part of another receiver or electronic navigation unit.

(c) Notwithstanding the provisions of paragraph (a) of this section, a person may operate an airplane on which no passengers are carried from a place where repairs or replacement cannot be made to a place where they can be made, if not more than one of each of the dual items of radio communication and navigational equipment specified in paragraphs (a)(1)(i) through (iv) and (a)(2) of this section malfunctions or becomes inoperative.

(d) Notwithstanding the provisions of paragraph (a) of this section, when both VHF and HF communications equipment are required for the route and the airplane has two VHF transmitters and two VHF receivers for communications, only one HF transmitter and one HF receiver is required for communications.

(e) As used in this section, the term *shore* means that area of the land adjacent to the water which is above the high-water mark and excludes land areas which are intermittently under water.

(f) Notwithstanding the requirements in paragraph (a)(2) of this section, a person may operate in the Gulf of Mexico, the Caribbean Sea, and the Atlantic Ocean west of a line which extends from 44° 47'00" N / 67° 00'00" W to 39° 00'00" N / 67° 00'00" W to 38° 30'00" N / 60° 00'00" W south along the 60° 00'00" W longitude line to the point where the line intersects with the northern coast of South America, when:

(1) A single long-range navigation system is installed, operational, and appropriate for the route; and

(2) Flight conditions and the aircraft's capabilities are such that no more than a 30-minute gap in two-way radio very high frequency communications is expected to exist.

[Docket No. 18334, 54 FR 334314, Aug. 18, 1989; as amended by Amdt. 91–249, 61 FR 7190, Feb. 26, 1996]

§ 91.513 Emergency equipment.

(a) No person may operate an airplane unless it is equipped with the emergency equipment listed in this section.

(b) Each item of equipment—

(1) Must be inspected in accordance with § 91.409 to ensure its continued serviceability and immediate readiness for its intended purposes;

(2) Must be readily accessible to the crew;

(3) Must clearly indicate its method of operation; and

(4) When carried in a compartment or container, must have that compartment or container marked as to contents and date of last inspection.

(c) Hand fire extinguishers must be provided for use in crew, passenger, and cargo compartments in accordance with the following:

(1) The type and quantity of extinguishing agent must be suitable for the kinds of fires likely to occur in the compartment where the extinguisher is intended to be used.

(2) At least one hand fire extinguisher must be provided and located on or near the flight deck in a place that is readily accessible to the flight crew.

(3) At least one hand fire extinguisher must be conveniently located in the passenger compartment of each airplane accommodating more than six but less than 31 passengers, and at least two hand fire extinguishers must be conveniently located in the passenger compartment of each airplane accommodating more than 30 passengers.

(4) Hand fire extinguishers must be installed and secured in such a manner that they will not interfere with the safe operation of the airplane or adversely affect the safety of the crew and passengers. They must be readily accessible and, unless the locations of the fire extinguishers are obvious, their stowage provisions must be properly identified.

(d) First aid kits for treatment of injuries likely to occur in flight or in minor accidents must be provided.

(e) Each airplane accommodating more than 19 passengers must be equipped with a crash axe.

(f) Each passenger-carrying airplane must have a portable battery-powered megaphone or megaphones readily accessible to the crewmembers assigned to direct emergency evacuation, installed as follows:

(1) One megaphone on each airplane with a seating capacity of more than 60 but less than 100 passengers, at the most rearward location in the passenger cabin where it would be readily accessible to a normal flight attendant seat. However, the Administrator may grant a deviation from the requirements of this subparagraph if the Administrator finds that a different location would be more useful for evacuation of persons during an emergency.

(2) On each airplane with a seating capacity of 100 or more passengers, one megaphone installed at the forward end and one installed at the most rearward location where it would be readily accessible to a normal flight attendant seat.

§ 91.515 Flight altitude rules.

(a) Notwithstanding § 91.119, and except as provided in paragraph (b) of this section, no person may operate an airplane under VFR at less than—

(1) One thousand feet above the surface, or 1,000 feet from any mountain, hill, or other obstruction to flight, for day operations; and

(2) The altitudes prescribed in § 91.177, for night operations.

(b) This section does not apply—

(1) During takeoff or landing;

(2) When a different altitude is authorized by a waiver to this section under subpart J of this part; or

(3) When a flight is conducted under the special VFR weather minimums of § 91.157 with an appropriate clearance from ATC.

§ 91.517 Passenger information.

(a) Except as provided in paragraph (b) of this section, no person may operate an airplane carrying passengers unless it is equipped with signs that are visible to passengers and flight attendants to notify them when smoking is prohibited and when safety belts must be fastened. The signs must be so constructed that the crew can turn them on and off. They must be turned on during airplane movement on the surface, for each takeoff, for each landing, and when otherwise considered to be necessary by the pilot in command.

(b) The pilot in command of an airplane that is not required, in accordance with applicable aircraft and equipment requirements of this chapter, to be equipped as provided in paragraph (a) of this section shall ensure that the passengers are notified orally each time that it is necessary to fasten their safety belts and when smoking is prohibited.

(c) If passenger information signs are installed, no passenger or crewmember may smoke while any "no smoking" sign is lighted nor may any passenger or crewmember smoke in any lavatory.

(d) Each passenger required by § 91.107 (a)(3) to occupy a seat or berth shall fasten his or her safety belt about him or her and keep it fastened while any "fasten seat belt" sign is lighted.

(e) Each passenger shall comply with instructions given him or her by crewmembers regarding compliance with paragraphs (b), (c), and (d) of this section.

[Docket No. 26142, 57 FR 42672, Sept. 15, 1992]

§ 91.519 Passenger briefing.

(a) Before each takeoff the pilot in command of an airplane carrying passengers shall ensure that all passengers have been orally briefed on—

(1) *Smoking.* Each passenger shall be briefed on when, where, and under what conditions smoking is prohibited. This briefing shall include a statement, as appropriate, that the Federal Aviation Regulations require passenger compliance with lighted passenger information signs and no smoking placards, prohibit smoking in the lavatories, and require compliance with crewmember instructions with regard to these items;

(2) *Use of safety belts and shoulder harnesses.* Each passenger shall be briefed on when, where, and under what conditions it is necessary to have his or her safety belt and, if installed, his or her shoulder harness fastened about him or her. The briefing shall include a statement, as appropriate, that Federal Aviation Regulations require passenger compliance with the lighted passenger sign and/or crewmember instructions with regard to these items;

(3) Location and means for opening the passenger entry door and emergency exits;

(4) Location of survival equipment;

(5) Ditching procedures and the use of flotation equipment required under § 91.509 for a flight over water; and

(6) The normal and emergency use of oxygen equipment installed on the airplane.

(b) The oral briefing required by paragraph (a) of this section shall be given by the pilot in command or a member of the crew, but need not be given when the pilot in command determines that the passengers are familiar with the contents of the briefing. It may be supplemented by printed cards for the use of each passenger containing—

(1) A diagram of, and methods of operating, the emergency exits; and

(2) Other instructions necessary for use of emergency equipment.

(c) Each card used under paragraph (b) must be carried in convenient locations on the airplane for the use of each passenger and must contain information that is pertinent only to the type and model airplane on which it is used.

[Docket No. 18334, 54 FR 34314, Aug. 18, 1989; as amended by Amdt. 91–231, 57 FR 42672, Sept. 15, 1992]

§ 91.521 Shoulder harness.

(a) No person may operate a transport category airplane that was type certificated after January 1, 1958, unless it is equipped at each seat at a flight deck station with a combined safety belt and shoulder harness that meets the applicable requirements specified in § 25.785 of this chapter, except that—

(1) Shoulder harnesses and combined safety belt and shoulder harnesses that were approved and installed before March 6, 1980, may continue to be used; and

(2) Safety belt and shoulder harness restraint systems may be designed to the inertia load factors established under the certification basis of the airplane.

(b) No person may operate a transport category airplane unless it is equipped at each required flight attendant seat in the passenger compartment with a combined safety belt and shoulder harness that meets the applicable requirements specified in § 25.785 of this chapter, except that—

(1) Shoulder harnesses and combined safety belt and shoulder harnesses that were approved and installed before March 6, 1980, may continue to be used; and

(2) Safety belt and shoulder harness restraint systems may be designed to the inertia load factors established under the certification basis of the airplane.

§ 91.523 Carry-on baggage.

No pilot in command of an airplane having a seating capacity of more than 19 passengers may permit a passenger to stow baggage aboard that airplane except—

(a) In a suitable baggage or cargo storage compartment, or as provided in § 91.525; or

(b) Under a passenger seat in such a way that it will not slide forward under crash impacts severe enough to induce the ultimate inertia forces specified in § 25.561(b)(3) of this chapter, or the

requirements of the regulations under which the airplane was type certificated. Restraining devices must also limit sideward motion of underseat baggage and be designed to withstand crash impacts severe enough to induce sideward forces specified in § 25.561(b)(3) of this chapter.

§ 91.525 Carriage of cargo.

(a) No pilot in command may permit cargo to be carried in any airplane unless—

(1) It is carried in an approved cargo rack, bin, or compartment installed in the airplane;

(2) It is secured by means approved by the Administrator; or

(3) It is carried in accordance with each of the following:

(i) It is properly secured by a safety belt or other tiedown having enough strength to eliminate the possibility of shifting under all normally anticipated flight and ground conditions.

(ii) It is packaged or covered to avoid possible injury to passengers.

(iii) It does not impose any load on seats or on the floor structure that exceeds the load limitation for those components.

(iv) It is not located in a position that restricts the access to or use of any required emergency or regular exit, or the use of the aisle between the crew and the passenger compartment.

(v) It is not carried directly above seated passengers.

(b) When cargo is carried in cargo compartments that are designed to require the physical entry of a crewmember to extinguish any fire that may occur during flight, the cargo must be loaded so as to allow a crewmember to effectively reach all parts of the compartment with the contents of a hand fire extinguisher.

§ 91.527 Operating in icing conditions.

(a) No pilot may take off an airplane that has—

(1) Frost, snow, or ice adhering to any propeller, windshield, or powerplant installation or to an airspeed, altimeter, rate of climb, or flight attitude instrument system;

(2) Snow or ice adhering to the wings or stabilizing or control surfaces; or

(3) Any frost adhering to the wings or stabilizing or control surfaces, unless that frost has been polished to make it smooth.

(b) Except for an airplane that has ice protection provisions that meet the requirements in section 34 of Special Federal Aviation Regulation No. 23, or those for transport category airplane type certification, no pilot may fly—

(1) Under IFR into known or forecast moderate icing conditions; or

(2) Under VFR into known light or moderate icing conditions unless the aircraft has functioning

de-icing or anti-icing equipment protecting each propeller, windshield, wing, stabilizing or control surface, and each airspeed, altimeter, rate of climb, or flight attitude instrument system.

(c) Except for an airplane that has ice protection provisions that meet the requirements in section 34 of Special Federal Aviation Regulation No. 23, or those for transport category airplane type certification, no pilot may fly an airplane into known or forecast severe icing conditions.

(d) If current weather reports and briefing information relied upon by the pilot in command indicate that the forecast icing conditions that would otherwise prohibit the flight will not be encountered during the flight because of changed weather conditions since the forecast, the restrictions in paragraphs (b) and (c) of this section based on forecast conditions do not apply.

§91.529 Flight engineer requirements.

(a) No person may operate the following airplanes without a flight crewmember holding a current flight engineer certificate:

(1) An airplane for which a type certificate was issued before January 2, 1964, having a maximum certificated takeoff weight of more than 80,000 pounds.

(2) An airplane type certificated after January 1, 1964, for which a flight engineer is required by the type certification requirements.

(b) No person may serve as a required flight engineer on an airplane unless, within the preceding 6 calendar months, that person has had at least 50 hours of flight time as a flight engineer on that type airplane or has been checked by the Administrator on that type airplane and is found to be familiar and competent with all essential current information and operating procedures.

§91.531 Second in command requirements.

(a) Except as provided in paragraph (b) of this section, no person may operate the following airplanes without a pilot who is designated as second in command of that airplane:

(1) A large airplane, except that a person may operate an airplane certificated under SFAR 41 without a pilot who is designated as second in command if that airplane is certificated for operation with one pilot.

(2) A turbojet-powered multiengine airplane for which two pilots are required under the type certification requirements for that airplane.

(3) A commuter category airplane, except that a person may operate a commuter category airplane notwithstanding paragraph (a)(1) of this section, that has a passenger seating configuration, excluding pilot seats, of nine or less without a

pilot who is designated as second in command if that airplane is type certificated for operations with one pilot.

(b) The Administrator may issue a letter of authorization for the operation of an airplane without compliance with the requirements of paragraph (a) of this section if that airplane is designed for and type certificated with only one pilot station. The authorization contains any conditions that the Administrator finds necessary for safe operation.

(c) No person may designate a pilot to serve as second in command, nor may any pilot serve as second in command, of an airplane required under this section to have two pilots unless that pilot meets the qualifications for second in command prescribed in §61.55 of this chapter.

§91.533 Flight attendant requirements.

(a) No person may operate an airplane unless at least the following number of flight attendants are on board the airplane:

(1) For airplanes having more than 19 but less than 51 passengers on board, one flight attendant.

(2) For airplanes having more than 50 but less than 101 passengers on board, two flight attendants.

(3) For airplanes having more than 100 passengers on board, two flight attendants plus one additional flight attendant for each unit (or part of a unit) of 50 passengers above 100.

(b) No person may serve as a flight attendant on an airplane when required by paragraph (a) of this section unless that person has demonstrated to the pilot in command familiarity with the necessary functions to be performed in an emergency or a situation requiring emergency evacuation and is capable of using the emergency equipment installed on that airplane.

§91.535 Stowage of food, beverage, and passenger service equipment during aircraft movement on the surface, takeoff, and landing.

(a) No operator may move an aircraft on the surface, takeoff or land when any food, beverage, or tableware furnished by the operator is located at any passenger seat.

(b) No operator may move an aircraft on the surface, takeoff, or land unless each food and beverage tray is secured in its stowed position.

(c) No operator may permit an aircraft to move on the surface, takeoff, or land unless each passenger serving cart is secured in its stowed position.

(d) No operator may permit an aircraft to move on the surface, takeoff, or land unless each movie screen that extends into the aisle is stowed.

(e) Each passenger shall comply with instructions given by a crewmember with regard to compliance with this section.

[Docket No. 26142, 57 FR 42672, Sept. 15, 1992]

§ 91.536 – 91.599 [Reserved]

Subpart G—
Additional Equipment and Operating Requirements for Large and Transport Category Aircraft

Source: Docket No. 18334, 54 FR 34318, Aug. 18, 1989, unless otherwise noted.

§ 91.601 Applicability.

This subpart applies to operation of large and transport category U.S.-registered civil aircraft.

§ 91.603 Aural speed warning device.

No person may operate a transport category airplane in air commerce unless that airplane is equipped with an aural speed warning device that complies with § 25.1303(c)(1).

§ 91.605 Transport category civil airplane weight limitations.

(a) No person may take off any transport category airplane (other than a turbine-engine-powered airplane certificated after September 30, 1958) unless—

(1) The takeoff weight does not exceed the authorized maximum takeoff weight for the elevation of the airport of takeoff;

(2) The elevation of the airport of takeoff is within the altitude range for which maximum takeoff weights have been determined;

(3) Normal consumption of fuel and oil in flight to the airport of intended landing will leave a weight on arrival not in excess of the authorized maximum landing weight for the elevation of that airport; and

(4) The elevations of the airport of intended landing and of all specified alternate airports are within the altitude range for which the maximum landing weights have been determined.

(b) No person may operate a turbine-engine-powered transport category airplane certificated after September 30, 1958, contrary to the Airplane Flight Manual, or take off that airplane unless—

(1) The takeoff weight does not exceed the takeoff weight specified in the Airplane Flight Manual for the elevation of the airport and for the ambient temperature existing at the time of takeoff;

(2) Normal consumption of fuel and oil in flight to the airport of intended landing and to the alternate airports will leave a weight on arrival not in excess of the landing weight specified in the Airplane Flight Manual for the elevation of each of the airports involved and for the ambient temperatures expected at the time of landing;

(3) The takeoff weight does not exceed the weight shown in the Airplane Flight Manual to correspond with the minimum distances required for takeoff, considering the elevation of the airport, the runway to be used, the effective runway gradient, and the ambient temperature and wind component at the time of takeoff, and, if operating limitations exist for the minimum distances required for takeoff from wet runways, the runway surface condition (dry or wet). Wet runway distances associated with grooved or porous friction course runways, if provided in the Airplane Flight Manual, may be used only for runways that are grooved or treated with a porous friction course (PFC) overlay, and that the operator determines are designed, constructed, and maintained in a manner acceptable to the Administrator.

(4) Where the takeoff distance includes a clearway, the clearway distance is not greater than one-half of—

(i) The takeoff run, in the case of airplanes certificated after September 30, 1958, and before August 30, 1959; or

(ii) The runway length, in the case of airplanes certificated after August 29, 1959.

(c) No person may take off a turbine-engine-powered transport category airplane certificated after August 29, 1959, unless, in addition to the requirements of paragraph (b) of this section—

(1) The accelerate-stop distance is no greater than the length of the runway plus the length of the stopway (if present); and

(2) The takeoff distance is no greater than the length of the runway plus the length of the clearway (if present); and

(3) The takeoff run is no greater than the length of the runway.

[Docket No. 18334, 54 FR 34318, Aug. 18, 1989; as amended by Amdt. 91–256, 63 FR 8321, Feb. 18, 1998]

§ 91.607 Emergency exits for airplanes carrying passengers for hire.

(a) Notwithstanding any other provision of this chapter, no person may operate a large airplane (type certificated under the Civil Air Regulations effective before April 9, 1957) in passenger-carrying operations for hire, with more than the number of occupants—

(1) Allowed under Civil Air Regulations § 4b.362 (a), (b), and (c) as in effect on December 20, 1951; or

(2) Approved under Special Civil Air Regulations SR–387, SR–389, SR–389A, or SR–389B, or under this section as in effect.

However, an airplane type listed in the following table may be operated with up to the listed number of occupants (including crewmembers) and the corresponding number of exits (including emergency exits and doors) approved for the emergency exit of passengers or with an occupant-exit configuration approved under paragraph (b) or (c) of this section.

Airplane type	Maximum number of occupants including all crewmembers	Corresponding number of exits authorized for passenger use
B-307	61	4
B-377	96	9
C-46	67	4
CV-240	53	6
CV-340 and CV-440	53	6
DC-3	35	4
DC-3 (Super)	39	5
DC-4	86	5
DC-6	87	7
DC-6B	112	11
L-18	17	3
L-049, L-649, L-749	87	7
L-1049 series	96	9
M-202	53	6
M-404	53	7
Viscount 700 series	53	7

(b) Occupants in addition to those authorized under paragraph (a) of this section may be carried as follows:

(1) For each additional floor-level exit at least 24 inches wide by 48 inches high, with an unobstructed 20-inch-wide access aisleway between the exit and the main passenger aisle, 12 additional occupants.

(2) For each additional window exit located over a wing that meets the requirements of the airworthiness standards under which the airplane was type certificated or that is large enough to inscribe an ellipse 19 X 26 inches, eight additional occupants.

(3) For each additional window exit that is not located over a wing but that otherwise complies with paragraph (b)(2) of this section, five additional occupants.

(4) For each airplane having a ratio (as computed from the table in paragraph (a) of this section) of maximum number of occupants to number of exits greater than 14:1, and for each airplane that does not have at least one full-size, door-type exit in the side of the fuselage in the rear part of the cabin, the first additional exit must be a floor-level exit that complies with paragraph (b)(1) of this section and must be located in the rear part of the cabin on the opposite side of the fuselage from the main entrance door. However, no person may operate an airplane under this section carrying more than 115 occupants unless there is such an exit on each side of the fuselage in the rear part of the cabin.

(c) No person may eliminate any approved exit except in accordance with the following:

(1) The previously authorized maximum number of occupants must be reduced by the same number of additional occupants authorized for that exit under this section.

(2) Exits must be eliminated in accordance with the following priority schedule: First, non-over-wing window exits; second, over-wing window exits; third, floor-level exits located in the forward part of the cabin; and fourth, floor-level exits located in the rear of the cabin.

(3) At least one exit must be retained on each side of the fuselage regardless of the number of occupants.

(4) No person may remove any exit that would result in a ratio of maximum number of occupants to approved exits greater than 14:1.

(d) This section does not relieve any person operating under part 121 of this chapter from complying with § 121.291.

§ 91.609 Flight recorders and cockpit voice recorders.

(a) No holder of an air carrier operating certificate or an operating certificate may conduct any operation under this part with an aircraft listed in the holder's operations specifications or current list of aircraft used in air transportation unless that aircraft complies with any applicable flight recorder and cockpit voice recorder requirements of the part under which its certificate is issued except that the operator may—

(1) Ferry an aircraft with an inoperative flight recorder or cockpit voice recorder from a place where repair or replacement cannot be made to a place where they can be made;

(2) Continue a flight as originally planned, if the flight recorder or cockpit voice recorder becomes inoperative after the aircraft has taken off;

(3) Conduct an airworthiness flight test during which the flight recorder or cockpit voice recorder is turned off to test it or to test any communications or electrical equipment installed in the aircraft; or

(4) Ferry a newly acquired aircraft from the place where possession of it is taken to a place where the flight recorder or cockpit voice recorder is to be installed.

(b) Notwithstanding paragraphs (c) and (e) of this section, an operator other than the holder of an air carrier or a commercial operator certificate may—

(1) Ferry an aircraft with an inoperative flight recorder or cockpit voice recorder from a place where repair or replacement cannot be made to a place where they can be made;

(2) Continue a flight as originally planned if the flight recorder or cockpit voice recorder becomes inoperative after the aircraft has taken off;

(3) Conduct an airworthiness flight test during which the flight recorder or cockpit voice recorder is turned off to test it or to test any communications or electrical equipment installed in the aircraft;

(4) Ferry a newly acquired aircraft from a place where possession of it was taken to a place where the flight recorder or cockpit voice recorder is to be installed; or

(5) Operate an aircraft:

(i) For not more than 15 days while the flight recorder and/or cockpit voice recorder is inoperative and/or removed for repair provided that the aircraft maintenance records contain an entry that indicates the date of failure, and a placard is located in view of the cockpit to show that the flight recorder or pilot voice recorder is inoperative.

(ii) For not more than an additional 15 days, provided that the requirements in paragraph (b)(5)(i) are met and that a certified pilot, or a certified person authorized to return an aircraft to service under § 43.7 of this chapter certifies in the aircraft maintenance records that additional time is required to complete repairs or obtain a replacement unit.

(c) No person may operate a U.S. civil registered, multiengine, turbine-powered airplane or rotorcraft having a passenger seating configuration, excluding any pilot seats of 10 or more that has been manufactured after October 11, 1991, unless it is equipped with one or more approved flight recorders that utilize a digital method of recording and storing data and a method of readily retrieving that data from the storage medium, that are capable of recording the data specified in Appendix E to this part, for an airplane, or Appendix F to this part, for a rotorcraft, of this part within the range, accuracy, and recording interval specified, and that are capable of retaining no less than 8 hours of aircraft operation.

(d) Whenever a flight recorder, required by this section, is installed, it must be operated continuously from the instant the airplane begins the takeoff roll or the rotorcraft begins lift-off until the airplane has completed the landing roll or the rotorcraft has landed at its destination.

(e) Unless otherwise authorized by the Administrator, after October 11, 1991, no person may operate a U.S. civil registered multiengine, turbine-powered airplane or rotorcraft having a passenger seating configuration of six passengers or more and for which two pilots are required by type certification or operating rule unless it is equipped with an approved cockpit voice recorder that:

(1) Is installed in compliance with § 23.1457(a) (1) and (2), (b), (c), (d), (e), (f), and (g); § 25.1457(a) (1) and (2), (b), (c), (d), (e), (f), and (g); § 27.1457(a) (1) and (2), (b), (c), (d), (e), (f), and (g); or § 29.1457(a) (1) and (2), (b), (c), (d), (e), (f), and (g) of this chapter, as applicable; and

(2) Is operated continuously from the use of the checklist before the flight to completion of the final checklist at the end of the flight.

(f) In complying with this section, an approved cockpit voice recorder having an erasure feature may be used, so that at any time during the operation of the recorder, information recorded more than 15 minutes earlier may be erased or otherwise obliterated.

(g) In the event of an accident or occurrence requiring immediate notification to the National Transportation Safety Board under part 830 of its regulations that results in the termination of the flight, any operator who has installed approved flight recorders and approved cockpit voice recorders shall keep the recorded information for at least 60 days or, if requested by the Administrator or the Board, for a longer period. Information obtained from the record is used to assist in determining the cause of accidents or occurrences in connection with the investigation under part 830. The Administrator does not use the cockpit voice recorder record in any civil penalty or certificate action.

[Docket No. 18334, 54 FR 34318, Aug. 18, 1989; as amended by Amdt. 91–226, 56 FR 51621, Oct. 11, 1991; Amdt. 91–228, 57 FR 19353, May 5, 1992]

§ 91.611 Authorization for ferry flight with one engine inoperative.

(a) *General.* The holder of an air carrier operating certificate or an operating certificate issued under part 125 may conduct a ferry flight of a four-engine airplane or a turbine-engine-powered airplane equipped with three engines, with one engine inoperative, to a base for the purpose of repairing that engine subject to the following:

(1) The airplane model has been test flown and found satisfactory for safe flight in accordance

with paragraph (b) or (c) of this section, as appropriate. However, each operator who before November 19, 1966, has shown that a model of airplane with an engine inoperative is satisfactory for safe flight by a test flight conducted in accordance with performance data contained in the applicable Airplane Flight Manual under paragraph (a)(2) of this section need not repeat the test flight for that model.

(2) The approved Airplane Flight Manual contains the following performance data and the flight is conducted in accordance with that data:

(i) Maximum weight.

(ii) Center of gravity limits.

(iii) Configuration of the inoperative propeller (if applicable).

(iv) Runway length for takeoff (including temperature accountability).

(v) Altitude range.

(vi) Certificate limitations.

(vii) Ranges of operational limits.

(viii) Performance information.

(ix) Operating procedures.

(3) The operator has FAA approved procedures for the safe operation of the airplane, including specific requirements for—

(i) Limiting the operating weight on any ferry flight to the minimum necessary for the flight plus the necessary reserve fuel load;

(ii) A limitation that takeoffs must be made from dry runways unless, based on a showing of actual operating takeoff techniques on wet runways with one engine inoperative, takeoffs with full controllability from wet runways have been approved for the specific model aircraft and included in the Airplane Flight Manual:

(iii) Operations from airports where the runways may require a takeoff or approach over populated areas; and

(iv) Inspection procedures for determining the operating condition of the operative engines.

(4) No person may take off an airplane under this section if—

(i) The initial climb is over thickly populated areas; or

(ii) Weather conditions at the takeoff or destination airport are less than those required for VFR flight.

(5) Persons other than required flight crewmembers shall not be carried during the flight.

(6) No person may use a flight crewmember for flight under this section unless that crewmember is thoroughly familiar with the operating procedures for one-engine inoperative ferry flight contained in the certificate holder's manual and the limitations and performance information in the Airplane Flight Manual.

(b) *Flight tests: reciprocating-engine-powered airplanes.* The airplane performance of a reciprocating-engine-powered airplane with one engine inoperative must be determined by flight test as follows:

(1) A speed not less than 1.3 V_{S1} must be chosen at which the airplane may be controlled satisfactorily in a climb with the critical engine inoperative (with its propeller removed or in a configuration desired by the operator and with all other engines operating at the maximum power determined in paragraph (b)(3) of this section.

(2) The distance required to accelerate to the speed listed in paragraph (b)(1) of this section and to climb to 50 feet must be determined with—

(i) The landing gear extended;

(ii) The critical engine inoperative and its propeller removed or in a configuration desired by the operator; and

(iii) The other engines operating at not more than maximum power established under paragraph (b)(3) of this section.

(3) The takeoff, flight and landing procedures, such as the approximate trim settings, method of power application, maximum power, and speed must be established.

(4) The performance must be determined at a maximum weight not greater than the weight that allows a rate of climb of at least 400 feet per minute in the en route configuration set forth in § 25.67(d) of this chapter in effect on January 31, 1977, at an altitude of 5,000 feet.

(5) The performance must be determined using temperature accountability for the takeoff field length, computed in accordance with § 25.61 of this chapter in effect on January 31, 1977.

(c) *Flight tests: Turbine-engine-powered airplanes.* The airplane performance of a turbine-engine-powered airplane with one engine inoperative must be determined by flight tests, including at least three takeoff tests, in accordance with the following:

(1) Takeoff speeds V_R and V_2, not less than the corresponding speeds under which the airplane was type certificated under § 25.107 of this chapter, must be chosen at which the airplane may be controlled satisfactorily with the critical engine inoperative (with its propeller removed or in a configuration desired by the operator, if applicable) and with all other engines operating at not more than the power selected for type certification as set forth in § 25.101 of this chapter.

(2) The minimum takeoff field length must be the horizontal distance required to accelerate and climb to the 35-foot height at V_2 speed (including any additional speed increment obtained in the tests) multiplied by 115 percent and determined with—

(i) The landing gear extended;

(ii) The critical engine inoperative and its propeller removed or in a configuration desired by the operator (if applicable); and

91

(iii) The other engine operating at not more than the power selected for type certification as set forth in § 25.101 of this chapter.

(3) The takeoff, flight, and landing procedures such as the approximate trim setting, method of power application, maximum power, and speed must be established. The airplane must be satisfactorily controllable during the entire takeoff run when operated according to these procedures.

(4) The performance must be determined at a maximum weight not greater than the weight determined under § 25.121(c) of this chapter but with—

(i) The actual steady gradient of the final takeoff climb requirement not less than 1.2 percent at the end of the takeoff path with two critical engines inoperative; and

(ii) The climb speed not less than the two-engine inoperative trim speed for the actual steady gradient of the final takeoff climb prescribed by paragraph (c)(4)(i) of this section.

(5) The airplane must be satisfactorily controllable in a climb with two critical engines inoperative. Climb performance may be shown by calculations based on, and equal in accuracy to, the results of testing.

(6) The performance must be determined using temperature accountability for takeoff distance and final takeoff climb computed in accordance with § 25.101 of this chapter.

For the purpose of paragraphs (c)(4) and (5) of this section, *two critical engines* means two adjacent engines on one side of an airplane with four engines, and the center engine and one outboard engine on an airplane with three engines.

§ 91.613 Materials for compartment interiors.

No person may operate an airplane that conforms to an amended or supplemental type certificate issued in accordance with SFAR No. 41 for a maximum certificated takeoff weight in excess of 12,500 pounds unless within 1 year after issuance of the initial airworthiness certificate under that SFAR the airplane meets the compartment interior requirements set forth in § 25.853 (a), (b), (b-1), (b-2), and (b-3) of this chapter in effect on September 26, 1978.

§ 91.615 – 91.699 [Reserved]

Subpart H— Foreign Aircraft Operations and Operations of U.S.-Registered Civil Aircraft Outside of the United States; and Rules Governing Persons On Board Such Aircraft

Source: Docket No. 18334, 54 FR 34320, Aug. 18, 1989, unless otherwise noted.

§ 91.701 Applicability.

(a) This subpart applies to the operations of civil aircraft of U.S. registry outside of the United States and the operations of foreign civil aircraft within the United States.

(b) Section 91.702 of this subpart also applies to each person on board an aircraft operated as follows:

(1) A U.S. registered civil aircraft operated outside the United States;

(2) Any aircraft operated outside the United States—

(i) That has its next scheduled destination or last place of departure in the United States if the aircraft next lands in the United States; or

(ii) If the aircraft lands in the United States with the individual still on the aircraft regardless of whether it was a scheduled or otherwise planned landing site.

[Docket No. 18334, 54 FR 34292, Aug. 18, 1989; as amended by Amdt. 91–257, 64 FR 1079, Jan. 7, 1999]

§ 91.702 Persons on board.

Section 91.11 of this part (Prohibitions on interference with crewmembers) applies to each person on board an aircraft.

[Docket No. 18334, 54 FR 34320, Aug. 18, 1989; as amended by Amdt. 91–257, 64 FR 1079, Jan. 7, 1999]

§ 91.703 Operations of civil aircraft of U.S. registry outside of the United States.

(a) Each person operating a civil aircraft of U.S. registry outside of the United States shall—

(1) When over the high seas, comply with annex 2 (Rules of the Air) to the Convention on International Civil Aviation and with §§ 91.117(c), 91.127, 91.129, and 91.131;

(2) When within a foreign country, comply with the regulations relating to the flight and maneuver of aircraft there in force;

(3) Except for §§ 91.307(b), 91.309, 91.323, and 91.711, comply with this part so far as it is not inconsistent with applicable regulations of the foreign country where the aircraft is operated or annex 2 of the Convention on International Civil Aviation; and

(4) When operating within airspace designated as Minimum Navigation Performance Specifications (MNPS) airspace, comply with § 91.705. When operating within airspace designated as Reduced Vertical Separation Minimum (RVSM) airspace, comply with § 91.706.

(b) Annex 2 to the Convention on International Civil Aviation, Ninth Edition—July 1990, with Amendments through Amendment 32 effective February 19, 1996, to which reference is made in this part, is incorporated into this part and made a part hereof as provided in 5 U.S.C. § 552 and pursuant to 1 CFR part 51. Annex 2 (including a complete historic file of changes thereto) is available for public inspection at the Rules Docket, AGC–200, Federal Aviation Administration, 800 Independence Avenue SW, Washington, DC 20591; or at the Office of the Federal Register, 800 North Capitol Street NW., Suite 700, Washington DC. In addition, Annex 2 may be purchased from the International Civil Aviation Organization (Attention: Distribution Officer), P.O. Box 400, Succursale, Place de L'Aviation Internationale, 1000 Sherbrooke Street West, Montreal, Quebec, Canada H3A 2R2.

[Docket No. 18834, 54 FR 34320, Aug. 18, 1989; as amended by Amdt. 91–227, 56 FR 65661, Dec. 17, 1991; Amdt. 91–254, 62 FR 17487, April 9, 1997]

§ 91.705 Operations within airspace designated as Minimum Navigation Performance Specification Airspace.

(a) Except as provided in paragraph (b) of this section, no person may operate a civil aircraft of U.S. registry in airspace designated as Minimum Navigation Performance Specifications airspace unless—

(1) The aircraft has approved navigation performance capability that complies with the requirements of Appendix C of this part; and

(2) The operator is authorized by the Administrator to perform such operations.

(b) The Administrator may authorize a deviation from the requirements of this section in accordance with Section 3 of Appendix C to this part.

[Docket No. 28870, 62 FR 17487, April 9, 1997]

§91.706 Operations within airspace designated as Reduced Vertical Separation Minimum Airspace.

(a) Except as provided in paragraph (b) of this section, no person may operate a civil aircraft of U.S. registry in airspace designated as Reduced Vertical Separation Minimum (RVSM) airspace unless—

(1) The operator and the operator's aircraft comply with the requirements of Appendix G of this part; and

(2) The operator is authorized by the Administrator to conduct such operations.

(b) The Administrator may authorize a deviation from the requirements of this section in accordance with Section 5 of Appendix G to this part.

[Docket No. 28870, 62 FR 17487, April 9, 1997]

§ 91.707 Flights between Mexico or Canada and the United States.

Unless otherwise authorized by ATC, no person may operate a civil aircraft between Mexico or Canada and the United States without filing an IFR or VFR flight plan, as appropriate.

§ 91.709 Operations to Cuba.

No person may operate a civil aircraft from the United States to Cuba unless—

(a) Departure is from an international airport of entry designated in § 6.13 of the Air Commerce Regulations of the Bureau of Customs (19 CFR 6.13); and

(b) In the case of departure from any of the 48 contiguous States or the District of Columbia, the pilot in command of the aircraft has filed—

(1) A DVFR or IFR flight plan as prescribed in § 99.11 or § 99.13 of this chapter; and

(2) A written statement, within 1 hour before departure, with the Office of Immigration and Naturalization Service at the airport of departure, containing—

(i) All information in the flight plan;

(ii) The name of each occupant of the aircraft;

(iii) The number of occupants of the aircraft; and

(iv) A description of the cargo, if any.

This section does not apply to the operation of aircraft by a scheduled air carrier over routes authorized in operations specifications issued by the Administrator.

(Approved by the Office of Management and Budget under control number 2120–0005)

91

§ 91.711 Special rules for foreign civil aircraft.

(a) *General.* In addition to the other applicable regulations of this part, each person operating a foreign civil aircraft within the United States shall comply with this section.

(b) *VFR.* No person may conduct VFR operations which require two-way radio communications under this part unless at least one crewmember of that aircraft is able to conduct two-way radio communications in the English language and is on duty during that operation.

(c) *IFR.* No person may operate a foreign civil aircraft under IFR unless—

(1) That aircraft is equipped with—

(i) Radio equipment allowing two-way radio communication with ATC when it is operated in controlled airspace; and

(ii) Radio navigational equipment appropriate to the navigational facilities to be used;

(2) Each person piloting the aircraft—

(i) Holds a current United States instrument rating or is authorized by his foreign airman certificate to pilot under IFR; and

(ii) Is thoroughly familiar with the United States en route, holding, and letdown procedures; and

(3) At least one crewmember of that aircraft is able to conduct two-way radiotelephone communications in the English language and that crewmember is on duty while the aircraft is approaching, operating within, or leaving the United States.

(d) *Over water.* Each person operating a foreign civil aircraft over water off the shores of the United States shall give flight notification or file a flight plan in accordance with the Supplementary Procedures for the ICAO region concerned.

(e) *Flight at and above FL 240.* If VOR navigational equipment is required under paragraph (c)(1)(ii) of this section, no person may operate a foreign civil aircraft within the 50 States and the District of Columbia at or above FL 240, unless the aircraft is equipped with distance measuring equipment (DME) capable of receiving and indicating distance information from the VORTAC facilities to be used. When DME required by this paragraph fails at and above FL 240, the pilot in command of the aircraft shall notify ATC immediately and may then continue operations at and above FL 240 to the next airport of intended landing at which repairs or replacement of the equipment can be made. However, paragraph (e) of this section does not apply to foreign civil aircraft that are not equipped with DME when operated for the following purposes and if ATC is notified prior to each takeoff:

(1) Ferry flights to and from a place in the United States where repairs or alterations are to be made.

(2) Ferry flights to a new country of registry.

(3) Flight of a new aircraft of U.S. manufacture for the purpose of—

(i) Flight testing the aircraft;

(ii) Training foreign flight crews in the operation of the aircraft; or

(iii) Ferrying the aircraft for export delivery outside the United States.

(4) Ferry, demonstration, and test flight of an aircraft brought to the United States for the purpose of demonstration or testing the whole or any part thereof.

[Docket No. 18834, 54 FR 34320, Aug. 18, 1989; as amended by Amdt. 91–227, 56 FR 65661, Dec. 17, 1991]

§ 91.713 Operation of civil aircraft of Cuban registry.

No person may operate a civil aircraft of Cuban registry except in controlled airspace and in accordance with air traffic clearance or air traffic control instructions that may require use of specific airways or routes and landings at specific airports.

§ 91.715 Special flight authorizations for foreign civil aircraft.

(a) Foreign civil aircraft may be operated without airworthiness certificates required under § 91.203 if a special flight authorization for that operation is issued under this section. Application for a special flight authorization must be made to the Flight Standards Division Manager or Aircraft Certification Directorate Manager of the FAA region in which the applicant is located or to the region within which the U.S. point of entry is located. However, in the case of an aircraft to be operated in the U.S. for the purpose of demonstration at an airshow, the application may be made to the Flight Standards Division Manager or Aircraft Certification Directorate Manager of the FAA region in which the airshow is located.

(b) The Administrator may issue a special flight authorization for a foreign civil aircraft subject to any conditions and limitations that the Administrator considers necessary for safe operation in the U.S. airspace.

(c) No person may operate a foreign civil aircraft under a special flight authorization unless that operation also complies with part 375 of the Special Regulations of the Department of Transportation (14 CFR part 375).

(Approved by the Office of Management and Budget under control number 2120–0005)

[Docket No. 18334, 54 FR 34320, Aug. 18, 1989; as amended by Amdt. 91–212, 54 FR 39293, Sept. 25, 1989]

§ 91.717 – 91.799 [Reserved]

Subpart I—
Operating Noise Limits

Source: Docket No. 18334, 54 FR 34321, Aug. 18, 1989, unless otherwise noted.

§ 91.801 Applicability: Relation to part 36.

(a) This subpart prescribes operating noise limits and related requirements that apply, as follows, to the operation of civil aircraft in the United States.

(1) Sections 91.803, 91.805, 91.807, 91.809, and 91.811 apply to civil subsonic turbojet airplanes with maximum weights of more than 75,000 pounds and—

(i) If U.S. registered, that have standard airworthiness certificates; or

(ii) If foreign registered, that would be required by this chapter to have a U.S. standard airworthiness certificate in order to conduct the operations intended for the airplane were it registered in the United States. Those sections apply to operations to or from airports in the United States under this part and parts 121, 125, 129, and 135 of this chapter.

(2) Section 91.813 applies to U.S. operators of civil subsonic turbojet airplanes covered by this subpart. This section applies to operators operating to or from airports in the United States under this part and parts 121, 125, and 135, but not to those operating under part 129 of this chapter.

(3) Sections 91.803, 91.819, and 91.821 apply to U.S.-registered civil supersonic airplanes having standard airworthiness certificates and to foreign-registered civil supersonic airplanes that, if registered in the United States, would be required by this chapter to have U.S. standard airworthiness certificates in order to conduct the operations intended for the airplane. Those sections apply to operations under this part and under parts 121, 125, 129, and 135 of this chapter.

(b) Unless otherwise specified, as used in this subpart "part 36" refers to 14 CFR part 36, including the noise levels under Appendix C of that part, notwithstanding the provisions of that part excepting certain airplanes from the specified noise requirements. For purposes of this subpart, the various stages of noise levels, the terms used to describe airplanes with respect to those levels, and the terms "subsonic airplane" and "supersonic airplane" have the meanings specified under part 36 of this chapter. For purposes of this subpart, for subsonic airplanes operated in foreign air commerce in the United States, the Administrator may accept compliance with the noise requirements under annex 16 of the International Civil Aviation Organization when those require-

ments have been shown to be substantially compatible with, and achieve results equivalent to those achievable under, part 36 for that airplane. Determinations made under these provisions are subject to the limitations of § 36.5 of this chapter as if those noise levels were part 36 noise levels.

(c) Sections 91.851 through 91.877 of this subpart prescribe operating noise limits and related requirements that apply to any civil subsonic turbojet airplane with a maximum certificated weight of more than 75,000 pounds operating to or from an airport in the 48 contiguous United States and the District of Columbia under this part, part 121, 125, 129, or 135 of this chapter on and after September 25, 1991.

(d) Section 91.877 prescribes reporting requirements that apply to any civil subsonic turbojet airplane with a maximum weight of more than 75,000 pounds operated by an air carrier or foreign air carrier between the contiguous United States and the State of Hawaii, between the State of Hawaii and any point outside of the 48 contiguous United States, or between the islands of Hawaii in turnaround service, under part 121 or 129 of this chapter on or after November 5, 1990.

[Docket No. 18334, 54 FR 34321, Aug. 18, 1989; as amended by Amdt. 91–211, 54 FR 41211, Oct. 5, 1989, Amdt. 91–225, 56 FR 48658, Sept. 25, 1991; Amdt. 91–252, 61 FR 66185, Dec. 16, 1996]

§ 91.803 Part 125 operators: Designation of applicable regulations.

For airplanes covered by this subpart and operated under part 125 of this chapter, the following regulations apply as specified:

(a) For each airplane operation to which requirements prescribed under this subpart applied before November 29, 1980, those requirements of this subpart continue to apply.

(b) For each subsonic airplane operation to which requirements prescribed under this subpart did not apply before November 29, 1980, because the airplane was not operated in the United States under this part or part 121, 129, or 135 of this chapter, the requirements prescribed under §§ 91.805, 91.809, 91.811, and 91.813 of this subpart apply.

(c) For each supersonic airplane operation to which requirements prescribed under this subpart did not apply before November 29, 1980, because the airplane was not operated in the United States under this part or part 121, 129, or 135 of this chapter, the requirements of §§ 91.819 and 91.821 of this subpart apply.

(d) For each airplane required to operate under part 125 for which a deviation under that part is approved to operate, in whole or in part, under this part or part 121, 129, or 135 of this chapter, notwithstanding the approval, the requirements prescribed under paragraphs (a), (b), and (c) of this section continue to apply.

§ 91.805 Final compliance: Subsonic airplanes.

Except as provided in §§ 91.809 and 91.811, on and after January 1, 1985, no person may operate to or from an airport in the United States any subsonic airplane covered by this subpart unless that airplane has been shown to comply with Stage 2 or Stage 3 noise levels under part 36 of this chapter.

§ 91.807 Phased compliance under parts 121, 125, and 135: Subsonic airplanes.

(a) *General.* Each person operating airplanes under part 121, 125, or 135 of this chapter, as prescribed under § 91.803 of this subpart, regardless of the state of registry of the airplane, shall comply with this section with respect to subsonic airplanes covered by this subpart.

(b) *Compliance schedules.* Except for airplanes shown to be operated in foreign air commerce under paragraph (c) of this section or covered by an exemption (including those issued under § 91.811), airplanes operated by U.S. operators in air commerce in the United States must be shown to comply with Stage 2 or Stage 3 noise levels under part 36 of this chapter, in accordance with the following schedule, or they may not be operated to or from airports in the United States:

(1) By January 1, 1981—

(i) At least one quarter of the airplanes that have four engines with no bypass ratio or with a bypass ratio less than two; and

(ii) At least half of the airplanes powered by engines with any other bypass ratio or by another number of engines.

(2) By January 1, 1983—

(i) At least one-half of the airplanes that have four engines with no bypass ratio or with a bypass ratio less than two; and

(ii) All airplanes powered by engines with any other bypass ratio or by another number of engines.

(c) *Apportionment of airplanes.* For purposes of paragraph (b) of this section, a person operating airplanes engaged in domestic and foreign air commerce in the United States may elect not to comply with the phased schedule with respect to that portion of the airplanes operated by that person shown, under an approved method of apportionment, to be engaged in foreign air commerce in the United States.

§ 91.809 Replacement airplanes.

A Stage 1 airplane may be operated after the otherwise applicable compliance dates prescribed under §§ 91.805 and 91.807 if, under an approved plan, a replacement airplane has been ordered by the operator under a binding contract as follows:

(a) For replacement of an airplane powered by two engines, until January 1, 1986, but not after the date specified in the plan, if the contract is entered into by January 1, 1983, and specifies delivery before January 1, 1986, of a replacement airplane which has been shown to comply with Stage 3 noise levels under part 36 of this chapter.

(b) For replacement of an airplane powered by three engines, until January 1, 1985, but not after the date specified in the plan, if the contract is entered into by January 1, 1983, and specifies delivery before January 1, 1985, of a replacement airplane which has been shown to comply with Stage 3 noise levels under part 36 of this chapter.

(c) For replacement of any other airplane, until January 1, 1985, but not after the date specified in the plan, if the contract specifies delivery before January 1, 1985, of a replacement airplane which—

(1) Has been shown to comply with Stage 2 or Stage 3 noise levels under part 36 of this chapter prior to issuance of an original standard airworthiness certificate; or

(2) Has been shown to comply with Stage 3 noise levels under part 36 of this chapter prior to issuance of a standard airworthiness certificate other than original issue.

(d) Each operator of a Stage 1 airplane for which approval of a replacement plan is requested under this section shall submit to the Director, Office of Environment and Energy, an application constituting the proposed replacement plan (or revised plan) that contains the information specified under this paragraph and which is certified (under penalty of 18 U.S.C. 1001) as true and correct. Each application for approval must provide information corresponding to that specified in the contract, upon which the FAA may rely in considering its approval, as follows:

(1) Name and address of the applicant.

(2) Aircraft type and model and registration number for each airplane to be replaced under the plan.

(3) Aircraft type and model of each replacement airplane.

(4) Scheduled dates of delivery and introduction into service of each replacement airplane.

(5) Names and addresses of the parties to the contract and any other persons who may effectively cancel the contract or otherwise control the performance of any party.

(6) Information specifying the anticipated disposition of the airplanes to be replaced.

(7) A statement that the contract represents a legally enforceable, mutual agreement for delivery of an eligible replacement airplane.

(8) Any other information or documentation requested by the Director, Office of Environment and Energy, reasonably necessary to determine whether the plan should be approved.

§ 91.811 Service to small communities exemption: Two-engine, subsonic airplanes.

(a) A Stage 1 airplane powered by two engines may be operated after the compliance dates prescribed under §§ 91.805, 91.807, and 91.809 when, with respect to that airplane, the Administrator issues an exemption to the operator from the noise level requirements under this subpart. Each exemption issued under this section terminates on the earliest of the following dates:

(1) For an exempted airplane sold, or otherwise disposed of, to another person on or after January 1, 1983, on the date of delivery to that person.

(2) For an exempted airplane with a seating configuration of 100 passenger seats or less, on January 1, 1988.

(3) For an exempted airplane with a seating configuration of more than 100 passenger seats, on January 1, 1985.

(b) For the purpose of this section, the seating configuration of an airplane is governed by that shown to exist on December 1, 1979, or an earlier date established for that airplane by the Administrator.

§ 91.813 Compliance plans and status: U.S. operations of subsonic airplanes.

(a) Each U.S. operator of a civil subsonic airplane covered by this subpart (regardless of the state of registry) shall submit to the Director, Office of Environment and Energy, in accordance with this section, the operator's current compliance status and plan for achieving and maintaining compliance with the applicable noise level requirements of this subpart. If appropriate, an operator may substitute for the required plan a notice, certified as true (under penalty of 18 U.S.C. 1001) by that operator, that no change in the plan or status of any airplane affected by the plan has occurred since the date of the plan most recently submitted under this section.

(b) Each compliance plan, including each revised plan, must contain the information specified under paragraph (c) of this section for each airplane covered by this section that is operated by the operator. Unless otherwise approved by the Administrator, compliance plans must provide the required plan and status information as it exists on the date 30 days before the date specified for submission of the plan. Plans must be certified by the operator as true and complete (under penalty of 18 U.S.C. 1001) and be submitted for each airplane covered by this section on or before 90 days after initially commencing operation of airplanes covered by this section, whichever is later, and thereafter—

(1) Thirty days after any change in the operator's fleet or compliance planning decisions that has a separate or cumulative effect on 10 percent or more of the airplanes in either class of airplanes covered by § 91.807(b); and

(2) Thirty days after each compliance date applicable to that airplane under this subpart, and annually thereafter through 1985, or until any later date for that airplane prescribed under this subpart, on the anniversary of that submission date, to show continuous compliance with this subpart.

(c) Each compliance plan submitted under this section must identify the operator and include information regarding the compliance plan and status for each airplane covered by the plan as follows:

(1) Name and address of the airplane operator.

(2) Name and telephone number of the person designated by the operator to be responsible for the preparation of the compliance plan and its submission.

(3) The total number of airplanes covered by this section and in each of the following classes and subclasses:

(i) For airplanes engaged in domestic air commerce—

(A) Airplanes powered by four turbojet engines with no bypass ratio or with a bypass ratio less than two;

(B) Airplanes powered by engines with any other bypass ratio or by another number of engines; and

(C) Airplanes covered by an exemption issued under § 91.811 of this subpart.

(ii) For airplanes engaged in foreign air commerce under an approved apportionment plan—

(A) Airplanes powered by four turbojet engines with no bypass ratio or with a bypass ratio less than two;

(B) Airplanes powered by engines with any other bypass ratio or by another number of engines; and

(C) Airplanes covered by an exemption issued under § 91.811 of this subpart.

(4) For each airplane covered by this section—

(i) Aircraft type and model;

(ii) Aircraft registration number;

(iii) Aircraft manufacturer serial number;

(iv) Aircraft powerplant make and model;

(v) Aircraft year of manufacture;

(vi) Whether part 36 noise level compliance has been shown, "Yes/No";

(vii) The appropriate code prescribed under paragraph (c)(5) of this section which indicates the acoustical technology installed, or to be installed, on the airplane;

(viii) For airplanes on which acoustical technology has been or will be applied, following the appropriate code entry, the actual or scheduled month and year of installation on the airplane;

(ix) For DC-8 and B-707 airplanes operated in domestic U.S. air commerce which have been or will be retired from service in the United States without replacement between January 24, 1977, and January 1, 1985, the appropriate code prescribed under paragraph (c)(5) of this section followed by the actual or scheduled month and year of retirement of the airplane from service;

(x) For DC-8 and B-707 airplanes operated in foreign air commerce in the United States which have been or will be retired from service in the United States without replacement between April 14, 1980, and January 1, 1985, the appropriate code prescribed under paragraph (c)(5) of this section followed by the actual or scheduled month and year of retirement of the airplane from service;

(xi) For airplanes covered by an approved replacement plan under § 91.807(c) of this subpart, the appropriate code prescribed under paragraph (c)(5) of this section followed by the scheduled month and year for replacement of the airplane;

(xii) For airplanes designated as "engaged in foreign commerce" in accordance with an approved method of apportionment under § 91.807(c) of this subpart, the appropriate code prescribed under paragraph (c)(5) of this section;

(xiii) For airplanes covered by an exemption issued to the operator granting relief from noise level requirements of this subpart, the appropriate code prescribed under paragraph (c)(5) of this section followed by the actual or scheduled month and year of expiration of the exemption and the appropriate code and applicable dates which indicate the compliance strategy planned or implemented for the airplane;

(xiv) For all airplanes covered by this section, the number of spare shipsets of acoustical components needed for continuous compliance and the number available on demand to the operator in support of those airplanes; and

(xv) For airplanes for which none of the other codes prescribed under paragraph (c)(5) of this section describes either the technology applied or to be applied to the airplane in accordance with the certification requirements under parts 21 and 36 of this chapter, or the compliance strategy or methodology following the code "OTH," enter the date of any certificate action and attach an addendum to the plan explaining the nature and the extent of the certificated technology, strategy, or

methodology employed, with reference to the type certificate documentation.

(5) Table of Acoustical Technology / Strategy Codes

Code	Airplane type / model	Certificate technology
A	B-707-120B; B-707-320B/C; B-720B	Quiet nacelles + 1-ring.
B	B-727-100	Double wall fan duct treatment.
C	B-727-200	Double wall fan duct treatment (pre-January 1977 installations and amended type certificate).
D	B-727-200; B-737-100; B-737-200	Quiet nacelles + double wall fan duct treatment.
E	B-747-100 (pre-December 1971); B-747-200 (pre-December 1971)	Fixed lip inlets + sound absorbing material treatment.
F	DC-8	New extended inlet and bullet with treatment + fan duct treatment areas.
G	DC-9	P-36 sound absorbing material treatment kit.
H	BAC-111-200	Silencer kit (BAC Acoustic Report 522).
I	BAC-111-400	Silencer kit (BAC Acoustic Report 598).
J	B-707; DC-8	Reengined with high bypass ratio turbojet engines + quiet nacelles (if certificated under stage 3 noise level requirements).

REP— For airplanes covered by an approved replacement plan under § 91.807(c) of this subpart.

EFC— For airplanes designated as "engaged in foreign commerce" in accordance with an approved method of apportionment under § 91.811 of this subpart.

RET— For DC-8 and B-707 airplanes operated in domestic U.S. air commerce and retired from service in the United States without replacement between January 24, 1977, and January 1, 1985.

RFC— For DC-8 and B-707 airplanes operated by U.S. operators in foreign air commerce in the United States and retired from service in the United States without replacement between April 14, 1980, and January 1, 1985.

EXD— For airplanes exempted from showing compliance with the noise level requirements of this subpart.

OTH— For airplanes for which no other prescribed code describes either the certificated technology applied or to be applied to the airplane, or the compliance strategy or methodology. (An addendum must explain the nature and extent of technology, strategy, or methodology and reference the type certificate documentation.)

§ 91.815 Agricultural and fire fighting airplanes: Noise operating limitations.

(a) This section applies to propeller-driven, small airplanes having standard airworthiness certificates that are designed for "agricultural aircraft operations" (as defined in § 137.3 of this chapter, as effective on January 1, 1966) or for dispensing fire fighting materials.

(b) If the Airplane Flight Manual, or other approved manual material information, markings, or placards for the airplane indicate that the airplane has not been shown to comply with the noise limits under part 36 of this chapter, no person may operate that airplane, except—

(1) To the extent necessary to accomplish the work activity directly associated with the purpose for which it is designed;

(2) To provide flight crewmember training in the special purpose operation for which the airplane is designed; and

(3) To conduct "nondispensing aerial work operations" in accordance with the requirements under § 137.29(c) of this chapter.

§ 91.817 Civil aircraft sonic boom.

(a) No person may operate a civil aircraft in the United States at a true flight Mach number greater than 1 except in compliance with conditions and limitations in an authorization to exceed Mach 1 issued to the operator under Appendix B of this part.

(b) In addition, no person may operate a civil aircraft for which the maximum operating limit speed M_{MO} exceeds a Mach number of 1, to or from an airport in the United States, unless—

(1) Information available to the flight crew includes flight limitations that ensure that flights entering or leaving the United States will not cause a sonic boom to reach the surface within the United States; and

(2) The operator complies with the flight limitations prescribed in paragraph (b)(1) of this section or complies with conditions and limitations in an authorization to exceed Mach 1 issued under Appendix B of this part.

(Approved by the Office of Management and Budget under control number 2120–0005)

§ 91.819 Civil supersonic airplanes that do not comply with part 36.

(a) *Applicability.* This section applies to civil supersonic airplanes that have not been shown to comply with the Stage 2 noise limits of part 36 in effect on October 13, 1977, using applicable trade-off provisions, and that are operated in the United States, after July 31, 1978.

(b) *Airport use.* Except in an emergency, the following apply to each person who operates a civil supersonic airplane to or from an airport in the United States:

(1) Regardless of whether a type design change approval is applied for under part 21 of this chapter, no person may land or take off an airplane covered by this section for which the type design is changed, after July 31, 1978, in a manner constituting an "acoustical change" under § 21.93 unless the acoustical change requirements of part 36 are complied with.

(2) No flight may be scheduled, or otherwise planned, for takeoff or landing after 10 p.m. and before 7 a.m. local time.

§ 91.821 Civil supersonic airplanes: Noise limits.

Except for Concorde airplanes having flight time before January 1, 1980, no person may operate in the United States, a civil supersonic airplane that does not comply with Stage 2 noise limits of part 36 in effect on October 13, 1977, using applicable trade-off provisions.

§ 91.823 – 91.849 [Reserved]

§ 91.851 Definitions.

For the purposes of §§ 91.851 through 91.877 of this subpart:

Contiguous United States means the area encompassed by the 48 contiguous United States and the District of Columbia.

Fleet means those civil subsonic turbojet airplanes with a maximum certificated weight of more than 75,000 pounds that are listed on an operator's operations specifications as eligible for operation in the contiguous United States.

Import means a change in ownership of an airplane from a non-U.S. person to a U.S. person when the airplane is brought into the United States for operation.

Operations specifications means an enumeration of airplanes by type, model, series, and serial number operated by the operator or foreign air carrier on a given day, regardless of how or whether such airplanes are formally listed or designated by the operator.

Owner means any person that has indicia of ownership sufficient to register the airplane in the United States pursuant to part 47 of this chapter.

New entrant means an air carrier or foreign air carrier that, on or before November 5, 1990, did not conduct operations under part 121 or 129 of this chapter using an airplane covered by this subpart to or from any airport in the contiguous United States, but that initiates such operation after that date.

Stage 2 noise levels mean the requirements for Stage 2 noise levels as defined in part 36 of this chapter in effect on November 5, 1990.

Stage 3 noise levels mean the requirements for Stage 3 noise levels as defined in part 36 of this chapter in effect on November 5, 1990.

Stage 2 airplane means a civil subsonic turbojet airplane with a maximum certificated weight of 75,000 pounds or more that complies with Stage 2 noise levels as defined in part 36 of this chapter.

Stage 3 airplane means a civil subsonic turbojet airplane with a maximum certificated weight of 75,000 pounds or more that complies with Stage 3 noise levels as defined in part 36 of this chapter.

[Docket No. 26433, 56 FR 48658, Sept. 25, 1991; as amended by Amdt. 91–252, 61 FR 66185, Dec. 16, 1996]

§ 91.853 Final compliance: Civil subsonic airplanes.

Except as provided in § 91.873, after December 31, 1999, no person shall operate to or from any airport in the contiguous United States any airplane subject to § 91.801(c) of this subpart, unless that airplane has been shown to comply with Stage 3 noise levels.

[Docket No. 26433, 56 FR 48658, Sept. 25, 1991]

§ 91.855 Entry and nonaddition rule.

No person may operate any airplane subject to § 91.801(c) of this subpart to or from an airport in the contiguous United States unless one or more of the following apply:

(a) The airplane complies with Stage 3 noise levels.

(b) The airplane complies with Stage 2 noise levels and was owned by a U.S. person on and since November 5, 1990. Stage 2 airplanes that meet these criteria and are leased to foreign airlines are also subject to the return provisions of paragraph (e) of this section.

(c) The airplane complies with Stage 2 noise levels, is owned by a non-U.S. person, and is the subject of a binding lease to a U.S. person effective before and on September 25, 1991. Any such airplane may be operated for the term of the lease in effect on that date, and any extensions thereof provided for in that lease.

(d) The airplane complies with Stage 2 noise levels and is operated by a foreign air carrier.

(e) The airplane complies with Stage 2 noise levels and is operated by a foreign operator other than for the purpose of foreign air commerce.

(f) The airplane complies with Stage 2 noise levels and—

(1) On November 5, 1990, was owned by:

(i) A corporation, trust, or partnership organized under the laws of the United States or any State (including individual States, territories, possessions, and the District of Columbia);

(ii) An individual who is a citizen of the United States; or

(iii) An entity owned or controlled by a corporation, trust, partnership, or individual described in paragraph (f)(1)(i) or (ii) of this section; and

(2) Enters into the United States not later than 6 months after the expiration of a lease agreement (including any extensions thereof) between an owner described in paragraph (f)(1) of this section and a foreign airline.

(g) The airplane complies with Stage 2 noise levels and was purchased by the importer under a written contract executed before November 5, 1990.

(h) Any Stage 2 airplane described in this section is eligible for operation in the contiguous United States only as provided under §§ 91.865 or 91.867.

[Docket No. 26433, 56 FR 48658, Sept. 25, 1991; 56 FR 51167, Oct. 10, 1991]

§ 91.857 Stage 2 operations outside of the 48 contiguous United States, and authorization for maintenance.

An operator of a Stage 2 airplane that is operating only between points outside the contiguous United States on or after November 5, 1990, shall—

(a) Include in its operations specifications a statement that such airplane may not be used to provide air transportation to or from any airport in the contiguous United States.

(b) Obtain a special flight authorization to operate that airplane into the contiguous United States for the purpose of maintenance. The special flight authorization must include a statement indicating that this regulation is the basis for the authorization.

[Docket No. 26433, 56 FR 48658, Sept. 25, 1991; as amended by Amdt. 91–252, 61 FR 66185, Dec. 16, 1996]

§ 91.859 Modification to meet Stage 3 noise levels.

For an airplane subject to § 91.801(c) of this subpart and otherwise prohibited from operation to or from an airport in the contiguous United States by § 91.855, any person may apply for a special flight authorization for that airplane to operate in the contiguous United States for the purpose of obtaining modifications to meet Stage 3 noise levels.

[Docket No. 26433, 56 FR 48658, Sept. 25, 1991]

§ 91.861 Base level.

(a) *U.S. Operators.* The base level of a U.S. operator is equal to the number of owned or leased Stage 2 airplanes subject to § 91.801(c) of this subpart that were listed on that operator's operations specifications for operations to or from airports in the contiguous United States on any one day selected by the operator during the period January 1, 1990, through July 1, 1991, plus or minus adjustments made pursuant to paragraphs (a)(1) and (2).

(1) The base level of a U.S. operator shall be increased by a number equal to the total of the following—

(i) The number of Stage 2 airplanes returned to service in the United States pursuant to § 91.855(f);

(ii) The number of Stage 2 airplanes purchased pursuant to § 91.855(g); and

(iii) Any U.S. operator base level acquired with a Stage 2 airplane transferred from another person under § 91.863.

(2) The base level of a U.S. operator shall be decreased by the amount of U.S. operator base level transferred with the corresponding number of Stage 2 airplanes to another person under § 91.863.

(b) Foreign air carriers. The base level of a foreign air carrier is equal to the number of owned or leased Stage 2 airplanes that were listed on that carrier's U.S. operations specifications on any one day during the period January 1, 1990, through July 1, 1991, plus or minus any adjustments to the base levels made pursuant to paragraphs (b)(1) and (2).

(1) The base level of a foreign air carrier shall be increased by the amount of foreign air carrier base level acquired with a Stage 2 airplane from another person under § 91.863.

(2) The base level of a foreign air carrier shall be decreased by the amount of foreign air carrier base level transferred with a Stage 2 airplane to another person under § 91.863.

(c) New entrants do not have a base level.

[Docket No. 26433, 56 FR 48659, Sept. 25, 1991; 56 FR 51167, Oct. 10, 1991]

§ 91.863 Transfers of Stage 2 airplanes with base level.

(a) Stage 2 airplanes may be transferred with or without the corresponding amount of base level. Base level may not be transferred without the corresponding number of Stage 2 airplanes.

(b) No portion of a U.S. operator's base level established under § 91.861(a) may be used for operations by a foreign air carrier. No portion of a foreign air carrier's base level established under § 91.861(b) may be used for operations by a U.S. operator.

(c) Whenever a transfer of Stage 2 airplanes with base level occurs, the transferring and acquiring parties shall, within 10 days, jointly submit written notification of the transfer to the FAA, Office of Environment and Energy. Such notification shall state:

(1) The names of the transferring and acquiring parties;

(2) The name, address, and telephone number of the individual responsible for submitting the notification on behalf of the transferring and acquiring parties;

(3) The total number of Stage 2 airplanes transferred, listed by airplane type, model, series, and serial number;

(4) The corresponding amount of base level transferred and whether it is U.S. operator or foreign air carrier base level; and

(5) The effective date of the transaction.

(d) If, taken as a whole, a transaction or series of transactions made pursuant to this section does not produce an increase or decrease in the number of Stage 2 airplanes for either the acquiring or transferring operator, such transaction or series of transactions may not be used to establish compliance with the requirements of § 91.865.

[Docket No. 26433, 56 FR 48659, Sept. 25, 1991]

§ 91.865 Phased compliance for operators with base level.

Except as provided in paragraph (a) of this section, each operator that operates an airplane under part 91, 121, 125, 129, or 135 of this chapter, regardless of the national registry of the airplane, shall comply with paragraph (b) or (d) of this section at each interim compliance date with regard to its subsonic airplane fleet covered by § 91.801(c) of this subpart.

(a) This section does not apply to new entrants covered by § 91.867 or to foreign operators not engaged in foreign air commerce.

(b) Each operator that chooses to comply with this paragraph pursuant to any interim compliance requirement shall reduce the number of Stage 2 airplanes it operates that are eligible for operation in the contiguous United States to a maximum of:

(1) After December 31, 1994, 75 percent of the base level held by the operator;

(2) After December 31, 1996, 50 percent of the base level held by the operator;

(3) After December 31, 1998, 25 percent of the base level held by the operator.

(c) Except as provided under § 91.871, the number of Stage 2 airplanes that must be reduced at each compliance date contained in paragraph (b) of this section shall be determined by reference to the amount of base level held by the operator on that compliance date, as calculated under § 91.861.

(d) Each operator that chooses to comply with this paragraph pursuant to any interim compliance requirement shall operate a fleet that consists of:

(1) After December 31, 1994, not less than 55 percent Stage 3 airplanes;

(2) After December 31, 1996, not less than 65 percent Stage 3 airplanes;

(3) After December 31, 1998, not less than 75 percent Stage 3 airplanes.

(e) Calculations resulting in fractions may be rounded to permit the continued operation of the next whole number of Stage 2 airplanes.

[Docket No. 26433, 56 FR 48659, Sept. 25, 1991]

§ 91.867 Phased compliance for new entrants.

(a) New entrant U.S. air carriers.

(1) A new entrant initiating operations under part 121 of this chapter on or before December 31, 1994, may initiate service without regard to the percentage of its fleet composed of Stage 3 airplanes.

(2) After December 31, 1994, at least 25 percent of the fleet of a new entrant must comply with Stage 3 noise levels.

(3) After December 31, 1996, at least 50 percent of the fleet of a new entrant must comply with Stage 3 noise levels.

(4) After December 31, 1998, at least 75 percent of the fleet of a new entrant must comply with Stage 3 noise levels.

(b) New entrant foreign air carriers.

(1) A new entrant foreign air carrier initiating part 129 operations on or before December 31, 1994, may initiate service without regard to the percentage of its fleet composed of Stage 3 airplanes.

(2) After December 31, 1994, at least 25 percent of the fleet on U.S. operations specifications

of a new entrant foreign air carrier must comply with Stage 3 noise levels.

(3) After December 31, 1996, at least 50 percent of the fleet on U.S. operations specifications of a new entrant foreign air carrier must comply with Stage 3 noise levels.

(4) After December 31, 1998, at least 75 percent of the fleet on U.S. operations specifications of a new entrant foreign air carrier must comply with Stage 3 noise levels.

(c) Calculations resulting in fractions may be rounded to permit the continued operation of the next whole number of Stage 2 airplanes.

[Docket No. 26433, 56 FR 48659, Sept. 25, 1991; as amended by Amdt. 91–252, 61 FR 66185, Dec. 16, 1996]

§ 91.869 Carry-forward compliance.

(a) Any operator that exceeds the requirements of paragraph (b) of § 91.865 of this part on or before December 31, 1994, or on or before December 31, 1996, may claim a credit that may be applied at a subsequent interim compliance date.

(b) Any operator that eliminates or modifies more Stage 2 airplanes pursuant to § 91.865(b) than required as of December 31, 1994, or December 31, 1996, may count the number of additional Stage 2 airplanes reduced as a credit toward—

(1) The number of Stage 2 airplanes it would otherwise be required to reduce following a subsequent interim compliance date specified in § 91.865(b); or

(2) The number of Stage 3 airplanes it would otherwise be required to operate in its fleet following a subsequent interim compliance date to meet the percentage requirements specified in § 91.865(d).

[Docket No. 26433, 56 FR 48659, Sept. 25, 1991; 56 FR 65783, Dec. 18, 1991]

§ 91.871 Waivers from interim compliance requirements.

(a) Any U.S. operator or foreign air carrier subject to the requirements of §§ 91.865 or 91.867 of this subpart may request a waiver from any individual compliance requirement.

(b) Applications must be filed with the Secretary of Transportation at least 120 days prior to the compliance date from which the waiver is requested.

(c) Applicants must show that a grant of waiver would be in the public interest, and must include in its application its plans and activities for modifying its fleet, including evidence of good faith efforts to comply with the requirements of §§ 91.865 or 91.867. The application should contain all information the applicant considers relevant, including, as appropriate, the following:

(1) The applicant's balance sheet and cash flow positions;

(2) The composition of the applicant's current fleet; and

(3) The applicant's delivery position with respect to new airplanes or noise-abatement equipment.

(d) Waivers will be granted only upon a showing by the applicant that compliance with the requirements of § 91.865 or 91.867 at a particular interim compliance date is financially onerous, physically impossible, or technologically infeasible, or that it would have an adverse effect on competition or on service to small communities.

(e) The conditions of any waiver granted under this section shall be determined by the circumstances presented in the application, but in no case may the term extend beyond the next interim compliance date.

(f) A summary of any request for a waiver under this section will be published in the Federal Register, and public comment will be invited. Unless the Secretary finds that circumstances require otherwise, the public comment period will be at least 14 days.

[Docket No. 26433, 56 FR 48660, Sept. 25, 1991]

§ 91.873 Waivers from final compliance.

(a) A U.S. air carrier may apply for a waiver from the prohibition contained in § 91.853 for its remaining Stage 2 airplanes, provided that, by July 1, 1999, at least 85 percent of the airplanes used by the carrier to provide service to or from an airport in the contiguous United States will comply with the Stage 3 noise levels.

(b) An application for the waiver described in paragraph (a) of this section must be filed with the Secretary of Transportation no later than January 1, 1999. Such application must include a plan with firm orders for replacing or modifying all airplanes to comply with Stage 3 noise levels at the earliest practicable time.

(c) To be eligible to apply for the waiver under this section, a new entrant U.S. air carrier must initiate service no later than January 1, 1999, and must comply fully with all provisions of this section.

(d) The Secretary may grant a waiver under this section if the Secretary finds that granting such waiver is in the public interest. In making such a finding, the Secretary shall include consideration of the effect of granting such waiver on competition in the air carrier industry and the effect on small community air service, and any other information submitted by the applicant that the Secretary considers relevant.

(e) The term of any waiver granted under this section shall be determined by the circumstances presented in the application, but in no case will the waiver permit the operation of any Stage 2 airplane covered by this subchapter in the contiguous United States after December 31, 2003.

(f) A summary of any request for a waiver under this section will be published in the Federal Register, and public comment will be invited. Unless the secretary finds that circumstances require otherwise, the public comment period will be at least 14 days.

[Docket No. 26433, 56 FR 48660, Sept. 25, 1991; 56 FR 51167 Oct. 10, 1991]

§ 91.875 Annual progress reports.

(a) Each operator subject to § 91.865 or § 91.867 of this chapter shall submit an annual report to the FAA, Office of Environment and Energy, on the progress it has made toward complying with the requirements of that section. Such reports shall be submitted no later than 45 days after the end of a calendar year. All progress reports must provide the information through the end of the calendar year, be certified by the operator as true and complete (under penalty of 18 U.S.C. 1001), and include the following information:

(1) The name and address of the operator;

(2) The name, title, and telephone number of the person designated by the operator to be responsible for ensuring the accuracy of the information in the report;

(3) The operator's progress during the reporting period toward compliance with the requirements of § 91.853, § 91.865 or § 91.867. For airplanes on U.S. operations specifications, each operator shall identify the airplanes by type, model, series, and serial number.

(i) Each Stage 2 airplane added or removed from operation or U.S. operations specifications (grouped separately by those airplanes acquired with and without base level);

(ii) Each Stage 2 airplane modified to Stage 3 noise levels (identifying the manufacturer and model of noise abatement retrofit equipment;

(iii) Each Stage 3 airplane on U.S. operations specifications as of the last day of the reporting period; and

(iv) For each Stage 2 airplane transferred or acquired, the name and address of the recipient or transferor; and, if base level was transferred, the person to or from whom base level was transferred or acquired pursuant to Section 91.863 along with the effective date of each base level transaction, and the type of base level transferred or acquired.

(b) Each operator subject to § 91.865 or § 91.867 of this chapter shall submit an initial progress report covering the period from January 1, 1990, through December 31, 1991, and provide:

(1) For each operator subject to § 91.865:

(i) The date used to establish its base level pursuant to § 91.861(a); and

(ii) A list of those Stage 2 airplanes (by type, model, series and serial number) in its base level, including adjustments made pursuant to § 91.861 after the date its base level was established.

(2) For each U.S. operator:

(i) A plan to meet the compliance schedules in § 91.865 or § 91.867 and the final compliance date of § 91.853, including the schedule for delivery of replacement Stage 3 airplanes or the installation of noise abatement retrofit equipment; and

(ii) A separate list (by type, model, series, and serial number) of those airplanes included in the operator's base level, pursuant to § 91.861(a)(1)(i) and (ii), under the categories "returned" or "purchased," along with the date each was added to its operations specifications.

(c) Each operator subject to § 91.865 or § 91.867 of this chapter shall submit subsequent annual progress reports covering the calendar year preceding the report and including any changes in the information provided in paragraphs (a) and (b) of this section; including the use of any carry-forward credits pursuant to § 91.869.

(d) An operator may request, in any report, that specific planning data be considered proprietary.

(e) If an operator's actions during any reporting period cause it to achieve compliance with § 91.853, the report should include a statement to that effect. Further progress reports are not required unless there is any change in the information reported pursuant to paragraph (a) of this section.

(f) For each U.S. operator subject to § 91.865, progress reports submitted for calendar years 1994, 1996, and 1998, shall also state how the operator achieved compliance with the requirements of that section, i.e.—

(1) By reducing the number of Stage 2 airplanes in its fleet to no more than the maximum permitted percentage of its base level under § 91.865(b), or

(2) By operating a fleet that consists of at least the minimum required percentage of Stage 3 airplanes under § 91.865(d).

(Approved by the Office of Management and Budget under control number 2120–0553)

[Docket No. 26433, 56 FR 48660, Sept. 25, 1991; 56 FR 51168, Oct. 10, 1991; as amended by 57 FR 5977, Feb. 19, 1992]

§ 91.877 Annual reporting of Hawaiian operations.

(a) Each air carrier or foreign air carrier subject to § 91.865 or § 91.867 of this part that conducts operations between the contiguous United States and the State of Hawaii, between the State of Hawaii and any point outside of the contiguous United States, or between the islands of Hawaii in turnaround service, on or since November 5, 1990, shall include in its annual report the information described in paragraph (c) of this section.

(b) Each air carrier or foreign air carrier not subject to § 91.865 or § 91.867 of this part that conducts operations between the contiguous U.S. and the State of Hawaii, between the State of Hawaii and any point outside of the contiguous United States, or between the islands of Hawaii in turnaround service, on or since November 5, 1990, shall submit an annual report to the FAA, Office of Environment and Energy, on its compliance with the Hawaiian operations provisions of 49 U.S.C. 47528. Such reports shall be submitted no later than 45 days after the end of a calendar year. All progress reports must provide the information through the end of the calendar year, be certified by the operator as true and complete (under penalty of 18 U.S.C. 1001), and include the following information—

(1) The name and address of the air carrier or foreign air carrier;

(2) The name, title, and telephone number of the person designated by the air carrier or foreign air carrier to be responsible for ensuring the accuracy of the information in the report; and

(3) The information specified in paragraph (c) of this section.

(c) The following information must be included in reports filed pursuant to this section—

(1) For operations conducted between the contiguous United States and the State of Hawaii—

(i) The number of Stage 2 airplanes used to conduct such operations as of November 5, 1990;

(ii) Any change to that number during the calendar year being reported, including the date of such change;

(2) For air carriers that conduct inter-island turnaround service in the State of Hawaii—

(i) The number of Stage 2 airplanes used to conduct such operations as of November 5, 1990;

(ii) Any change to that number during the calendar year being reported, including the date of such change;

(iii) For an air carrier that provided inter-island turnaround service within the State of Hawaii on November 5, 1990, the number reported under paragraph (c)(2)(i) of this section may include all Stage 2 airplanes with a maximum certificated takeoff weight of more than 75,000 pounds that were owned or leased by the air carrier on November 5, 1990, regardless of whether such airplanes were operated by that air carrier or foreign air carrier on that date.

(3) For operations conducted between the State of Hawaii and a point outside the contiguous United States—

(i) The number of Stage 2 airplanes used to conduct such operations as of November 5, 1990; and

(ii) Any change to that number during the calendar year being reported, including the date of such change.

(d) Reports or amended reports for years predating this regulation are required to be filed concurrently with the next annual report.

[Docket No. 28213, 61 FR 66185, Dec. 16, 1996]

§ 91.879 – 91.899 [Reserved]

Subpart J—Waivers

§ 91.901 [Reserved]

§ 91.903 Policy and procedures.

(a) The Administrator may issue a certificate of waiver authorizing the operation of aircraft in deviation from any rule listed in this subpart if the Administrator finds that the proposed operation can be safely conducted under the terms of that certificate of waiver.

(b) An application for a certificate of waiver under this part is made on a form and in a manner prescribed by the Administrator and may be submitted to any FAA office.

(c) A certificate of waiver is effective as specified in that certificate of waiver.

[Docket No. 18334, 54 FR 34325, Aug. 18, 1989]

§ 91.905 List of rules subject to waivers.

[Docket No. 18334, 54 FR 34325, Aug. 18, 1989; as amended by Amdt. 91–227, 56 FR 65661, Dec. 17, 1991]

§ 91.907 – 91.999 [Reserved]

APPENDICES TO PART 91

APPENDIX A TO PART 91
CATEGORY II OPERATIONS: MANUAL,
INSTRUMENTS, EQUIPMENT, AND
MAINTENANCE

1. CATEGORY II MANUAL

(a) *Application for approval.* An applicant for approval of a Category II manual or an amendment to an approved Category II manual must submit the proposed manual or amendment to the Flight Standards District Office having jurisdiction of the area in which the applicant is located. If the application requests an evaluation program, it must include the following:

(1) The location of the aircraft and the place where the demonstrations are to be conducted; and

(2) The date the demonstrations are to commence (at least 10 days after filing the application).

(b) *Contents.* Each Category II manual must contain:

(1) The registration number, make, and model of the aircraft to which it applies;

(2) A maintenance program as specified in section 4 of this appendix; and

(3) The procedures and instructions related to recognition of decision height, use of runway visual range information, approach monitoring, the decision region (the region between the middle marker and the decision height), the maximum permissible deviations of the basic ILS indicator within the decision region, a missed approach, use of airborne low approach equipment, minimum altitude for the use of the autopilot, instrument and equipment failure warning systems, instrument failure, and other procedures, instructions, and limitations that may be found necessary by the Administrator.

2. REQUIRED INSTRUMENTS AND EQUIPMENT

The instruments and equipment listed in this section must be installed in each aircraft operated in a Category II operation. This section does not require duplication of instruments and equipment required by § 91.205 or any other provisions of this chapter.

(a) *Group I.*

(1) Two localizer and glide slope receiving systems. Each system must provide a basic ILS display and each side of the instrument panel must have a basic ILS display. However, a single localizer antenna and a single glide slope antenna may be used.

(2) A communications system that does not affect the operation of at least one of the ILS systems.

(3) A marker beacon receiver that provides distinctive aural and visual indications of the outer and the middle markers.

(4) Two gyroscopic pitch and bank indicating systems.

(5) Two gyroscopic direction indicating systems.

(6) Two airspeed indicators.

(7) Two sensitive altimeters adjustable for barometric pressure, each having a placarded correction for altimeter scale error and for the wheel height of the aircraft. After June 26, 1979, two sensitive altimeters adjustable for barometric pressure, having markings at 20-foot intervals and each having a placarded correction for altimeter scale error and for the wheel height of the aircraft.

(8) Two vertical speed indicators.

(9) A flight control guidance system that consists of either an automatic approach coupler or a flight director system. A flight director system must display computed information as steering command in relation to an ILS localizer and, on the same instrument, either computed information as pitch command in relation to an ILS glide slope or basic ILS glide slope information. An automatic approach coupler must provide at least automatic steering in relation to an ILS localizer. The flight control guidance system may be operated from one of the receiving systems required by subparagraph (1) of this paragraph.

(10) For Category II operations with decision heights below 150 feet either a marker beacon receiver providing aural and visual indications of the inner marker or a radio altimeter.

(b) *Group II.*

(1) Warning systems for immediate detection by the pilot of system faults in items (1), (4), (5), and (9) of Group I and, if installed for use in Category III operations, the radio altimeter and autothrottle system.

(2) Dual controls.

(3) An externally vented static pressure system with an alternate static pressure source.

(4) A windshield wiper or equivalent means of providing adequate cockpit visibility for a safe visual transition by either pilot to touchdown and rollout.

(5) A heat source for each airspeed system pitot tube installed or an equivalent means of preventing malfunctioning due to icing of the pitot system.

3. INSTRUMENTS AND EQUIPMENT APPROVAL

(a) *General.* The instruments and equipment required by section 2 of this appendix must be approved as provided in this section before being used in Category II operations. Before presenting an aircraft for approval of the instruments and equipment, it must be shown that since the beginning of the 12th calendar month before the date of submission—

(1) The ILS localizer and glide slope equipment were bench checked according to the manufacturer's instructions and found to meet those standards specified in RTCA Paper 23–63/DO–117 dated March 14, 1963, "Standard Adjustment Criteria for Airborne Localizer and Glide Slope Receivers," which may be obtained from the RTCA Secretariat, 1425 K St. NW., Washington, DC 20005.

(2) The altimeters and the static pressure systems were tested and inspected in accordance with Appendix E to part 43 of this chapter; and

(3) All other instruments and items of equipment specified in section 2(a) of this appendix that are listed in the proposed maintenance program were bench checked and found to meet the manufacturer's specifications.

(b) *Flight control guidance system.* All components of the flight control guidance system must be approved as installed by the evaluation program specified in paragraph (e) of this section if they have not been approved for Category III operations under applicable type or supplemental type certification procedures. In addition, subsequent changes to make, model, or design of the components must be approved under this paragraph. Related systems or devices, such as the autothrottle and computed missed approach guidance system, must be approved in the same manner if they are to be used for Category II operations.

(c) *Radio altimeter.* A radio altimeter must meet the performance criteria of this paragraph for original approval and after each subsequent alteration.

(1) It must display to the flight crew clearly and positively the wheel height of the main landing gear above the terrain.

(2) It must display wheel height above the terrain to an accuracy of plus or minus 5 feet or 5 percent, whichever is greater, under the following conditions:

(i) Pitch angles of zero to plus or minus 5 degrees about the mean approach attitude.

(ii) Roll angles of zero to 20 degrees in either direction.

(iii) Forward velocities from minimum approach speed up to 200 knots.

(iv) Sink rates from zero to 15 feet per second at altitudes from 100 to 200 feet.

(3) Over level ground, it must track the actual altitude of the aircraft without significant lag or oscillation.

(4) With the aircraft at an altitude of 200 feet or less, any abrupt change in terrain representing no more than 10 percent of the aircraft's altitude must not cause the altimeter to unlock, and indicator response to such changes must not exceed 0.1 seconds and, in addition, if the system unlocks for greater changes, it must reacquire the signal in less than 1 second.

(5) Systems that contain a push-to-test feature must test the entire system (with or without an antenna) at a simulated altitude of less than 500 feet.

(6) The system must provide to the flight crew a positive failure warning display any time there is a loss of power or an absence of ground return signals within the designed range of operating altitudes.

(d) *Other instruments and equipment.* All other instruments and items of equipment required by § 2 of this appendix must be capable of performing as necessary for Category II operations. Approval is also required after each subsequent alteration to these instruments and items of equipment.

(e) *Evaluation program—*

(1) *Application.* Approval by evaluation is requested as a part of the application for approval of the Category II manual.

(2) *Demonstrations.* Unless otherwise authorized by the Administrator, the evaluation program for each aircraft requires the demonstrations specified in this paragraph. At least 50 ILS approaches must be flown with at least five approaches on each of three different ILS facilities and no more than one half of the total approaches on any one ILS facility. All approaches shall be flown under simulated instrument conditions to a 100-foot decision height and 90 percent of the total approaches made must be successful. A successful approach is one in which—

(i) At the 100-foot decision height, the indicated airspeed and heading are satisfactory for a normal flare and landing (speed must be plus or minus 5 knots of programmed airspeed, but may not be less than computed threshold speed if autothrottles are used);

(ii) The aircraft at the 100-foot decision height, is positioned so that the cockpit is within, and tracking so as to remain within, the lateral confines of the runway extended;

(iii) Deviation from glide slope after leaving the outer marker does not exceed 50 percent of full-scale deflection as displayed on the ILS indicator;

(iv) No unusual roughness or excessive attitude changes occur after leaving the middle marker; and

91

(v) In the case of an aircraft equipped with an approach coupler, the aircraft is sufficiently in trim when the approach coupler is disconnected at the decision height to allow for the continuation of a normal approach and landing.

(3) *Records.* During the evaluation program the following information must be maintained by the applicant for the aircraft with respect to each approach and made available to the Administrator upon request:

(i) Each deficiency in airborne instruments and equipment that prevented the initiation of an approach.

(ii) The reasons for discontinuing an approach, including the altitude above the runway at which it was discontinued.

(iii) Speed control at the 100-foot decision height if auto throttles are used.

(iv) Trim condition of the aircraft upon disconnecting the auto coupler with respect to continuation to flare and landing.

(v) Position of the aircraft at the middle marker and at the decision height indicated both on a diagram of the basic ILS display and a diagram of the runway extended to the middle marker. Estimated touchdown point must be indicated on the runway diagram.

(vi) Compatibility of flight director with the auto coupler, if applicable.

(vii) Quality of overall system performance.

(4) *Evaluation.* A final evaluation of the flight control guidance system is made upon successful completion of the demonstrations. If no hazardous tendencies have been displayed or are otherwise known to exist, the system is approved as installed.

4. MAINTENANCE PROGRAM

(a) Each maintenance program must contain the following:

(1) A list of each instrument and item of equipment specified in § 2 of this appendix that is installed in the aircraft and approved for Category II operations, including the make and model of those specified in § 2(a).

(2) A schedule that provides for the performance of inspections under subparagraph (5) of this paragraph within 3 calendar months after the date of the previous inspection. The inspection must be performed by a person authorized by part 43 of this chapter, except that each alternate inspection may be replaced by a functional flight check. This functional flight check must be performed by a pilot holding a Category II pilot authorization for the type aircraft checked.

(3) A schedule that provides for the performance of bench checks for each listed instrument and item of equipment that is specified in section

2(a) within 12 calendar months after the date of the previous bench check.

(4) A schedule that provides for the performance of a test and inspection of each static pressure system in accordance with Appendix E to part 43 of this chapter within 12 calendar months after the date of the previous test and inspection.

(5) The procedures for the performance of the periodic inspections and functional flight checks to determine the ability of each listed instrument and item of equipment specified in section 2(a) of this appendix to perform as approved for Category II operations including a procedure for recording functional flight checks.

(6) A procedure for assuring that the pilot is informed of all defects in listed instruments and items of equipment.

(7) A procedure for assuring that the condition of each listed instrument and item of equipment upon which maintenance is performed is at least equal to its Category II approval condition before it is returned to service for Category II operations.

(8) A procedure for an entry in the maintenance records required by § 43.9 of this chapter that shows the date, airport, and reasons for each discontinued Category II operation because of a malfunction of a listed instrument or item of equipment.

(b) *Bench check.* A bench check required by this section must comply with this paragraph.

(1) It must be performed by a certificated repair station holding one of the following ratings as appropriate to the equipment checked:

(i) An instrument rating.

(ii) A radio rating.

(iii) A rating issued under subpart D of part 145 of this chapter.

(2) It must consist of removal of an instrument or item of equipment and performance of the following:

(i) A visual inspection for cleanliness, impending failure, and the need for lubrication, repair, or replacement of parts;

(ii) Correction of items found by that visual inspection; and

(iii) Calibration to at least the manufacturer's specifications unless otherwise specified in the approved Category II manual for the aircraft in which the instrument or item of equipment is installed.

(c) *Extensions.* After the completion of one maintenance cycle of 12 calendar months, a request to extend the period for checks, tests, and inspections is approved if it is shown that the performance of particular equipment justifies the requested extension.

[Docket No. 18334, 54 FR 34325, Aug. 18, 1989]

APPENDIX B TO PART 91
AUTHORIZATIONS TO EXCEED MACH 1
(SECTION 91.817)

SECTION 1. APPLICATION

(a) An applicant for an authorization to exceed Mach 1 must apply in a form and manner prescribed by the Administrator and must comply with this appendix.

(b) In addition, each application for an authorization to exceed Mach 1 covered by section 2(a) of this appendix must contain all information requested by the Administrator necessary to assist him in determining whether the designation of a particular test area or issuance of a particular authorization is a "major Federal action significantly affecting the quality of the human environment" within the meaning of the National Environmental Policy Act of 1969 (42 U.S.C. 4321 *et seq.*), and to assist him in complying with that act and with related Executive Orders, guidelines, and orders prior to such action.

(c) In addition, each application for an authorization to exceed Mach 1 covered by section 2(a) of this appendix must contain—

(1) Information showing that operation at a speed greater than Mach 1 is necessary to accomplish one or more of the purposes specified in section 2(a) of this appendix, including a showing that the purpose of the test cannot be safely or properly accomplished by overocean testing;

(2) A description of the test area proposed by the applicant, including an environmental analysis of that area meeting the requirements of paragraph (b) of this section; and

(3) Conditions and limitations that will ensure that no measurable sonic boom overpressure will reach the surface outside of the designated test area.

(d) An application is denied if the Administrator finds that such action is necessary to protect or enhance the environment.

SECTION 2. ISSUANCE

(a) For a flight in a designated test area, an authorization to exceed Mach 1 may be issued when the Administrator has taken the environmental protective actions specified in section 1(b) of this appendix and the applicant shows one or more of the following:

(1) The flight is necessary to show compliance with airworthiness requirements.

(2) The flight is necessary to determine the sonic boom characteristics of the airplane or to establish means of reducing or eliminating the effects of sonic boom.

(3) The flight is necessary to demonstrate the conditions and limitations under which speeds greater than a true flight Mach number of 1 will not cause a measurable sonic boom overpressure to reach the surface.

(b) For a flight outside of a designated test area, an authorization to exceed Mach 1 may be issued if the applicant shows conservatively under paragraph (a)(3) of this section that—

(1) The flight will not cause a measurable sonic boom overpressure to reach the surface when the aircraft is operated under conditions and limitations demonstrated under paragraph (a)(3) of this section; and

(2) Those conditions and limitations represent all foreseeable operating conditions.

SECTION 3. DURATION

(a) An authorization to exceed Mach 1 is effective until it expires or is surrendered, or until it is suspended or terminated by the Administrator. Such an authorization may be amended or suspended by the Administrator at any time if the Administrator finds that such action is necessary to protect the environment. Within 30 days of notification of amendment, the holder of the authorization must request reconsideration or the amendment becomes final. Within 30 days of notification of suspension, the holder of the authorization must request reconsideration or the authorization is automatically terminated. If reconsideration is requested within the 30-day period, the amendment or suspension continues until the holder shows why the authorization should not be amended or terminated. Upon such showing, the Administrator may terminate or amend the authorization if the Administrator finds that such action is necessary to protect the environment, or he may reinstate the authorization without amendment if he finds that termination or amendment is not necessary to protect the environment.

(b) Findings and actions by the Administrator under this section do not affect any certificate issued under title VI of the Federal Aviation Act of 1958.

[Docket No. 18334, 54 FR 34327, Aug. 18, 1989]

APPENDIX C TO PART 91
OPERATIONS IN THE NORTH ATLANTIC (NAT)
MINIMUM NAVIGATION PERFORMANCE
SPECIFICATIONS (MNPS) AIRSPACE

SECTION 1

NAT MNPS airspace is that volume of airspace between FL 285 and FL 420 extending between latitude 27 degrees north and the North Pole, bounded in the east by the eastern boundaries of control areas Santa Maria Oceanic, Shanwick Oceanic, and Reykjavik Oceanic and in the west by the western boundary of Reykjavik Oceanic Control Area, the western boundary of Gander Oceanic Control Area, and the western boundary of New York Oceanic Control Area, excluding the areas west of 60 degrees west and south of 38 degrees 30 minutes north.

SECTION 2

The navigation performance capability required for aircraft to be operated in the airspace defined in section 1 of this appendix is as follows:

(a) The standard deviation of lateral track errors shall be less than 6.3 NM (11.7 Km). Standard deviation is a statistical measure of data about a mean value. The mean is zero nautical miles. The overall form of data is such that the plus and minus 1 standard deviation about the mean encompasses approximately 68 percent of the data and plus or minus 2 deviations encompasses approximately 95 percent.

(b) The proportion of the total flight time spent by aircraft 30 NM (55.6 Km) or more off the cleared track shall be less than 5.3×10^{-4} (less than 1 hour in 1,887 flight hours).

(c) The proportion of the total flight time spent by aircraft between 50 NM and 70 NM (92.6 Km and 129.6 Km) off the cleared track shall be less than 13×10^{-5} (less than 1 hour in 7,693 flight hours.)

SECTION 3

Air traffic control (ATC) may authorize an aircraft operator to deviate from the requirements of § 91.705 for a specific flight if, at the time of flight plan filing for that flight, ATC determines that the aircraft may be provided appropriate separation and that the flight will not interfere with, or impose a burden upon, the operations of other aircraft which meet the requirements of § 91.705.

[Docket No. 18334, 54 FR 34327, Aug. 18, 1989; as amended by Amdt. 91–254, 62 FR 17487, April 9, 1997]

APPENDIX D TO PART 91
AIRPORTS/LOCATIONS:
SPECIAL OPERATING RESTRICTIONS

Section 1. Locations at which the requirements of § 91.215(b)(2) apply.

The requirements of § 91.215(b)(2) apply below 10,000 feet above the surface within a 30-nautical-mile radius of each location in the following list:

Atlanta, GA (The William B. Hartsfield Atlanta International Airport)
Baltimore, MD
(Baltimore Washington International Airport)
Boston, MA (General Edward Lawrence Logan International Airport)
Chantilly, VA
(Washington Dulles International Airport)
Charlotte, NC
(Charlotte/Douglas International Airport)
Chicago, IL
(Chicago-O'Hare International Airport)
Cleveland, OH
(Cleveland-Hopkins International Airport)
Dallas, TX (Dallas/Fort Worth Regional Airport)
Denver, CO (Denver International Airport)
Detroit, MI (Metropolitan Wayne County Airport)
Honolulu, HI (Honolulu International Airport)
Houston, TX (Houston Intercontinental Airport)
Kansas City, KS
(Mid-Continent International Airport)
Las Vegas, NV (McCarran International Airport)
Los Angeles, CA
(Los Angeles International Airport)
Memphis, TN (Memphis International Airport)
Miami, FL (Miami International Airport)
Minneapolis, MN
(Minneapolis-St. Paul International Airport)
Newark, NJ (Newark International Airport)
New Orleans, LA (New Orleans International Airport —Moisant Field)
New York, NY
(John F. Kennedy International Airport)
New York, NY (LaGuardia Airport)
Orlando, FL
(Orlando International Airport)
Philadelphia, PA
(Philadelphia International Airport)
Phoenix, AZ
(Phoenix Sky Harbor International Airport)
Pittsburgh, PA
(Greater Pittsburgh International Airport)
St. Louis, MO
(Lambert-St. Louis International Airport)
Salt Lake City, UT
(Salt Lake City International Airport)

San Diego, CA (San Diego International
    Airport)
San Francisco, CA
    (San Francisco International Airport)
Seattle, WA
    (Seattle-Tacoma International Airport)
Tampa, FL (Tampa International Airport)
Washington, DC (Washington National Airport)

Section 2. Airports at which the requirements
of § 91.215(b)(5)(ii) apply.

Section 3. Locations at which fixed-wing Special VFR operations are prohibited.

The Special VFR weather minimums of
§ 91.157 do not apply to the following airports:

Atlanta, GA (The William B. Hartsfield Atlanta
    International Airport)
Baltimore, MD
    (Baltimore/Washington International Airport)
Boston, MA (General Edward Lawrence Logan
    International Airport)
Buffalo, NY
    (Greater Buffalo International Airport)
Chicago, IL
    (Chicago-O'Hare International Airport)
Cleveland, OH
    (Cleveland-Hopkins International Airport)
Columbus, OH
    (Port Columbus International Airport)
Covington, KY
    (Greater Cincinnati International Airport)
Dallas, TX (Dallas/Fort Worth Regional Airport)
Dallas, TX (Love Field)
Denver, CO (Denver International Airport)
Detroit, MI (Metropolitan Wayne County
    Airport)
Honolulu, HI (Honolulu International Airport)
Houston, TX (Houston Intercontinental Airport)
Indianapolis, IN
    (Indianapolis International Airport)
Los Angeles, CA
    (Los Angeles International Airport)
Louisville, KY (Standiford Field)
Memphis, TN (Memphis International Airport)
Miami, FL (Miami International Airport)
Minneapolis, MN
    (Minneapolis-St. Paul International Airport)
Newark, NJ (Newark International Airport)
New York, NY
    (John F. Kennedy International Airport)
New York, NY (LaGuardia Airport)

New Orleans, LA (New Orleans International
    Airport—Moisant Field)
Philadelphia, PA
    (Philadelphia International Airport)
Pittsburgh, PA
    (Greater Pittsburgh International Airport)
Portland, OR (Portland International Airport)
San Francisco, CA
    (San Francisco International Airport)
Seattle, WA
    (Seattle-Tacoma International Airport)
St. Louis, MO
    (Lambert-St. Louis International Airport)
Tampa, FL (Tampa International Airport)
Washington, DC (Washington National Airport)

Section 4. Locations at which solo student pilot
activity is not permitted.

Pursuant to § 91.131(b)(2), solo student pilot
operations are not permitted at any of the following airports.

Atlanta, GA (The William B. Hartsfield Atlanta
    International Airport)
Boston, MA (General Edward Lawrence Logan
    International Airport)
Chicago, IL
    (Chicago-O'Hare International Airport)
Dallas, TX (Dallas/Fort Worth Regional Airport)
Los Angeles, CA
    (Los Angeles International Airport)
Miami, FL (Miami International Airport)
Newark, NJ (Newark International Airport)
New York, NY
    (John F. Kennedy International Airport)
New York, NY (LaGuardia Airport)
San Francisco, CA
    (San Francisco International Airport)
Washington, DC (Washington National Airport)
Andrews Air Force Base, MD

[Docket No. 24458, Amdt. 91–227, 56 FR 65661, Dec.
17, 1991; as amended by Amdt. 91–237, 59 FR 6547,
Feb. 11, 1994; 59 FR 37667, July 25, 1994]

91

APPENDIX E TO PART 91
AIRPLANE FLIGHT RECORDER SPECIFICATIONS

Parameters	Range	Installed system¹ minimum accuracy (to recovered data)	Sampling interval (per second)	Resolution⁴ read out
Relative Time (From Recorded on Prior to Takeoff)	8 hr minimum	±0.125% per hour	1	1 sec.
Indicated Airspeed	V_S0 to V_D (KIAS)	±5% or ±10 kts, whichever is greater. Resolution 2 kts. below 175 KIAS.	1	1%³
Altitude	–1,000 ft. to max cert. alt. of A/C	–100 to ±700 ft. (see Table 1. TSO C51-a)	11	25 to 150 ft.
Magnetic Heading	360°	±5°	1	1°
Vertical Acceleration	–3g to +6g	±0.2g in addition to ±0.3g maximum datum	4 (or 1 per second where peaks, ref. to 1g are recorded)	0.03g
Longitudinal Acceleration	±1.0g	±1.5% max. range excluding datum error of ±5%	2	0.01g
Pitch Attitude	100% of usable	±2°	1	0.8°
Roll Attitude	±60° of 100% of usable range, whichever is greater	±2°	1	0.8°
Stabilizer Trim Position, or Pitch Control Position	Full Range	±3% unless higher uniquely required	1	1%³
Engine Power, Each Engine: Fan or N1 Speed or EPR or cockpit indications used for aircraft certification OR	Full Range	±3% unless higher uniquely required	1	1%³
	Maximum Range	±5%	1	1%³
Prop. speed and Torque (sample once/sec as close together as practicable)	—	—	1 (prop speed) / 1 (torque)	1%³ / 1%³
Altitude Rate² (need depends on altitude resolution)	±8,000 fpm	±10%. Resolution 250 fpm below 12,000 ft. indicated	1	250 fpm below 12,000
Angle of Attack² (need depends on altitude resolution)	–20° to 40° or 100% of usable range	±2°	1	0.8%³
Radio Transmitter Keying (Discrete)	On/Off	—	1	—
TE Flaps (Discrete or Analog)	Each discrete position (U.D. T/O, AAP) OR	—	1	—
LE Flaps (Discrete or Analog)	Analog 0–100% range / Each discrete position (U.D. T/O, AAP) OR	±3%	1 / 1	1%³ / —
Thrust Reverser, Each Engine (Discrete)	Analog 0–100% range / Stowed or full reverse	±3°	1 / —	1%³
Spoiler/Speed brake (Discrete)	Stowed or out	—	1	—
Autopilot Engaged (Discrete)	Engaged or Disengaged	—	1	—

¹ When data sources are aircraft instruments (except altimeters) of acceptable quality to fly the aircraft the recording system excluding these sensors (but including all other characteristics of the recording system) shall contribute no more than half of the values in this column.

² If data from the altitude encoding altimeter (100 ft. resolution) is used, then either one of these parameters should also be recorded. If however, altitude is recorded at a minimum resolution of 25 feet, then these two parameters can be omitted.

³ Percent of full range.   ⁴ This column applies to aircraft manufactured after October 11, 1991.

[Docket No. 18334, 54 FR 34327, Aug. 18, 1989]

APPENDIX F TO PART 91
HELICOPTER FLIGHT RECORDER SPECIFICATIONS

Parameters	Range	Installed system[1] minimum accuracy (to recovered data)	Sampling interval (per second)	Resolution[3] read out
Relative Time (from recorded on prior to takeoff)	4 hr minimum	±0.125% per hour	1	1 sec.
Indicated Airspeed	V_{min} to V_D (KIAS) (minimum airspeed signal attainable with installed pilot-static system)	±5% or ±10 kts, whichever is greater	1	1 kt.
Altitude	−1,000 ft. to 20,000 ft. pressure altitude	±100 to ±700 ft. (see Table 1. TSO C51-a)	1	25 to 150 ft.
Magnetic Heading	360°	±5°	1	1°
Vertical Acceleration	−3g to +6g	±0.2g in addition to ±0.3g maximum datum	4 (or 1 per second where peaks, ref. to 1g are recorded)	0.05g
Longitudinal Acceleration	±1.0g	±1.5% max. range excluding datum error of ±5%	2	0.03g
Pitch Attitude	100% of usable range	±2°	1	0.8°
Roll Attitude	±60 or 100% of usable range, whichever is greater	±2°	1	0.8°
Altitude Rate	±8,000 fpm	±10% Resolution 250 fpm below 12,000 ft. indicated	1	250 fpm below 12,000
Engine Power, Each Engine:				
Main Rotor Speed	Maximum Range	±5%	1	1%[2]
Free or Power Turbine	Maximum Range	±5%	1	1%[2]
Engine Torque	Maximum Range	±5%	1	1%[2]
Flight Control Hydraulic Pressure:				
Primary (Discrete)	High / Low		1	
Secondary – if applicable (Discrete)	High / Low		1	
Radio Transmitter Keying (Discrete)	On / Off		1	
Autopilot Engaged (Discrete)	Engaged or Disengaged		1	
SAS Status – Engaged (Discrete)	Engaged or Disengaged		1	
SAS Fault Status (Discrete)	Fault / OK		1	
Flight Controls:				
Collective	Full range	±3%	2	1%[2]
Pedal Position	Full range	±3%	2	1%[2]
Lat. Cyclic	Full range	±3%	2	1%[2]
Long. Cyclic	Full range	±3%	2	1%[2]
Controllable Stabilizer Position	Full range	±3%	2	1%[2]

[1] When data sources are aircraft instruments (except altimeters) of acceptable quality to fly the aircraft the recording system excluding these sensors (but including all other characteristics of the recording system) shall contribute no more than half of the values in this column.
[2] Percent of full range.
[3] This column applies to aircraft manufactured after October 11, 1991.

[Docket No. 18334, 54 FR 34328, Aug. 18, 1989; 54 FR 41211, Oct. 5, 1989; 54 FR 53036, Dec. 26, 1989]

91

APPENDIX G TO PART 91

OPERATIONS IN REDUCED VERTICAL
SEPARATION MINIMUM (RVSM) AIRSPACE

SECTION 1. DEFINITIONS

Reduced Vertical Separation Minimum (RVSM) Airspace. Within RVSM airspace, air traffic control (ATC) separates aircraft by a minimum of 1,000 feet vertically between flight level (FL) 290 and FL 410 inclusive. RVSM airspace is special qualification airspace; the operator and the aircraft used by the operator must be approved by the Administrator. Air-traffic control notifies operators of RVSM by providing route planning information. Section 8 of this appendix identifies airspace where RVSM may be applied.

RVSM Group Aircraft. Aircraft within a group of aircraft, approved as a group by the Administrator, in which each of the aircraft satisfy each of the following:

(a) The aircraft have been manufactured to the same design, and have been approved under the same type certificate, amended type certificate, or supplemental type certificate.

(b) The static system of each aircraft is installed in a manner and position that is the same as those of the other aircraft in the group. The same static source error correction is incorporated in each aircraft of the group.

(c) The avionics units installed in each aircraft to meet the minimum RVSM equipment requirements of this appendix are:

(1) Manufactured to the same manufacturer specification and have the same part number; or

(2) Of a different manufacturer or part number, if the applicant demonstrates that the equipment provides equivalent system performance.

RVSM Nongroup Aircraft. An aircraft that is approved for RVSM operations as an individual aircraft.

RVSM Flight envelope. An RVSM flight envelope includes the range of Mach number, weight divided by atmospheric pressure ratio, and altitudes over which an aircraft is approved to be operated in cruising flight within RVSM airspace. RVSM flight envelopes are defined as follows:

(a) The *full RVSM flight envelope* is bounded as follows:

(1) The altitude flight envelope extends from FL 290 upward to the lowest altitude of the following:

(i) FL 410 (the RVSM altitude limit);

(ii) The maximum certificated altitude for the aircraft; or

(iii) The altitude limited by cruise thrust, buffet, or other flight limitations.

(2) The airspeed flight envelopes extends:

(i) From the airspeed of the slats/flaps-up maximum endurance (holding) airspeed, or the maneuvering airspeed, whichever is lower;

(ii) To the maximum operating airspeed (V_{MO}/M_{MO}), or airspeed limited by cruise thrust buffet, or other flight limitations, whichever is lower.

(3) All permissible gross weights within the flight envelopes defined in paragraphs (1) and (2) of this definition.

(b) The *basic RVSM flight envelope* is the same as the full RVSM flight envelope except that the airspeed flight envelope extends:

(1) From the airspeed of the slats/flaps-up maximum endurance (holding) airspeed, or the maneuver airspeed, whichever is lower;

(2) To the upper Mach/airspeed boundary defined for the full RVSM flight envelope, or a specified lower value not less than the long-range cruise Mach number plus .04 Mach, unless further limited by available cruise thrust, buffet, or other flight limitations.

SECTION 2. AIRCRAFT APPROVAL

(a) An operator may be authorized to conduct RVSM operations if the Administrator finds that its aircraft comply with this section.

(b) The application for authorization shall submit the appropriate data package for aircraft approval. The package must consist of at least the following:

(1) An identification of the RVSM aircraft group or the nongroup aircraft;

(2) A definition of the RVSM flight envelopes applicable to the subject aircraft;

(3) Documentation that establishes compliance with the applicable RVSM aircraft requirements of this section; and

(4) The conformity tests used to ensure that aircraft approved with the data package meet the RVSM aircraft requirements.

(c) *Altitude-keeping equipment: All aircraft.* To approve an aircraft group or a nongroup aircraft, the Administrator must find that the aircraft meets the following requirements:

(1) The aircraft must be equipped with two operational independent altitude measurement systems.

(2) The aircraft must be equipped with at least one automatic altitude control system that controls the aircraft altitude—

(i) Within a tolerance band of ±65 feet about an acquired altitude when the aircraft is operated in straight and level flight under nonturbulent, nongust conditions; or

(ii) Within a tolerance band of ±130 feet under nonturbulent, nongust conditions for aircraft for which application for type certification occurred on or before April 9, 1997 that are equipped with an automatic altitude control system with flight management/performance system inputs.

(3) The aircraft must be equipped with an altitude alert system that signals an alert when the altitude displayed to the flight crew deviates from the selected altitude by more than:

(i) ±300 feet for aircraft for which application for type certification was made on or before April 9, 1997; or

(ii) ±200 feet for aircraft for which application for type certification is made after April 9, 1997.

(d) *Altimetry system error containment: Group aircraft for which application for type certification was made on or before April 9, 1997.* To approve group aircraft for which application for type certification was made on or before April 9, 1997, the Administrator must find that the altimetry system error (ASE) is contained as follows:

(1) At the point in the basic RVSM flight envelope where mean ASE reaches its largest absolute value, the absolute value may not exceed 80 feet.

(2) At the point in the basic RVSM flight envelope where mean ASE plus three standard deviations reaches its largest absolute value, the absolute value may not exceed 200 feet.

(3) At the point in the full RVSM flight envelope where mean ASE reaches its largest absolute value, the absolute value may not exceed 120 feet.

(4) At the point in the full RVSM flight envelope where mean ASE plus three standard deviations reaches its largest absolute value, the absolute value may not exceed 245 feet.

(5) *Necessary operating restrictions.* If the applicant demonstrates that its aircraft otherwise comply with the ASE containment requirements, the Administrator may establish an operating restriction on that applicant's aircraft to restrict the aircraft from operating in areas of the basic RVSM flight envelope where the absolute value of mean ASE exceeds 80 feet, and/or the absolute value of mean ASE plus three standard deviations exceeds 200 feet; or from operating in areas of the full RVSM flight envelope where the absolute value of the mean ASE exceeds 120 feet and/or the absolute value of the mean ASE plus three standard deviations exceeds 245 feet.

(e) *Altimetry system error containment: Group aircraft for which application for type certification is made after April 9, 1997.* To approve group aircraft for which application for type certification is made after April 9, 1997, the Administrator must find that the altimetry system error (ASE) is contained as follows:

(1) At the point in the full RVSM flight envelope where mean ASE reaches its largest absolute value, the absolute value may not exceed 80 feet.

(2) At the point in the full RVSM flight envelope where mean ASE plus three standard deviations reaches its largest absolute value, the absolute value may not exceed 200 feet.

(f) *Altimetry system error containment: Nongroup aircraft.* To approve a nongroup aircraft, the Administrator must find that the altimetry system error (ASE) is contained as follows:

(1) For each condition in the basic RVSM flight envelope, the largest combined absolute value for residual static source error plus the avionics error may not exceed 160 feet.

(2) For each condition in the full RVSM flight envelope, the largest combined absolute value for residual static source error plus the avionics error may not exceed 200 feet.

(g) If the Administrator finds that the applicant's aircraft comply with this section, the Administrator notifies the applicant in writing.

SECTION 3. OPERATOR AUTHORIZATION

(a) Authority for an operator to conduct flight in airspace where RVSM is applied is issued in operations specifications or a Letter of Authorization, as appropriate. To issue an RVSM authorization, the Administrator must find that the operator's aircraft have been approved in accordance with Section 2 of this appendix and that the operator complies with this section.

(b) An applicant for authorization to operate within RVSM airspace shall apply in a form and manner prescribed by the Administrator. The application must include the following:

(1) An approved RVSM maintenance program outlining procedures to maintain RVSM aircraft in accordance with the requirements of this appendix. Each program must contain the following:

(i) Periodic inspections, functional flight tests, and maintenance and inspection procedures, with acceptable maintenance practices, for ensuring continued compliance with the RVSM aircraft requirements.

(ii) A quality assurance program for ensuring continuing accuracy and reliability of test equipment used for testing aircraft to determine compliance with the RVSM aircraft requirements.

(iii) Procedures for returning noncompliant aircraft to service.

(2) For an applicant who operates under part 121 or 135, initial and recurring pilot training requirements.

(3) Policies and Procedures. An applicant who operates under part 121 or 135 shall submit RVSM policies and procedures that will enable it to conduct RVSM operations safely.

(c) Validation and Demonstration. In a manner prescribed by the Administrator, the operator must provide evidence that:

(1) It is capable to operate and maintain each aircraft or aircraft group for which it applies for approval to operate in RVSM airspace; and

(2) Each pilot has an adequate knowledge of RVSM requirements, policies, and procedures.

Section 4. RVSM Operations

(a) Each person requesting a clearance to operate within RVSM airspace shall correctly annotate the flight plan filed with air traffic control with the status of the operator and aircraft with regard to RVSM approval. Each operator shall verify RVSM applicability for the flight planned route through the appropriate flight planning information sources.

(b) No person may show, on the flight plan filed with air traffic control, an operator or aircraft as approved for RVSM operations, or operate on a route or in an area where RVSM approval is required, unless:

(1) The operator is authorized by the Administrator to perform such operations; and

(2) The aircraft has been approved and complies with the requirements of Section 2 of this appendix.

Section 5. Deviation Authority Approval

The Administrator may authorize an aircraft operator to deviate from the requirements of § 91.706 for a specific flight in RVSM airspace if that operator has not been approved in accordance with Section 3 of this appendix, and if:

(a) The operator submits an appropriate request with the air traffic control center controlling the airspace, (request should be made at least 48 hours in advance of the operation unless prevented by exceptional circumstances); and

(b) At the time of filing the flight plan for that flight, ATC determines that the aircraft may be provided appropriate separation and that the flight will not interfere with, or impose a burden on, the operations of operators who have been approved for RVSM operations in accordance with Section 3 of this appendix.

Section 6.
Reporting altitude-Keeping Errors

Each operator shall report to the Administrator each event in which the operator's aircraft has exhibited the following altitude-keeping performance:

(a) Total vertical error of 300 feet or more;

(b) Altimetry system error of 245 feet or more; or

(c) Assigned altitude deviation of 300 feet or more.

Section 7.
Removal or Amendment of Authority

The Administrator may amend operations specifications to revoke or restrict an RVSM authorization, or may revoke or restrict an RVSM letter of authorization, if the Administrator determines that the operator is not complying, or is unable to comply, with this appendix or subpart H of this part. Examples of reasons for amendment, revocation, or restriction include, but are not limited to, an operator's:

(a) Committing one of more altitude-keeping errors in RVSM airspace;

(b) Failing to make an effective and timely response to identify and correct an altitude-keeping error; or

(c) Failing to report an altitude-keeping error.

Section 8. Airspace Designation

RVSM may be applied in the following ICAO Flight Information Regions (FIRs): New York Oceanic, Gander Oceanic, Sondrestrom FIR, Reykjavik Oceanic, Shanwick Oceanic, and Santa Maria Oceanic.

RVSM may be effective in the Minimum Navigation Performance Specification (MNPS) airspace with the NAT. The MNPS airspace within the NAT is defined by the volume of airspace FL 285 and FL 420 extending between latitude 27 degrees north and the North Pole, bounded in the east by the eastern boundaries of control areas Santa Maria Oceanic, Shanwick Oceanic, and Reykjavik Oceanic and in the west by the western boundaries of control areas Reykjavik Oceanic, Gander Oceanic, and New York Oceanic, excluding the areas west of 60 degrees west and south of 38 degrees 30 minutes north.

[Docket No. 28870, 62 FR 17487, April 9, 1997]

PART 97
STANDARD INSTRUMENT APPROACH PROCEDURES

Subpart A — General

Sec.
97.1   Applicability.
97.3   Symbols and terms used in procedures.
97.5   Bearings; courses; headings; radials; miles.

Subpart B — Procedures

97.10   General.

Subpart C — TERPS Procedures

97.20   General.

Authority: 49 U.S.C. 106(g), 40103, 40113, 40120, 44701; and 14 CFR 11.49(b)(2).

Source: Docket No. 1580, 28 FR 6719, June 29, 1963, unless otherwise noted.

Subpart A — General

§ 97.1 Applicability.

This part prescribes standard instrument approach procedures for instrument letdown to airports in the United States and the weather minimums that apply to takeoffs and landings under IFR at those airports.

§ 97.3 Symbols and terms used in procedures.

As used in the standard terminal instrument procedures prescribed in this part—

(a) *A* means alternate airport weather minimum.

(b) *Aircraft approach category* means a grouping of aircraft based on a speed of 1.3 V_{S0} (at maximum certificated landing weight). V_{S0} and the maximum certificated landing weight are those values as established for the aircraft by the certificating authority of the country of registry. The categories are as follows:

(1) Category A: Speed less than 91 knots.

(2) Category B: Speed 91 knots or more but less than 121 knots.

(3) Category C: Speed 121 knots or more but less than 141 knots.

(4) Category D: Speed 141 knots or more but less than 166 knots.

(5) Category E: Speed 166 knots or more.

(c) Approach procedure segments for which altitudes (all altitudes prescribed are minimum altitudes unless otherwise specified) or courses, or both, are prescribed in procedures, are as follows:

(1) *Initial approach* is the segment between the initial approach fix and the intermediate fix or the point where the aircraft is established on the intermediate course or final approach course.

(2) *Initial approach altitude* means the altitude (or altitudes, in High Altitude Procedures) prescribed for the initial approach segment of an instrument approach.

(3) *Intermediate approach* is the segment between the intermediate fix or point and the final approach fix.

(4) *Final approach* is the segment between the final approach fix or point and the runway, airport, or missed-approach point.

(5) *Missed approach* is the segment between the missed-approach point, or point of arrival at decision height, and the missed-approach fix at the prescribed altitude.

(d) *C* means circling landing minimum, a statement of ceiling and visibility values, or minimum descent altitude and visibility, required for the circle-to-land maneuver.

(d–1) *Copter procedures* means helicopter procedures, with applicable minimums as prescribed in § 97.35 of this part. Helicopters may also use other procedures prescribed in Subpart C of this part and may use the Category A minimum descent altitude (MDA) or decision height (DH). The required visibility minimum may be reduced to one-half the published visibility minimum for Category A aircraft, but in no case may it be reduced to less than one-quarter mile or 1,200 feet RVR.

(e) *Ceiling minimum* means the minimum ceiling, expressed in feet above the surface of the airport, required for takeoff or required for designating an airport as an alternate airport.

(f) *D* means day.

(g) *FAF* means final approach fix.

(h) *HAA* means height above airport.

(h–1) *HAL* means height above a designated helicopter landing area used for helicopter instrument approach procedures.

(i) *HAT* means height above touchdown.

(j) *MAP* means missed approach point.

(k) *More than 65 knots* means an aircraft that has a stalling speed of more than 65 knots (as established in an approved flight manual) at maximum certificated landing weight with full flaps, landing gear extended, and power off.

(l) *MSA* means minimum safe altitude, an emergency altitude expressed in feet above mean sea level, which provides 1,000 feet clearance over all obstructions in that sector within 25 miles of the facility on which the procedure is based (LOM in ILS procedures).

97

(m) *N* means night.

(n) *NA* means not authorized.

(o) *NOPT* means no procedure turn required (altitude prescribed applies only if procedure turn is not executed).

(o-1) *Point in space approach* means a helicopter instrument approach procedure to a missed approach point that is more than 2,600 feet from an associated helicopter landing area.

(p) *Procedure turn* means the maneuver prescribed when it is necessary to reverse direction to establish the aircraft on an intermediate or final approach course. The outbound course, direction of turn, distance within which the turn must be completed, and minimum altitude are specified in the procedure. However, the point at which the turn may be commenced, and the type and rate of turn, is left to the discretion of the pilot.

(q) *RA* means radio altimeter setting height.

(r) *RVV* means runway visibility value.

(s) *S* means straight-in landing minimum, a statement of ceiling and visibility, minimum descent altitude and visibility, or decision height and visibility, required for a straight-in landing on a specified runway. The number appearing with the *S* indicates the runway to which the minimum applies. If a straight-in minimum is not prescribed in the procedure, the circling minimum specified applies to a straight-in landing.

(t) *Shuttle* means a shuttle, or race-track-type, pattern with 2-minute legs prescribed in lieu of a procedure turn.

(u) *65 knots or less* means an aircraft that has a stalling speed of 65 knots or less (as established in an approved flight manual) at maximum certificated landing weight with full flaps, landing gear extended, and power off.

(v) *T* means takeoff minimum.

(w) *TDZ* means touchdown zone.

(x) *Visibility minimum* means the minimum visibility specified for approach, or landing, or takeoff, expressed in statute miles, or in feet where RVR is reported.

(Secs. 307(c), 313(a), 601, Federal Aviation Act of 1958, as amended (49 U.S.C. 1348(c), 1354(a), 1421); sec. 6(c), Department of Transportation Act (49 U.S.C. 1655(c)))

[Docket No. 8130 32 FR 13911, Oct. 6, 1967; as amended by Amdt. 97–803, 37 FR 6287, March 28, 1972; Amdt. 97–1133, 44 FR 15659, March 15, 1979]

§ 97.5 Bearings; courses; headings; radials; miles.

(a) All bearings, courses, headings, and radials in this part are magnetic.

(b) RVR values are stated in feet. Other visibility values are stated in statute miles. All other mileages are stated in nautical miles.

[Docket No. 561, 32 FR 13912, Oct. 6, 1967]

Subpart B — Procedures

EDITORIAL NOTE: The procedures set forth in this subpart were formerly carried as §§ 609.100 through 609.500 of this title and were transferred to part 97 as §§ 97.11 through 97.19, respectively, but are not carried in the Code of Federal Regulations. For Federal Register citations affecting these procedures, see the List of CFR Sections Affected in the Finding Aids section of this volume.

§ 97.10 General.

This subpart prescribes standard instrument approach procedures other than those based on the criteria contained in the U.S. Standard for Terminal Instrument Approach Procedures (TERPs). Standard instrument approach procedures adopted by the FAA and described on FAA Form 3139 are incorporated into this part and made a part hereof as provided in 5 U.S.C. 552(a)(1) and pursuant to 1 CFR part 20. The incorporated standard instrument approach procedures are available for examination at the Rules Docket and at the National Flight Data Center, Federal Aviation Administration, 800 Independence Avenue SW., Washington, DC 20590. Copies of SIAPs adopted in a particular FAA Region are also available for examination at the headquarters of that region. Moreover, copies of SIAPs originating in a particular Flight Inspection District Office are available for examination at that office. Based on the information contained on FAA Form 3139, standard instrument approach procedures are portrayed on charts prepared for the use of pilots by the U.S. Coast and Geodetic Survey and other publishers of aeronautical charts.

[Docket No. 9748, 35 FR 5609, April 7, 1970]

Subpart C— TERPS Procedures

Source: Docket No. 8130, 32 FR 13912, Oct. 6, 1967, unless otherwise noted.

EDITORIAL NOTE: The procedures for §§ 97.21 through 97.35, respectively, are not carried in the Code of Federal Regulations. For FEDERAL REGISTER citations affecting these procedures, see the List of CFR Sections Affected in the Finding Aids section of this volume.

§ 97.20 General.

This subpart prescribes standard instrument approach procedures based on the criteria contained in the U.S. Standard for Terminal Instrument Approach Procedures (TERPs). The standard instrument approach procedures adopted by the FAA and described on FAA Form 8260–3, 8260–4, or 8260–5 are incorporated into this part

and made a part hereof as provided in 5 U.S.C. 552(a)(1) and pursuant to 1 CFR part 20. The incorporated standard instrument approach procedures are available for examination at the Rules Docket and at the National Flight Data Center, Federal Aviation Administration, 800 Independence Avenue SW, Washington, DC 20590. Copies of SIAPs adopted in a particular FAA Region are also available for examination at the headquarters of that Region. Moreover, copies of SIAPs originating in a particular Flight Inspection District Office are available for examination at that Office. Based on the information contained on FAA Form 8260–3, 8260–4, and 8260-5, standard instrument approach procedures are portrayed on charts prepared for the use of pilots by the U.S. Coast and Geodetic Survey and other publishers of aeronautical charts.

(Sec. 6(c) Department of Transportation Act. 49 U.S.C. 1655(c) and 5 U.S.C. 552(a)(1))

[Docket No. 9748, 35 FR 5609, April 7, 1970]

PART 103
ULTRALIGHT VEHICLES

Subpart A—General

Sec.

Authority: 49 U.S.C. 106(g), 40103–40104, 40113, 44701.

Source: Docket No. 21631, 47 FR 38776, Sept. 2, 1982, unless otherwise noted.

Subpart A—General

§ 103.1 Applicability.

This part prescribes rules governing the operation of ultralight vehicles in the United States. For the purposes of this part, an ultralight vehicle is a vehicle that:

(a) Is used or intended to be used for manned operation in the air by a single occupant;

(b) Is used or intended to be used for recreation or sport purposes only;

(c) Does not have any U.S. or foreign airworthiness certificate; and

(d) If unpowered, weighs less than 155 pounds; or

(e) If powered:

(1) Weighs less than 254 pounds empty weight, excluding floats and safety devices which are intended for deployment in a potentially catastrophic situation;

(2) Has a fuel capacity not exceeding 5 U.S. gallons;

(3) Is not capable of more than 55 knots calibrated airspeed at full power in level flight; and

(4) Has a power-off stall speed which does not exceed 24 knots calibrated airspeed.

§ 103.3 Inspection requirements.

(a) Any person operating an ultralight vehicle under this part shall, upon request, allow the Administrator, or his designee, to inspect the vehicle to determine the applicability of this part.

(b) The pilot or operator of an ultralight vehicle must, upon request of the Administrator, furnish satisfactory evidence that the vehicle is subject only to the provisions of this part.

§ 103.5 Waivers.

No person may conduct operations that require a deviation from this part except under a written waiver issued by the Administrator.

§ 103.7 Certification and registration.

(a) Notwithstanding any other section pertaining to certification of aircraft or their parts or equipment, ultralight vehicles and their component parts and equipment are not required to meet the airworthiness certification standards specified for aircraft or to have certificates of airworthiness.

(b) Notwithstanding any other section pertaining to airman certification, operators of ultralight vehicles are not required to meet any aeronautical knowledge, age, or experience requirements to operate those vehicles or to have airman or medical certificates.

(c) Notwithstanding any other section pertaining to registration and marking of aircraft, ultralight vehicles are not required to be registered or to bear markings of any type.

Subpart B—
Operating Rules

§ 103.9 Hazardous operations.

(a) No person may operate any ultralight vehicle in a manner that creates a hazard to other persons or property.

(b) No person may allow an object to be dropped from an ultralight vehicle if such action creates a hazard to other persons or property.

§ 103.11 Daylight operations.

(a) No person may operate an ultralight vehicle except between the hours of sunrise and sunset.

(b) Notwithstanding paragraph (a) of this section, ultralight vehicles may be operated during the twilight periods 30 minutes before official sunrise and 30 minutes after official sunset or, in Alaska, during the period of civil twilight as defined in the Air Almanac, if:

103

(1) The vehicle is equipped with an operating anticollision light visible for at least 3 statute miles; and

(2) All operations are conducted in uncontrolled airspace.

§ 103.13 Operation near aircraft; right-of-way rules.

(a) Each person operating an ultralight vehicle shall maintain vigilance so as to see and avoid aircraft and shall yield the right-of-way to all aircraft.

(b) No person may operate an ultralight vehicle in a manner that creates a collision hazard with respect to any aircraft.

(c) Powered ultralights shall yield the right-of-way to unpowered ultralights.

§ 103.15 Operations over congested areas.

No person may operate an ultralight vehicle over any congested area of a city, town, or settlement, or over any open air assembly of persons.

§ 103.17 Operations in certain airspace.

No person may operate an ultralight vehicle within Class A, Class B, Class C, or Class D airspace or within the lateral boundaries of the surface area of Class E airspace designated for an airport unless that person has prior authorization from the ATC facility having jurisdiction over that airspace.

[Docket No. 21631, 47 FR 38776, Sept. 2, 1982; as amended by Amdt. 103–17, 56 FR 65662, Dec. 17, 1991]

§ 103.19 Operations in prohibited or restricted areas.

No person may operate an ultralight vehicle in prohibited or restricted areas unless that person has permission from the using or controlling agency, as appropriate.

§ 103.20 Flight restrictions in the proximity of certain areas designated by notice to airmen.

No person may operate an ultralight vehicle in areas designated in a Notice to Airmen under § 91.143 or § 91.141 of this chapter, unless authorized by ATC.

[Docket No. 24454, 50 FR 4969, Feb. 5, 1985; as amended by Amdt. 103–3, 54 FR 34331, Aug. 18, 1989]

§ 103.21 Visual reference with the surface.

No person may operate an ultralight vehicle except by visual reference with the surface.

§ 103.23 Flight visibility and cloud clearance requirements.

No person may operate an ultralight vehicle when the flight visibility or distance from clouds is less than that in the table found below. All operations in Class A, Class B, Class C, and Class D airspace or Class E airspace designated for an airport must receive prior ATC authorization as required in § 103.17 of this part.

Airspace	Flight visibility	Distance from clouds
Class A	Not applicable	Not applicable
Class B	3 statute miles	Clear of clouds
Class C	3 statute miles	500 feet below 1,000 feet above 2,000 feet horizontal
Class D	3 statute miles	500 feet below 1,000 feet above 2,000 feet horizontal
Class E: Less than 10,000 feet MSL	3 statute miles	500 feet below 1,000 feet above 2,000 feet horizontal
At or above 10,000 feet MSL	5 statute miles	1,000 feet below 1,000 feet above 1 statute mile horizontal
Class G: 1,200 feet or less above the surface (regardless of MSL altitude)	1 statute mile	Clear of clouds
More than 1,200 feet above the surface but less than 10,000 feet MSL	1 statute mile	500 feet below 1,000 feet above 2,000 feet horizontal
More than 1,200 feet above the surface and at or above 10,000 feet MSL	5 statute miles	1,000 feet below 1,000 feet above 1 statute mile horizontal.

[Docket No. 21631, 47 FR 38776, Sept. 2, 1982; as amended by Amdt. 103–17, 56 FR 65662, Dec. 17, 1991]

PART 105
PARACHUTE JUMPING

Subpart A—General

Sec.
105.1   Applicability.

Subpart B—Operating Rules

105.11   Applicability.
105.13   General.
105.14   Radio equipment and use requirements.
105.15   Jumps over or into congested areas or open air assembly of persons.
105.17   Jumps over or onto airports.
105.19   Jumps in or into Class A, Class B, Class C, and Class D airspace.
105.23   Jumps in or into other airspace.
105.25   Information required, and notice of cancellation or postponement of jump.
105.27   Jumps over or within restricted or prohibited areas.
105.29   Flight visibility and clearance from clouds requirements.
105.33   Parachute jumps between sunset and sunrise.
105.35   Liquor and drugs.
105.37   Inspections.

Subpart C—Parachute Equipment

105.41   Applicability.
105.43   Parachute equipment and packing requirements.

Authority: 49 U.S.C. 106(g), 40113–40114, 44701–44702, 44721.

Source: Docket No. 1491, 27 FR 11636, Nov. 27, 1962, unless otherwise noted.

Subpart A—General

§ 105.1 Applicability.

(a) This part prescribes rules governing parachute jumps made in the United States except parachute jumps necessary because of an inflight emergency.

(b) For the purposes of this part, a *parachute jump* means the descent of a person, to the surface from an aircraft in flight, when he intends to use, or uses, a parachute during all or part of that descent.

Subpart B— Operating Rules

§ 105.11 Applicability.

(a) Except as provided in paragraphs (b) and (c) of this section, this subpart prescribes operating rules governing parachute jumps to which this part applies.

(b) This subpart does not apply to a parachute jump necessary to meet an emergency on the surface, when it is made at the direction, or with the approval, of an agency of the United States, or of a State, Puerto Rico, the District of Columbia, or a possession of the United States, or of a political subdivision of any of them.

(c) Sections 105.13 through 105.17 and §§ 105.27 through 105.37 of this subpart do not apply to a parachute jump made by a member of an Armed Force:

(1) Over or within a restricted area when that area is under the control of an Armed Force; or

(2) In military operations in uncontrolled airspace.

(d) Section 105.23 does not apply to a parachute jump made by a member of an Armed Force within a restricted area that extends upward from the surface when that area is under the control of an Armed Force.

[Docket No. 1491, 27 FR 11636, Nov. 27, 1962; as amended by Amdt. 105–4, 33 FR 11901, Aug. 22, 1968]

§ 105.13 General.

No person may make a parachute jump, and no pilot in command of an aircraft may allow a parachute jump to be made from that aircraft, if that jump creates a hazard to air traffic or to persons or property on the surface.

§ 105.14 Radio equipment and use requirements.

(a) Except when otherwise authorized by ATC—

(1) No person may make a parachute jump, and no pilot in command of an aircraft may allow a parachute jump to be made from that aircraft, in or into controlled airspace unless, during that flight—

(i) The aircraft is equipped with a functioning two-way radio communications system appropriate to the ATC facilities to be used;

(ii) Radio communications have been established between the aircraft and the nearest FAA air traffic control facility or FAA flight service station at least 5 minutes before the jumping activity is to begin, for the purpose of receiving information in the aircraft about known air traffic in the vicinity of the jumping activity; and

105

(iii) The information described in paragraph (a)(1)(ii) of this section has been received by the pilot in command and the jumpers in that flight; and

(2) The pilot in command of an aircraft used for any jumping activity in or into controlled airspace shall, during each flight—

(i) Maintain or have maintained a continuous watch on the appropriate frequency of the aircraft's radio communications system from the time radio communications are first established between the aircraft and ATC, until he advises ATC that the jumping activity is ended from that flight; and

(ii) Advise ATC that the jumping activity is ended for that flight when the last parachute jumper from the aircraft reaches the ground.

(b) If, during any flight, the required radio communications system is or becomes inoperative, any jumping activity from the aircraft in or into controlled airspace shall be abandoned. However, if the communications system becomes inoperative in flight after receipt of a required ATC authorization, the jumping activity from that flight may be continued.

[Docket No. 7824, 31 FR 16612, Dec. 29, 1966]

§ 105.15 Jumps over or into congested areas or open air assembly of persons.

(a) No person may make a parachute jump, and no pilot in command of an aircraft may allow a parachute jump to be made from that aircraft, over or into a congested area of a city, town, or settlement, or an open air assembly of person unless a certificate of authorization for that jump has been issued under this section. However, a parachutist may drift over that congested area or open air assembly with a fully deployed and properly functioning parachute if he is at a sufficient altitude to avoid creating a hazard to persons and property on the ground.

(b) An application for a certificate of authorization issued under this section is made in a form and in a manner prescribed by the Administrator and must be submitted to the FAA Flight Standards District Office having jurisdiction over the area in which the parachute jump is to be made, at least 4 days before the day of that jump.

(c) Each holder of a certificate of authorization issued under this section shall present that certificate for inspection upon the request of the Administrator, or any Federal, State, or local official.

[Docket No. 1491, 27 FR 11636, Nov. 27, 1962, as amended by, Amdt. 105–1, 29 FR 14920, Nov. 4, 1964; Amdt. 105–7, 43 FR 22641, May 25, 1978]

§ 105.17 Jumps over or onto airports.

Unless prior approval has been given by the airport management, no person may make a parachute jump, and no pilot in command of an aircraft may allow a parachute jump to be made from that aircraft—

(a) Over an airport that does not have a functioning control tower operated by the United States; or

(b) Onto any airport.

However, a parachutist may drift over that airport with a fully deployed and properly functioning parachute if he is at least 2,000 feet above that airport's traffic pattern, and avoids creating a hazard to air traffic or to persons and property on the ground.

[Docket No. 4057, 29 FR 14920, Nov. 4, 1964]

§ 105.19 Jumps in or into Class A, Class B, Class C, and Class D airspace.

(a) No person may make a parachute jump, and no pilot in command may allow a parachute jump to be made from that aircraft, in or into Class A, Class B, Class C, and Class D airspace without, or in violation of, the terms of an ATC authorization issued under this section.

(b) Each request for an authorization under this section must be submitted to the nearest FAA air traffic control facility or FAA flight service station and must include the information prescribed by § 105.25(a).

[Docket No. 1491, 27 FR 11636, Nov. 27, 1962; as amended by Amdt. 105–10, 56 FR 65658, Dec. 17, 1991]

§ 105.23 Jumps in or into other airspace.

(a) No person may make a parachute jump, and no pilot in command of an aircraft may allow a parachute jump to be made from that aircraft, in or into airspace unless the nearest FAA air traffic control facility or FAA flight service station was notified of that jump at least 1 hour before the jump is to be made, but not more than 24 hours before the jumping is to be completed, and the notice contained the information prescribed in § 105.25(a).

(b) Notwithstanding paragraph (a) of this section, ATC may accept from a parachute jumping organization a written notification of a scheduled series of jumps to be made over a stated period of time not longer than 12 calendar months. The notification must contain the information prescribed by § 105.25(a), identify the responsible persons associated with that jumping activity, and be submitted at least 15 days, but not more than 30 days, before the jumping is to begin. ATC may revoke the acceptance of the notification for any failure of the jumping organization to comply with its terms.

(c) This section does not apply to parachute jumps in or into any airspace or place described in § 105.15, § 105.19, or § 105.21.

[Docket No. 7824, 31 FR 16612, Dec. 29, 1966]

§ 105.25 Information required, and notice of cancellation or postponement of jump.

(a) Each person requesting an authorization under § 105.19 or § 105.21, and each person submitting a notice under § 105.23, must include the following information (on an individual or group basis) in that request or notice:

(1) The date and time jumping will begin.

(2) The size of the jump zone expressed in nautical mile radius around the target.

(3) The location of the center of the jump zone in relation to—

(i) The nearest VOR facility in terms of the VOR radial on which it is located, and its distance in nautical miles from the VOR facility when that facility is 30 nautical miles or less from the drop zone target; or

(ii) The nearest airport, town, or city depicted on the appropriate Coast and Geodetic Survey WAC or Sectional Aeronautical chart, when the nearest VOR facility is more than 30 nautical miles from the drop zone target.

(4) The altitudes above mean sea level at which jumping will take place.

(5) The duration of the intended jump.

(6) The name, address, and telephone number of the person requesting the authorization or giving notice.

(7) The identification of the aircraft to be used.

(8) The radio frequencies, if any, available in the aircraft.

(b) Each person requesting an authorization under § 105.19 or § 105.21, and each person submitting a notice under § 105.23, must promptly notify the FAA air traffic control facility or FAA flight service station from which it requested authorization or which it notified, if the proposed or scheduled jumping activity is canceled or postponed.

[Docket No. 7824, 31 FR 16612, Dec. 29, 1966; as amended by Amdt. 105–6, 41 FR 47229, Oct. 28, 1976; Amdt. 105–9, 51 FR 21907, June 17, 1986]

§ 105.27 Jumps over or within restricted or prohibited areas.

No person may make a parachute jump, and no pilot in command may allow a parachute jump to be made from that aircraft, over or within a restricted area or prohibited area unless the controlling agency of the area concerned has authorized that jump.

§ 105.29 Flight visibility and clearance from clouds requirements.

No person may make a parachute jump, and no pilot in command of an aircraft may allow a parachute jump to be made from that aircraft—

(a) Into or through a cloud; or

(b) When the flight visibility is less, or at a distance from clouds that is less, than that prescribed in the following table:

Altitude	Flight visibility (statute miles)	Distance from clouds
(1) 1,200 feet or less above the surface regardless of the MSL altitude	3	500 feet below. 1,000 feet above. 2,000 feet horizontal.
(2) More than 1,200 feet above the surface but less than 10,000 feet MSL	3	500 feet below. 1,000 feet above. 2,000 feet horizontal.
(3) More than 1,200 feet above the surface and at or above 10,000 feet MSL	5	1,000 feet below. 1,000 feet above. 1 mile horizontal.

[Docket No. 9937, 36 FR 8775, May 13, 1971]

§ 105.33 Parachute jumps between sunset and sunrise.

(a) No person may make a parachute jump, and no pilot in command of an aircraft may allow any person to make a parachute jump from that aircraft, between sunset and sunrise, unless that person is equipped with a means of producing a light visible for at least 3 statute miles.

(b) Each person making a parachute jump between sunset and sunrise shall display the light required by paragraph (a) of this section from the time that person exits the aircraft until that person reaches the surface.

[Docket No. 16383, 43 FR 22641, May 25, 1978]

§ 105.35 Liquor and drugs.

No person may make a parachute jump while, and no pilot in command of an aircraft may allow a person to make a parachute jump from that aircraft if that person appears to be:

(a) Under the influence of intoxicating liquor; or

(b) Using any drug that affects his faculties in any way contrary to safety.

§ 105.37 Inspections.

The Administrator may inspect (including inspections at the jump site), any parachute jump operation to which this part applies, to determine compliance with the regulations of this part.

Subpart C— Parachute Equipment

§ 105.41 Applicability.

(a) Except as provided in paragraph (b) of this section, this subpart prescribes rules governing parachute equipment used in parachute jumps to which this part applies.

(b) This subpart does not apply to a parachute jump made by a member of an Armed Force using parachute equipment of an Armed Force.

§ 105.43 Parachute equipment and packing requirements.

(a) No person may make a parachute jump, and no pilot in command of an aircraft may allow any person to make a parachute jump from that aircraft, unless that person is wearing a single harness dual parachute pack, having at least one main parachute and one approved auxiliary parachute that are packed as follows:

(1) The main parachute must have been packed by a certificated parachute rigger, or by the person making the jump, within 120 days before the date of its use.

(2) The auxiliary must have been packed by a certificated and appropriately rated parachute rigger:

(i) Within 120 days before the date of use, if its canopy, shroud, and harness are composed exclusively of nylon, rayon, or other similar synthetic fiber or material that is substantially resistant to damage from mold, mildew, or other fungi and other rotting agents propagated in a moist environment; or

(ii) Within 60 days before the date of use, if it is composed in any amount of silk, pongee, or other natural fiber, or material not specified in paragraph (a)(2)(i) of this section.

(b) No person may make a parachute jump using a static line attached to the aircraft and the main parachute unless an assist device, described and attached as follows, is used to aid the pilot chute in performing its function, or, if no pilot chute is used, to aid in the direct deployment of the main parachute canopy.

(1) The assist device must be long enough to allow the container to open before a load is placed on the device.

(2) The assist device must have a static load strength of—

(i) At least 28 pounds but not more than 160 pounds, if it is used to aid the pilot chute in performing its function; or

(ii) At least 56 pounds but not more than 320 pounds, if it is used to aid in the direct deployment of the main parachute canopy.

(3) The assist device must be attached—

(i) At one end, to the static line above the static line pins, or, if static pins are not used, above the static line ties to the parachute cone; and

(ii) At the other end, to the pilot chute apex, bridle cord or bridle loop, or, if no pilot chute is used, to the main parachute canopy.

(c) No person may attach an assist device required by paragraph (b) of this section to any main parachute unless he has a current parachute rigger certificate issued under part 65 of this chapter or is the person who makes the jump with that parachute.

(d) For the purpose of this section, an *approved* parachute is:

(1) A parachute manufactured under a type certificate or a technical standard order (C–23 series); or

(2) A personnel-carrying military parachute (other than a high altitude, high-speed, or ejection kind) identified by an NAF, AAF, or AN drawing number, an AAF order number, or any other military designation or specification number.

[Docket No. 1491, 27 FR 11636, Nov. 27, 1962; as amended by Amdt. 105–3, 33 FR 8481, June 8, 1968; Amdt. 105–7, 43 FR 22641, May 25, 1978]

SUBCHAPTER G

AIR CARRIERS AND OPERATORS FOR COMPENSATION OR HIRE: CERTIFICATION AND OPERATIONS

PART 119

CERTIFICATION: AIR CARRIERS AND COMMERCIAL OPERATORS

SPECIAL FEDERAL AVIATION REGULATION

SFAR No. 78 [Note]

Authority: 49 U.S.C. 106(g), 1153, 40101, 40102, 40103, 40113, 44105, 44106, 44111, 44701–44717, 44722, 44901, 44903, 44904, 44906, 44912, 44914, 44936, 44938, 46103, 46105.

Source: Docket No. 28154, 60 FR 65913, Dec. 20, 1995, unless otherwise noted.

SPECIAL FEDERAL AVIATION REGULATION

SFAR NO. 78 TO PART 119

SPECIAL OPERATING RULES FOR COMMERCIAL AIR TOUR OPERATORS IN THE VICINITY OF THE ROCKY MOUNTAIN NATIONAL PARK

EDITORIAL NOTE: FOR THE TEXT OF SFAR NO. 78, SEE PART 91 OF THIS CHAPTER.

Subpart A — General

§ 119.1 Applicability.

(a) This part applies to each person operating or intending to operate civil aircraft—

(1) As an air carrier or commercial operator, or both, in air commerce or

(2) When common carriage is not involved, in operations of U.S.-registered civil airplanes with a seat configuration of 20 or more passengers, or a maximum payload capacity of 6,000 pounds or more.

(b) This part prescribes—

(1) The types of air operator certificates issued by the Federal Aviation Administration, including air carrier certificates and operating certificates;

(2) The certification requirements an operator must meet in order to obtain and hold a certificate authorizing operations under part 121, 125, or 135 of this chapter and operations specifications for each kind of operation to be conducted and each class and size of aircraft to be operated under part 121 or 135 of this chapter;

(3) The requirements an operator must meet to conduct operations under part 121, 125, or 135 of this chapter and in operating each class and size of aircraft authorized in its operations specifications;

(4) Requirements affecting wet leasing of aircraft and other arrangements for transportation by air;

(5) Requirements for obtaining deviation authority to perform operations under a military contract and obtaining deviation authority to perform an emergency operation; and

(6) Requirements for management personnel for operations conducted under part 121 or part 135 of this chapter.

(c) Persons subject to this part must comply with the other requirements of this chapter, except where those requirements are modified by or where additional requirements are imposed by part 119, 121, 125, or 135 of this chapter.

(d) This part does not govern operations conducted under part 129, 133, 137, or 139 of this chapter.

(e) Except for operations when common carriage is not involved conducted with airplanes having a passenger-seat configuration of 20 seats or more, excluding any required crewmember seat, or a payload capacity of 6,000 pounds or more, this part does not apply to—

(1) Student instruction;

(2) Nonstop sightseeing flights conducted with aircraft having a passenger seat configuration of 30 or fewer, excluding each crewmember seat, and a payload capacity of 7,500 pounds or less, that begin and end at the same airport, and are conducted within a 25 statute mile radius of that airport; however, for nonstop sightseeing flights for compensation or hire conducted in the vicinity of the Grand Canyon National Park, Arizona, the requirements of SFAR 50–2 of this part and SFAR 38–2 of 14 CFR part 121 or 14 CFR part 119, as applicable, apply;

(3) Ferry or training flights;

(4) Aerial work operations, including—

(i) Crop dusting, seeding, spraying, and bird chasing;

(ii) Banner towing;

(iii) Aerial photography or survey;

(iv) Fire fighting;

(v) Helicopter operations in construction or repair work (but it does apply to transportation to and from the site of operations); and

(vi) Powerline or pipeline patrol;

(5) Sightseeing flights conducted in hot air balloons;

(6) Nonstop flights conducted within a 25 statute mile radius of the airport of takeoff carrying persons for the purpose of intentional parachute jumps;

(7) Helicopter flights conducted within a 25 statute mile radius of the airport of takeoff if—

(i) Not more than two passengers are carried in the helicopter in addition to the required flightcrew;

(ii) Each flight is made under day VFR conditions;

(iii) The helicopter used is certificated in the standard category and complies with the 100-hour inspection requirements of part 91 of this chapter;

(iv) The operator notifies the FAA Flight Standards District Office responsible for the geographic area concerned at least 72 hours before each flight and furnishes any essential information that the office requests;

(v) The number of flights does not exceed a total of six in any calendar year;

(vi) Each flight has been approved by the Administrator; and

(vii) Cargo is not carried in or on the helicopter;

(8) Operations conducted under part 133 of this chapter or 375 of this title;

(9) Emergency mail service conducted under 49 U.S.C. 41906; or

(10) Operations conducted under the provisions of § 91.321 of this chapter.

§ 119.2 Compliance with 14 CFR part 119 or SFAR 38–2 of parts 121 and 135 of this chapter.

(a) Each certificate holder that before January 19, 1996, was issued an air carrier certificate or operating certificate and operations specifications under the requirements of part 121, 135, or SFAR 38–2 of parts 121 and 135 of this chapter shall continue to comply with SFAR 38–2 of parts 121 and 135 of this chapter until March 20, 1997, or until the date on which the certificate holder is issued operations specifications in accordance with part 119, whichever occurs first. In addition, persons conducting operations under SFAR 38–2 of parts 121 and 135 of this chapter shall continue to comply with the applicable requirements of §§ 121.6, 121.57, 121.59, 121.61, 121.71 through 121.83, 135.5, 135.11(c), 135.15, 135.17, 135.27, 135.29, 135.33, 135.35, 135.37, and 135.39 of this chapter as in effect on January 18, 1996, until March 20, 1997, or until the date on which the certificate holder is issued operations specifications in accordance with part 119, whichever occurs first. If a certificate holder is issued operations specifications in accordance with part 119 before March 20, 1997, then, notwithstanding all provisions in SFAR 38–2 of parts 121 and 135 of this chapter, such certificate holder shall comply with the provisions of part 119.

A copy of these regulations may be obtained from the Federal Aviation Administration, Office of Rulemaking (ARM), 800 Independence Ave. SW, Washington, DC 20591, or by phone (202) 267-9677.

(b) Each person who on or after January 19, 1996, applies for or obtains an initial air carrier certificate or operating certificate and operations specifications to conduct operations under part 121 or 135 of this chapter shall comply with this part, notwithstanding all provisions of SFAR 38–2 of parts 121 and 135 of this chapter.

[Docket No. 28154, 61 FR 30433, June 14, 1996]

§ 119.3 Definitions.

For the purpose of subchapter G of this chapter, the term—

All-cargo operation means any operation for compensation or hire that is other than a passenger-carrying operation or, if passengers are carried, they are only those specified in §§ 121.583(a) or 135.85 of this chapter.

Certificate-holding district office means the Flight Standards District Office that has responsibility for administering the certificate and is charged with the overall inspection of the certificate holder's operations.

Commuter operation means any scheduled operation conducted by any person operating one of the following types of aircraft with a frequency of operations of at least five round trips per week on at least one route between two or more points according to the published flight schedules:

(1) Airplanes, other than turbojet powered airplanes, having a maximum passenger-seat configuration of 9 seats or less, excluding each crewmember seat, and a maximum payload capacity of 7,500 pounds or less; or

(2) Rotorcraft.

Direct air carrier means a person who provides or offers to provide air transportation and who has control over the operational functions performed in providing that transportation.

Domestic operation means any scheduled operation conducted by any person operating any airplane described in paragraph (1) of this definition at locations described in paragraph (2) of this definition:

(1) Airplanes:

(i) Turbojet-powered airplanes;

(ii) Airplanes having a passenger-seat configuration of more than 9 passenger seats, excluding each crewmember seat; or

(iii) Airplanes having a payload capacity of more than 7,500 pounds.

(2) Locations:

(i) Between any points within the 48 contiguous States of the United States or the District of Columbia; or

(ii) Operations solely within the 48 contiguous States of the United States or the District of Columbia; or

(iii) Operations entirely within any State, territory, or possession of the United States; or

(iv) When specifically authorized by the Administrator, operations between any point within the 48 contiguous States of the United States or the District of Columbia and any specifically authorized point located outside the 48 contiguous States of the United States or the District of Columbia.

Empty weight means the weight of the airframe, engines, propellers, rotors, and fixed equipment. Empty weight excludes the weight of the crew and payload, but includes the weight of all fixed ballast, unusable fuel supply, undrainable oil, total quantity of engine coolant, and total quantity of hydraulic fluid.

Flag operation means any scheduled operation conducted by any person operating any airplane described in paragraph (1) of this definition at the locations described in paragraph (2) of this definition:

(1) Airplanes:

(i) Turbojet-powered airplanes;

(ii) Airplanes having a passenger-seat configuration of more than 9 passenger seats, excluding each crewmember seat; or

(iii) Airplanes having a payload capacity of more than 7,500 pounds.

(2) Locations:

(i) Between any point within the State of Alaska or the State of Hawaii or any territory or possession of the United States and any point outside the State of Alaska or the State of Hawaii or any territory or possession of the United States, respectively; or

(ii) Between any point within the 48 contiguous States of the United States or the District of Columbia and any point outside the 48 contiguous States of the United States and the District of Columbia.

(iii) Between any point outside the U.S. and another point outside the U.S.

Justifiable aircraft equipment means any equipment necessary for the operation of the aircraft. It does not include equipment or ballast specifically installed, permanently or otherwise, for the purpose of altering the empty weight of an aircraft to meet the maximum payload capacity.

Kind of operation means one of the various operations a certificate holder is authorized to conduct, as specified in its operations specifications, i.e., domestic, flag, supplemental, commuter, or on-demand operations.

Maximum payload capacity means:

(1) For an aircraft for which a maximum zero fuel weight is prescribed in FAA technical specifications, the maximum zero fuel weight, less empty weight, less all justifiable aircraft equipment, and less the operating load (consisting of minimum flightcrew, foods and beverages, and supplies and equipment related to foods and beverages, but not including disposable fuel or oil).

(2) For all other aircraft, the maximum certificated takeoff weight of an aircraft, less the empty weight, less all justifiable aircraft equipment, and less the operating load (consisting of minimum fuel load, oil, and flightcrew). The allowance for the weight of the crew, oil, and fuel is as follows:

(i) Crew—for each crewmember required by the Federal Aviation Regulations—

(A) For male flight crewmembers—180 pounds.

(B) For female flight crewmembers—140 pounds.

(C) For male flight attendants—180 pounds.

(D) For female flight attendants—130 pounds.

(E) For flight attendants not identified by gender—140 pounds.

(ii) Oil—350 pounds or the oil capacity as specified on the Type Certificate Data Sheet.

(iii) Fuel—the minimum weight of fuel required by the applicable Federal Aviation Regulations for a flight between domestic points 174 nautical miles apart under VFR weather conditions that does not involve extended overwater operations.

Maximum zero fuel weight means the maximum permissible weight of an aircraft with no disposable fuel or oil. The zero fuel weight figure may be found in either the aircraft type certificate data sheet, the approved Aircraft Flight Manual, or both.

Noncommon carriage means an aircraft operation for compensation or hire that does not involve a holding out to others.

On-demand operation means any operation for compensation or hire that is one of the following:

(1) Passenger-carrying operations conducted as a public charter under part 380 of this title or any operations in which the departure time, departure location, and arrival location are specifically negotiated with the customer or the customer's representative that are any of the following types of operations:

(i) Common carriage operations conducted with airplanes, including turbojet-powered airplanes, having a passenger-seat configuration of 30 seats or fewer, excluding each crewmember seat, and a payload capacity of 7,500 pounds or less, except that operations using a specific airplane that is also used in domestic or flag operations and that is so listed in the operations specifications as required by § 119.49(a)(4) for those operations are considered supplemental operations;

(ii) Noncommon or private carriage operations conducted with airplanes having a passenger-seat configuration of less than 20 seats, excluding each crewmember seat, and a payload capacity of less than 6,000 pounds; or

(iii) Any rotorcraft operation.

(2) Scheduled passenger-carrying operations conducted with one of the following types of aircraft with a frequency of operations of less than five round trips per week on at least one route between two or more points according to the published flight schedules:

(i) Airplanes, other than turbojet powered airplanes, having a maximum passenger-seat configuration of 9 seats or less, excluding each crewmember seat, and a maximum payload capacity of 7,500 pounds or less; or

(ii) Rotorcraft.

(3) All-cargo operations conducted with airplanes having a payload capacity of 7,500 pounds or less, or with rotorcraft.

Passenger-carrying operation means any aircraft operation carrying any person, unless the only persons on the aircraft are those identified in §§ 121.583(a) or 135.85 of this chapter, as applicable. An aircraft used in a passenger-carrying operation may also carry cargo or mail in addition to passengers.

Principal base of operations means the primary operating location of a certificate holder as established by the certificate holder.

Provisional airport means an airport approved by the Administrator for use by a certificate holder for the purpose of providing service to a community when the regular airport used by the certificate holder is not available.

Regular airport means an airport used by a certificate holder in scheduled operations and listed in its operations specifications.

Scheduled operation means any common carriage passenger-carrying operation for compensation or hire conducted by an air carrier or commercial operator for which the certificate holder or its representative offers in advance the departure location, departure time, and arrival location. It does not include any passenger-carrying operation that is conducted as a public charter operation under part 380 of this title.

Supplemental operation means any common carriage operation for compensation or hire conducted with any airplane described in paragraph (1) of this definition that is a type of operation described in paragraph (2) of this definition:

(1) Airplanes:

(i) Airplanes having a passenger-seat configuration of more than 30 seats, excluding each crewmember seat;

(ii) Airplanes having a payload capacity of more than 7,500 pounds; or

(iii) Each propeller-powered airplane having a passenger-seat configuration of more than 9 seats and less than 31 seats, excluding each crewmember seat, that is also used in domestic or flag operations and that is so listed in the operations specifications as required by §119.49(a)(4) for those operations; or

(iv) Each turbojet powered airplane having a passenger seat configuration of 1 or more and less than 31 seats, excluding each crewmember seat, that is also used in domestic or flag operations and that is so listed in the operations specifications as required by §119.49(a)(4) for those operations.

(2) Types of operation:

(i) Operations for which the departure time, departure location, and arrival location are specifically negotiated with the customer or the customer's representative;

(ii) All-cargo operations; or

(iii) Passenger-carrying public charter operations conducted under part 380 of this title.

Wet lease means any leasing arrangement whereby a person agrees to provide an entire aircraft and at least one crewmember. A wet lease does not include a code-sharing arrangement.

When common carriage is not involved or operations not involving common carriage means any of the following:

(1) Noncommon carriage.

(2) Operations in which persons or cargo are transported without compensation or hire.

(3) Operations not involving the transportation of persons or cargo.

(4) Private carriage.

[Docket No. 28154, 60 FR 65913, Dec. 28, 1995; as amended by Amdt. 119–1, 61 FR 2609, Jan. 26, 1996; Amdt. 119–2, 61 FR 30433, June 14, 1996; Amdt. 119–3, 62 FR 13253, March 19, 1997]

§119.5 Certifications, authorizations, and prohibitions.

(a) A person authorized by the Administrator to conduct operations as a direct air carrier will be issued an Air Carrier Certificate.

(b) A person who is not authorized to conduct direct air carrier operations, but who is authorized by the Administrator to conduct operations as a U.S. commercial operator, will be issued an Operating Certificate.

(c) A person who is not authorized to conduct direct air carrier operations, but who is authorized by the Administrator to conduct operations when common carriage is not involved as an operator of U.S.-registered civil airplanes with a seat configuration of 20 or more passengers, or a maximum payload capacity of 6,000 pounds or more, will be issued an Operating Certificate.

(d) A person authorized to engage in common carriage under part 121 or part 135 of this chapter, or both, shall be issued only one certificate authorizing such common carriage, regardless of the kind of operation or the class or size of aircraft to be operated.

(e) A person authorized to engage in noncommon or private carriage under part 125 or part 135 of this chapter, or both, shall be issued only one certificate authorizing such carriage, regardless of the kind of operation or the class or size of aircraft to be operated.

(f) A person conducting operations under more than one paragraph of §§119.21, 119.23, or 119.25 shall conduct those operations in compliance with—

(1) The requirements specified in each paragraph of those sections for the kind of operation conducted under that paragraph; and

(2) The appropriate authorizations, limitations, and procedures specified in the operations specifications for each kind of operation.

(g) No person may operate as a direct air carrier or as a commercial operator without, or in violation of, an appropriate certificate and appropriate operations specifications. No person may operate as a direct air carrier or as a commercial operator in violation of any deviation or exemption authority, if issued to that person or that person's representative.

(h) A person holding an Operating Certificate authorizing noncommon or private carriage operations shall not conduct any operations in common carriage. A person holding an Air Carrier Certificate or Operating Certificate authorizing common carriage operations shall not conduct any operations in noncommon carriage.

(i) No person may operate as a direct air carrier without holding appropriate economic authority from the Department of Transportation.

(j) A certificate holder under this part may not operate aircraft under part 121 or part 135 of this chapter in a geographical area unless its operations specifications specifically authorize the certificate holder to operate in that area.

(k) No person may advertise or otherwise offer to perform an operation subject to this part unless that person is authorized by the Federal Aviation Administration to conduct that operation.

(l) No person may operate an aircraft under this part, part 121 of this chapter, or part 135 of this chapter in violation of an air carrier operating certificate, operating certificate, or appropriate operations specifications issued under this part.

[Docket No. 28154, 60 FR 65913, Dec. 20, 1995; as amended by Amdt. 119–3, 62 FR 13253, March 19, 1997]

§ 119.7 Operations specifications.

(a) Each certificate holder's operations specifications must contain—

(1) The authorizations, limitations, and certain procedures under which each kind of operation, if applicable, is to be conducted; and

(2) Certain other procedures under which each class and size of aircraft is to be operated.

(b) Except for operations specifications paragraphs identifying authorized kinds of operations, operations specifications are not a part of a certificate.

§ 119.9 Use of business names.

(a) A certificate holder under this part may not operate an aircraft under part 121 or part 135 of this chapter using a business name other than a business name appearing in the certificate holder's operations specifications.

(b) No person may operate an aircraft under part 121 or part 135 of this chapter unless the name of the certificate holder who is operating the aircraft, or the air carrier or operating certificate number of the certificate holder who is operating the aircraft, is legibly displayed on the aircraft and is clearly visible and readable from the outside of the aircraft to a person standing on the ground at any time except during flight time. The means of displaying the name on the aircraft and its readability must be acceptable to the Administrator.

[Docket No. 28154, 60 FR 65913, Dec. 20, 1995; as amended by Amdt. 119–3, 62 FR 13253, March 19, 1997]

Subpart B— Applicability of Operating Requirements to Different Kinds of Operations Under Parts 121, 125, and 135 of this Chapter

§ 119.21 Commercial operators engaged in intrastate common carriage and direct air carriers.

(a) Each person who conducts airplane operations as a commercial operator engaged in intrastate common carriage of persons or property for compensation or hire in air commerce, or as a direct air carrier, shall comply with the certification and operations specifications requirements in subpart C of this part, and shall conduct its:

(1) Domestic operations in accordance with the applicable requirements of part 121 of this chapter, and shall be issued operations specifications for those operations in accordance with those requirements. However, based on a showing of safety in air commerce, the Administrator may permit persons who conduct domestic operations between any point located within any of the following Alaskan islands and any point in the State of Alaska to comply with the requirements applicable to flag operations contained in subpart U of part 121 of this chapter:

(i) The Aleutian Islands.

(ii) The Pribilof Islands.

(iii) The Shumagin Islands.

(2) Flag operations in accordance with the applicable requirements of part 121 of this chapter, and shall be issued operations specifications for those operations in accordance with those requirements.

(3) Supplemental operations in accordance with the applicable requirements of part 121 of this chapter, and shall be issued operations specifications for those operations in accordance with those requirements. However, based on a determination of safety in air commerce, the Administrator may authorize or require those operations to be conducted under paragraph (a)(1) or (a)(2) of this section:

(i) Passenger-carrying operations which are conducted between points that are also served by the certificate holder's domestic or flag operations.

(ii) All-cargo operations which are conducted regularly and frequently between the same two points.

(4) Commuter operations in accordance with the applicable requirements of part 135 of this chapter, and shall be issued operations specifications for those operations in accordance with those requirements.

(5) On-demand operations in accordance with the applicable requirements of part 135 of this chapter, and shall be issued operations specifications for those operations in accordance with those requirements.

(b) Persons who are subject to the requirements of paragraph (a)(4) of this section may conduct those operations in accordance with the requirements of paragraph (a)(1) or (a)(2) of this section, provided they obtain authorization from the Administrator.

(c) Persons who are subject to the requirements of paragraph (a)(5) of this section may conduct those operations in accordance with the requirements of paragraph (a)(3) of this section, provided they obtain authorization from the Administrator.

[Docket No. 28154, 60 FR 65913, Dec. 20, 1995; as amended by Amdt. 119–2, 61 FR 30433, June 14, 1996; Amdt. 119–3, 62 FR 13254, March 19, 1997]

§ 119.23 Operators engaged in passenger-carrying operations, cargo operations, or both with airplanes when common carriage is not involved.

(a) Each person who conducts operations when common carriage is not involved with airplanes having a passenger-seat configuration of 20 seats or more, excluding each crewmember seat, or a payload capacity of 6,000 pounds or more, shall, unless deviation authority is issued—

(1) Comply with the certification and operations specifications requirements of part 125 of this chapter;

(2) Conduct its operations with those airplanes in accordance with the requirements of part 125 of this chapter; and

(3) Be issued operations specifications in accordance with those requirements.

(b) Each person who conducts noncommon carriage (except as provided in § 91.501(b) of this chapter) or private carriage operations for compensation or hire with airplanes having a passenger-seat configuration of less than 20 seats, excluding each crewmember seat, and a payload capacity of less than 6,000 pounds shall—

(1) Comply with the certification and operations specifications requirements in subpart C of this part;

(2) Conduct those operations in accordance with the requirements of part 135 of this chapter, except for those requirements applicable only to commuter operations; and

(3) Be issued operations specifications in accordance with those requirements.

[Docket No. 28154, 60 FR 65913, Dec. 20, 1995; as amended by Amdt. 119–2, 61 FR 30434, June 14, 1996]

§ 119.25 Rotorcraft operations: Direct air carriers and commercial operators.

Each person who conducts rotorcraft operations for compensation or hire must comply with the certification and operations specifications requirements of Subpart C of this part, and shall conduct its:

(a) Commuter operations in accordance with the applicable requirements of part 135 of this chapter, and shall be issued operations specifications for those operations in accordance with those requirements.

(b) On-demand operations in accordance with the applicable requirements of part 135 of this chapter, and shall be issued operations specifications for those operations in accordance with those requirements.

Subpart C— Certification, Operations Specifications, and Certain Other Requirements for Operations Conducted Under Part 121 or Part 135 of this Chapter

§ 119.31 Applicability.

This subpart sets out certification requirements and prescribes the content of operations specifications and certain other requirements for operations conducted under part 121 or part 135 of this chapter.

§ 119.33 General requirements.

(a) A person may not operate as a direct air carrier unless that person—

(1) Is a citizen of the United States;

(2) Obtains an Air Carrier Certificate; and

(3) Obtains operations specifications that prescribe the authorizations, limitations, and procedures under which each kind of operation must be conducted.

(b) A person other than a direct air carrier may not conduct any commercial passenger or cargo aircraft operation for compensation or hire under part 121 or part 135 of this chapter unless that person—

(1) Is a citizen of the United States;

(2) Obtains an Operating Certificate; and

(3) Obtains operations specifications that prescribe the authorizations, limitations, and procedures under which each kind of operation must be conducted.

(c) Each applicant for a certificate under this part and each applicant for operations specifications authorizing a new kind of operation that is subject to § 121.163 or § 135.145 of this chapter shall conduct proving tests as authorized by the Administrator during the application process for authority to conduct operations under part 121 or part 135 of this chapter. All proving tests must be conducted under the appropriate operating and maintenance requirements of part 121 or 135 of this chapter that would apply if the applicant were fully certificated. The Administrator will issue a letter of authorization to each person stating the various authorities under which the proving tests shall be conducted.

[Docket No. 28154, 60 FR 65913, Dec. 20, 1995; as amended by Amdt. 119–2, 61 FR 30434, June 14, 1996]

§ 119.35 Certificate application requirements for all operators.

(a) A person applying to the Administrator for an Air Carrier Certificate or Operating Certificate under this part (applicant) must submit an application—

(1) In a form and manner prescribed by the Administrator; and

(2) Containing any information the Administrator requires the applicant to submit.

(b) Each applicant must submit the application to the Administrator at least 90 days before the date of intended operation.

[Docket No. 28154, 62 FR 13254, March 19, 1997; as amended by Amdt. 119–3, 62 FR 15570, April 1, 1997]

§ 119.36 Additional certificate application requirements for commercial operators.

(a) Each applicant for the original issue of an operating certificate for the purpose of conducting intrastate common carriage operations under part 121 or part 135 of this chapter must submit an application in a form and manner prescribed by the Administrator to the Flight Standards District Office in whose area the applicant proposes to establish or has established his or her principal base of operations.

(b) Each application submitted under paragraph (a) of this section must contain a signed statement showing the following:

(1) For corporate applicants:

(i) The name and address of each stockholder who owns 5 percent or more of the total voting stock of the corporation, and if that stockholder is not the sole beneficial owner of the stock, the name and address of each beneficial owner. An individual is considered to own the stock owned, directly or indirectly, by or for his or her spouse, children, grandchildren, or parents.

(ii) The name and address of each director and each officer and each person employed or who will be employed in a management position described in §§ 119.65 and 119.69, as applicable.

(iii) The name and address of each person directly or indirectly controlling or controlled by the applicant and each person under direct or indirect control with the applicant.

(2) For non-corporate applicants:

(i) The name and address of each person having a financial interest therein and the nature and extent of that interest.

(ii) The name and address of each person employed or who will be employed in a management position described in §§ 119.65 and 119.69, as applicable.

(c) In addition, each applicant for the original issue of an operating certificate under paragraph (a) of this section must submit with the application a signed statement showing—

(1) The nature and scope of its intended operation, including the name and address of each person, if any, with whom the applicant has a contract to provide services as a commercial operator and the scope, nature, date, and duration of each of those contracts; and

(2) For applicants intending to conduct operations under part 121 of this chapter, the financial information listed in paragraph (e) of this section.

(d) Each applicant for, or holder of, a certificate issued under paragraph (a) of this section, shall notify the Administrator within 10 days after—

(1) A change in any of the persons, or the names and addresses of any of the persons, submitted to the Administrator under paragraph (b)(1) or (b)(2) of this section; or

(2) For applicants intending to conduct operations under part 121 of this chapter, a change in the financial information submitted to the Administrator under paragraph (e) of this section that occurs while the application for the issue is pending before the FAA and that would make the applicant's financial situation substantially less favorable than originally reported.

(e) Each applicant for the original issue of an operating certificate under paragraph (a) of this section who intends to conduct operations under part 121 of this chapter must submit the following financial information:

(1) A balance sheet that shows assets, liabilities, and net worth, as of a date not more than 60 days before the date of application.

(2) An itemization of liabilities more than 60 days past due on the balance sheet date, if any,

showing each creditor's name and address, a description of the liability, and the amount and due date of the liability.

(3) An itemization of claims in litigation, if any, against the applicant as of the date of application showing each claimant's name and address and a description and the amount of the claim.

(4) A detailed projection of the proposed operation covering 6 complete months after the month in which the certificate is expected to be issued including—

(i) Estimated amount and source of both operating and nonoperating revenue, including identification of its existing and anticipated income producing contracts and estimated revenue per mile or hour of operation by aircraft type;

(ii) Estimated amount of operating and nonoperating expenses by expense objective classification; and

(iii) Estimated net profit or loss for the period.

(5) An estimate of the cash that will be needed for the proposed operations during the first 6 months after the month in which the certificate is expected to be issued, including—

(i) Acquisition of property and equipment (explain);

(ii) Retirement of debt (explain);

(iii) Additional working capital (explain);

(iv) Operating losses other than depreciation and amortization (explain); and

(v) Other (explain).

(6) An estimate of the cash that will be available during the first 6 months after the month in which the certificate is expected to be issued, from—

(i) Sale of property or flight equipment (explain);

(ii) New debt (explain);

(iii) New equity (explain);

(iv) Working capital reduction (explain);

(v) Operations (profits) (explain);

(vi) Depreciation and amortization (explain); and

(vii) Other (explain).

(7) A schedule of insurance coverage in effect on the balance sheet date showing insurance companies; policy numbers; types, amounts, and period of coverage; and special conditions, exclusions, and limitations.

(8) Any other financial information that the Administrator requires to enable him or her to determine that the applicant has sufficient financial resources to conduct his or her operations with the degree of safety required in the public interest.

(f) Each financial statement containing financial information required by paragraph (e) of this section must be based on accounts prepared and maintained on an accrual basis in accordance with generally accepted accounting principles applied on a consistent basis, and must contain the name and address of the applicant's public accounting firm, if any. Information submitted must be signed by an officer, owner, or partner of the applicant or certificate holder.

[Docket No. 28154, 62 FR 133254, March 19, 1999; as amended by Amdt. 119–3, 62 FR 15570, April 1, 1997]

§ 119.37 Contents of an Air Carrier Certificate or Operating Certificate.

The Air Carrier Certificate or Operating Certificate includes—

(a) The certificate holder's name;

(b) The location of the certificate holder's principal base of operations;

(c) The certificate number;

(d) The certificate's effective date; and

(e) The name or the designator of the certificate-holding district office.

§ 119.39 Issuing or denying a certificate.

(a) An applicant may be issued an Air Carrier Certificate or Operating Certificate if, after investigation, the Administrator finds that the applicant—

(1) Meets the applicable requirements of this part;

(2) Holds the economic authority applicable to the kinds of operations to be conducted, issued by the Department of Transportation, if required; and

(3) Is properly and adequately equipped in accordance with the requirements of this chapter and is able to conduct a safe operation under appropriate provisions of part 121 or part 135 of this chapter and operations specifications issued under this part.

(b) An application for a certificate may be denied if the Administrator finds that—

(1) The applicant is not properly or adequately equipped or is not able to conduct safe operations under this subchapter;

(2) The applicant previously held an Air Carrier Certificate or Operating Certificate which was revoked;

(3) The applicant intends to or fills a key management position listed in § 119.65(a) or § 119.69(a), as applicable, with an individual who exercised control over or who held the same or a similar position with a certificate holder whose certificate was revoked, or is in the process of being revoked, and that individual materially contributed to the circumstances causing revocation or causing the revocation process;

(4) An individual who will have control over or have a substantial ownership interest in the applicant had the same or similar control or interest in a certificate holder whose certificate was revoked, or is in the process of being revoked, and that individual materially contributed to the circum-

stances causing revocation or causing the revocation process; or

(5) In the case of an applicant for an Operating Certificate for intrastate common carriage, that for financial reasons the applicant is not able to conduct a safe operation.

§ 119.41 Amending a certificate.

(a) The Administrator may amend any certificate issued under this part if—

(1) The Administrator determines, under 49 U.S.C. 44709 and part 13 of this chapter, that safety in air commerce and the public interest requires the amendment; or

(2) The certificate holder applies for the amendment and the certificate-holding district office determines that safety in air commerce and the public interest allows the amendment.

(b) When the Administrator proposes to issue an order amending, suspending, or revoking all or part of any certificate, the procedure in § 13.19 of this chapter applies.

(c) When the certificate holder applies for an amendment of its certificate, the following procedure applies:

(1) The certificate holder must file an application to amend its certificate with the certificate-holding district office at least 15 days before the date proposed by the applicant for the amendment to become effective, unless the administrator approves filing within a shorter period; and

(2) The application must be submitted to the certificate-holding district office in the form and manner prescribed by the Administrator.

(d) When a certificate holder seeks reconsideration of a decision from the certificate-holding district office concerning amendments of a certificate, the following procedure applies:

(1) The petition for reconsideration must be made within 30 days after the certificate holder receives the notice of denial; and

(2) The certificate holder must petition for reconsideration to the Director, Flight Standards Service.

§ 119.43 Certificate holder's duty to maintain operations specifications.

(a) Each certificate holder shall maintain a complete and separate set of its operations specifications at its principal base of operations.

(b) Each certificate holder shall insert pertinent excerpts of its operations specifications, or references thereto, in its manual and shall—

(1) Clearly identify each such excerpt as a part of its operations specifications; and

(2) State that compliance with each operations specifications requirement is mandatory.

(c) Each certificate holder shall keep each of its employees and other persons used in its operations informed of the provisions of its operations specifications that apply to that employee's or person's duties and responsibilities.

§ 119.45 [Reserved]

§ 119.47 Maintaining a principal base of operations, main operations base, and main maintenance base; change of address.

(a) Each certificate holder must maintain a principal base of operations. Each certificate holder may also establish a main operations base and a main maintenance base which may be located at either the same location as the principal base of operations or at separate locations.

(b) At least 30 days before it proposes to establish or change the location of its principal base of operations, its main operations base, or its main maintenance base, a certificate holder must provide written notification to its certificate-holding district office.

§ 119.49 Contents of operations specifications.

(a) Each certificate holder conducting domestic, flag, or commuter operations must obtain operations specifications containing all of the following:

(1) The specific location of the certificate holder's principal base of operations and, if different, the address that shall serve as the primary point of contact for correspondence between the FAA and the certificate holder and the name and mailing address of the certificate holder's agent for service.

(2) Other business names under which the certificate holder may operate.

(3) Reference to the economic authority issued by the Department of Transportation, if required.

(4) Type of aircraft, registration markings, and serial numbers of each aircraft authorized for use, each regular and alternate airport to be used in scheduled operations, and, except for commuter operations, each provisional and refueling airport.

(i) Subject to the approval of the Administrator with regard to form and content, the certificate holder may incorporate by reference the items listed in paragraph (a)(4) of this section into the certificate holder's operations specifications by maintaining a current listing of those items and by referring to the specific list in the applicable paragraph of the operations specifications.

(ii) The certificate holder may not conduct any operation using any aircraft or airport not listed.

(5) Kinds of operations authorized.

(6) Authorization and limitations for routes and areas of operations.

(7) Airport limitations.

(8) Time limitations, or standards for determining time limitations, for overhauling, inspecting, and checking airframes, engines, propellers, rotors, appliances, and emergency equipment.

(9) Authorization for the method of controlling weight and balance of aircraft.

(10) Interline equipment interchange requirements, if relevant.

(11) Aircraft wet lease information required by § 119.53(c).

(12) Any authorized deviation and exemption granted from any requirement of this chapter.

(13) Any other item the Administrator determines is necessary.

(b) Each certificate holder conducting supplemental operations must obtain operations specifications containing all of the following:

(1) The specific location of the certificate holder's principal base of operations, and, if different, the address that shall serve as the primary point of contact for correspondence between the FAA and the certificate holder and the name and mailing address of the certificate holder's agent for service.

(2) Other business names under which the certificate holder may operate.

(3) Reference to the economic authority issued by the Department of Transportation, if required.

(4) Type of aircraft, registration markings, and serial number of each aircraft authorized for use.

(i) Subject to the approval of the Administrator with regard to form and content, the certificate holder may incorporate by reference the items listed in paragraph (b)(4) of this section into the certificate holder's operations specifications by maintaining a current listing of those items and by referring to the specific list in the applicable paragraph of the operations specifications.

(ii) The certificate holder may not conduct any operation using any aircraft not listed.

(5) Kinds of operations authorized.

(6) Authorization and limitations for routes and areas of operations.

(7) Special airport authorizations and limitations.

(8) Time limitations, or standards for determining time limitations, for overhauling, inspecting, and checking airframes, engines, propellers, appliances, and emergency equipment.

(9) Authorization for the method of controlling weight and balance of aircraft.

(10) Aircraft wet lease information required by § 119.53(c).

(11) Any authorization or requirement to conduct supplemental operations as provided by § 119.21(a)(3)(i) or (ii).

(12) Any authorized deviation or exemption from any requirement of this chapter.

(13) Any other item the Administrator determines is necessary.

(c) Each certificate holder conducting on-demand operations must obtain operations specifications containing all of the following:

(1) The specific location of the certificate holder's principal base of operations, and if different, the address that shall serve as the primary point of contact for correspondence between the FAA and the name and mailing address of the certificate holder's agent for service.

(2) Other business names under which the certificate holder may operate.

(3) Reference to the economic authority issued by the Department of Transportation, if required.

(4) Kind and area of operations authorized.

(5) Category and class of aircraft that may be used in those operations.

(6) Type of aircraft, registration markings, and serial number of each aircraft that is subject to an airworthiness maintenance program required by § 135.411(a)(2) of this chapter.

(i) Subject to the approval of the Administrator with regard to form and content, the certificate holder may incorporate by reference the items listed in paragraph (c)(6) of this section into the certificate holder's operations specifications by maintaining a current listing of those items and by referring to the specific list in the applicable paragraph of the operations specifications.

(ii) The certificate holder may not conduct any operation using any aircraft not listed.

(7) Registration markings of each aircraft that is to be inspected under an approved aircraft inspection program under § 135.419 of this chapter.

(8) Time limitations or standards for determining time limitations, for overhauls, inspections, and checks for airframes, engines, propellers, rotors, appliances, and emergency equipment of aircraft that are subject to an airworthiness maintenance program required by § 135.411(a)(2) of this chapter.

(9) Additional maintenance items required by the Administrator under § 135.421 of this chapter.

(10) Aircraft wet lease information required by § 119.53(c).

(11) Any authorized deviation or exemption from any requirement of this chapter.

(12) Any other item the Administrator determines is necessary.

§ 119.51 Amending operations specifications.

(a) The Administrator may amend any operations specifications issued under this part if—

(1) The Administrator determines that safety in air commerce and the public interest require the amendment; or

(2) The certificate holder applies for the amendment, and the Administrator determines that safety in air commerce and the public interest allows the amendment.

(b) Except as provided in paragraph (e) of this section, when the Administrator initiates an amendment to a certificate holder's operations specifications, the following procedure applies:

(1) The certificate-holding district office notifies the certificate holder in writing of the proposed amendment.

(2) The certificate-holding district office sets a reasonable period (but not less than 7 days) within which the certificate holder may submit written information, views, and arguments on the amendment.

(3) After considering all material presented, the certificate-holding district office notifies the certificate holder of—

(i) The adoption of the proposed amendment;

(ii) The partial adoption of the proposed amendment; or

(iii) The withdrawal of the proposed amendment.

(4) If the certificate-holding district office issues an amendment to the operations specifications, it becomes effective not less than 30 days after the certificate holder receives notice of it unless—

(i) The certificate-holding district office finds under paragraph (e) of this section that there is an emergency requiring immediate action with respect to safety in air commerce; or

(ii) The certificate holder petitions for reconsideration of the amendment under paragraph (d) of this section.

(c) When the certificate holder applies for an amendment to its operations specifications, the following procedure applies:

(1) The certificate holder must file an application to amend its operations specifications—

(i) At least 90 days before the date proposed by the applicant for the amendment to become effective, unless a shorter time is approved, in cases of mergers; acquisitions of airline operational assets that require an additional showing of safety (e.g., proving tests); changes in the kind of operation as defined in § 119.3; resumption of operations following a suspension of operations as a result of bankruptcy actions; or the initial introduction of aircraft not before proven for use in air carrier or commercial operator operations.

(ii) At least 15 days before the date proposed by the applicant for the amendment to become effective in all other cases.

(2) The application must be submitted to the certificate-holding district office in a form and manner prescribed by the Administrator.

(3) After considering all material presented, the certificate-holding district office notifies the certificate holder of—

(i) The adoption of the applied for amendment;

(ii) The partial adoption of the applied for amendment; or

(iii) The denial of the applied for amendment. The certificate holder may petition for reconsideration of a denial under paragraph (d) of this section.

(4) If the certificate-holding district office approves the amendment, following coordination with the certificate holder regarding its implementation, the amendment is effective on the date the Administrator approves it.

(d) When a certificate holder seeks reconsideration of a decision from the certificate-holding district office concerning the amendment of operations specifications, the following procedure applies:

(1) The certificate holder must petition for reconsideration of that decision within 30 days of the date that the certificate holder receives a notice of denial of the amendment to its operations specifications, or of the date it receives notice of an FAA-initiated amendment to its operations specifications, whichever circumstance applies.

(2) The certificate holder must address its petition to the Director, Flight Standards Service.

(3) A petition for reconsideration, if filed within the 30-day period, suspends the effectiveness of any amendment issued by the certificate-holding district office unless the certificate-holding district office has found, under paragraph (e) of this section, that an emergency exists requiring immediate action with respect to safety in air transportation or air commerce.

(4) If a petition for reconsideration is not filed within 30 days, the procedures of paragraph (c) of this section apply.

(e) If the certificate-holding district office finds that an emergency exists requiring immediate action with respect to safety in air commerce or air transportation that makes the procedures set out in this section impracticable or contrary to the public interest:

(1) The certificate-holding district office amends the operations specifications and makes the amendment effective on the day the certificate holder receives notice of it.

(2) In the notice to the certificate holder, the certificate-holding district office articulates the reasons for its finding that an emergency exists requiring immediate action with respect to safety

in air transportation or air commerce or that makes it impracticable or contrary to the public interest to stay the effectiveness of the amendment.

§ 119.53 Wet leasing of aircraft and other arrangements for transportation by air.

(a) Unless otherwise authorized by the Administrator, prior to conducting operations involving a wet lease, each certificate holder under this part authorized to conduct common carriage operations under this subchapter shall provide the Administrator with a copy of the wet lease to be executed which would lease the aircraft to any other person engaged in common carriage operations under this subchapter, including foreign air carriers, or to any other foreign person engaged in common carriage wholly outside the United States.

(b) No certificate holder under this part may wet lease from a foreign air carrier or any other foreign person or any person not authorized to engage in common carriage.

(c) Upon receiving a copy of a wet lease, the Administrator determines which party to the agreement has operational control of the aircraft and issues amendments to the operations specifications of each party to the agreement, as needed. The lessor must provide the following information to be incorporated into the operations specifications of both parties, as needed.

(1) The names of the parties to the agreement and the duration thereof.

(2) The nationality and registration markings of each aircraft involved in the agreement.

(3) The kind of operation (e.g., domestic, flag, supplemental, commuter, or on-demand).

(4) The airports or areas of operation.

(5) A statement specifying the party deemed to have operational control and the times, airports, or areas under which such operational control is exercised.

(d) In making the determination of paragraph (c) of this section, the Administrator will consider the following:

(1) Crewmembers and training.

(2) Airworthiness and performance of maintenance.

(3) Dispatch.

(4) Servicing the aircraft.

(5) Scheduling.

(6) Any other factor the Administrator considers relevant.

(e) Other arrangements for transportation by air: Except as provided in paragraph (f) of this section, a certificate holder under this part operating under part 121 or 135 of this chapter may not conduct any operation for another certificate holder under this part or a foreign air carrier under part 129 of this chapter or a foreign person engaged in common carriage wholly outside the United States unless it holds applicable Department of Transportation economic authority, if required, and is authorized under its operations specifications to conduct the same kinds of operations (as defined in § 119.3). The certificate holder conducting the substitute operation must conduct that operation in accordance with the same operations authority held by the certificate holder arranging for the substitute operation. These substitute operations must be conducted between airports for which the substitute certificate holder holds authority for scheduled operations or within areas of operations for which the substitute certificate holder has authority for supplemental or on-demand operations.

(f) A certificate holder under this part may, if authorized by the Department of Transportation under § 380.3 of this title and the Administrator in the case of interstate commuter, interstate domestic, and flag operations, or the Administrator in the case of scheduled intrastate common carriage operations, conduct one or more flights for passengers who are stranded because of the cancellation of their scheduled flights. These flights must be conducted under the rules of part 121 or part 135 of this chapter applicable to supplemental or on-demand operations.

§ 119.55 Obtaining deviation authority to perform operations under a U.S. military contract.

(a) The Administrator may authorize a certificate holder that is authorized to conduct supplemental or on-demand operations to deviate from the applicable requirements of this part, part 121, or part 135 of this chapter in order to perform operations under a U.S. military contract.

(b) A certificate holder that has a contract with the U.S. Department of Defense's Air Mobility Command (AMC) must submit a request for deviation authority to AMC. AMC will review the requests, then forward the carriers' consolidated requests, along with AMC's recommendations, to the FAA for review and action.

(c) The Administrator may authorize a deviation to perform operations under a U.S. military contract under the following conditions—

(1) The Department of Defense certifies to the Administrator that the operation is essential to the national defense;

(2) The Department of Defense further certifies that the certificate holder cannot perform the operation without deviation authority;

(3) The certificate holder will perform the operation under a contract or subcontract for the benefit of a U.S. armed service; and

(4) The Administrator finds that the deviation is based on grounds other than economic advantage either to the certificate holder or to the United States.

(d) In the case where the Administrator authorizes a deviation under this section, the Administrator will issue an appropriate amendment to the certificate holder's operations specifications.

(e) The Administrator may, at any time, terminate any grant of deviation authority issued under this section.

§ 119.57 Obtaining deviation authority to perform an emergency operation.

(a) In emergency conditions, the Administrator may authorize deviations if—

(1) Those conditions necessitate the transportation of persons or supplies for the protection of life or property; and

(2) The Administrator finds that a deviation is necessary for the expeditious conduct of the operations.

(b) When the Administrator authorizes deviations for operations under emergency conditions—

(1) The Administrator will issue an appropriate amendment to the certificate holder's operations specifications; or

(2) If the nature of the emergency does not permit timely amendment of the operations specifications—

(i) The Administrator may authorize the deviation orally; and

(ii) The certificate holder shall provide documentation describing the nature of the emergency to the certificate-holding district office within 24 hours after completing the operation.

§ 119.59 Conducting tests and inspections.

(a) At any time or place, the Administrator may conduct an inspection or test to determine whether a certificate holder under this part is complying with title 49 of the United States Code, applicable regulations, the certificate, or the certificate holder's operations specifications.

(b) The certificate holder must—

(1) Make available to the Administrator at the certificate holder's principal base of operations—

(i) The certificate holder's Air Carrier Certificate or the certificate holder's Operating Certificate and the certificate holder's operations specifications; and

(ii) A current listing that will include the location and persons responsible for each record, document, and report required to be kept by the certificate holder under title 49 of the United States

Code applicable to the operation of the certificate holder.

(2) Allow the Administrator to make any test or inspection to determine compliance respecting any matter stated in paragraph (a) of this section.

(c) Each employee of, or person used by, the certificate holder who is responsible for maintaining the certificate holder's records must make those records available to the Administrator.

(d) The Administrator may determine a certificate holder's continued eligibility to hold its certificate and/or operations specifications on any grounds listed in paragraph (a) of this section, or any other appropriate grounds.

(e) Failure by any certificate holder to make available to the Administrator upon request, the certificate, operations specifications, or any required record, document, or report is grounds for suspension of all or any part of the certificate holder's certificate and operations specifications.

(f) In the case of operators conducting intrastate common carriage operations, these inspections and tests include inspections and tests of financial books and records.

§ 119.61 Duration and surrender of certificate and operations specifications.

(a) An Air Carrier Certificate or Operating Certificate issued under this part is effective until—

(1) The certificate holder surrenders it to the Administrator; or

(2) The Administrator suspends, revokes, or otherwise terminates the certificate.

(b) Operations specifications issued under this part, part 121, or part 135 of this chapter are effective unless—

(1) The Administrator suspends, revokes, or otherwise terminates the certificate;

(2) The operations specifications are amended as provided in § 119.51;

(3) The certificate holder does not conduct a kind of operation for more than the time specified in § 119.63 and fails to follow the procedures of § 119.63 upon resuming that kind of operation; or

(4) The Administrator suspends or revokes the operations specifications for a kind of operation.

(c) Within 30 days after a certificate holder terminates operations under part 135 of this chapter, the operating certificate and operations specifications must be surrendered by the certificate holder to the certificate-holding district office.

§ 119.63 Recency of operation.

(a) Except as provided in paragraph (b) of this section, no certificate holder may conduct a kind of operation for which it holds authority in its operations specifications unless the certificate holder has conducted that kind of operation within the preceding number of consecutive calendar days specified in this paragraph:

(1) For domestic, flag, or commuter operations—30 days.

(2) For supplemental or on-demand operations—90 days, except that if the certificate holder has authority to conduct domestic, flag, or commuter operations, and has conducted domestic, flag or commuter operations within the previous 30 days, this paragraph does not apply.

(b) If a certificate holder does not conduct a kind of operation for which it is authorized in its operations specifications within the number of calendar days specified in paragraph (a) of this section, it shall not conduct such kind of operation unless—

(1) It advises the Administrator at least 5 consecutive calendar days before resumption of that kind of operation; and

(2) It makes itself available and accessible during the 5 consecutive calendar day period in the event that the FAA decides to conduct a full inspection reexamination to determine whether the certificate holder remains properly and adequately equipped and able to conduct a safe operation.

[Docket No. 28154, 60 FR 65913, Dec. 20, 1995; as amended by Amdt. 119–2, 61 FR 30434, June 14, 1996]

§ 119.65 Management personnel required for operations conducted under part 121 of this chapter.

(a) Each certificate holder must have sufficient qualified management and technical personnel to ensure the highest degree of safety in its operations. The certificate holder must have qualified personnel serving full-time in the following or equivalent positions:

(1) Director of Safety.

(2) Director of Operations.

(3) Chief Pilot.

(4) Director of Maintenance.

(5) Chief Inspector.

(b) The Administrator may approve positions or numbers of positions other than those listed in paragraph (a) of this section for a particular operation if the certificate holder shows that it can perform the operation with the highest degree of safety under the direction of fewer or different categories of management personnel due to—

(1) The kind of operation involved;

(2) The number and type of airplanes used; and

(3) The area of operations.

(c) The title of the positions required under paragraph (a) of this section or the title and number of equivalent positions approved under paragraph (b) of this section shall be set forth in the certificate holder's operations specifications.

(d) The individuals who serve in the positions required or approved under paragraph (a) or (b) of this section and anyone in a position to exercise control over operations conducted under the operating certificate must—

(1) Be qualified through training, experience, and expertise;

(2) To the extent of their responsibilities, have a full understanding of the following materials with respect to the certificate holder's operation—

(i) Aviation safety standards and safe operating practices;

(ii) 14 CFR Chapter I (Federal Aviation Regulations);

(iii) The certificate holder's operations specifications;

(iv) All appropriate maintenance and airworthiness requirements of this chapter (e.g., parts 1, 21, 23, 25, 43, 45, 47, 65, 91, and 121 of this chapter); and

(v) The manual required by § 121.133 of this chapter; and

(3) Discharge their duties to meet applicable legal requirements and to maintain safe operations.

(e) Each certificate holder must:

(1) State in the general policy provisions of the manual required by § 121.133 of this chapter, the duties, responsibilities, and authority of personnel required under paragraph (a) of this section;

(2) List in the manual the names and business addresses of the individuals assigned to those positions; and

(3) Notify the certificate-holding district office within 10 days of any change in personnel or any vacancy in any position listed.

§ 119.67 Management personnel: Qualifications for operations conducted under part 121 of this chapter.

(a) To serve as Director of Operations under § 119.65(a) a person must—

(1) Hold an airline transport pilot certificate;

(2) Have at least 3 years supervisory or managerial experience within the last 6 years in a position that exercised operational control over any operations conducted with large airplanes under part 121 or part 135 of this chapter, or if the certificate holder uses only small airplanes in its operations, the experience may be obtained in large or small airplanes; and

(3) In the case of a person becoming a Director of Operations—

(i) For the first time ever, have at least 3 years experience, within the past 6 years, as pilot in command of a large airplane operated under part 121 or part 135 of this chapter, if the certificate holder operates large airplanes. If the certificate holder uses only small airplanes in its operation, the experience may be obtained in either large or small airplanes.

(ii) In the case of a person with previous experience as a Director of Operations, have at least 3 years experience as pilot in command of a large airplane operated under part 121 or part 135 of this chapter, if the certificate holder operates large airplanes. If the certificate holder uses only small airplanes in its operation, the experience may be obtained in either large or small airplanes.

(b) To serve as Chief Pilot under § 119.65(a) a person must hold an airline transport pilot certificate with appropriate ratings for at least one of the airplanes used in the certificate holder's operation and:

(1) In the case of a person becoming a Chief Pilot for the first time ever, have at least 3 years experience, within the past 6 years, as pilot in command of a large airplane operated under part 121 or part 135 of this chapter, if the certificate holder operates large airplanes. If the certificate holder uses only small airplanes in its operation, the experience may be obtained in either large or small airplanes.

(2) In the case of a person with previous experience as a Chief Pilot, have at least 3 years experience, as pilot in command of a large airplane operated under part 121 or part 135 of this chapter, if the certificate holder operates large airplanes. If the certificate holder uses only small airplanes in its operation, the experience may be obtained in either large or small airplanes.

(c) To serve as Director of Maintenance under § 119.65(a) a person must—

(1) Hold a mechanic certificate with airframe and powerplant ratings;

(2) Have 1 year of experience in a position responsible for returning airplanes to service;

(3) Have at least 1 year of experience in a supervisory capacity under either paragraph (c)(4)(i) or (c)(4)(ii) of this section maintaining the same category and class of airplane as the certificate holder uses; and

(4) Have 3 years experience within the past 6 years in one or a combination of the following—

(i) Maintaining large airplanes with 10 or more passenger seats, including at the time of appointment as Director of Maintenance, experience in maintaining the same category and class of airplane as the certificate holder uses; or

(ii) Repairing airplanes in a certificated airframe repair station that is rated to maintain airplanes in the same category and class of airplane as the certificate holder uses.

(d) To serve as Chief Inspector under § 119.65(a) a person must—

(1) Hold a mechanic certificate with both airframe and powerplant ratings, and have held these ratings for at least 3 years;

(2) Have at least 3 years of maintenance experience on different types of large airplanes with 10 or more passenger seats with an air carrier or certificated repair station, 1 year of which must have been as maintenance inspector; and

(3) Have at least 1 year of experience in a supervisory capacity maintaining the same category and class of aircraft as the certificate holder uses.

(e) A certificate holder may request a deviation to employ a person who does not meet the appropriate airman experience, managerial experience, or supervisory experience requirements of this section if the Manager of the Air Transportation Division, AFS–200, or the Manager of the Aircraft Maintenance Division, AFS–300, as appropriate, finds that the person has comparable experience, and can effectively perform the functions associated with the position in accordance with the requirements of this chapter and the procedures outlined in the certificate holder's manual. Grants of deviation under this paragraph may be granted after consideration of the size and scope of the operation and the qualifications of the intended personnel. The Administrator may, at any time, terminate any grant of deviation authority issued under this paragraph.

[Docket No. 28154, 60 FR 65913, Dec. 20, 1995; as amended by Amdt. 119–2, 61 FR 30434, June 14, 1996; Amdt. 119–3, 62 FR 13255, March 19, 1997]

§ 119.69 Management personnel required for operations conducted under part 135 of this chapter.

(a) Each certificate holder must have sufficient qualified management and technical personnel to ensure the safety of its operations. Except for a certificate holder using only one pilot in its operations, the certificate holder must have qualified personnel serving in the following or equivalent positions:

(1) Director of Operations.

(2) Chief Pilot.

(3) Director of Maintenance.

(b) The Administrator may approve positions or numbers of positions other than those listed in paragraph (a) of this section for a particular operation if the certificate holder shows that it can perform the operation with the highest degree of safety under the direction of fewer or different categories of management personnel due to—

(1) The kind of operation involved;

(2) The number and type of aircraft used; and

(3) The area of operations.

(c) The title of the positions required under paragraph (a) of this section or the title and number of equivalent positions approved under paragraph (b) of this section shall be set forth in the certificate holder's operations specifications.

(d) The individuals who serve in the positions required or approved under paragraph (a) or (b) of this section and anyone in a position to exercise control over operations conducted under the operating certificate must—

(1) Be qualified through training, experience, and expertise;

(2) To the extent of their responsibilities, have a full understanding of the following material with respect to the certificate holder's operation—

(i) Aviation safety standards and safe operating practices;

(ii) 14 CFR Chapter I (Federal Aviation Regulations);

(iii) The certificate holder's operations specifications;

(iv) All appropriate maintenance and airworthiness requirements of this chapter (e.g., parts 1, 21, 23, 25, 43, 45, 47, 65, 91, and 135 of this chapter); and

(v) The manual required by § 135.21 of this chapter; and

(3) Discharge their duties to meet applicable legal requirements and to maintain safe operations.

(e) Each certificate holder must—

(1) State in the general policy provisions of the manual required by § 135.21 of this chapter, the duties, responsibilities, and authority of personnel required or approved under paragraph (a) or (b), respectively, of this section;

(2) List in the manual the names and business addresses of the individuals assigned to those positions; and

(3) Notify the certificate-holding district office within 10 days of any change in personnel or any vacancy in any position listed.

§ 119.71 Management personnel: Qualifications for operations conducted under part 135 of this chapter.

(a) To serve as Director of Operations under § 119.69(a) for a certificate holder conducting any operations for which the pilot in command is required to hold an airline transport pilot certificate a person must hold an airline transport pilot certificate and either:

(1) Have at least 3 years supervisory or managerial experience within the last 6 years in a position that exercised operational control over any operations conducted under part 121 or part 135 of this chapter; or

(2) In the case of a person becoming Director of Operations—

(i) For the first time ever, have at least 3 years experience, within the past 6 years, as pilot in command of an aircraft operated under part 121 or part 135 of this chapter.

(ii) In the case of a person with previous experience as a Director of Operations, have at least 3 years experience, as pilot in command of an aircraft operated under part 121 or part 135 of this chapter.

(b) To serve as Director of Operations under § 119.69(a) for a certificate holder that only conducts operations for which the pilot in command is required to hold a commercial pilot certificate, a person must hold at least a commercial pilot certificate. If an instrument rating is required for any pilot in command for that certificate holder, the Director of Operations must also hold an instrument rating. In addition, the Direction of Operations must either—

(1) Have at least 3 years supervisory or managerial experience within the last 6 years in a position that exercised operational control over any operations conducted under part 121 or part 135 of this chapter; or

(2) In the case of a person becoming Director of Operations—

(i) For the first time ever, have at least 3 years experience, within the past 6 years, as pilot in command of an aircraft operated under part 121 or part 135 of this chapter.

(ii) In the case of a person with previous experience as a Director of Operations, have at least 3 years experience as pilot in command of an aircraft operated under part 121 or part 135 of this chapter.

(c) To serve as Chief Pilot under § 119.69(a) for a certificate holder conducting any operation for which the pilot in command is required to hold an airline transport pilot certificate a person must hold an airline transport pilot certificate with appropriate ratings and be qualified to serve as pilot in command in at least one aircraft used in the certificate holder's operation and:

(1) In the case of a person becoming a Chief Pilot for the first time ever, have at least 3 years experience, within the past 6 years, as pilot in command of an aircraft operated under part 121 or part 135 of this chapter.

(2) In the case of a person with previous experience as a Chief Pilot, have at least 3 years experience as pilot in command of an aircraft operated under part 121 or part 135 of this chapter.

(d) To serve as Chief Pilot under § 119.69(a) for a certificate holder that only conducts operations for which the pilot in command is required to hold a commercial pilot certificate, a person must hold at least a commercial pilot certificate. If an instrument rating is required for any pilot in com-

119

mand for that certificate holder, the Chief Pilot must also hold an instrument rating. The Chief Pilot must be qualified to serve as pilot in command in at least one aircraft used in the certificate holder's operation. In addition, the Chief Pilot must:

(1) In the case of a person becoming a Chief Pilot for the first time ever, have at least 3 years experience, within the past 6 years, as pilot in command of an aircraft operated under part 121 or part 135 of this chapter.

(2) In the case of a person with previous experience as a Chief Pilot, have at least 3 years experience as pilot in command of an aircraft operated under part 121 or part 135 of this chapter.

(e) To serve as Director of Maintenance under § 119.69(a) a person must hold a mechanic certificate with airframe and powerplant ratings and either:

(1) Have 3 years of experience within the past 3 years maintaining aircraft as a certificated mechanic, including, at the time of appointment as Director of Maintenance, experience in maintaining the same category and class of aircraft as the certificate holder uses; or

(2) Have 3 years of experience within the past 3 years repairing aircraft in a certificated airframe repair station, including 1 year in the capacity of approving aircraft for return to service.

(f) A certificate holder may request a deviation to employ a person who does not meet the appropriate airmen experience requirements, managerial experience requirements, or supervisory experience requirements of this section if the Manager of the Air Transportation Division, AFS–200, or the Manager of the Aircraft Maintenance Division, AFS–300, as appropriate, find that the person has comparable experience, and can effectively perform the functions associated with the position in accordance with the requirements of this chapter and the procedures outlined in the certificate holder's manual. Grants of deviation under this paragraph may be granted after consideration of the size and scope of the operation and the qualifications of the intended personnel. The Administrator may, at any time, terminate any grant of deviation authority issued under this paragraph.

[Docket No. 28154, 60 FR 65913, Dec. 20, 1995; as amended by Amdt. 119–3, 62 FR 13255, March 19, 1997]

135

135

Authority: 49 U.S.C. 106(g), 44113, 44701, 44702, 44705, 44709, 44711–44713, 44715–44717, 44722.

Source: Docket No. 16097, 43 FR 46783, Oct. 10, 1978, unless otherwise noted.

SPECIAL FEDERAL AVIATION REGULATIONS

SFAR No. 36 TO PART 135

Editorial Note: For the text of SFAR No. 36, see Part 121 of this chapter.

SFAR No. 38–2 TO PART 135
CERTIFICATION AND OPERATING REQUIREMENTS

Editorial Note: For the text of SFAR No. 38–2, see Part 121 of this chapter.

SFAR No. 50–2 TO PART 135
SPECIAL FLIGHT RULES IN THE VICINITY OF THE GRAND CANYON NATIONAL PARK, AZ

Editorial Note: For the text of SFAR No. 50–2, see Part 91 of this chapter.

SFAR No. 52 TO PART 135
EXTENSION OF COMPLIANCE DATE OF SEAT CUSHION FLAMMABILITY REGULATION FOR LARGE AIRPLANES OPERATED UNDER PART 135 IN OTHER THAN COMMUTER AIR CARRIER OPERATIONS

Contrary provisions of §§ 121.312 and 135.169 of this chapter notwithstanding, for airplanes type certificated after January 1, 1958, after February 24, 1988, seat cushions in any compartment occupied by crew or passengers (except those on flight crewmember seats) in large airplanes operated under part 135 of this chapter, except large airplanes used in commuter air carrier operations, must comply with the requirements pertaining to fire protection of seat cushions in § 25.853(c), effective November 26, 1984, and Appendix F to part 25 of this chapter, effective November 26, 1984, unless an alternative compliance plan has been approved by the Administrator.

For airplanes type certificated after January 1, 1958, after November 26, 1987, seat cushions in any compartment occupied by crew or passengers (except those on flight crewmember seats) in large airplanes operated under part 135 of this chapter and used in commuter air carrier operations must comply with the requirements pertaining to fire protection of seat cushions in § 25.853(c), effective November 26, 1984, and Appendix F to part 25 of this chapter, effective November 26, 1984.

This Special Federal Aviation Regulation terminates on December 1, 1988.

[Docket No. 25477, 52 FR 45913, Dec. 2, 1987]

SFAR No. 58 TO PART 135
ADVANCED QUALIFICATION PROGRAM

Editorial Note: For the text of SFAR No. 58, see Part 121 of this chapter.

SFAR No. 71 TO PART 135
SPECIAL OPERATING RULES FOR AIR TOUR OPERATORS IN THE STATE OF HAWAII

Editorial Note: For the text of SFAR No. 71, see Part 91 of this chapter.

SFAR No. 78 TO PART 135

SFAR No. 78 TO PART 135

SPECIAL OPERATING RULES FOR COMMERCIAL
AIR TOUR OPERATORS IN THE VICINITY OF
THE ROCKY MOUNTAIN NATIONAL PARK

*Editorial Note: For the text of SFAR No. 78, see Part 91
of this chapter.*

Subpart A—General

§ 135.1 Applicability.

(a) This part prescribes rules governing—

(1) The commuter or on-demand operations of
each person who holds or is required to hold an
Air Carrier Certificate or Operating Certificate under part 119 of this chapter.

(2) Each person employed or used by a certificate holder conducting operations under this part
including the maintenance, preventative maintenance and alteration of an aircraft.

(3) The transportation of mail by aircraft conducted under a postal service contract awarded
under 39 U.S.C. 5402c.

(4) Each person who applies for provisional approval of an Advanced Qualification Program curriculum, curriculum segment, or portion of a curriculum segment under SFAR No. 58 of 14 CFR
part 121 and each person employed or used by
an air carrier or commercial operator under this
part to perform training, qualification, or evaluation functions under an Advanced Qualification
Program under SFAR No. 58 of 14 CFR part 121.

(5) Nonstop sightseeing flights for compensation or hire that begin and end at the same airport,
and are conducted within a 25 statute mile radius
of that airport; however, except for operations
subject to SFAR 50–2, these operations, when
conducted for compensation or hire, must comply
only with §§ 135.249, 135.251, 135.253, 135.255,
and 135.353.

(6) Each person who is on board an aircraft being operated under this part.

(7) Each person who is an applicant for an Air
Carrier Certificate or an Operating Certificate under 119 of this chapter, when conducting proving
tests.

(b) [Reserved]

(c) For the purpose of §§ 135.249, 135.251,
135.253, 135.255, and 135.353, *operator* means
any person or entity conducting non-stop sightseeing flights for compensation or hire in an airplane
or rotorcraft that begin and end at the same airport and are conducted within a 25 statute mile
radius of that airport.

(d) Notwithstanding the provisions of this part
and Appendices I and J to part 121 of this chapter, an operator who does not hold a part 121 or

part 135 certificate is permitted to use a person
who is otherwise authorized to perform aircraft
maintenance or preventive maintenance duties
and who is not subject to FAA-approved anti-drug
and alcohol misuse prevention programs to
perform—

(1) Aircraft maintenance or preventive maintenance on the operator's aircraft if the operator
would otherwise be required to transport the aircraft more than 50 nautical miles further than the
repair point closest to operator's principal place of
operation to obtain these services; or

(2) Emergency repairs on the operator's aircraft
if the aircraft cannot be safely operated to a location where an employee subject to FAA-approved
programs can perform the repairs.

[Docket No. 16097, 43 FR 46783, Oct. 10, 1978; as
amended by Amdt. 135–5, 45 FR 43162, June 26, 1980;
Amdt. 135–7, 45 FR 67235, Oct. 9, 1980; Amdt. 135–20,
51 FR 40709, Nov. 7, 1986; Amdt. 135–28, 53 FR
47060, Nov. 21, 1988; Amdt. 135–32, 54 FR 34332, Aug.
18, 1989; Amdt. 135–37, 55 FR 40278, Oct. 2, 1990;
Amdt. 135–41, 56 FR 43976, Sept. 5, 1991; Amdt. 135–
48, 59 FR 7396, Feb. 15, 1994; Amdt. 135–58, 60 FR
65938, Dec. 20, 1995]

§ 135.2 Compliance schedule for operators that transition to part 121 of this chapter; certain new entrant operators.

(a) *Applicability.* This section applies to the following:

(1) Each certificate holder that was issued an
air carrier or operating certificate and operations
specifications under the requirements of part 135
of this chapter or under SFAR No. 38–2 of 14
CFR part 121 before January 19, 1996, and that
conducts scheduled passenger-carrying operations with:

(i) Nontransport category turbopropeller powered airplanes type certificated after December
31, 1964, that have a passenger seat configuration of 10–19 seats;

(ii) Transport category turbopropeller powered
airplanes that have a passenger seat configuration of 20–30 seats; or

(iii) Turbojet engine powered airplanes having a
passenger seat configuration of 1–30 seats.

(2) Each person who, after January 19, 1996,
applies for or obtains an initial air carrier or operating certificate and operations specifications to
conduct scheduled passenger-carrying operations in the kinds of airplanes described in paragraphs (a)(1)(i), (a)(1)(ii), or paragraph (a)(1)(iii)
of this section.

(b) *Obtaining operations specifications.* A certificate holder described in paragraph (a)(1) of
this section may not, after March 20, 1997, operate an airplane described in paragraphs (a)(1)(i),

135

(a)(1)(ii), or (a)(1)(iii) of this section in scheduled passenger-carrying operations, unless it obtains operations specifications to conduct its scheduled operations under part 121 of this chapter on or before March 20, 1997.

(c) *Regular or accelerated compliance.* Except as provided in paragraphs (d) and (e) of this section, each certificate holder described in paragraphs (a)(1) of this section shall comply with each applicable requirement of part 121 of this chapter on and after March 20, 1997 or on and after the date on which the certificate holder is issued operations specifications under this part, whichever occurs first. Except as provided in paragraphs (d) and (e) of this section, each person described in paragraph (a)(2) of this section shall comply with each applicable requirement of part 121 of this chapter on and after the date on which that person is issued a certificate and operations specifications under part 121 of this chapter.

(d) *Delayed compliance dates.* Unless paragraph (e) of this section specifies an earlier compliance date, no certificate holder that is covered by paragraph (a) of this section may operate an airplane in 14 CFR part 121 operations on or after a date listed in this paragraph unless that airplane meets the applicable requirement of this paragraph:

(1) *Nontransport category turbopropeller powered airplanes type certificated after December 31, 1964, that have a passenger seat configuration of 10–19 seats.* No certificate holder may operate under this part an airplane that is described in paragraph (a)(1)(i) of this section on or after a date listed in paragraph (d)(1) of this section unless that airplane meets the applicable requirement listed in paragraph (d)(1) of this section:

(i) December 20, 1997:

(A) Section 121.289, Landing gear aural warning.

(B) Section 121.308, Lavatory fire protection.

(C) Section 121.310(e), Emergency exit handle illumination.

(D) Section 121.337(b)(8), Protective breathing equipment.

(E) Section 121.340, Emergency flotation means.

(ii) December 20, 1999: Section 121.342, Pitot heat indication system.

(iii) December 20, 2010:

(A) For airplanes described in § 121.157(f), the Airplane Performance Operating Limitations in §§ 121.189 through 121.197.

(B) Section 121.161(b), Ditching approval.

(C) Section 121.305(j), Third attitude indicator.

(D) Section 121.312(c), Passenger seat cushion flammability.

(iv) March 12, 1999: Section 121.310(b)(1), Interior emergency exit locating sign.

(2) *Transport category turbopropeller powered airplanes that have a passenger seat configuration of 20–30 seats.* No certificate holder may operate under this part an airplane that is described in paragraph (a)(1)(ii) of this section on or after a date listed in paragraph (d)(2) of this section unless that airplane meets the applicable requirement listed in paragraph (d)(2) of this section:

(i) December 20, 1997:

(A) Section 121.308, Lavatory fire protection.

(B) Section 121.337(b)(8) and (9), Protective breathing equipment.

(C) Section 121.340, Emergency flotation means.

(ii) December 20, 2010: Section 121.305(j), Third attitude indicator.

(e) *Newly manufactured airplanes.* No certificate holder that is described in paragraph (a) of this section may operate under part 121 of this chapter an airplane manufactured on or after a date listed in this paragraph (e) unless that airplane meets the applicable requirement listed in this paragraph (e).

(1) For nontransport category turbopropeller powered airplanes type certificated after December 31, 1964, that have a passenger seat configuration of 10–19 seats:

(i) Manufactured on or after March 20, 1997:

(A) Section 121.305(j), Third attitude indicator.

(B) Section 121.311(f), Safety belts and shoulder harnesses.

(ii) Manufactured on or after December 20, 1997: Section 121.317(a), Fasten seat belt light.

(iii) Manufactured on or after December 20, 1999: Section 121.293, Takeoff warning system.

(iv) Manufactured on or after March 12, 1999: Section 121.310(b)(1), Interior emergency exit locating sign.

(2) For transport category turbopropeller powered airplanes that have a passenger seat configuration of 20–30 seats manufactured on or after March 20, 1997: Section 121.305(j), Third attitude indicator.

(f) *New type certification requirements.* No person may operate an airplane for which the application for a type certificate was filed after March 29, 1995, in 14 CFR part 121 operations unless that airplane is type certificated under part 25 of this chapter.

(g) *Transition plan.* Before March 19, 1996, each certificate holder described in paragraph (a)(1) of this section must submit to the FAA a transition plan (containing a calendar of events) for moving from conducting its scheduled operations under the commuter requirements of part 135 of this chapter to the requirements for domestic or flag operations under part 121 of this chapter. Each transition plan must contain details on the following:

(1) Plans for obtaining new operations specifications authorizing domestic or flag operations;

(2) Plans for being in compliance with the applicable requirements of part 121 of this chapter on or before March 20, 1997; and

(3) Plans for complying with the compliance date schedules contained in paragraphs (d) and (e) of this section.

[Docket. No. 28154, 60 FR 65938, Dec. 20, 1995; as amended by Amdt. 135–65, 61 FR 30435, June 14, 1996; Amdt. 135–66, 62 FR 13257, March 19, 1997]

§ 135.3 Rules applicable to operations subject to this part.

(a) Each person operating an aircraft in operations under this part shall—

(1) While operating inside the United States, comply with the applicable rules of this chapter; and

(2) While operating outside the United States, comply with Annex 2, Rules of the Air, to the Convention on International Civil Aviation or the regulations of any foreign country, whichever applies, and with any rules of parts 61 and 91 of this chapter and this part that are more restrictive than that Annex or those regulations and that can be complied with without violating that Annex or those regulations. Annex 2 is incorporated by reference in § 91.703(b) of this chapter.

(b) After March 19, 1997, each certificate holder that conducts commuter operations under this part with airplanes in which two pilots are required by the type certification rules of this chapter shall comply with subparts N and O of part 121 of this chapter instead of the requirements of subparts E, G, and H of this part. Each affected certificate holder must submit to the Administrator and obtain approval of a transition plan (containing a calendar of events) for moving from its present part 135 training, checking, testing, and qualification requirements to the requirements of part 121 of this chapter. Each transition plan must be submitted by March 19, 1996, and must contain details on how the certificate holder plans to be in compliance with subparts N and O of part 121 on or before March 19, 1997.

(c) If authorized by the Administrator upon application, each certificate holder that conducts operations under this part to which paragraph (b) of this section does not apply, may comply with the applicable sections of subparts N and O of part 121 instead of the requirements of subparts E, G, and H of this part, except that those authorized certificate holders may choose to comply with the operating experience requirements of § 135.244, instead of the requirements of § 121.434 of this chapter.

[Docket No. 27993, 60 FR 65949, Dec. 20, 1995; as amended by Amdt. 135–65, 61 FR 30435, June 14, 1996]

§ 135.7 Applicability of rules to unauthorized operators.

The rules in this part which apply to a person certificated under part 119 of this chapter also apply to a person who engages in any operation governed by this part without an appropriate certificate and operations specifications required by part 119 of this chapter.

[Docket No. 16097, 43 FR 46783, Oct. 10, 1978; as amended by Amdt. 135–58, 60 FR 65939, Dec. 20, 1995]

§ 135.12 Previously trained crewmembers.

A certificate holder may use a crewmember who received the certificate holder's training in accordance with subparts E, G, and H of this part before March 19, 1997, without complying with initial training and qualification requirements of subparts N and O of part 121 of this chapter. The crewmember must comply with the applicable recurrent training requirements of part 121 of this chapter.

[Docket No. 27993, 60 FR 65950, Dec. 20, 1995]

§ 135.19 Emergency operations.

(a) In an emergency involving the safety of persons or property, the certificate holder may deviate from the rules of this part relating to aircraft and equipment and weather minimums to the extent required to meet that emergency.

(b) In an emergency involving the safety of persons or property, the pilot in command may deviate from the rules of this part to the extent required to meet that emergency.

(c) Each person who, under the authority of this section, deviates from a rule of this part shall, within 10 days, excluding Saturdays, Sundays, and Federal holidays, after the deviation, send to the FAA Flight Standards District Office charged with the overall inspection of the certificate holder a complete report of the aircraft operation involved, including a description of the deviation and reasons for it.

§ 135.21 Manual requirements.

(a) Each certificate holder, other than one who uses only one pilot in the certificate holder's operations, shall prepare and keep current a manual setting forth the certificate holder's procedures and policies acceptable to the Administrator. This manual must be used by the certificate holder's flight, ground, and maintenance personnel in conducting its operations. However, the Administrator may authorize a deviation from this paragraph if the Administrator finds that, because of the limited size of the operation, all or part of the manual is not necessary for guidance of flight, ground, or maintenance personnel.

(b) Each certificate holder shall maintain at least one copy of the manual at its principal base of operations.

(c) The manual must not be contrary to any applicable Federal regulations, foreign regulation applicable to the certificate holder's operations in foreign countries, or the certificate holder's operating certificate or operations specifications.

(d) A copy of the manual, or appropriate portions of the manual (and changes and additions) shall be made available to maintenance and ground operations personnel by the certificate holder and furnished to —

(1) Its flight crewmembers; and

(2) Representatives of the Administrator assigned to the certificate holder.

(e) Each employee of the certificate holder to whom a manual or appropriate portions of it are furnished under paragraph (d)(1) of this section shall keep it up to date with the changes and additions furnished to them.

(f) For the purpose of complying with paragraph (d) of this section, a certificate holder may furnish the persons listed therein with the maintenance part of its manual in printed form or other form, acceptable to the Administrator, that is retrievable in the English language. If the certificate holder furnishes the maintenance part of the manual in other than printed form, it must ensure there is a compatible reading device available to those persons that provide a legible image of the maintenance information and instructions, or a system that is able to retrieve the maintenance information and instructions in the English language.

(g) If a certificate holder conducts aircraft inspections or maintenance at specified stations where it keeps the approved inspection program manual, it is not required to carry the manual aboard the aircraft en route to those stations.

[Docket No. 16097, 43 FR 46783, Oct. 10, 1978; as amended by Amdt. 135–18, 47 FR 33396, Aug. 2, 1982; Amdt. 135–58, 60 FR 65939, Dec. 20, 1995; Amdt. 135–66, 62 FR 13257, March 19, 1997]

§ 135.23 Manual contents.

Each manual shall have the date of the last revision on each revised page. The manual must include—

(a) The name of each management person required under § 119.69(a) of this chapter who is authorized to act for the certificate holder, the person's assigned area of responsibility, the person's

duties, responsibilities, and authority, and the name and title of each person authorized to exercise operational control under § 135.77;

(b) Procedures for ensuring compliance with aircraft weight and balance limitations and, for multiengine aircraft, for determining compliance with § 135.185;

(c) Copies of the certificate holder's operations specifications or appropriate extracted information, including area of operations authorized, category and class of aircraft authorized, crew complements, and types of operations authorized;

(d) Procedures for complying with accident notification requirements;

(e) Procedures for ensuring that the pilot in command knows that required airworthiness inspections have been made and that the aircraft has been approved for return to service in compliance with applicable maintenance requirements;

(f) Procedures for reporting and recording mechanical irregularities that come to the attention of the pilot in command before, during, and after completion of a flight;

(g) Procedures to be followed by the pilot in command for determining that mechanical irregularities or defects reported for previous flights have been corrected or that correction has been deferred;

(h) Procedures to be followed by the pilot in command to obtain maintenance, preventive maintenance, and servicing of the aircraft at a place where previous arrangements have not been made by the operator, when the pilot is authorized to so act for the operator;

(i) Procedures under § 135.179 for the release for, or continuation of, flight if any item of equipment required for the particular type of operation becomes inoperative or unserviceable en route;

(j) Procedures for refueling aircraft, eliminating fuel contamination, protecting from fire (including electrostatic protection), and supervising and protecting passengers during refueling;

(k) Procedures to be followed by the pilot in command in the briefing under § 135.117;

(l) Flight locating procedures, when applicable;

(m) Procedures for ensuring compliance with emergency procedures, including a list of the functions assigned each category of required crewmembers in connection with an emergency and emergency evacuation duties under § 135.123;

(n) En route qualification procedures for pilots, when applicable;

(o) The approved aircraft inspection program, when applicable;

(p) Procedures and instructions to enable personnel to recognize hazardous materials, as defined in title 49 CFR, and if these materials are to be carried, stored, or handled, procedures and instructions for—

(1) Accepting shipment of hazardous material required by title 49 CFR, to assure proper packaging, marking, labeling, shipping documents, compatibility of articles, and instructions on their loading, storage, and handling;

(2) Notification and reporting hazardous material incidents as required by title 49 CFR; and

(3) Notification of the pilot in command when there are hazardous materials aboard, as required by title 49 CFR;

(q) Procedures for the evacuation of persons who may need the assistance of another person to move expeditiously to an exit if an emergency occurs; and

(r) Other procedures and policy instructions regarding the certificate holder's operations, that are issued by the certificate holder.

[Docket No. 16097, 43 FR 46783, Oct. 10, 1978; as amended by Amdt. 135–20, 51 FR 40709, Nov. 7, 1986; Amdt. 135–58, 60 FR 65939, Dec. 20, 1995]

§ 135.25 Aircraft requirements.

(a) Except as provided in paragraph (d) of this section, no certificate holder may operate an aircraft under this part unless that aircraft —

(1) Is registered as a civil aircraft of the United States and carries an appropriate and current airworthiness certificate issued under this chapter; and

(2) Is in an airworthy condition and meets the applicable airworthiness requirements of this chapter, including those relating to identification and equipment.

(b) Each certificate holder must have the exclusive use of at least one aircraft that meets the requirements for at least one kind of operation authorized in the certificate holder's operations specifications. In addition, for each kind of operation for which the certificate holder does not have the exclusive use of an aircraft, the certificate holder must have available for use under a written agreement (including arrangements for performing required maintenance) at least one aircraft that meets the requirements for that kind of operation. However, this paragraph does not prohibit the operator from using or authorizing the use of the aircraft for other than operations under this part and does not require the certificate holder to have exclusive use of all aircraft that the certificate holder uses.

(c) For the purposes of paragraph (b) of this section, a person has exclusive use of an aircraft if that person has the sole possession, control, and use of it for flight, as owner, or has a written agreement (including arrangements for performing required maintenance), in effect when the aircraft is operated, giving the person that possession, control, and use for at least 6 consecutive months.

(d) A certificate holder may operate in common carriage, and for the carriage of mail, a civil aircraft which is leased or chartered to it without crew and is registered in a country which is a party to the Convention on International Civil Aviation if —

(1) The aircraft carries an appropriate airworthiness certificate issued by the country of registration and meets the registration and identification requirements of that country;

(2) The aircraft is of a type design which is approved under a U.S. type certificate and complies with all of the requirements of this chapter (14 CFR chapter 1) that would be applicable to that aircraft were it registered in the United States, including the requirements which must be met for issuance of a U.S. standard airworthiness certificate (including type design conformity, condition for safe operation, and the noise, fuel venting, and engine emission requirements of this chapter), except that a U.S. registration certificate and a U.S. standard airworthiness certificate will not be issued for the aircraft;

(3) The aircraft is operated by U.S.-certificated airmen employed by the certificate holder; and

(4) The certificate holder files a copy of the aircraft lease or charter agreement with the FAA Aircraft Registry, Department of Transportation, 6400 South MacArthur Boulevard, Oklahoma City, OK (Mailing address: P.O. Box 25504, Oklahoma City, OK 73125).

[Docket No. 16097, 43 FR 46783, Oct. 10, 1978; as amended by Amdt. 135–8, 45 FR 68649, Oct. 16, 1980; Amdt. 135–66, 62 FR 13257, March 19, 1997]

§ 135.41 Carriage of narcotic drugs, marihuana, and depressant or stimulant drugs or substances.

If the holder of a certificate operating under this part allows any aircraft owned or leased by that holder to be engaged in any operation that the certificate holder knows to be in violation of § 91.19(a) of this chapter, that operation is a basis for suspending or revoking the certificate.

[Docket No. 28154, 60 FR 65939, Dec. 20, 1995]

§ 135.43 Crewmember certificates: International operations.

(a) This section describes the certificates that were issued to United States citizens who were employed by air carriers at the time of issuance as flight crewmembers on United States registered aircraft engaged in international air commerce. The purpose of the certificate is to facilitate the entry and clearance of those crewmembers into ICAO contracting states. They were issued under Annex 9, as amended, to the Convention on International Civil Aviation.

(b) The holder of a certificate issued under this section, or the air carrier by whom the holder is employed, shall surrender the certificate for cancellation at the nearest FAA Flight Standards District Office at the termination of the holder's employment with that air carrier.

[Docket No. 28154, 61 FR 30435, June 14, 1996]

Subpart B— Flight Operations

§ 135.61 General.

This subpart prescribes rules, in addition to those in part 91 of this chapter, that apply to operations under this part.

§ 135.63 Recordkeeping requirements.

(a) Each certificate holder shall keep at its principal business office or at other places approved by the Administrator, and shall make available for inspection by the Administrator the following—

(1) The certificate holder's operating certificate;

(2) The certificate holder's operations specifications;

(3) A current list of the aircraft used or available for use in operations under this part and the operations for which each is equipped;

(4) An individual record of each pilot used in operations under this part, including the following information:

(i) The full name of the pilot.

(ii) The pilot certificate (by type and number) and ratings that the pilot holds.

(iii) The pilot's aeronautical experience in sufficient detail to determine the pilot's qualifications to pilot aircraft in operations under this part.

(iv) The pilot's current duties and the date of the pilot's assignment to those duties.

(v) The effective date and class of the medical certificate that the pilot holds.

(vi) The date and result of each of the initial and recurrent competency tests and proficiency and route checks required by this part and the type of aircraft flown during that test or check.

(vii) The pilot's flight time in sufficient detail to determine compliance with the flight time limitations of this part.

(viii) The pilot's check pilot authorization, if any.

(ix) Any action taken concerning the pilot's release from employment for physical or professional disqualification.

(x) The date of the completion of the initial phase and each recurrent phase of the training required by this part; and

(5) An individual record for each flight attendant who is required under this part, maintained in sufficient detail to determine compliance with the applicable portions of § 135.273 of this part.

(b) Each certificate holder must keep each record required by paragraph (a)(3) of this section for at least 6 months, and must keep each record required by paragraphs (a)(4) and (a)(5) of this section for at least 12 months.

(c) For multiengine aircraft, each certificate holder is responsible for the preparation and accuracy of a load manifest in duplicate containing information concerning the loading of the aircraft. The manifest must be prepared before each takeoff and must include:

(1) The number of passengers;

(2) The total weight of the loaded aircraft;

(3) The maximum allowable takeoff weight for that flight;

(4) The center of gravity limits;

(5) The center of gravity of the loaded aircraft, except that the actual center of gravity need not be computed if the aircraft is loaded according to a loading schedule or other approved method that ensures that the center of gravity of the loaded aircraft is within approved limits. In those cases, an entry shall be made on the manifest indicating that the center of gravity is within limits according to a loading schedule or other approved method;

(6) The registration number of the aircraft or flight number;

(7) The origin and destination; and

(8) Identification of crew members and their crew position assignments.

(d) The pilot in command of an aircraft for which a load manifest must be prepared shall carry a copy of the completed load manifest in the aircraft to its destination. The certificate holder shall keep copies of completed load manifests for at least 30 days at its principal operations base, or at another location used by it and approved by the Administrator.

[Docket No. 16097, 43 FR 46783, Oct. 10, 1978; as amended by Amdt. 135–52, 59 FR 42993, Aug. 19, 1994]

§ 135.64 Retention of contracts and amendments: Commercial operators who conduct intrastate operations for compensation or hire.

Each commercial operator who conducts intrastate operations for compensation or hire shall keep a copy of each written contract under which it provides services as a commercial operator for a period of at least one year after the date of execution of the contract. In the case of an oral contract, it shall keep a memorandum stating its elements, and of any amendments to it, for a period of at least one year after the execution of that contract or change.

[Docket No. 28154, 60 FR 65939, Dec. 20, 1995; as amended by Amdt. 135–65, 61 FR 30435, June 14, 1996; Amdt. 135–66, 62 FR 13257, March 19, 1997]

§ 135.65 Reporting mechanical irregularities.

(a) Each certificate holder shall provide an aircraft maintenance log to be carried on board each aircraft for recording or deferring mechanical irregularities and their correction.

(b) The pilot in command shall enter or have entered in the aircraft maintenance log each mechanical irregularity that comes to the pilot's attention during flight time. Before each flight, the pilot in command shall, if the pilot does not already know, determine the status of each irregularity entered in the maintenance log at the end of the preceding flight.

(c) Each person who takes corrective action or defers action concerning a reported or observed failure or malfunction of an airframe, powerplant, propeller, rotor, or appliance, shall record the action taken in the aircraft maintenance log under the applicable maintenance requirements of this chapter.

(d) Each certificate holder shall establish a procedure for keeping copies of the aircraft maintenance log required by this section in the aircraft for access by appropriate personnel and shall include that procedure in the manual required by § 135.21.

§ 135.67 Reporting potentially hazardous meteorological conditions and irregularities of communications or navigation facilities.

Whenever a pilot encounters a potentially hazardous meteorological condition or an irregularity in a ground communications or navigational facility in flight, the knowledge of which the pilot considers essential to the safety of other flights, the pilot shall notify an appropriate ground radio station as soon as practicable.

[Docket No. 16097, 43 FR 46783, Oct. 1, 1978; as amended by Amdt. 135–1, 44 FR 26737, May 7, 1979]

§ 135.69 Restriction or suspension of operations: Continuation of flight in an emergency.

(a) During operations under this part, if a certificate holder or pilot in command knows of conditions, including airport and runway conditions, that are a hazard to safe operations, the certificate holder or pilot in command, as the case may be, shall restrict or suspend operations as necessary until those conditions are corrected.

(b) No pilot in command may allow a flight to continue toward any airport of intended landing under the conditions set forth in paragraph (a) of this section, unless, in the opinion of the pilot in command, the conditions that are a hazard to safe operations may reasonably be expected to be corrected by the estimated time of arrival or, unless there is no safer procedure. In the latter event, the continuation toward that airport is an emergency situation under § 135.19.

§ 135.71 Airworthiness check.

The pilot in command may not begin a flight unless the pilot determines that the airworthiness inspections required by § 91.409 of this chapter, or § 135.419, whichever is applicable, have been made.

[Docket No. 16097, 43 FR 46783, Oct. 10, 1978; as amended by Amdt. 135–32, 54 FR 34332, Aug. 18, 1989]

§ 135.73 Inspections and tests.

Each certificate holder and each person employed by the certificate holder shall allow the Administrator, at any time or place, to make inspections or tests (including en route inspections) to determine the holder's compliance with the Federal Aviation Act of 1958, applicable regulations, and the certificate holder's operating certificate, and operations specifications.

§ 135.75 Inspectors credentials: admission to pilots' compartment: Forward observer's seat.

(a) Whenever, in performing the duties of conducting an inspection, an FAA inspector presents an Aviation Safety Inspector credential, FAA Form 110A, to the pilot in command of an aircraft operated by the certificate holder, the inspector must be given free and uninterrupted access to the pilot compartment of that aircraft. However, this paragraph does not limit the emergency authority of the pilot in command to exclude any person from the pilot compartment in the interest of safety.

(b) A forward observer's seat on the flight deck, or forward passenger seat with headset or speaker must be provided for use by the Administrator while conducting en route inspections. The suitability of the location of the seat and the headset or speaker for use in conducting en route inspections is determined by the Administrator.

§ 135.77 Responsibility for operational control.

Each certificate holder is responsible for operational control and shall list, in the manual required by § 135.21, the name and title of each person authorized by it to exercise operational control.

§ 135.79 Flight locating requirements.

(a) Each certificate holder must have procedures established for locating each flight, for which an FAA flight plan is not filed, that—

(1) Provide the certificate holder with at least the information required to be included in a VFR flight plan;

(2) Provide for timely notification of an FAA facility or search and rescue facility, if an aircraft is overdue or missing; and

(3) Provide the certificate holder with the location, date, and estimated time for reestablishing radio or telephone communications, if the flight will operate in an area where communications cannot be maintained.

(b) Flight locating information shall be retained at the certificate holder's principal place of business, or at other places designated by the certificate holder in the flight locating procedures, until the completion of the flight.

(c) Each certificate holder shall furnish the representative of the Administrator assigned to it with a copy of its flight locating procedures and any changes or additions, unless those procedures are included in a manual required under this part.

§ 135.81 Informing personnel of operational information and appropriate changes.

Each certificate holder shall inform each person in its employment of the operations specifications that apply to that person's duties and responsibilities and shall make available to each pilot in the certificate holder's employ the following materials in current form:

(a) Airman's Information Manual (Alaska Supplement in Alaska and Pacific Chart Supplement in Pacific-Asia Regions) or a commercial publication that contains the same information.

(b) This part and part 91 of this chapter.

(c) Aircraft Equipment Manuals, and Aircraft Flight Manual or equivalent.

(d) For foreign operations, the International Flight Information Manual or a commercial publication that contains the same information concerning the pertinent operational and entry requirements of the foreign country or countries involved.

§ 135.83 Operating information required.

(a) The operator of an aircraft must provide the following materials, in current and appropriate form, accessible to the pilot at the pilot station, and the pilot shall use them:

(1) A cockpit checklist.

(2) For multiengine aircraft or for aircraft with retractable landing gear, an emergency cockpit checklist containing the procedures required by paragraph (c) of this section, as appropriate.

(3) Pertinent aeronautical charts.

(4) For IFR operations, each pertinent navigational en route, terminal area, and approach and letdown chart.

(5) For multiengine aircraft, one-engine-inoperative climb performance data and if the aircraft is approved for use in IFR or over-the-top operations, that data must be sufficient to enable the pilot to determine compliance with § 135.181(a)(2).

(b) Each cockpit checklist required by paragraph (a)(1) of this section must contain the following procedures:

(1) Before starting engines;

(2) Before takeoff;

(3) Cruise;

(4) Before landing;

(5) After landing;

(6) Stopping engines.

(c) Each emergency cockpit checklist required by paragraph (a)(2) of this section must contain the following procedures, as appropriate:

(1) Emergency operation of fuel, hydraulic, electrical, and mechanical systems.

(2) Emergency operation of instruments and controls.

(3) Engine inoperative procedures.

(4) Any other emergency procedures necessary for safety.

§ 135.85 Carriage of persons without compliance with the passenger-carrying provisions of this part.

The following persons may be carried aboard an aircraft without complying with the passenger-carrying requirements of this part:

(a) A crewmember or other employee of the certificate holder.

(b) A person necessary for the safe handling of animals on the aircraft.

(c) A person necessary for the safe handling of hazardous materials (as defined in subchapter C of title 49 CFR).

(d) A person performing duty as a security or honor guard accompanying a shipment made by or under the authority of the U.S. Government.

(e) A military courier or a military route supervisor carried by a military cargo contract air carrier or commercial operator in operations under a military cargo contract, if that carriage is specifically authorized by the appropriate military service.

(f) An authorized representative of the Administrator conducting an en route inspection.

(g) A person, authorized by the Administrator, who is performing a duty connected with a cargo operation of the certificate holder.

§ 135.87 Carriage of cargo including carry-on baggage.

No person may carry cargo, including carry-on baggage, in or on any aircraft unless—

(a) It is carried in an approved cargo rack, bin, or compartment installed in or on the aircraft;

(b) It is secured by an approved means; or

(c) It is carried in accordance with each of the following:

(1) For cargo, it is properly secured by a safety belt or other tie-down having enough strength to eliminate the possibility of shifting under all normally anticipated flight and ground conditions, or for carry-on baggage, it is restrained so as to prevent its movement during air turbulence.

(2) It is packaged or covered to avoid possible injury to occupants.

(3) It does not impose any load on seats or on the floor structure that exceeds the load limitation for those components.

(4) It is not located in a position that obstructs the access to, or use of, any required emergency or regular exit, or the use of the aisle between the crew and the passenger compartment, or located in a position that obscures any passenger's view of the "seat belt" sign, "no smoking" sign, or any required exit sign, unless an auxiliary sign or other approved means for proper notification of the passengers is provided.

(5) It is not carried directly above seated occupants.

(6) It is stowed in compliance with this section for takeoff and landing.

(7) For cargo only operations, paragraph (c)(4) of this section does not apply if the cargo is loaded so that at least one emergency or regular exit is available to provide all occupants of the aircraft a means of unobstructed exit from the aircraft if an emergency occurs.

(d) Each passenger seat under which baggage is stowed shall be fitted with a means to prevent articles of baggage stowed under it from sliding under crash impacts severe enough to induce the ultimate inertia forces specified in the emergency landing condition regulations under which the aircraft was type certificated.

(e) When cargo is carried in cargo compartments that are designed to require the physical entry of a crewmember to extinguish any fire that may occur during flight, the cargo must be loaded so as to allow a crewmember to effectively reach all parts of the compartment with the contents of a hand fire extinguisher.

§ 135.89 Pilot requirements: Use of oxygen.

(a) *Unpressurized aircraft.* Each pilot of an unpressurized aircraft shall use oxygen continuously when flying—

(1) At altitudes above 10,000 feet through 12,000 feet MSL for that part of the flight at those altitudes that is of more than 30 minutes duration; and

(2) Above 12,000 feet MSL.

(b) *Pressurized aircraft.*

(1) Whenever a pressurized aircraft is operated with the cabin pressure altitude more than 10,000 feet MSL, each pilot shall comply with paragraph (a) of this section.

(2) Whenever a pressurized aircraft is operated at altitudes above 25,000 feet through 35,000 feet MSL, unless each pilot has an approved quick-donning type oxygen mask—

(i) At least one pilot at the controls shall wear, secured and sealed, an oxygen mask that either supplies oxygen at all times or automatically supplies oxygen whenever the cabin pressure altitude exceeds 12,000 feet MSL; and

(ii) During that flight, each other pilot on flight deck duty shall have an oxygen mask, connected to an oxygen supply, located so as to allow immediate placing of the mask on the pilot's face sealed and secured for use.

(3) Whenever a pressurized aircraft is operated at altitudes above 35,000 feet MSL, at least one pilot at the controls shall wear, secured and sealed, an oxygen mask required by paragraph (b)(2)(i) of this section.

(4) If one pilot leaves a pilot duty station of an aircraft when operating at altitudes above 25,000 feet MSL, the remaining pilot at the controls shall put on and use an approved oxygen mask until the other pilot returns to the pilot duty station of the aircraft.

§ 135.91 Oxygen for medical use by passengers.

(a) Except as provided in paragraphs (d) and (e) of this section, no certificate holder may allow the carriage or operation of equipment for the storage, generation or dispensing of medical oxygen unless the unit to be carried is constructed so that all valves, fittings, and gauges are protected from damage during that carriage or operation and unless the following conditions are met—

(1) The equipment must be—

(i) Of an approved type or in conformity with the manufacturing, packaging, marking, labeling, and maintenance requirements of title 49 CFR parts 171, 172, and 173, except § 173.24(a)(1);

(ii) When owned by the certificate holder, maintained under the certificate holder's approved maintenance program;

(iii) Free of flammable contaminants on all exterior surfaces; and

(iv) Appropriately secured.

(2) When the oxygen is stored in the form of a liquid, the equipment must have been under the certificate holder's approved maintenance program since its purchase new or since the storage container was last purged.

(3) When the oxygen is stored in the form of a compressed gas as defined in title 49 CFR 173.300(a) —

(i) When owned by the certificate holder, it must be maintained under its approved maintenance program; and

(ii) The pressure in any oxygen cylinder must not exceed the rated cylinder pressure.

(4) The pilot in command must be advised when the equipment is on board, and when it is intended to be used.

(5) The equipment must be stowed, and each person using the equipment must be seated, so as not to restrict access to or use of any required emergency or regular exit, or of the aisle in the passenger compartment.

(b) No person may smoke and no certificate holder may allow any person to smoke within 10 feet of oxygen storage and dispensing equipment carried under paragraph (a) of this section.

(c) No certificate holder may allow any person other than a person trained in the use of medical oxygen equipment to connect or disconnect oxygen bottles or any other ancillary component while any passenger is aboard the aircraft.

(d) Paragraph (a)(1)(i) of this section does not apply when that equipment is furnished by a professional or medical emergency service for use on board an aircraft in a medical emergency when no other practical means of transportation (including any other properly equipped certificate holder) is reasonably available and the person carried under the medical emergency is accompanied by a person trained in the use of medical oxygen.

(e) Each certificate holder who, under the authority of paragraph (d) of this section, deviates from paragraph (a)(1)(i) of this section under a medical emergency shall, within 10 days, excluding Saturdays, Sundays, and Federal holidays, after the deviation, send to the certificate-holding district office a complete report of the operation involved, including a description of the deviation and the reasons for it.

[Docket No. 16097, 43 FR 46783, Oct. 10, 1978; as amended by Amdt. 135–60, 61 FR 2616, Jan. 26, 1996]

§ 135.93 Autopilot: Minimum altitudes for use.

(a) Except as provided in paragraphs (b), (c), (d), and (e) of this section, no person may use an autopilot at an altitude above the terrain which is less than 500 feet or less than twice the maximum altitude loss specified in the approved Aircraft Flight Manual or equivalent for a malfunction of the autopilot, whichever is higher.

(b) When using an instrument approach facility other than ILS, no person may use an autopilot at an altitude above the terrain that is less than 50 feet below the approved minimum descent altitude for that procedure, or less than twice the maximum loss specified in the approved Airplane Flight Manual or equivalent for a malfunction of the autopilot under approach conditions, whichever is higher.

(c) For ILS approaches, when reported weather conditions are less than the basic weather conditions in § 91.155 of this chapter, no person may use an autopilot with an approach coupler at an altitude above the terrain that is less than 50 feet above the terrain, or the maximum altitude loss specified in the approved Airplane Flight Manual or equivalent for the malfunction of the autopilot with approach coupler, whichever is higher.

(d) Without regard to paragraph (a), (b), or (c) of this section, the Administrator may issue operations specifications to allow the use, to touchdown, of an approved flight control guidance system with automatic capability, if —

(1) The system does not contain any altitude loss (above zero) specified in the approved Aircraft Flight Manual or equivalent for malfunction of the autopilot with approach coupler; and

(2) The Administrator finds that the use of the system to touchdown will not otherwise adversely affect the safety standards of this section.

(e) Notwithstanding paragraph (a) of this section, the Administrator issues operations specifications to allow the use of an approved autopilot system with automatic capability during the takeoff and initial climb phase of flight provided:

(1) The Airplane Flight Manual specifies a minimum altitude engagement certification restriction;

(2) The system is not engaged prior to the minimum engagement certification restriction specified in the Airplane Flight Manual or an altitude specified by the Administrator, whichever is higher; and

(3) The Administrator finds that the use of the system will not otherwise affect the safety standards required by this section.

(f) This section does not apply to operations conducted in rotorcraft.

[Docket No. 16097, 43 FR 46783, Oct. 10, 1978; as amended by Amdt. 135–32, 54 FR 34332, Aug. 18, 1989; Amdt. 135–68, 62 FR 27923, May 21, 1997]

§ 135.95 Airmen:
Limitations on use of services.

No certificate holder may use the services of any person as an airman unless the person performing those services —

(a) Holds an appropriate and current airman certificate; and

(b) Is qualified, under this chapter, for the operation for which the person is to be used.

§ 135.97 Aircraft and facilities for recent flight experience.

Each certificate holder shall provide aircraft and facilities to enable each of its pilots to maintain and demonstrate the pilot's ability to conduct all operations for which the pilot is authorized.

§ 135.99 Composition of flight crew.

(a) No certificate holder may operate an aircraft with less than the minimum flight crew specified in the aircraft operating limitations or the Aircraft Flight Manual for that aircraft and required by this part for the kind of operation being conducted.

(b) No certificate holder may operate an aircraft without a second in command if that aircraft has a passenger seating configuration, excluding any pilot seat, of ten seats or more.

§ 135.100 Flight crewmember duties.

(a) No certificate holder shall require, nor may any flight crewmember perform, any duties during a critical phase of flight except those duties required for the safe operation of the aircraft. Duties such as company required calls made for such nonsafety related purposes as ordering galley supplies and confirming passenger connections, announcements made to passengers promoting the air carrier or pointing out sights of interest, and filling out company payroll and related records are not required for the safe operation of the aircraft.

(b) No flight crewmember may engage in, nor may any pilot in command permit, any activity during a critical phase of flight which could distract any flight crewmember from the performance of his or her duties or which could interfere in any way with the proper conduct of those duties. Activities such as eating meals, engaging in nonessential conversations within the cockpit and nonessential communications between the cabin and cockpit crews, and reading publications not related to the proper conduct of the flight are not required for the safe operation of the aircraft.

(c) For the purposes of this section, critical phases of flight includes all ground operations involving taxi, takeoff and landing, and all other flight operations conducted below 10,000 feet, except cruise flight.

Note: Taxi is defined as "movement of an airplane under its own power on the surface of an airport."

[Docket No. 20661, 46 FR 5502, Jan. 19, 1981]

§ 135.101 Second in command required under IFR.

Except as provided in §§ 135.105, no person may operate an aircraft carrying passengers under IFR unless there is a second in command in the aircraft.

[Docket No. 28743, 62 FR 42374, Aug. 6, 1997]

§ 135.103 [Reserved]

§ 135.105 Exception to second in command requirement:
Approval for use of autopilot system.

(a) Except as provided in §§ 135.99 and 135.111, unless two pilots are required by this chapter for operations under VFR, a person may operate an aircraft without a second in command, if it is equipped with an operative approved autopilot system and the use of that system is authorized by appropriate operations specifications. No certificate holder may use any person, nor may any person serve, as a pilot in command under this section of an aircraft operated in a commuter operation, as defined in part 119 of this chapter unless that person has at least 100 hours pilot in command flight time in the make and model of aircraft to be flown and has met all other applicable requirements of this part.

(b) The certificate holder may apply for an amendment of its operations specifications to authorize the use of an autopilot system in place of a second in command.

(c) The Administrator issues an amendment to the operations specifications authorizing the use of an autopilot system, in place of a second in command, if —

(1) The autopilot is capable of operating the aircraft controls to maintain flight and maneuver it about the three axes; and

(2) The certificate holder shows, to the satisfaction of the Administrator, that operations using the autopilot system can be conducted safely and in compliance with this part.

The amendment contains any conditions or limitations on the use of the autopilot system that the Administrator determines are needed in the interest of safety.

[Docket No. 16097, 43 FR 46783, Oct. 10, 1978; as amended by Amdt. 135–3, 45 FR 7542, Feb. 4, 1980; Amdt. 135–58, 60 FR 65939, Dec. 20, 1995]

§ 135.107 Flight attendant crewmember requirement.

No certificate holder may operate an aircraft that has a passenger seating configuration, excluding any pilot seat, of more than 19 unless there is a flight attendant crewmember on board the aircraft.

§ 135.109 Pilot in command or second in command: Designation required.

(a) Each certificate holder shall designate a—
(1) Pilot in command for each flight; and
(2) Second in command for each flight requiring two pilots.
(b) The pilot in command, as designated by the certificate holder, shall remain the pilot in command at all times during that flight.

§ 135.111 Second in command required in Category II operations.

No person may operate an aircraft in a Category II operation unless there is a second in command of the aircraft.

§ 135.113 Passenger occupancy of pilot seat.

No certificate holder may operate an aircraft type certificated after October 15, 1971, that has a passenger seating configuration, excluding any pilot seat, of more than eight seats if any person other than the pilot in command, a second in command, a company check airman, or an authorized representative of the Administrator, the National Transportation Safety Board, or the United States Postal Service occupies a pilot seat.

§ 135.115 Manipulation of controls.

No pilot in command may allow any person to manipulate the flight controls of an aircraft during flight conducted under this part, nor may any person manipulate the controls during such flight unless that person is—
(a) A pilot employed by the certificate holder and qualified in the aircraft; or
(b) An authorized safety representative of the Administrator who has the permission of the pilot in command, is qualified in the aircraft, and is checking flight operations.

§ 135.117 Briefing of passengers before flight.

(a) Before each takeoff each pilot in command of an aircraft carrying passengers shall ensure that all passengers have been orally briefed on—
(1) *Smoking.* Each passenger shall be briefed on when, where, and under what conditions smoking is prohibited (including, but not limited to, any applicable requirements of part 252 of this title). This briefing shall include a statement that the Federal Aviation Regulations require passenger compliance with the lighted passenger information signs (if such signs are required), posted placards, areas designated for safety purposes as no smoking areas, and crewmember instructions with regard to these items. The briefing shall also include a statement (if the aircraft is equipped with a lavatory) that Federal law prohibits: tampering with, disabling, or destroying any smoke detector installed in an aircraft lavatory; smoking in lavatories; and when applicable, smoking in passenger compartments.
(2) Use of safety belts, including instructions on how to fasten and unfasten the safety belts. Each passenger shall be briefed on when, where and under what conditions the safety belt must be fastened about that passenger. This briefing shall include a statement that the Federal Aviation Regulations require passenger compliance with lighted passenger information signs and crewmember instructions concerning the use of safety belts.
(3) The placement of seat backs in an upright position before takeoff and landing;
(4) Location and means for opening the passenger entry door and emergency exits;
(5) Location of survival equipment;
(6) If the flight involves extended overwater operation, ditching procedures and the use of required flotation equipment;
(7) If the flight involves operations above 12,000 feet MSL, the normal and emergency use of oxygen; and
(8) Location and operation of fire extinguishers.
(b) Before each takeoff the pilot in command shall ensure that each person who may need the assistance of another person to move expeditiously to an exit if an emergency occurs and that person's attendant, if any, has received a briefing as to the procedures to be followed if an evacuation occurs. This paragraph does not apply to a person who has been given a briefing before a previous leg of a flight in the same aircraft.
(c) The oral briefing required by paragraph (a) of this section shall be given by the pilot in command or a crewmember.
(d) Notwithstanding the provisions of paragraph (c) of this section, for aircraft certificated to carry 19 passengers or less, the oral briefing required by paragraph (a) of this section shall be given by the pilot in command, a crewmember, or other qualified person designated by the certificate holder and approved by the Administrator.
(e) The oral briefing required by paragraph (a) shall be supplemented by printed cards which must be carried in the aircraft in locations convenient for the use of each passenger. The cards must—

(1) Be appropriate for the aircraft on which they are to be used;

(2) Contain a diagram of, and method of operating, the emergency exits; and

(3) Contain other instructions necessary for the use of emergency equipment on board the aircraft.

(f) The briefing required by paragraph (a) may be delivered by means of an approved recording playback device that is audible to each passenger under normal noise levels.

[Docket No. 16097, 43 FR 46783, Oct. 10, 1978; as amended by Amdt. 135–9, 51 FR 40709, Nov. 7, 1986; Amdt. 135–25, 53 FR 12362, Apr. 13, 1988; Amdt. 135–44, 57 FR 42675, Sept. 15, 1992; 57 FR 43776, Sept. 22, 1992]

§ 135.119 Prohibition against carriage of weapons.

No person may, while on board an aircraft being operated by a certificate holder, carry on or about that person a deadly or dangerous weapon, either concealed or unconcealed. This section does not apply to—

(a) Officials or employees of a municipality or a State, or of the United States, who are authorized to carry arms; or

(b) Crewmembers and other persons authorized by the certificate holder to carry arms.

§ 135.120 Prohibition on interference with crewmembers.

No person may assault, threaten, intimidate, or interfere with a crewmember in the performance of the crewmember's duties aboard an aircraft being operated under this part.

[Docket No. 16097, 43 FR 46783, Oct. 10, 1978; as amended by Amdt. 135–73, 64 FR 1080, Jan. 7, 1999]

§ 135.121 Alcoholic beverages.

(a) No person may drink any alcoholic beverage aboard an aircraft unless the certificate holder operating the aircraft has served that beverage.

(b) No certificate holder may serve any alcoholic beverage to any person aboard its aircraft if that person appears to be intoxicated.

(c) No certificate holder may allow any person to board any of its aircraft if that person appears to be intoxicated.

§ 135.122 Stowage of food, beverage, and passenger service equipment during aircraft movement on the surface, takeoff, and landing.

(a) No certificate holder may move an aircraft on the surface, takeoff, or land when any food, beverage, or tableware furnished by the certificate holder is located at any passenger seat.

(b) No certificate holder may move an aircraft on the surface, takeoff, or land unless each food and beverage tray and seat back tray table is secured in its stowed position.

(c) No certificate holder may permit an aircraft to move on surface, takeoff or land unless each passenger serving cart is secured in its stowed position.

(d) Each passenger shall comply with instructions given by a crewmember with regard to compliance with this section.

[Docket No. 26142, 57 FR 42675, Sept. 15, 1992]

§ 135.123 Emergency and emergency evacuation duties.

(a) Each certificate holder shall assign to each required crewmember for each type of aircraft as appropriate, the necessary functions to be performed in an emergency or in a situation requiring emergency evacuation. The certificate holder shall ensure that those functions can be practicably accomplished, and will meet any reasonably anticipated emergency including incapacitation of individual crewmembers or their inability to reach the passenger cabin because of shifting cargo in combination cargo-passenger aircraft.

(b) The certificate holder shall describe in the manual required under § 135.21 the functions of each category of required crewmembers assigned under paragraph (a) of this section.

§ 135.125 Airplane security.

Certificate holders conducting operations under this part shall comply with the applicable security requirements in part 108 of this chapter.

[Docket No. 108, 46 FR 3791, Jan. 15, 1981]

§ 135.127 Passenger information.

(a) No person may conduct a scheduled flight segment on which smoking is prohibited unless the "No Smoking" passenger information signs are lighted during the entire flight segment, or one or more "No Smoking" placards meeting the requirements of § 25.1541 are posted during the entire flight segment. If both the lighted signs and the placards are used, the signs must remain lighted during the entire flight segment. Smoking is prohibited on scheduled flight segments:

(1) Between any two points within Puerto Rico, the United States Virgin Islands, the District of Columbia, or any State of the United States (other than Alaska or Hawaii) or between any two points in any one of the above-mentioned jurisdictions (other than Alaska or Hawaii);

(2) Within the State of Alaska or within the State of Hawaii; or

(3) Scheduled in the current Worldwide or North American Edition of the *Official Airline Guide* or 6 hours or less in duration and between any point listed in paragraph (a)(1) of this section and any point in Alaska or Hawaii, or between any point in Alaska and any point in Hawaii.

(b) No person may smoke while a "No Smoking" sign is lighted or while "No Smoking" placards are posted, except that the pilot in command may authorize smoking on the flight deck (if it is physically separated from the passenger compartment) except during any movement of an aircraft on the surface, takeoff, and landing.

(c) No person may smoke in any aircraft lavatory.

(d) No person may operate an aircraft with a lavatory equipped with a smoke detector unless there is in that lavatory a sign or placard which reads: "Federal law provides for a penalty of up to $2,000 for tampering with the smoke detector installed in this lavatory."

(e) No person may tamper with, disable, or destroy any smoke detector installed in any aircraft lavatory.

(f) On flight segments other than those described in paragraph (a) of this section, the "No Smoking" signs required by § 135.177 (a)(3) of this part must be turned on during any movement of the aircraft on the surface, for each takeoff and landing, and at any other time considered necessary by the pilot in command.

(g) The passenger information requirements prescribed in § 91.517(b) and (d) of this chapter are in addition to the requirements prescribed in this section.

(h) Each passenger shall comply with instructions given him or her by crewmembers regarding compliance with paragraphs (b), (c), and (e) of this section.

[Docket No. 25590, 55 FR 8367, March 7, 1990; as amended by Amdt. 135–35, 55 FR 20135, May 15, 1990; Amdt. 135–44, 57 FR 42675, Sept. 15, 1992; Amdt. 135–60, 61 FR 2616, Jan. 26, 1996]

§ 135.128 Use of safety belts and child restraint systems.

(a) Except as provided in this paragraph, each person on board an aircraft operated under this part shall occupy an approved seat or berth with a separate safety belt properly secured about him or her during movement on the surface, takeoff and landing. For seaplane and float equipped ro-

torcraft operations during movement on the surface, the person pushing off the seaplane or rotorcraft from the dock and the person mooring the seaplane or rotorcraft at the dock are excepted from the preceding seating and safety belt requirements. A safety belt provided for the occupant of a seat may not be used by more than one person who has reached his or her second birthday. Not withstanding the preceding requirements, a child may:

(1) Be held by an adult who is occupying an approved seat or berth, provided the child has not reached his or her second birthday and the child does not occupy or use any restraining device; or

(2) Notwithstanding any other requirement of this chapter, occupy an approved child restraint system furnished by the certificate holder or one of the persons described in paragraph (a)(2)(i) of this section, provided:

(i) The child is accompanied by a parent, guardian, or attendant designated by the child's parent or guardian to attend to the safety of the child during flight;

(ii) Except as provided in paragraph (a)(2)(ii)(D) of this section, the approved child restraint system bears one or more labels as follows:

(A) Seats manufactured to U.S. standards between January 1, 1981, and February 25, 1985, must bear the label: "This child restraint system conforms to all applicable Federal motor vehicle safety standards";

(B) Seats manufactured to U.S. standards on or after February 26, 1985, must bear two labels:

(1) "This child restraint system conforms to all applicable Federal motor vehicle safety standards"; and

(2) "THIS RESTRAINT IS CERTIFIED FOR USE IN MOTOR VEHICLES AND AIRCRAFT" in red lettering;

(C) Seats that do not qualify under paragraphs (a)(2)(ii)(A) and (a)(2)(ii)(B) of this section must bear either a label showing approval of a foreign government or a label showing that the seat was manufactured under the standards of the United Nations;

(D) Notwithstanding any other provisions of this section, booster-type child restraint systems (as defined in Federal Motor Vehicle Standard No. 213 (49 CFR 571.213)), vest- and harness-type child restraint systems, and lap held child restraints are not approved for use in aircraft; and

(iii) The certificate holder complies with the following requirements:

(A) The restraint system must be properly secured to an approved forward-facing seat or berth;

(B) The child must be properly secured in the restraint system and must not exceed the specified weight limit for the restraint system; and

(C) The restraint system must bear the appropriate label(s).

(b) Except as provided in paragraph (b)(3) of this section, the following prohibitions apply to certificate holders:

(1) No certificate holder may permit a child, in an aircraft, to occupy a booster-type child restraint system, a vest-type child restraint system, a harness-type child restraint system, or a lap held child restraint system during take off, landing, or movement on the surface.

(2) Except as required in paragraph (b)(1) of this section, no certificate holder may prohibit a child, if requested by the child's parent, guardian, or designated attendant, from occupying a child restraint system furnished by the child's parent, guardian, or designated attendant provided:

(i) The child holds a ticket for an approved seat or berth or such seat or berth is otherwise made available by the certificate holder for the child's use;

(ii) The requirements of paragraph (a)(2)(i) of this section are met;

(iii) The requirements of paragraph (a)(2)(iii) of this section are met; and

(iv) The child restraint system has one or more of the labels described in paragraphs (a)(2)(ii)(A) through (a)(2)(ii)(C) of this section.

(3) This section does not prohibit the certificate holder from providing child restraint systems authorized by this or, consistent with safe operating practices, determining the most appropriate passenger seat location for the child restraint system.

[Docket No. 26142, 57 FR 42676, Sept. 15, 1992; as amended by Amdt. 135–62, 61 FR 28422, June 4, 1996]

§ 135.129 Exit seating.

(a)(1) *Applicability.* This section applies to all certificate holders operating under this part, except for on-demand operations with aircraft having 19 or fewer passenger seats and commuter operations with aircraft having 9 or fewer passenger seats.

(2) *Duty to make determination of suitability.* Each certificate holder shall determine, to the extent necessary to perform the applicable functions of paragraph (d) of this section, the suitability of each person it permits to occupy an exit seat. For the purpose of this section —

(i) *Exit seat* means —

(A) Each seat having direct access to an exit; and

(B) Each seat in a row of seats through which passengers would have to pass to gain access to an exit, from the first seat inboard of the exit to the first aisle inboard of the exit.

(ii) A passenger seat having *direct access* means a seat from which a passenger can proceed directly to the exit without entering an aisle or passing around an obstruction.

(3) *Persons designated to make determination.* Each certificate holder shall make the passenger exit seating determinations required by the paragraph in a non-discriminatory manner consistent with the requirements of this section, by persons designated in the certificate holder's required operations manual.

(4) *Submission of designation for approval.* Each certificate holder shall designate the exit seats for each passenger seating configuration in its fleet in accordance with the definitions in this paragraph and submit those designations for approval as part of the procedures required to be submitted for approval under paragraphs (n) and (p) of this section.

(b) No certificate holder may seat a person in a seat affected by this section if the certificate holder determines that it is likely that the person would be unable to perform one or more of the applicable functions listed in paragraph (d) of this section because —

(1) The person lacks sufficient mobility, strength, or dexterity in both arms and hands, and both legs:

(i) To reach upward, sideways, and downward to the location of emergency exit and exit-slide operating mechanisms;

(ii) To grasp and push, pull, turn, or otherwise manipulate those mechanisms;

(iii) To push, shove, pull, or otherwise open emergency exits;

(iv) To lift out, hold, deposit on nearby seats, or maneuver over the seatbacks to the next row objects the size and weight of over-wing window exit doors;

(v) To remove obstructions of size and weight similar over-wing exit doors;

(vi) To reach the emergency exit expeditiously;

(vii) To maintain balance while removing obstructions;

(viii) To exit expeditiously;

(ix) To stabilize an escape slide after deployment; or

(x) To assist others in getting off an escape slide;

(2) The person is less than 15 years of age or lacks the capacity to perform one or more of the applicable functions listed in paragraph (d) of this section without the assistance of an adult companion, parent, or other relative;

(3) The person lacks the ability to read and understand instructions required by this section and related to emergency evacuation provided by the certificate holder in printed or graphic form or the ability to understand oral crew commands.

(4) The person lacks sufficient visual capacity to perform one or more of the applicable functions in paragraph (d) of this section without the assis-

tance of visual aids beyond contact lenses or eyeglasses;

(5) The person lacks sufficient aural capacity to hear and understand instructions shouted by flight attendants, without assistance beyond a hearing aid;

(6) The person lacks the ability adequately to impart information orally to other passengers; or,

(7) The person has:

(i) A condition or responsibilities, such as caring for small children, that might prevent the person from performing one or more of the applicable functions listed in paragraph (d) of this section; or

(ii) A condition that might cause the person harm if he or she performs one or more of the applicable functions listed in paragraph (d) of this section.

(c) Each passenger shall comply with instructions given by a crewmember or other authorized employee of the certificate holder implementing exit seating restrictions established in accordance with this section.

(d) Each certificate holder shall include on passenger information cards, presented in the languages in which briefings and oral commands are given by the crew, at each exit seat affected by this section, information that, in the event of an emergency in which a crewmember is not available to assist, a passenger occupying an exit row seat may use if called upon to perform the following functions:

(1) Locate the emergency exit;

(2) Recognize the emergency exit opening mechanism;

(3) Comprehend the instructions for operating the emergency exit;

(4) Operate the emergency exit;

(5) Assess whether opening the emergency exit will increase the hazards to which passengers may be exposed;

(6) Follow oral directions and hand signals given by a crewmember;

(7) Stow or secure the emergency exit door so that it will not impede use of the exit;

(8) Assess the condition of an escape slide, activate the slide, and stabilize the slide after deployment to assist others in getting off the slide;

(9) Pass expeditiously through the emergency exit; and

(10) Assess, select, and follow a safe path away from the emergency exit.

(e) Each certificate holder shall include on passenger information cards, at each exit seat—

(1) In the primary language in which emergency commands are given by the crew, the selection criteria set forth in paragraph (b) of this section, and a request that a passenger identify himself or herself to allow reseating if he or she—

(i) Cannot meet the selection criteria set forth in paragraph (b) of this section;

(ii) Has a nondiscernible condition that will prevent him or her from performing the applicable functions listed in paragraph (d) of this section;

(iii) May suffer bodily harm as the result of performing one or more of those functions; or,

(iv) Does not wish to perform those functions; and,

(2) In each language used by the certificate holder for passenger information cards, a request that a passenger identify himself or herself to allow reseating if he or she lacks the ability to read, speak, or understand the language or the graphic form in which instructions required by this section and related to emergency evacuation are provided by the certificate holder, or the ability to understand the specified language in which crew commands will be given in an emergency;

(3) May suffer bodily harm as the result of performing one or more of those functions; or,

(4) Does not wish to perform those functions.

A certificate holder shall not require the passenger to disclose his or her reason for needing reseating.

(f) Each certificate holder shall make available for inspection by the public at all passenger loading gates and ticket counters at each airport where it conducts passenger operations, written procedures established for making determinations in regard to exit row seating.

(g) No certificate holder may allow taxi or pushback unless at least one required crewmember has verified that no exit row seat is occupied by a person the crewmember determines is likely to be unable to perform the applicable functions listed in paragraph (d) of this section.

(h) Each certificate holder shall include in its passenger briefings a reference to the passenger information cards, required by paragraphs (d) and (e), the selection criteria set forth in paragraph (b), and the functions to be performed, set forth in paragraph (d) of this section.

(i) Each certificate holder shall include in its passenger briefings a request that a passenger identify himself or herself to allow reseating if he or she—

(1) Cannot meet the selection criteria set forth in paragraph (b) of this section;

(2) Has a nondiscernible condition that will prevent him or her from performing the applicable functions listed in paragraph (d) of this section;

(3) May suffer bodily harm as the result of performing one or more of those functions; or,

(4) Does not wish to perform those functions.

A certificate holder shall not require the passenger to disclose his or her reason for needing reseating.

(j) [Reserved]

(k) In the event a certificate holder determines in accordance with this section that it is likely that a passenger assigned to an exit row seat would be unable to perform the functions listed in paragraph (d) of this section or a passenger requests a non-exit seat, the certificate holder shall expeditiously relocate the passenger to a non-exit seat.

(l) In the event of full booking in the non-exit seats, and if necessary to accommodate a passenger being relocated from an exit seat, the certificate holder shall move a passenger who is willing and able to assume the evacuation functions that may be required, to an exit seat.

(m) A certificate holder may deny transportation to any passenger under this section only because—

(1) The passenger refuses to comply with instructions given by a crewmember or other authorized employee of the certificate holder implementing exit seating restrictions established in accordance with this section, or

(2) The only seat that will physically accommodate the person's handicap is an exit seat.

(n) In order to comply with this section certificate holders shall—

(1) Establish procedures that address:

(i) The criteria listed in paragraph (b) of this section;

(ii) The functions listed in paragraph (d) of this section;

(iii) The requirements for airport information, passenger information cards, crewmember verification of appropriate seating in exit rows, passenger briefings, seat assignments, and denial of transportation as set forth in this section;

(iv) How to resolve disputes arising from implementation of this section, including identification of the certificate holder employee on the airport to whom complaints should be addressed for resolution; and,

(2) Submit their procedures for preliminary review and approval to the principal operations inspectors assigned to them at the certificate-holding district office.

(o) Certificate holders shall assign seats prior to boarding consistent with the criteria listed in paragraph (b) and the functions listed in paragraph (d) of this section, to the maximum extent feasible.

(p) The procedures required by paragraph (n) of this section will not become effective until final approval is granted by the Director, Flight Standards Service, Washington, DC. Approval will be based solely upon the safety aspects of the certificate holder's procedures.

[Docket No. 25821, 55 FR 8073, March 6, 1990; as amended by Amdt. 135–45, 57 FR 48664, Oct. 27, 1992; Amdt. 135–50, 59 FR 33603, June 29, 1994; Amdt. 135–60, 61 FR 2616, Jan. 26, 1996]

Subpart C— Aircraft and Equipment

§ 135.141 Applicability.

This subpart prescribes aircraft and equipment requirements for operations under this part. The requirements of this subpart are in addition to the aircraft and equipment requirements of part 91 of this chapter. However, this part does not require the duplication of any equipment required by this chapter.

§ 135.143 General requirements.

(a) No person may operate an aircraft under this part unless that aircraft and its equipment meet the applicable regulations of this chapter.

(b) Except as provided in § 135.179, no person may operate an aircraft under this part unless the required instruments and equipment in it have been approved and are in an operable condition.

(c) ATC transponder equipment installed within the time periods indicated below must meet the performance and environmental requirements of the following TSOs:

(1) *Through January 1, 1992:*

(i) Any class of TSO-C74b or any class of TSO-C74c as appropriate, provided that the equipment was manufactured before January 1, 1990; or

(ii) The appropriate class of TSO-C112 (Mode S).

(2) *After January 1, 1992:* The appropriate class of TSO-C112 (Mode S). For purposes of paragraph (c)(2) of this section, "installation" does not include—

(i) Temporary installation of TSO-C74b or TSO-C74c substitute equipment, as appropriate, during maintenance of the permanent equipment;

(ii) Reinstallation of equipment after temporary removal for maintenance; or

(iii) For fleet operations, installation of equipment in a fleet aircraft after removal of the equipment for maintenance from another aircraft in the same operator's fleet.

[Docket No. 16097, 43 FR 46783, Oct. 10, 1978; as amended by Amdt. 135–22, 52 FR 3392, Feb. 3, 1987]

135

§ 135.144 Portable electronic devices.

(a) Except as provided in paragraph (b) of this section, no person may operate, nor may any operator or pilot in command of an aircraft allow the operation of, any portable electronic device on any U.S.-registered civil aircraft operating under this part.

(b) Paragraph (a) of this section does not apply to—

(1) Portable voice recorders;

(2) Hearing aids;

(3) Heart pacemakers;

(4) Electric shavers; or

(5) Any other portable electronic device that the part 119 certificate holder has determined will not cause interference with the navigation or communication system of the aircraft on which it is to be used.

(c) The determination required by paragraph (b)(5) of this section shall be made by that part 119 certificate holder operating the aircraft on which the particular device is to be used.

[Docket No. 16097, 43 FR 46783, Oct. 10, 1978; as amended by Amdt. 135–73, 64 FR 1080, Jan. 7, 1999]

§ 135.145 Aircraft proving tests.

(a) No certificate holder may operate a turbojet airplane, or an aircraft for which two pilots are required by this chapter for operations under VFR, if it has not previously proved that aircraft or an aircraft of the same make and similar design in any operation under this part unless, in addition to the aircraft certification tests, at least 25 hours of proving tests acceptable to the Administrator have been flown by that certificate holder including—

(1) Five hours of night time, if night flights are to be authorized;

(2) Five instrument approach procedures under simulated or actual instrument weather conditions, if IFR flights are to be authorized; and

(3) Entry into a representative number of en route airports as determined by the Administrator.

(b) No certificate holder may carry passengers in an aircraft during proving tests, except those needed to make the tests and those designated by the Administrator to observe the tests. However, pilot flight training may be conducted during the proving tests.

(c) For the purposes of paragraph (a) of this section an aircraft is not considered to be of similar design if an alteration includes—

(1) The installation of powerplants other than those of a type similar to those with which it is certificated; or

(2) Alterations to the aircraft or its components that materially affect flight characteristics.

(d) The Administrator may authorize deviations from this section if the Administrator finds that special circumstances make full compliance with this section unnecessary.

§ 135.147 Dual controls required.

No person may operate an aircraft in operations requiring two pilots unless it is equipped with functioning dual controls. However, if the aircraft type certification operating limitations do not require two pilots, a throwover control wheel may be used in place of two control wheels.

§ 135.149 Equipment requirements: General.

No person may operate an aircraft unless it is equipped with—

(a) A sensitive altimeter that is adjustable for barometric pressure;

(b) Heating or deicing equipment for each carburetor or, for a pressure carburetor, an alternate air source;

(c) For turbojet airplanes, in addition to two gyroscopic bank-and-pitch indicators (artificial horizons) for use at the pilot stations, a third indicator that is installed in accordance with the instrument requirements prescribed in § 121.305(j) of this chapter.

(d) [Reserved]

(e) For turbine powered aircraft, any other equipment as the Administrator may require.

[Docket No. 16097, 43 FR 46783, Oct. 10, 1978; as amended by Amdt. 135–1, 44 FR 26737, May 7, 1979; Amdt. 135–34, 54 FR 43926, Oct. 27, 1989; Amdt. 135–38, 55 FR 43310, Oct. 26, 1990]

§ 135.150 Public address and crewmember interphone systems.

No person may operate an aircraft having a passenger seating configuration, excluding any pilot seat, of more than 19 unless it is equipped with—

(a) A public address system which—

(1) Is capable of operation independent of the crewmember interphone system required by paragraph (b) of this section, except for handsets, headsets, microphones, selector switches, and signaling devices;

(2) Is approved in accordance with § 21.305 of this chapter;

(3) Is accessible for immediate use from each of two flight crewmember stations in the pilot compartment;

(4) For each required floor-level passenger emergency exit which has an adjacent flight attendant seat, has a microphone which is readily accessible to the seated flight attendant, except that one microphone may serve more than one exit, provided the proximity of the exits allows un-

assisted verbal communication between seated flight attendants;

(5) Is capable of operation within 10 seconds by a flight attendant at each of those stations in the passenger compartment from which its use is accessible;

(6) Is audible at all passenger seats, lavatories, and flight attendant seats and work stations; and

(7) For transport category airplanes manufactured on or after November 27, 1990, meets the requirements of § 25.1423 of this chapter.

(b) A crewmember interphone system which—

(1) Is capable of operation independent of the public address system required by paragraph (a) of this section, except for handsets, headsets, microphones, selector switches, and signaling devices;

(2) Is approved in accordance with § 21.305 of this chapter;

(3) Provides a means of two-way communication between the pilot compartment and—

(i) Each passenger compartment; and

(ii) Each galley located on other than the main passenger deck level;

(4) Is accessible for immediate use from each of two flight crewmember stations in the pilot compartment;

(5) Is accessible for use from at least one normal flight attendant station in each passenger compartment;

(6) Is capable of operation within 10 seconds by a flight attendant at each of those stations in each passenger compartment from which its use is accessible; and

(7) For large turbojet-powered airplanes—

(i) Is accessible for use at enough flight attendant stations so that all floor-level emergency exits (or entryways to those exits in the case of exits located within galleys) in each passenger compartment are observable from one or more of those stations so equipped;

(ii) Has an alerting system incorporating aural or visual signals for use by flight crewmembers to alert flight attendants and for use by flight attendants to alert flight crewmembers;

(iii) For the alerting system required by paragraph (b)(7)(ii) of this section, has a means for the recipient of a call to determine whether it is a normal call or an emergency call; and

(iv) When the airplane is on the ground, provides a means of two-way communication between ground personnel and either of at least two flight crewmembers in the pilot compartment. The interphone system station for use by ground personnel must be so located that personnel using the system may avoid visible detection from within the airplane.

[Docket No. 24995, 54 FR 43926, Oct. 27, 1989]

§ 135.151 Cockpit voice recorders.

(a) No person may operate a multiengine, turbine-powered airplane or rotorcraft having a passenger seating configuration of six or more and for which two pilots are required by certification or operating rules unless it is equipped with an approved cockpit voice recorder that:

(1) Is installed in compliance with § 23.1457(a) (1) and (2), (b), (c), (d), (e), (f), and (g); § 25.1457(a)(1) and (2), (b), (c), (d), (e), (f), and (g); § 27.1457(a)(1) and (2), (b), (c), (d), (e), (f), and (g); or § 29.1457(a)(1) and (2), (b), (c), (d), (e), (f), and (g) of this chapter, as applicable; and

(2) Is operated continuously from the use of the check list before the flight to completion of the final check list at the end of the flight.

(b) No person may operate a multiengine, turbine-powered airplane or rotorcraft having a passenger seating configuration of 20 or more seats unless it is equipped with an approved cockpit voice recorder that—

(1) Is installed in compliance with § 23.1457, § 25.1457, § 27.1457 or § 29.1457 of this chapter, as applicable; and

(2) Is operated continuously from the use of the check list before the flight to completion of the final check list at the end of the flight.

(c) In the event of an accident, or occurrence requiring immediate notification of the National Transportation Safety Board which results in termination of the flight, the certificate holder shall keep the recorded information for at least 60 days or, if requested by the Administrator or the Board, for a longer period. Information obtained from the record may be used to assist in determining the cause of accidents or occurrences in connection with investigations. The Administrator does not use the record in any civil penalty or certificate action.

(d) For those aircraft equipped to record the uninterrupted audio signals received by a boom or a mask microphone the flight crewmembers are required to use the boom microphone below 18,000 feet mean sea level. No person may operate a large turbine engine powered airplane manufactured after October 11, 1991, or on which a cockpit voice recorder has been installed after October 11, 1991, unless it is equipped to record the uninterrupted audio signal received by a boom or mask microphone in accordance with § 25.1457(c)(5) of this chapter.

(e) In complying with this section, an approved cockpit voice recorder having an erasure feature may be used, so that during the operation of the recorder, information:

(1) Recorded in accordance with paragraph (a) of this section and recorded more than 15 minutes earlier; or

(2) Recorded in accordance with paragraph (b) of this section and recorded more than 30 minutes earlier; may be erased or otherwise obliterated.

[Docket No. 16097, 43 FR 46783, Oct. 10, 1978; as amended by Amdt. 135–23, 52 FR 9637, March 25, 1987; Amdt. 135–26, 53 FR 26151, July 11, 1988; Amdt. 135–60, 61 FR 2616, Jan. 26, 1996]

§ 135.152 Flight recorders.

(a) Except as provided in paragraph (k) of this section, no person may operate under this part a multi-engine, turbine-engine powered airplane or rotorcraft having a passenger seating configuration, excluding any required crewmember seat, of 10 to 19 seats, that was either brought onto the U.S. register after, or was registered outside the United States and added to the operator's U.S. operations specifications after, October 11, 1991, unless it is equipped with one or more approved flight recorders that use a digital method of recording and storing data and a method of readily retrieving that data from the storage medium. The parameters specified in either Appendix B or C of this part, as applicable must be recorded within the range, accuracy, resolution, and recording intervals as specified. The recorder shall retain no less than 25 hours of aircraft operation.

(b) After October 11, 1991, no person may operate a multiengine, turbine-powered airplane having a passenger seating configuration of 20 to 30 seats or a multiengine, turbine-powered rotorcraft having a passenger seating configuration of 20 or more seats unless it is equipped with one or more approved flight recorders that utilize a digital method of recording and storing data, and a method of readily retrieving that data from the storage medium. The parameters in Appendix D or E of this part, as applicable, that are set forth below, must be recorded within the ranges, accuracies, resolutions, and sampling intervals as specified.

(1) Except as provided in paragraph (b)(3) of this section for aircraft type certificated before October 1, 1969, the following parameters must be recorded:

(i) Time;
(ii) Altitude;
(iii) Airspeed;
(iv) Vertical acceleration;
(v) Heading;
(vi) Time of each radio transmission to or from air traffic control;
(vii) Pitch attitude;
(viii) Roll attitude;
(ix) Longitudinal acceleration;
(x) Control column or pitch control surface position; and
(xi) Thrust of each engine.

(2) Except as provided in paragraph (b)(3) of this section for aircraft type certificated after September 30, 1969, the following parameters must be recorded:

(i) Time;
(ii) Altitude;
(iii) Airspeed;
(iv) Vertical acceleration;
(v) Heading;
(vi) Time of each radio transmission either to or from air traffic control;
(vii) Pitch attitude;
(viii) Roll attitude;
(ix) Longitudinal acceleration;
(x) Pitch trim position;
(xi) Control column or pitch control surface position;
(xii) Control wheel or lateral control surface position;
(xiii) Rudder pedal or yaw control surface position;
(xiv) Thrust of each engine;
(xv) Position of each thrust reverser;
(xvi) Trailing edge flap or cockpit flap control position; and
(xvii) Leading edge flap or cockpit flap control position.

(3) For aircraft manufactured after October 11, 1991, all of the parameters listed in Appendix D or E of this part, as applicable, must be recorded.

(c) Whenever a flight recorder required by this section is installed, it must be operated continuously from the instant the airplane begins the takeoff roll or the rotorcraft begins the lift-off until the airplane has completed the landing roll or the rotorcraft has landed at its destination.

(d) Except as provided in paragraph (c) of this section, and except for recorded data erased as authorized in this paragraph, each certificate holder shall keep the recorded data prescribed in paragraph (a) of this section until the aircraft has been operating for at least 25 hours of the operating time specified in paragraph (c) of this section. In addition, each certificate holder shall keep the recorded data prescribed in paragraph (b) of this section for an airplane until the airplane has been operating for at least 25 hours, and for a rotorcraft until the rotorcraft has been operating for at least 10 hours, of the operating time specified in paragraph (c) of this section. A total of 1 hour of recorded data may be erased for the purpose of testing the flight recorder or the flight recorder system. Any erasure made in accordance with this paragraph must be of the oldest recorded data accumulated at the time of testing. Except as provided in paragraph (c) of this section, no record need be kept more than 60 days.

(e) In the event of an accident or occurrence that requires the immediate notification of the National Transportation Safety Board under 49 CFR part 830 of its regulations and that results in termination of the flight, the certificate holder shall remove the recording media from the aircraft and keep the recorded data required by paragraphs (a) and (b) of this section for at least 60 days or for a longer period upon request of the Board or the Administrator.

(f)(1) For airplanes manufactured on or before August 18, 2000, and all other aircraft, each flight recorder required by this section must be installed in accordance with the requirements of § 23.1459, 25.1459, 27.1459, or 29.1459, as appropriate, of this chapter. The correlation required by paragraph (c) of § 23.1459, 25.1459, 27.1459, or 29.1459, as appropriate, of this chapter need be established only on one aircraft of a group of aircraft:

(i) That are of the same type;

(ii) On which the flight recorder models and their installations are the same; and

(iii) On which there are no differences in the type designs with respect to the installation of the first pilot's instruments associated with the flight recorder. The most recent instrument calibration, including the recording medium from which this calibration is derived, and the recorder correlation must be retained by the certificate holder.

(f)(2) For airplanes manufactured after August 18, 2000, each flight data recorder system required by this section must be installed in accordance with the requirements of § 23.1459 (a), (b), (d) and (e) of this chapter, or § 25.1459 (a), (b), (d), and (e) of this chapter. A correlation must be established between the values recorded by the flight data recorder and the corresponding values being measured. The correlation must contain a sufficient number of correlation points to accurately establish the conversion from the recorded values to engineering units or discrete state over the full operating range of the parameter. Except for airplanes having separate altitude and airspeed sensors that are an integral part of the flight data recorder system, a single correlation may be established for any group of airplanes—

(i) That are of the same type;

(ii) On which the flight recorder system and its installation are the same; and

(iii) On which there is no difference in the type design with respect to the installation of those sensors associated with the flight data recorder system. Documentation sufficient to convert recorded data into the engineering units and discrete values specified in the applicable appendix must be maintained by the certificate holder.

(g) Each flight recorder required by this section that records the data specified in paragraphs (a) and (b) of this section must have an approved device to assist in locating that recorder under water.

(h) The operational parameters required to be recorded by digital flight data recorders required by paragraphs (i) and (j) of this section are as follows, the phrase "when an information source is installed" following a parameter indicates that recording of that parameter is not intended to require a change in installed equipment.

(1) Time;

(2) Pressure altitude;

(3) Indicated airspeed;

(4) Heading—primary flight crew reference (if selectable, record discrete, true or magnetic);

(5) Normal acceleration (Vertical);

(6) Pitch attitude;

(7) Roll attitude;

(8) Manual radio transmitter keying, or CVR/DFDR synchronization reference;

(9) Thrust/power of each engine—primary flight crew reference;

(10) Autopilot engagement status;

(11) Longitudinal acceleration;

(12) Pitch control input;

(13) Lateral control input;

(14) Rudder pedal input;

(15) Primary pitch control surface position;

(16) Primary lateral control surface position;

(17) Primary yaw control surface position;

(18) Lateral acceleration;

(19) Pitch trim surface position or parameters of paragraph (h)(82) of this section if currently recorded;

(20) Trailing edge flap or cockpit flap control selection (except when parameters of paragraph (h)(85) of this section apply);

(21) Leading edge flap or cockpit flap control selection (except when parameters of paragraph (h)(86) of this section apply);

(22) Each Thrust reverser position (or equivalent for propeller airplane);

(23) Ground spoiler position or speed brake selection (except when parameters of paragraph (h)(87) of this section apply);

(24) Outside or total air temperature;

(25) Automatic Flight Control System (AFCS) modes and engagement status, including autothrottle;

(26) Radio altitude (when an information source is installed);

(27) Localizer deviation, MLS Azimuth;

(28) Glideslope deviation, MLS Elevation;

(29) Marker beacon passage;

(30) Master warning;

(31) Air/ground sensor (primary airplane system reference nose or main gear);

(32) Angle of attack (when information source is installed);

135

(33) Hydraulic pressure low (each system);

(34) Ground speed (when an information source is installed);

(35) Ground proximity warning system;

(36) Landing gear position or landing gear cockpit control selection;

(37) Drift angle (when an information source is installed);

(38) Wind speed and direction (when an information source is installed);

(39) Latitude and longitude (when an information source is installed);

(40) Stick shaker/pusher (when an information source is installed);

(41) Windshear (when an information source is installed);

(42) Throttle/power lever position;

(43) Additional engine parameters (as designated in Appendix F of this part);

(44) Traffic alert and collision avoidance system;

(45) DME 1 and 2 distances;

(46) Nav 1 and 2 selected frequency;

(47) Selected barometric setting (when an information source is installed);

(48) Selected altitude (when an information source is installed);

(49) Selected speed (when an information source is installed);

(50) Selected mach (when an information source is installed);

(51) Selected vertical speed (when an information source is installed);

(52) Selected heading (when an information source is installed);

(53) Selected flight path (when an information source is installed);

(54) Selected decision height (when an information source is installed);

(55) EFIS display format;

(56) Multi-function/engine/alerts display format;

(57) Thrust command (when an information source is installed);

(58) Thrust target (when an information source is installed);

(59) Fuel quantity in CG trim tank (when an information source is installed);

(60) Primary Navigation System Reference;

(61) Icing (when an information source is installed);

(62) Engine warning each engine vibration (when an information source is installed);

(63) Engine warning each engine over temp. (when an information source is installed);

(64) Engine warning each engine oil pressure low (when an information source is installed);

(65) Engine warning each engine over speed (when an information source is installed;

(66) Yaw trim surface position;

(67) Roll trim surface position;

(68) Brake pressure (selected system);

(69) Brake pedal application (left and right);

(70) Yaw or sideslip angle (when an information source is installed);

(71) Engine bleed valve position (when an information source is installed);

(72) De-icing or anti-icing system selection (when an information source is installed);

(73) Computed center of gravity (when an information source is installed);

(74) AC electrical bus status;

(75) DC electrical bus status;

(76) APU bleed valve position (when an information source is installed);

(77) Hydraulic pressure (each system);

(78) Loss of cabin pressure;

(79) Computer failure;

(80) Heads-up display (when an information source is installed);

(81) Para-visual display (when an information source is installed);

(82) Cockpit trim control input position — pitch;

(83) Cockpit trim control input position — roll;

(84) Cockpit trim control input position — yaw;

(85) Trailing edge flap and cockpit flap control position;

(86) Leading edge flap and cockpit flap control position;

(87) Ground spoiler position and speed brake selection; and

(88) All cockpit flight control input forces (control wheel, control column, rudder pedal).

(i) For all turbine-engine powered airplanes with a seating configuration, excluding any required crewmember seat, of 10 to 30 passenger seats, manufactured after August 18, 2000 —

(1) The parameters listed in paragraphs (h)(1) through (h)(57) of this section must be recorded within the ranges, accuracies, resolutions, and recording intervals specified in Appendix F of this part.

(2) Commensurate with the capacity of the recording system, all additional parameters for which information sources are installed and which are connected to the recording system must be recorded within the ranges, accuracies, resolutions, and sampling intervals specified in Appendix F of this part.

(j) For all turbine-engine-powered airplanes with a seating configuration, excluding any required crewmember seat, of 10 to 30 passenger seats, that are manufactured after August 19, 2002 the parameters listed in paragraph (a)(1) through (a)(88) of this section must be recorded within the ranges, accuracies, resolutions, and recording intervals specified in Appendix F of this part.

(k) For airplanes manufactured before August 18, 1997 the following airplane type need not comply with this section: deHavilland DHC-6.

[Docket No. 25530, 53 FR 26151, July 11, 1988; as amended by Amdt. 135–69, 62 FR 38396, July 17, 1997; Amdt. 135–69, 62 FR 48135, Sept. 12, 1997]

§ 135.153 Ground proximity warning system.

(a) No person may operate a turbine-powered airplane having a passenger seat configuration of 10 seats or more, excluding any pilot seat, unless it is equipped with an approved ground proximity warning system.

(b) [Reserved]

(c) For a system required by this section, the Airplane Flight Manual shall contain—

(1) Appropriate procedures for—

(i) The use of the equipment;

(ii) Proper flight crew action with respect to the equipment; and

(iii) Deactivation for planned abnormal and emergency conditions; and

(2) An outline of all input sources that must be operating.

(d) No person may deactivate a system required by this section except under procedures in the Airplane Flight Manual.

(e) Whenever a system required by this section is deactivated, an entry shall be made in the airplane maintenance record that includes the date and time of deactivation.

[Docket No. 26202, 57 FR 9951, March 20, 1992; as amended by Amdt. 135–60, 61 FR 2616, Jan. 26, 1996; Amdt. 135–66, 62 FR 13257, March 19, 1997]

§ 135.155 Fire extinguishers: Passenger-carrying aircraft.

No person may operate an aircraft carrying passengers unless it is equipped with hand fire extinguishers of an approved type for use in crew and passenger compartments as follows—

(a) The type and quantity of extinguishing agent must be suitable for the kinds of fires likely to occur;

(b) At least one hand fire extinguisher must be provided and conveniently located on the flight deck for use by the flight crew; and

(c) At least one hand fire extinguisher must be conveniently located in the passenger compartment of each aircraft having a passenger seating configuration, excluding any pilot seat, of at least 10 seats but less than 31 seats.

§ 135.157 Oxygen equipment requirements.

(a) *Unpressurized aircraft.* No person may operate an unpressurized aircraft at altitudes prescribed in this section unless it is equipped with enough oxygen dispensers and oxygen to supply the pilots under § 135.89(a) and to supply, when flying—

(1) At altitudes above 10,000 feet through 15,000 feet MSL, oxygen to at least 10 percent of the occupants of the aircraft, other than the pilots, for that part of the flight at those altitudes that is of more than 30 minutes duration; and

(2) Above 15,000 feet MSL, oxygen to each occupant of the aircraft other than the pilots.

(b) *Pressurized aircraft.* No person may operate a pressurized aircraft—

(1) At altitudes above 25,000 feet MSL, unless at least a 10-minute supply of supplemental oxygen is available for each occupant of the aircraft, other than the pilots, for use when a descent is necessary due to loss of cabin pressurization; and

(2) Unless it is equipped with enough oxygen dispensers and oxygen to comply with paragraph (a) of this section whenever the cabin pressure altitude exceeds 10,000 feet MSL and, if the cabin pressurization fails, to comply with § 135.89 (a) or to provide a 2-hour supply for each pilot, whichever is greater, and to supply when flying—

(i) At altitudes above 10,000 feet through 15,000 feet MSL, oxygen to at least 10 percent of the occupants of the aircraft, other than the pilots, for that part of the flight at those altitudes that is of more than 30 minutes duration; and

(ii) Above 15,000 feet MSL, oxygen to each occupant of the aircraft, other than the pilots, for one hour unless, at all times during flight above that altitude, the aircraft can safely descend to 15,000 feet MSL within four minutes, in which case only a 30-minute supply is required.

(c) The equipment required by this section must have a means—

(1) To enable the pilots to readily determine, in flight, the amount of oxygen available in each source of supply and whether the oxygen is being delivered to the dispensing units; or

(2) In the case of individual dispensing units, to enable each user to make those determinations with respect to that person's oxygen supply and delivery; and

(3) To allow the pilots to use undiluted oxygen at their discretion at altitudes above 25,000 feet MSL.

135

§ 135.158 Pitot heat indication systems.

(a) Except as provided in paragraph (b) of this section, after April 12, 1981, no person may operate a transport category airplane equipped with a flight instrument pitot heating system unless the airplane is also equipped with an operable pitot heat indication system that complies with § 25.1326 of this chapter in effect on April 12, 1978.

(b) A certificate holder may obtain an extension of the April 12, 1981, compliance date specified in paragraph (a) of this section, but not beyond April 12, 1983, from the Director, Flight Standards Service if the certificate holder—

(1) Shows that due to circumstances beyond its control it cannot comply by the specified compliance date; and

(2) Submits by the specified compliance date a schedule for compliance, acceptable to the Director, indicating that compliance will be achieved at the earliest practicable date.

[Docket No. 18094, Amdt. 135–17, 46 FR 48306, Aug. 31, 1981; as amended by Amdt. 135–33, 54 FR 39294, Sept. 25, 1989]

§ 135.159 Equipment requirements: Carrying passengers under VFR at night or under VFR over-the-top conditions.

No person may operate an aircraft carrying passengers under VFR at night or under VFR over-the-top, unless it is equipped with—

(a) A gyroscopic rate-of-turn indicator except on the following aircraft:

(1) Airplanes with a third attitude instrument system usable through flight attitudes of 360 degrees of pitch-and-roll and installed in accordance with the instrument requirements prescribed in § 121.305(j) of this chapter.

(2) Helicopters with a third attitude instrument system usable through flight attitudes of ±80 degrees of pitch and ±120 degrees of roll and installed in accordance with § 29.1303(g) of this chapter.

(3) Helicopters with a maximum certificated takeoff weight of 6,000 pounds or less.

(b) A slip skid indicator.

(c) A gyroscopic bank-and-pitch indicator.

(d) A gyroscopic direction indicator.

(e) A generator or generators able to supply all probable combinations of continuous in-flight electrical loads for required equipment and for recharging the battery.

(f) For night flights—

(1) An anticollision light system;

(2) Instrument lights to make all instruments, switches, and gauges easily readable, the direct rays of which are shielded from the pilots' eyes; and

(3) A flashlight having at least two size "D" cells or equivalent.

(g) For the purpose of paragraph (e) of this section, a continuous in-flight electrical load includes one that draws current continuously during flight, such as radio equipment and electrically driven instruments and lights, but does not include occasional intermittent loads.

(h) Notwithstanding provisions of paragraphs (b), (c), and (d), helicopters having a maximum certificated takeoff weight of 6,000 pounds or less may be operated until January 6, 1988, under visual flight rules at night without a slip skid indicator, a gyroscopic bank-and-pitch indicator, or a gyroscopic direction indicator.

[Docket No. 24550, 51 FR 40709, Nov. 7, 1986; as amended by Amdt. 135–38, 55 FR 43310, Oct. 26, 1990]

§ 135.161 Radio and navigational equipment: Carrying passengers under VFR at night or under VFR over-the-top.

(a) No person may operate an aircraft carrying passengers under VFR at night, or under VFR over-the-top, unless it has two-way radio communications equipment able, at least in flight, to transmit to, and receive from, ground facilities 25 miles away.

(b) No person may operate an aircraft carrying passengers under VFR over-the-top unless it has radio navigational equipment able to receive radio signals from the ground facilities to be used.

(c) No person may operate an airplane carrying passengers under VFR at night unless it has radio navigational equipment able to receive radio signals from the ground facilities to be used.

§ 135.163 Equipment requirements: Aircraft carrying passengers under IFR.

No person may operate an aircraft under IFR, carrying passengers, unless it has—

(a) A vertical speed indicator;

(b) A free-air temperature indicator;

(c) A heated pitot tube for each airspeed indicator;

(d) A power failure warning device or vacuum indicator to show the power available for gyroscopic instruments from each power source;

(e) An alternate source of static pressure for the altimeter and the airspeed and vertical speed indicators;

(f) For a single-engine aircraft:

(1) Two independent electrical power generating sources each of which is able to supply all probable combinations of continuous inflight elec-

trical loads for required instruments and equipment; or

(2) In addition to the primary electrical power generating source, a standby battery or an alternate source of electric power that is capable of supplying 150% of the electrical loads of all required instruments and equipment necessary for safe emergency operation of the aircraft for at least one hour;

(g) For multi-engine aircraft, at least two generators or alternators each of which is on a separate engine, of which any combination of one-half of the total number are rated sufficiently to supply the electrical loads of all required instruments and equipment necessary for safe emergency operation of the aircraft except that for multi-engine helicopters, the two required generators may be mounted on the main rotor drive train; and

(h) Two independent sources of energy (with means of selecting either) of which at least one is an engine-driven pump or generator, each of which is able to drive all required gyroscopic instruments powered by, or to be powered by, that particular source and installed so that failure of one instrument or source, does not interfere with the energy supply to the remaining instruments or the other energy source unless, for single-engine aircraft in all cargo operations only, the rate of turn indicator has a source of energy separate from the bank and pitch and direction indicators. For the purpose of this paragraph, for multi-engine aircraft, each engine-driven source of energy must be on a different engine.

(i) For the purpose of paragraph (f) of this section, a continuous inflight electrical load includes one that draws current continuously during flight, such as radio equipment, electrically driven instruments, and lights, but does not include occasional intermittent loads.

[Docket No. 16097, 43 FR 46783, Oct. 10, 1978; as amended by Amdt. 135–70, 62 FR 42374, Aug. 6, 1997; Amdt. 135–73, 63 FR 25573, May 8, 1998]

§ 135.165 Radio and navigational equipment: Extended overwater or IFR operations.

(a) No person may operate a turbojet airplane having a passenger seating configuration, excluding any pilot seat, of 10 seats or more, or a multi-engine airplane in a commuter operation, as defined in part 119 of this chapter, under IFR or in extended overwater operations unless it has at least the following radio communication and navigational equipment appropriate to the facilities to be used which are capable of transmitting to, and receiving from, at any place on the route to be flown, at least one ground facility:

(1) Two transmitters, (2) two microphones, (3) two headsets or one headset and one speaker,

(4) a marker beacon receiver, (5) two independent receivers for navigation, and (6) two independent receivers for communications.

(b) No person may operate an aircraft other than that specified in paragraph (a) of this section, under IFR or in extended overwater operations unless it has at least the following radio communication and navigational equipment appropriate to the facilities to be used and which are capable of transmitting to, and receiving from, at any place on the route, at least one ground facility:

(1) A transmitter, (2) two microphones, (3) two headsets or one headset and one speaker, (4) a marker beacon receiver, (5) two independent receivers for navigation, (6) two independent receivers for communications, and (7) for extended overwater operations only, an additional transmitter.

(c) For the purpose of paragraphs (a)(5), (a)(6), (b)(5), and (b)(6) of this section, a receiver is independent if the function of any part of it does not depend on the functioning of any part of another receiver. However, a receiver that can receive both communications and navigational signals may be used in place of a separate communications receiver and a separate navigational signal receiver.

(d) Notwithstanding the requirements of paragraphs (a) and (b) of this section, installation and use of a single long-range navigation system and a single long-range communication system, for extended overwater operations, may be authorized by the Administrator and approved in the certificate holder's operations specifications. The following are among the operational factors the Administrator may consider in granting an authorization:

(1) The ability of the flightcrew to reliably fix the position of the airplane within the degree of accuracy required by ATC,

(2) The length of the route being flown, and

(3) The duration of the very high frequency communications gap.

[Docket No. 16097, 43 FR 46073, Oct. 10, 1978; as amended by Amdt. 135–58, 60 FR 65939, Dec. 20, 1995; Amdt. 135–61, 61 FR 7191, Feb. 26, 1996]

§ 135.167 Emergency equipment: Extended overwater operations.

(a) No person may operate an aircraft in extended overwater operations unless it carries, installed in conspicuously marked locations easily accessible to the occupants if a ditching occurs, the following equipment:

(1) An approved life preserver equipped with an approved survivor locator light for each occupant of the aircraft. The life preserver must be easily accessible to each seated occupant.

(2) Enough approved liferafts of a rated capacity and buoyancy to accommodate the occupants

of the aircraft.

(b) Each liferaft required by paragraph (a) of this section must be equipped with or contain at least the following:

(1) One approved survivor locator light.

(2) One approved pyrotechnic signaling device.

(3) Either—

(i) One survival kit, appropriately equipped for the route to be flown; or

(ii) One canopy (for sail, sunshade, or rain catcher);

(iii) One radar reflector;

(iv) One liferaft repair kit;

(v) One bailing bucket;

(vi) One signaling mirror;

(vii) One police whistle;

(viii) One raft knife;

(ix) One CO_2 bottle for emergency inflation;

(x) One inflation pump;

(xi) Two oars;

(xii) One 75-foot retaining line;

(xiii) One magnetic compass;

(xiv) One dye marker;

(xv) One flashlight having at least two size "D" cells or equivalent;

(xvi) A 2-day supply of emergency food rations supplying at least 1,000 calories per day for each person;

(xvii) For each two persons the raft is rated to carry, two pints of water or one sea water desalting kit;

(xviii) One fishing kit; and

(xix) One book on survival appropriate for the area in which the aircraft is operated.

(c) No person may operate an airplane in extended overwater operations unless there is attached to one of the life rafts required by paragraph (a) of this section, an approved survival type emergency locator transmitter. Batteries used in this transmitter must be replaced (or recharged, if the batteries are rechargeable) when the transmitter has been in use for more than 1 cumulative hour, or, when 50 percent of their useful life (or for rechargeable batteries, 50 percent of their useful life of charge) has expired, as established by the transmitter manufacturer under its approval. The new expiration date for replacing (or recharging) the battery must be legibly marked on the outside of the transmitter. The battery useful life (or useful life of charge) requirements of this paragraph do not apply to batteries (such as water-activated batteries) that are essentially unaffected during probable storage intervals.

[Docket No. 16097, 43 FR 46783, Oct. 10, 1978; as amended by Amdt. 135–4, 45 FR 38348, June 30, 1980; Amdt. 135–20, 51 FR 40710, Nov. 7, 1986; Amdt. 135–49, 59 FR 32058, June 21, 1994]

§ 135.169 Additional airworthiness requirements.

(a) Except for commuter category airplanes, no person may operate a large airplane unless it meets the additional airworthiness requirements of §§ 121.213 through 121.283 and 121.307 of this chapter.

(b) No person may operate a reciprocating-engine or turbopropeller-powered small airplane that has a passenger seating configuration, excluding pilot seats, of 10 seats or more unless it is type certificated—

(1) In the transport category;

(2) Before July 1, 1970, in the normal category and meets special conditions issued by the Administrator for airplanes intended for use in operations under this part;

(3) Before July 19, 1970, in the normal category and meets the additional airworthiness standards in Special Federal Aviation Regulation No. 23;

(4) In the normal category and meets the additional airworthiness standards in Appendix A;

(5) In the normal category and complies with section 1.(a) of Special Federal Aviation Regulation No. 41;

(6) In the normal category and complies with section 1.(b) of Special Federal Aviation Regulation No. 41; or

(7) In the commuter category.

(c) No person may operate a small airplane with a passenger seating configuration, excluding any pilot seat, of 10 seats or more, with a seating configuration greater than the maximum seating configuration used in that type airplane in operations under this part before August 19, 1977. This paragraph does not apply to—

(1) An airplane that is type certificated in the transport category; or

(2) An airplane that complies with—

(i) Appendix A of this part provided that its passenger seating configuration, excluding pilot seats, does not exceed 19 seats; or

(ii) Special Federal Aviation Regulation No. 41.

(d) Cargo or baggage compartments:

(1) After March 20, 1991, each Class C or D compartment, as defined in § 25.857 of part 25 of this chapter, greater than 200 cubic feet in volume in a transport category airplane type certificated after January 1, 1958, must have ceiling and sidewall panels which are constructed of:

(i) Glass fiber reinforced resin;

(ii) Materials which meet the test requirements of part 25, Appendix F, part III of this chapter; or

(iii) In the case of liner installations approved prior to March 20, 1989, aluminum.

(2) For compliance with this paragraph, the term "liner" includes any design feature, such as a

joint or fastener, which would affect the capability of the liner to safely contain a fire.

[Docket No. 16097, 43 FR 46783, Oct. 10, 1978; as amended by Amdt. 135–2, 44 FR 53731, Sept. 17, 1979; Amdt. 135–21, 52 FR 1836, Jan. 15, 1987; 52 FR 34745, Sept. 14, 1987; Amdt. 135–31, 54 FR 7389, Feb. 17, 1989; Amdt. 135–55, 60 FR 6628, Feb. 2, 1995]

§ 135.170 Materials for compartment interiors.

(a) No person may operate an airplane that conforms to an amended or supplemental type certificate issued in accordance with SFAR No. 41 for a maximum certificated takeoff weight in excess of 12,500 pounds unless within one year after issuance of the initial airworthiness certificate under that SFAR, the airplane meets the compartment interior requirements set forth in § 25.853(a) in effect March 6, 1995 (formerly § 25.853(a), (b), (b-1), (b-2), and (b-3) of this chapter in effect on September 26, 1978).

(b) Except for commuter category airplanes and airplanes certificated under Special Federal Aviation Regulation No. 41, no person may operate a large airplane unless it meets the following additional airworthiness requirements:

(1) Except for those materials covered by paragraph (b)(2) of this section, all materials in each compartment used by the crewmembers or passengers must meet the requirements of § 25.853 of this chapter in effect as follows or later amendment thereto:

(i) Except as provided in paragraph (b)(1)(iv) of this section, each airplane with a passenger capacity of 20 or more and manufactured after August 19, 1988, but prior to August 20, 1990, must comply with the heat release rate testing provisions of § 25.853(d) in effect March 6, 1995 (formerly § 25.853(a-1) in effect on August 20, 1986), except that the total heat release over the first 2 minutes of sample exposure rate must not exceed 100 kilowatt minutes per square meter and the peak heat release rate must not exceed 100 kilowatts per square meter.

(ii) Each airplane with a passenger capacity of 20 or more and manufactured after August 19, 1990, must comply with the heat release rate and smoke testing provisions of § 25.853(d) in effect March 6, 1995 (formerly § 25.83(a-1) in effect on September 26, 1988).

(iii) Except as provided in paragraph (b)(1)(v) or (vi) of this section, each airplane for which the application for type certificate was filed prior to May 1, 1972, must comply with the provisions of § 25.853 in effect on April 30, 1972, regardless of the passenger capacity, if there is a substantially complete replacement of the cabin interior after April 30, 1972.

(iv) Except as provided in paragraph (b)(1)(v) or (vi) of this section, each airplane for which the application for type certificate was filed after May 1, 1972, must comply with the material requirements under which the airplane was type certificated regardless of the passenger capacity if there is a substantially complete replacement of the cabin interior after that date.

(v) Except as provided in paragraph (b)(1)(vi) of this section, each airplane that was type certificated after January 1, 1958, must comply with the heat release testing provisions of § 25.853(d) in effect March 6, 1995 (formerly § 25.853(a-1) in effect on August 20, 1986), if there is a substantially complete replacement of the cabin interior components identified in that paragraph on or after that date, except that the total heat release over the first 2 minutes of sample exposure shall not exceed 100 kilowatt-minutes per square meter and the peak heat release rate shall not exceed 100 kilowatts per square meter.

(vi) Each airplane that was type certificated after January 1, 1958, must comply with the heat release rate and smoke testing provisions of § 25.853(d) in effect March 6, 1995 (formerly § 25.853(a-1) in effect on August 20, 1986), if there is a substantially complete replacement of the cabin interior components identified in that paragraph after August 19, 1990.

(vii) Contrary provisions of this section notwithstanding, the Manager of the Transport Airplane Directorate, Aircraft Certification Service, Federal Aviation Administration, may authorize deviation from the requirements of paragraph (b)(1)(i), (b)(1)(ii), (b)(1)(v), or (b)(1)(vi) of this section for specific components of the cabin interior that do not meet applicable flammability and smoke emission requirements, if the determination is made that special circumstances exist that make compliance impractical. Such grants of deviation will be limited to those airplanes manufactured within 1 year after the applicable date specified in this section and those airplanes in which the interior is replaced within 1 year of that date. A request for such grant of deviation must include a thorough and accurate analysis of each component subject to § 25.853(d) in effect March 6, 1995 (formerly § 25.853(a-1) in effect on August 20, 1986), the steps being taken to achieve compliance, and for the few components for which timely compliance will not be achieved, credible reasons for such noncompliance.

(viii) Contrary provisions of this section notwithstanding, galley carts and standard galley containers that do not meet the flammability and smoke emission requirements of § 25.853(d) in effect March 6, 1995 (formerly § 25.853(a-1) in effect on August 20, 1986), may be used in airplanes that must meet the requirements of paragraph (b)(1)(i), (b)(1)(ii), (b)(1)(iv) or (b)(1)(vi) of

135

this section provided the galley carts or standard containers were manufactured prior to March 6, 1995.

(2) For airplanes type certificated after January 1, 1958, seat cushions, except those on flight crewmember seats, in any compartment occupied by crew or passengers must comply with the requirements pertaining to fire protection of seat cushions in § 25.853(c) effective November 26, 1984.

[Docket No. 26192, 60 FR 6628, Feb. 2, 1995; as amended by Amdt. 135–55, 60 FR 11194, March 1, 1995; Amdt. 135–56, 60 FR 13011, March 9, 1995]

§ 135.171 Shoulder harness installation at flight crewmember stations.

(a) No person may operate a turbojet aircraft or an aircraft having a passenger seating configuration, excluding any pilot seat, of 10 seats or more unless it is equipped with an approved shoulder harness installed for each flight crewmember station.

(b) Each flight crewmember occupying a station equipped with a shoulder harness must fasten the shoulder harness during takeoff and landing, except that the shoulder harness may be unfastened if the crewmember cannot perform the required duties with the shoulder harness fastened.

§ 135.173 Airborne thunderstorm detection equipment requirements.

(a) No person may operate an aircraft that has a passenger seating configuration, excluding any pilot seat, of 10 seats or more in passenger-carrying operations, except a helicopter operating under day VFR conditions, unless the aircraft is equipped with either approved thunderstorm detection equipment or approved airborne weather radar equipment.

(b) No person may operate a helicopter that has a passenger seating configuration, excluding any pilot seat, of 10 seats or more in passenger-carrying operations, under night VFR when current weather reports indicate that thunderstorms or other potentially hazardous weather conditions that can be detected with airborne thunderstorm detection equipment may reasonably be expected along the route to be flown, unless the helicopter is equipped with either approved thunderstorm detection equipment or approved airborne weather radar equipment.

(c) No person may begin a flight under IFR or night VFR conditions when current weather reports indicate that thunderstorms or other potentially hazardous weather conditions that can be detected with airborne thunderstorm detection equipment, required by paragraph (a) or (b) of this

section, may reasonably be expected along the route to be flown, unless the airborne thunderstorm detection equipment is in satisfactory operating condition.

(d) If the airborne thunderstorm detection equipment becomes inoperative en route, the aircraft must be operated under the instructions and procedures specified for that event in the manual required by § 135.21.

(e) This section does not apply to aircraft used solely within the State of Hawaii, within the State of Alaska, within that part of Canada west of longitude 130 degrees W, between latitude 70 degrees N, and latitude 53 degrees N, or during any training, test, or ferry flight.

(f) Without regard to any other provision of this part, an alternate electrical power supply is not required for airborne thunderstorm detection equipment.

[Docket No. 16097, 43 FR 46783, Oct. 10, 1978; as amended by Amdt. 135–20, 51 FR 40710, Nov. 7, 1986; Amdt. 135–60, 61 FR 2616, Jan. 26, 1996]

§ 135.175 Airborne weather radar equipment requirements.

(a) No person may operate a large, transport category aircraft in passenger-carrying operations unless approved airborne weather radar equipment is installed in the aircraft.

(b) No person may begin a flight under IFR or night VFR conditions when current weather reports indicate that thunderstorms, or other potentially hazardous weather conditions that can be detected with airborne weather radar equipment, may reasonably be expected along the route to be flown, unless the airborne weather radar equipment required by paragraph (a) of this section is in satisfactory operating condition.

(c) If the airborne weather radar equipment becomes inoperative en route, the aircraft must be operated under the instructions and procedures specified for that event in the manual required by § 135.21.

(d) This section does not apply to aircraft used solely within the State of Hawaii, within the State of Alaska, within that part of Canada west of longitude 130 degrees W, between latitude 70 degrees N, and latitude 53 degrees N, or during any training, test, or ferry flight.

(e) Without regard to any other provision of this part, an alternate electrical power supply is not required for airborne weather radar equipment.

§ 135.177 Emergency equipment requirements for aircraft having a passenger seating configuration of more than 19 passengers.

(a) No person may operate an aircraft having a passenger seating configuration, excluding any pilot seat, of more than 19 seats unless it is equipped with the following emergency equipment:

(1) One approved first aid kit for treatment of injuries likely to occur in flight or in a minor accident, which meets the following specifications and requirements:

(i) Each first aid kit must be dust and moisture proof, and contain only materials that either meet Federal Specifications GGK-319a, as revised, or as approved by the Administrator.

(ii) Required first aid kits must be readily accessible to the cabin flight attendants.

(iii) Except as provided in paragraph (a)(1)(iv) of this section, at time of takeoff, each first aid kit must contain at least the following or other contents approved by the Administrator:

Contents	Quantity
Adhesive bandage compressors, 1 in	16
Antiseptic swabs	20
Ammonia inhalants	10
Bandage compressors, 4 in	8
Triangular bandage compressors, 40 in	5
Arm splint, noninflatable	1
Leg splint, noninflatable	1
Roller bandage, 4 in	4
Adhesive tape, 1-in standard roll	2
Bandage scissors	1
Protective latex gloves or equivalent nonpermeable gloves	1 pair

(iv) Protective latex gloves or equivalent nonpermeable gloves may be placed in the first aid kit or in a location that is readily accessible to crewmembers.

(2) A crash axe carried so as to be accessible to the crew but inaccessible to passengers during normal operations.

(3) Signs that are visible to all occupants to notify them when smoking is prohibited and when safety belts must be fastened. The signs must be constructed so that they can be turned on during any movement by the aircraft on the surface, for each takeoff and landing, and at other times considered necessary by the pilot in command. "No smoking" signs shall be turned on when required by § 135.127.

(4) [Reserved]

(b) Each item of equipment must be inspected regularly under inspection periods established in the operations specifications to ensure its condition for continued serviceability and immediate readiness to perform its intended emergency purposes.

[Docket No. 16097, 43 FR 46783, Oct. 10, 1978; as amended by Amdt. 135–25, 53 FR 12362, April 13, 1988; Amdt. 135–43, 57 FR 19245, May 4, 1992; Amdt. 135–44, 57 FR 42676, Sept. 15, 1992; Amdt. 135–47, 59 FR 1781, Jan. 12, 1994; Amdt. 135–53, 59 FR 52643, Oct. 18, 1994, 59 FR 55208, Nov. 4, 1994]

§ 135.178 Additional emergency equipment.

No person may operate an airplane having a passenger seating configuration of more than 19 seats, unless it has the additional emergency equipment specified in paragraphs (a) through (l) of this section.

(a) *Means for emergency evacuation.* Each passenger-carrying landplane emergency exit (other than over-the-wing) that is more than 6 feet from the ground, with the airplane on the ground and the landing gear extended, must have an approved means to assist the occupants in descending to the ground. The assisting means for a floor-level emergency exit must meet the requirements of § 25.809(f)(1) of this chapter in effect on April 30, 1972, except that, for any airplane for which the application for the type certificate was filed after the date, it must meet the requirements under which the airplane was type certificated. An assisting means that deploys automatically must be armed during taxiing, takeoffs, and landings; however, the Administrator may grant a deviation from the requirement of automatic deployment if he finds that the design of the exit makes compliance impractical, if the assisting means automatically erects upon deployment and, with respect to require emergency exits, if an emergency evacuation demonstration is conducted in accordance with § 121.291(a) of this chapter. This paragraph does not apply to the rear window emergency exit of Douglas DC-3 airplanes operated with fewer than 36 occupants, including crewmembers, and fewer than five exits authorized for passenger use.

(b) *Interior emergency exit marking.* The following must be complied with for each passenger-carrying airplane:

(1) Each passenger emergency exit, its means of access, and its means of opening must be conspicuously marked. The identity and locating of each passenger emergency exit must be recognizable from a distance equal to the width of the cabin. The location of each passenger emergency exit must be indicated by a sign visible to occupants approaching along the main passenger aisle. There must be a locating sign —

(i) Above the aisle near each over-the-wing passenger emergency exit, or at another ceiling location if it is more practical because of low headroom;

(ii) Next to each floor level passenger emergency exit, except that one sign may serve two such exits if they both can be seen readily from that sign; and

(iii) On each bulkhead or divider that prevents fore and aft vision along the passenger cabin, to indicate emergency exits beyond and obscured by it, except that if this is not possible, the sign may be placed at another appropriate location.

(2) Each passenger emergency exit marking and each locating sign must meet the following:

(i) For an airplane for which the application for the type certificate was filed prior to May 1, 1972, each passenger emergency exit marking and each locating sign must be manufactured to meet the requirements of § 25.812(b) of this chapter in effect on April 30, 1972. On these airplanes, no sign may continue to be used if its luminescence (brightness) decreases to below 100 microlamberts. The colors may be reversed if it increases the emergency illumination of the passenger compartment. However, the Administrator may authorize deviation from the 2-inch background requirements if he finds that special circumstances exist that make compliance impractical and that the proposed deviation provides an equivalent level of safety.

(ii) For an airplane for which the application for the type certificate was filed on or after May 1, 1972, each passenger emergency exit marking and each locating sign must be manufactured to meet the interior emergency exit marking requirements under which the airplane was type certificated. On these airplanes, no sign may continue to be used if its luminescence (brightness) decreases to below 250 microlamberts.

(c) *Lighting for interior emergency exit markings.* Each passenger-carrying airplane must have an emergency lighting system, independent of the main lighting system; however, sources of general cabin illumination may be common to both the emergency and the main lighting systems if the power supply to the emergency lighting system is independent of the power supply to the main lighting system. The emergency lighting system must—

(1) Illuminate each passenger exit marking and locating sign;

(2) Provide enough general lighting in the passenger cabin so that the average illumination when measured at 40-inch intervals at seat armrest height, on the centerline of the main passenger aisle, is at least 0.05 foot-candles; and

(3) For airplanes type certificated after January 1, 1958, include floor proximity emergency escape path marking which meets the requirements of § 25.812(e) of this chapter in effect on November 26, 1984.

(d) *Emergency light operation.* Except for lights forming part of emergency lighting subsystems provided in compliance with § 25.812(h) of this chapter (as prescribed in paragraph (h) of this section) that serve no more than one assist means, are independent of the airplane's main emergency lighting systems, and are automatically activated when the assist means is deployed, each light required by paragraphs (c) and (h) of this section must:

(1) Be operable manually both from the flightcrew station and from a point in the passenger compartment that is readily accessible to a normal flight attendant seat;

(2) Have a means to prevent inadvertent operation of the manual controls;

(3) When armed or turned on at either station, remain lighted or become lighted upon interruption of the airplane's normal electric power;

(4) Be armed or turned on during taxiing, takeoff, and landing. In showing compliance with this paragraph, a transverse vertical separation of the fuselage need not be considered;

(5) Provide the required level of illumination for at least 10 minutes at the critical ambient conditions after emergency landing; and

(6) Have a cockpit control device that has an "on," "off," and "armed" position.

(e) *Emergency exit operating handles.*

(1) For a passenger-carrying airplane for which the application for the type certificate was filed prior to May 1, 1972, the location of each passenger emergency exit operating handle, and instructions for opening the exit, must be shown by a marking on or near the exit that is readable from a distance of 30 inches. In addition, for each Type I and Type II emergency exit with a locking mechanism released by rotary motion of the handle, the instructions for opening must be shown by—

(i) A red arrow with a shaft at least three-fourths inch wide and a head twice the width of the shaft, extending along at least 70° of arc at a radius approximately equal to three-fourths of the handle length; and

(ii) The word "open" in red letters 1 inch high placed horizontally near the head of the arrow.

(2) For a passenger-carrying airplane for which the application for the type certificate was filed on or after May 1, 1972, the location of each passenger emergency exit operating handle and instructions for opening the exit must be shown in accordance with the requirements under which the airplane was type certificated. On these airplanes, no operating handle or operating handle cover may continue to be used if its luminescence (brightness) decreases to below 100 microlamberts.

(f) *Emergency exit access.* Access to emergency exits must be provided as follows for each passenger-carrying airplane:

(1) Each passageway between individual passenger areas, or leading to a Type I or Type II emergency exit, must be unobstructed and at least 20 inches wide.

(2) There must be enough space next to each Type I or Type II emergency exit to allow a crewmember to assist in the evacuation of passengers without reducing the unobstructed width of the passageway below that required in paragraph (f)(1) of this section; however, the Administrator may authorize deviation from this requirement for an airplane certificated under the provisions of part 4b of the Civil Air Regulations in effect before December 20, 1951, if he finds that special circumstances exist that provide an equivalent level of safety.

(3) There must be access from the main aisle to each Type III and Type IV exit. The access from the aisle to these exits must not be obstructed by seats, berths, or other protrusions in a manner that would reduce the effectiveness of the exit. In addition, for a transport category airplane type certificated after January 1, 1958, there must be placards installed in accordance with § 25.813(c)(3) of this chapter for each Type III exit after December 3, 1992.

(4) If it is necessary to pass through a passageway between passenger compartments to reach any required emergency exit from any seat in the passenger cabin, the passageway must not be obstructed. Curtains may, however, be used if they allow free entry through the passageway.

(5) No door may be installed in any partition between passenger compartments.

(6) If it is necessary to pass through a doorway separating the passenger cabin from other areas to reach a required emergency exit from any passenger seat, the door must have a means to latch it in the open position, and the door must be latched open during each takeoff and landing. The latching means must be able to withstand the loads imposed upon it when the door is subjected to the ultimate inertia forces, relative to the surrounding structure, listed in § 25.561(b) of this chapter.

(g) *Exterior exit markings.* Each passenger emergency exit and the means of opening that exit from the outside must be marked on the outside of the airplane. There must be a 2-inch colored band outlining each passenger emergency exit on the side of the fuselage. Each outside marking, including the band, must be readily distinguishable from the surrounding fuselage area by contrast in color. The markings must comply with the following:

(1) If the reflectance of the darker color is 15 percent or less, the reflectance of the lighter color must be at least 45 percent.

(2) If the reflectance of the darker color is greater than 15 percent, at least a 30 percent difference between its reflectance and the reflectance of the lighter color must be provided.

(3) Exits that are not in the side of the fuselage must have the external means of opening and applicable instructions marked conspicuously in red or, if red is inconspicuous against the background color, in bright chrome yellow and, when the opening means for such an exit is located on only one side of the fuselage, a conspicuous marking to that effect must be provided on the other side. "Reflectance" is the ratio of the luminous flux reflected by a body to the luminous flux it receives.

(h) *Exterior emergency lighting and escape route.*

(1) Each passenger-carrying airplane must be equipped with exterior lighting that meets the following requirements:

(i) For an airplane for which the application for the type certificate was filed prior to May 1, 1972, the requirements of § 25.812(f) and (g) of this chapter in effect on April 30, 1972.

(ii) For an airplane for which the application for the type certificate was filed on or after May 1, 1972, the exterior emergency lighting requirements under which the airplane was type certificated.

(2) Each passenger-carrying airplane must be equipped with a slip-resistant escape route that meets the following requirements:

(i) For an airplane for which the application for the type certificate was filed prior to May 1, 1972, the requirements of § 25.803(e) of this chapter in effect on April 30, 1972.

(ii) For an airplane for which the application for the type certificate was filed on or after May 1, 1972, the slip-resistant escape route requirements under which the airplane was type certificated.

(i) *Floor level exits.* Each floor level door or exit in the side of the fuselage (other than those leading into a cargo or baggage compartment that is not accessible from the passenger cabin) that is 44 or more inches high and 20 or more inches wide, but not wider than 46 inches, each passenger ventral exit (except the ventral exits on Martin 404 and Convair 240 airplanes), and each tail cone exit, must meet the requirements of this section for floor level emergency exits. However, the Administrator may grant a deviation from this paragraph if he finds that circumstances make full compliance impractical and that an acceptable level of safety has been achieved.

(j) *Additional emergency exits.* Approved emergency exits in the passenger compartments that are in excess of the minimum number of required emergency exits must meet all of the applicable provisions of this section, except paragraphs (f)(1), (2), and (3) of this section, and must be readily accessible.

135

(k) On each large passenger-carrying turbojet-powered airplane, each ventral exit and tailcone exit must be—

(1) Designed and constructed so that it cannot be opened during flight; and

(2) Marked with a placard readable from a distant of 30 inches and installed at a conspicuous location near the means of opening the exit, stating that the exit has been designed and constructed so that it cannot be opened during flight.

(l) *Portable lights.* No person may operate a passenger-carrying airplane unless it is equipped with flashlight stowage provisions accessible from each flight attendant seat.

[Docket No. 26530, 57 FR 19245, May 4, 1992; 57 FR 29120, June 30, 1992; as amended by 57 FR 34682, Aug. 6, 1992]

§ 135.179 Inoperable instruments and equipment.

(a) No person may take off an aircraft with inoperable instruments or equipment installed unless the following conditions are met:

(1) An approved Minimum Equipment List exists for that aircraft.

(2) The certificate-holding district office has issued the certificate holder operations specifications authorizing operations in accordance with an approved Minimum Equipment List. The flight crew shall have direct access at all times prior to flight to all of the information contained in the approved Minimum Equipment List through printed or other means approved by the Administrator in the certificate holder's operations specifications. An approved Minimum Equipment List, as authorized by the operations specifications, constitutes an approved change to the type design without requiring recertification.

(3) The approved Minimum Equipment List must:

(i) Be prepared in accordance with the limitations specified in paragraph (b) of this section.

(ii) Provide for the operation of the aircraft with certain instruments and equipment in an inoperable condition.

(4) Records identifying the inoperable instruments and equipment and the information required by (a)(3)(ii) of this section must be available to the pilot.

(5) The aircraft is operated under all applicable conditions and limitations contained in the Minimum Equipment List and the operations specifications authorizing use of the Minimum Equipment List.

(b) The following instruments and equipment may not be included in the Minimum Equipment List:

(1) Instruments and equipment that are either specifically or otherwise required by the airworthiness requirements under which the airplane is type certificated and which are essential for safe operations under all operating conditions.

(2) Instruments and equipment required by an airworthiness directive to be in operable condition unless the airworthiness directive provides otherwise.

(3) Instruments and equipment required for specific operations by this part.

(c) Notwithstanding paragraphs (b)(1) and (b)(3) of this section, an aircraft with inoperable instruments or equipment may be operated under a special flight permit under §§ 179.197 and 21.199 of this chapter.

[Docket No. 25780, 56 FR 12311, March 22, 1991; 56 FR 14920, April 8, 1991; as amended by Amdt. 135–60, 61 FR 2616, Jan. 26, 1996]

§ 135.180 Traffic Alert and Collision Avoidance System.

(a) Unless otherwise authorized by the Administrator, after December 31, 1995, no person may operate a turbine powered airplane that has a passenger seat configuration, excluding any pilot seat, of 10 to 30 seats unless it is equipped with an approved traffic alert and collision avoidance system. If a TCAS II system is installed, it must be capable of coordinating with TCAS units that meet TSO C-119.

(b) The airplane flight manual required by § 135.21 of this part shall contain the following information on the TCAS I system required by this section:

(1) Appropriate procedures for—

(i) The use of the equipment; and

(ii) Proper flightcrew action with respect to the equipment operation.

(2) An outline of all input sources that must be operating for the TCAS to function properly.

[Docket No. 25355, 54 FR 951, Jan. 10, 1989; as amended by Amdt. 135–54, 59 FR 67587, Dec. 29, 1994]

§ 135.181 Performance requirements: Aircraft operated over-the-top or in IFR conditions.

(a) Except as provided in paragraphs (b) and (c) of this section, no person may—

(1) Operate a single-engine aircraft carrying passengers over-the-top; or

(2) Operate a multiengine aircraft carrying passengers over-the-top or in IFR conditions at a weight that will not allow it to climb, with the critical engine inoperative, at least 50 feet a minute when operating at the MEAs of the route to be flown or 5,000 feet MSL, whichever is higher.

(b) Notwithstanding the restrictions in paragraph (a)(2) of this section, multiengine helicopters carrying passengers offshore may conduct such operations in over-the-top or in IFR conditions at a weight that will allow the helicopter to climb at least 50 feet per minute with the critical engine inoperative when operating at the MEA of the route to be flown or 1,500 feet MSL, whichever is higher.

(c) Without regard to paragraph (a) of this section, if the latest weather reports or forecasts, or any combination of them, indicate that the weather along the planned route (including takeoff and landing) allows flight under VFR under the ceiling (if a ceiling exists) and that the weather is forecast to remain so until at least 1 hour after the estimated time of arrival at the destination, a person may operate an aircraft over-the-top.

(d) Without regard to paragraph (a) of this section, a person may operate an aircraft over-the-top under conditions allowing—

(1) For multiengine aircraft, descent or continuance of the flight under VFR if its critical engine fails; or

(2) For single-engine aircraft, descent under VFR if its engine fails.

[Docket No. 16097, 43 FR 46783, Oct. 10, 1978; as amended by Amdt. 135–20, 51 FR 40710, Nov. 7, 1986; Amdt. 135–70, 62 FR 42374, Aug. 6, 1997]

§135.183 Performance requirements: Land aircraft operated over water.

No person may operate a land aircraft carrying passengers over water unless—

(a) It is operated at an altitude that allows it to reach land in the case of engine failure;

(b) It is necessary for takeoff or landing;

(c) It is a multiengine aircraft operated at a weight that will allow it to climb, with the critical engine inoperative, at least 50 feet a minute, at an altitude of 1,000 feet above the surface; or

(d) It is a helicopter equipped with helicopter flotation devices.

§135.185 Empty weight and center of gravity: Currency requirement.

(a) No person may operate a multiengine aircraft unless the current empty weight and center of gravity are calculated from values established by actual weighing of the aircraft within the preceding 36 calendar months.

(b) Paragraph (a) of this section does not apply to—

(1) Aircraft issued an original airworthiness certificate within the preceding 36 calendar months; and

(2) Aircraft operated under a weight and balance system approved in the operations specifications of the certificate holder.

Subpart D— VFR/IFR Operating Limitations and Weather Requirements

§135.201 Applicability.

This subpart prescribes the operating limitations for VFR/IFR flight operations and associated weather requirements for operations under this part.

§135.203 VFR: Minimum altitudes.

Except when necessary for takeoff and landing, no person may operate under VFR—

(a) An airplane—

(1) During the day, below 500 feet above the surface or less than 500 feet horizontally from any obstacle; or

(2) At night, at an altitude less than 1,000 feet above the highest obstacle within a horizontal distance of 5 miles from the course intended to be flown or, in designated mountainous terrain, less than 2,000 feet above the highest obstacle within a horizontal distance of 5 miles from the course intended to be flown; or

(b) A helicopter over a congested area at an altitude less than 300 feet above the surface.

§135.205 VFR: Visibility requirements.

(a) No person may operate an airplane under VFR in uncontrolled airspace when the ceiling is less than 1,000 feet unless flight visibility is at least 2 miles.

(b) No person may operate a helicopter under VFR in Class G airspace at an altitude of 1,200 feet or less above the surface or within the lateral boundaries of the surface areas of Class B, Class C, Class D, or Class E airspace designated for an airport unless the visibility is at least—

(1) During the day—½ mile; or

(2) At night—1 mile.

[Docket No. 16097, 43 FR 46783, Oct. 10, 1978; as amended by Amdt. 135–41, 56 FR 65663, Dec. 17, 1991]

§135.207 VFR: Helicopter surface reference requirements.

No person may operate a helicopter under VFR unless that person has visual surface reference or, at night, visual surface light reference, sufficient to safely control the helicopter.

135

§ 135.209 VFR: Fuel supply.

(a) No person may begin a flight operation in an airplane under VFR unless, considering wind and forecast weather conditions, it has enough fuel to fly to the first point of intended landing and, assuming normal cruising fuel consumption—

(1) During the day, to fly after that for at least 30 minutes; or

(2) At night, to fly after that for at least 45 minutes.

(b) No person may begin a flight operation in a helicopter under VFR unless, considering wind and forecast weather conditions, it has enough fuel to fly to the first point of intended landing and, assuming normal cruising fuel consumption, to fly after that for at least 20 minutes.

§ 135.211 VFR: Over-the-top carrying passengers: Operating limitations.

Subject to any additional limitations in §135.181, no person may operate an aircraft under VFR over-the-top carrying passengers, unless—

(a) Weather reports or forecasts, or any combination of them, indicate that the weather at the intended point of termination of over-the-top flight—

(1) Allows descent to beneath the ceiling under VFR and is forecast to remain so until at least 1 hour after the estimated time of arrival at that point; or

(2) Allows an IFR approach and landing with flight clear of the clouds until reaching the prescribed initial approach altitude over the final approach facility, unless the approach is made with the use of radar under § 91.175(f) of this chapter; or

(b) It is operated under conditions allowing—

(1) For multiengine aircraft, descent or continuation of the flight under VFR if its critical engine fails; or

(2) For single-engine aircraft, descent under VFR if its engine fails.

[Docket No. 16097, 43 FR 46783, Oct. 10, 1978; as amended by Amdt. 135–32, 54 FR 34332, Aug. 18, 1989]

§ 135.213 Weather reports and forecasts.

(a) Whenever a person operating an aircraft under this part is required to use a weather report or forecast, that person shall use that of the U.S. National Weather Service, a source approved by the U.S. National Weather Service, or a source approved by the Administrator. However, for operations under VFR, the pilot in command may, if such a report is not available, use weather information based on that pilot's own observations or on those of other persons competent to supply appropriate observations.

(b) For the purposes of paragraph (a) of this section, weather observations made and furnished to pilots to conduct IFR operations at an airport must be taken at the airport where those IFR operations are conducted, unless the Administrator issues operations specifications allowing the use of weather observations taken at a location not at the airport where the IFR operations are conducted. The Administrator issues such operations specifications when, after investigation by the U.S. National Weather Service and the certificate-holding district office, it is found that the standards of safety for that operation would allow the deviation from this paragraph for a particular operation for which an air carrier operating certificate or operating certificate has been issued.

[Docket No. 16097, 43 FR 46783, Oct. 10, 1978; as amended by Amdt. 135–60, 61 FR 2616, Jan. 26, 1996]

§ 135.215 IFR: Operating limitations.

(a) Except as provided in paragraphs (b), (c) and (d) of this section, no person may operate an aircraft under IFR outside of controlled airspace or at any airport that does not have an approved standard instrument approach procedure.

(b) The Administrator may issue operations specifications to the certificate holder to allow it to operate under IFR over routes outside controlled airspace if—

(1) The certificate holder shows the Administrator that the flight crew is able to navigate, without visual reference to the ground, over an intended track without deviating more than 5 degrees or 5 miles, whichever is less, from that track; and

(2) The Administrator determines that the proposed operations can be conducted safely.

(c) A person may operate an aircraft under IFR outside of controlled airspace if the certificate holder has been approved for the operations and that operation is necessary to—

(1) Conduct an instrument approach to an airport for which there is in use a current approved standard or special instrument approach procedure; or

(2) Climb into controlled airspace during an approved missed approach procedure; or

(3) Make an IFR departure from an airport having an approved instrument approach procedure.

(d) The Administrator may issue operations specifications to the certificate holder to allow it to depart at an airport that does not have an approved standard instrument approach procedure when the Administrator determines that it is necessary to make an IFR departure from that airport and that the proposed operations can be conducted safely. The approval to operate at that airport does not include an approval to make an IFR approach to that airport.

§ 135.217 IFR: Takeoff limitations.

No person may takeoff an aircraft under IFR from an airport where weather conditions are at or above takeoff minimums but are below authorized IFR landing minimums unless there is an alternate airport within 1 hour's flying time (at normal cruising speed, in still air) of the airport of departure.

§ 135.219 IFR: Destination airport weather minimums.

No person may take off an aircraft under IFR or begin an IFR or over-the-top operation unless the latest weather reports or forecasts, or any combination of them, indicate that weather conditions at the estimated time of arrival at the next airport of intended landing will be at or above authorized IFR landing minimums.

§ 135.221 IFR: Alternate airport weather minimums.

No person may designate an alternate airport unless the weather reports or forecasts, or any combination of them, indicate that the weather conditions will be at or above authorized alternate airport landing minimums for that airport at the estimated time of arrival.

§ 135.223 IFR: Alternate airport requirements.

(a) Except as provided in paragraph (b) of this section, no person may operate an aircraft in IFR conditions unless it carries enough fuel (considering weather reports or forecasts or any combination of them) to —

(1) Complete the flight to the first airport of intended landing;

(2) Fly from that airport to the alternate airport; and

(3) Fly after that for 45 minutes at normal cruising speed or, for helicopters, fly after that for 30 minutes at normal cruising speed.

(b) Paragraph (a)(2) of this section does not apply if part 97 of this chapter prescribes a standard instrument approach procedure for the first airport of intended landing and, for at least one hour before and after the estimated time of arrival, the appropriate weather reports or forecasts, or any combination of them, indicate that —

(1) The ceiling will be at least 1,500 feet above the lowest circling approach MDA; or

(2) If a circling instrument approach is not authorized for the airport, the ceiling will be at least 1,500 feet above the lowest published minimum or 2,000 feet above the airport elevation, whichever is higher; and

(3) Visibility for that airport is forecast to be at least three miles, or two miles more than the lowest applicable visibility minimums, whichever is the greater, for the instrument approach procedure to be used at the destination airport.

[Docket No. 16097, 43 FR 46783, Oct. 10, 1978; as amended by Amdt. 135–20, 51 FR 40710, Nov. 7, 1986]

§ 135.225 IFR: Takeoff, approach and landing minimums.

(a) No pilot may begin an instrument approach procedure to an airport unless —

(1) That airport has a weather reporting facility operated by the U.S. National Weather Service, a source approved by U.S. National Weather Service, or a source approved by the Administrator; and

(2) The latest weather report issued by that weather reporting facility indicates that weather conditions are at or above the authorized IFR landing minimums for that airport.

(b) No pilot may begin the final approach segment of an instrument approach procedure to an airport unless the latest weather reported by the facility described in paragraph (a)(1) of this section indicates that weather conditions are at or above the authorized IFR landing minimums for that procedure.

(c) If a pilot has begun the final approach segment of an instrument approach to an airport under paragraph (b) of this section and a later weather report indicating below minimum conditions is received after the aircraft is —

(1) On an ILS final approach and has passed the final approach fix; or

(2) On an ASR or PAR final approach and has been turned over to the final approach controller; or

(3) On a final approach using a VOR, NDB, or comparable approach procedure; and the aircraft—

(i) Has passed the appropriate facility or final approach fix; or

(ii) Where a final approach fix is not specified, has completed the procedure turn and is established inbound toward the airport on the final approach course within the distance prescribed in the procedure; the approach may be continued and a landing made if the pilot finds, upon reaching the authorized MDA or DH, that actual weather conditions are at least equal to the minimums prescribed for the procedure.

(d) The MDA or DH and visibility landing minimums prescribed in part 97 of this chapter or in the operator's operations specifications are increased by 100 feet and $\frac{1}{2}$ mile respectively, but not to exceed the ceiling and visibility minimums for that airport when used as an alternate airport, for each pilot in command of a turbine-powered airplane who has not served at least 100 hours as pilot in command in that type of airplane.

(e) Each pilot making an IFR takeoff or approach and landing at a military or foreign airport shall comply with applicable instrument approach procedures and weather minimums prescribed by the authority having jurisdiction over that airport. In addition, no pilot may, at that airport—

(1) Take off under IFR when the visibility is less than 1 mile; or

(2) Make an instrument approach when the visibility is less than $\frac{1}{2}$ mile.

(f) If takeoff minimums are specified in part 97 of this chapter for the takeoff airport, no pilot may take off an aircraft under IFR when the weather conditions reported by the facility described in paragraph (a)(1) of this section are less than the takeoff minimums specified for the takeoff airport in part 97 or in the certificate holder's operations specifications.

(g) Except as provided in paragraph (h) of this section, if takeoff minimums are not prescribed in part 97 of this chapter for the takeoff airport, no pilot may take off an aircraft under IFR when the weather conditions reported by the facility described in paragraph (a)(1) of this section are less than that prescribed in part 91 of this chapter or in the certificate holder's operations specifications.

(h) At airports where straight-in instrument approach procedures are authorized, a pilot may take off an aircraft under IFR when the weather conditions reported by the facility described in paragraph (a)(1) of this section are equal to or better than the lowest straight-in landing minimums, unless otherwise restricted, if—

(1) The wind direction and velocity at the time of takeoff are such that a straight-in instrument approach can be made to the runway served by the instrument approach;

(2) The associated ground facilities upon which the landing minimums are predicated and the related airborne equipment are in normal operation; and

(3) The certificate holder has been approved for such operations.

§ 135.227 Icing conditions: Operating limitations.

(a) No pilot may take off an aircraft that has frost, ice, or snow adhering to any rotor blade, propeller, windshield, wing, stabilizing or control surface, to a powerplant installation, or to an airspeed, altimeter, rate of climb, or flight attitude instrument system, except under the following conditions:

(1) Takeoffs may be made with frost adhering to the wings, or stabilizing or control surfaces, if the frost has been polished to make it smooth.

(2) Takeoffs may be made with frost under the wing in the area of the fuel tanks if authorized by the Administrator.

(b) No certificate holder may authorize an airplane to take off and no pilot may take off an airplane any time conditions are such that frost, ice, or snow may reasonably be expected to adhere to the airplane unless the pilot has completed all applicable training as required by § 135.341 and unless one of the following requirements is met:

(1) A pretakeoff contamination check, that has been established by the certificate holder and approved by the Administrator for the specific airplane type, has been completed within 5 minutes prior to beginning takeoff. A pretakeoff contamination check is a check to make sure the wings and control surfaces are free of frost, ice, or snow.

(2) The certificate holder has an approved alternative procedure and under that procedure the airplane is determined to be free of frost, ice, or snow.

(3) The certificate holder has an approved deicing/anti-icing program that complies with § 121.629(c) of this chapter and the takeoff complies with that program.

(c) Except for an airplane that has ice protection provisions that meet section 34 of Appendix A, or those for transport category airplane type certification, no pilot may fly—

(1) Under IFR into known or forecast light or moderate icing conditions; or

(2) Under VFR into known light or moderate icing conditions; unless the aircraft has functioning deicing or anti-icing equipment protecting each rotor blade, propeller, windshield, wing, stabilizing or control surface, and each airspeed, altimeter, rate of climb, or flight attitude instrument system.

(d) No pilot may fly a helicopter under IFR into known or forecast icing conditions or under VFR into known icing conditions unless it has been type certificated and appropriately equipped for operations in icing conditions.

(e) Except for an airplane that has ice protection provisions that meet section 34 of Appendix A, or those for transport category airplane type certification, no pilot may fly an aircraft into known or forecast severe icing conditions.

(f) If current weather reports and briefing information relied upon by the pilot in command indicate that the forecast icing condition that would otherwise prohibit the flight will not be encountered during the flight because of changed weather conditions since the forecast, the restrictions in paragraphs (c), (d), and (e) of this section based on forecast conditions do not apply.

[Docket No. 16097, 43 FR 46783, Oct. 10, 1978; as amended by Amdt. 133–20, 51 FR 40710, Nov. 7, 1986; Amdt. 135–46, 58 FR 69629, Dec. 30, 1993; Amdt. 135–46, 58 FR 69629, Dec. 30, 1993; Amdt. 135–60, 61 FR, Jan. 26, 1996]

§ 135.229 Airport requirements.

(a) No certificate holder may use any airport unless it is adequate for the proposed operation, considering such items as size, surface, obstructions, and lighting.

(b) No pilot of an aircraft carrying passengers at night may take off from, or land on, an airport unless—

(1) That pilot has determined the wind direction from an illuminated wind direction indicator or local ground communications or, in the case of takeoff, that pilot's personal observations; and

(2) The limits of the area to be used for landing or takeoff are clearly shown—

(i) For airplanes, by boundary or runway marker lights;

(ii) For helicopters, by boundary or runway marker lights or reflective material.

(c) For the purpose of paragraph (b) of this section, if the area to be used for takeoff or landing is marked by flare pots or lanterns, their use must be approved by the Administrator.

Subpart E— Flight Crewmember Requirements

§ 135.241 Applicability.

Except as provided in § 135.3, this subpart prescribes the flight crewmember requirements for operations under this part.

[Docket No. 16097, 43 FR 46783, Oct. 10, 1978; as amended by Amdt. 135–57, 60 FR 65950, Dec. 20, 1995]

§ 135.243 Pilot in command qualifications.

(a) No certificate holder may use a person, nor may any person serve, as pilot in command in passenger-carrying operations—

(1) Of a turbojet airplane, of an airplane having a passenger-seat configuration, excluding each crewmember seat, of 10 seats or more, or of a multiengine airplane in a commuter operation as defined in part 119 in this chapter, unless that person holds an airline transport pilot certificate with appropriate category and class ratings and, if required, an appropriate type rating for that airplane.

(2) Of a helicopter in a scheduled interstate air transportation operation by an air carrier within the 48 contiguous states unless that person holds an airline transport pilot certificate, appropriate type ratings, and an instrument rating.

(b) Except as provided in paragraph (a) of this section, no certificate holder may use a person,

nor may any person serve, as pilot in command of an aircraft under VFR unless that person—

(1) Holds at least a commercial pilot certificate with appropriate category and class ratings and, if required, an appropriate type rating for that aircraft; and

(2) Has had at least 500 hours of flight time as a pilot, including at least 100 hours of cross-country flight time, at least 25 hours of which were at night; and

(3) For an airplane, holds an instrument rating or an airline transport pilot certificate with an airplane category rating; or

(4) For helicopter operations conducted VFR over-the-top, holds a helicopter instrument rating, or an airline transport pilot certificate with a category and class rating for that aircraft, not limited to VFR.

(c) Except as provided in paragraph (a) of this section, no certificate holder may use a person, nor may any person serve, as pilot in command of an aircraft under IFR unless that person—

(1) Holds at least a commercial pilot certificate with appropriate category and class ratings and, if required, an appropriate type rating for that aircraft; and

(2) Has had at least 1,200 hours of flight time as a pilot, including 500 hours of cross country flight time, 100 hours of night flight time, and 75 hours of actual or simulated instrument time at least 50 hours of which were in actual flight; and

(3) For an airplane, holds an instrument rating or an airline transport pilot certificate with an airplane category rating; or

(4) For a helicopter, holds a helicopter instrument rating, or an airline transport pilot certificate with a category and class rating for that aircraft, not limited to VFR.

(d) Paragraph (b)(3) of this section does not apply when—

(1) The aircraft used is a single reciprocating-engine-powered airplane;

(2) The certificate holder does not conduct any operation pursuant to a published flight schedule which specifies five or more round trips a week between two or more points and places between which the round trips are performed, and does not transport mail by air under a contract or contracts with the United States Postal Service having total amount estimated at the beginning of any semi-annual reporting period (January 1–June 30; July 1–December 31) to be in excess of $20,000 over the 12 months commencing with the beginning of the reporting period;

(3) The area, as specified in the certificate holder's operations specifications, is an isolated area, as determined by the Flight Standards district office, if it is shown that—

(i) The primary means of navigation in the area is by pilotage, since radio navigational aids are largely ineffective; and

(ii) The primary means of transportation in the area is by air;

(4) Each flight is conducted under day VFR with a ceiling of not less than 1,000 feet and visibility not less than 3 statute miles;

(5) Weather reports or forecasts, or any combination of them, indicate that for the period commencing with the planned departure and ending 30 minutes after the planned arrival at the destination the flight may be conducted under VFR with a ceiling of not less than 1,000 feet and visibility of not less than 3 statute miles, except that if weather reports and forecasts are not available, the pilot in command may use that pilot's observations or those of other persons competent to supply weather observations if those observations indicate the flight may be conducted under VFR with the ceiling and visibility required in this paragraph;

(6) The distance of each flight from the certificate holder's base of operation to destination does not exceed 250 nautical miles for a pilot who holds a commercial pilot certificate with an airplane rating without an instrument rating, provided the pilot's certificate does not contain any limitation to the contrary; and

(7) The areas to be flown are approved by the certificate-holding FAA Flight Standards district office and are listed in the certificate holder's operations specifications.

[Docket No. 16097, 43 FR 46783, Oct. 10, 1978; as amended by Amdt. 135–1, 43 FR 49975, Oct. 26, 1978; Amdt. 135–15, 46 FR 30971, June 11, 1981; Amdt. 135–58, 60 FR 65939, Dec. 20, 1995; 63 FR 53804, Oct. 7, 1998]

§ 135.244 Operating experience.

(a) No certificate holder may use any person, nor may any person serve, as a pilot in command of an aircraft operated in a commuter operation, as defined in part 119 of this chapter, unless that person has completed, prior to designation as pilot in command, on that make and basic model aircraft and in that crewmember position, the following operating experience in each make and basic model of aircraft to be flown:

(1) Aircraft, single engine—10 hours.

(2) Aircraft multiengine, reciprocating engine-powered —15 hours.

(3) Aircraft multiengine, turbine engine-powered — 20 hours.

(4) Airplane, turbojet-powered—25 hours.

(b) In acquiring the operating experience, each person must comply with the following:

(1) The operating experience must be acquired after satisfactory completion of the appropriate

ground and flight training for the aircraft and crewmember position. Approved provisions for the operating experience must be included in the certificate holder's training program.

(2) The experience must be acquired in flight during commuter passenger-carrying operations under this part. However, in the case of an aircraft not previously used by the certificate holder in operations under this part, operating experience acquired in the aircraft during proving flights or ferry flights may be used to meet this requirement.

(3) Each person must acquire the operating experience while performing the duties of a pilot in command under the supervision of a qualified check pilot.

(4) The hours of operating experience may be reduced to not less than 50 percent of the hours required by this section by the substitution of one additional takeoff and landing for each hour of flight.

[Docket No. 20011, 45 FR 7541, Feb. 4, 1980; as amended by Amdt. 135–9, 45 FR 80461, Dec. 14, 1980; Amdt. 135–58, 60 FR 65940, Dec. 20, 1995]

§ 135.245 Second in command qualifications.

(a) Except as provided in paragraph (b), no certificate holder may use any person, nor may any person serve, as second in command of an aircraft unless that person holds at least a commercial pilot certificate with appropriate category and class ratings and an instrument rating. For flight under IFR, that person must meet the recent instrument experience requirements of part 61 of this chapter.

(b) A second in command of a helicopter operated under VFR, other than over-the-top, must have at least a commercial pilot certificate with an appropriate aircraft category and class rating.

[44 FR 26738, May 7, 1979]

§ 135.247 Pilot qualifications: Recent experience.

(a) No certificate holder may use any person, nor may any person serve, as pilot in command of an aircraft carrying passengers unless, within the preceding 90 days, that person has—

(1) Made three takeoffs and three landings as the sole manipulator of the flight controls in an aircraft of the same category and class and, if a type rating is required, of the same type in which that person is to serve; or

(2) For operation during the period beginning 1 hour after sunset and ending 1 hour before sunrise (as published in the Air Almanac), made three takeoffs and three landings during that period as the sole manipulator of the flight controls in an aircraft of the same category and class and, if a type

rating is required, of the same type in which that person is to serve.

A person who complies with paragraph (a)(2) of this section need not comply with paragraph (a)(1) of this section.

(b) For the purpose of paragraph (a) of this section, if the aircraft is a tailwheel airplane, each takeoff must be made in a tailwheel airplane and each landing must be made to a full stop in a tailwheel airplane.

§ 135.249 Use of prohibited drugs.

(a) This section applies to persons who perform a function listed in Appendix I to part 121 of this chapter for a certificate holder or an operator. For the purpose of this section, a person who performs such a function pursuant to a contract with the certificate holder or the operator is considered to be performing that function for the certificate holder or the operator.

(b) No certificate holder or operator may knowingly use any person to perform, nor may any person perform for a certificate holder or an operator, either directly or by contract, any function listed in Appendix I to part 121 of this chapter while that person has a prohibited drug, as defined in that appendix, in his or her system.

(c) No certificate holder or operator shall knowingly use any person to perform, nor shall any person perform for a certificate holder or operator, either directly or by contract, any safety-sensitive function if the person has a verified positive drug test result on or has refused to submit to a drug test required by Appendix I to part 121 of this chapter and the person has not met the requirements of Appendix I to part 121 of this chapter for returning to the performance of safety-sensitive duties.

[Docket No. 25148, 53 FR 47061, Nov. 21, 1988; as amended by Amdt. 135–51, 59 FR 42933, Aug. 19, 1994]

§ 135.251 Testing for prohibited drugs.

(a) Each certificate holder or operator shall test each of its employees who performs a function listed in Appendix I to part 121 of this chapter in accordance with that appendix.

(b) No certificate holder or operator may use any contractor to perform a function listed in Appendix I to part 121 of this chapter unless that contractor tests each employee performing such a function for the certificate holder or operator in accordance with that appendix.

[Docket No. 25148, 53 FR 47061, Nov. 21, 1988]

§ 135.253 Misuse of alcohol.

(a) This section applies to employees who perform a function listed in Appendix J to part 121 of this chapter for a certificate holder or operator (*covered employees*). For the purpose of this section, a person who meets the definition of covered employee in Appendix J is considered to be performing the function for the certificate holder or operator.

(b) *Alcohol concentration.* No covered employee shall report for duty or remain on duty requiring the performance of safety-sensitive functions while having an alcohol concentration of 0.04 or greater. No certificate holder or operator having actual knowledge that an employee has an alcohol concentration of 0.04 or greater shall permit the employee to perform or continue to perform safety-sensitive functions.

(c) *On-duty use.* No covered employee shall use alcohol while performing safety-sensitive functions. No certificate holder or operator having actual knowledge that a covered employee is using alcohol while performing safety-sensitive functions shall permit the employee to perform or continue to perform safety-sensitive functions.

(d) *Pre-duty use.*

(1) No covered employee shall perform flight crewmember or flight attendant duties within 8 hours after using alcohol. No certificate holder or operator having actual knowledge that such an employee has used alcohol within 8 hours shall permit the employee to perform or continue to perform the specified duties.

(2) No covered employee shall perform safety-sensitive duties other than those specified in paragraph (d)(1) of this section within 4 hours after using alcohol. No certificate holder or operator having actual knowledge that such an employee has used alcohol within 4 hours shall permit the employee to perform or continue to perform safety-sensitive functions.

(e) *Use following an accident.* No covered employee who has actual knowledge of an accident involving an aircraft for which he or she performed a safety-sensitive function at or near the time of the accident shall use alcohol for 8 hours following the accident, unless he or she has been given a post-accident test under Appendix J of part 121 of this chapter, or the employer has determined that the employee's performance could not have contributed to the accident.

(f) *Refusal to submit to a required alcohol test.* No covered employee shall refuse to submit to a post-accident, random, reasonable suspicion, or follow-up alcohol test required under Appendix J to part 121 of this chapter. No operator or certificate holder shall permit a covered employee who refuses to submit to such a test to perform or continue to perform safety-sensitive functions.

[Docket No. 16097, 43 FR 46783, Oct. 10, 1978; as amended by Amdt. 135–48, 59 FR 7396, Feb. 15, 1994]

§ 135.255 Testing for alcohol.

(a) Each certificate holder and operator must establish an alcohol misuse prevention program in accordance with the provisions of Appendix J to part 121 of this chapter.

(b) No certificate holder or operator shall use any person who meets the definition of "covered employee" in Appendix J to part 121 to perform a safety-sensitive function listed in that appendix unless such person is subject to testing for alcohol misuse in accordance with the provisions of Appendix J.

[Docket No. 16097, 43 FR 46783, Oct. 10, 1978; as amended by Amdt. 135–48, 59 FR 7397, Feb. 15, 1994]

Subpart F— Crewmember Flight Time and Duty Period Limitations and Rest Requirements

SOURCE: Docket No. 23634, 50 FR 29320, July 18, 1985, unless otherwise noted.

§ 135.261 Applicability.

Sections 135.263 through 135.273 of this part prescribe flight time limitations, duty period limitations, and rest requirements for operations conducted under this part as follows:

(a) Section 135.263 applies to all operations under this subpart.

(b) Section 135.265 applies to:

(1) Scheduled passenger-carrying operations except those conducted solely within the state of Alaska. "Scheduled passenger-carrying operations" means passenger-carrying operations that are conducted in accordance with a published schedule which covers at least five round trips per week on at least one route between two or more points, includes dates or times (or both), and is openly advertised or otherwise made readily available to the general public, and

(2) Any other operation under this part, if the operator elects to comply with § 135.265 and obtains an appropriate operations specification amendment.

(c) Sections 135.267 and 135.269 apply to any operation that is not a scheduled passenger-carrying operation and to any operation conducted solely within the State of Alaska, unless the oper-

ator elects to comply with § 135.265 as authorized under paragraph (b)(2) of this section.

(d) Section 135.271 contains special daily flight time limits for operations conducted under the helicopter emergency medical evacuation service (HEMES).

(e) Section 135.273 prescribes duty period limitations and rest requirements for flight attendants in all operations conducted under this part.

[Docket No. 23634, 50 FR 29320, July 18, 1985; as amended by Amdt. 135–52, 59 FR 42993, Aug. 19, 1994]

§ 135.263 Flight time limitations and rest requirements: All certificate holders.

(a) A certificate holder may assign a flight crewmember and a flight crewmember may accept an assignment for flight time only when the applicable requirements of §§ 135.263 through 135.271 are met.

(b) No certificate holder may assign any flight crewmember to any duty with the certificate holder during any required rest period.

(c) Time spent in transportation, not local in character, that a certificate holder requires of a flight crewmember and provides to transport the crewmember to an airport at which he is to serve on a flight as a crewmember, or from an airport at which he was relieved from duty to return to his home station, is not considered part of a rest period.

(d) A flight crewmember is not considered to be assigned flight time in excess of flight time limitations if the flights to which he is assigned normally terminate within the limitations, but due to circumstances beyond the control of the certificate holder or flight crewmember (such as adverse weather conditions), are not at the time of departure expected to reach their destination within the planned flight time.

§ 135.265 Flight time limitations and rest requirements: Scheduled operations.

(a) No certificate holder may schedule any flight crewmember, and no flight crewmember may accept an assignment, for flight time in scheduled operations or in other commercial flying if that crewmember's total flight time in all commercial flying will exceed—

(1) 1,200 hours in any calendar year.

(2) 120 hours in any calendar month.

(3) 34 hours in any 7 consecutive days.

(4) 8 hours during any 24 consecutive hours for a flight crew consisting of one pilot.

(5) 8 hours between required rest periods for a flight crew consisting of two pilots qualified under this part for the operation being conducted.

(b) Except as provided in paragraph (c) of this section, no certificate holder may schedule a flight crewmember, and no flight crewmember may accept an assignment, for flight time during the 24 consecutive hours preceding the scheduled completion of any flight segment without a scheduled rest period during that 24 hours of at least the following:

(1) 9 consecutive hours of rest for less than 8 hours of scheduled flight time.

(2) 10 consecutive hours of rest for 8 or more but less than 9 hours of scheduled flight time.

(3) 11 consecutive hours of rest for 9 or more hours of scheduled flight time.

(c) A certificate holder may schedule a flight crewmember for less than the rest required in paragraph (b) of this section or may reduce a scheduled rest under the following conditions:

(1) A rest required under paragraph (b)(1) of this section may be scheduled for or reduced to a minimum of 8 hours if the flight crewmember is given a rest period of at least 10 hours that must begin no later than 24 hours after the commencement of the reduced rest period.

(2) A rest required under paragraph (b)(2) of this section may be scheduled for or reduced to a minimum of 8 hours if the flight crewmember is given a rest period of at least 11 hours that must begin no later than 24 hours after the commencement of the reduced rest period.

(3) A rest required under paragraph (b)(3) of this section may be scheduled for or reduced to a minimum of 9 hours if the flight crewmember is given a rest period of at least 12 hours that must begin no later than 24 hours after the commencement of the reduced rest period.

(d) Each certificate holder shall relieve each flight crewmember engaged in scheduled air transportation from all further duty for at least 24 consecutive hours during any 7 consecutive days.

§ 135.267 Flight time limitations and rest requirements: Unscheduled one- and two-pilot crews.

(a) No certificate holder may assign any flight crewmember, and no flight crewmember may accept an assignment, for flight time as a member of a one- or two-pilot crew if that crewmember's total flight time in all commercial flying will exceed—

(1) 500 hours in any calendar quarter.

(2) 800 hours in any two consecutive calendar quarters.

(3) 1,400 hours in any calendar year.

(b) Except as provided in paragraph (c) of this section, during any 24 consecutive hours the total flight time of the assigned flight when added to any other commercial flying by that flight crewmember may not exceed—

(1) 8 hours for a flight crew consisting of one pilot; or

(2) 10 hours for a flight crew consisting of two pilots qualified under this part for the operation being conducted.

(c) A flight crewmember's flight time may exceed the flight time limits of paragraph (b) of this section if the assigned flight time occurs during a regularly assigned duty period of no more than 14 hours and—

(1) If this duty period is immediately preceded by and followed by a required rest period of at least 10 consecutive hours of rest;

(2) If flight time is assigned during this period, that total flight time when added to any other commercial flying by the flight crewmember may not exceed—

(i) 8 hours for a flight crew consisting of one pilot; or

(ii) 10 hours for a flight crew consisting of two pilots; and

(3) If the combined duty and rest periods equal 24 hours.

(d) Each assignment under paragraph (b) of this section must provide for at least 10 consecutive hours of rest during the 24-hour period that precedes the planned completion time of the assignment.

(e) When a flight crewmember has exceeded the daily flight time limitations in this section, because of circumstances beyond the control of the certificate holder or flight crewmember (such as adverse weather conditions), that flight crewmember must have a rest period before being assigned or accepting an assignment for flight time of at least—

(1) 11 consecutive hours of rest if the flight time limitation is exceeded by not more than 30 minutes;

(2) 12 consecutive hours of rest if the flight time limitation is exceeded by more than 30 minutes, but not more than 60 minutes; and

(3) 16 consecutive hours of rest if the flight time limitation is exceeded by more than 60 minutes.

(f) The certificate holder must provide each flight crewmember at least 13 rest periods of at least 24 consecutive hours each in each calendar quarter.

[Docket No. 23634, 50 FR 29320, July 18, 1989; as amended by Amdt. 135–33, 54 FR 39294, Sept. 25, 1989; Amdt. 135–60, 61 FR 2616, Jan. 26, 1996]

135

§ 135.269 Flight time limitations and rest requirements: Unscheduled three- and four-pilot crews.

(a) No certificate holder may assign any flight crewmember, and no flight crewmember may accept an assignment, for flight time as a member of a three- or four-pilot crew if that crewmember's total flight time in all commercial flying will exceed—

(1) 500 hours in any calendar quarter.

(2) 800 hours in any two consecutive calendar quarters.

(3) 1,400 hours in any calendar year.

(b) No certificate holder may assign any pilot to a crew of three or four pilots, unless that assignment provides—

(1) At least 10 consecutive hours of rest immediately preceding the assignment;

(2) No more than 8 hours of flight deck duty in any 24 consecutive hours;

(3) No more than 18 duty hours for a three-pilot crew or 20 duty hours for a four-pilot crew in any 24 consecutive hours;

(4) No more than 12 hours aloft for a three-pilot crew or 16 hours aloft for a four-pilot crew during the maximum duty hours specified in paragraph (b)(3) of this section;

(5) Adequate sleeping facilities on the aircraft for the relief pilot;

(6) Upon completion of the assignment, a rest period of at least 12 hours;

(7) For a three-pilot crew, a crew which consists of at least the following:

(i) A pilot in command (PIC) who meets the applicable flight crewmember requirements of subpart E of part 135;

(ii) A PIC who meets the applicable flight crewmember requirements of subpart E of part 135, except those prescribed in §§ 135.244 and 135.247; and

(iii) A second in command (SIC) who meets the SIC qualifications of § 135.245.

(8) For a four-pilot crew, at least three pilots who meet the conditions of paragraph (b)(7) of this section, plus a fourth pilot who meets the SIC qualifications of § 135.245.

(c) When a flight crewmember has exceeded the daily flight deck duty limitation in this section by more than 60 minutes, because of circumstances beyond the control of the certificate holder or flight crewmember, that flight crewmember must have a rest period before the next duty period of at least 16 consecutive hours.

(d) A certificate holder must provide each flight crewmember at least 13 rest periods of at least 24 consecutive hours each in each calendar quarter.

§ 135.271 Helicopter hospital emergency medical evacuation service (HEMES).

(a) No certificate holder may assign any flight crewmember, and no flight crewmember may accept an assignment for flight time if that crewmember's total flight time in all commercial flight will exceed—

(1) 500 hours in any calendar quarter.

(2) 800 hours in any two consecutive calendar quarters.

(3) 1,400 hours in any calendar year.

(b) No certificate holder may assign a helicopter flight crewmember, and no flight crewmember may accept an assignment, for hospital emergency medical evacuation service helicopter operations unless that assignment provides for at least 10 consecutive hours of rest immediately preceding reporting to the hospital for availability for flight time.

(c) No flight crewmember may accrue more than 8 hours of flight time during any 24-consecutive hour period of a HEMES assignment, unless an emergency medical evacuation operation is prolonged. Each flight crewmember who exceeds the daily 8 hour flight time limitation in this paragraph must be relieved of the HEMES assignment immediately upon the completion of that emergency medical evacuation operation and must be given a rest period in compliance with paragraph (h) of this section.

(d) Each flight crewmember must receive at least 8 consecutive hours of rest during any 24 consecutive hour period of a HEMES assignment. A flight crewmember must be relieved of the HEMES assignment if he or she has not or cannot receive at least 8 consecutive hours of rest during any 24 consecutive hour period of a HEMES assignment.

(e) A HEMES assignment may not exceed 72 consecutive hours at the hospital.

(f) An adequate place of rest must be provided at, or in close proximity to, the hospital at which the HEMES assignment is being performed.

(g) No certificate holder may assign any other duties to a flight crewmember during a HEMES assignment.

(h) Each pilot must be given a rest period upon completion of the HEMES assignment and prior to being assigned any further duty with the certificate holder of—

(1) At least 12 consecutive hours for an assignment of less than 48 hours.

(2) At least 16 consecutive hours for an assignment of more than 48 hours.

(i) The certificate holder must provide each flight crewmember at least 13 rest periods of at least 24 consecutive hours each in each calendar quarter.

§ 135.273 Duty period limitations and rest time requirements.

(a) For purposes of this section—

Calendar day means the period of elapsed time, using Coordinated Universal Time or local time, that begins at midnight and ends 24 hours later at the next midnight.

Duty period means the period of elapsed time between reporting for an assignment involving flight time and release from that assignment by the certificate holder. The time is calculated using either Coordinated Universal Time or local time to reflect the total elapsed time.

Flight attendant means an individual, other than a flight crewmember, who is assigned by the certificate holder, in accordance with the required minimum crew complement under the certificate holder's operations specifications or in addition to that minimum complement, to duty in an aircraft during flight time and whose duties include but are not necessarily limited to cabin-safety-related responsibilities.

Rest period means the period free of all responsibility for work or duty should the occasion arise.

(b) Except as provided in paragraph (c) of this section, a certificate holder may assign a duty period to a flight attendant only when the applicable duty period limitations and rest requirements of this paragraph are met.

(1) Except as provided in paragraphs (b)(4), (b)(5), and (b)(6) of this section, no certificate holder may assign a flight attendant to a scheduled duty period of more than 14 hours.

(2) Except as provided in paragraph (b)(3) of this section, a flight attendant scheduled to a duty period of 14 hours or less as provided under paragraph (b)(1) of this section must be given a scheduled rest period of at least 9 consecutive hours. This rest period must occur between the completion of the scheduled duty period and the commencement of the subsequent duty period.

(3) The rest period required under paragraph (b)(2) of this section may be scheduled or reduced to 8 consecutive hours if the flight attendant is provided a subsequent rest period of at least 10 consecutive hours; this subsequent rest period must be scheduled to begin no later than 24 hours after the beginning of the reduced rest period and must occur between the completion of the scheduled duty period and the commencement of the subsequent duty period.

(4) A certificate holder may assign a flight attendant to a scheduled duty period of more than 14 hours, but no more than 16 hours, if the certificate holder has assigned to the flight or flights in that duty period at least one flight attendant in addition to the minimum flight attendant complement required for the flight or flights in that duty period under the certificate holder's operations specifications.

(5) A certificate holder may assign a flight attendant to a scheduled duty period of more than 16 hours, but no more than 18 hours, if the certificate holder has assigned to the flight or flights in that duty period at least two flight attendants in addition to the minimum flight attendant complement required for the flight or flights in that duty period under the certificate holder's operations specifications.

(6) A certificate holder may assign a flight attendant to a scheduled duty period of more than 18 hours, but no more than 20 hours, if the scheduled duty period includes one or more flights that land or take off outside the 48 contiguous states and the District of Columbia, and if the certificate holder has assigned to the flight or flights in that duty period at least three flight attendants in addition to the minimum flight attendant complement required for the flight or flights in that duty period under the certificate holder's operations specifications.

(7) Except as provided in paragraph (b)(8) of this section, a flight attendant scheduled to a duty period of more than 14 hours but no more than 20 hours, as provided in paragraphs (b)(4), (b)(5), and (b)(6) of this section, must be given a scheduled rest period of at least 12 consecutive hours. This rest period must occur between the completion of the scheduled duty period and the commencement of the subsequent duty period.

(8) The rest period required under paragraph (b)(7) of this section may be scheduled or reduced to 10 consecutive hours if the flight attendant is provided a subsequent rest period of at least 14 consecutive hours; this subsequent rest period must be scheduled to begin no later than 24 hours after the beginning of the reduced rest period and must occur between the completion of the scheduled duty period and the commencement of the subsequent duty period.

(9) Notwithstanding paragraphs (b)(4), (b)(5), and (b)(6) of this section, if a certificate holder elects to reduce the rest period to 10 hours as authorized by paragraph (b)(8) of this section, the certificate holder may not schedule a flight attendant for a duty period of more than 14 hours during the 24-hour period commencing after the beginning of the reduced rest period.

(10) No certificate holder may assign a flight attendant any duty period with the certificate holder unless the flight attendant has had at least the minimum rest required under this section.

(11) No certificate holder may assign a flight attendant to perform any duty with the certificate holder during any required rest period.

(12) Time spent in transportation, not local in character, that a certificate holder requires of a flight attendant and provides to transport the flight

attendant to an airport at which that flight attendant is to serve on a flight as a crewmember, or from an airport at which the flight attendant was relieved from duty to return to the flight attendant's home station, is not considered part of a rest period.

(13) Each certificate holder must relieve each flight attendant engaged in air transportation from all further duty for at least 24 consecutive hours during any 7 consecutive calendar days.

(14) A flight attendant is not considered to be scheduled for duty in excess of duty period limitations if the flights to which the flight attendant is assigned are scheduled and normally terminate within the limitations but due to circumstances beyond the control of the certificate holder (such as adverse weather conditions) are not at the time of departure expected to reach their destination within the scheduled time.

(c) Notwithstanding paragraph (b) of this section, a certificate holder may apply the flight crewmember flight time and duty limitations and rest requirements of this part to flight attendants for all operations conducted under this part provided that—

(1) The certificate holder establishes written procedures that—

(i) Apply to all flight attendants used in the certificate holder's operation;

(ii) Include the flight crewmember requirements contained in subpart F of this part, as appropriate to the operation being conducted, except that rest facilities on board the aircraft are not required; and

(iii) Include provisions to add one flight attendant to the minimum flight attendant complement for each flight crewmember who is in excess of the minimum number required in the aircraft type certificate data sheet and who is assigned to the aircraft under the provisions of subpart F of this part, as applicable.

(iv) Are approved by the Administrator and described or referenced in the certificate holder's operations specifications; and

(2) Whenever the Administrator finds that revisions are necessary for the continued adequacy of duty period limitation and rest requirement procedures that are required by paragraph (c)(1) of this section and that had been granted final approval, the certificate holder must, after notification by the Administrator, make any changes in the procedures that are found necessary by the Administrator. Within 30 days after the certificate holder receives such notice, it may file a petition to reconsider the notice with the certificate-holding district office. The filing of a petition to reconsider stays the notice, pending decision by the Administrator. However, if the Administrator finds that there is an emergency that requires immediate action in the interest of safety, the Administra-

tor may, upon a statement of the reasons, require a change effective without stay.

[Docket No. 23634, 50 FR 29320, July 18, 1985; as amended by Amdt. 135–52, 59 FR 42993, Aug. 19, 1994; Amdt. 135–60, 61 FR 2616, Jan. 26, 1996]

Subpart G—Crewmember Testing Requirements

§ 135.291 Applicability.

Except as provided in § 135.3, this subpart—

(a) Prescribes the tests and checks required for pilot and flight attendant crewmembers and for the approval of check pilots in operations under this part; and

(b) Permits training center personnel authorized under part 142 of this chapter who meet the requirements of § 135.337 and § 135.339 to provide training, testing, and checking under contract or other arrangement to those persons subject to the requirements of this subpart.

[Docket No. 26933, 61 FR 34561, July 2, 1996]

§ 135.293 Initial and recurrent pilot testing requirements.

(a) No certificate holder may use a pilot, nor may any person serve as a pilot, unless, since the beginning of the 12th calendar month before that service, that pilot has passed a written or oral test, given by the Administrator or an authorized check pilot, on that pilot's knowledge in the following areas—

(1) The appropriate provisions of parts 61, 91, and 135 of this chapter and the operations specifications and the manual of the certificate holder;

(2) For each type of aircraft to be flown by the pilot, the aircraft powerplant, major components and systems, major appliances, performance and operating limitations, standard and emergency operating procedures, and the contents of the approved Aircraft Flight Manual or equivalent, as applicable;

(3) For each type of aircraft to be flown by the pilot, the method of determining compliance with weight and balance limitations for takeoff, landing and en route operations;

(4) Navigation and use of air navigation aids appropriate to the operation or pilot authorization, including, when applicable, instrument approach facilities and procedures;

(5) Air traffic control procedures, including IFR procedures when applicable;

(6) Meteorology in general, including the principles of frontal systems, icing, fog, thunderstorms, and windshear, and, if appropriate for the operation of the certificate holder, high altitude weather;

(7) Procedures for—

(i) Recognizing and avoiding severe weather situations;

(ii) Escaping from severe weather situations, in case of inadvertent encounters, including low-altitude windshear (except that rotorcraft pilots are not required to be tested on escaping from low-altitude windshear); and

(iii) Operating in or near thunderstorms (including best penetrating altitudes), turbulent air (including clear air turbulence), icing, hail, and other potentially hazardous meteorological conditions; and

(8) New equipment, procedures, or techniques, as appropriate.

(b) No certificate holder may use a pilot, nor may any person serve as a pilot, in any aircraft unless, since the beginning of the 12th calendar month before that service, that pilot has passed a competency check given by the Administrator or an authorized check pilot in that class of aircraft, if single-engine airplane other than turbojet, or that type of aircraft, if helicopter, multiengine airplane, or turbojet airplane, to determine the pilot's competence in practical skills and techniques in that aircraft or class of aircraft. The extent of the competency check shall be determined by the Administrator or authorized check pilot conducting the competency check. The competency check may include any of the maneuvers and procedures currently required for the original issuance of the particular pilot certificate required for the operations authorized and appropriate to the category, class and type of aircraft involved. For the purposes of this paragraph, type, as to an airplane, means any one of a group of airplanes determined by the Administrator to have a similar means of propulsion, the same manufacturer, and no significantly different handling or flight characteristics. For the purposes of this paragraph, type, as to a helicopter, means a basic make and model.

(c) The instrument proficiency check required by § 135.297 may be substituted for the competency check required by this section for the type of aircraft used in the check.

(d) For the purpose of this part, competent performance of a procedure or maneuver by a person to be used as a pilot requires that the pilot be the obvious master of the aircraft, with the successful outcome of the maneuver never in doubt.

(e) The Administrator or authorized check pilot certifies the competency of each pilot who passes the knowledge or flight check in the certificate holder's pilot records.

(f) Portions of a required competency check may be given in an aircraft simulator or other appropriate training device, if approved by the Administrator.

[Docket No. 16097, 43 FR 46783, Oct. 10, 1978; as amended by Amdt. 135–27, 53 FR 37697, Sept. 27, 1988]

§ 135.295 Initial and recurrent flight attendant crewmember testing requirements.

No certificate holder may use a flight attendant crewmember, nor may any person serve as a flight attendant crewmember unless, since the beginning of the 12th calendar month before that service, the certificate holder has determined by appropriate initial and recurrent testing that the person is knowledgeable and competent in the following areas as appropriate to assigned duties and responsibilities—

(a) Authority of the pilot in command;

(b) Passenger handling, including procedures to be followed in handling deranged persons or other persons whose conduct might jeopardize safety;

(c) Crewmember assignments, functions, and responsibilities during ditching and evacuation of persons who may need the assistance of another person to move expeditiously to an exit in an emergency;

(d) Briefing of passengers;

(e) Location and operation of portable fire extinguishers and other items of emergency equipment;

(f) Proper use of cabin equipment and controls;

(g) Location and operation of passenger oxygen equipment;

(h) Location and operation of all normal and emergency exits, including evacuation chutes and escape ropes; and

(i) Seating of persons who may need assistance of another person to move rapidly to an exit in an emergency as prescribed by the certificate holder's operations manual.

§ 135.297 Pilot in command: Instrument proficiency check requirements.

(a) No certificate holder may use a pilot, nor may any person serve, as a pilot in command of an aircraft under IFR unless, since the beginning of the 6th calendar month before that service, that pilot has passed an instrument proficiency check under this section administered by the Administrator or an authorized check pilot.

(b) No pilot may use any type of precision instrument approach procedure under IFR unless, since the beginning of the 6th calendar month before that use, the pilot satisfactorily demonstrated that type of approach procedure. No pilot may use any type of nonprecision approach procedure under IFR unless, since the beginning of the 6th calendar month before that use, the pilot has satisfactorily demonstrated either that type of approach procedure or any other two different types of nonprecision approach procedures. The instrument approach procedure or procedures must in-

135

clude at least one straight-in approach, one circling approach, and one missed approach. Each
type of approach procedure demonstrated must
be conducted to published minimums for that procedure.

(c) The instrument proficiency check required by
paragraph (a) of this section consists of an oral or
written equipment test and a flight check under
simulated or actual IFR conditions. The equipment
test includes questions on emergency procedures,
engine operation, fuel and lubrication systems,
power settings, stall speeds, best engine-out
speed, propeller and supercharger operations, and
hydraulic, mechanical, and electrical systems, as
appropriate. The flight check includes navigation
by instruments, recovery from simulated emergencies, and standard instrument approaches involving navigational facilities which that pilot is to be
authorized to use. Each pilot taking the instrument
proficiency check must show that standard of competence required by § 135.293(d).

(1) The instrument proficiency check must —

(i) For a pilot in command of an airplane under
§ 135.243(a), include the procedures and maneuvers for an airline transport pilot certificate in the
particular type of airplane, if appropriate; and

(ii) For a pilot in command of an airplane or helicopter under § 135.243(c), include the procedures and maneuvers for a commercial pilot certificate with an instrument rating and, if required,
for the appropriate type rating.

(2) The instrument proficiency check must be
given by an authorized check airman or by the Administrator.

(d) If the pilot in command is assigned to pilot
only one type of aircraft, that pilot must take the
instrument proficiency check required by paragraph (a) of this section in that type of aircraft.

(e) If the pilot in command is assigned to pilot
more than one type of aircraft, that pilot must take
the instrument proficiency check required by
paragraph (a) of this section in each type of aircraft to which that pilot is assigned, in rotation, but
not more than one flight check during each period
described in paragraph (a) of this section.

(f) If the pilot in command is assigned to pilot
both single-engine and multiengine aircraft, that
pilot must initially take the instrument proficiency
check required by paragraph (a) of this section in
a multiengine aircraft, and each succeeding
check alternately in single-engine and multiengine aircraft, but not more than one flight check
during each period described in paragraph (a) of
this section. Portions of a required flight check
may be given in an aircraft simulator or other appropriate training device, if approved by the Administrator.

(g) If the pilot in command is authorized to use
an autopilot system in place of a second in command, that pilot must show, during the required instrument proficiency check, that the pilot is able
(without a second in command) both with and
without using the autopilot to —

(1) Conduct instrument operations compe-
tently; and

(2) Properly conduct air-ground communications and comply with complex air traffic control
instructions.

(3) Each pilot taking the autopilot check must
show that, while using the autopilot, the airplane
can be operated as proficiently as it would be if a
second in command were present to handle air-
ground communications and air traffic control instructions. The autopilot check need only be demonstrated once every 12 calendar months during
the instrument proficiency check required under
paragraph (a) of this section.

[Docket No. 16097, 43 FR 46783, Oct. 10, 1978; as
amended by Amdt. 135–15, 46 FR 30971, June 11,
1981]

§ 135.299 Pilot in command: Line checks: Routes and airports.

(a) No certificate holder may use a pilot, nor
may any person serve, as a pilot in command of a
flight unless, since the beginning of the 12th calendar month before that service, that pilot has
passed a flight check in one of the types of aircraft
which that pilot is to fly. The flight check shall —

(1) Be given by an approved check pilot or by
the Administrator;

(2) Consist of at least one flight over one route
segment; and

(3) Include takeoffs and landings at one or
more representative airports. In addition to the requirements of this paragraph, for a pilot authorized to conduct IFR operations, at least one flight
shall be flown over a civil airway, an approved off-
airway route, or a portion of either of them.

(b) The pilot who conducts the check shall determine whether the pilot being checked satisfactorily performs the duties and responsibilities of a
pilot in command in operations under this part,
and shall so certify in the pilot training record.

(c) Each certificate holder shall establish in the
manual required by § 135.21 a procedure which
will ensure that each pilot who has not flown over
a route and into an airport within the preceding 90
days will, before beginning the flight, become familiar with all available information required for the
safe operation of that flight.

§ 135.301 Crewmember:
Tests and checks, grace provisions, training to accepted standards.

(a) If a crewmember who is required to take a test or a flight check under this part, completes the test or flight check in the calendar month before or after the calendar month in which it is required, that crewmember is considered to have completed the test or check in the calendar month in which it is required.

(b) If a pilot being checked under this subpart fails any of the required maneuvers, the person giving the check may give additional training to the pilot during the course of the check. In addition to repeating the maneuvers failed, the person giving the check may require the pilot being checked to repeat any other maneuvers that are necessary to determine the pilot's proficiency. If the pilot being checked is unable to demonstrate satisfactory performance to the person conducting the check, the certificate holder may not use the pilot, nor may the pilot serve, as a flight crewmember in operations under this part until the pilot has satisfactorily completed the check.

Subpart H—Training

§ 135.321 Applicability and terms used.

(a) Except as provided in § 135.3, this subpart prescribes the requirements applicable to—

(1) A certificate holder under this part which contracts with, or otherwise arranges to use the services of a training center certificated under part 142 to perform training, testing, and checking functions;

(2) Each certificate holder for establishing and maintaining an approved training program for crewmembers, check airmen and instructors, and other operations personnel employed or used by that certificate holder; and

(3) Each certificate holder for the qualification, approval, and use of aircraft simulators and flight training devices in the conduct of the program.

(b) For the purposes of this subpart, the following terms and definitions apply:

(1) *Initial training.* The training required for crewmembers who have not qualified and served in the same capacity on an aircraft.

(2) *Transition training.* The training required for crewmembers who have qualified and served in the same capacity on another aircraft.

(3) *Upgrade training.* The training required for crewmembers who have qualified and served as second in command on a particular aircraft type, before they serve as pilot in command on that aircraft.

(4) *Differences training.* The training required for crewmembers who have qualified and served on a particular type aircraft, when the Administrator finds differences training is necessary before a crewmember serves in the same capacity on a particular variation of that aircraft.

(5) *Recurrent training.* The training required for crewmembers to remain adequately trained and currently proficient for each aircraft, crewmember position, and type of operation in which the crewmember serves.

(6) *In flight.* The maneuvers, procedures, or functions that must be conducted in the aircraft.

(7) *Training center.* An organization governed by the applicable requirements of part 142 of this chapter that provides training, testing, and checking under contract or other arrangement to certificate holders subject to the requirements of this part.

(8) *Requalification training.* The training required for crewmembers previously trained and qualified, but who have become unqualified due to not having met within the required period the—

(i) Recurrent pilot testing requirements of § 135.293;

(ii) Instrument proficiency check requirements of § 135.297; or

(iii) Line checks required by § 135.299.

[Docket No. 16097, 43 FR 46783, Oct. 10, 1978; as amended by Amdt. 135–57, 60 FR 65950, Dec. 20, 1995; Amdt. 135–63, 61 FR 34561, July 2, 1996]

§ 135.323 Training program: General.

(a) Each certificate holder required to have a training program under § 135.341 shall:

(1) Establish, obtain the appropriate initial and final approval of, and provide a training program that meets this subpart and that ensures that each crewmember, flight instructor, check airman, and each person assigned duties for the carriage and handling of hazardous materials (as defined in 49 CFR 171.8) is adequately trained to perform their assigned duties.

(2) Provide adequate ground and flight training facilities and properly qualified ground instructors for the training required by this subpart.

(3) Provide and keep current for each aircraft type used and, if applicable, the particular variations within the aircraft type, appropriate training material, examinations, forms, instructions, and procedures for use in conducting the training and checks required by this subpart.

(4) Provide enough flight instructors, check airmen, and simulator instructors to conduct required flight training and flight checks, and simulator training courses allowed under this subpart.

(b) Whenever a crewmember who is required to take recurrent training under this subpart completes the training in the calendar month before, or the calendar month after, the month in which that training is required, the crewmember is considered to have completed it in the calendar month in which it was required.

(c) Each instructor, supervisor, or check airman who is responsible for a particular ground training subject, segment of flight training, course of training, flight check, or competence check under this part shall certify as to the proficiency and knowledge of the crewmember, flight instructor, or check airman concerned upon completion of that training or check. That certification shall be made a part of the crewmember's record. When the certification required by this paragraph is made by an entry in a computerized recordkeeping system, the certifying instructor, supervisor, or check airman, must be identified with that entry. However, the signature of the certifying instructor, supervisor, or check airman, is not required for computerized entries.

(d) Training subjects that apply to more than one aircraft or crewmember position and that have been satisfactorily completed during previous training while employed by the certificate holder for another aircraft or another crewmember position, need not be repeated during subsequent training other than recurrent training.

(e) Aircraft simulators and other training devices may be used in the certificate holder's training program if approved by the Administrator.

§ 135.324 Training program: Special rules.

(a) Other than the certificate holder, only another certificate holder certificated under this part or a training center certificated under part 142 of this chapter is eligible under this subpart to provide training, testing, and checking under contract or other arrangement to those persons subject to the requirements of this subpart.

(b) A certificate holder may contract with, or otherwise arrange to use the services of, a training center certificated under part 142 of this chapter to provide training, testing, and checking required by this part only if the training center—

(1) Holds applicable training specifications issued under part 142 of this chapter;

(2) Has facilities, training equipment, and course-ware meeting the applicable requirements of part 142 of this chapter;

(3) Has approved curriculums, curriculum segments, and portions of curriculum segments applicable for use in training courses required by this subpart; and

(4) Has sufficient instructor and check airmen qualified under the applicable requirements of §§ 135.337 through 135.340 to provide training, testing, and checking to persons subject to the requirements of this subpart.

[Docket No. 26933, 61 FR 34562, July 2, 1996; as amended by Amdt. 135–67, 62 FR 13791, March 21, 1997]

§ 135.325 Training program and revision: Initial and final approval.

(a) To obtain initial and final approval of a training program, or a revision to an approved training program, each certificate holder must submit to the Administrator—

(1) An outline of the proposed or revised curriculum, that provides enough information for a preliminary evaluation of the proposed training program or revision; and

(2) Additional relevant information that may be requested by the Administrator.

(b) If the proposed training program or revision complies with this subpart, the Administrator grants initial approval in writing after which the certificate holder may conduct the training under that program. The Administrator then evaluates the effectiveness of the training program and advises the certificate holder of deficiencies, if any, that must be corrected.

(c) The Administrator grants final approval of the proposed training program or revision if the certificate holder shows that the training conducted under the initial approval in paragraph (b) of this section ensures that each person who successfully completes the training is adequately trained to perform that person's assigned duties.

(d) Whenever the Administrator finds that revisions are necessary for the continued adequacy of a training program that has been granted final approval, the certificate holder shall, after notification by the Administrator, make any changes in the program that are found necessary by the Administrator. Within 30 days after the certificate holder receives the notice, it may file a petition to reconsider the notice with the Administrator. The filing of a petition to reconsider stays the notice pending a decision by the Administrator. However, if the Administrator finds that there is an emergency that requires immediate action in the interest of safety, the Administrator may, upon a statement of the reasons, require a change effective without stay.

§ 135.327 Training program: Curriculum.

(a) Each certificate holder must prepare and keep current a written training program curriculum for each type of aircraft for each crewmember required for that type aircraft. The curriculum must include ground and flight training required by this subpart.

(b) Each training program curriculum must include the following:

(1) A list of principal ground training subjects, including emergency training subjects, that are provided.

(2) A list of all the training devices, mockups, systems trainers, procedures trainers, or other training aids that the certificate holder will use.

(3) Detailed descriptions or pictorial displays of the approved normal, abnormal, and emergency maneuvers, procedures and functions that will be performed during each flight training phase or flight check, indicating those maneuvers, procedures and functions that are to be performed during the inflight portions of flight training and flight checks.

§ 135.329 Crewmember training requirements.

(a) Each certificate holder must include in its training program the following initial and transition ground training as appropriate to the particular assignment of the crewmember:

(1) Basic indoctrination ground training for newly hired crewmembers including instruction in at least the —

(i) Duties and responsibilities of crewmembers as applicable;

(ii) Appropriate provisions of this chapter;

(iii) Contents of the certificate holder's operating certificate and operations specifications (not required for flight attendants); and

(iv) Appropriate portions of the certificate holder's operating manual.

(2) The initial and transition ground training in §§ 135.345 and 135.349, as applicable.

(3) Emergency training in § 135.331.

(b) Each training program must provide the initial and transition flight training in § 135.347, as applicable.

(c) Each training program must provide recurrent ground and flight training in § 135.351.

(d) Upgrade training in §§ 135.345 and 135.347 for a particular type aircraft may be included in the training program for crewmembers who have qualified and served as second in command on that aircraft.

(e) In addition to initial, transition, upgrade and recurrent training, each training program must provide ground and flight training, instruction, and practice necessary to ensure that each crewmember—

(1) Remains adequately trained and currently proficient for each aircraft, crewmember position, and type of operation in which the crewmember serves; and

(2) Qualifies in new equipment, facilities, procedures, and techniques, including modifications to aircraft.

§ 135.331 Crewmember emergency training.

(a) Each training program must provide emergency training under this section for each aircraft type, model, and configuration, each crewmember, and each kind of operation conducted, as appropriate for each crewmember and the certificate holder.

(b) Emergency training must provide the following:

(1) Instruction in emergency assignments and procedures, including coordination among crewmembers.

(2) Individual instruction in the location, function, and operation of emergency equipment including—

(i) Equipment used in ditching and evacuation;

(ii) First aid equipment and its proper use; and

(iii) Portable fire extinguishers, with emphasis on the type of extinguisher to be used on different classes of fires.

(3) Instruction in the handling of emergency situations including—

(i) Rapid decompression;

(ii) Fire in flight or on the surface and smoke control procedures with emphasis on electrical equipment and related circuit breakers found in cabin areas;

(iii) Ditching and evacuation;

(iv) Illness, injury, or other abnormal situations involving passengers or crewmembers; and

(v) Hijacking and other unusual situations.

(4) Review of the certificate holder's previous aircraft accidents and incidents involving actual emergency situations.

(c) Each crewmember must perform at least the following emergency drills, using the proper emergency equipment and procedures, unless the Administrator finds that, for a particular drill, the crewmember can be adequately trained by demonstration:

(1) Ditching, if applicable.

(2) Emergency evacuation.

(3) Fire extinguishing and smoke control.

(4) Operation and use of emergency exits, including deployment and use of evacuation chutes, if applicable.

(5) Use of crew and passenger oxygen.

(6) Removal of life rafts from the aircraft, inflation of the life rafts, use of life lines, and boarding of passengers and crew, if applicable.

(7) Donning and inflation of life vests and the use of other individual flotation devices, if applicable.

(d) Crewmembers who serve in operations above 25,000 feet must receive instruction in the following:

(1) Respiration.

(2) Hypoxia.

(3) Duration of consciousness without supplemental oxygen at altitude.

(4) Gas expansion.

(5) Gas bubble formation.

(6) Physical phenomena and incidents of decompression.

§ 135.333 Training requirements: Handling and carriage of hazardous materials.

(a) Except as provided in paragraph (d) of this section, no certificate holder may use any person to perform, and no person may perform, any assigned duties and responsibilities for the handling or carriage of hazardous materials (as defined in 49 CFR 171.8), unless within the preceding 12 calendar months that person has satisfactorily completed initial or recurrent training in an appropriate training program established by the certificate holder, which includes instruction regarding—

(1) The proper shipper certification, packaging, marking, labeling, and documentation for hazardous materials; and

(2) The compatibility, loading, storage, and handling characteristics of hazardous materials.

(b) Each certificate holder shall maintain a record of the satisfactory completion of the initial and recurrent training given to crewmembers and ground personnel who perform assigned duties and responsibilities for the handling and carriage of hazardous materials.

(c) Each certificate holder that elects not to accept hazardous materials shall ensure that each crewmember is adequately trained to recognize those items classified as hazardous materials.

(d) If a certificate holder operates into or out of airports at which trained employees or contract personnel are not available, it may use persons not meeting the requirements of paragraphs (a) and (b) of this section to load, offload, or otherwise handle hazardous materials if these persons are supervised by a crewmember who is qualified under paragraphs (a) and (b) of this section.

§ 135.335 Approval of aircraft simulators and other training devices.

(a) Training courses using aircraft simulators and other training devices may be included in the certificate holder's training program if approved by the Administrator.

(b) Each aircraft simulator and other training device that is used in a training course or in checks required under this subpart must meet the following requirements:

(1) It must be specifically approved for—

(i) The certificate holder; and

(ii) The particular maneuver, procedure, or crewmember function involved.

(2) It must maintain the performance, functional, and other characteristics that are required for approval.

(3) Additionally, for aircraft simulators, it must be—

(i) Approved for the type aircraft and, if applicable, the particular variation within type for which the training or check is being conducted; and

(ii) Modified to conform with any modification to the aircraft being simulated that changes the performance, functional, or other characteristics required for approval.

(c) A particular aircraft simulator or other training device may be used by more than one certificate holder.

(d) In granting initial and final approval of training programs or revisions to them, the Administrator considers the training devices, methods and procedures listed in the certificate holder's curriculum under § 135.327.

[Docket No. 16907, 43 FR 46783, Oct. 10, 1978; as amended by Amdt. 135–1, 44 FR 26738, May 7, 1979]

§ 135.337 Qualifications: Check airmen (aircraft) and check airmen (simulator).

(a) For the purposes of this section and § 135.339:

(1) A check airman (aircraft) is a person who is qualified to conduct flight checks in an aircraft, in a flight simulator, or in a flight training device for a particular type aircraft.

(2) A check airman (simulator) is a person who is qualified to conduct flight checks, but only in a flight simulator, in a flight training device, or both, for a particular type aircraft.

(3) Check airmen (aircraft) and check airmen (simulator) are those check airmen who perform the functions described in §§ 135.321(a) and 135.323(a)(4) and (c).

(b) No certificate holder may use a person, nor may any person serve as a check airman (aircraft) in a training program established under this subpart unless, with respect to the aircraft type involved, that person —

(1) Holds the airman certificates and ratings required to serve as a pilot in command in operations under this part;

(2) Has satisfactorily completed the training phases for the aircraft, including recurrent training, that are required to serve as a pilot in command in operations under this part;

(3) Has satisfactorily completed the proficiency or competency checks that are required to serve as a pilot in command in operations under this part;

(4) Has satisfactorily completed the applicable training requirements of § 135.339;

(5) Holds at least a Class III medical certificate unless serving as a required crewmember, in which case holds a Class I or Class II medical certificate as appropriate.

(6) Has satisfied the recency of experience requirements of § 135.247; and

(7) Has been approved by the Administrator for the check airman duties involved.

(c) No certificate holder may use a person, nor may any person serve as a check airman (simulator) in a training program established under this subpart unless, with respect to the aircraft type involved, that person meets the provisions of paragraph (b) of this section, or —

(1) Holds the applicable airman certificates and ratings, except medical certificate, required to serve as a pilot in command in operations under this part;

(2) Has satisfactorily completed the appropriate training phases for the aircraft, including recurrent training, that are required to serve as a pilot in command in operations under this part;

(3) Has satisfactorily completed the appropriate proficiency or competency checks that are required to serve as a pilot in command in operations under this part;

(4) Has satisfactorily completed the applicable training requirements of § 135.339; and

(5) Has been approved by the Administrator for the check airman (simulator) duties involved.

(d) Completion of the requirements in paragraphs (b)(2), (3), and (4) or (c)(2), (3), and (4) of this section, as applicable, shall be entered in the individual's training record maintained by the certificate holder.

(e) Check airmen who do not hold an appropriate medical certificate may function as check airmen (simulator), but may not serve as flightcrew members in operations under this part.

(f) A check airman (simulator) must accomplish the following —

(1) Fly at least two flight segments as a required crewmember for the type, class, or category aircraft involved within the 12-month preceding the performance of any check airman duty in a flight simulator; or

(2) Satisfactorily complete an approved line-observation program within the period prescribed by that program and that must precede the performance of any check airman duty in a flight simulator.

(g) The flight segments or line-observation program required in paragraph (f) of this section are considered to be completed in the month required if completed in the calendar month before or the calendar month after the month in which they are due.

[Docket No. 28471, 61 FR 30744, June 17, 1996]

§ 135.338 Qualifications: Flight instructors (aircraft) and flight instructors (simulator).

(a) For the purposes of this section and § 135.340:

(1) A flight instructor (aircraft) is a person who is qualified to instruct in an aircraft, in a flight simulator, or in a flight training device for a particular type, class, or category aircraft.

(2) A flight instructor (simulator) is a person who is qualified to instruct in a flight simulator, in a flight training device, or in both, for a particular type, class, or category aircraft.

(3) Flight instructors (aircraft) and flight instructors (simulator) are those instructors who perform the functions described in §§ 135.321(a) and 135.323(a)(4) and (c).

(b) No certificate holder may use a person, nor may any person serve as a flight instructor (aircraft) in a training program established under this subpart unless, with respect to the type, class, or category aircraft involved, that person —

(1) Holds the airman certificates and ratings required to serve as a pilot in command in operations under this part;

(2) Has satisfactorily completed the training phases for the aircraft, including recurrent training, that are required to serve as a pilot in command in operations under this part;

(3) Has satisfactorily completed the proficiency or competency checks that are required to serve as a pilot in command in operations under this part;

(4) Has satisfactorily completed the applicable training requirements of § 135.340;

(5) Holds at least a Class III medical certificate; and

(6) Has satisfied the recency of experience requirements of § 135.247.

(c) No certificate holder may use a person, nor may any person serve as a flight instructor (simulator) in a training program established under this subpart, unless, with respect to the type, class, or

135

category aircraft involved, that person meets the provisions of paragraph (b) of this section, or—

(1) Holds the airman certificates and ratings, except medical certificate, required to serve as a pilot in command in operations under this part except before March 19, 1997 that person need not hold a type rating for the type, class, or category of aircraft involved.

(2) Has satisfactorily completed the appropriate training phases for the aircraft, including recurrent training, that are required to serve as a pilot in command in operations under this part;

(3) Has satisfactorily completed the appropriate proficiency or competency checks that are required to serve as a pilot in command in operations under this part; and

(4) Has satisfactorily completed the applicable training requirements of § 135.340.

(d) Completion of the requirements in paragraphs (b)(2), (3), and (4) or (c)(2), (3), and (4) of this section, as applicable, shall be entered in the individual's training record maintained by the certificate holder.

(e) An airman who does not hold a medical certificate may function as a flight instructor in an aircraft if functioning as a non-required crewmember, but may not serve as a flightcrew member in operations under this part.

(f) A flight instructor (simulator) must accomplish the following—

(1) Fly at least two flight segments as a required crewmember for the type, class, or category aircraft involved within the 12-month period preceding the performance of any flight instructor duty in a flight simulator; or

(2) Satisfactorily complete an approved line-observation program within the period prescribed by that program and that must precede the performance of any check airman duty in a flight simulator.

(g) The flight segments or line-observation program required in paragraph (f) of this section are considered completed in the month required if completed in the calendar month before, or in the calendar month after, the month in which they are due.

[Docket No. 28471, 61 FR 30744, June 17, 1996; as amended by Amdt. 135–64, 62 FR 3739, Jan. 24, 1997]

§ 135.339 Initial and transition training and checking: Check airmen (aircraft), check airmen (simulator).

(a) No certificate holder may use a person nor may any person serve as a check airman unless—

(1) That person has satisfactorily completed initial or transition check airman training; and

(2) Within the preceding 24 calendar months, that person satisfactorily conducts a proficiency

or competency check under the observation of an FAA inspector or an aircrew designated examiner employed by the operator. The observation check may be accomplished in part or in full in an aircraft, in a flight simulator, or in a flight training device. This paragraph applies after March 19, 1997.

(b) The observation check required by paragraph (a)(2) of this section is considered to have been completed in the month required if completed in the calendar month before or the calendar month after the month in which it is due.

(c) The initial ground training for check airmen must include the following:

(1) Check airman duties, functions, and responsibilities.

(2) The applicable Code of Federal Regulations and the certificate holder's policies and procedures.

(3) The applicable methods, procedures, and techniques for conducting the required checks.

(4) Proper evaluation of student performance including the detection of—

(i) Improper and insufficient training; and

(ii) Personal characteristics of an applicant that could adversely affect safety.

(5) The corrective action in the case of unsatisfactory checks.

(6) The approved methods, procedures, and limitations for performing the required normal, abnormal, and emergency procedures in the aircraft.

(d) The transition ground training for check airmen must include the approved methods, procedures, and limitations for performing the required normal, abnormal, and emergency procedures applicable to the aircraft to which the check airman is in transition.

(e) The initial and transition flight training for check airmen (aircraft) must include the following—

(1) The safety measures for emergency situations that are likely to develop during a check;

(2) The potential results of improper, untimely, or nonexecution of safety measures during a check;

(3) Training and practice in conducting flight checks from the left and right pilot seats in the required normal, abnormal, and emergency procedures to ensure competence to conduct the pilot flight checks required by this part; and

(4) The safety measures to be taken from either pilot seat for emergency situations that are likely to develop during checking.

(f) The requirements of paragraph (e) of this section may be accomplished in full or in part in flight, in a flight simulator, or in a flight training device, as appropriate.

(g) The initial and transition flight training for check airmen (simulator) must include the following:

(1) Training and practice in conducting flight checks in the required normal, abnormal, and emergency procedures to ensure competence to conduct the flight checks required by this part. This training and practice must be accomplished in a flight simulator or in a flight training device.

(2) Training in the operation of flight simulators, flight training devices, or both, to ensure competence to conduct the flight checks required by this part.

[Docket No. 28471, 61 FR 30745, June 17, 1996; as amended by Amdt. 135–64, 62 FR 3739, Jan. 24, 1997]

§ 135.340 Initial and transition training and checking: Flight instructors (aircraft), flight instructors (simulator).

(a) No certificate holder may use a person nor may any person serve as a flight instructor unless—

(1) That person has satisfactorily completed initial or transition flight instructor training; and

(2) Within the preceding 24 calendar months, that person satisfactorily conducts instruction under the observation of an FAA inspector, an operator check airman, or an aircrew designated examiner employed by the operator. The observation check may be accomplished in part or in full in an aircraft, in a flight simulator, or in a flight training device. This paragraph applies after March 19, 1997.

(b) The observation check required by paragraph (a)(2) of this section is considered to have been completed in the month required if completed in the calendar month before, or the calendar month after, the month in which it is due.

(c) The initial ground training for flight instructors must include the following:

(1) Flight instructor duties, functions, and responsibilities.

(2) The applicable Code of Federal Regulations and the certificate holder's policies and procedures.

(3) The applicable methods, procedures, and techniques for conducting flight instruction.

(4) Proper evaluation of student performance including the detection of—

(i) Improper and insufficient training; and

(ii) Personal characteristics of an applicant that could adversely affect safety.

(5) The corrective action in the case of unsatisfactory training progress.

(6) The approved methods, procedures, and limitations for performing the required normal, abnormal, and emergency procedures in the aircraft.

(7) Except for holders of a flight instructor certificate—

(i) The fundamental principles of the teaching-learning process;

(ii) Teaching methods and procedures; and

(iii) The instructor-student relationship.

(d) The transition ground training for flight instructors must include the approved methods, procedures, and limitations for performing the required normal, abnormal, and emergency procedures applicable to the type, class, or category aircraft to which the flight instructor is in transition.

(e) The initial and transition flight training for flight instructors (aircraft) must include the following—

(1) The safety measures for emergency situations that are likely to develop during instruction;

(2) The potential results of improper or untimely safety measures during instruction;

(3) Training and practice from the left and right pilot seats in the required normal, abnormal, and emergency maneuvers to ensure competence to conduct the flight instruction required by this part; and

(4) The safety measures to be taken from either the left or right pilot seat for emergency situations that are likely to develop during instruction.

(f) The requirements of paragraph (e) of this section may be accomplished in full or in part in flight, in a flight simulator, or in a flight training device, as appropriate.

(g) The initial and transition flight training for a flight instructor (simulator) must include the following:

(1) Training and practice in the required normal, abnormal, and emergency procedures to ensure competence to conduct the flight instruction required by this part. These maneuvers and procedures must be accomplished in full or in part in a flight simulator or in a flight training device.

(2) Training in the operation of flight simulators, flight training devices, or both, to ensure competence to conduct the flight instruction required by this part.

[Docket No. 28471, 61 FR 30745, June 17, 1996; as amended by Amdt. 135–64, 62 FR 3739, Jan. 24, 1997]

§ 135.341 Pilot and flight attendant crewmember training programs.

(a) Each certificate holder, other than one who uses only one pilot in the certificate holder's operations, shall establish and maintain an approved pilot training program, and each certificate holder who uses a flight attendant crewmember shall establish and maintain an approved flight attendant training program, that is appropriate to the operations to which each pilot and flight attendant is to be assigned, and will ensure that they are adequately trained to meet the applicable knowledge and practical testing requirements of §§ 135.293 through 135.301. However, the Administrator may authorize a deviation from this section if the Administrator finds that, because of the limited size and scope of the operation, safety will allow a deviation from these requirements.

(b) Each certificate holder required to have a training program by paragraph (a) of this section shall include in that program ground and flight training curriculums for—

(1) Initial training;

(2) Transition training;

(3) Upgrade training;

(4) Differences training; and

(5) Recurrent training.

(c) Each certificate holder required to have a training program by paragraph (a) of this section shall provide current and appropriate study materials for use by each required pilot and flight attendant.

(d) The certificate holder shall furnish copies of the pilot and flight attendant crewmember training program, and all changes and additions, to the assigned representative of the Administrator. If the certificate holder uses training facilities of other persons, a copy of those training programs or appropriate portions used for those facilities shall also be furnished. Curricula that follow FAA published curricula may be cited by reference in the copy of the training program furnished to the representative of the Administrator and need not be furnished with the program.

[Docket No. 16097, 43 FR 46783, Oct. 10, 1978; as amended by Amdt. 135–18, 47 FR 33396, Aug. 2, 1982]

§ 135.343 Crewmember initial and recurrent training requirements.

No certificate holder may use a person, nor may any person serve, as a crewmember in operations under this part unless that crewmember has completed the appropriate initial or recurrent training phase of the training program appropriate to the type of operation in which the crewmember is to serve since the beginning of the 12th calendar month before that service. This section does not apply to a certificate holder that uses only one pilot in the certificate holder's operations.

[Docket No. 16097, 43 FR 46783, Oct. 10, 1978; as amended by Amdt. 135–18, 47 FR 33396, Aug. 2, 1982]

§ 135.345 Pilots: Initial, transition, and upgrade ground training.

Initial, transition, and upgrade ground training for pilots must include instruction in at least the following, as applicable to their duties:

(a) General subjects—

(1) The certificate holder's flight locating procedures;

(2) Principles and methods for determining weight and balance, and runway limitations for takeoff and landing;

(3) Enough meteorology to ensure a practical knowledge of weather phenomena, including the principles of frontal systems, icing, fog, thunderstorms, windshear and, if appropriate, high altitude weather situations;

(4) Air traffic control systems, procedures, and phraseology;

(5) Navigation and the use of navigational aids, including instrument approach procedures;

(6) Normal and emergency communication procedures;

(7) Visual cues before and during descent below DH or MDA; and

(8) Other instructions necessary to ensure the pilot's competence.

(b) For each aircraft type—

(1) A general description;

(2) Performance characteristics;

(3) Engines and propellers;

(4) Major components;

(5) Major aircraft systems (i.e., flight controls, electrical, and hydraulic), other systems, as appropriate, principles of normal, abnormal, and emergency operations, appropriate procedures and limitations;

(6) Knowledge and procedures for—

(i) Recognizing and avoiding severe weather situations;

(ii) Escaping from severe weather situations, in case of inadvertent encounters, including low-altitude windshear (except that rotorcraft pilots are not required to be trained in escaping from low-altitude windshear);

(iii) Operating in or near thunderstorms (including best penetrating altitudes), turbulent air (including clear air turbulence), icing, hail, and other potentially hazardous meteorological conditions; and

(iv) Operating airplanes during ground icing conditions, (i.e., any time conditions are such that frost, ice, or snow may reasonably be expected to adhere to the airplane), if the certificate holder expects to authorize takeoffs in ground icing conditions, including:

(A) The use of holdover times when using deicing/anti-icing fluids:

(B) Airplane deicing/anti-icing procedures, including inspection and check procedures and responsibilities.

(C) Communications;

(D) Airplane surface contamination (i.e., adherence of frost, ice, or snow) and critical area identification, and knowledge of how contamination adversely affects airplane performance and flight characteristics;

(E) Types and characteristics of deicing/anti-icing fluids, if used by the certificates holder;

(F) Cold weather preflight inspection procedures;

(G) Techniques for recognizing contamination on the airplane;

(7) Operating limitations;

(8) Fuel consumption and cruise control;

(9) Flight planning;

(10) Each normal and emergency procedure; and

(11) The approved Aircraft Flight Manual, or equivalent.

[Docket No. 16097, 43 FR 46783, Oct. 10, 1978; as amended by Amdt. 135–27, 53 FR 37697, Sept. 27, 1988; Amdt. 135–46, 58 FR 69630, Dec. 30, 1993]

§ 135.347 Pilots: Initial, transition, upgrade, and differences flight training.

(a) Initial, transition, upgrade, and differences training for pilots must include flight and practice in each of the maneuvers and procedures in the approved training program curriculum.

(b) The maneuvers and procedures required by paragraph (a) of this section must be performed in flight, except to the extent that certain maneuvers and procedures may be performed in an aircraft simulator, or an appropriate training device, as allowed by this subpart.

(c) If the certificate holder's approved training program includes a course of training using an aircraft simulator or other training device, each pilot must successfully complete—

(1) Training and practice in the simulator or training device in at least the maneuvers and procedures in this subpart that are capable of being performed in the aircraft simulator or training device; and

(2) A flight check in the aircraft or a check in the simulator or training device to the level of proficiency of a pilot in command or second in command, as applicable, in at least the maneuvers and procedures that are capable of being performed in an aircraft simulator or training device.

§ 135.349 Flight attendants: Initial and transition ground training.

Initial and transition ground training for flight attendants must include instruction in at least the following—

(a) General subjects—

(1) The authority of the pilot in command; and

(2) Passenger handling, including procedures to be followed in handling deranged persons or other persons whose conduct might jeopardize safety.

(b) For each aircraft type—

(1) A general description of the aircraft emphasizing physical characteristics that may have a bearing on ditching, evacuation, and inflight emergency procedures and on other related duties;

(2) The use of both the public address system and the means of communicating with other flight crewmembers, including emergency means in the case of attempted hijacking or other unusual situations; and

(3) Proper use of electrical galley equipment and the controls for cabin heat and ventilation.

§ 135.351 Recurrent training.

(a) Each certificate holder must ensure that each crewmember receives recurrent training and is adequately trained and currently proficient for the type aircraft and crewmember position involved.

(b) Recurrent ground training for crewmembers must include at least the following:

(1) A quiz or other review to determine the crewmember's knowledge of the aircraft and crewmember position involved.

(2) Instruction as necessary in the subjects required for initial ground training by this subpart, as appropriate, including low-altitude windshear training and training on operating during ground icing conditions, as prescribed in § 135.341 and described in § 135.345, and emergency training.

(c) Recurrent flight training for pilots must include, at least, flight training in the maneuvers or procedures in this subpart, except that satisfactory completion of the check required by § 135.293 within the preceding 12 calendar months may be substituted for recurrent flight training.

[Docket No. 16097, 43 FR 46783, Oct. 10, 1978; as amended by Amdt. 135–27, 53 FR 37698, Sept. 27, 1988; Amdt. 135–46, 58 FR 69630, Dec. 30, 1993]

§ 135.353 Prohibited drugs.

(a) Each certificate holder or operator shall provide each employee performing a function listed in Appendix I to part 121 of this chapter and his or her supervisor with the training specified in that appendix.

(b) No certificate holder or operator may use any contractor to perform a function specified in Appendix I to part 121 of this chapter unless that contractor provides each of its employees performing that function for the certificate holder or the operator and his or her supervisor with the training specified in that appendix.

[Docket No. 25148, 53 FR 47061, Nov. 21, 1988]

Subpart I— Airplane Performance Operating Limitations

§ 135.361 Applicability.

(a) This subpart prescribes airplane performance operating limitations applicable to the operation of the categories of airplanes listed in § 135.363 when operated under this part.

(b) For the purpose of this subpart, *effective length of the runway*, for landing means the distance from the point at which the obstruction clearance plane associated with the approach end of the runway intersects the centerline of the runway to the far end of the runway.

(c) For the purpose of this subpart, *obstruction clearance plane* means a plane sloping upward from the runway at a slope of 1:20 to the horizontal, and tangent to or clearing all obstructions within a specified area surrounding the runway as shown in a profile view of that area. In the plan view, the centerline of the specified area coincides with the centerline of the runway, beginning at the point where the obstruction clearance plane intersects the centerline of the runway and proceeding to a point at least 1,500 feet from the beginning point. After that the centerline coincides with the takeoff path over the ground for the runway (in the case of takeoffs) or with the instrument approach counterpart (for landings), or, where the applicable one of these paths has not been established, it proceeds consistent with turns of at least 4,000-foot radius until a point is reached beyond which the obstruction clearance plane clears all obstructions. This area extends laterally 200 feet on each side of the centerline at the point where the obstruction clearance plane intersects the runway and continues at this width to the end of the runway; then it increases uniformly to 500 feet on each side of the centerline at a point 1,500 feet from the intersection of the obstruction clearance plane with the runway; after that it extends laterally 500 feet on each side of the centerline.

§ 135.363 General.

(a) Each certificate holder operating a reciprocating engine powered large transport category airplane shall comply with §§ 135.365 through 135.377.

(b) Each certificate holder operating a turbine engine powered large transport category airplane shall comply with §§ 135.379 through 135.387, except that when it operates a turbopropeller-powered large transport category airplane certificated after August 29, 1959, but previously type certificated with the same number of reciprocating engines, it may comply with §§ 135.365 through 135.377.

(c) Each certificate holder operating a large nontransport category airplane shall comply with §§ 135.389 through 135.395 and any determination of compliance must be based only on approved performance data. For the purpose of this subpart, a large nontransport category airplane is an airplane that was type certificated before July 1, 1942.

(d) Each certificate holder operating a small transport category airplane shall comply with § 135.397.

(e) Each certificate holder operating a small nontransport category airplane shall comply with § 135.399.

(f) The performance data in the Airplane Flight Manual applies in determining compliance with §§ 135.365 through 135.387. Where conditions are different from those on which the performance data is based, compliance is determined by interpolation or by computing the effects of change in the specific variables, if the results of the interpolation or computations are substantially as accurate as the results of direct tests.

(g) No person may take off a reciprocating engine powered large transport category airplane at a weight that is more than the allowable weight for the runway being used (determined under the runway takeoff limitations of the transport category operating rules of this subpart) after taking into account the temperature operating correction factors in section 4a.749a-T or section 4b.117 of the Civil Air Regulations in effect on January 31, 1965, and in the applicable Airplane Flight Manual.

(h) The Administrator may authorize in the operations specifications deviations from this subpart if special circumstances make a literal observance of a requirement unnecessary for safety.

(i) The 10-mile width specified in §§ 135.369 through 135.373 may be reduced to 5 miles, for not more than 20 miles, when operating under VFR or where navigation facilities furnish reliable and accurate identification of high ground and obstructions located outside of 5 miles, but within 10 miles, on each side of the intended track.

(j) Each certificate holder operating a commuter category airplane shall comply with § 135.398.

[Docket No. 16097, 43 FR 46783, Oct. 10, 1978; as amended by Amdt. 135–21, 52 FR 1836, Jan. 15, 1987]

§ 135.365 Large transport category airplanes: Reciprocating engine powered: Weight limitations.

(a) No person may take off a reciprocating engine powered large transport category airplane from an airport located at an elevation outside of the range for which maximum takeoff weights have been determined for that airplane.

(b) No person may take off a reciprocating engine powered large transport category airplane for an airport of intended destination that is located at an elevation outside of the range for which maximum landing weights have been determined for that airplane.

(c) No person may specify, or have specified, an alternate airport that is located at an elevation outside of the range for which maximum landing weights have been determined for the reciprocating engine powered large transport category airplane concerned.

(d) No person may take off a reciprocating engine powered large transport category airplane at a weight more than the maximum authorized takeoff weight for the elevation of the airport.

(e) No person may take off a reciprocating engine powered large transport category airplane if its weight on arrival at the airport of destination will be more than the maximum authorized landing weight for the elevation of that airport, allowing for normal consumption of fuel and oil en route.

§ 135.367 Large transport category airplanes: Reciprocating engine powered: Takeoff limitations.

(a) No person operating a reciprocating engine powered large transport category airplane may take off that airplane unless it is possible—

(1) To stop the airplane safely on the runway, as shown by the accelerate-stop distance data, at any time during takeoff until reaching critical-engine failure speed;

(2) If the critical engine fails at any time after the airplane reaches critical-engine failure speed V_1, to continue the takeoff and reach a height of 50 feet, as indicated by the takeoff path data, before passing over the end of the runway; and

(3) To clear all obstacles either by at least 50 feet vertically (as shown by the takeoff path data) or 200 feet horizontally within the airport boundaries and 300 feet horizontally beyond the boundaries, without banking before reaching a height of 50 feet (as shown by the takeoff path data) and after that without banking more than 15 degrees.

(b) In applying this section, corrections must be made for any runway gradient. To allow for wind effect, takeoff data based on still air may be corrected by taking into account not more than 50 percent of any reported headwind component and not less than 150 percent of any reported tailwind component.

§ 135.369 Large transport category airplanes: Reciprocating engine powered: En route limitations: All engines operating.

(a) No person operating a reciprocating engine powered large transport category airplane may take off that airplane at a weight, allowing for normal consumption of fuel and oil, that does not allow a rate of climb (in feet per minute), with all engines operating, of at least $6.90 V_{SO}$ (that is, the number of feet per minute obtained by multiplying the number of knots by 6.90) at an altitude of at least 1,000 feet above the highest ground or obstruction within ten miles of each side of the intended track.

(b) This section does not apply to large transport category airplanes certificated under part 4a of the Civil Air Regulations.

§ 135.371 Large transport category airplanes: Reciprocating engine powered: En route limitations: One engine inoperative.

(a) Except as provided in paragraph (b) of this section, no person operating a reciprocating engine powered large transport category airplane may take off that airplane at a weight, allowing for normal consumption of fuel and oil, that does not allow a rate of climb (in feet per minute), with one engine inoperative, of at least $(0.079-0.106/N)$ V_{SO}^2 (where N is the number of engines installed and V_{SO} is expressed in knots) at an altitude of at least 1,000 feet above the highest ground or obstruction within 10 miles of each side of the intended track. However, for the purposes of this paragraph the rate of climb for transport category airplanes certificated under part 4a of the Civil Air Regulations is $0.026 V_{SO}^2$.

(b) In place of the requirements of paragraph (a) of this section, a person may, under an approved procedure, operate a reciprocating engine powered large transport category airplane at an all-engines-operating altitude that allows the airplane to continue, after an engine failure, to an alternate airport where a landing can be made under § 135.377, allowing for normal consumption of fuel and oil. After the assumed failure, the flight path must clear the ground and any obstruction within five miles on each side of the intended track by at least 2,000 feet.

(c) If an approved procedure under paragraph (b) of this section is used, the certificate holder shall comply with the following:

(1) The rate of climb (as prescribed in the Airplane Flight Manual for the appropriate weight and altitude) used in calculating the airplane's flight path shall be diminished by an amount in feet per minute, equal to $(0.079-0.106/N)$ V_{SO}^2

135

(when N is the number of engines installed and V_{S0} is expressed in knots) for airplanes certificated under part 25 of this chapter and by 0.026 V_{S0}^2 for airplanes certificated under part 4a of the Civil Air Regulations.

(2) The all-engines-operating altitude shall be sufficient so that in the event the critical engine becomes inoperative at any point along the route, the flight will be able to proceed to a predetermined alternate airport by use of this procedure. In determining the takeoff weight, the airplane is assumed to pass over the critical obstruction following engine failure at a point no closer to the critical obstruction than the nearest approved radio navigational fix, unless the Administrator approves a procedure established on a different basis upon finding that adequate operational safeguards exist.

(3) The airplane must meet the provisions of paragraph (a) of this section at 1,000 feet above the airport used as an alternate in this procedure.

(4) The procedure must include an approved method of accounting for winds and temperatures that would otherwise adversely affect the flight path.

(5) In complying with this procedure, fuel jettisoning is allowed if the certificate holder shows that it has an adequate training program, that proper instructions are given to the flight crew, and all other precautions are taken to ensure a safe procedure.

(6) The certificate holder and the pilot in command shall jointly elect an alternate airport for which the appropriate weather reports or forecasts, or any combination of them, indicate that weather conditions will be at or above the alternate weather minimum specified in the certificate holder's operations specifications for that airport when the flight arrives.

§ 135.373 Part 25 transport category airplanes with four or more engines: Reciprocating engine powered: En route limitations: Two engines inoperative.

(a) No person may operate an airplane certificated under part 25 and having four or more engines unless—

(1) There is no place along the intended track that is more than 90 minutes (with all engines operating at cruising power) from an airport that meets § 135.377; or

(2) It is operated at a weight allowing the airplane, with the two critical engines inoperative, to climb at 0.013 V_{S0}^2 feet per minute (that is, the number of feet per minute obtained by multiplying the number of knots squared by 0.013) at an altitude of 1,000 feet above the highest ground or obstruction within 10 miles on each side of the in-

tended track, or at an altitude of 5,000 feet, whichever is higher.

(b) For the purposes of paragraph (a)(2) of this section, it is assumed that—

(1) The two engines fail at the point that is most critical with respect to the takeoff weight;

(2) Consumption of fuel and oil is normal with all engines operating up to the point where the two engines fail with two engines operating beyond that point;

(3) Where the engines are assumed to fail at an altitude above the prescribed minimum altitude, compliance with the prescribed rate of climb at the prescribed minimum altitude need not be shown during the descent from the cruising altitude to the prescribed minimum altitude, if those requirements can be met once the prescribed minimum altitude is reached, and assuming descent to be along a net flight path and the rate of descent to be 0.013 V_{S0}^2 greater than the rate in the approved performance data; and

(4) If fuel jettisoning is provided, the airplane's weight at the point where the two engines fail is considered to be not less than that which would include enough fuel to proceed to an airport meeting § 135.377 and to arrive at an altitude of at least 1,000 feet directly over that airport.

§ 135.375 Large transport category airplanes: Reciprocating engine powered: Landing limitations: Destination airports.

(a) Except as provided in paragraph (b) of this section, no person operating a reciprocating engine powered large transport category airplane may take off that airplane, unless its weight on arrival, allowing for normal consumption of fuel and oil in flight, would allow a full stop landing at the intended destination within 60 percent of the effective length of each runway described below from a point 50 feet directly above the intersection of the obstruction clearance plane and the runway. For the purposes of determining the allowable landing weight at the destination airport the following is assumed:

(1) The airplane is landed on the most favorable runway and in the most favorable direction in still air.

(2) The airplane is landed on the most suitable runway considering the probable wind velocity and direction (forecast for the expected time of arrival), the ground handling characteristics of the type of airplane, and other conditions such as landing aids and terrain, and allowing for the effect of the landing path and roll of not more than 50 percent of the headwind component or not less than 150 percent of the tailwind component.

(b) An airplane that would be prohibited from being taken off because it could not meet paragraph (a)(2) of this section may be taken off if an alternate airport is selected that meets all of this section except that the airplane can accomplish a full stop landing within 70 percent of the effective length of the runway.

§ 135.377 Large transport category airplanes: Reciprocating engine powered: Landing limitations: Alternate airports.

No person may list an airport as an alternate airport in a flight plan unless the airplane (at the weight anticipated at the time of arrival at the airport), based on the assumptions in § 135.375(a) (1) and (2), can be brought to a full stop landing within 70 percent of the effective length of the runway.

§ 135.379 Large transport category airplanes: Turbine engine powered: Takeoff limitations.

(a) No person operating a turbine engine powered large transport category airplane may take off that airplane at a weight greater than that listed in the Airplane Flight Manual for the elevation of the airport and for the ambient temperature existing at take off.

(b) No person operating a turbine engine powered large transport category airplane certificated after August 26, 1957, but before August 30, 1959 (SR422, 422A), may take off that airplane at a weight greater than that listed in the Airplane Flight Manual for the minimum distance required for takeoff. In the case of an airplane certificated after September 30, 1958 (SR422A, 422B), the takeoff distance may include a clearway distance but the clearway distance included may not be greater than one-half of the takeoff run.

(c) No person operating a turbine engine powered large transport category airplane certificated after August 29, 1959 (SR422B), may take off that airplane at a weight greater than that listed in the Airplane Flight Manual at which compliance with the following may be shown:

(1) The accelerate-stop distance, as defined in § 25.109 of this chapter, must not exceed the length of the runway plus the length of any stopway.

(2) The takeoff distance must not exceed the length of the runway plus the length of any clearway except that the length of any clearway included must not be greater than one-half the length of the runway.

(3) The takeoff run must not be greater than the length of the runway.

(d) No person operating a turbine engine powered large transport category airplane may take off that airplane at a weight greater than that listed in the Airplane Flight Manual—

(1) For an airplane certificated after August 26, 1957, but before October 1, 1958 (SR422), that allows a takeoff path that clears all obstacles either by at least (35+0.01 D) feet vertically (D is the distance along the intended flight path from the end of the runway in feet), or by at least 200 feet horizontally within the airport boundaries and by at least 300 feet horizontally after passing the boundaries; or

(2) For an airplane certificated after September 30, 1958 (SR422A, 422B), that allows a net takeoff flight path that clears all obstacles either by a height of at least 35 feet vertically, or by at least 200 feet horizontally within the airport boundaries and by at least 300 feet horizontally after passing the boundaries.

(e) In determining maximum weights, minimum distances, and flight paths under paragraphs (a) through (d) of this section, correction must be made for the runway to be used, the elevation of the airport, the effective runway gradient, the ambient temperature and wind component at the time of takeoff, and, if operating limitations exist for the minimum distances required for takeoff from wet runways, the runway surface condition (dry or wet). Wet runway distances associated with grooved or porous friction course runways, if provided in the Airplane Flight Manual, may be used only for runways that are grooved or treated with a porous friction course (PFC) overlay, and that the operator determines are designed, constructed, and maintained in a manner acceptable to the Administrator.

(f) For the purposes of this section, it is assumed that the airplane is not banked before reaching a height of 50 feet, as shown by the takeoff path or net takeoff flight path data (as appropriate) in the Airplane Flight Manual, and after that the maximum bank is not more than 15 degrees.

(g) For the purposes of this section, the terms, takeoff distance, takeoff run, net takeoff flight path, have the same meanings as set forth in the rules under which the airplane was certificated.

[Docket No. 16097, 43 FR 46783, Oct. 10, 1978; as amended by Amdt. 135–71, 63 FR 8321, Feb. 18, 1998]

§ 135.381 Large transport category airplanes: Turbine engine powered: En route limitations: One engine inoperative.

(a) No person operating a turbine engine powered large transport category airplane may take off that airplane at a weight, allowing for normal consumption of fuel and oil, that is greater than that which (under the approved, one engine inoperative, en route net flight path data in the Airplane Flight Manual for that airplane) will allow compliance with paragraph (a)(1) or (2) of this section, based on the ambient temperatures expected en route.

(1) There is a positive slope at an altitude of at least 1,000 feet above all terrain and obstructions within five statute miles on each side of the intended track, and, in addition, if that airplane was certificated after August 29, 1958 (SR422B), there is a positive slope at 1,500 feet above the airport where the airplane is assumed to land after an engine fails.

(2) The net flight path allows the airplane to continue flight from the cruising altitude to an airport where a landing can be made under § 135.387 clearing all terrain and obstructions within five statute miles of the intended track by at least 2,000 feet vertically and with a positive slope at 1,000 feet above the airport where the airplane lands after an engine fails, or, if that airplane was certificated after September 30, 1958 (SR422A, 422B), with a positive slope at 1,500 feet above the airport where the airplane lands after an engine fails.

(b) For the purpose of paragraph (a)(2) of this section, it is assumed that—

(1) The engine fails at the most critical point en route;

(2) The airplane passes over the critical obstruction, after engine failure at a point that is no closer to the obstruction than the approved radio navigation fix, unless the Administrator authorizes a different procedure based on adequate operational safeguards;

(3) An approved method is used to allow for adverse winds;

(4) Fuel jettisoning will be allowed if the certificate holder shows that the crew is properly instructed, that the training program is adequate, and that all other precautions are taken to ensure a safe procedure;

(5) The alternate airport is selected and meets the prescribed weather minimums; and

(6) The consumption of fuel and oil after engine failure is the same as the consumption that is allowed for in the approved net flight path data in the Airplane Flight Manual.

§ 135.383 Large transport category airplanes: Turbine engine powered: En route limitations: Two engines inoperative.

(a) Airplanes certificated after August 26, 1957, but before October 1, 1958 (SR422). No person may operate a turbine engine powered large transport category airplane along an intended route unless that person complies with either of the following:

(1) There is no place along the intended track that is more than 90 minutes (with all engines operating at cruising power) from an airport that meets § 135.387.

(2) Its weight, according to the two-engine-inoperative, en route, net flight path data in the Airplane Flight Manual, allows the airplane to fly from the point where the two engines are assumed to fail simultaneously to an airport that meets § 135.387, with a net flight path (considering the ambient temperature anticipated along the track) having a positive slope at an altitude of at least 1,000 feet above all terrain and obstructions within five statute miles on each side of the intended track, or at an altitude of 5,000 feet, whichever is higher.

For the purposes of paragraph (a)(2) of this section, it is assumed that the two engines fail at the most critical point en route, that if fuel jettisoning is provided, the airplane's weight at the point where the engines fail includes enough fuel to continue to the airport and to arrive at an altitude of at least 1,000 feet directly over the airport, and that the fuel and oil consumption after engine failure is the same as the consumption allowed for in the net flight path data in the Airplane Flight Manual.

(b) Airplanes certificated after September 30, 1958, but before August 30, 1959 (SR422A). No person may operate a turbine engine powered large transport category airplane along an intended route unless that person complies with either of the following:

(1) There is no place along the intended track that is more than 90 minutes (with all engines operating at cruising power) from an airport that meets § 135.387.

(2) Its weight, according to the two-engine-inoperative, en route, net flight path data in the Airplane Flight Manual allows the airplane to fly from the point where the two engines are assumed to fail simultaneously to an airport that meets § 135.387 with a net flight path (considering the ambient temperatures anticipated along the track) having a positive slope at an altitude of at least 1,000 feet above all terrain and obstructions within five statute miles on each side of the intended track, or at an altitude of 2,000 feet, whichever is higher.

For the purpose of paragraph (b)(2) of this section, it is assumed that the two engines fail at the most critical point en route, that the airplane's weight at the point where the engines fail includes enough fuel to continue to the airport, to arrive at an altitude of at least 1,500 feet directly over the airport, and after that to fly for 15 minutes at cruise power or thrust, or both, and that the consumption of fuel and oil after engine failure is the same as the consumption allowed for in the net flight path data in the Airplane Flight Manual.

(c) Aircraft certificated after August 29, 1959 (SR422B). No person may operate a turbine engine powered large transport category airplane along an intended route unless that person complies with either of the following:

(1) There is no place along the intended track that is more than 90 minutes (with all engines operating at cruising power) from an airport that meets § 135.387.

(2) Its weight, according to the two-engine-inoperative, en route, net flight path data in the Airplane Flight Manual, allows the airplane to fly from the point where the two engines are assumed to fail simultaneously to an airport that meets § 135.387, with the net flight path (considering the ambient temperatures anticipated along the track) clearing vertically by at least 2,000 feet all terrain and obstructions within five statute miles on each side of the intended track. For the purposes of this paragraph, it is assumed that—

(i) The two engines fail at the most critical point en route;

(ii) The net flight path has a positive slope at 1,500 feet above the airport where the landing is assumed to be made after the engines fail;

(iii) Fuel jettisoning will be approved if the certificate holder shows that the crew is properly instructed, that the training program is adequate, and that all other precautions are taken to ensure a safe procedure;

(iv) The airplane's weight at the point where the two engines are assumed to fail provides enough fuel to continue to the airport, to arrive at an altitude of at least 1,500 feet directly over the airport, and after that to fly for 15 minutes at cruise power or thrust, or both; and

(v) The consumption of fuel and oil after the engines fail is the same as the consumption that is allowed for in the net flight path data in the Airplane Flight Manual.

§ 135.385 Large transport category airplanes: Turbine engine powered: Landing limitations: Destination airports.

(a) No person operating a turbine engine powered large transport category airplane may take off that airplane at a weight that (allowing for normal consumption of fuel and oil in flight to the destination or alternate airport) the weight of the airplane on arrival would exceed the landing weight in the Airplane Flight Manual for the elevation of the destination or alternate airport and the ambient temperature anticipated at the time of landing.

(b) Except as provided in paragraph (c), (d), or (e) of this section, no person operating a turbine engine powered large transport category airplane

may take off that airplane unless its weight on arrival, allowing for normal consumption of fuel and oil in flight (in accordance with the landing distance in the Airplane Flight Manual for the elevation of the destination airport and the wind conditions anticipated there at the time of landing), would allow a full stop landing at the intended destination airport within 60 percent of the effective length of each runway described below from a point 50 feet above the intersection of the obstruction clearance plane and the runway. For the purpose of determining the allowable landing weight at the destination airport the following is assumed:

(1) The airplane is landed on the most favorable runway and in the most favorable direction, in still air.

(2) The airplane is landed on the most suitable runway considering the probable wind velocity and direction and the ground handling characteristics of the airplane, and considering other conditions such as landing aids and terrain.

(c) A turbopropeller powered airplane that would be prohibited from being taken off because it could not meet paragraph (b)(2) of this section, may be taken off if an alternate airport is selected that meets all of this section except that the airplane can accomplish a full stop landing within 70 percent of the effective length of the runway.

(d) Unless, based on a showing of actual operating landing techniques on wet runways, a shorter landing distance (but never less than that required by paragraph (b) of this section) has been approved for a specific type and model airplane and included in the Airplane Flight Manual, no person may take off a turbojet airplane when the appropriate weather reports or forecasts, or any combination of them, indicate that the runways at the destination airport may be wet or slippery at the estimated time of arrival unless the effective runway length at the destination airport is at least 115 percent of the runway length required under paragraph (b) of this section.

(e) A turbojet airplane that would be prohibited from being taken off because it could not meet paragraph (b)(2) of this section may be taken off if an alternate airport is selected that meets all of paragraph (b) of this section.

§ 135.387 Large transport category airplanes: Turbine engine powered: Landing limitations: Alternate airports.

No person may select an airport as an alternate airport for a turbine engine powered large transport category airplane unless (based on the assumptions in § 135.385(b)) that airplane, at the weight anticipated at the time of arrival, can be brought to a full stop landing within 70 percent of the effective length of the runway for turbopropeller-powered airplanes and 60 percent of the effective length of the runway for turbojet airplanes, from a point 50 feet above the intersection of the obstruction clearance plane and the runway.

§ 135.389 Large nontransport category airplanes: Takeoff limitations.

(a) No person operating a large nontransport category airplane may take off that airplane at a weight greater than the weight that would allow the airplane to be brought to a safe stop within the effective length of the runway, from any point during the takeoff before reaching 105 percent of minimum control speed (the minimum speed at which an airplane can be safely controlled in flight after an engine becomes inoperative) or 115 percent of the power off stalling speed in the takeoff configuration, whichever is greater.

(b) For the purposes of this section—

(1) It may be assumed that takeoff power is used on all engines during the acceleration;

(2) Not more than 50 percent of the reported headwind component, or not less than 150 percent of the reported tailwind component, may be taken into account;

(3) The average runway gradient (the difference between the elevations of the endpoints of the runway divided by the total length) must be considered if it is more than one-half of one percent;

(4) It is assumed that the airplane is operating in standard atmosphere; and

(5) For takeoff, *effective length of the runway* means the distance from the end of the runway at which the takeoff is started to a point at which the obstruction clearance plane associated with the other end of the runway intersects the runway centerline.

§ 135.391 Large nontransport category airplanes: En route limitations: One engine inoperative.

(a) Except as provided in paragraph (b) of this section, no person operating a large nontransport category airplane may take off that airplane at a weight that does not allow a rate of climb of at least 50 feet a minute, with the critical engine inoperative, at an altitude of at least 1,000 feet above the highest obstruction within five miles on each side of the intended track, or 5,000 feet, whichever is higher.

(b) Without regard to paragraph (a) of this section, if the Administrator finds that safe operations are not impaired, a person may operate the airplane at an altitude that allows the airplane, in case of engine failure, to clear all obstructions within five miles on each side of the intended track by 1,000 feet. If this procedure is used, the rate of descent for the appropriate weight and altitude is assumed to be 50 feet a minute greater than the rate in the approved performance data. Before approving such a procedure, the Administrator considers the following for the route, route segment, or area concerned:

(1) The reliability of wind and weather forecasting.

(2) The location and kinds of navigation aids.

(3) The prevailing weather conditions, particularly the frequency and amount of turbulence normally encountered.

(4) Terrain features.

(5) Air traffic problems.

(6) Any other operational factors that affect the operations.

(c) For the purposes of this section, it is assumed that—

(1) The critical engine is inoperative;

(2) The propeller of the inoperative engine is in the minimum drag position;

(3) The wing flaps and landing gear are in the most favorable position;

(4) The operating engines are operating at the maximum continuous power available;

(5) The airplane is operating in standard atmosphere; and

(6) The weight of the airplane is progressively reduced by the anticipated consumption of fuel and oil.

§ 135.393 Large nontransport category airplanes: Landing limitations: Destination airports.

(a) No person operating a large nontransport category airplane may take off that airplane at a weight that—

(1) Allowing for anticipated consumption of fuel and oil, is greater than the weight that would allow a full stop landing within 60 percent of the effective length of the most suitable runway at the destination airport; and

(2) Is greater than the weight allowable if the landing is to be made on the runway—

(i) With the greatest effective length in still air; and

(ii) Required by the probable wind, taking into account not more than 50 percent of the headwind component or not less than 150 percent of the tailwind component.

(b) For the purpose of this section, it is assumed that—

(1) The airplane passes directly over the intersection of the obstruction clearance plane and the runway at a height of 50 feet in a steady gliding approach at a true indicated airspeed of at least $1.3\,V_{S0}$;

(2) The landing does not require exceptional pilot skill; and

(3) The airplane is operating in standard atmosphere.

§ 135.395 Large nontransport category airplanes: Landing limitations: Alternate airports.

No person may select an airport as an alternate airport for a large nontransport category airplane unless that airplane (at the weight anticipated at the time of arrival), based on the assumptions in § 135.393(b), can be brought to a full stop landing within 70 percent of the effective length of the runway.

§ 135.397 Small transport category airplane performance operating limitations.

(a) No person may operate a reciprocating engine powered small transport category airplane unless that person complies with the weight limitations in § 135.365, the takeoff limitations in § 135.367 (except paragraph (a)(3)), and the landing limitations in §§ 135.375 and 135.377.

(b) No person may operate a turbine engine powered small transport category airplane unless that person complies with the takeoff limitations in § 135.379 (except paragraphs (d) and (f)) and the landing limitations in §§ 135.385 and 135.387.

§ 135.398 Commuter category airplanes performance operating limitations.

(a) No person may operate a commuter category airplane unless that person complies with the takeoff weight limitations in the approved Airplane Flight Manual.

(b) No person may take off an airplane type certificated in the commuter category at a weight greater than that listed in the Airplane Flight Manual that allows a net takeoff flight path that clears all obstacles either by a height of at least 35 feet vertically, or at least 200 feet horizontally within the airport boundaries and by at least 300 feet horizontally after passing the boundaries.

(c) No person may operate a commuter category airplane unless that person complies with the landing limitations prescribed in §§ 135.385 and 135.387 of this part. For purposes of this paragraph, §§ 135.385 and 135.387 are applicable to all commuter category airplanes notwithstanding their stated applicability to turbine-engine-powered large transport category airplanes.

(d) In determining maximum weights, minimum distances and flight paths under paragraphs (a) through (c) of this section, correction must be made for the runway to be used, the elevation of the airport, the effective runway gradient, and ambient temperature, and wind component at the time of takeoff.

(e) For the purposes of this section, the assumption is that the airplane is not banked before reaching a height of 50 feet as shown by the net takeoff flight path data in the Airplane Flight Manual and thereafter the maximum bank is not more than 15 degrees.

[Docket No. 23516, 52 FR 1836, Jan. 15, 1987]

§ 135.399 Small nontransport category airplane performance operating limitations.

(a) No person may operate a reciprocating engine or turbopropeller-powered small airplane that is certificated under § 135.169(b)(2), (3), (4), (5), or (6) unless that person complies with the takeoff weight limitations in the approved Airplane Flight Manual or equivalent for operations under this part, and, if the airplane is certificated under § 135.169(b)(4) or (5) with the landing weight limitations in the Approved Airplane Flight Manual or equivalent for operations under this part.

(b) No person may operate an airplane that is certificated under § 135.169(b)(6) unless that person complies with the landing limitations prescribed in §§ 135.385 and 135.387 of this part. For purposes of this paragraph, §§ 135.385 and 135.387 are applicable to reciprocating and turbopropeller-powered small airplanes notwithstanding their stated applicability to turbine engine powered large transport category airplanes.

[44 FR 53731, Sept. 17, 1979]

Subpart J—Maintenance, Preventive Maintenance, and Alterations

§ 135.411 Applicability.

(a) This subpart prescribes rules in addition to those in other parts of this chapter for the maintenance, preventive maintenance, and alterations for each certificate holder as follows:

(1) Aircraft that are type certificated for a passenger seating configuration, excluding any pilot seat, of nine seats or less, shall be maintained under parts 91 and 43 of this chapter and §§ 135.415, 135.417, and 135.421. An approved aircraft inspection program may be used under § 135.419.

(2) Aircraft that are type certificated for a passenger seating configuration, excluding any pilot seat, of ten seats or more, shall be maintained under a maintenance program in §§ 135.415, 135.417, and 135.423 through 135.443.

(b) A certificate holder who is not otherwise required, may elect to maintain its aircraft under paragraph (a)(2) of this section.

(c) Single engine aircraft used in passenger-carrying IFR operations shall also be maintained in accordance with § 135.421 (c), (d), and (e).

[Docket No. 16097, 43 FR 46783, Oct. 10, 1978; as amended by Amdt. 135–70, 62 FR 42374, Aug. 6, 1997]

§ 135.413 Responsibility for airworthiness.

(a) Each certificate holder is primarily responsible for the airworthiness of its aircraft, including airframes, aircraft engines, propellers, rotors, appliances, and parts, and shall have its aircraft maintained under this chapter, and shall have defects repaired between required maintenance under part 43 of this chapter.

(b) Each certificate holder who maintains its aircraft under § 135.411(a)(2) shall—

(1) Perform the maintenance, preventive maintenance, and alteration of its aircraft, including airframe, aircraft engines, propellers, rotors, appliances, emergency equipment and parts, under its manual and this chapter; or

(2) Make arrangements with another person for the performance of maintenance, preventive maintenance, or alteration. However, the certificate holder shall ensure that any maintenance, preventive maintenance, or alteration that is performed by another person is performed under the certificate holder's manual and this chapter.

§ 135.415 Mechanical reliability reports.

(a) Each certificate holder shall report the occurrence or detection of each failure, malfunction, or defect in an aircraft concerning—

(1) Fires during flight and whether the related fire-warning system functioned properly;

(2) Fires during flight not protected by related fire-warning system;

(3) False fire-warning during flight;

(4) An exhaust system that causes damage during flight to the engine, adjacent structure, equipment, or components;

(5) An aircraft component that causes accumulation or circulation of smoke, vapor, or toxic or noxious fumes in the crew compartment or passenger cabin during flight;

(6) Engine shutdown during flight because of flameout;

(7) Engine shutdown during flight when external damage to the engine or aircraft structure occurs;

(8) Engine shutdown during flight due to foreign object ingestion or icing;

(9) Shutdown of more than one engine during flight;

(10) A propeller feathering system or ability of the system to control overspeed during flight;

(11) A fuel or fuel-dumping system that affects fuel flow or causes hazardous leakage during flight;

(12) An unwanted landing gear extension or retraction or opening or closing of landing gear doors during flight;

(13) Brake system components that result in loss of brake actuating force when the aircraft is in motion on the ground;

(14) Aircraft structure that requires major repair;

(15) Cracks, permanent deformation, or corrosion of aircraft structures, if more than the maximum acceptable to the manufacturer or the FAA; and

(16) Aircraft components or systems that result in taking emergency actions during flight (except action to shut-down an engine).

(b) For the purpose of this section, *during flight* means the period from the moment the aircraft leaves the surface of the earth on takeoff until it touches down on landing.

(c) In addition to the reports required by paragraph (a) of this section, each certificate holder shall report any other failure, malfunction, or defect in an aircraft that occurs or is detected at any time if, in its opinion, the failure, malfunction, or defect has endangered or may endanger the safe operation of the aircraft.

(d) Each certificate holder shall send each report required by this section, in writing, covering each 24-hour period beginning at 0900 hours local time of each day and ending at 0900 hours local time on the next day to the FAA Flight Standards District Office charged with the overall inspection of the certificate holder. Each report of occurrences during a 24-hour period must be mailed or delivered to that office within the next 72 hours. However, a report that is due on Saturday or Sunday may be mailed or delivered on the following Monday and one that is due on a holiday may be mailed or delivered on the next work day. For aircraft operated in areas where mail is not collected, reports may be mailed or delivered within 72 hours after the aircraft returns to a point where the mail is collected.

(e) The certificate holder shall transmit the reports required by this section on a form and in a manner prescribed by the Administrator, and shall include as much of the following as is available:

(1) The type and identification number of the aircraft.

(2) The name of the operator.

(3) The date.

(4) The nature of the failure, malfunction, or defect.

(5) Identification of the part and system involved, including available information pertaining

to type designation of the major component and time since last overhaul, if known.

(6) Apparent cause of the failure, malfunction or defect (e.g., wear, crack, design deficiency, or personnel error).

(7) Other pertinent information necessary for more complete identification, determination of seriousness, or corrective action.

(f) A certificate holder that is also the holder of a type certificate (including a supplemental type certificate), a Parts Manufacturer Approval, or a Technical Standard Order Authorization, or that is the licensee of a type certificate need not report a failure, malfunction, or defect under this section if the failure, malfunction, or defect has been reported by it under § 21.3 or § 37.17 of this chapter or under the accident reporting provisions of part 830 of the regulations of the National Transportation Safety Board.

(g) No person may withhold a report required by this section even though all information required by this section is not available.

(h) When the certificate holder gets additional information, including information from the manufacturer or other agency, concerning a report required by this section, it shall expeditiously submit it as a supplement to the first report and reference the date and place of submission of the first report.

§ 135.417 Mechanical interruption summary report.

Each certificate holder shall mail or deliver, before the end of the 10th day of the following month, a summary report of the following occurrences in multiengine aircraft for the preceding month to the certificate-holding district office:

(a) Each interruption to a flight, unscheduled change of aircraft en route, or unscheduled stop or diversion from a route, caused by known or suspected mechanical difficulties or malfunctions that are not required to be reported under § 135.415.

(b) The number of propeller featherings in flight, listed by type of propeller and engine and aircraft on which it was installed. Propeller featherings for training, demonstration, or flight check purposes need not be reported.

[Docket No. 16097, 43 FR 46783, Oct. 10, 1978; as amended by Amdt. 135–60, 61 FR 2616, Jan. 26, 1996]

§ 135.419 Approved aircraft inspection program.

(a) Whenever the Administrator finds that the aircraft inspections required or allowed under part 91 of this chapter are not adequate to meet this part, or upon application by a certificate holder, the Administrator may amend the certificate

holder's operations specifications under § 135.17, to require or allow an approved aircraft inspection program for any make and model aircraft of which the certificate holder has the exclusive use of at least one aircraft (as defined in § 135.25(b)).

(b) A certificate holder who applies for an amendment of its operations specifications to allow an approved aircraft inspection program must submit that program with its application for approval by the Administrator.

(c) Each certificate holder who is required by its operations specifications to have an approved aircraft inspection program shall submit a program for approval by the Administrator within 30 days of the amendment of its operations specifications or within any other period that the Administrator may prescribe in the operations specifications.

(d) The aircraft inspection program submitted for approval by the Administrator must contain the following:

(1) Instructions and procedures for the conduct of aircraft inspections (which must include necessary tests and checks), setting forth in detail the parts and areas of the airframe, engines, propellers, rotors, and appliances, including emergency equipment, that must be inspected.

(2) A schedule for the performance of the aircraft inspections under paragraph (d)(1) of this section expressed in terms of the time in service, calendar time, number of system operations, or any combination of these.

(3) Instructions and procedures for recording discrepancies found during inspections and correction or deferral of discrepancies including form and disposition of records.

(e) After approval, the certificate holder shall include the approved aircraft inspection program in the manual required by § 135.21.

(f) Whenever the Administrator finds that revisions to an approved aircraft inspection program are necessary for the continued adequacy of the program, the certificate holder shall, after notification by the Administrator, make any changes in the program found by the Administrator to be necessary. The certificate holder may petition the Administrator to reconsider the notice to make any changes in a program. The petition must be filed with the representatives of the Administrator assigned to it within 30 days after the certificate holder receives the notice. Except in the case of an emergency requiring immediate action in the interest of safety, the filing of the petition stays the notice pending a decision by the Administrator.

(g) Each certificate holder who has an approved aircraft inspection program shall have each aircraft that is subject to the program inspected in accordance with the program.

(h) The registration number of each aircraft that is subject to an approved aircraft inspection program must be included in the operations specifications of the certificate holder.

§ 135.421 Additional maintenance requirements.

(a) Each certificate holder who operates an aircraft type certificated for a passenger seating configuration, excluding any pilot seat, of nine seats or less, must comply with the manufacturer's recommended maintenance programs, or a program approved by the Administrator, for each aircraft engine, propeller, rotor, and each item of emergency equipment required by this chapter.

(b) For the purpose of this section, a manufacturer's maintenance program is one which is contained in the maintenance manual or maintenance instructions set forth by the manufacturer as required by this chapter for the aircraft, aircraft engine, propeller, rotor or item of emergency equipment.

(c) For each single engine aircraft to be used in passenger-carrying IFR operations, each certificate holder must incorporate into its maintenance program either:

(1) the manufacturer's recommended engine trend monitoring program, which includes an oil analysis, if appropriate, or

(2) an FAA approved engine trend monitoring program that includes an oil analysis at each 100 hour interval or at the manufacturer's suggested interval, whichever is more frequent.

(d) For single engine aircraft to be used in passenger-carrying IFR operations, written maintenance instructions containing the methods, techniques, and practices necessary to maintain the equipment specified in §§ 135.105, and 135.163 (f) and (h) are required.

(e) No certificate holder may operate a single engine aircraft under IFR, carrying passengers, unless the certificate holder records and maintains in the engine maintenance records the results of each test, observation, and inspection required by the applicable engine trend monitoring program specified in (c)(1) and (c)(2) of this section.

[Docket No. 16097, 43 FR 46783, Oct. 10, 1978; as amended by Amdt. 135–70, 62 FR 42374, Aug. 6, 1997]

§ 135.423 Maintenance, preventive maintenance, and alteration organization.

(a) Each certificate holder that performs any of its maintenance (other than required inspections), preventive maintenance, or alterations, and each person with whom it arranges for the performance of that work, must have an organization adequate to perform the work.

(b) Each certificate holder that performs any inspections required by its manual under § 135.427(b)(2) or (3), (in this subpart referred to as *required inspections*), and each person with whom it arranges for the performance of that work, must have an organization adequate to perform that work.

(c) Each person performing required inspections in addition to other maintenance, preventive maintenance, or alterations, shall organize the performance of those functions so as to separate the required inspection functions from the other maintenance, preventive maintenance, and alteration functions. The separation shall be below the level of administrative control at which overall responsibility for the required inspection functions and other maintenance, preventive maintenance, and alteration functions is exercised.

§ 135.425 Maintenance, preventive maintenance, and alteration programs.

Each certificate holder shall have an inspection program and a program covering other maintenance, preventive maintenance, and alterations, that ensures that—

(a) Maintenance, preventive maintenance, and alterations performed by it, or by other persons, are performed under the certificate holder's manual;

(b) Competent personnel and adequate facilities and equipment are provided for the proper performance of maintenance, preventive maintenance, and alterations; and

(c) Each aircraft released to service is airworthy and has been properly maintained for operation under this part.

§ 135.427 Manual requirements.

(a) Each certificate holder shall put in its manual the chart or description of the certificate holder's organization required by § 135.423 and a list of persons with whom it has arranged for the performance of any of its required inspections, other maintenance, preventive maintenance, or alterations, including a general description of that work.

(b) Each certificate holder shall put in its manual the programs required by § 135.425 that must be followed in performing maintenance, preventive maintenance, and alterations of that certificate holder's aircraft, including airframes, aircraft engines, propellers, rotors, appliances, emergency equipment, and parts, and must include at least the following:

(1) The method of performing routine and non-routine maintenance (other than required inspections), preventive maintenance, and alterations.

(2) A designation of the items of maintenance and alteration that must be inspected (required inspections) including at least those that could result in a failure, malfunction, or defect endangering the safe operation of the aircraft, if not performed properly or if improper parts or materials are used.

(3) The method of performing required inspections and a designation by occupational title of personnel authorized to perform each required inspection.

(4) Procedures for the reinspection of work performed under previous required inspection findings (*buy-back procedures*).

(5) Procedures, standards, and limits necessary for required inspections and acceptance or rejection of the items required to be inspected and for periodic inspection and calibration of precision tools, measuring devices, and test equipment.

(6) Procedures to ensure that all required inspections are performed.

(7) Instructions to prevent any person who performs any item of work from performing any required inspection of that work.

(8) Instructions and procedures to prevent any decision of an inspector regarding any required inspection from being countermanded by persons other than supervisory personnel of the inspection unit, or a person at the level of administrative control that has overall responsibility for the management of both the required inspection functions and the other maintenance, preventive maintenance, and alterations functions.

(9) Procedures to ensure that required inspections, other maintenance, preventive maintenance, and alterations that are not completed as a result of work interruptions are properly completed before the aircraft is released to service.

(c) Each certificate holder shall put in its manual a suitable system (which may include a coded system) that provides for the retention of the following information —

(1) A description (or reference to data acceptable to the Administrator) of the work performed;

(2) The name of the person performing the work if the work is performed by a person outside the organization of the certificate holder; and

(3) The name or other positive identification of the individual approving the work.

(d) For the purposes of this part, the certificate holder must prepare that part of its manual containing maintenance information and instructions, in whole or in part, in printed form or other form, acceptable to the Administrator, that is retrievable in the English language.

[Docket No. 16097, 43 FR 46783, Oct. 10, 1978; as amended by Amdt. 135–66, 62 FR 13257, March 19, 1997]

§135.429 Required inspection personnel.

(a) No person may use any person to perform required inspections unless the person performing the inspection is appropriately certificated, properly trained, qualified, and authorized to do so.

(b) No person may allow any person to perform a required inspection unless, at the time, the person performing that inspection is under the supervision and control of an inspection unit.

(c) No person may perform a required inspection if that person performed the item of work required to be inspected.

(d) In the case of rotorcraft that operate in remote areas or sites, the Administrator may approve procedures for the performance of required inspection items by a pilot when no other qualified person is available, provided —

(1) The pilot is employed by the certificate holder;

(2) It can be shown to the satisfaction of the Administrator that each pilot authorized to perform required inspections is properly trained and qualified;

(3) The required inspection is a result of a mechanical interruption and is not a part of a certificate holder's continuous airworthiness maintenance program;

(4) Each item is inspected after each flight until the item has been inspected by an appropriately certificated mechanic other than the one who originally performed the item of work; and

(5) Each item of work that is a required inspection item that is part of the flight control system shall be flight tested and reinspected before the aircraft is approved for return to service.

(e) Each certificate holder shall maintain, or shall determine that each person with whom it arranges to perform its required inspections maintains, a current listing of persons who have been trained, qualified, and authorized to conduct required inspections. The persons must be identified by name, occupational title and the inspections that they are authorized to perform. The certificate holder (or person with whom it arranges to perform its required inspections) shall give written information to each person so authorized, describing the extent of that person's responsibilities, authorities, and inspectional limitations. The list shall be made available for inspection by the Administrator upon request.

[Docket No. 16097, 43 FR 46783, Oct. 10, 1978; as amended by Amdt. 135–20, 51 FR 40710, Nov. 7, 1986]

135

§ 135.431 Continuing analysis and surveillance.

(a) Each certificate holder shall establish and maintain a system for the continuing analysis and surveillance of the performance and effectiveness of its inspection program and the program covering other maintenance, preventive maintenance, and alterations and for the correction of any deficiency in those programs, regardless of whether those programs are carried out by the certificate holder or by another person.

(b) Whenever the Administrator finds that either or both of the programs described in paragraph (a) of this section does not contain adequate procedures and standards to meet this part, the certificate holder shall, after notification by the Administrator, make changes in those programs requested by the Administrator.

(c) A certificate holder may petition the Administrator to reconsider the notice to make a change in a program. The petition must be filed with the certificate-holding district office within 30 days after the certificate holder receives the notice. Except in the case of an emergency requiring immediate action in the interest of safety, the filing of the petition stays the notice pending a decision by the Administrator.

[Docket No. 16097, 43 FR 46783, Oct. 10, 1978; as amended by Amdt. 135–60, 61 FR 2617, Jan. 26, 1996]

§ 135.433 Maintenance and preventive maintenance training program.

Each certificate holder or a person performing maintenance or preventive maintenance functions for it shall have a training program to ensure that each person (including inspection personnel) who determines the adequacy of work done is fully informed about procedures and techniques and new equipment in use and is competent to perform that person's duties.

§ 135.435 Certificate requirements.

(a) Except for maintenance, preventive maintenance, alterations, and required inspections performed by repair stations certificated under the provisions of subpart C of part 145 of this chapter, each person who is directly in charge of maintenance, preventive maintenance, or alterations, and each person performing required inspections must hold an appropriate airman certificate.

(b) For the purpose of this section, a person *directly in charge* is each person assigned to a position in which that person is responsible for the work of a shop or station that performs maintenance, preventive maintenance, alterations, or other functions affecting airworthiness. A person who is *directly in charge* need not physically observe and direct each worker constantly but must

be available for consultation and decision on matters requiring instruction or decision from higher authority than that of the person performing the work.

§ 135.437 Authority to perform and approve maintenance, preventive maintenance, and alterations.

(a) A certificate holder may perform or make arrangements with other persons to perform maintenance, preventive maintenance, and alterations as provided in its maintenance manual. In addition, a certificate holder may perform these functions for another certificate holder as provided in the maintenance manual of the other certificate holder.

(b) A certificate holder may approve any airframe, aircraft engine, propeller, rotor, or appliance for return to service after maintenance, preventive maintenance, or alterations that are performed under paragraph (a) of this section. However, in the case of a major repair or alteration, the work must have been done in accordance with technical data approved by the Administrator.

§ 135.439 Maintenance recording requirements.

(a) Each certificate holder shall keep (using the system specified in the manual required in § 135.427) the following records for the periods specified in paragraph (b) of this section:

(1) All the records necessary to show that all requirements for the issuance of an airworthiness release under § 135.443 have been met.

(2) Records containing the following information:

(i) The total time in service of the airframe, engine, propeller, and rotor.

(ii) The current status of life-limited parts of each airframe, engine, propeller, rotor, and appliance.

(iii) The time since last overhaul of each item installed on the aircraft which are required to be overhauled on a specified time basis.

(iv) The identification of the current inspection status of the aircraft, including the time since the last inspections required by the inspection program under which the aircraft and its appliances are maintained.

(v) The current status of applicable airworthiness directives, including the date and methods of compliance, and, if the airworthiness directive involves recurring action, the time and date when the next action is required.

(vi) A list of current major alterations and repairs to each airframe, engine, propeller, rotor, and appliance.

(b) Each certificate holder shall retain the records required to be kept by this section for the following periods:

(1) Except for the records of the last complete overhaul of each airframe, engine, propeller, rotor, and appliance the records specified in paragraph (a)(1) of this section shall be retained until the work is repeated or superseded by other work or for one year after the work is performed.

(2) The records of the last complete overhaul of each airframe, engine, propeller, rotor, and appliance shall be retained until the work is superseded by work of equivalent scope and detail.

(3) The records specified in paragraph (a)(2) of this section shall be retained and transferred with the aircraft at the time the aircraft is sold.

(c) The certificate holder shall make all maintenance records required to be kept by this section available for inspection by the Administrator or any representative of the National Transportation Safety Board.

[Docket No. 16097, 43 FR 46783, Oct. 10, 1978; 43 FR 49975, Oct. 26, 1978]

§ 135.441 Transfer of maintenance records.

Each certificate holder who sells a United States registered aircraft shall transfer to the purchaser, at the time of the sale, the following records of that aircraft, in plain language form or in coded form which provides for the preservation and retrieval of information in a manner acceptable to the Administrator:

(a) The records specified in § 135.439(a)(2).

(b) The records specified in § 135.439(a)(1) which are not included in the records covered by paragraph (a) of this section, except that the purchaser may allow the seller to keep physical custody of such records. However, custody of records by the seller does not relieve the purchaser of its responsibility under § 135.439(c) to make the records available for inspection by the Administrator or any representative of the National Transportation Safety Board.

§ 135.443 Airworthiness release or aircraft log entry.

(a) No certificate holder may operate an aircraft after maintenance, preventive maintenance, or alterations are performed on the aircraft unless the certificate holder prepares, or causes the person with whom the certificate holder arranges for the performance of the maintenance, preventive maintenance, or alterations, to prepare—

(1) An airworthiness release; or

(2) An appropriate entry in the aircraft maintenance log.

(b) The airworthiness release or log entry required by paragraph (a) of this section must—

(1) Be prepared in accordance with the procedure in the certificate holder's manual;

(2) Include a certification that—

(i) The work was performed in accordance with the requirements of the certificate holder's manual;

(ii) All items required to be inspected were inspected by an authorized person who determined that the work was satisfactorily completed;

(iii) No known condition exists that would make the aircraft unairworthy;

(iv) So far as the work performed is concerned, the aircraft is in condition for safe operation; and

(3) Be signed by an authorized certificated mechanic or repairman, except that a certificated repairman may sign the release or entry only for the work for which that person is employed and for which that person is certificated.

Notwithstanding paragraph (b)(3) of this section, after maintenance, preventive maintenance, or alterations performed by a repair station certificated under the provisions of subpart C of part 145, the airworthiness release or log entry required by paragraph (a) of this section may be signed by a person authorized by that repair station.

(c) Instead of restating each of the conditions of the certification required by paragraph (b) of this section, the certificate holder may state in its manual that the signature of an authorized certificated mechanic or repairman constitutes that certification.

[Docket No. 16097, 43 FR 46783, Oct. 10, 1978; as amended by Amdt. 135–29, 53 FR 47375, Nov. 22, 1988]

APPENDIX A TO PART 135
ADDITIONAL AIRWORTHINESS STANDARDS FOR 10 OR MORE PASSENGER AIRPLANES

APPLICABILITY

1. *Applicability.* This appendix prescribes the additional airworthiness standards required by § 135.169.

2. *References.* Unless otherwise provided, references in this appendix to specific sections of part 23 of the Federal Aviation Regulations (FAR part 23) are to those sections of part 23 in effect on March 30, 1967.

FLIGHT REQUIREMENTS

3. *General.* Compliance must be shown with the applicable requirements of subpart B of FAR part 23, as supplemented or modified in §§ 4 through 10.

PERFORMANCE

4. *General.*

(a) Unless otherwise prescribed in this appendix, compliance with each applicable performance requirement in sections 4 through 7 must be shown for ambient atmospheric conditions and still air.

(b) The performance must correspond to the propulsive thrust available under the particular ambient atmospheric conditions and the particular flight condition. The available propulsive thrust must correspond to engine power or thrust, not exceeding the approved power or thrust less—

(1) Installation losses; and

(2) The power or equivalent thrust absorbed by the accessories and services appropriate to the particular ambient atmospheric conditions and the particular flight condition.

(c) Unless otherwise prescribed in this appendix, the applicant must select the takeoff, en route, and landing configurations for the airplane.

(d) The airplane configuration may vary with weight, altitude, and temperature, to the extent they are compatible with the operating procedures required by paragraph (e) of this section.

(e) Unless otherwise prescribed in this appendix, in determining the critical engine inoperative takeoff performance, the accelerate-stop distance, takeoff distance, changes in the airplane's configuration, speed, power, and thrust must be made under procedures established by the applicant for operation in service.

(f) Procedures for the execution of balked landings must be established by the applicant and included in the Airplane Flight Manual.

(g) The procedures established under paragraphs (e) and (f) of this section must—

(1) Be able to be consistently executed in service by a crew of average skill;

(2) Use methods or devices that are safe and reliable; and

(3) Include allowance for any time delays in the execution of the procedures, that may reasonably be expected in service.

5. *Takeoff—*

(a) *General.* Takeoff speeds the accelerate-stop distance, the takeoff distance, and the one-engine-inoperative takeoff flight path data (described in paragraphs (b), (c), (d), and (f) of this section), must be determined for—

(1) Each weight, altitude, and ambient temperature within the operational limits selected by the applicant;

(2) The selected configuration for takeoff;

(3) The center of gravity in the most unfavorable position;

(4) The operating engine within approved operating limitations; and

(5) Takeoff data based on smooth, dry, hard-surface runway.

(b) *Takeoff speeds.*

(1) The decision speed V_1 is the calibrated airspeed on the ground at which, as a result of engine failure or other reasons, the pilot is assumed to have made a decision to continue or discontinue the takeoff. The speed V_1 must be selected by the applicant but may not be less than—

(i) $1.10\,V_{S1}$;

(ii) $1.10\,V_{MC}$;

(iii) A speed that allows acceleration to V_1 and stop under paragraph (c) of this section; or

(iv) A speed at which the airplane can be rotated for takeoff and shown to be adequate to safely continue the takeoff, using normal piloting skill, when the critical engine is suddenly made inoperative.

(2) The initial climb out speed V_2 in terms of calibrated airspeed, must be selected by the applicant so as to allow the gradient of climb required in section 6(b)(2), but it must not be less than V_1 or less than $1.2\,V_{S1}$.

(3) Other essential take off speeds necessary for safe operation of the airplane.

(c) *Accelerate-stop distance.*

(1) The accelerate-stop distance is the sum of the distances necessary to—

(i) Accelerate the airplane from a standing start to V_1; and

(ii) Come to a full stop from the point at which V_1 is reached assuming that in the case of engine failure, failure of the critical engine is recognized by the pilot at the speed V_1.

(2) Means other than wheel brakes may be used to determine the accelerate-stop distance if that means is available with the critical engine inoperative and—

(i) Is safe and reliable;

(ii) Is used so that consistent results can be expected under normal operating conditions; and

(iii) Is such that exceptional skill is not required to control the airplane.

(d) *All engines operating takeoff distance.* The all engine operating takeoff distance is the horizontal distance required to takeoff and climb to a height of 50 feet above the takeoff surface under the procedures in FAR 23.51(a).

(e) *One-engine-inoperative takeoff.* Determine the weight for each altitude and temperature within the operational limits established for the airplane, at which the airplane has the capability, after failure of the critical engine at V_1 determined under paragraph (b) of this section, to take off and climb at not less than V_2, to a height 1,000 feet above the takeoff surface and attain the speed and configuration at which compliance is shown with the en route one engine-inoperative gradient of climb specified in section 6(c).

(f) *One-engine-inoperative takeoff flight path data.* The one-engine-inoperative takeoff flight path data consist of takeoff flight paths extending from a standing start to a point in the takeoff at which the airplane reaches a height 1,000 feet above the takeoff surface under paragraph (e) of this section.

6. *Climb—*

(a) *Landing climb: All-engines operating.* The maximum weight must be determined with the airplane in the landing configuration, for each altitude, and ambient temperature within the operational limits established for the airplane, with the most unfavorable center of gravity, and out-of-ground effect in free air, at which the steady gradient of climb will not be less than 3.3 percent, with:

(1) The engines at the power that is available 8 seconds after initiation of movement of the power or thrust controls from the minimum flight idle to the takeoff position.

(2) A climb speed not greater than the approach speed established under section 7 and not less than the greater of $1.05\,V_{MC}$ or $1.10\,V_{S1}$.

(b) *Takeoff climb: one-engine-inoperative.* The maximum weight at which the airplane meets the minimum climb performance specified in paragraphs (1) and (2) of this paragraph must be determined for each altitude and ambient temperature within the operational limits established for the airplane, out of ground effect in free air, with the airplane in the takeoff configuration, with the most unfavorable center of gravity, the critical engine inoperative, the remaining engines at the maximum takeoff power or thrust, and the propeller of the inoperative engine windmilling with the propeller controls in the normal position except that, if an approved automatic feathering system is installed, the propellers may be in the feathered position:

(1) *Takeoff: landing gear extended.* The minimum steady gradient of climb must be measurably positive at the speed V_1.

(2) *Takeoff: landing gear retracted.* The minimum steady gradient of climb may not be less than 2 percent at speed V_2. For airplanes with fixed landing gear this requirement must be met with the landing gear extended.

(c) *En route climb: one-engine-inoperative.* The maximum weight must be determined for each altitude and ambient temperature within the operational limits established for the airplane, at which the steady gradient of climb is not less 1.2 percent at an altitude 1,000 feet above the takeoff surface, with the airplane in the en route configuration, the critical engine inoperative, the remaining engine at the maximum continuous power or thrust, and the most unfavorable center of gravity.

7. *Landing.*

(a) The landing field length described in paragraph (b) of this section must be determined for

standard atmosphere at each weight and altitude within the operational limits established by the applicant.

(b) The landing field length is equal to the landing distance determined under FAR 23.75(a) divided by a factor of 0.6 for the destination airport and 0.7 for the alternate airport. Instead of the gliding approach specified in FAR 23.75(a)(1), the landing may be preceded by a steady approach down to the 50-foot height at a gradient of descent not greater than 5.2 percent (3°) at a calibrated airspeed not less than $1.3\,V_{S1}$.

TRIM

8. *Trim*

(a) *Lateral and directional trim.* The airplane must maintain lateral and directional trim in level flight at a speed of V_H or V_{MO}/M_{MO}, whichever is lower, with landing gear and wing flaps retracted.

(b) *Longitudinal trim.* The airplane must maintain longitudinal trim during the following conditions, except that it need not maintain trim at a speed greater than V_{MO}/M_{MO}.

(1) In the approach conditions specified in FAR 23.161(c)(3) through (5), except that instead of the speeds specified in those paragraphs, trim must be maintained with a stick force of not more than 10 pounds down to a speed used in showing compliance with section 7 or $1.4\,V_{S1}$ whichever is lower.

(2) In level flight at any speed from V_H or V_{MO}/M_{MO}, whichever is lower, to either V_X or $1.4\,V_{S1}$, with the landing gear and wing flaps retracted.

STABILITY

9. *Static longitudinal stability.*

(a) In showing compliance with FAR 23.175(b) and with paragraph (b) of this section, the airspeed must return to within $\pm 7\frac{1}{2}$ percent of the trim speed.

(b) *Cruise stability.* The stick force curve must have a stable slope for a speed range of ±50 knots from the trim speed except that the speeds need not exceed V_{FC}/M_{FC} or be less than $1.4\,V_{S1}$. This speed range will be considered to begin at the outer extremes of the friction band and the stick force may not exceed 50 pounds with—

(1) Landing gear retracted;

(2) Wing flaps retracted;

(3) The maximum cruising power as selected by the applicant as an operating limitation for turbine engines or 75 percent of maximum continuous power for reciprocating engines except that the power need not exceed that required at V_{MO}/M_{MO};

(4) Maximum takeoff weight; and

(5) The airplane trimmed for level flight with the power specified in paragraph (3) of this paragraph.

V_{FC}/M_{FC} may not be less than a speed midway between V_{MO}/M_{MO} and V_{DF}/M_{DF}, except that, for altitudes where Mach number is the limiting factor, M_{FC} need not exceed the Mach number at which effective speed warning occurs.

(c) *Climb stability (turbopropeller powered airplanes only)*. In showing compliance with FAR 23.175(a), an applicant must, instead of the power specified in FAR 23.175(a)(4), use the maximum power or thrust selected by the applicant as an operating limitation for use during climb at the best rate of climb speed, except that the speed need not be less than 1.4 V_{S1}.

STALLS

10. *Stall warning.* If artificial stall warning is required to comply with FAR 23.207, the warning device must give clearly distinguishable indications under expected conditions of flight. The use of a visual warning device that requires the attention of the crew within the cockpit is not acceptable by itself.

CONTROL SYSTEMS

11. *Electric trim tabs.* The airplane must meet FAR 23.677 and in addition it must be shown that the airplane is safely controllable and that a pilot can perform all the maneuvers and operations necessary to effect a safe landing following any probable electric trim tab runaway which might be reasonably expected in service allowing for appropriate time delay after pilot recognition of the runaway. This demonstration must be conducted at the critical airplane weights and center of gravity positions.

INSTRUMENTS: INSTALLATION

12. *Arrangement and visibility.* Each instrument must meet FAR 23.1321 and in addition:

(a) Each flight, navigation, and powerplant instrument for use by any pilot must be plainly visible to the pilot from the pilot's station with the minimum practicable deviation from the pilot's normal position and line of vision when the pilot is looking forward along the flight path.

(b) The flight instruments required by FAR 23.1303 and by the applicable operating rules must be grouped on the instrument panel and centered as nearly as practicable about the vertical plane of each pilot's forward vision. In addition—

(1) The instrument that most effectively indicates the attitude must be in the panel in the top center position;

(2) The instrument that most effectively indicates the airspeed must be on the panel directly to the left of the instrument in the top center position;

(3) The instrument that most effectively indicates altitude must be adjacent to and directly to the right of the instrument in the top center position; and

(4) The instrument that most effectively indicates direction of flight must be adjacent to and directly below the instrument in the top center position.

13. *Airspeed indicating system.* Each airspeed indicating system must meet FAR 23.1323 and in addition:

(a) Airspeed indicating instruments must be of an approved type and must be calibrated to indicate true airspeed at sea level in the standard atmosphere with a minimum practicable instrument calibration error when the corresponding pitot and static pressures are supplied to the instruments.

(b) The airspeed indicating system must be calibrated to determine the system error, i.e., the relation between IAS and CAS, in flight and during the accelerate-takeoff ground run. The ground run calibration must be obtained between 0.8 of the minimum value of V_1 and 1.2 times the maximum value of V_1, considering the approved ranges of altitude and weight. The ground run calibration is determined assuming an engine failure at the minimum value of V_1.

(c) The airspeed error of the installation excluding the instrument calibration error, must not exceed 3 percent or 5 knots whichever is greater, throughout the speed range from V_{MO} to 1.3 V_{S1} with flaps retracted and from 1.3 V_{S0} to V_{FE} with flaps in the landing position.

(d) Information showing the relationship between IAS and CAS must be shown in the Airplane Flight manual.

14. *Static air vent system.* The static air vent system must meet FAR 23.1325. The altimeter system calibration must be determined and shown in the Airplane Flight Manual.

OPERATING LIMITATIONS AND INFORMATION

15. *Maximum operating limit speed V_{MO}/M_{MO}.* Instead of establishing operating limitations based on V_{NE} and V_{NO}, the applicant must establish a maximum operating limit speed V_{MO}/M_{MO} as follows:

(a) The maximum operating limit speed must not exceed the design cruising speed V_C and must be sufficiently below V_D/M_D or V_{DF}/M_{DF} to make it highly improbable that the latter speeds will be inadvertently exceeded in flight.

(b) The speed V_{MO} must not exceed 0.8 V_D/M_D or 0.8 V_{DF}/M_{DF} unless flight demonstrations involving upsets as specified by the Administrator indicates a lower speed margin will not result in speeds exceeding V_D/M_D or V_{DF}. Atmospheric variations, horizontal gusts, system and equipment errors, and airframe production variations are taken into account.

16. *Minimum flight crew.* In addition to meeting FAR 23.1523, the applicant must establish the minimum number and type of qualified flight crew personnel sufficient for safe operation of the airplane considering—

(a) Each kind of operation for which the applicant desires approval;

(b) The workload on each crewmember considering the following:

(1) Flight path control.

(2) Collision avoidance.

(3) Navigation.

(4) Communications.

(5) Operation and monitoring of all essential aircraft systems.

(6) Command decisions; and

(c) The accessibility and ease of operation of necessary controls by the appropriate crewmember during all normal and emergency operations when at the crewmember flight station.

17. *Airspeed indicator.* The airspeed indicator must meet FAR 23.1545 except that, the airspeed notations and markings in terms of V_{NO} and V_{NH} must be replaced by the V_{MO}/M_{MO} notations. The airspeed indicator markings must be easily read and understood by the pilot. A placard adjacent to the airspeed indicator is an acceptable means of showing compliance with FAR 23.1545(c).

AIRPLANE FLIGHT MANUAL

18. *General.* The Airplane Flight Manual must be prepared under FARs 23.1583 and 23.1587, and in addition the operating limitations and performance information in sections 19 and 20 must be included.

19. *Operating limitations.* The Airplane Flight Manual must include the following limitations—

(a) *Airspeed limitations.*

(1) The maximum operating limit speed V_{MO}/M_{MO} and a statement that this speed limit may not be deliberately exceeded in any regime of flight (climb. cruise, or descent) unless a higher speed is authorized for flight test or pilot training;

(2) If an airspeed limitation is based upon compressibility effects, a statement to this effect and information as to any symptoms the probable behavior of the airplane, and the recommended recovery procedures; and

(3) The airspeed limits, shown in terms of V_{MO}/M_{MO} instead of V_{NO} and V_{NE}.

(b) *Takeoff weight limitations.* The maximum takeoff weight for each airport elevation, ambient temperature, and available takeoff runway length within the range selected by the applicant may not exceed the weight at which—

(1) The all-engine-operating takeoff distance determined under section 5(b) or the accelerate-stop distance determined under section 5(c), whichever is greater, is equal to the available runway length;

(2) The airplane complies with the one-engine-inoperative takeoff requirements specified in section 5(e); and

(3) The airplane complies with the one-engine-inoperative takeoff and en route climb requirements specified in sections 6 (b) and (c).

(c) *Landing weight limitations.* The maximum landing weight for each airport elevation (standard temperature) and available landing runway length, within the range selected by the applicant. This weight may not exceed the weight at which the landing field length determined under section 7(b) is equal to the available runway length. In showing compliance with this operating limitation, it is acceptable to assume that the landing weight at the destination will be equal to the takeoff weight reduced by the normal consumption of fuel and oil en route.

20. *Performance information.* The Airplane Flight Manual must contain the performance information determined under the performance requirements of this appendix. The information must include the following:

(a) Sufficient information so that the takeoff weight limits specified in section 19(b) can be determined for all temperatures and altitudes within the operation limitations selected by the applicant.

(b) The conditions under which the performance information was obtained, including the airspeed at the 50-foot height used to determine landing distances.

(c) The performance information (determined by extrapolation and computed for the range of weights between the maximum landing and takeoff weights) for—

(1) Climb in the landing configuration; and

(2) Landing distance.

(d) Procedure established under section 4 related to the limitations and information required by this section in the form of guidance material including any relevant limitations or information.

(e) An explanation of significant or unusual flight or ground handling characteristics of the airplane.

(f) Airspeeds, as indicated airspeeds, corresponding to those determined for takeoff under section 5(b).

21. *Maximum operating altitudes.* The maximum operating altitude to which operation is allowed, as limited by flight, structural, powerplant, functional, or equipment characteristics, must be specified in the Airplane Flight Manual.

22. *Stowage provision for airplane flight manual.* Provision must be made for stowing the Airplane Flight Manual in a suitable fixed container which is readily accessible to the pilot.

23. *Operating procedures.* Procedures for restarting turbine engines in flight (including the effects of altitude) must be set forth in the Airplane Flight Manual.

AIRFRAME REQUIREMENTS
FLIGHT LOADS

24. *Engine torque.*

(a) Each turbopropeller engine mount and its supporting structure must be designed for the torque effects of:

(1) The conditions in FAR 23.361(a).

(2) The limit engine torque corresponding to takeoff power and propeller speed multiplied by a factor accounting for propeller control system malfunction, including quick feathering action, simultaneously with 1g level flight loads. In the absence of a rational analysis, a factor of 1.6 must be used.

(b) The limit torque is obtained by multiplying the mean torque by a factor of 1.25.

25. *Turbine engine gyroscopic loads.* Each turbopropeller engine mount and its supporting structure must be designed for the gyroscopic loads that result, with the engines at maximum continuous r.p.m., under either—

(a) The conditions in FARs 23.351 and 23.423; or

(b) All possible combinations of the following:

(1) A yaw velocity of 2.5 radians per second.

(2) A pitch velocity of 1.0 radians per second.

(3) A normal load factor of 2.5.

(4) Maximum continuous thrust.

26. *Unsymmetrical loads due to engine failure.*

(a) Turbopropeller powered airplanes must be designed for the unsymmetrical loads resulting from the failure of the critical engine including the following conditions in combination with a single malfunction of the propeller drag limiting system, considering the probable pilot corrective action on the flight controls:

(1) At speeds between V_{MO} and V_D, the loads resulting from power failure because of fuel flow interruption are considered to
be limit loads.

(2) At speeds between V_{MO} and V_C, the loads resulting from the disconnection of the engine compressor from the turbine or from loss of the turbine blades are considered to be ultimate loads.

(3) The time history of the thrust decay and drag buildup occurring as a result of the prescribed engine failures must be substantiated by test or other data applicable to the particular engine-propeller combination.

(4) The timing and magnitude of the probable pilot corrective action must be conservatively esti-

mated, considering the characteristics of the particular engine-propeller-airplane combination.

(b) Pilot corrective action may be assumed to be initiated at the time maximum yawing velocity is reached, but not earlier than 2 seconds after the engine failure. The magnitude of the corrective action may be based on the control forces in FAR 23.397 except that lower forces may be assumed where it is shown by analysis or test that these forces can control the yaw and roll resulting from the prescribed engine failure conditions.

GROUND LOADS

27. *Dual wheel landing gear units.* Each dual wheel landing gear unit and its supporting structure must be shown to comply with the following:

(a) *Pivoting.* The airplane must be assumed to pivot about one side of the main gear with the brakes on that side locked. The limit vertical load factor must be 1.0 and the coefficient of friction 0.8. This condition need apply only to the main gear and its supporting structure.

(b) *Unequal tire inflation.* A 60–40 percent distribution of the loads established under FAR 23.471 through FAR 23.483 must be applied to the dual wheels.

(c) *Flat tire.*

(1) Sixty percent of the loads in FAR 23.471 through FAR 23.483 must be applied to either wheel in a unit.

(2) Sixty percent of the limit drag and side loads and 100 percent of the limit vertical load established under FARs 23.493 and 23.485 must be applied to either wheel in a unit except that the vertical load need not exceed the maximum vertical load in paragraph (c)(1) of this section.

FATIGUE EVALUATION

28. *Fatigue evaluation of wing and associated structure.* Unless it is shown that the structure, operating stress levels, materials and expected use are comparable from a fatigue standpoint to a similar design which has had substantial satisfactory service experience, the strength, detail design, and the fabrication of those parts of the wing, wing carry through, and attaching structure whose failure would be catastrophic must be evaluated under either—

(a) A fatigue strength investigation in which the structure is shown by analysis, tests, or both to be able to withstand the repeated loads of variable magnitude expected in service, or

(b) A fail-safe strength investigation in which it is shown by analysis, tests, or both that catastrophic failure of the structure is not probable after fatigue, or obvious partial failure, of a principal structural element, and that the remaining structure is able to withstand a static ultimate load factor of 75 percent of the critical limit load factor at

V_C. These loads must be multiplied by a factor of 1.15 unless the dynamic effects of failure under static load are otherwise considered.

DESIGN AND CONSTRUCTION

29. *Flutter.* For multiengine turbopropeller powered airplanes, a dynamic evaluation must be made and must include—

(a) The significant elastic, inertia, and aerodynamic forces associated with the rotations and displacements of the plane of the propeller; and

(b) Engine-propeller-nacelle stiffness and damping variations appropriate to the particular configuration.

LANDING GEAR

30. *Flap operated landing gear warning device.* Airplanes having retractable landing gear and wing flaps must be equipped with a warning device that functions continuously when the wing flaps are extended to a flap position that activates the warning device to give adequate warning before landing, using normal landing procedures, if the landing gear is not fully extended and locked. There may not be a manual shut off for this warning device. The flap position sensing unit may be installed at any suitable location. The system for this device may use any part of the system (including the aural warning device) provided for other landing gear warning devices.

PERSONNEL AND CARGO ACCOMMODATIONS

31. *Cargo and baggage compartments.* Cargo and baggage compartments must be designed to meet FAR 23.787 (a) and (b), and in addition means must be provided to protect passengers from injury by the contents of any cargo or baggage compartment when the ultimate forward inertia force is 9g.

32. *Doors and exits.* The airplane must meet FAR 23.783 and FAR 23.807 (a)(3), (b), and (c), and in addition:

(a) There must be a means to lock and safeguard each external door and exit against opening in flight either inadvertently by persons, or as a result of mechanical failure. Each external door must be operable from both the inside and the outside.

(b) There must be means for direct visual inspection of the locking mechanism by crewmembers to determine whether external doors and exits, for which the initial opening movement is outward, are fully locked. In addition, there must be a visual means to signal to crewmembers when normally used external doors are closed and fully locked.

(c) The passenger entrance door must qualify as a floor level emergency exit. Each additional required emergency exit except floor level exits must be located over the wing or must be provided with acceptable means to assist the occupants in descending to the ground. In addition to the passenger entrance door:

(1) For a total seating capacity of 15 or less, an emergency exit as defined in FAR 23.807(b) is required on each side of the cabin.

(2) For a total seating capacity of 16 through 23, three emergency exits as defined in FAR 23.807(b) are required with one on the same side as the door and two on the side opposite the door.

(d) An evacuation demonstration must be conducted utilizing the maximum number of occupants for which certification is desired. It must be conducted under simulated night conditions utilizing only the emergency exits on the most critical side of the aircraft. The participants must be representative of average airline passengers with no previous practice or rehearsal for the demonstration. Evacuation must be completed within 90 seconds.

(e) Each emergency exit must be marked with the word "Exit" by a sign which has white letters 1 inch high on a red background 2 inches high, be self-illuminated or independently internally electrically illuminated, and have a minimum luminescence (brightness) of at least 160 microlamberts. The colors may be reversed if the passenger compartment illumination is essentially the same.

(f) Access to window type emergency exits must not be obstructed by seats or seat backs.

(g) The width of the main passenger aisle at any point between seats must equal or exceed the values in the following table:

Total seating capacity	Minimum main passenger aisle width	
	Less than 25 inches from floor	25 inches and more from floor
10 through 23	9 inches	15 inches

MISCELLANEOUS

33. *Lightning strike protection.* Parts that are electrically insulated from the basic airframe must be connected to it through lightning arrestors unless a lightning strike on the insulated part—

(a) Is improbable because of shielding by other parts; or

(b) Is not hazardous.

34. *Ice protection.* If certification with ice protection provisions is desired, compliance with the following must be shown:

(a) The recommended procedures for the use of the ice protection equipment must be set forth in the Airplane Flight Manual.   •

(b) An analysis must be performed to establish, on the basis of the airplane's operational needs, the adequacy of the ice protection system for the various components of the airplane. In addition,

135

tests of the ice protection system must be conducted to demonstrate that the airplane is capable of operating safely in continuous maximum and intermittent maximum icing conditions as described in Appendix C of part 25 of this chapter.

(c) Compliance with all or portions of this section may be accomplished by reference, where applicable because of similarity of the designs, to analysis and tests performed by the applicant for a type certificated model.

35. *Maintenance information.* The applicant must make available to the owner at the time of delivery of the airplane the information the applicant considers essential for the proper maintenance of the airplane. That information must include the following:

(a) Description of systems, including electrical, hydraulic, and fuel controls.

(b) Lubrication instructions setting forth the frequency and the lubricants and fluids which are to be used in the various systems.

(c) Pressures and electrical loads applicable to the various systems.

(d) Tolerances and adjustments necessary for proper functioning.

(e) Methods of leveling, raising, and towing.

(f) Methods of balancing control surfaces.

(g) Identification of primary and secondary structures.

(h) Frequency and extent of inspections necessary to the proper operation of the airplane.

(i) Special repair methods applicable to the airplane.

(j) Special inspection techniques, such as X-ray, ultrasonic, and magnetic particle inspection.

(k) List of special tools.

PROPULSION

GENERAL

36. *Vibration characteristics.* For turbopropeller powered airplanes, the engine installation must not result in vibration characteristics of the engine exceeding those established during the type certification of the engine.

37. *In flight restarting of engine.* If the engine on turbopropeller powered airplanes cannot be restarted at the maximum cruise altitude, a determination must be made of the altitude below which restarts can be consistently accomplished. Restart information must be provided in the Airplane Flight Manual.

38. *Engines.*

(a) *For turbopropeller powered airplanes.* The engine installation must comply with the following:

(1) *Engine isolation.* The powerplants must be arranged and isolated from each other to allow operation, in at least one configuration, so that the failure or malfunction of any engine, or of any system that can affect the engine, will not—

(i) Prevent the continued safe operation of the remaining engines; or

(ii) Require immediate action by any crewmember for continued safe operation.

(2) *Control of engine rotation.* There must be a means to individually stop and restart the rotation of any engine in flight except that engine rotation need not be stopped if continued rotation could not jeopardize the safety of the airplane. Each component of the stopping and restarting system on the engine side of the firewall, and that might be exposed to fire, must be at least fire resistant. If hydraulic propeller feathering systems are used for this purpose, the feathering lines must be at least fire resistant under the operating conditions that may be expected to exist during feathering.

(3) *Engine speed and gas temperature control devices.* The powerplant systems associated with engine control devices, systems, and instrumentation must provide reasonable assurance that those engine operating limitations that adversely affect turbine rotor structural integrity will not be exceeded in service.

(b) *For reciprocating engine powered airplanes.* To provide engine isolation, the powerplants must be arranged and isolated from each other to allow operation, in at least one configuration, so that the failure or malfunction of any engine, or of any system that can affect that engine, will not—

(1) Prevent the continued safe operation of the remaining engines: or

(2) Require immediate action by any crewmember for continued safe operation.

39. *Turbopropeller reversing systems.*

(a) Turbopropeller reversing systems intended for ground operation must be designed so that no single failure or malfunction of the system will result in unwanted reverse thrust under any expected operating condition. Failure of structural elements need not be considered if the probability of this kind of failure is extremely remote.

(b) Turbopropeller reversing systems intended for in flight use must be designed so that no unsafe condition will result during normal operation of the system, or from any failure (or reasonably likely combination of failures) of the reversing system, under any anticipated condition of operation of the airplane. Failure of structural elements need not be considered if the probability of this kind of failure is extremely remote.

(c) Compliance with this section may be shown by failure analysis, testing, or both for propeller systems that allow propeller blades to move from the flight low-pitch position to a position that is substantially less than that at the normal flight low-pitch stop position. The analysis may include or be supported by the analysis made to show compliance with the type certification of the propeller and associated installation components.

Credit will be given for pertinent analysis and testing completed by the engine and propeller manufacturers.

40. *Turbopropeller drag-limiting systems.* Turbopropeller drag-limiting systems must be designed so that no single failure or malfunction of any of the systems during normal or emergency operation results in propeller drag in excess of that for which the airplane was designed. Failure of structural elements of the drag-limiting systems need not be considered if the probability of this kind of failure is extremely remote.

41. *Turbine engine powerplant operating characteristics.* For turbopropeller powered airplanes, the turbine engine powerplant operating characteristics must be investigated in flight to determine that no adverse characteristics (such as stall, surge, or flameout) are present to a hazardous degree, during normal and emergency operation within the range of operating limitations of the airplane and of the engine.

42. *Fuel flow.*

(a) For turbopropeller powered airplanes —

(1) The fuel system must provide for continuous supply of fuel to the engines for normal operation without interruption due to depletion of fuel in any tank other than the main tank; and

(2) The fuel flow rate for turbopropeller engine fuel pump systems must not be less than 125 percent of the fuel flow required to develop the standard sea level atmospheric conditions takeoff power selected and included as an operating limitation in the Airplane Flight Manual.

(b) For reciprocating engine powered airplanes, it is acceptable for the fuel flow rate for each pump system (main and reserve supply) to be 125 percent of the takeoff fuel consumption of the engine.

FUEL SYSTEM COMPONENTS

43. *Fuel pumps.* For turbopropeller powered airplanes, a reliable and independent power source must be provided for each pump used with turbine engines which do not have provisions for mechanically driving the main pumps. It must be demonstrated that the pump installations provide a reliability and durability equivalent to that in FAR 23.991(a).

44. *Fuel strainer or filter.* For turbopropeller powered airplanes, the following apply:

(a) There must be a fuel strainer or filter between the tank outlet and the fuel metering device of the engine. In addition, the fuel strainer or filter must be —

(1) Between the tank outlet and the engine-driven positive displacement pump inlet, if there is an engine-driven positive displacement pump;

(2) Accessible for drainage and cleaning and, for the strainer screen, easily removable; and

(3) Mounted so that its weight is not supported by the connecting lines or by the inlet or outlet connections of the strainer or filter itself.

(b) Unless there are means in the fuel system to prevent the accumulation of ice on the filter, there must be means to automatically maintain the fuel-flow if ice-clogging of the filter occurs; and

(c) The fuel strainer or filter must be of adequate capacity (for operating limitations established to ensure proper service) and of appropriate mesh to insure proper engine operation, with the fuel contaminated to a degree (for particle size and density) that can be reasonably expected in service. The degree of fuel filtering may not be less than that established for the engine type certification.

45. *Lightning strike protection.* Protection must be provided against the ignition of flammable vapors in the fuel vent system due to lightning strikes.

COOLING

46. *Cooling test procedures for turbopropeller powered airplanes.*

(a) Turbopropeller powered airplanes must be shown to comply with FAR 23.1041 during takeoff, climb, en route, and landing stages of flight that correspond to the applicable performance requirements. The cooling tests must be conducted with the airplane in the configuration, and operating under the conditions that are critical relative to cooling during each stage of flight. For the cooling tests a temperature is "stabilized" when its rate of change is less than 2°F per minute.

(b) Temperatures must be stabilized under the conditions from which entry is made into each stage of flight being investigated unless the entry condition is not one during which component and engine fluid temperatures would stabilize, in which case, operation through the full entry condition must be conducted before entry into the stage of flight being investigated to allow temperatures to reach their natural levels at the time of entry. The takeoff cooling test must be preceded by a period during which the powerplant component and engine fluid temperatures are stabilized with the engines at ground idle.

(c) Cooling tests for each stage of flight must be continued until —

(1) The component and engine fluid temperatures stabilize;

(2) The stage of flight is completed; or

(3) An operating limitation is reached.

INDUCTION SYSTEM

47. *Air induction.* For turbopropeller powered airplanes —

(a) There must be means to prevent hazardous quantities of fuel leakage or overflow from drains, vents, or other components of flammable fluid systems from entering the engine intake systems; and

(b) The air inlet ducts must be located or protected so as to minimize the ingestion of foreign matter during takeoff, landing, and taxiing.

48. *Induction system icing protection.* For turbopropeller powered airplanes, each turbine engine must be able to operate throughout its flight power range without adverse effect on engine operation or serious loss of power or thrust, under the icing conditions specified in Appendix C of part 25 of this chapter. In addition, there must be means to indicate to appropriate flight crewmembers the functioning of the powerplant ice protection system.

49. *Turbine engine bleed air systems.* Turbine engine bleed air systems of turbopropeller powered airplanes must be investigated to determine—

(a) That no hazard to the airplane will result if a duct rupture occurs. This condition must consider that a failure of the duct can occur anywhere between the engine port and the airplane bleed service; and

(b) That, if the bleed air system is used for direct cabin pressurization, it is not possible for hazardous contamination of the cabin air system to occur in event of lubrication system failure.

EXHAUST SYSTEM

50. *Exhaust system drains.* Turbopropeller engine exhaust systems having low spots or pockets must incorporate drains at those locations. These drains must discharge clear of the airplane in normal and ground attitudes to prevent the accumulation of fuel after the failure of an attempted engine start.

POWERPLANT CONTROLS AND ACCESSORIES

51. *Engine controls.* If throttles or power levers for turbopropeller powered airplanes are such that any position of these controls will reduce the fuel flow to the engine(s) below that necessary for satisfactory and safe idle operation of the engine while the airplane is in flight, a means must be provided to prevent inadvertent movement of the control into this position. The means provided must incorporate a positive lock or stop at this idle position and must require a separate and distinct operation by the crew to displace the control from the normal engine operating range.

52. *Reverse thrust controls.* For turbopropeller powered airplanes, the propeller reverse thrust controls must have a means to prevent their inadvertent operation. The means must have a positive lock or stop at the idle position and must require a separate and distinct operation by the crew to displace the control from the flight regime.

53. *Engine ignition systems.* Each turbopropeller airplane ignition system must be considered an essential electrical load.

54. *Powerplant accessories.* The powerplant accessories must meet FAR 23.1163, and if the continued rotation of any accessory remotely driven by the engine is hazardous when malfunctioning occurs, there must be means to prevent rotation without interfering with the continued operation of the engine.

POWERPLANT FIRE PROTECTION

55. *Fire detector system.* For turbopropeller powered airplanes, the following apply:

(a) There must be a means that ensures prompt detection of fire in the engine compartment. An overtemperature switch in each engine cooling air exit is an acceptable method of meeting this requirement.

(b) Each fire detector must be constructed and installed to withstand the vibration, inertia, and other loads to which it may be subjected in operation.

(c) No fire detector may be affected by any oil, water, other fluids, or fumes that might be present.

(d) There must be means to allow the flight crew to check, in flight, the functioning of each fire detector electric circuit.

(e) Wiring and other components of each fire detector system in a fire zone must be at least fire resistant.

56. *Fire protection, cowling and nacelle skin.* For reciprocating engine powered airplanes, the engine cowling must be designed and constructed so that no fire originating in the engine compartment can enter either through openings or by burn through, any other region where it would create additional hazards.

57. *Flammable fluid fire protection.* If flammable fluids or vapors might be liberated by the leakage of fluid systems in areas other than engine compartments, there must be means to —

(a) Prevent the ignition of those fluids or vapors by any other equipment; or

(b) Control any fire resulting from that ignition.

EQUIPMENT

58. *Powerplant instruments.*

(a) The following are required for turbopropeller airplanes:

(1) The instruments required by FAR 23.1305 (a)(1) through (4), (b)(2) and (4).

(2) A gas temperature indicator for each engine.

(3) Free air temperature indicator.

(4) A fuel flowmeter indicator for each engine.

(5) Oil pressure warning means for each engine.

(6) A torque indicator or adequate means for indicating power output for each engine.

(7) Fire warning indicator for each engine.

(8) A means to indicate when the propeller blade angle is below the low-pitch position corresponding to idle operation in flight.

(9) A means to indicate the functioning of the ice protection system for each engine.

(b) For turbopropeller powered airplanes, the turbopropeller blade position indicator must begin indicating when the blade has moved below the flight low-pitch position.

(c) The following instruments are required for reciprocating engine powered airplanes:

(1) The instruments required by FAR 23.1305.

(2) A cylinder head temperature indicator for each engine.

(3) A manifold pressure indicator for each engine.

Systems and Equipment

General

59. *Function and installation.* The systems and equipment of the airplane must meet FAR 23.1301, and the following:

(a) Each item of additional installed equipment must—

(1) Be of a kind and design appropriate to its intended function;

(2) Be labeled as to its identification, function, or operating limitations, or any applicable combination of these factors, unless misuse or inadvertent actuation cannot create a hazard

(3) Be installed according to limitations specified for that equipment; and

(4) Function properly when installed.

(b) Systems and installations must be designed to safeguard against hazards to the aircraft in the event of their malfunction or failure.

(c) Where an installation, the functioning of which is necessary in showing compliance with the applicable requirements, requires a power supply, that installation must be considered an essential load on the power supply, and the power sources and the distribution system must be capable of supplying the following power loads in probable operation combinations and for probable durations:

(1) All essential loads after failure of any prime mover, power converter, or energy storage device.

(2) All essential loads after failure of any one engine on two-engine airplanes.

(3) In determining the probable operating combinations and durations of essential loads for the power failure conditions described in paragraphs

(1) and (2) of this paragraph, it is permissible to assume that the power loads are reduced in accordance with a monitoring procedure which is consistent with safety in the types of operations authorized.

60. *Ventilation.* The ventilation system of the airplane must meet FAR 23.831, and in addition, for pressurized aircraft, the ventilating air in flight crew and passenger compartments must be free of harmful or hazardous concentrations of gases and vapors in normal operation and in the event of reasonably probable failures or malfunctioning of the ventilating, heating, pressurization, or other systems, and equipment. If accumulation of hazardous quantities of smoke in the cockpit area is reasonably probable, smoke evacuation must be readily accomplished.

Electrical Systems and Equipment

61. *General.* The electrical systems and equipment of the airplane must meet FAR 23.1351, and the following:

(a) *Electrical system capacity.* The required generating capacity, and number and kinds of power sources must—

(1) Be determined by an electrical load analysis; and

(2) Meet FAR 23.1301.

(b) *Generating system.* The generating system includes electrical power sources, main power busses, transmission cables, and associated control, regulation and protective devices. It must be designed so that—

(1) The system voltage and frequency (as applicable) at the terminals of all essential load equipment can be maintained within the limits for which the equipment is designed, during any probable operating conditions;

(2) System transients due to switching, fault clearing, or other causes do not make essential loads inoperative, and do not cause a smoke or fire hazard;

(3) There are means, accessible in flight to appropriate crewmembers, for the individual and collective disconnection of the electrical power sources from the system; and

(4) There are means to indicate to appropriate crewmembers the generating system quantities essential for the safe operation of the system, including the voltage and current supplied by each generator.

62. *Electrical equipment and installation.* Electrical equipment, controls, and wiring must be installed so that operation of any one unit or system of units will not adversely affect the simultaneous operation of any other electrical unit or system essential to the safe operation.

63. *Distribution system.*

(a) For the purpose of complying with this section, the distribution system includes the distribution busses, their associated feeders, and each control and protective device.

(b) Each system must be designed so that essential load circuits can be supplied in the event of reasonably probable faults or open circuits, including faults in heavy current carrying cables.

(c) If two independent sources of electrical power for particular equipment or systems are required under this appendix, their electrical energy supply must be ensured by means such as duplicate electrical equipment, throwover switching, or multichannel or loop circuits separately routed.

64. *Circuit protective devices.* The circuit protective devices for the electrical circuits of the airplane must meet FAR 23.1357, and in addition circuits for loads which are essential to safe operation must have individual and exclusive circuit protection.

APPENDIX B TO PART 135
AIRPLANE FLIGHT RECORDER SPECIFICATIONS

Parameters	Range	Installed system[1] minimum accuracy (to recovered data)	Sampling interval (per second)	Resolution[4] readout
Relative time (from recorded on prior to takeoff)	25 hr minimum	±0.125% per hour	1	1 sec.
Indicated airspeed	V_{SO} to V_D (KIAS)	±5% or ±10 knots, whichever is greater. Resolution 2 knots below 175 KIAS	1	1%[3]
Altitude	−1,000 feet to max cert. alt of A/C	±100 to ±700 feet (see Table 1, TSO C51-a)	1	25 to 150
Magnetic heading	360°	±5°	1	1°
Vertical acceleration	−3g to +6g	±0.2g in addition to ±0.3g maximum datum	4 (or 1 per second where peaks, ref. to 1g are recorded)	0.03g
Longitudinal acceleration	±1.0g	±1.5% max. range excluding datum error of ±5%	2	0.01g
Pitch attitude	100% of usable	±2°	1	0.8°
Roll attitude	±60° or 100% of usable range, which-ever is greater	±2°	1	0.8°
Stabilizer trim position Or	Full range	±3% unless higher uniquely required	1	1%[3]
Pitch control position	Full range	±3% unless higher uniquely required	1	1%[3]
Engine Power, Each Engine				
Fan or N_1 speed or EPR or cockpit indications used for aircraft certification Or	Maximum range	±5%	1	1%[3]
Prop. speed and torque (sample once/sec as close together as practicable)			1 (prop speed), 1 (torque)	
Altitude rate[2] (need depends on altitude resolution)	±8,000 fpm	±10%. Resolution 250 fpm below 12,000 feet indicated	1	250 fpm below 12,000
Angle of attack[2] (need depends on altitude resolution)	−20° to 40° or of usable range	±2°	1	0.8%[3]
Radio transmitter keying (discrete)	On/off		1	
TE flaps (discrete or analog)	Each discrete position (U, D, T/O, AAP) Or		1	
	Analog 0–100% range	±3°	1	1%[3]
LE flaps (discrete or analog)	Each discrete position (U, D, T/O, AAP) Or		1	
	Analog 0–100% range	±3°	1	1%[3]
Thrust reverser, each engine (discrete)	Stowed or full reverse		1	
Spoiler/speedbrake (discrete)	Stowed or out		1	
Autopilot engaged (discrete)	Engaged or disengaged		1	

[1] When data sources are aircraft instruments (except altimeters) of acceptable quality to fly the aircraft the recording system excluding these sensors (but including all other characteristics of the recording system) shall contribute no more than half of the values in this column.

[2] If data from the altitude encoding altimeter (100 ft. resolution) is used, then either one of these parameters should also be recorded. If however, altitude is recorded at a minimum resolution of 25 feet, then these two parameters can be omitted.

[3] Percent of full range.

[4] This column applies to aircraft manufacturing after October 11, 1991.

[Docket No. 25530, 53 FR 26152, July 11, 1988; 53 FR 30906, Aug. 16, 1988; as amended by Amdt. 135-69, 62 FR 38397, July 17, 1997]

APPENDIX C TO PART 135
HELICOPTER FLIGHT RECORDER SPECIFICATIONS

Parameters	Range	Installed system[1] minimum accuracy (to recovered data)	Sampling interval (per second)	Resolution[3] readout
Relative time (from recorded on prior to takeoff)	25 hr minimum	±0.125% per hour	1	1 sec.
Indicated airspeed	V_{MIN} to V_D (KIAS) (minimum airspeed signal attainable with installed pilot-static system)	±5% or ±10 kts, whichever is greater	1	1 kt.
Altitude	−1,000 feet to 20,000 ft pressure altitude	±100 to ±700 ft (see Table 1, TSO C51-a)	1	25 to 150 ft.
Magnetic heading	360°	±5°	1	1°
Vertical acceleration	−3g to +6g	±0.2g in addition to ±0.3g maximum datum	4 (or 1 per second where peaks, ref. to 1g are recorded)	0.05g
Longitudinal acceleration	±1.0g	±1.5% max. range excluding datum error of ±5%	2	0.03g
Pitch attitude	100% of usable range	±2°	1	0.8°
Roll attitude	±60° or 100% of usable range, whichever is greater	±2°	1	0.8°
Altitude rate	±8,000 fpm	±10%. Resolution 250 fpm below 12,000 ft indicated	1	250 fpm below 12,000
Engine Power, Each Engine				
Main rotor speed	Maximum range	±5%	1	1%[2]
Free or power turbine	Maximum range	±5%	1	1%[2]
Engine torque	Maximum range	±5%	1	1%[2]
Flight Control— Hydraulic Pressure				
Primary (discrete)	High/low		1	
Secondary— if applicable (discrete)	High/low		1	
Radio transmitter keying (discrete)	On/off		1	
Autopilot engaged (discrete)	Engaged or disengaged		1	
SAS status—engaged (discrete)	Engaged/ disengaged		1	
SAS fault status (discrete)	Fault/OK		1	
Flight Controls				
Collective	Full range	±3%	2	1%[2]
Pedal position	Full range	±3%	2	1%[2]
Lat. cyclic	Full range	±3%	2	1%[2]
Long. cyclic	Full range	±3%	2	1%[2]
Controllable stabilator position	Full range	±3%	2	1%[2]

[1] When data sources are aircraft instruments (except altimeters) of acceptable quality to fly the aircraft the recording system excluding these sensors (but including all other characteristics of the recording system) shall contribute no more than half of the values in this column.

[2] Percent of full range.

[3] This column applies to aircraft manufactured after October 11, 1991.

[Docket No. 25530, 53 FR 26152, July 11, 1988; 53 FR 30906, Aug. 16, 1988; as amended by Amdt. 135-69, 62 FR 38397, July 17, 1997]

APPENDIX D TO PART 135
AIRPLANE FLIGHT RECORDER SPECIFICATIONS

Parameters	Range	Accuracy sensor input to DFDR readout	Sampling interval (per second)	Resolution[4] readout
Time (GMT or Frame Counter) (range 0 to 4095, sampled 1 per frame)	24 Hrs	±0.125% per hour	0.25 (1 per 4 seconds)	1 sec.
Altitude	−1,000 ft to max certificated altitude of aircraft	±100 to ±700 ft (See Table 1, TSO–C51a)	1	5' to 35'[1]
Airspeed	50 KIAS to V_{SO}, and V_{SO} to 1.2 V_D	±5%, ±3%	1	1 kt.
Heading	360°	±2°	1	0.5°
Normal Acceleration (Vertical)	−3g to +6g	±1% of max range excluding datum error of ±5%	8	0.01g
Pitch Attitude	±75°	±2°	1	0.5°
Roll Attitude	±180°	±2°	1	0.5°
Radio Transmitter Keying	On-Off (Discrete)		1	
Thrust / Power on Each Engine	Full range forward	±2°	1 (per engine)	0.2%[2]
Trailing Edge Flap or Cockpit Control Selection	Full range or each discrete position	±3° or as pilot's indicator	0.5	0.5%[2]
Leading Edge Flap or Cockpit Control Selection	Full range or each discrete position	±3° or as pilot's indicator	0.5	0.5%[2]
Thrust Reverser Position	Stowed, in transit, and reverse (discretion)		1 (per 4 seconds per engine)	
Ground Spoiler Position / Speed Brake Selection	Full range or each discrete position	±2% unless higher accuracy uniquely required	1	0.2%[2]
Marker Beacon Passage	Discrete		1	
Autopilot Engagement	Discrete		1	
Longitudinal Acceleration	±1g	±1.5% max range excluding datum error of ±5%	4	0.01g
Pilot Input and/or Surface Position — Primary Controls (Pitch, Roll, Yaw)[3]	Full Range	±2° unless higher accuracy uniquely required	1	0.2%[2]
Lateral Acceleration	±1g	±1.5% max range excluding datum error of ±5%	4	0.01g
Pitch Trim Position	Full Range	±3% unless higher accuracy uniquely required	1	0.3%[2]
Glideslope Deviation	±400 Microamps	±3%	1	0.3%[2]
Localizer Deviation	±400 Microamps	±3%	1	0.3%[2]
AFCS Mode and Engagement Status	Discrete		1	
Radio Altitude	−20 ft to 2,500 ft	±2 Ft or ±3% whichever is greater below 500 ft and ±5% above 500 ft	1	1 ft + 5%[2] above 500'
Master Warning	Discrete		1	
Main Gear Squat Switch Status	Discrete		1	
Angle of Attack (if recorded directly)	As installed	As installed	2	0.3%[2]
Outside Air Temperature or Total Air Temperature	−50°C to +90°C	±2°C	0.5	0.3°C
Hydraulics, Each System Low Pressure	Discrete		0.5	or 0.5%[2]
Groundspeed	As installed	Most accurate systems installed (IMS equipped aircraft only)	1	0.2%[2]

135

APPENDIX D TO PART 135

AIRPLANE FLIGHT RECORDER SPECIFICATION (*CONTINUED*)

If additional recording capacity is available, recording of the following parameters is recommended. The parameters are listed in order of significance:

Parameters	Range	Accuracy sensor input to DFDR readout	Sampling interval (per second)	Resolution[4] readout
Drift Angle	When available, As installed	As installed	4	
Wind Speed and Direction	When available, As installed	As installed	4	
Latitude and Longitude	When available, As installed	As installed	4	
Brake pressure / Brake pedal position	As installed	As installed	1	
Additional engine parameters:				
EPR	As installed	As installed	1 (per engine)	
N[1]	As installed	As installed	1 (per engine)	
N[2]	As installed	As installed	1 (per engine)	
EGT	As installed	As installed	1 (per engine)	
Throttle Lever Position	As installed	As installed	1 (per engine)	
Fuel Flow	As installed	As installed	1 (per engine)	
TCAS:				
TA	As installed	As installed	1	
RA	As installed	As installed	1	
Sensitivity level (as selected by crew)	As installed	As installed	2	
GPWS (ground proximity warning system)	Discrete		1	
Landing gear or gear selector position	Discrete		0.25 (1 per 4 seconds)	
DME 1 and 2 Distance	0–200 NM	As installed	0.25	1 mi.
Nav 1 and 2 Frequency Selection	Full range	As installed	0.25	

[1] When altitude rate is recorded. Altitude rate must have sufficient resolution and sampling to permit the derivation of altitude to 5 feet.
[2] Percent of full range
[3] For airplanes that can demonstrate the capability of deriving either the control input on control movement (one from the other) for all modes of operation and flight regimes, the "or" applies. For airplanes with non-mechanical control systems (fly-by-wire) the "and" applies. In airplanes with split surfaces, suitable combination of inputs is acceptable in lieu of recording each surface separately.
[4] This column applies to aircraft manufactured after October 11, 1991.

[Docket No. 25530, 53 FR 26153, July 11, 1988; 53 FR 30906, Aug. 16, 1988]

APPENDIX E TO PART 135
HELICOPTER FLIGHT RECORDER SPECIFICATIONS

Parameters	Range	Installed system[1] minimum accuracy (to recovered data)	Sampling interval (per second)	Resolution[2] read out
Time (GMT)	24 Hrs	±0.125% per hour	0.25 (1 per 4 seconds)	1 sec
Altitude	−1,000 ft to max certificated altitude of aircraft	±100 to ±700 ft (see Table 1. TSO C51-a)	1	5' to 30'
Airspeed	As the installed measuring system	±3%	1	1 kt
Heading	360°	±2°	1	0.5°
Normal Acceleration (vertical)	−3g to +6g	±1% of max range excluding datum error of ±5%	8	0.01g
Pitch Attitude	±75°	±2°	2	0.5°
Roll Attitude	±180°	±2°	2	0.5°
Radio Transmitter Keying	On-Off (Discrete)		1	0.25 sec
Power in Each Engine: Free Power Turbine Speed *and* Engine Torque	0–130% (power Turbine Speed) Full range (Torque)	±2%	1 speed 1 torque (per engine)	0.2%[1] to 0.4%[1]
Main Rotor Speed	0–130%	±2%	2	0.3%[1]
Altitude Rate	±6,000 ft/min	As installed	2	0.2%[1]
Pilot input—Primary Controls (Collective, Longitudinal Cyclic, Lateral Cyclic, Pedal)	Full Range	±3%	2	0.5%[1]
Flight Control Hydraulic Pressure Low	Discrete, each circuit		1	
Flight Control Hydraulic Pressure Selector Switch Position, 1st and 2nd stage	Discrete		1	
AFCS Mode and Engagement Status	Discrete (5 bits necessary)		1	
Stability Augmentation System Engage	Discrete		1	
SAS Fault Status	Discrete		0.25	
Main Gearbox Temperature Low	As installed	As installed	0.25	0.5%[1]
Main Gearbox Temperature High	As installed	As installed	0.5	0.5%[1]
Controllable Stabilator Position	Full range ±3%		2	0.4%[1]
Longitudinal Acceleration	±1g	±1.5% max range excluding datum of ±5%	4	0.01g
Lateral Acceleration	±1g	±1.5% max range excluding datum of ±5%		0.01g
Master Warning	Discrete		1	
Nav 1 and 2 Frequency Selection	Full range	As installed	0.25	
Outside Air Temperature	−50°C to +90°C	±2°C	0.5	0.3°C

[1] Percent of full range.
[2] This column applies to aircraft manufactured after October 11, 1991.

[Docket No. 25530, 53 FR 26154, July 11, 1988; 53 FR 30906, Aug. 16, 1988]

135

Appendix F to Part 135
Airplane Flight Recorder Specification

The recorded values must meet the designated range, resolution, and accuracy requirements during dynamic and static conditions. All data recorded must be correlated in time to within one second.

Parameters	Range	Accuracy (sensor input)	Seconds per sampling interval	Resolution	Remarks
1. Time or Relative Times Counts	24 Hrs, 0 to 4095	±0.125% Per Hour	4	1 sec	UTC time preferred when available. Counter increments each 4 seconds of system operation.
2. Pressure Altitude	−1000 ft to max certificated altitude of aircraft. +5000 ft.	±100 to ±700 ft (see table, TSO C124a or TSO C51a)	1	5' to 35'	Data should be obtained from the air data computer when practicable.
3. Indicated airspeed or Calibrated airspeed	50 KIAS or minimum value to Max V_{S0} to 1.2 V_D	±5% and ±3%	1	1 kt	Data should be obtained from the air data computer when practicable.
4. Heading (Primary flight crew reference)	0–360° and Discrete "true" or "mag"	±2°	1	0.5°	When true or magnetic heading can be selected as the primary heading reference, a discrete indicating selection must be recorded.
5. Normal Acceleration (Vertical)	−3g to +6g	±1% of max range excluding datum error of ±5	0.125	0.004g	—
6. Pitch Attitude	±75°	±2°	1 or 0.25 for airplanes operated under §135.152(j)	0.5°	A sampling rate of 0.25 is recommended.
7. Roll Attitude	±180°	±2°	1 or 0.5 for airplanes operated under §135.152(j)	0.5°	A sampling rate of 0.5 is recommended.
8. Manual Radio Transmitter Keying or CVR/DFDR synchronization reference	On-Off (Discrete) None	—	1	—	Preferably each crewmember but one discrete acceptable for all transmission provided the CVR/FDR system complies with TSO C124a CVR synchronization requirements (paragraph 4.2.1 ED-55).
9. Thrust/Power on Each Engine — primary flight crew reference	Full Range Forward	±2%	1 (per engine)	0.2% of full range	Sufficient parameters (e.g. EPR, N1 or Torque, NP) as appropriate to the particular engine be recorded to determine power in forward and reverse thrust, including potential overspeed conditions.
10. Autopilot Engagement	Discrete "on" or "off"	—	1	—	—
11. Longitudinal Acceleration	±1g	±1.5% max. range excluding datum error of ±5%	0.25	0.004g	—

Appendix F to Part 135
Airplane Flight Recorder Specification (Continued)

The recorded values must meet the designated range, resolution, and accuracy requirements during dynamic and static conditions. All data recorded must be correlated in time to within one second.

Parameters	Range	Accuracy (sensor input)	Seconds per sampling interval	Resolution	Remarks
12a. Pitch Control(s) position (non-fly-by-wire systems)	Full Range	±2% Unless Higher Accuracy Uniquely Required	0.5 or 0.25 for airplanes operated under §135.152(i)	0.2% of full range	For airplanes that have a flight control break away capability that allows either pilot to operate the controls independently, record both control inputs. The control inputs may be sampled alternately once per second to produce the sampling interval of 0.5 or 0.25, as applicable.
12b. Pitch Control(s) position (fly-by-wire systems)	Full Range	±2° Unless Higher Accuracy Uniquely Required	0.5 or 0.25 for airplanes operated under §135.152(i)	0.2% of full range	—
13a. Lateral Control position(s) (non-fly-by-wire)	Full Range	±2° Unless Higher Accuracy Uniquely Required	0.5 or 0.25 for airplanes operated under §135.152(i)	0.2% of full range	For airplanes that have a flight control break away capability that allows either pilot to operate the controls independently, record both control inputs. The control inputs may be sampled alternately once per second to produce the sampling interval of 0.5 or 0.25, as applicable.
13b. Lateral Control position(s) (fly-by-wire)	Full Range	±2° Unless Higher Accuracy Uniquely Required	0.5 or 0.25 for airplanes operated under §135.152(i)	0.2% of full range	—
14a. Yaw Control position(s) (non-fly-by-wire)	Full Range	±2° Unless Higher Accuracy Uniquely Required	0.5 or 0.25 for airplanes operated under §135.152(i)	0.2% of full range	For airplanes that have a flight control break away capability that allows either pilot to operate the controls independently, record both control inputs. The control inputs may be sampled alternately once per second to produce the sampling interval of 0.5.
14b. Yaw Control position(s) (fly-by-wire)	Full Range	±2° Unless Higher Accuracy Uniquely Required	0.5	0.2% of full range	—
15. Pitch Control Surface(s) Position	Full Range	±2° Unless Higher Accuracy Uniquely Required	0.5 or 0.25 for airplanes operated under §135.152(i)	0.2% of full range	For airplanes fitted with multiple or split surfaces, a suitable combination of inputs is acceptable in lieu of recording each surface separately. The control surfaces may be sampled alternately to produce the sampling interval of 0.5 or 0.25.

135

Appendix F to Part 135
Airplane Flight Recorder Specification (Continued)

The recorded values must meet the designated range, resolution, and accuracy requirements during dynamic and static conditions. All data recorded must be correlated in time to within one second.

Parameters	Range	Accuracy (sensor input)	Seconds per sampling interval	Resolution	Remarks
16. Lateral Control Surface(s) Position	Full Range	±2° Unless Higher Accuracy Uniquely Required	0.5 or 0.25 for airplanes operated under §135.152(j)	0.2% of full range	A suitable combination of surface position sensors is acceptable in lieu of recording each surface separately. The control surfaces may be sampled alternately to produce the sampling interval of 0.5 or 0.25.
17. Yaw Control Surface(s) Position	Full Range	±2° Unless Higher Accuracy Uniquely Required	0.5	0.2% of full range	For airplanes with multiple or split surfaces, a suitable combination of surface position sensors is acceptable in lieu of recording each surface separately. The control surfaces may be sampled alternately to produce the sampling interval of 0.5.
18. Lateral Acceleration	±1g	±1.5% max. range excluding datum error of ±5%	0.25	0.004g	—
19. Pitch Trim Surface Position	Full Range	±3% Unless Higher Accuracy Uniquely Required	1	0.3% of full range	—
20. Trailing Edge Flap or Cockpit Control Selection	Full Range or Each Position (discrete)	±3° or as Pilot's indicator	2	0.5% of full range	Flap position and cockpit control may each be sampled alternately at 4 second intervals, to give a data point every 2 seconds.
21. Leading Edge Flap or Cockpit Control Selection	Full Range or Each Discrete Position	±3° or as Pilot's indicator and sufficient to determine each discrete position	2	0.5% of full range	Left and right sides, or flap position and cockpit control may each be sampled at 4 second intervals, so as to give a data point every 2 seconds.
22. Each Thrust Reverser Position (or equivalent for propeller airplane)	Stowed, In Transit, and Reverse (Discrete)	—	1 (per engine)	—	Turbo-jet – 2 discretes enable the 3 states to be determined. Turbo-prop – 1 discrete.
23. Ground Spoiler Position or Speed Brake Selection	Full Range or Each Position (discrete)	±2° Unless Higher Accuracy Uniquely Required	1 or 0.5 for airplanes operated under §135.152(j)	0.2% of full range	—
24. Outside Air Temperature or Total Air Temperature	–50°C to +90°C	±2°C	2	0.3°C	—
25. Autopilot/Autothrottle/AFCS Mode and Engagement Status	A suitable combination of discretes	—	1	—	Discretes should show which systems are engaged and which primary modes are controlling the flight path and speed of the aircraft.

Appendix F to Part 135
Airplane Flight Recorder Specification (Continued)

The recorded values must meet the designated range, resolution, and accuracy requirements during dynamic and static conditions. All data recorded must be correlated in time to within one second.

Parameters	Range	Accuracy (sensor input)	Seconds per sampling interval	Resolution	Remarks
26. Radio Altitude	–20 ft to 2,500 ft	±2 ft or ±3% Whichever is Greater Below 500 ft and ±5% Above 500 ft	1	1 ft + 5% above 500 ft	For autoland/category 3 operations. Each radio altimeter should be recorded, but arranged so that at least one is recorded each second.
27. Localizer Deviation, MLS Azimuth, or GPS Latitude Deviation	±400 Microamps or available sensor range as installed ±62°	As installed ±3% recommended	1	0.3% of full range	For autoland/category 3 operations. Each system should be recorded, but arranged so that at least one is recorded each second. It is not necessary to record ILS and MLS at the same time, only the approach aid in use need be recorded.
28. Glideslope Deviation, MLS Elevation, or GPS Vertical Deviation	±400 Microamps or available sensor range as installed 0.9 to +30°	As installed ±3% recommended	1	0.3% of full range	For autoland/category 3 operations. Each system should be recorded, but arranged so that at least one is recorded each second. It is not necessary to record ILS and MLS at the same time, only the approach aid in use need be recorded.
29. Marker Beacon Passage	Discrete "on" or "off"		1	—	A single discrete is acceptable for all markers.
30. Master Warning	Discrete		1	—	Record the master warning and record each "red" warning that cannot be determined from other parameters or from the cockpit voice recorder.
31. Air/ground sensor (primary airplane system reference nose or main gear)	Discrete "air" or "ground"		1 (0.25 recommended)	—	—
32. Angle of Attack (if measured directly)	As installed	As installed	2 or 0.5 for airplanes operated under §135.152(j)	0.3% of full range	If left and right sensors are available, each may be recorded at 4 or 1 second intervals, as appropriate, so as to give a data point at 2 seconds or 0.5 second, as required.
33. Hydraulic Pressure Low, Each System	Discrete or available sensor range, "low" or "normal"	±5%	2	0.5% of full range	—
34. Groundspeed	As installed	Most Accurate Systems Installed	1	0.2% of full range	—
35. GPWS (ground proximity warning system)	Discrete "warning" or "off"		1	—	A suitable combination of discretes unless recorder capacity is limited in which case a single discrete for all modes is acceptable.

135

Appendix F to Part 135
Airplane Flight Recorder Specification (Continued)

The recorded values must meet the designated range, resolution, and accuracy requirements during dynamic and static conditions. All data recorded must be correlated in time to within one second.

Parameters	Range	Accuracy (sensor input)	Seconds per sampling interval	Resolution	Remarks
36. Landing Gear Position or Landing gear cockpit control selection	Discrete	—	4	—	A suitable combination of discretes should be recorded.
37. Drift Angle	As installed	As installed	4	0.1°	—
38. Wind Speed and Direction	As installed	As installed	4	1 knot, and 1.0°	—
39. Latitude and Longitude	As installed	As installed	4	0.002°, or as installed	Provided by the Primary Navigation System Reference. Where capacity permits latitude/longitude resolution should be 0.0002°.
40. Stick shaker and pusher activation	Discrete(s) "on" or "off"	—	1	—	A suitable combination of discretes to determine activation.
41. Windshear Detection	Discrete "warning" or "off"	—	1	—	—
42. Throttle/power lever position	Full Range	±2%	1 for each lever	2% of full range	For airplanes with non-mechanically linked cockpit engine controls.
43. Additional Engine Parameters	As installed	As installed	Each engine, each second	2% of full range	Where capacity permits, the preferred priority is indicated vibration level, N2, EGT, Fuel Flow, Fuel Cut-off lever position and N3, unless engine manufacturer recommends otherwise.
44. Traffic Alert and Collision Avoidance System (TCAS)	Discretes	As installed	1	—	A suitable combination of discretes should be recorded to determine the status of – Combined Control, Vertical Control, Up Advisory, and Down Advisory. (ref. ARINC Characteristic 735 Attachment 6E, TCAS VERTICAL RA DATA OUTPUT WORD.)
45. DME 1 and 2 Distance	0–200 NM	As installed	4	1 NM	1 mile
46. Nav 1 and 2 Selected Frequency	Full Range	As installed	4	—	Sufficient to determine selected frequency.
47. Selected barometric setting	Full Range	±5%	(1 per 64 sec.)	0.2% of full range	—
48. Selected altitude	Full Range	±5%	1	100 ft	—
49. Selected speed	Full Range	±5%	1	1 knot	—

Appendix F to Part 135
Airplane Flight Recorder Specification (Continued)

The recorded values must meet the designated range, resolution, and accuracy requirements during dynamic and static conditions. All data recorded must be correlated in time to within one second.

Parameters	Range	Accuracy (sensor input)	Seconds per sampling interval	Resolution	Remarks
50. Selected Mach	Full Range	±5%	1	.01	—
51. Selected vertical speed	Full Range	±5%	1	100 ft/min	—
52. Selected heading	Full Range	±5%	1	1°	—
53. Selected flight path	Full Range	±5%	1	1°	—
54. Selected decision height	Full Range	±5%	64	1 ft	—
55. EFIS display format	Discrete(s)	—	4	—	Discretes should show the display system status (e.g., off, normal, fail, composite, sector, plan, nav aids, weather radar, range, copy).
56. Multi-function/Engine Alerts Display format	Discrete(s)	—	4	—	Discretes should show the display system status (e.g., off, normal, fail, and the identity of display pages for emergency procedures, need not be recorded.)
57. Thrust command	Full Range	±2%	2	2% of full range	—
58. Thrust target	Full Range	±2%	4	2% of full range	—
59. Fuel quantity in CG trim tank	Full Range	±5%	(1 per 64 sec.)	1% of full range	—
60. Primary Navigation System Reference	Discrete GPS, INS, VOR/DME, MLS, Loran C, Omega, Localizer Glideslope	—	4	—	A suitable combination of discretes to determine the Primary Navigation System reference.
61. Ice Detection	Discrete "ice" or "no ice"	—	4	—	—
62. Engine warning each engine vibration	Discrete	—	1	—	—
63. Engine warning each engine over temp	Discrete	—	1	—	—
64. Engine warning each engine oil pressure low	Discrete	—	1	—	—
65. Engine warning each engine over speed	Discrete	—	1	—	—

Appendix F to Part 135
Airplane Flight Recorder Specification (Continued)

The recorded values must meet the designated range, resolution, and accuracy requirements during dynamic and static conditions. All data recorded must be correlated in time to within one second.

Parameters	Range	Accuracy (sensor input)	Seconds per sampling interval	Resolution	Remarks
66. Yaw Trim Surface Position	Full Range	±3% Unless Higher Accuracy Uniquely Required	2	0.3% of full range	—
67. Roll Trim Surface Position	Full Range	±3% Unless Higher Accuracy Uniquely Required	2	0.3% of full range	—
68. Brake Pressure (left and right)	As installed	±5%	1	—	To determine braking effort applied by pilots or by autobrakes.
69. Brake Pedal Application (left and right)	Discrete or Analog "applied" or "off"	±5% (Analog)	1	—	To determine braking applied by pilots.
70. Yaw or sideslip angle	Full Range	±5%	1	0.5°	—
71. Engine bleed valve position	Discrete "open" or "closed"	—	4	—	—
72. De-icing or anti-icing system selection	Discrete "on" or "off"	—	4	—	—
73. Computed center of gravity	Full Range	±5%	(1 per 64 sec.)	1% of full range	—
74. AC electrical bus status	Discrete "power" or "off"	—	4	—	Each bus.
75. DC electrical bus status	Discrete "power" or "off"	—	4	—	Each bus.
76. APU bleed valve position	Discrete "open" or "closed"	—	4	—	—
77. Hydraulic Pressure (each system)	Full Range	±5%	2	100 psi	—
78. Loss of cabin pressure	Discrete "loss" or "normal"	—	1	—	—
79. Computer failure (critical flight and engine control systems)	Discrete "fail" or "normal"	—	4	—	—
80. Heads-up display (when an information source is installed)	Discrete(s) "on" or "off"	—	4	—	—
81. Para-visual display (when an information source is installed)	Discrete(s) "on" or "off"	—	1	—	—
82. Cockpit trim control input position – pitch	Full Range	±5%	1	0.2% of full range	Where mechanical means for control inputs are not available, cockpit display trim positions should be recorded.

Appendix F to Part 135
Airplane Flight Recorder Specification (Continued)

The recorded values must meet the designated range, resolution, and accuracy requirements during dynamic and static conditions. All data recorded must be correlated in time to within one second.

Parameters	Range	Accuracy (sensor input)	Seconds per sampling interval	Resolution	Remarks
83. Cockpit trim control input position – roll	Full Range	±5%	1	0.2% of full range	Where mechanical means for control inputs are not available, cockpit display trim positions should be recorded.
84. Cockpit trim control input position – yaw	Full Range	±5%	1	0.2% of full range	Where mechanical means for control inputs are not available, cockpit display trim positions should be recorded.
85. Trailing edge flap and cockpit flap control position	Full Range	±5%	2	0.5% of full range	Trailing edge flaps and cockpit flap control position may each be sampled alternately at 4 second intervals to provide a sample each 0.5 second.
86. Leading edge flap and cockpit flap control position	Full Range or Discrete	±5%	1	0.5% of full range	—
87. Ground spoiler position and speed brake selection	Full Range or Discrete	±5%	0.5	0.2% of full range	—
88. All cockpit flight control input forces (control wheel, control column, rudder pedal)	Full Range Control wheel ±70 lbs Control column ±85 lbs Rudder pedal ±165 lbs	±5%	1	0.2% of full range	For fly-by-wire flight control systems, where flight control surface position is a function of the displacement of the control input device only, it is not necessary to record this parameter. For airplanes that have a flight control break away capability that allows either pilot to operate the control independently, record both control force inputs. The control force inputs may be sampled alternately once per 2 seconds to produce the sampling interval of 1.

[Docket No. 28109, 62 FR 38396, July 17, 1997; as amended by Amdt. 135–69, 62 FR 48135, Sept. 12, 1997]

135

PART 137
AGRICULTURAL AIRCRAFT OPERATIONS

Subpart A—General

Authority: 49 U.S.C. 106(g), 40103, 40113, 44701–44702.

Source: Docket No. 1464, 30 FR 8106, June 24, 1965, unless otherwise noted.

Subpart A—General

§ 137.1 Applicability.

(a) This part prescribes rules governing—

(1) Agricultural aircraft operations within the United States; and

(2) The issue of commercial and private agricultural aircraft operator certificates for those operations.

(b) In a public emergency, a person conducting agricultural aircraft operations under this part may, to the extent necessary, deviate from the operating rules of this part for relief and welfare activities approved by an agency of the United States or of a State or local government.

(c) Each person who, under the authority of this section, deviates from a rule of this part shall, within 10 days after the deviation send to the nearest FAA Flight Standards District Office a complete report of the aircraft operation involved, including a description of the operation and the reasons for it.

[Docket No. 1464, 30 FR 8106, June 24, 1965; as amended by Amdt. 137–13, 54 FR 39294, Sept. 25, 1989]

§ 137.3 Definition of terms.

For the purposes of this part—

Agricultural aircraft operation means the operation of an aircraft for the purpose of (1) dispensing any economic poison, (2) dispensing any other substance intended for plant nourishment, soil treatment, propagation of plant life, or pest control, or (3) engaging in dispensing activities directly affecting agriculture, horticulture, or forest preservation, but not including the dispensing of live insects.

Economic poison means (1) any substance or mixture of substances intended for preventing, destroying, repelling, or mitigating any insects, rodents, nematodes, fungi, weeds, and other forms of plant or animal life or viruses, except viruses on or in living man or other animals, which the Secretary of Agriculture shall declare to be a pest, and (2) any substance or mixture of substances intended for use as a plant regulator, defoliant or desiccant.

[Docket No. 1464, 30 FR 8106, June 24, 1965; as amended by Amdt. 137–3, 33 FR 9601, July 2, 1968]

137

Subpart B— Certification Rules

§ 137.11 Certificate required.

(a) Except as provided in paragraphs (c) and (d) of this section, no person may conduct agricultural aircraft operations without, or in violation of, an agricultural aircraft operator certificate issued under this part.

(b) Notwithstanding part 133 of this chapter, an operator may, if he complies with this part, conduct agricultural aircraft operations with a rotorcraft with external dispensing equipment in place without a rotorcraft external-load operator certificate.

(c) A Federal, State, or local government conducting agricultural aircraft operations with public aircraft need not comply with this subpart.

(d) The holder of a rotorcraft external-load operator certificate under part 133 of this chapter conducting an agricultural aircraft operation, involving only the dispensing of water on forest fires by rotorcraft external-load means, need not comply with this subpart.

[Docket No. 1464, 30 FR 8106, June 24, 1965; as amended by Amdt. 137–3, 33 FR 9601, July 2, 1968; Amdt. 137–6, 41 FR 35060, Aug. 19, 1976]

§ 137.15 Application for certificate.

An application for an agricultural aircraft operator certificate is made on a form and in a manner prescribed by the Administrator, and filed with the FAA Flight Standards District Office that has jurisdiction over the area in which the applicant's home base of operations is located.

[Docket No. 1464, 30 FR 8106, June 24, 1965; as amended by Amdt. 137–13, 54 FR 39294, Sept. 25, 1989]

§ 137.17 Amendment of certificate.

(a) An agricultural aircraft operator certificate may be amended—

(1) On the Administrator's own initiative, under section 609 of the Federal Aviation Act of 1958 (49 U.S.C. 1429) and part 13 of this chapter; or

(2) Upon application by the holder of that certificate.

(b) An application to amend an agricultural aircraft operator certificate is submitted on a form and in a manner prescribed by the Administrator. The applicant must file the application with the FAA Flight Standards District Office having jurisdiction over the area in which the applicant's home base of operations is located at least 15 days before the date that it proposes the amendment become effective, unless a shorter filing period is approved by that office.

(c) The Flight Standards District Office grants a request to amend a certificate if it determines that safety in air commerce and the public interest so allow.

(d) Within 30 days after receiving a refusal to amend, the holder may petition the Director, Flight Standards Service, to reconsider the refusal.

[Docket No. 1464, 30 FR 8106, June 24, 1965; as amended by Amdt. 137–9, 43 FR 52206, Nov. 9, 1978; Amdt. 137–11, 45 FR 47838, July 17, 1980; Amdt. 137–13, 54 FR 39294, Sept. 25, 1989]

§ 137.19 Certification requirements.

(a) *General.* An applicant for a private agricultural aircraft operator certificate is entitled to that certificate if he shows that he meets the requirements of paragraphs (b), (d), and (e) of this section. An applicant for a commercial agricultural aircraft operator certificate is entitled to that certificate if he shows that he meets the requirements of paragraphs (c), (d), and (e) of this section. However, if an applicant applies for an agricultural aircraft operator certificate containing a prohibition against the dispensing of economic poisons, that applicant is not required to demonstrate the knowledge required in paragraphs (e)(1)(ii) through (iv) of this section.

(b) *Private operator—pilot.* The applicant must hold a current U.S. private, commercial, or airline transport pilot certificate and be properly rated for the aircraft to be used.

(c) *Commercial operator—pilots.* The applicant must have available the services of at least one person who holds a current U.S. commercial or airline transport pilot certificate and who is properly rated for the aircraft to be used. The applicant himself may be the person available.

(d) *Aircraft.* The applicant must have at least one certificated and airworthy aircraft, equipped for agricultural operation.

(e) *Knowledge and skill tests.* The applicant must show, or have the person who is designated as the chief supervisor of agricultural aircraft operations for him show, that he has satisfactory knowledge and skill regarding agricultural aircraft operations, as described in paragraphs (e)(1) and (2) of this section.

(1) The test of knowledge consists of the following:

(i) Steps to be taken before starting operations, including survey of the area to be worked.

(ii) Safe handling of economic poisons and the proper disposal of used containers for those poisons.

(iii) The general effects of economic poisons and agricultural chemicals on plants, animals, and persons, with emphasis on those normally used in the areas of intended operations; and the precautions to be observed in using poisons and chemicals.

(iv) Primary symptoms of poisoning of persons from economic poisons, the appropriate emergency measures to be taken, and the location of poison control centers.

(v) Performance capabilities and operating limitations of the aircraft to be used.

(vi) Safe flight and application procedures.

(2) The test of skill consists of the following maneuvers that must be shown in any of the aircraft specified in paragraph (d) of this section, and at that aircraft's maximum certificated take-off weight, or the maximum weight established for the special purpose load, whichever is greater:

(i) Short-field and soft-field takeoffs (airplanes and gyroplanes only).

(ii) Approaches to the working area.

(iii) Flare-outs.

(iv) Swath runs.

(v) Pullups and turnarounds.

(vi) Rapid deceleration (quick stops) in helicopters only.

[Docket No. 1464, 30 FR 8106, June 24, 1965; as amended by Amdt. 137–1, 30 FR 15143, Dec. 8, 1965; Amdt. 137–7, 43 FR 22643, May 25, 1978]

§ 137.21 Duration of certificate.

An agricultural aircraft operator certificate is effective until it is surrendered, suspended, or revoked. The holder of an agricultural aircraft operator certificate that is suspended or revoked shall return it to the Administrator.

§ 137.23 Carriage of narcotic drugs, marihuana, and depressant or stimulant drugs or substances.

If the holder of a certificate issued under this part permits any aircraft owned or leased by that holder to be engaged in any operation that the certificate holder knows to be in violation of § 91.19(a) of this chapter, that operation is a basis for suspending or revoking the certificate.

[Docket No. 12035, 38 FR 17493, July 2, 1973; as amended by Amdt. 137–12, 54 FR 34332, Aug. 18, 1989]

Subpart C— Operating Rules

§ 137.29 General.

(a) Except as provided in paragraphs (d) and (e) of this section, this subpart prescribes rules that apply to persons and aircraft used in agricultural aircraft operations conducted under this part.

(b) [Reserved]

(c) The holder of an agricultural aircraft operator certificate may deviate from the provisions of part 91 of this chapter without a certificate of waiver, as authorized in this subpart for dispensing operations, when conducting nondispensing aerial work operations related to agriculture, horticulture, or forest preservation in accordance with the operating rules of this subpart.

(d) Sections 137.31 through 137.35, §§ 137.41, and 137.53 through 137.59 do not apply to persons and aircraft used in agricultural aircraft operations conducted with public aircraft.

(e) Sections 137.31 through 137.35, §§ 137.39, 137.41, 137.51 through 137.59, and subpart D do not apply to persons and rotorcraft used in agricultural aircraft operations conducted by a person holding a certificate under part 133 of this chapter and involving only the dispensing of water on forest fires by rotorcraft external-load means. However, the operation shall be conducted in accordance with—

(1) The rules of part 133 of this chapter governing rotorcraft external-load operations; and

(2) The operating rules of this subpart contained in §§ 137.29, 137.37, and §§ 137.43 through 137.49.

[Docket No. 1464, 30 FR 8106, June 24, 1965; as amended by Amdt. 137–3, 33 FR 9601, July 2, 1968; Amdt. 137–6, 41 FR 35060, Aug. 19, 1976]

§ 137.31 Aircraft requirements.

No person may operate an aircraft unless that aircraft—

(a) Meets the requirements of § 137.19(d); and

(b) Is equipped with a suitable and properly installed shoulder harness for use by each pilot.

§ 137.33 Carrying of certificate.

(a) No person may operate an aircraft unless a facsimile of the agricultural aircraft operator certificate, under which the operation is conducted, is carried on that aircraft. The facsimile shall be presented for inspection upon the request of the Administrator or any Federal, State, or local law enforcement officer.

(b) Notwithstanding part 91 of this chapter, the registration and airworthiness certificates issued for the aircraft need not be carried in the aircraft. However, when those certificates are not carried in the aircraft they shall be kept available for inspection at the base from which the dispensing operation is conducted.

[Docket No. 1464, 30 FR 8106, June 24, 1965; as amended by Amdt. 137–3, 33 FR 9601, July 2, 1968]

§ 137.35 Limitations on private agricultural aircraft operator.

No person may conduct an agricultural aircraft operation under the authority of a private agricultural aircraft operator certificate—

(a) For compensation or hire;

(b) Over a congested area; or

(c) Over any property unless he is the owner or lessee of the property, or has ownership or other property interest in the crop located on that property.

§ 137.37 Manner of dispensing.

No persons may dispense, or cause to be dispensed, from an aircraft, any material or substance in a manner that creates a hazard to persons or property on the surface.

[Docket No. 1464, 30 FR 8106, June 24, 1965; as amended by Amdt. 137–3, 33 FR 9601, July 2, 1968]

§ 137.39 Economic poison dispensing.

(a) Except as provided in paragraph (b) of this section, no person may dispense or cause to be dispensed from an aircraft, any economic poison that is registered with the U.S. Department of Agriculture under the Federal Insecticide, Fungicide, and Rodenticide Act (7 U.S.C. 135–135k)—

(1) For a use other than that for which it is registered;

(2) Contrary to any safety instructions or use limitations on its label; or

(3) In violation of any law or regulation of the United States.

(b) This section does not apply to any person dispensing economic poisons for experimental purposes under—

(1) The supervision of a Federal or State agency authorized by law to conduct research in the field of economic poisons; or

(2) A permit from the U.S. Department of Agriculture issued pursuant to the Federal Insecticide, Fungicide, and Rodenticide Act (7 U.S.C. 135–135k).

[Amdt. 137–2, 31 FR 6686, May 5, 1966]

§ 137.41 Personnel.

(a) *Information.* The holder of an agricultural aircraft operator certificate shall insure that each person used in the holder's agricultural aircraft operation is informed of that person's duties and responsibilities for the operation.

(b) *Supervisors.* No person may supervise an agricultural aircraft operation unless he has met the knowledge and skill requirements of § 137.19(e).

(c) *Pilot-in-command.* No person may act as pilot in command of an aircraft unless he holds a pilot certificate and rating prescribed by § 137.19(b) or (c), as appropriate to the type of operation conducted. In addition, he must demonstrate to the holder of the Agricultural Aircraft Operator Certificate conducting the operation that he has met the knowledge and skill requirements of § 137.19(e). If the holder of that certificate has designated a person under § 137.19(e) to supervise his agricultural aircraft operations the demonstration must be made to the person so designated. However, a demonstration of the knowledge and skill requirement is not necessary for any pilot in command who—

(1) Is, at the time of the filing of an application by an agricultural aircraft operator, working as a pilot in command for that operator; and

(2) Has a record of operation under that applicant that does not disclose any question regarding the safety of his flight operations or his competence in dispensing agricultural materials or chemicals.

§ 137.42 Fastening of safety belts and shoulder harnesses.

No person may operate an aircraft in operations required to be conducted under part 137 without a safety belt and shoulder harness properly secured about that person except that the shoulder harness need not be fastened if that person would be unable to perform required duties with the shoulder harness fastened.

[Amdt. 137–10, 44 FR 61325, Oct. 25, 1979]

§ 137.43 Operations in controlled airspace designated for an airport.

(a) Except for flights to and from a dispensing area, no person may operate an aircraft within the lateral boundaries of the surface area of Class D airspace designated for an airport unless authorization for that operation has been obtained from the ATC facility having jurisdiction over that area.

(b) No person may operate an aircraft in weather conditions below VFR minimums within the lateral boundaries of a Class E airspace area that extends upward from the surface unless authorization for that operation has been obtained from the ATC facility having jurisdiction over that area.

(c) Notwithstanding § 91.157(a)(2) of this chapter, an aircraft may be operated under the special VFR weather minimums without meeting the requirements prescribed therein.

[Docket No. 24456, 56 FR 65664, Dec. 17, 1991; as amended by Amdt. 137–14, 58 FR 32840, June 14, 1993]

§ 137.45 Nonobservance of airport traffic pattern.

Notwithstanding part 91 of this chapter, the pilot in command of an aircraft may deviate from an airport traffic pattern when authorized by the control tower concerned. At an airport without a functioning control tower, the pilot in command may deviate from the traffic pattern if—

(a) Prior coordination is made with the airport management concerned;

(b) Deviations are limited to the agricultural aircraft operation;

(c) Except in an emergency, landing and takeoffs are not made on ramps, taxiways, or other areas of the airport not intended for such use; and

(d) The aircraft at all times remains clear of, and gives way to, aircraft conforming to the traffic pattern for the airport.

§ 137.47 Operation without position lights.

Notwithstanding part 91 of this chapter, an aircraft may be operated without position lights if prominent unlighted objects are visible for at least 1 mile and takeoffs and landings at—

(a) Airports with a functioning control tower are made only as authorized by the control tower operator; and

(b) Other airports are made only with the permission of the airport management and no other aircraft operations requiring position lights are in progress at that airport.

§ 137.49 Operations over other than congested areas.

Notwithstanding part 91 of this chapter, during the actual dispensing operation, including approaches, departures, and turnarounds reasonably necessary for the operation, an aircraft may be operated over other than congested areas below 500 feet above the surface and closer than 500 feet to persons, vessels, vehicles, and structures, if the operations are conducted without creating a hazard to persons or property on the surface.

[Amdt. 137–3, 33 FR 9601, July 2, 1968]

§ 137.51 Operation over congested areas: General.

(a) Notwithstanding part 91 of this chapter, an aircraft may be operated over a congested area at altitudes required for the proper accomplishment of the agricultural aircraft operation if the operation is conducted—

(1) With the maximum safety to persons and property on the surface, consistent with the operation; and

(2) In accordance with the requirements of paragraph (b) of this section.

(b) No person may operate an aircraft over a congested area except in accordance with the requirements of this paragraph.

(1) Prior written approval must be obtained from the appropriate official or governing body of the political subdivision over which the operations are conducted.

(2) Notice of the intended operation must be given to the public by some effective means, such as daily newspapers, radio, television, or door-to-door notice.

(3) A plan for each complete operation must be submitted to, and approved by appropriate personnel of the FAA Flight Standards District Office having jurisdiction over the area where the operation is to be conducted. The plan must include consideration of obstructions to flight; the emergency landing capabilities of the aircraft to be used; and any necessary coordination with air traffic control.

(4) Single engine aircraft must be operated as follows:

(i) Except for helicopters, no person may take off a loaded aircraft, or make a turnaround over a congested area.

(ii) No person may operate an aircraft over a congested area below the altitudes prescribed in part 91 of this chapter except during the actual dispensing operation, including the approaches and departures necessary for that operation.

(iii) No person may operate an aircraft over a congested area during the actual dispensing operation, including the approaches and departures for that operation, unless it is operated in a pattern and at such an altitude that the aircraft can land, in an emergency, without endangering persons or property on the surface.

(5) Multiengine aircraft must be operated as follows:

(i) No person may take off a multiengine airplane over a congested area except under conditions that will allow the airplane to be brought to a safe stop within the effective length of the runway from any point on takeoff up to the time of attaining, with all engines operating at normal takeoff power, 105 percent of the minimum control speed with the critical engine inoperative in the takeoff configuration or 115 percent of the power-off stall speed in the takeoff configuration, whichever is greater, as shown by the accelerate stop distance data. In applying this requirement, takeoff data is based upon still-air conditions, and no correction is made for any uphill gradient of 1 percent or less when the percentage is measured as the difference between elevation at the end points of the runway divided by the total length. For uphill gradients greater than 1 percent, the effective takeoff length of the runway is reduced 20 percent for each 1-percent grade.

(ii) No person may operate a multiengine airplane at a weight greater than the weight that, with the critical engine inoperative, would permit a rate of climb of at least 50 feet per minute at an altitude of at least 1,000 feet above the elevation of the highest ground or obstruction within the area to be worked or at an altitude of 5,000 feet, whichever is higher. For the purposes of this subdivision, it is assumed that the propeller of the inoperative engine is in the minimum drag position; that the wing flaps and landing gear are in the most favorable positions; and that the remaining engine or engines are operating at the maximum continuous power available.

(iii) No person may operate any multiengine aircraft over a congested area below the altitudes prescribed in part 91 of this chapter except during the actual dispensing operation, including the approaches, departures, and turnarounds necessary for that operation.

[Docket No. 1464, 30 FR 8106, June 24, 1965; as amended by Docket No. 8084, 32 FR 5769, April 11, 1967; Amdt. 137–13, 54 FR 39294, Sept. 25, 1989]

§ 137.53 Operation over congested areas: Pilots and aircraft.

(a) *General.* No person may operate an aircraft over a congested area except in accordance with the pilot and aircraft rules of this section.

(b) *Pilots.* Each pilot in command must have at least—

(1) 25 hours of pilot-in-command flight time in the make and basic model of the aircraft, at least 10 hours of which must have been acquired within the preceding 12 calendar months; and

(2) 100 hours of flight experience as pilot in command in dispensing agricultural materials or chemicals.

(c) *Aircraft.*

(1) Each aircraft must—

(i) If it is an aircraft not specified in paragraph (c)(1)(ii) of this section, have had within the preceding 100 hours of time in service a 100-hour or annual inspection by a person authorized by part 65 or 145 of this chapter, or have been inspected under a progressive inspection system; and

(ii) If it is a large or turbine-powered multiengine civil airplane of U.S. registry, have been inspected in accordance with the applicable inspection program requirements of § 91.409 of this chapter.

(2) If other than a helicopter, it must be equipped with a device capable of jettisoning at least one-half of the aircraft's maximum authorized load of agricultural material within 45 seconds. If the aircraft is equipped with a device for releasing the tank or hopper as a unit, there must be a means to prevent inadvertent release by the pilot or other crewmember.

[Docket No. 1464, 30 FR 8106, June 24, 1965; as amended by Amdt. 137–5, 41 FR 16796, April 22, 1976; Amdt. 137–12, 54 FR 34332, Aug. 18, 1989]

§ 137.55 Business name: Commercial agricultural aircraft operator.

No person may operate under a business name that is not shown on his commercial agricultural aircraft operator certificate.

§ 137.57 Availability of certificate.

Each holder of an agricultural aircraft operator certificate shall keep that certificate at his home base of operations and shall present it for inspection on the request of the Administrator or any Federal, State, or local law enforcement officer.

§ 137.59 Inspection authority.

Each holder of an agricultural aircraft operator certificate shall allow the Administrator at any time and place to make inspections, including on-the-job inspections, to determine compliance with applicable regulations and his agricultural aircraft operator certificate.

Subpart D— Records and Reports

§ 137.71 Records: Commercial agricultural aircraft operator.

(a) Each holder of a commercial agricultural aircraft operator certificate shall maintain and keep current, at the home base of operations designated in his application, the following records:

(1) The name and address of each person for whom agricultural aircraft services were provided;

(2) The date of the service;

(3) The name and quantity of the material dispensed for each operation conducted; and

(4) The name, address, and certificate number of each pilot used in agricultural aircraft operations and the date that pilot met the knowledge and skill requirements of § 137.19(e).

(b) The records required by this section must be kept at least 12 months and made available for inspection by the Administrator upon request.

§ 137.75 Change of address.

Each holder of an agricultural aircraft operator certificate shall notify the FAA in writing in advance of any change in the address of his home base of operations.

§ 137.77 Termination of operations.

Whenever a person holding an agricultural aircraft operator certificate ceases operations under this part, he shall surrender that certificate to the FAA Flight Standards District Office last having jurisdiction over his operation.

[Docket No. 1464, 30 FR 8106, June 24, 1965; as amended by Amdt. 137–13, 54 FR 39294, Sept. 25, 1989; 54 FR 52872, Dec. 22, 1989]

SUBCHAPTER H
SCHOOLS AND OTHER CERTIFICATED AGENCIES

PART 141
PILOT SCHOOLS

141

Authority: 49 U.S.C. 106(g), 40113, 44701–44703, 44707, 44709, 44711, 45102–45103, 45301–45302.

Source: Docket No. 25910, 62 FR 16347, April 4, 1997, unless otherwise noted.

Subpart A—General

§ 141.1 Applicability.

This part prescribes the requirements for issuing pilot school certificates, provisional pilot school certificates, and associated ratings, and the general operating rules applicable to a holder of a certificate or rating issued under this part.

§ 141.3 Certificate required.

No person may operate as a certificated pilot school without, or in violation of, a pilot school certificate or provisional pilot school certificate issued under this part.

§ 141.5 Requirements for a pilot school certificate.

An applicant may be issued a pilot school certificate with associated ratings if the applicant:

(a) Completes the application for a pilot school certificate on a form and in a manner prescribed by the Administrator;

(b) Holds a provisional pilot school certificate, issued under this part, for at least 24 calendar months preceding the month in which the application for a pilot school certificate is made;

(c) Meets the applicable requirements of subparts A through C of this part for the school ratings sought; and

(d) Has trained and recommended for pilot certification and rating tests, within 24 calendar months preceding the month the application is made for the pilot school certificate, at least 10 students for a knowledge or practical test for a pilot certificate, flight instructor certificate, ground instructor certificate, an additional rating, an end-of-course test for a training course specified in Appendix K to this part, or any combination of those tests, and at least 80 percent of all tests administered were passed on the first attempt.

§ 141.7 Provisional pilot school certificate.

An applicant that meets the applicable requirements of subparts A, B, and C of this part, but does not meet the recent training activity requirements of § 141.5(d) of this part, may be issued a provisional pilot school certificate with ratings.

§ 141.9 Examining authority.

An applicant is issued examining authority for its pilot school certificate if the applicant meets the requirements of subpart D of this part.

§ 141.11 Pilot school ratings.

(a) The ratings listed in paragraph (b) of this section may be issued to an applicant for:

(1) A pilot school certificate, provided the applicant meets the requirements of § 141.5 of this part; or

(2) A provisional pilot school certificate, provided the applicant meets the requirements of § 141.7 of this part.

(b) An applicant may be authorized to conduct the following courses:

(1) *Certification and rating courses.* (Appendixes A through J).

(i) Recreational pilot course.

(ii) Private pilot course.

(iii) Commercial pilot course.

(iv) Instrument rating course.

(v) Airline transport pilot course.

(vi) Flight instructor course.

(vii) Flight instructor instrument course.

(viii) Ground instructor course.

(ix) Additional aircraft category or class rating course.

(x) Aircraft type rating course.

(2) *Special preparation courses.* (Appendix K).

(i) Pilot refresher course.

(ii) Flight instructor refresher course.

(iii) Ground instructor refresher course.

(iv) Agricultural aircraft operations course.

(v) Rotorcraft external-load operations course.

(vi) Special operations course.

(vii) Test pilot course.

(3) *Pilot ground school course.* (Appendix L).

§ 141.13 Application for issuance, amendment, or renewal.

(a) Application for an original certificate and rating, an additional rating, or the renewal of a certificate under this part must be made on a form and in a manner prescribed by the Administrator.

(b) Application for the issuance or amendment of a certificate or rating must be accompanied by two copies of each proposed training course curriculum for which approval is sought.

§ 141.17 Duration of certificate and examining authority.

(a) Unless surrendered, suspended, or revoked, a pilot school's certificate or a provisional pilot school's certificate expires:

(1) On the last day of the 24th calendar month from the month the certificate was issued;

(2) Except as provided in paragraph (b) of this section, on the date that any change in ownership of the school occurs;

(3) On the date of any change in the facilities upon which the school's certificate is based occurs; or

(4) Upon notice by the Administrator that the school has failed for more than 60 days to maintain the facilities, aircraft, or personnel required for any one of the school's approved training courses.

(b) A change in the ownership of a pilot school or provisional pilot school does not terminate that school's certificate if, within 30 days after the date that any change in ownership of the school occurs:

(1) Application is made for an appropriate amendment to the certificate; and

(2) No change in the facilities, personnel, or approved training courses is involved.

(c) An examining authority issued to the holder of a pilot school certificate expires on the date that the pilot school certificate expires, or is surrendered, suspended, or revoked.

§ 141.18 Carriage of narcotic drugs, marijuana, and depressant or stimulant drugs or substances.

If the holder of a certificate issued under this part permits any aircraft owned or leased by that holder to be engaged in any operation that the certificate holder knows to be in violation of § 91.19(a) of this chapter, that operation is a basis for suspending or revoking the certificate.

§ 141.19 Display of certificate.

(a) Each holder of a pilot school certificate or a provisional pilot school certificate must display that certificate in a place in the school that is normally accessible to the public and is not obscured.

(b) A certificate must be made available for inspection upon request by:

(1) The Administrator;

(2) An authorized representative of the National Transportation Safety Board; or

(3) A Federal, State, or local law enforcement officer.

§ 141.21 Inspections.

Each holder of a certificate issued under this part must allow the Administrator to inspect its personnel, facilities, equipment, and records to determine the certificate holder's:

(a) Eligibility to hold its certificate;

(b) Compliance with 49 U.S.C. 40101 *et seq.*, formerly the Federal Aviation Act of 1958, as amended; and

(c) Compliance with the Federal Aviation Regulations.

§ 141.23 Advertising limitations.

(a) The holder of a pilot school certificate or a provisional pilot school certificate may not make any statement relating to its certification and ratings that is false or designed to mislead any person contemplating enrollment in that school.

(b) The holder of a pilot school certificate or a provisional pilot school certificate may not advertise that the school is certificated unless it clearly differentiates between courses that have been approved under part 141 of this chapter and those that have not been approved under part 141 of this chapter.

(c) The holder of a pilot school certificate or a provisional pilot school certificate must promptly remove:

(1) From vacated premises, all signs indicating that the school was certificated by the Administrator; or

(2) All indications (including signs), wherever located, that the school is certificated by the Administrator when its certificate has expired or has been surrendered, suspended, or revoked.

§ 141.25 Business office and operations base.

(a) Each holder of a pilot school or a provisional pilot school certificate must maintain a principal business office with a mailing address in the name shown on its certificate.

(b) The facilities and equipment at the principal business office must be adequate to maintain the files and records required to operate the business of the school.

(c) The principal business office may not be shared with, or used by, another pilot school.

(d) Before changing the location of the principal business office or the operations base, each certificate holder must notify the FAA Flight Standards District Office having jurisdiction over the area of the new location, and the notice must be:

(1) Submitted in writing at least 30 days before the change of location; and

(2) Accompanied by any amendments needed for the certificate holder's approved training course outline.

141

(e) A certificate holder may conduct training at an operations base other than the one specified in its certificate, if:

(1) The Administrator has inspected and approved the base for use by the certificate holder; and

(2) The course of training and any needed amendments have been approved for use at that base.

§ 141.26 Training agreements.

A training center certificated under part 142 of this chapter may provide the training, testing, and checking for pilot schools certificated under part 141 of this chapter, and is considered to meet the requirements of part 141, provided—

(a) There is a training agreement between the certificated training center and the pilot school;

(b) The training, testing, and checking provided by the certificated training center is approved and conducted under part 142;

(c) The pilot school certificated under part 141 obtains the Administrator's approval for a training course outline that includes the training, testing, and checking to be conducted under part 141 and the training, testing, and checking to be conducted under part 142; and

(d) Upon completion of the training, testing, and checking conducted under part 142, a copy of each student's training record is forwarded to the part 141 school and becomes part of the student's permanent training record.

§ 141.27 Renewal of certificates and ratings.

(a) *Pilot school.*

(1) A pilot school may apply for renewal of its school certificate and ratings within 30 days preceding the month the pilot school's certificate expires, provided the school meets the requirements prescribed in paragraph (a)(2) of this section for renewal of its certificate and ratings.

(2) A pilot school may have its school certificate and ratings renewed for an additional 24 calendar months if the Administrator determines the school's personnel, aircraft, facility and airport, approved training courses, training records, and recent training ability and quality meet the requirements of this part.

(3) A pilot school that does not meet the renewal requirements in paragraph (a)(2) of this section, may apply for a provisional pilot school certificate if the school meets the requirements of § 141.7 of this part.

(b) *Provisional pilot school.*

(1) Except as provided in paragraph (b)(3) of this section, a provisional pilot school may not

have its provisional pilot school certificate or the ratings on that certificate renewed.

(2) A provisional pilot school may apply for a pilot school certificate and associated ratings provided that school meets the requirements of § 141.5 of this part.

(3) A former provisional pilot school may apply for another provisional pilot school certificate, provided 180 days have elapsed since its last provisional pilot school certificate expired.

§ 141.29 [Reserved]

Subpart B— Personnel, Aircraft, and Facilities Requirements

§ 141.31 Applicability.

(a) This subpart prescribes:

(1) The personnel and aircraft requirements for a pilot school certificate or a provisional pilot school certificate; and

(2) The facilities that a pilot school or provisional pilot school must have available on a continuous basis.

(b) As used in this subpart, to have continuous use of a facility, including an airport, the school must have:

(1) Ownership of the facility or airport for at least 6 calendar months after the date the application for initial certification and on the date of renewal of the school's certificate is made; or

(2) A written lease agreement for the facility or airport for at least 6 calendar months after the date the application for initial certification and on the date of renewal of the school's certificate is made.

[Docket No. 25910, 62 FR 16347, April 4, 1997; as amended by Amdt. 141–9, 62 FR 40907, July 30, 1997]

§ 141.33 Personnel.

(a) An applicant for a pilot school certificate or for a provisional pilot school certificate must meet the following personnel requirements:

(1) Each applicant must have adequate personnel, including certificated flight instructors, certificated ground instructors, or holders of a commercial pilot certificate with a lighter-than-air rating, and a chief instructor for each approved course of training who is qualified and competent to perform the duties to which that instructor is assigned.

(2) If the school employs dispatchers, aircraft handlers, and line and service personnel, then it must instruct those persons in the procedures and responsibilities of their employment.

(3) Each instructor to be used for ground or flight training must hold a flight instructor certificate, ground instructor certificate, or commercial pilot certificate with a lighter-than-air rating, as appropriate, with ratings for the approved course of training and any aircraft used in that course.

(b) An applicant for a pilot school certificate or for a provisional pilot school certificate must designate a chief instructor for each of the school's approved training courses, who must meet the requirements of § 141.35 of this part.

(c) When necessary, an applicant for a pilot school certificate or for a provisional pilot school certificate may designate a person to be an assistant chief instructor for an approved training course, provided that person meets the requirements of § 141.36 of this part.

(d) A pilot school and a provisional pilot school may designate a person to be a check instructor for conducting student stage checks, end-of-course tests, and instructor proficiency checks, provided:

(1) That person meets the requirements of § 141.37 of this part; and

(2) That school has a student enrollment of at least 50 students at the time designation is sought.

(e) A person, as listed in this section, may serve in more than one position for a school, provided that person is qualified for each position.

[Docket No. 25910, 62 FR 16347, April 4, 1997; as amended by Amdt. 141–9, 62 FR 40907, July 30, 1997]

§ 141.35 Chief instructor qualifications.

(a) To be eligible for designation as a chief instructor for a course of training, a person must meet the following requirements:

(1) Hold a commercial pilot certificate or an airline transport pilot certificate, and, except for a chief instructor for a course of training solely for a lighter-than-air rating, a current flight instructor certificate. The certificates must contain the appropriate aircraft category and class ratings for the category and class of aircraft used in the course and an instrument rating, if an instrument rating is required for enrollment in the course of training;

(2) Meet the pilot-in-command recent flight experience requirements of § 61.57 of this chapter;

(3) Pass a knowledge test on—

(i) Teaching methods;

(ii) Applicable provisions of the "Aeronautical Information Manual";

(iii) Applicable provisions of parts 61, 91, and 141 of this chapter; and

(iv) The objectives and approved course completion standards of the course for which the person seeks to obtain designation.

(4) Pass a proficiency test on instructional skills and ability to train students on the flight procedures and maneuvers appropriate to the course;

(5) Except for a course of training for gliders, balloons, or airships, the chief instructor must meet the applicable requirements in paragraphs (b), (c), and (d) of this section; and

(6) A chief instructor for a course of training for gliders, balloons or airships is only required to have 40 percent of the hours required in paragraphs (b) and (d) of this section.

(b) For a course of training leading to the issuance of a recreational or private pilot certificate or rating, a chief instructor must have:

(1) At least 1,000 hours as pilot in command; and

(2) Primary flight training experience, acquired as either a certificated flight instructor or an instructor in a military pilot flight training program, or a combination thereof, consisting of at least—

(i) 2 years and a total of 500 flight hours; or

(ii) 1,000 flight hours.

(c) For a course of training leading to the issuance of an instrument rating or a rating with instrument privileges, a chief instructor must have:

(1) At least 100 hours of flight time under actual or simulated instrument conditions;

(2) At least 1,000 hours as pilot in command; and

(3) Instrument flight instructor experience, acquired as either a certificated flight instructor–instrument or an instructor in a military pilot flight training program, or a combination thereof, consisting of at least—

(i) 2 years and a total of 250 flight hours; or

(ii) 400 flight hours.

(d) For a course of training other than one leading to the issuance of a recreational or private pilot certificate or rating, or an instrument rating or a rating with instrument privileges, a chief instructor must have:

(1) At least 2,000 hours as pilot in command; and

(2) Flight training experience, acquired as either a certificated flight instructor or an instructor in a military pilot flight training program, or a combination thereof, consisting of at least—

(i) 3 years and a total of 1,000 flight hours; or

(ii) 1,500 flight hours.

(e) To be eligible for designation as chief instructor for a ground school course, a person must have 1 year of experience as a ground school instructor at a certificated pilot school.

[Docket No. 25910, 62 FR 16347, April 4, 1997; as amended by Amdt. 141–9, 62 FR 40907, July 30, 1997; Amdt. No. 141–10, 63 FR 20289, April 23, 1998]

§ 141.36 Assistant chief instructor qualifications.

(a) To be eligible for designation as an assistant chief instructor for a course of training, a person must meet the following requirements:

(1) Hold a commercial pilot or an airline transport pilot certificate and, except for the assistant chief instructor for a course of training solely for a lighter-than-air rating, a current flight instructor certificate. The certificates must contain the appropriate aircraft category, class, and instrument ratings if an instrument rating is required by the course of training for the category and class of aircraft used in the course;

(2) Meet the pilot-in-command recent flight experience requirements of § 61.57 of this chapter;

(3) Pass a knowledge test on—

(i) Teaching methods;

(ii) Applicable provisions of the "Aeronautical Information Manual";

(iii) Applicable provisions of parts 61, 91, and 141 of this chapter; and

(iv) The objectives and approved course completion standards of the course for which the person seeks to obtain designation.

(4) Pass a proficiency test on the flight procedures and maneuvers appropriate to that course; and

(5) Meet the applicable requirements in paragraphs (b), (c), and (d) of this section. However, an assistant chief instructor for a course of training for gliders, balloons, or airships is only required to have 40 percent of the hours required in paragraphs (b) and (d) of this section.

(b) For a course of training leading to the issuance of a recreational or private pilot certificate or rating, an assistant chief instructor must have:

(1) At least 500 hours as pilot in command; and

(2) Flight training experience, acquired as either a certificated flight instructor or an instructor in a military pilot flight training program, or a combination thereof, consisting of at least—

(i) 1 year and a total of 250 flight hours; or

(ii) 500 flight hours.

(c) For a course of training leading to the issuance of an instrument rating or a rating with instrument privileges, an assistant chief flight instructor must have:

(1) At least 50 hours of flight time under actual or simulated instrument conditions;

(2) At least 500 hours as pilot in command; and

(3) Instrument flight instructor experience, acquired as either a certificated flight instructor–instrument or an instructor in a military pilot flight training program, or a combination thereof, consisting of at least—

(i) 1 year and a total of 125 flight hours; or

(ii) 200 flight hours.

(d) For a course of training other than one leading to the issuance of a recreational or private pilot certificate or rating, or an instrument rating or a rating with instrument privileges, an assistant chief instructor must have:

(1) At least 1,000 hours as pilot in command; and

(2) Flight training experience, acquired as either a certificated flight instructor or an instructor in a military pilot flight training program, or a combination thereof, consisting of at least—

(i) 1½ years and a total of 500 flight hours; or

(ii) 750 flight hours.

(e) To be eligible for designation as an assistant chief instructor for a ground school course, a person must have 6 months of experience as a ground school instructor at a certificated pilot school.

[Docket No. 25910, 62 FR 16347, April 4, 1997; as amended by Amdt. 141–9, 62 FR 40907, July 30, 1997; Amdt. No. 141–10, 63 FR 20289, April 23, 1998]

§ 141.37 Check instructor qualifications.

(a) To be designated as a check instructor for conducting student stage checks, end-of-course tests, and instructor proficiency checks under this part, a person must meet the eligibility requirements of this section:

(1) For checks and tests that relate to either flight or ground training, the person must pass a test, given by the chief instructor, on—

(i) Teaching methods;

(ii) Applicable provisions of the "Aeronautical Information Manual";

(iii) Applicable provisions of parts 61, 91, and 141 of this chapter; and

(iv) The objectives and course completion standards of the approved training course for the designation sought.

(2) For checks and tests that relate to a flight training course, the person must—

(i) Meet the requirements in paragraph (a)(1) of this section;

(ii) Hold a commercial pilot certificate or an airline transport pilot certificate and, except for a check instructor for a course of training for a lighter-than-air rating, a current flight instructor certificate. The certificates must contain the appropriate aircraft category, class, and instrument ratings for the category and class of aircraft used in the course;

(iii) Meet the pilot-in-command recent flight experience requirements of § 61.57 of this chapter; and

(iv) Pass a proficiency test, given by the chief instructor or assistant chief instructor, on the flight procedures and maneuvers of the approved training course for the designation sought.

(3) For checks and tests that relate to ground training, the person must—

(i) Meet the requirements in paragraph (a)(1) of this section;

(ii) Except for a course of training for a lighter-than-air rating, hold a current flight instructor certificate or ground instructor certificate with ratings appropriate to the category and class of aircraft used in the course; and

(iii) For a course of training for a lighter-than-air rating, hold a commercial pilot certificate with a lighter-than-air category rating and the appropriate class rating.

(b) A person who meets the eligibility requirements in paragraph (a) of this section must:

(1) Be designated, in writing, by the chief instructor to conduct student stage checks, end-of-course tests, and instructor proficiency checks; and

(2) Be approved by the FAA Flight Standards District Office having jurisdiction over the school.

(c) A check instructor may not conduct a stage check or an end-of-course test of any student for whom the check instructor has:

(1) Served as the principal instructor; or

(2) Recommended for a stage check or end-of-course test.

[Docket No. 25910, 62 FR 16347, April 4, 1997; as amended by Amdt. 141–9, 62 FR 40907, July 30, 1997]

§ 141.38 Airports.

(a) An applicant for a pilot school certificate or a provisional pilot school certificate must show that he or she has continuous use of each airport at which training flights originate.

(b) Each airport used for airplanes and gliders must have at least one runway or takeoff area that allows training aircraft to make a normal takeoff or landing under the following conditions at the aircraft's maximum certificated takeoff gross weight:

(1) Under wind conditions of not more than 5 miles per hour;

(2) At temperatures in the operating area equal to the mean high temperature for the hottest month of the year;

(3) If applicable, with the powerplant operation, and landing gear and flap operation recommended by the manufacturer; and

(4) In the case of a takeoff—

(i) With smooth transition from liftoff to the best rate of climb speed without exceptional piloting skills or techniques; and

(ii) Clearing all obstacles in the takeoff flight path by at least 50 feet.

(c) Each airport must have a wind direction indicator that is visible from the end of each runway at ground level;

(d) Each airport must have a traffic direction indicator when:

(1) The airport does not have an operating control tower; and

(2) UNICOM advisories are not available.

(e) Except as provided in paragraph (f) of this section, each airport used for night training flights must have permanent runway lights;

(f) An airport or seaplane base used for night training flights in seaplanes is permitted to use adequate nonpermanent lighting or shoreline lighting, if approved by the Administrator.

[Docket No. 25910, 62 FR 16347, April 4, 1997; as amended by Amdt. 141–9, 62 FR 40907, July 30, 1997]

§ 141.39 Aircraft.

An applicant for a pilot school certificate or provisional pilot school certificate must show that each aircraft used by that school for flight training and solo flights meets the following requirements:

(a) Each aircraft must be registered as a civil aircraft in the United States;

(b) Each aircraft must be certificated with a standard airworthiness certificate or a primary airworthiness certificate, unless the Administrator determines that due to the nature of the approved course, an aircraft not having a standard airworthiness certificate or primary airworthiness certificate may be used;

(c) Each aircraft must be maintained and inspected in accordance with the requirements under subpart E of part 91 of this chapter that apply to aircraft operated for hire;

(d) Each aircraft used in flight training must have at least two pilot stations with engine-power controls that can be easily reached and operated in a normal manner from both pilot stations; and

(e) Each aircraft used in a course involving IFR en route operations and instrument approaches must be equipped and maintained for IFR operations. For training in the control and precision maneuvering of an aircraft by reference to instruments, the aircraft may be equipped as provided in the approved course of training.

[Docket No. 25910, 62 FR 16347, April 4, 1997; as amended by Amdt. 141–9, 62 FR 40908, July 30, 1997]

§ 141.41 Flight simulators, flight training devices, and training aids.

An applicant for a pilot school certificate or a provisional pilot school certificate must show that its flight simulators, flight training devices, training aids, and equipment meet the following requirements:

(a) *Flight simulators.* Each flight simulator used to obtain flight training credit allowed for flight simulators in an approved pilot training course curriculum must—

141

(1) Be a full-size aircraft cockpit replica of a specific type of aircraft, or make, model, and series of aircraft;

(2) Include the hardware and software necessary to represent the aircraft in ground operations and flight operations;

(3) Use a force cueing system that provides cues at least equivalent to those cues provided by a 3 degree freedom of motion system;

(4) Use a visual system that provides at least a 45-degree horizontal field of view and a 30-degree vertical field of view simultaneously for each pilot; and

(5) Have been evaluated, qualified, and approved by the Administrator.

(b) *Flight training devices.* Each flight training device used to obtain flight training credit allowed for flight training devices in an approved pilot training course curriculum must—

(1) Be a full-size replica of instruments, equipment panels, and controls of an aircraft, or set of aircraft, in an open flight deck area or in an enclosed cockpit, including the hardware and software for the systems installed that is necessary to simulate the aircraft in ground and flight operations;

(2) Need not have a force (motion) cueing or visual system; and

(3) Have been evaluated, qualified, and approved by the Administrator.

(c) *Training aids and equipment.* Each training aid, including any audiovisual aid, projector, tape recorder, mockup, chart, or aircraft component listed in the approved training course outline, must be accurate and appropriate to the course for which it is used.

[Docket No. 25910, 62 FR 16347, April 4, 1997; as amended by Amdt. 141–9, 62 FR 40908, July 30, 1997]

§ 141.43 Pilot briefing areas.

(a) An applicant for a pilot school certificate or provisional pilot school certificate must show that the applicant has continuous use of a briefing area located at each airport at which training flights originate that is:

(1) Adequate to shelter students waiting to engage in their training flights;

(2) Arranged and equipped for the conduct of pilot briefings; and

(3) Except as provided in paragraph (c) of this section, for a school with an instrument rating or commercial pilot course, equipped with private landline or telephone communication to the nearest FAA Flight Service Station.

(b) A briefing area required by paragraph (a) of this section may not be used by the applicant if it is available for use by any other pilot school during the period it is required for use by the applicant.

(c) The communication equipment required by paragraph (a)(3) of this section is not required if the briefing area and the flight service station are located on the same airport, and are readily accessible to each other.

§ 141.45 Ground training facilities.

An applicant for a pilot school or provisional pilot school certificate must show that:

(a) Each room, training booth, or other space used for instructional purposes is heated, lighted, and ventilated to conform to local building, sanitation, and health codes; and

(b) The training facility is so located that the students in that facility are not distracted by the training conducted in other rooms, or by flight and maintenance operations on the airport.

Subpart C— Training Course Outline and Curriculum

§ 141.51 Applicability.

This subpart prescribes the curriculum and course outline requirements for the issuance of a pilot school certificate or provisional pilot school certificate and ratings.

§ 141.53 Approval procedures for a training course: General.

(a) *General.* An applicant for a pilot school certificate or provisional pilot school certificate must obtain the Administrator's approval of the outline of each training course for which certification and rating is sought.

(b) *Application.*

(1) An application for the approval of an initial or amended training course must be submitted in duplicate to the FAA Flight Standards District Office having jurisdiction over the area where the school is based.

(2) An application for the approval of an initial or amended training course must be submitted at least 30 days before any training under that course, or any amendment thereto, is scheduled to begin.

(3) An application for amending a training course must be accompanied by two copies of the amendment.

(c) *Training courses.*

(1) A training course submitted for approval prior to August 4, 1997 may, if approved, retain that approval until 1 year after August 4, 1997.

(2) An applicant for a pilot school certificate or provisional pilot school certificate may request

approval of the training courses specified in § 141.11(b) of this part.

[Docket No. 25910, 62 FR 16347, April 4, 1997; as amended by Amdt. 141–9, 62 FR 40908, July 30, 1997]

§ 141.55 Training course: Contents.

(a) Each training course for which approval is requested must meet the minimum curriculum requirements in accordance with the appropriate appendix of this part.

(b) Except as provided in paragraphs (d) and (e) of this section, each training course for which approval is requested must meet the minimum ground and flight training time requirements in accordance with the appropriate appendix of this part.

(c) Each training course for which approval is requested must contain:

(1) A description of each room used for ground training, including the room's size and the maximum number of students that may be trained in the room at one time;

(2) A description of each type of audiovisual aid, projector, tape recorder, mockup, chart, aircraft component, and other special training aids used for ground training;

(3) A description of each flight simulator or flight training device used for training;

(4) A listing of the airports at which training flights originate and a description of the facilities, including pilot briefing areas that are available for use by the school's students and personnel at each of those airports;

(5) A description of the type of aircraft including any special equipment used for each phase of training;

(6) The minimum qualifications and ratings for each instructor assigned to ground or flight training; and

(7) A training syllabus that includes the following information—

(i) The prerequisites for enrolling in the ground and flight portion of the course that include the pilot certificate and rating (if required by this part), training, pilot experience, and pilot knowledge;

(ii) A detailed description of each lesson, including the lesson's objectives, standards, and planned time for completion;

(iii) A description of what the course is expected to accomplish with regard to student learning;

(iv) The expected accomplishments and the standards for each stage of training; and

(v) A description of the checks and tests to be used to measure a student's accomplishments for each stage of training.

(d) A pilot school may request and receive initial approval for a period of not more than 24 calendar months for any of the training courses of this part without specifying the minimum ground and flight training time requirements of this part, provided the following provisions are met:

(1) The school holds a pilot school certificate issued under this part and has held that certificate for a period of at least 24 consecutive calendar months preceding the month of the request;

(2) In addition to the information required by paragraph (c) of this section, the training course specifies planned ground and flight training time requirements for the course;

(3) The school does not request the training course to be approved for examining authority, nor may that school hold examining authority for that course; and

(4) The practical test or knowledge test for the course is to be given by—

(i) An FAA inspector; or

(ii) An examiner who is not an employee of the school.

(e) A certificated pilot school may request and receive final approval for any of the training courses of this part without specifying the minimum ground and flight training time requirements of this part, provided the following conditions are met:

(1) The school has held initial approval for that training course for at least 24 calendar months.

(2) The school has—

(i) Trained at least 10 students in that training course within the preceding 24 calendar months and recommended those students for a pilot, flight instructor, or ground instructor certificate or rating; and

(ii) At least 80 percent of those students passed the practical or knowledge test, or any combination thereof, on the first attempt, and that test was given by—

(A) An FAA inspector; or

(B) An examiner who is not an employee of the school.

(3) In addition to the information required by paragraph (c) of this section, the training course specifies planned ground and flight training time requirements for the course.

(4) The school does not request that the training course be approved for examining authority nor may that school hold examining authority for that course.

§ 141.57 Special curricula.

An applicant for a pilot school certificate or provisional pilot school certificate may apply for approval to conduct a special course of airman training for which a curriculum is not prescribed in the appendixes of this part, if the applicant shows that the training course contains features that could achieve a level of pilot proficiency equivalent to that achieved by a training course prescribed in the appendixes of this part or the requirements of part 61 of this chapter.

Subpart D— Examining Authority

§ 141.61 Applicability.

This subpart prescribes the requirements for the issuance of examining authority to the holder of a pilot school certificate, and the privileges and limitations of that examining authority.

§ 141.63 Examining authority qualification requirements.

(a) A pilot school must meet the following prerequisites to receive initial approval for examining authority:

(1) The school must complete the application for examining authority on a form and in a manner prescribed by the Administrator;

(2) The school must hold a pilot school certificate and rating issued under this part;

(3) The school must have held the rating in which examining authority is sought for at least 24 consecutive calendar months preceding the month of application for examining authority;

(4) The training course for which examining authority is requested may not be a course that is approved without meeting the minimum ground and flight training time requirements of this part; and

(5) Within 24 calendar months before the date of application for examining authority, that school must meet the following requirements—

(i) The school must have trained at least 10 students in the training course for which examining authority is sought and recommended those students for a pilot, flight instructor, or ground instructor certificate or rating; and

(ii) At least 90 percent of those students passed the required practical or knowledge test, or any combination thereof, for the pilot, flight instructor, or ground instructor certificate or rating on the first attempt, and that test was given by—

(A) An FAA inspector; or

(B) An examiner who is not an employee of the school.

(b) A pilot school must meet the following requirements to retain approval of its examining authority:

(1) The school must complete the application for renewal of its examining authority on a form and in a manner prescribed by the Administrator;

(2) The school must hold a pilot school certificate and rating issued under this part;

(3) The school must have held the rating for which continued examining authority is sought for at least 24 calendar months preceding the month of application for renewal of its examining authority; and

(4) The training course for which continued examining authority is requested may not be a course that is approved without meeting the minimum ground and flight training time requirements of this part.

[Docket No. 25910, 62 FR 16347, April 4, 1997; as amended by Amdt. 141–9, 62 FR 40908, July 30, 1997]

§ 141.65 Privileges.

A pilot school that holds examining authority may recommend a person who graduated from its course for the appropriate pilot, flight instructor, or ground instructor certificate or rating without taking the FAA knowledge test or practical test in accordance with the provisions of this subpart.

§ 141.67 Limitations and reports.

A pilot school that holds examining authority may only recommend the issuance of a pilot, flight instructor, or ground instructor certificate and rating to a person who does not take an FAA knowledge test or practical test, if the recommendation for the issuance of that certificate or rating is in accordance with the following requirements:

(a) The person graduated from a training course for which the pilot school holds examining authority.

(b) Except as provided in this paragraph, the person satisfactorily completed all the curriculum requirements of that pilot school's approved training course. A person who transfers from one part 141 approved pilot school to another part 141 approved pilot school may receive credit for that previous training, provided the following requirements are met:

(1) The maximum credited training time does not exceed one-half of the receiving school's curriculum requirements;

(2) The person completes a knowledge and proficiency test conducted by the receiving school for the purpose of determining the amount of pilot experience and knowledge to be credited;

(3) The receiving school determines (based on the person's performance on the knowledge and proficiency test required by paragraph (b)(2) of this section) the amount of credit to be awarded, and records that credit in the person's training record;

(4) The person who requests credit for previous pilot experience and knowledge obtained the experience and knowledge from another part 141 approved pilot school and training course; and

(5) The receiving school retains a copy of the person's training record from the previous school.

(c) Tests given by a pilot school that holds examining authority must be approved by the Administrator and be at least equal in scope, depth, and difficulty to the comparable knowledge and practical tests prescribed by the Administrator under part 61 of this chapter.

(d) A pilot school that holds examining authority may not use its knowledge or practical tests if the school:

(1) Knows, or has reason to believe, the test has been compromised; or

(2) Is notified by an FAA Flight Standards District Office that there is reason to believe or it is known that the test has been compromised.

(e) A pilot school that holds examining authority must maintain a record of all temporary airman certificates it issues, which consist of the following information:

(1) A chronological listing that includes—

(i) The date the temporary airman certificate was issued;

(ii) The student to whom the temporary airman certificate was issued, and that student's permanent mailing address and telephone number;

(iii) The training course from which the student graduated;

(iv) The name of person who conducted the knowledge or practical test;

(v) The type of temporary airman certificate or rating issued to the student; and

(vi) The date the student's airman application file was sent to the FAA for processing for a permanent airman certificate.

(2) A copy of the record containing each student's graduation certificate, airman application, temporary airman certificate, superseded airman certificate (if applicable), and knowledge test or practical test results; and

(3) The records required by paragraph (e) of this section must be retained for 1 year and made available to the Administrator upon request. These records must be surrendered to the Administrator when the pilot school ceases to have examining authority.

(f) Except for pilot schools that have an airman certification representative, when a student passes the knowledge test or practical test, the pilot school that holds examining authority must submit that student's airman application file and training record to the FAA for processing for the issuance of a permanent airman certificate.

[Docket No. 25910, 62 FR 16347, April 4, 1997; as amended by Amdt. 141–9, 62 FR 40908, July 30, 1997]

Subpart E— Operating Rules

§ 141.71 Applicability.

This subpart prescribes the operating rules applicable to a pilot school or provisional pilot school certificated under the provisions of this part.

§ 141.73 Privileges.

(a) The holder of a pilot school certificate or a provisional pilot school certificate may advertise and conduct approved pilot training courses in accordance with the certificate and any ratings that it holds.

(b) A pilot school that holds examining authority for an approved training course may recommend a graduate of that course for the issuance of an appropriate pilot, flight instructor, or ground instructor certificate and rating, without taking an FAA knowledge test or practical test, provided the training course has been approved and meets the minimum ground and flight training time requirements of this part.

§ 141.75 Aircraft requirements.

The following items must be carried on each aircraft used for flight training and solo flights:

(a) A pretakeoff and prelanding checklist; and

(b) The operator's handbook for the aircraft, if one is furnished by the manufacturer, or copies of the handbook if furnished to each student using the aircraft.

[Docket No. 25910, 62 FR 40908, July 30, 1997]

§ 141.77 Limitations.

(a) The holder of a pilot school certificate or a provisional pilot school certificate may not issue a graduation certificate to a student, or recommend a student for a pilot certificate or rating, unless the student has:

(1) Completed the training specified in the pilot school's course of training; and

(2) Passed the required final tests.

(b) Except as provided in paragraph (c) of this section, the holder of a pilot school certificate or a provisional pilot school certificate may not graduate a student from a course of training unless the student has completed all of the curriculum requirements of that course;

(c) A student may be given credit towards the curriculum requirements of a course for previous pilot experience and knowledge, provided the following conditions are met:

(1) If the credit is based upon a part 141-approved training course, the credit given that student for the previous pilot experience and knowl-

edge may be 50 percent of the curriculum requirements and must be based upon a proficiency test
or knowledge test, or both, conducted by the receiving pilot school;

(2) If the credit is not based upon a part 141-
approved training course, the credit given that student for the previous pilot experience and knowledge shall not exceed more than 25 percent of
the curriculum requirements and must be based
upon a proficiency test or knowledge test, or both,
conducted by the receiving pilot school;

(3) The receiving school determines the
amount of course credit to be transferred under
paragraph (c)(1) or paragraph (c)(2) of this section, based on a proficiency test or knowledge
test, or both, of the student; and

(4) Credit for training specified in paragraph
(c)(1) or paragraph (c)(2) of this section may be
given only if the previous provider of the training
has certified in writing, or other form acceptable to
the Administrator as to the kind and amount of
training provided, and the result of each stage
check and end-of-course test, if applicable, given
to the student.

[Docket No. 25910, 62 FR 16347, April 4, 1997; as
amended by Amdt. 141–9, 62 FR 40908, July 30, 1997]

§ 141.79 Flight training.

(a) No person other than a certificated flight instructor or commercial pilot with a lighter-than-air
rating who has the ratings and the minimum qualifications specified in the approved training course
outline may give a student flight training under an
approved course of training.

(b) No student pilot may be authorized to start
a solo practice flight from an airport until the flight
has been approved by a certificated flight instructor or commercial pilot with a lighter-than-air rating who is present at that airport.

(c) Each chief instructor and assistant chief instructor assigned to a training course must complete, at least once every 12 calendar months, an
approved syllabus of training consisting of ground
or flight training, or both, or an approved flight instructor refresher course.

(d) Each certificated flight instructor or commercial pilot with a lighter-than-air rating who is
assigned to a flight training course must satisfactorily complete the following tasks, which must be
administered by the school's chief instructor, assistant chief instructor, or check instructor:

(1) Prior to receiving authorization to train students in a flight training course, must—

(i) Accomplish a review of and receive a briefing on the objectives and standards of that training course; and

(ii) Accomplish an initial proficiency check in
each make and model of aircraft used in that

training course in which that person provides
training; and

(2) Every 12 calendar months after the month
in which the person last complied with the requirements of paragraph (d)(1)(ii) of this section, accomplish a recurrent proficiency check in one of
the aircraft in which the person trains students.

[Docket No. 25910, 62 FR 16347, April 4, 1997; as
amended by Amdt. 141–9, 62 FR 40908, July 30, 1997]

§ 141.81 Ground training.

(a) Except as provided in paragraph (b) of this
section, each instructor who is assigned to a
ground training course must hold a flight or
ground instructor certificate, or a commercial pilot
certificate with a lighter-than-air rating, with the
appropriate rating for that course of training.

(b) A person who does not meet the requirements of paragraph (a) of this section may be assigned ground training duties in a ground training
course, if:

(1) The chief instructor who is assigned to that
ground training course finds the person qualified
to give that training; and

(2) The training is given while under the supervision of the chief instructor or the assistant chief
instructor who is present at the facility when the
training is given.

(c) An instructor may not be used in a ground
training course until that instructor has been
briefed on the objectives and standards of that
course by the chief instructor, assistant chief instructor, or check instructor.

[Docket No. 25910, 62 FR 16347, April 4, 1997; as
amended by Amdt. 141–9, 62 FR 40908, July 30, 1997]

§ 141.83 Quality of training.

(a) Each pilot school or provisional pilot school
must meet the following requirements:

(1) Comply with its approved training course;
and

(2) Provide training of such quality that meets
the requirements of § 141.5(d) of this part.

(b) The failure of a pilot school or provisional pilot school to maintain the quality of training specified in paragraph (a) of this section may be the
basis for suspending or revoking that school's certificate.

(c) When requested by the Administrator, a pilot school or provisional pilot school must allow
the FAA to administer any knowledge test, practical test, stage check, or end-of-course test to its
students.

(d) When a stage check or end-of-course test is
administered by the FAA under the provisions of
paragraph (c) of this section, and the student has
not completed the training course, then that test

will be based on the standards prescribed in the school's approved training course.

(e) When a practical test or knowledge test is administered by the FAA under the provisions of paragraph (c) of this section, to a student who has completed the school's training course, that test will be based upon the areas of operation approved by the Administrator.

[Docket No. 25910, 62 FR 16347, April 4, 1997; as amended by Amdt. 141–9, 62 FR 40908, July 30, 1997]

§ 141.85 Chief instructor responsibilities.

(a) Each person designated as a chief instructor for a pilot school or provisional pilot school shall be responsible for:

(1) Certifying each student's training record, graduation certificate, stage check and end-of-course test report, recommendation for course completion, and application;

(2) Ensuring that each certificated flight instructor, certificated ground instructor, or commercial pilot with a lighter-than-air rating passes an initial proficiency check prior to that instructor being assigned instructing duties in the school's approved training course, and thereafter that the instructor passes a recurrent proficiency check every 12 calendar months after the month in which the initial test was accomplished;

(3) Ensuring that each student accomplishes the required stage checks and end-of-course tests in accordance with the school's approved training course; and

(4) Maintaining training techniques, procedures, and standards for the school that are acceptable to the Administrator.

(b) The chief instructor or an assistant chief instructor must be available at the pilot school or, if away from the pilot school, be available by telephone, radio, or other electronic means during the time that training is given for an approved training course.

(c) The chief instructor may delegate authority for conducting stage checks, end-of-course tests, and flight instructor proficiency checks to the assistant chief instructor or a check instructor.

[Docket No. 25910, 62 FR 16347, April 4, 1997; as amended by Amdt. 141–9, 62 FR 40908, July 30, 1997]

§ 141.87 Change of chief instructor.

Whenever a pilot school or provisional pilot school makes a change of designation of its chief instructor, that school:

(a) Must immediately provide the FAA Flight Standards District Office that has jurisdiction over the area in which the school is located with written notification of the change;

(b) May conduct training without a chief instructor for that training course for a period not to exceed 60 days while awaiting the designation and approval of another chief instructor;

(c) May, for a period not to exceed 60 days, have the stage checks and end-of-course tests administered by:

(1) The training course's assistant chief instructor, if one has been designated;

(2) The training course's check instructor, if one has been designated;

(3) An FAA inspector; or

(4) An examiner.

(d) Must, after 60 days without a chief instructor, cease operations and surrender its certificate to the Administrator; and

(e) May have its certificate reinstated, upon:

(1) Designating and approving another chief instructor;

(2) Showing it meets the requirements of § 141.27(a)(2) of this part; and

(3) Applying for reinstatement on a form and in a manner prescribed by the Administrator.

§ 141.89 Maintenance of personnel, facilities, and equipment.

The holder of a pilot school certificate or provisional pilot school certificate may not provide training to a student who is enrolled in an approved course of training unless:

(a) Each airport, aircraft, and facility necessary for that training meets the standards specified in the holder's approved training course outline and the appropriate requirements of this part; and

(b) Except as provided in § 141.87 of this part, each chief instructor, assistant chief instructor, check instructor, or instructor meets the qualifications specified in the holder's approved course of training and the appropriate requirements of this part.

§ 141.91 Satellite bases.

The holder of a pilot school certificate or provisional pilot school certificate may conduct ground training or flight training in an approved course of training at a base other than its main operations base if:

(a) An assistant chief instructor is designated for each satellite base, and that assistant chief instructor is available at that base or, if away from the premises, by telephone, radio, or other electronic means during the time that training is provided for an approved training course;

(b) The airport, facilities, and personnel used at the satellite base meet the appropriate requirements of subpart B of this part and its approved training course outline;

141

(c) The instructors are under the direct supervision of the chief instructor or assistant chief instructor for the appropriate training course, who is readily available for consultation in accordance with § 141.85(b) of this part; and

(d) The FAA Flight Standards District Office having jurisdiction over the area in which the school is located is notified in writing if training is conducted at a base other than the school's main operations base for more than 7 consecutive days.

[Docket No. 25910, 62 FR 16347, April 4, 1997; as amended by Amdt. 141–9, 62 FR 40908, July 30, 1997]

§ 141.93 Enrollment.

(a) The holder of a pilot school certificate or a provisional pilot school certificate must, at the time a student is enrolled in an approved training course, furnish that student with a copy of the following:

(1) A certificate of enrollment containing—

(i) The name of the course in which the student is enrolled; and

(ii) The date of that enrollment.

(2) A copy of the student's training syllabus.

(3) A copy of the safety procedures and practices developed by the school that describe the use of the school's facilities and the operation of its aircraft. Those procedures and practices shall include training on at least the following information—

(i) The weather minimums required by the school for dual and solo flights;

(ii) The procedures for starting and taxiing aircraft on the ramp;

(iii) Fire precautions and procedures;

(iv) Redispatch procedures after unprogrammed landings, on and off airports;

(v) Aircraft discrepancies and approval for return-to-service determinations;

(vi) Securing of aircraft when not in use;

(vii) Fuel reserves necessary for local and cross-country flights;

(viii) Avoidance of other aircraft in flight and on the ground;

(ix) Minimum altitude limitations and simulated emergency landing instructions; and

(x) A description of and instructions regarding the use of assigned practice areas.

(b) The holder of a pilot school certificate or provisional pilot school certificate must maintain a monthly listing of persons enrolled in each training course offered by the school.

[Docket No. 25910, 62 FR 16347, April 4, 1997; as amended by Amdt. 141–9, 62 FR 40908, July 30, 1997]

§ 141.95 Graduation certificate.

(a) The holder of a pilot school certificate or provisional pilot school certificate must issue a graduation certificate to each student who completes its approved course of training.

(b) The graduation certificate must be issued to the student upon completion of the course of training and contain at least the following information:

(1) The name of the school and the certificate number of the school;

(2) The name of the graduate to whom it was issued;

(3) The course of training for which it was issued;

(4) The date of graduation;

(5) A statement that the student has satisfactorily completed each required stage of the approved course of training including the tests for those stages;

(6) A certification of the information contained on the graduation certificate by the chief instructor for that course of training; and

(7) A statement showing the cross-country training that the student received in the course of training.

[Docket No. 25910, 62 FR 16347, April 4, 1997; as amended by Amdt. 141–9, 62 FR 40908, July 30, 1997]

Subpart F—Records

§ 141.101 Training records.

(a) Each holder of a pilot school certificate or provisional pilot school certificate must establish and maintain a current and accurate record of the participation of each student enrolled in an approved course of training conducted by the school that includes the following information:

(1) The date the student was enrolled in the approved course;

(2) A chronological log of the student's course attendance, subjects, and flight operations covered in the student's training, and the names and grades of any tests taken by the student; and

(3) The date the student graduated, terminated training, or transferred to another school.

(b) The records required to be maintained in a student's logbook will not suffice for the record required by paragraph (a) of this section.

(c) Whenever a student graduates, terminates training, or transfers to another school, the student's record must be certified to that effect by the chief instructor.

(d) The holder of a pilot school certificate or a provisional pilot school certificate must retain each student record required by this section for at least 1 year from the date that the student:

(1) Graduates from the course to which the record pertains;

(2) Terminates enrollment in the course to which the record pertains; or

(3) Transfers to another school.

(e) The holder of a pilot school certificate or a provisional pilot school certificate must make a copy of the student's training record available upon request by the student.

[Docket No. 25910, 62 FR 16347, April 4, 1997; as amended by Amdt. 141–9, 62 FR 40908, July 30, 1997]

APPENDIX A TO PART 141

RECREATIONAL PILOT CERTIFICATION COURSE

1. *Applicability.* This appendix prescribes the minimum curriculum required for a recreational pilot certification course under this part, for the following ratings:

(a) Airplane single-engine.

(b) Rotorcraft helicopter.

(c) Rotorcraft gyroplane.

2. *Eligibility for enrollment.* A person must hold a student pilot certificate prior to enrolling in the flight portion of the recreational pilot certification course.

3. *Aeronautical knowledge training.* Each approved course must include at least 20 hours of ground training on the following aeronautical knowledge areas, appropriate to the aircraft category and class for which the course applies:

(a) Applicable Federal Aviation Regulations for recreational pilot privileges, limitations, and flight operations;

(b) Accident reporting requirements of the National Transportation Safety Board;

(c) Applicable subjects in the "Aeronautical Information Manual" and the appropriate FAA advisory circulars;

(d) Use of aeronautical charts for VFR navigation using pilotage with the aid of a magnetic compass;

(e) Recognition of critical weather situations from the ground and in flight, windshear avoidance, and the procurement and use of aeronautical weather reports and forecasts;

(f) Safe and efficient operation of aircraft, including collision avoidance, and recognition and avoidance of wake turbulence;

(g) Effects of density altitude on takeoff and climb performance;

(h) Weight and balance computations;

(i) Principles of aerodynamics, powerplants, and aircraft systems;

(j) Stall awareness, spin entry, spins, and spin recovery techniques, if applying for an airplane single-engine rating;

(k) Aeronautical decision making and judgment; and

(l) Preflight action that includes—

(1) How to obtain information on runway lengths at airports of intended use, data on takeoff and landing distances, weather reports and forecasts, and fuel requirements; and

(2) How to plan for alternatives if the planned flight cannot be completed or delays are encountered.

4. *Flight training.*

(a) Each approved course must include at least 30 hours of flight training (of which 15 hours must be with a certificated flight instructor and 3 hours must be solo flight training as provided in section No. 5 of this appendix) on the approved areas of operation listed in paragraph (c) of this section that are appropriate to the aircraft category and class rating for which the course applies, including:

(1) Except as provided in § 61.100 of this chapter, 2 hours of dual flight training to and at an airport that is located more than 25 nautical miles from the airport where the applicant normally trains, with at least three takeoffs and three landings; and

(2) 3 hours of dual flight training in an aircraft that is appropriate to the aircraft category and class for which the course applies, in preparation for the practical test within 60 days preceding the date of the test.

(b) Each training flight must include a preflight briefing and a postflight critique of the student by the flight instructor assigned to that flight.

(c) Flight training must include the following approved areas of operation appropriate to the aircraft category and class rating—

(1) *For an airplane single-engine course:*
(i) Preflight preparation;
(ii) Preflight procedures;
(iii) Airport operations;
(iv) Takeoffs, landings, and go-arounds;
(v) Performance maneuvers;
(vi) Ground reference maneuvers;
(vii) Navigation;
(viii) Slow flight and stalls;
(ix) Emergency operations; and
(x) Postflight procedures.

(2) *For a rotorcraft helicopter course:*
(i) Preflight preparation;
(ii) Preflight procedures;
(iii) Airport and heliport operations;
(iv) Hovering maneuvers;
(v) Takeoffs, landings, and go-arounds;
(vi) Performance maneuvers;
(vii) Navigation;
(viii) Emergency operations; and
(ix) Postflight procedures.

(3) *For a rotorcraft gyroplane course:*
(i) Preflight preparation;
(ii) Preflight procedures;

141

(iii) Airport operations;
(iv) Takeoffs, landings, and go-arounds;
(v) Performance maneuvers;
(vi) Ground reference maneuvers;
(vii) Navigation;
(viii) Flight at slow airspeeds;
(ix) Emergency operations; and
(x) Postflight procedures.

5. *Solo flight training.* Each approved course must include at least 3 hours of solo flight training on the approved areas of operation listed in paragraph (c) of section No. 4 of this appendix that are appropriate to the aircraft category and class rating for which the course applies.

6. *Stage checks and end-of-course tests.*

(a) Each student enrolled in a recreational pilot course must satisfactorily accomplish the stage checks and end-of-course tests, in accordance with the school's approved training course, consisting of the approved areas of operation listed in paragraph (c) of section No. 4 of this appendix that are appropriate to the aircraft category and class rating for which the course applies.

(b) Each student must demonstrate satisfactory proficiency prior to receiving an endorsement to operate an aircraft in solo flight.

[Docket No. 25910, 62 FR 16347, April 4, 1997; as amended by Amdt. 141–9, 62 FR 40908, July 30, 1997]

APPENDIX B TO PART 141

PRIVATE PILOT CERTIFICATION COURSE

1. *Applicability.* This appendix prescribes the minimum curriculum for a private pilot certification course required under this part, for the following ratings:

(a) Airplane single-engine.
(b) Airplane multiengine.
(c) Rotorcraft helicopter.
(d) Rotorcraft gyroplane.
(e) Powered-lift.
(f) Glider.
(g) Lighter-than-air airship.
(h) Lighter-than-air balloon.

2. *Eligibility for enrollment.* A person must hold a recreational or student pilot certificate prior to enrolling in the flight portion of the private pilot certification course.

3. *Aeronautical knowledge training.*

(a) Each approved course must include at least the following ground training on the aeronautical knowledge areas listed in paragraph (b) of this section, appropriate to the aircraft category and class rating:

(1) 35 hours of training if the course is for an airplane, rotorcraft, or powered-lift category rating.

(2) 15 hours of training if the course is for a glider category rating.

(3) 10 hours of training if the course is for a lighter-than-air category with a balloon class rating.

(4) 35 hours of training if the course is for a lighter-than-air category with an airship class rating.

(b) Ground training must include the following aeronautical knowledge areas:

(1) Applicable Federal Aviation Regulations for private pilot privileges, limitations, and flight operations;

(2) Accident reporting requirements of the National Transportation Safety Board;

(3) Applicable subjects of the "Aeronautical Information Manual" and the appropriate FAA advisory circulars;

(4) Aeronautical charts for VFR navigation using pilotage, dead reckoning, and navigation systems;

(5) Radio communication procedures;

(6) Recognition of critical weather situations from the ground and in flight, windshear avoidance, and the procurement and use of aeronautical weather reports and forecasts;

(7) Safe and efficient operation of aircraft, including collision avoidance, and recognition and avoidance of wake turbulence;

(8) Effects of density altitude on takeoff and climb performance;

(9) Weight and balance computations;

(10) Principles of aerodynamics, powerplants, and aircraft systems;

(11) If the course of training is for an airplane category or glider category rating, stall awareness, spin entry, spins, and spin recovery techniques;

(12) Aeronautical decision making and judgment; and

(13) Preflight action that includes—

(i) How to obtain information on runway lengths at airports of intended use, data on takeoff and landing distances, weather reports and forecasts, and fuel requirements; and

(ii) How to plan for alternatives if the planned flight cannot be completed or delays are encountered.

4. *Flight training.*

(a) Each approved course must include at least the following flight training, as provided in this section and section No. 5 of this appendix, on the approved areas of operation listed in paragraph (d) of this section, appropriate to the aircraft category and class rating:

(1) 35 hours of training if the course is for an airplane, rotorcraft, powered-lift, or airship rating.

(2) 6 hours of training if the course is for a glider rating.

(3) 8 hours of training if the course is for a balloon rating.

(b) Each approved course must include at least the following flight training:

(1) *For an airplane single-engine course:* 20 hours of flight training from a certificated flight instructor on the approved areas of operation in paragraph (d)(1) of this section that includes at least—

(i) Except as provided in § 61.111 of this chapter, 3 hours of cross-country flight training in a single-engine airplane;

(ii) 3 hours of night flight training in a single-engine airplane that includes—

(A) One cross-country flight of more than 100-nautical-miles total distance; and

(B) 10 takeoffs and 10 landings to a full stop (with each landing involving a flight in the traffic pattern) at an airport.

(iii) 3 hours of instrument training in a single-engine airplane; and

(iv) 3 hours of flight training in a single-engine airplane in preparation for the practical test within 60 days preceding the date of the test.

(2) *For an airplane multiengine course:* 20 hours of flight training from a certificated flight instructor on the approved areas of operation in paragraph (d)(2) of this section that includes at least—

(i) Except as provided in § 61.111 of this chapter, 3 hours of cross-country flight training in a multiengine airplane;

(ii) 3 hours of night flight training in a multiengine airplane that includes—

(A) One cross-country flight of more than 100-nautical-miles total distance; and

(B) 10 takeoffs and 10 landings to a full stop (with each landing involving a flight in the traffic pattern) at an airport.

(iii) 3 hours of instrument training in a multiengine airplane; and

(iv) 3 hours of flight training in a multiengine airplane in preparation for the practical test within 60 days preceding the date of the test.

(3) *For a rotorcraft helicopter course:* 20 hours of flight training from a certificated flight instructor on the approved areas of operation in paragraph (d)(3) of this section that includes at least—

(i) Except as provided in § 61.111 of this chapter, 3 hours of cross-country flight training in a helicopter.

(ii) 3 hours of night flight training in a helicopter that includes—

(A) One cross-country flight of more than 50-nautical-miles total distance; and

(B) 10 takeoffs and 10 landings to a full stop (with each landing involving a flight in the traffic pattern) at an airport.

(iii) 3 hours of flight training in a helicopter in preparation for the practical test within 60 days preceding the date of the test.

(4) *For a rotorcraft gyroplane course:* 20 hours of flight training from a certificated flight instructor on the approved areas of operation in paragraph (d)(4) of this section that includes at least—

(i) Except as provided in § 61.111 of this chapter, 3 hours of cross-country flight training in a gyroplane.

(ii) 3 hours of night flight training in a gyroplane that includes—

(A) One cross-country flight over 50-nautical-miles total distance; and

(B) 10 takeoffs and 10 landings to a full stop (with each landing involving a flight in the traffic pattern) at an airport.

(iii) 3 hours of flight training in a gyroplane in preparation for the practical test within 60 days preceding the date of the test.

(5) *For a powered-lift course:* 20 hours of flight training from a certificated flight instructor on the approved areas of operation in paragraph (d)(5) of this section that includes at least—

(i) Except as provided in § 61.111 of this chapter, 3 hours of cross-country flight training in a powered-lift;

(ii) 3 hours of night flight training in a powered-lift that includes—

(A) One cross-country flight of more than 100-nautical-miles total distance; and

(B) 10 takeoffs and 10 landings to a full stop (with each landing involving a flight in the traffic pattern) at an airport.

(iii) 3 hours of instrument training in a powered-lift; and

(iv) 3 hours of flight training in a powered-lift in preparation for the practical test, within 60 days preceding the date of the test.

(6) *For a glider course:* 4 hours of flight training from a certificated flight instructor on the approved areas of operation in paragraph (d)(6) of this section that includes at least—

(i) Five training flights in a glider with a certificated flight instructor on the launch/tow procedures approved for the course and on the appropriate approved areas of operation listed in paragraph (d)(6) of this section; and

(ii) Three training flights in a glider with a certificated flight instructor in preparation for the practical test within 60 days preceding the date of the test.

(7) *For a lighter-than-air airship course:* 20 hours of flight training from a commercial pilot with an airship rating on the approved areas of operation in paragraph (d)(7) of this section that includes at least—

(i) Except as provided in § 61.111 of this chapter, 3 hours of cross-country flight training in an airship;

(ii) 3 hours of night flight training in an airship that includes—

(A) One cross-country flight over 25-nautical-miles total distance; and

(B) Five takeoffs and five landings to a full stop (with each landing involving a flight in the traffic pattern) at an airport.

(iii) 3 hours of instrument training in an airship; and

(iv) 3 hours of flight training in an airship in preparation for the practical test within 60 days preceding the date of the test.

(8) *For a lighter-than-air balloon course:* 8 hours of flight training, including at least five training flights, from a commercial pilot with a balloon rating on the approved areas of operation in paragraph (d)(8) of this section, that includes—

(i) If the training is being performed in a gas balloon—

(A) Two flights of 1 hour each;

(B) One flight involving a controlled ascent to 3,000 feet above the launch site; and

(C) Two flights in preparation for the practical test within 60 days preceding the date of the test.

(ii) If the training is being performed in a balloon with an airborne heater—

(A) Two flights of 30 minutes each;

(B) One flight involving a controlled ascent to 2,000 feet above the launch site; and

(C) Two flights in preparation for the practical test within 60 days preceding the date of the test.

(c) For use of flight simulators or flight training devices:

(1) The course may include training in a flight simulator or flight training device, provided it is representative of the aircraft for which the course is approved, meets the requirements of this paragraph, and the training is given by an authorized instructor.

(2) Training in a flight simulator that meets the requirements of § 141.41(a) of this part may be credited for a maximum of 20 percent of the total flight training hour requirements of the approved course, or of this section, whichever is less.

(3) Training in a flight training device that meets the requirements of § 141.41(b) of this part may be credited for a maximum of 15 percent of the total flight training hour requirements of the approved course, or of this section, whichever is less.

(4) Training in flight simulators or flight training devices described in paragraphs (c)(2) and (c)(3) of this section, if used in combination, may be credited for a maximum of 20 percent of the total flight training hour requirements of the approved course, or of this section, whichever is less. However, credit for training in a flight training device that meets the requirements of § 141.41(b) cannot exceed the limitation provided for in paragraph (c)(3) of this section.

(d) Each approved course must include the flight training on the approved areas of operation listed in this paragraph that are appropriate to the aircraft category and class rating—

(1) *For a single-engine airplane course:*
(i) Preflight preparation;
(ii) Preflight procedures;
(iii) Airport and seaplane base operations;
(iv) Takeoffs, landings, and go-arounds;
(v) Performance maneuvers;
(vi) Ground reference maneuvers;
(vii) Navigation;
(viii) Slow flight and stalls;
(ix) Basic instrument maneuvers;
(x) Emergency operations;
(xi) Night operations, and
(xii) Postflight procedures.

(2) *For a multiengine airplane course:*
(i) Preflight preparation;
(ii) Preflight procedures;
(iii) Airport and seaplane base operations;
(iv) Takeoffs, landings, and go-arounds;
(v) Performance maneuvers;
(vi) Ground reference maneuvers;
(vii) Navigation;
(viii) Slow flight and stalls;
(ix) Basic instrument maneuvers;
(x) Emergency operations;
(xi) Multiengine operations;
(xii) Night operations; and
(xiii) Postflight procedures.

(3) *For a rotorcraft helicopter course:*
(i) Preflight preparation;
(ii) Preflight procedures;
(iii) Airport and heliport operations;
(iv) Hovering maneuvers;
(v) Takeoffs, landings, and go-arounds;
(vi) Performance maneuvers;
(vii) Navigation;
(viii) Emergency operations;
(ix) Night operations; and
(x) Postflight procedures.

(4) *For a rotorcraft gyroplane course:*
(i) Preflight preparation;
(ii) Preflight procedures;
(iii) Airport operations;
(iv) Takeoffs, landings, and go-arounds;
(v) Performance maneuvers;
(vi) Ground reference maneuvers;
(vii) Navigation;
(viii) Flight at slow airspeeds;
(ix) Emergency operations;
(x) Night operations; and
(xi) Postflight procedures.

(5) *For a powered-lift course:*
(i) Preflight preparation;
(ii) Preflight procedures;
(iii) Airport and heliport operations;
(iv) Hovering maneuvers;
(v) Takeoffs, landings, and go-arounds;

(vi) Performance maneuvers;
(vii) Ground reference maneuvers;
(viii) Navigation;
(ix) Slow flight and stalls;
(x) Basic instrument maneuvers;
(xi) Emergency operations;
(xii) Night operations; and
(xiii) Postflight procedures.

(6) *For a glider course:*
(i) Preflight preparation;
(ii) Preflight procedures;
(iii) Airport and gliderport operations;
(iv) Launches/tows, as appropriate, and landings;
(v) Performance speeds;
(vi) Soaring techniques;
(vii) Performance maneuvers;
(viii) Navigation;
(ix) Slow flight and stalls;
(x) Emergency operations; and
(xi) Postflight procedures.

(7) *For a lighter-than-air airship course:*
(i) Preflight preparation;
(ii) Preflight procedures;
(iii) Airport operations;
(iv) Takeoffs, landings, and go-arounds;
(v) Performance maneuvers;
(vi) Ground reference maneuvers;
(vii) Navigation;
(viii) Emergency operations; and
(ix) Postflight procedures.

(8) *For a lighter-than-air balloon course:*
(i) Preflight preparation;
(ii) Preflight procedures;
(iii) Airport operations;
(iv) Launches and landings;
(v) Performance maneuvers;
(vi) Navigation;
(vii) Emergency operations; and
(viii) Postflight procedures.

5. *Solo flight training.* Each approved course must include at least the following solo flight training:
(a) *For an airplane single-engine course:* 5 hours of solo flight training in a single-engine airplane on the approved areas of operation in paragraph (d)(1) of section No. 4 of this appendix that includes at least—
(1) One solo cross-country flight of at least 100 nautical miles with landings at a minimum of three points, and one segment of the flight consisting of a straight-line distance of at least 50 nautical miles between the takeoff and landing locations; and
(2) Three takeoffs and three landings to a full stop (with each landing involving a flight in the traffic pattern) at an airport with an operating control tower.

(b) *For an airplane multiengine course:* 5 hours of flight training in a multiengine airplane performing the duties of a pilot in command while under the supervision of a certificated flight instructor. The training must consist of the approved areas of operation in paragraph (d)(2) of section No. 4 of this appendix, and include at least—
(1) One cross-country flight of at least 100 nautical miles with landings at a minimum of three points, and one segment of the flight consisting of a straight-line distance of at least 50 nautical miles between the takeoff and landing locations; and
(2) Three takeoffs and three landings to a full stop (with each landing involving a flight in the traffic pattern) at an airport with an operating control tower.

(c) *For a rotorcraft helicopter course:* 5 hours of solo flight training in a helicopter on the approved areas of operation in paragraph (d)(3) of section No. 4 of this appendix that includes at least—
(1) One solo cross-country flight of more than 50 nautical miles with landings at a minimum of three points, and one segment of the flight consisting of a straight-line distance of at least 25 nautical miles between the takeoff and landing locations; and
(2) Three takeoffs and three landings to a full stop (with each landing involving a flight in the traffic pattern) at an airport with an operating control tower.

(d) *For a rotorcraft gyroplane course:* 5 hours of solo flight training in gyroplanes on the approved areas of operation in paragraph (d)(4) of section No. 4 of this appendix that includes at least—
(1) One solo cross-country flight of more than 50 nautical miles with landings at a minimum of three points, and one segment of the flight consisting of a straight-line distance of at least 25 nautical miles between the takeoff and landing locations; and
(2) Three takeoffs and three landings to a full stop (with each landing involving a flight in the traffic pattern) at an airport with an operating control tower.

(e) *For a powered-lift course:* 5 hours of solo flight training in a powered-lift on the approved areas of operation in paragraph (d)(5) of section No. 4 of this appendix that includes at least—
(1) One solo cross-country flight of at least 100 nautical miles with landings at a minimum of three points, and one segment of the flight consisting of a straight-line distance of at least 50 nautical miles between the takeoff and landing locations; and
(2) Three takeoffs and three landings to a full stop (with each landing involving a flight in the traffic pattern) at an airport with an operating control tower.

(f) *For a glider course:* Two solo flights in a glider on the approved areas of operation in paragraph (d)(6) of section No. 4 of this appendix, and the launch and tow procedures appropriate for the approved course.

(g) *For a lighter-than-air airship course:* 5 hours of flight training in an airship performing the duties of pilot in command while under the supervision of a commercial pilot with an airship rating. The training must consist of the approved areas of operation in paragraph (d)(7) of section No. 4 of this appendix.

(h) *For a lighter-than-air balloon course:* Two solo flights in a balloon with an airborne heater if the course involves a balloon with an airborne heater, or, if the course involves a gas balloon, at least two flights in a gas balloon performing the duties of pilot in command while under the supervision of a commercial pilot with a balloon rating. The training must consist of the approved areas of operation in paragraph (d)(8) of section No. 4 of this appendix, in the kind of balloon for which the course applies.

6. *Stage checks and end-of-course tests.*

(a) Each student enrolled in a private pilot course must satisfactorily accomplish the stage checks and end-of-course tests in accordance with the school's approved training course, consisting of the approved areas of operation listed in paragraph (d) of section No. 4 of this appendix that are appropriate to the aircraft category and class rating for which the course applies.

(b) Each student must demonstrate satisfactory proficiency prior to receiving an endorsement to operate an aircraft in solo flight.

[Docket No. 25910, 62 FR 16347, April 4, 1997; as amended by Amdt. 141–9, 62 FR 40908, July 30, 1997; Amdt. No. 141–10, 63 FR 20289, April 23, 1998]

APPENDIX C TO PART 141
INSTRUMENT RATING COURSE

1. *Applicability.* This appendix prescribes the minimum curriculum for an instrument rating course and an additional instrument rating course, required under this part, for the following ratings:

(a) Instrument — airplane.

(b) Instrument — helicopter.

(c) Instrument — powered-lift.

2. *Eligibility for enrollment.* A person must hold at least a private pilot certificate with an aircraft category and class rating appropriate to the instrument rating for which the course applies prior to enrolling in the flight portion of the instrument rating course.

3. *Aeronautical knowledge training.*

(a) Each approved course must include at least the following ground training on the aeronautical

knowledge areas listed in paragraph (b) of this section appropriate to the instrument rating for which the course applies:

(1) 30 hours of training if the course is for an initial instrument rating.

(2) 20 hours of training if the course is for an additional instrument rating.

(b) Ground training must include the following aeronautical knowledge areas:

(1) Applicable Federal Aviation Regulations for IFR flight operations;

(2) Appropriate information in the "Aeronautical Information Manual";

(3) Air traffic control system and procedures for instrument flight operations;

(4) IFR navigation and approaches by use of navigation systems;

(5) Use of IFR en route and instrument approach procedure charts;

(6) Procurement and use of aviation weather reports and forecasts, and the elements of forecasting weather trends on the basis of that information and personal observation of weather conditions;

(7) Safe and efficient operation of aircraft under instrument flight rules and conditions;

(8) Recognition of critical weather situations and windshear avoidance;

(9) Aeronautical decision making and judgment; and

(10) Crew resource management, to include crew communication and coordination.

4. *Flight training.*

(a) Each approved course must include at least the following flight training on the approved areas of operation listed in paragraph (d) of this section, appropriate to the instrument-aircraft category and class rating for which the course applies:

(1) 35 hours of instrument training if the course is for an initial instrument rating.

(2) 15 hours of instrument training if the course is for an additional instrument rating.

(b) For the use of flight simulators or flight training devices—

(1) The course may include training in a flight simulator or flight training device, provided it is representative of the aircraft for which the course is approved, meets the requirements of this paragraph, and the training is given by an authorized instructor.

(2) Training in a flight simulator that meets the requirements of § 141.41(a) of this part may be credited for a maximum of 50 percent of the total flight training hour requirements of the approved course, or of this section, whichever is less.

(3) Training in a flight training device that meets the requirements of § 141.41(b) of this part may be credited for a maximum of 40 percent of the total flight training hour requirements of the ap-

proved course, or of this section, whichever is less.

(4) Training in flight simulators or flight training devices described in paragraphs (b)(2) and (b)(3) of this section, if used in combination, may be credited for a maximum of 50 percent of the total flight training hour requirements of the approved course, or of this section, whichever is less. However, credit for training in a flight training device that meets the requirements of § 141.41(b) cannot exceed the limitation provided for in paragraph (b)(3) of this section.

(c) Each approved course must include the following flight training—

(1) *For an instrument airplane course:* Instrument training time from a certificated flight instructor with an instrument rating on the approved areas of operation in paragraph (d) of this section including at least one cross-country flight that—

(i) Is in the category and class of airplane that the course is approved for, and is performed under IFR;

(ii) Is a distance of at least 250 nautical miles along airways or ATC-directed routing with one segment of the flight consisting of at least a straight-line distance of 100 nautical miles between airports;

(iii) Involves an instrument approach at each airport; and

(iv) Involves three different kinds of approaches with the use of navigation systems.

(2) *For an instrument helicopter course:* Instrument training time from a certificated flight instructor with an instrument rating on the approved areas of operation in paragraph (d) of this section including at least one cross-country flight that—

(i) Is in a helicopter and is performed under IFR;

(ii) Is a distance of at least 100 nautical miles along airways or ATC-directed routing with one segment of the flight consisting of at least a straight-line distance of 50 nautical miles between airports;

(iii) Involves an instrument approach at each airport; and

(iv) Involves three different kinds of approaches with the use of navigation systems.

(3) *For an instrument powered-lift course:* Instrument training time from a certificated flight instructor with an instrument rating on the approved areas of operation in paragraph (d) of this section including at least one cross-country flight that—

(i) Is in a powered-lift and is performed under IFR;

(ii) Is a distance of at least 250 nautical miles along airways or ATC-directed routing with one segment of the flight consisting of at least a straight-line distance of 100 nautical miles between airports;

(iii) Involves an instrument approach at each airport; and

(iv) Involves three different kinds of approaches with the use of navigation systems.

(d) Each approved course must include the flight training on the approved areas of operation listed in this paragraph appropriate to the instrument aircraft category and class rating for which the course applies:

(1) Preflight preparation;
(2) Preflight procedures;
(3) Air traffic control clearances and procedures;
(4) Flight by reference to instruments;
(5) Navigation systems;
(6) Instrument approach procedures;
(7) Emergency operations; and
(8) Postflight procedures.

5. *Stage checks and end-of-course tests.*

Each student enrolled in an instrument rating course must satisfactorily accomplish the stage checks and end-of-course tests, in accordance with the school's approved training course, consisting of the approved areas of operation listed in paragraph (d) of section No. 4 of this appendix that are appropriate to the aircraft category and class rating for which the course applies.

[Docket No. 25910, 62 FR 16347, April 4, 1997; as amended by Amdt. 141–9, 62 FR 40909, July 30, 1997]

APPENDIX D TO PART 141
COMMERCIAL PILOT CERTIFICATION COURSE

1. *Applicability.* This appendix prescribes the minimum curriculum for a commercial pilot certification course required under this part, for the following ratings:

(a) Airplane single-engine.
(b) Airplane multiengine.
(c) Rotorcraft helicopter.
(d) Rotorcraft gyroplane.
(e) Powered-lift.
(f) Glider.
(g) Lighter-than-air airship.
(h) Lighter-than-air balloon.

2. *Eligibility for enrollment.* A person must hold the following prior to enrolling in the flight portion of the commercial pilot certification course:

(a) At least a private pilot certificate; and
(b) If the course is for a rating in an airplane or a powered-lift category, then the person must:

(1) Hold an instrument rating in the aircraft that is appropriate to the aircraft category rating for which the course applies; or

(2) Be concurrently enrolled in an instrument rating course that is appropriate to the aircraft category rating for which the course applies, and pass the required instrument rating practical test prior to completing the commercial pilot certification course.

3. *Aeronautical knowledge training.*

(a) Each approved course must include at least the following ground training on the aeronautical knowledge areas listed in paragraph (b) of this section, appropriate to the aircraft category and class rating for which the course applies:

(1) 35 hours of training if the course is for an airplane category rating or a powered-lift category rating.

(2) 65 hours of training if the course is for a lighter-than-air category with an airship class rating.

(3) 30 hours of training if the course is for a rotorcraft category rating.

(4) 20 hours of training if the course is for a glider category rating.

(5) 20 hours of training if the course is for lighter-than-air category with a balloon class rating.

(b) Ground training must include the following aeronautical knowledge areas:

(1) Federal Aviation Regulations that apply to commercial pilot privileges, limitations, and flight operations;

(2) Accident reporting requirements of the National Transportation Safety Board;

(3) Basic aerodynamics and the principles of flight;

(4) Meteorology, to include recognition of critical weather situations, windshear recognition and avoidance, and the use of aeronautical weather reports and forecasts;

(5) Safe and efficient operation of aircraft;

(6) Weight and balance computations;

(7) Use of performance charts;

(8) Significance and effects of exceeding aircraft performance limitations;

(9) Use of aeronautical charts and a magnetic compass for pilotage and dead reckoning;

(10) Use of air navigation facilities;

(11) Aeronautical decision making and judgment;

(12) Principles and functions of aircraft systems;

(13) Maneuvers, procedures, and emergency operations appropriate to the aircraft;

(14) Night and high-altitude operations;

(15) Descriptions of and procedures for operating within the National Airspace System; and

(16) Procedures for flight and ground training for lighter-than-air ratings.

4. *Flight training.*

(a) Each approved course must include at least the following flight training, as provided in this section and section No. 5 of this appendix, on the approved areas of operation listed in paragraph (d) of this section that are appropriate to the aircraft category and class rating for which the course applies:

(1) 120 hours of training if the course is for an airplane or powered-lift rating.

(2) 155 hours of training if the course is for a airship rating.

(3) 115 hours of training if the course is for a rotorcraft rating.

(4) 6 hours of training if the course is for a glider rating.

(5) 10 hours of training and 8 training flights if the course is for a balloon rating.

(b) Each approved course must include at least the following flight training:

(1) *For an airplane single-engine course:* 55 hours of flight training from a certificated flight instructor on the approved areas of operation listed in paragraph (d)(1) of this section that includes at least—

(i) 5 hours of instrument training in a single-engine airplane;

(ii) 10 hours of training in a single-engine airplane that has retractable landing gear, flaps, and a controllable pitch propeller, or is turbine-powered;

(iii) One cross-country flight in a single-engine airplane of at least a 2-hour duration, a total straight-line distance of more than 100 nautical miles from the original point of departure, and occurring in day VFR conditions;

(iv) One cross-country flight in a single-engine airplane of at least a 2-hour duration, a total straight-line distance of more than 100 nautical miles from the original point of departure, and occurring in night VFR conditions; and

(v) 3 hours in a single-engine airplane in preparation for the practical test within 60 days preceding the date of the test.

(2) *For an airplane multiengine course:* 55 hours of flight training from a certificated flight instructor on the approved areas of operation listed in paragraph (d)(2) of this section that includes at least—

(i) 5 hours of instrument training in a multiengine airplane;

(ii) 10 hours of training in a multiengine airplane that has retractable landing gear, flaps, and a controllable pitch propeller, or is turbine-powered;

(iii) One cross-country flight in a multiengine airplane of at least a 2-hour duration, a total straight-line distance of more than 100 nautical miles from the original point of departure, and occurring in day VFR conditions;

(iv) One cross-country flight in a multiengine airplane of at least a 2-hour duration, a total straight-line distance of more than 100 nautical miles from the original point of departure, and occurring in night VFR conditions; and

(v) 3 hours in a multiengine airplane in preparation for the practical test within 60 days preceding the date of the test.

(3) *For a rotorcraft helicopter course:* 30 hours of flight training from a certificated flight instructor

on the approved areas of operation listed in paragraph (d)(3) of this section that includes at least—

(i) 5 hours of instrument training;

(ii) One cross-country flight in a helicopter of at least a 2-hour duration, a total straight-line distance of more than 50 nautical miles from the original point of departure and occurring in day VFR conditions;

(iii) One cross-country flight in a helicopter of at least a 2-hour duration, a total straight-line distance of more than 50 nautical miles from the original point of departure, and occurring in night VFR conditions; and

(iv) 3 hours in a helicopter in preparation for the practical test within 60 days preceding the date of the test.

(4) *For a rotorcraft gyroplane course:* 30 hours of flight training from a certificated flight instructor on the approved areas of operation listed in paragraph (d)(4) of this section that includes at least—

(i) 5 hours of instrument training;

(ii) One cross-country flight in a gyroplane of at least a 2-hour duration, a total straight-line distance of more than 50 nautical miles from the original point of departure, and occurring in day VFR conditions;

(iii) One cross-country flight in a gyroplane of at least a 2-hour duration, a total straight-line distance of more than 50 nautical miles from the original point of departure, and occurring in night VFR conditions; and

(iv) 3 hours in a gyroplane in preparation for the practical test within 60 days preceding the date of the test.

(5) *For a powered-lift course:* 55 hours of flight training from a certificated flight instructor on the approved areas of operation listed in paragraph (d)(5) of this section that includes at least—

(i) 5 hours of instrument training in a powered-lift;

(ii) One cross-country flight in a powered-lift of at least a 2-hour duration, a total straight-line distance of more than 100 nautical miles from the original point of departure, and occurring in day VFR conditions;

(iii) One cross-country flight in a powered-lift of at least a 2-hour duration, a total straight-line distance of more than 100 nautical miles from the original point of departure, and occurring in night VFR conditions; and

(iv) 3 hours in a powered-lift in preparation for the practical test within 60 days preceding the date of the test.

(6) *For a glider course:* 4 hours of flight training from a certificated flight instructor on the approved areas of operation in paragraph (d)(6) of this section, that includes at least—

(i) Five training flights in a glider with a certificated flight instructor on the launch/tow procedures approved for the course and on the appropriate approved areas of operation listed in paragraph (d)(6) of this section; and

(ii) Three training flights in a glider a certificated flight instructor in preparation for the practical test within 60 days preceding the date of the test.

(7) *For a lighter-than-air airship course:* 55 hours of flight training in airships from a commercial pilot with an airship rating on the approved areas of operation in paragraph (d)(7) of this section that includes at least—

(i) 3 hours of instrument training in an airship;

(ii) One cross-country flight in an airship of at least a 1-hour duration, a total straight-line distance of more than 25 nautical miles from the original point of departure, and occurring in day VFR conditions; and

(iii) One cross-country flight in an airship of at least a 1-hour duration, a total straight-line distance of more than 25 nautical miles from the original point of departure, and occurring in night VFR conditions; and

(iv) 3 hours in an airship, in preparation for the practical test within 60 days preceding the date of the test.

(8) *For a lighter-than-air balloon course:* Flight training from a commercial pilot with a balloon rating on the approved areas of operation in paragraph (d)(8) of this section that includes at least—

(i) If the course involves training in a gas balloon:

(A) Two flights of 1 hour each;

(B) One flight involving a controlled ascent to at least 5,000 feet above the launch site; and

(C) Two flights in preparation for the practical test within 60 days preceding the date of the test.

(ii) If the course involves training in a balloon with an airborne heater:

(A) Two flights of 30 minutes each;

(B) One flight involving a controlled ascent to at least 3,000 feet above the launch site; and

(C) Two flights in preparation for the practical test within 60 days preceding the date of the test.

(c) For the use of flight simulators or flight training devices:

(1) The course may include training in a flight simulator or flight training device, provided it is representative of the aircraft for which the course is approved, meets the requirements of this paragraph, and is given by an authorized instructor.

(2) Training in a flight simulator that meets the requirements of § 141.41(a) of this part may be credited for a maximum of 30 percent of the total flight training hour requirements of the approved course, or of this section, whichever is less.

(3) Training in a flight training device that meets the requirements of § 141.41(b) of this part may be credited for a maximum of 20 percent of the total flight training hour requirements of the approved course, or of this section, whichever is less.

141

(4) Training in the flight training devices described in paragraphs (c)(2) and (c)(3) of this section, if used in combination, may be credited for a maximum of 30 percent of the total flight training hour requirements of the approved course, or of this section, whichever is less. However, credit for training in a flight training device that meets the requirements of § 141.41(b) cannot exceed the limitation provided for in paragraph (c)(3) of this section.

(d) Each approved course must include the flight training on the approved areas of operation listed in this paragraph that are appropriate to the aircraft category and class rating—

(1) *For an airplane single-engine course:*
(i) Preflight preparation;
(ii) Preflight procedures;
(iii) Airport and seaplane base operations;
(iv) Takeoffs, landings, and go-arounds;
(v) Performance maneuvers;
(vi) Navigation;
(vii) Slow flight and stalls;
(viii) Emergency operations;
(ix) High-altitude operations; and
(x) Postflight procedures.

(2) *For an airplane multiengine course:*
(i) Preflight preparation;
(ii) Preflight procedures;
(iii) Airport and seaplane base operations;
(iv) Takeoffs, landings, and go-arounds;
(v) Performance maneuvers;
(vi) Navigation;
(vii) Slow flight and stalls;
(viii) Emergency operations;
(ix) Multiengine operations;
(x) High-altitude operations; and
(xi) Postflight procedures.

(3) *For a rotorcraft helicopter course:*
(i) Preflight preparation;
(ii) Preflight procedures;
(iii) Airport and heliport operations;
(iv) Hovering maneuvers;
(v) Takeoffs, landings, and go-arounds;
(vi) Performance maneuvers;
(vii) Navigation;
(viii) Emergency operations;
(ix) Special operations; and
(x) Postflight procedures.

(4) *For a rotorcraft gyroplane course:*
(i) Preflight preparation;
(ii) Preflight procedures;
(iii) Airport operations;
(iv) Takeoffs, landings, and go-arounds;
(v) Performance maneuvers;
(vi) Navigation;
(vii) Flight at slow airspeeds;
(viii) Emergency operations; and
(ix) Postflight procedures.

(5) *For a powered-lift course:*
(i) Preflight preparation;
(ii) Preflight procedures;
(iii) Airport and heliport operations;
(iv) Hovering maneuvers;
(v) Takeoffs, landings, and go-arounds;
(vi) Performance maneuvers;
(vii) Navigation;
(viii) Slow flight and stalls;
(ix) Emergency operations;
(x) High altitude operations;
(xi) Special operations; and
(xii) Postflight procedures.

(6) *For a glider course:*
(i) Preflight preparation;
(ii) Preflight procedures;
(iii) Airport and gliderport operations;
(iv) Launches/tows, as appropriate, and landings;
(v) Performance speeds;
(vi) Soaring techniques;
(vii) Performance maneuvers;
(viii) Navigation;
(ix) Slow flight and stalls;
(x) Emergency operations; and
(xi) Postflight procedures.

(7) *For a lighter-than-air airship course:*
(i) Fundamentals of instructing;
(ii) Technical subjects;
(iii) Preflight preparation;
(iv) Preflight lessons on a maneuver to be performed in flight;
(v) Preflight procedures;
(vi) Airport operations;
(vii) Takeoffs, landings, and go-arounds;
(viii) Performance maneuvers;
(ix) Navigation;
(x) Emergency operations; and
(xi) Postflight procedures.

(8) *For a lighter-than-air balloon course:*
(i) Fundamentals of instructing;
(ii) Technical subjects;
(iii) Preflight preparation;
(iv) Preflight lesson on a maneuver to be performed in flight;
(v) Preflight procedures;
(vi) Airport operations;
(vii) Launches and landings;
(viii) Performance maneuvers;
(ix) Navigation;
(x) Emergency operations; and
(xi) Postflight procedures.

5. *Solo training.* Each approved course must include at least the following solo flight training:

(a) *For an airplane single-engine course:* 10 hours of solo flight training in a single-engine airplane on the approved areas of operation in paragraph (d)(1) of section No. 4 of this appendix that includes at least—

(1) One cross-country flight, if the training is being performed in the State of Hawaii, with landings at a minimum of three points, and one of the segments consisting of a straight-line distance of at least 150 nautical miles;

(2) One cross-country flight, if the training is being performed in a State other than Hawaii, with landings at a minimum of three points, and one segment of the flight consisting of a straight-line distance of at least 250 nautical miles; and

(3) 5 hours in night VFR conditions with 10 takeoffs and 10 landings (with each landing involving a flight with a traffic pattern) at an airport with an operating control tower.

(b) *For an airplane multiengine course:* 10 hours of flight training in a multiengine airplane performing the duties of pilot in command while under the supervision of a certificated flight instructor. The training must consist of the approved areas of operation in paragraph (d)(2) of section No. 4 of this appendix, and include at least—

(1) One cross-country flight, if the training is being performed in the State of Hawaii, with landings at a minimum of three points, and one of the segments consisting of a straight-line distance of at least 150 nautical miles;

(2) One cross-country flight, if the training is being performed in a State other than Hawaii, with landings at a minimum of three points and one segment of the flight consisting of straight-line distance of at least 250 nautical miles; and

(3) 5 hours in night VFR conditions with 10 takeoffs and 10 landings (with each landing involving a flight with a traffic pattern) at an airport with an operating control tower.

(c) *For a rotorcraft helicopter course:* 10 hours of solo flight training in a helicopter on the approved areas of operation in paragraph (d)(3) of section No. 4 of this appendix that includes at least—

(1) One cross-country flight with landings at a minimum of three points and one segment of the flight consisting of a straight-line distance of at least 50 nautical miles from the original point of departure; and

(2) 5 hours in night VFR conditions with 10 takeoffs and 10 landings (with each landing involving a flight with a traffic pattern) at an airport with an operating control tower.

(d) *For a rotorcraft-gyroplane course:* 10 hours of solo flight training in a gyroplane on the approved areas of operation in paragraph (d)(4) of section No. 4 of this appendix that includes at least—

(1) One cross-country flight with landings at a minimum of three points, and one segment of the flight consisting of a straight-line distance of at

least 50 nautical miles from the original point of departure; and

(2) 5 hours in night VFR conditions with 10 takeoffs and 10 landings (with each landing involving a flight with a traffic pattern) at an airport with an operating control tower.

(e) *For a powered-lift course:* 10 hours of solo flight training in a powered-lift on the approved areas of operation in paragraph (d)(5) of section No. 4 of this appendix that includes at least—

(1) One cross-country flight, if the training is being performed in the State of Hawaii, with landings at a minimum of three points, and one segment of the flight consisting of a straight-line distance of at least 150 nautical miles;

(2) One cross-country flight, if the training is being performed in a State other than Hawaii, with landings at a minimum of three points, and one segment of the flight consisting of a straight-line distance of at least 250 nautical miles; and

(3) 5 hours in night VFR conditions with 10 takeoffs and 10 landings (with each landing involving a flight with a traffic pattern) at an airport with an operating control tower.

(f) *For a glider course:* 5 solo flights in a glider on the approved areas of operation in paragraph (d)(6) of section No. 4 of this appendix.

(g) *For a lighter-than-air airship course:* 10 hours of flight training in an airship performing the duties of pilot in command under the supervision of a commercial pilot with an airship rating. The training must consist of the approved areas of operation in paragraph (d)(7) of section No. 4 of this appendix and include at least—

(1) One cross-country flight with landings at a minimum of three points, and one segment of the flight consisting of a straight-line distance of at least 25 nautical miles from the original point of departure; and

(2) 5 hours in night VFR conditions with 10 takeoffs and 10 landings (with each landing involving a flight with a traffic pattern).

(h) *For a lighter-than-air balloon course:* Two solo flights if the course is for a hot air balloon rating, or, if the course is for a gas balloon rating, at least two flights in a gas balloon, while performing the duties of pilot in command under the supervision of a commercial pilot with a balloon rating. The training shall consist of the approved areas of operation in paragraph (d)(8) of section No. 4 of this appendix, in the kind of balloon for which the course applies.

6. *Stage checks and end-of-course tests.*

(a) Each student enrolled in a commercial pilot course must satisfactorily accomplish the stage checks and end-of-course tests, in accordance with the school's approved training course, consisting of the approved areas of operation listed in paragraph (d) of section No. 4 of this appendix that are appropriate to aircraft category and class rating for which the course applies.

(b) Each student must demonstrate satisfactory proficiency prior to receiving an endorsement to operate an aircraft in solo flight.

[Docket No. 25910, 62 FR 16347, April 4, 1997; as amended by Amdt. 141–9, 62 FR 40909, July 30, 1997; Amdt. No. 141–10, 63 FR 20290, April 23, 1998]

APPENDIX E TO PART 141
AIRLINE TRANSPORT PILOT CERTIFICATION COURSE

1. *Applicability.* This appendix prescribes the minimum curriculum for an airline transport pilot certification course under this part, for the following ratings:

(a) Airplane single-engine.

(b) Airplane multiengine.

(c) Rotorcraft helicopter.

(d) Powered-lift.

2. *Eligibility for enrollment.* Prior to enrolling in the flight portion of the airline transport pilot certification course, a person must:

(a) Meet the aeronautical experience requirements prescribed in subpart G of part 61 of this chapter for an airline transport pilot certificate that is appropriate to the aircraft category and class rating for which the course applies;

(b) Hold at least a commercial pilot certificate and an instrument rating;

(c) Meet the military experience requirements under § 61.73 of this chapter to qualify for a commercial pilot certificate and an instrument rating, if the person is a rated military pilot or former rated military pilot of an Armed Force of the United States; or

(d) Hold either a foreign airline transport pilot license or foreign commercial pilot license and an instrument rating, if the person holds a pilot license issued by a contracting State to the Convention on International Civil Aviation.

3. *Aeronautical knowledge areas.*

(a) Each approved course must include at least 40 hours of ground training on the aeronautical knowledge areas listed in paragraph (b) of this section, appropriate to the aircraft category and class rating for which the course applies.

(b) Ground training must include the following aeronautical knowledge areas:

(1) Applicable Federal Aviation Regulations of this chapter that relate to airline transport pilot privileges, limitations, and flight operations;

(2) Meteorology, including knowledge of and effects of fronts, frontal characteristics, cloud formations, icing, and upper-air data;

(3) General system of weather and NOTAM collection, dissemination, interpretation, and use;

(4) Interpretation and use of weather charts, maps, forecasts, sequence reports, abbreviations, and symbols;

(5) National Weather Service functions as they pertain to operations in the National Airspace System;

(6) Windshear and microburst awareness, identification, and avoidance;

(7) Principles of air navigation under instrument meteorological conditions in the National Airspace System;

(8) Air traffic control procedures and pilot responsibilities as they relate to en route operations, terminal area and radar operations, and instrument departure and approach procedures;

(9) Aircraft loading; weight and balance; use of charts, graphs, tables, formulas, and computations; and the effects on aircraft performance;

(10) Aerodynamics relating to an aircraft's flight characteristics and performance in normal and abnormal flight regimes;

(11) Human factors;

(12) Aeronautical decision making and judgment; and

(13) Crew resource management to include crew communication and coordination.

4. *Flight training.*

(a) Each approved course must include at least 25 hours of flight training on the approved areas of operation listed in paragraph (c) of this section appropriate to the aircraft category and class rating for which the course applies. At least 15 hours of this flight training must be instrument flight training.

(b) For the use of flight simulators or flight training devices—

(1) The course may include training in a flight simulator or flight training device, provided it is representative of the aircraft for which the course is approved, meets the requirements of this paragraph, and the training is given by an authorized instructor.

(2) Training in a flight simulator that meets the requirements of § 141.41(a) of this part may be credited for a maximum of 50 percent of the total flight training hour requirements of the approved course, or of this section, whichever is less.

(3) Training in a flight training device that meets the requirements of § 141.41(b) of this part may be credited for a maximum of 25 percent of the total flight training hour requirements of the approved course, or of this section, whichever is less.

(4) Training in flight simulators or flight training devices described in paragraphs (b)(2) and (b)(3) of this section, if used in combination, may be credited for a maximum of 50 percent of the total flight training hour requirements of the approved course, or of this section, whichever is less. However, credit for training in a flight training device that meets the requirements of § 141.41(b) can-

not exceed the limitation provided for in paragraph (b)(3) of this section.

(c) Each approved course must include flight training on the approved areas of operation listed in this paragraph appropriate to the aircraft category and class rating for which the course applies:

(1) Preflight preparation;

(2) Preflight procedures;

(3) Takeoff and departure phase;

(4) In-flight maneuvers;

(5) Instrument procedures;

(6) Landings and approaches to landings;

(7) Normal and abnormal procedures;

(8) Emergency procedures; and

(9) Postflight procedures.

5. *Stage checks and end-of-course tests.*

(a) Each student enrolled in an airline transport pilot course must satisfactorily accomplish the stage checks and end-of-course tests, in accordance with the school's approved training course, consisting of the approved areas of operation listed in paragraph (c) of section No. 4 of this appendix that are appropriate to the aircraft category and class rating for which the course applies.

(b) Each student must demonstrate satisfactory proficiency prior to receiving an endorsement to operate an aircraft in solo flight.

[Docket No. 25910, 62 FR 16347, April 4, 1997; as amended by Amdt. 141–9, 62 FR 40909, July 30, 1997]

APPENDIX F TO PART 141

FLIGHT INSTRUCTOR CERTIFICATION COURSE

1. *Applicability.* This appendix prescribes the minimum curriculum for a flight instructor certification course and an additional flight instructor rating course required under this part, for the following ratings:

(a) Airplane single-engine.

(b) Airplane multiengine.

(c) Rotorcraft helicopter.

(d) Rotorcraft gyroplane.

(e) Powered-lift.

(f) Glider category.

2. *Eligibility for enrollment.* A person must hold the following prior to enrolling in the flight portion of the flight instructor or additional flight instructor rating course:

(a) A commercial pilot certificate or an airline transport pilot certificate, with an aircraft category and class rating appropriate to the flight instructor rating for which the course applies; and

(b) An instrument rating or privilege in an aircraft that is appropriate to the aircraft category and class rating for which the course applies, if the course is for a flight instructor airplane or powered-lift instrument rating.

3. *Aeronautical knowledge training.*

(a) Each approved course must include at least the following ground training in the aeronautical knowledge areas listed in paragraph (b) of this section:

(1) 40 hours of training if the course is for an initial issuance of a flight instructor certificate; or

(2) 20 hours of training if the course is for an additional flight instructor rating.

(b) Ground training must include the following aeronautical knowledge areas:

(1) The fundamentals of instructing including—

(i) The learning process;

(ii) Elements of effective teaching;

(iii) Student evaluation and testing;

(iv) Course development;

(v) Lesson planning; and

(vi) Classroom training techniques.

(2) The aeronautical knowledge areas in which training is required for—

(i) A recreational, private, and commercial pilot certificate that is appropriate to the aircraft category and class rating for which the course applies; and

(ii) An instrument rating that is appropriate to the aircraft category and class rating for which the course applies, if the course is for an airplane or powered-lift aircraft rating.

(c) A student who satisfactorily completes 2 years of study on the principles of education at a college or university may be credited with no more than 20 hours of the training required in paragraph (a)(1) of this section.

4. *Flight training.*

(a) Each approved course must include at least the following flight training on the approved areas of operation of paragraph (c) of this section appropriate to the flight instructor rating for which the course applies:

(1) 25 hours, if the course is for an airplane, rotorcraft, or powered-lift rating; and

(2) 10 hours, which must include 10 flights, if the course is for a glider category rating.

(b) For the use of flight simulators or flight training devices:

(1) The course may include training in a flight simulator or flight training device, provided it is representative of the aircraft for which the course is approved, meets the requirements of this paragraph, and the training is given by an authorized instructor.

(2) Training in a flight simulator that meets the requirements of § 141.41(a) of this part, may be credited for a maximum of 10 percent of the total flight training hour requirements of the approved course, or of this section, whichever is less.

(3) Training in a flight training device that meets the requirements of § 141.41(b) of this part, may be credited for a maximum of 5 percent of the total

flight training hour requirements of the approved course, or of this section, whichever is less.

(4) Training in flight simulators or flight training devices described in paragraphs (b)(2) and (b)(3) of this section, if used in combination, may be credited for a maximum of 10 percent of the total flight training hour requirements of the approved course, or of this section, whichever is less. However, credit for training in a flight training device that meets the requirements of § 141.41(b) cannot exceed the limitation provided for in paragraph (b)(3) of this section.

(c) Each approved course must include flight training on the approved areas of operation listed in this paragraph that are appropriate to the aircraft category and class rating for which the course applies—

(1) *For an airplane — single-engine course:*
(i) Fundamentals of instructing;
(ii) Technical subject areas;
(iii) Preflight preparation;
(iv) Preflight lesson on a maneuver to be performed in flight;
(v) Preflight procedures;
(vi) Airport and seaplane base operations;
(vii) Takeoffs, landings, and go-arounds;
(viii) Fundamentals of flight;
(ix) Performance maneuvers;
(x) Ground reference maneuvers;
(xi) Slow flight, stalls, and spins;
(xii) Basic instrument maneuvers;
(xiii) Emergency operations; and
(xiv) Postflight procedures.

(2) *For an airplane — multiengine course:*
(i) Fundamentals of instructing;
(ii) Technical subject areas;
(iii) Preflight preparation;
(iv) Preflight lesson on a maneuver to be performed in flight;
(v) Preflight procedures;
(vi) Airport and seaplane base operations;
(vii) Takeoffs, landings, and go-arounds;
(viii) Fundamentals of flight;
(ix) Performance maneuvers;
(x) Ground reference maneuvers;
(xi) Slow flight and stalls;
(xii) Basic instrument maneuvers;
(xiii) Emergency operations;
(xiv) Multiengine operations; and
(xv) Postflight procedures.

(3) *For a rotorcraft — helicopter course:*
(i) Fundamentals of instructing;
(ii) Technical subject areas;
(iii) Preflight preparation;
(iv) Preflight lesson on a maneuver to be performed in flight;
(v) Preflight procedures;
(vi) Airport and heliport operations;
(vii) Hovering maneuvers;

(viii) Takeoffs, landings, and go-arounds;
(ix) Fundamentals of flight;
(x) Performance maneuvers;
(xi) Emergency operations;
(xii) Special operations; and
(xiii) Postflight procedures.

(4) *For a rotorcraft — gyroplane course:*
(i) Fundamentals of instructing;
(ii) Technical subject areas;
(iii) Preflight preparation;
(iv) Preflight lesson on a maneuver to be performed in flight;
(v) Preflight procedures;
(vi) Airport operations;
(vii) Takeoffs, landings, and go-arounds;
(viii) Fundamentals of flight;
(ix) Performance maneuvers;
(x) Flight at slow airspeeds;
(xi) Ground reference maneuvers;
(xii) Emergency operations; and
(xiii) Postflight procedures.

(5) *For a powered-lift course:*
(i) Fundamentals of instructing;
(ii) Technical subject areas;
(iii) Preflight preparation;
(iv) Preflight lesson on a maneuver to be performed in flight;
(v) Preflight procedures;
(vi) Airport and heliport operations;
(vii) Hovering maneuvers;
(viii) Takeoffs, landings, and go-arounds;
(ix) Fundamentals of flight;
(x) Performance maneuvers;
(xi) Ground reference maneuvers;
(xii) Slow flight and stalls;
(xiii) Basic instrument maneuvers;
(xiv) Emergency operations;
(xv) Special operations; and
(xvi) Postflight procedures.

(6) *For a glider course:*
(i) Fundamentals of instructing;
(ii) Technical subject areas;
(iii) Preflight preparation;
(iv) Preflight lesson on a maneuver to be performed in flight;
(v) Preflight procedures;
(vi) Airport and gliderport operations;
(vii) Tows and launches, landings, and go-arounds, if applicable;
(viii) Fundamentals of flight;
(ix) Performance speeds;
(x) Soaring techniques;
(xi) Performance maneuvers;
(xii) Slow flight, stalls, and spins;
(xiii) Emergency operations; and
(xiv) Postflight procedures.

5. *Stage checks and end-of-course tests.*

(a) Each student enrolled in a flight instructor course must satisfactorily accomplish the stage checks and end-of-course tests, in accordance with the school's approved training course, consisting of the appropriate approved areas of operation listed in paragraph (c) of section No. 4 of this appendix appropriate to the flight instructor rating for which the course applies.

(b) In the case of a student who is enrolled in a flight instructor–airplane rating or flight instructor–glider rating course, that student must have:

(1) Received a logbook endorsement from a certificated flight instructor certifying the student received ground and flight training on stall awareness, spin entry, spins, and spin recovery procedures in an aircraft that is certificated for spins and is appropriate to the rating sought; and

(2) Demonstrated instructional proficiency in stall awareness, spin entry, spins, and spin recovery procedures.

[Docket No. 25910, 62 FR 16347, April 4, 1997; as amended by Amdt. 141–9, 62 FR 40909, July 30, 1997]

APPENDIX G TO PART 141
FLIGHT INSTRUCTOR INSTRUMENT
(FOR AN AIRPLANE, HELICOPTER, OR
POWERED-LIFT INSTRUMENT INSTRUCTOR
RATING, AS APPROPRIATE)
CERTIFICATION COURSE

1. *Applicability.* This appendix prescribes the minimum curriculum for a flight instructor instrument certification course required under this part, for the following ratings:

(a) Flight Instructor Instrument — Airplane.

(b) Flight Instructor Instrument — Helicopter.

(c) Flight Instructor Instrument — Powered-lift aircraft.

2. *Eligibility for enrollment.* A person must hold the following prior to enrolling in the flight portion of the flight instructor instrument course:

(a) A commercial pilot certificate or airline transport pilot certificate with an aircraft category and class rating appropriate to the flight instructor category and class rating for which the course applies; and

(b) An instrument rating or privilege on that flight instructor applicant's pilot certificate that is appropriate to the flight instructor instrument rating (for an airplane-, helicopter-, or powered-lift-instrument rating, as appropriate) for which the course applies.

3. *Aeronautical knowledge training.*

(a) Each approved course must include at least 15 hours of ground training on the aeronautical knowledge areas listed in paragraph (b) of this section, appropriate to the flight instructor instru-

ment rating (for an airplane-, helicopter-, or powered-lift-instrument rating, as appropriate) for which the course applies:

(b) Ground training must include the following aeronautical knowledge areas:

(1) The fundamentals of instructing including:

(i) The learning process;

(ii) Elements of effective teaching;

(iii) Student evaluation and testing;

(iv) Course development;

(v) Lesson planning; and

(vi) Classroom training techniques.

(2) The aeronautical knowledge areas in which training is required for an instrument rating that is appropriate to the aircraft category and class rating for the course which applies.

4. *Flight training.*

(a) Each approved course must include at least 15 hours of flight training in the approved areas of operation of paragraph (c) of this section appropriate to the flight instructor rating for which the course applies.

(b) For the use of flight simulators or flight training devices:

(1) The course may include training in a flight simulator or flight training device, provided it is representative of the aircraft for which the course is approved for, meets requirements of this paragraph, and the training is given by an instructor.

(2) Training in a flight simulator that meets the requirements of § 141.41(a) of this part, may be credited for a maximum of 10 percent of the total flight training hour requirements of the approved course, or of this section, whichever is less.

(3) Training in a flight training device that meets the requirements of § 141.41(b) of this part, may be credited for a maximum of 5 percent of the total flight training hour requirements of the approved course, or of this section, whichever is less.

(4) Training in flight simulators or flight training devices described in paragraphs (b)(2) and (b)(3) of this section, if used in combination, may be credited for a maximum of 10 percent of the total flight training hour requirements of the approved course, or of this section, whichever is less. However, credit for training in a flight training device that meets the requirements of § 141.41(b) cannot exceed the limitation provided for in paragraph (b)(3) of this section.

(c) An approved course for the flight instructor–instrument rating must include flight training on the following approved areas of operation that are appropriate to the instrument-aircraft category and class rating for which the course applies:

(1) Fundamentals of instructing;

(2) Technical subject areas;

(3) Preflight preparation;

(4) Preflight lesson on a maneuver to be performed in flight;

(5) Air traffic control clearances and procedures;

141

(6) Flight by reference to instruments;
(7) Navigation systems;
(8) Instrument approach procedures;
(9) Emergency operations; and
(10) Postflight procedures.
5. *Stage checks and end-of-course tests.*

Each student enrolled in a flight instructor instrument course must satisfactorily accomplish the stage checks and end-of-course tests, in accordance with the school's approved training course, consisting of the approved areas of operation listed in paragraph (c) of section No. 4 of this appendix that are appropriate to the flight instructor instrument rating (for an airplane-, helicopter-, or powered-lift-instrument rating, as appropriate) for which the course applies.

[Docket No. 25910, 62 FR 16347, April 4, 1997; as amended by Amdt. 141–9, 62 FR 40909, July 30, 1997]

APPENDIX H TO PART 141
GROUND INSTRUCTOR
CERTIFICATION COURSE

1. *Applicability.* This appendix prescribes the minimum curriculum for a ground instructor certification course and an additional ground instructor rating course, required under this part, for the following ratings:

(a) Ground Instructor—Basic.
(b) Ground Instructor—Advanced.
(c) Ground Instructor—Instrument.
2. *Aeronautical knowledge training.*
(a) Each approved course must include at least the following ground training on the knowledge areas listed in paragraphs (b), (c), (d), and (e) of this section, appropriate to the ground instructor rating for which the course applies:

(1) 20 hours of training if the course is for an initial issuance of a ground instructor certificate; or

(2) 10 hours of training if the course is for an additional ground instructor rating.

(b) Ground training must include the following aeronautical knowledge areas:

(1) Learning process;
(2) Elements of effective teaching;
(3) Student evaluation and testing;
(4) Course development;
(5) Lesson planning; and
(6) Classroom training techniques.

(c) Ground training for a basic ground instructor certificate must include the aeronautical knowledge areas applicable to a recreational and private pilot.

(d) Ground training for an advanced ground instructor rating must include the aeronautical knowledge areas applicable to a recreational, private, commercial, and airline transport pilot.

(e) Ground training for an instrument ground instructor rating must include the aeronautical knowledge areas applicable to an instrument rating.

(f) A student who satisfactorily completed 2 years of study on the principles of education at a college or university may be credited with 10 hours of the training required in paragraph (a)(1) of this section.

3. *Stage checks and end-of-course tests.*

Each student enrolled in a ground instructor course must satisfactorily accomplish the stage checks and end-of-course tests, in accordance with the school's approved training course, consisting of the approved knowledge areas in paragraph (b), (c), (d), and (e) of section No. 2 of this appendix appropriate to the ground instructor rating for which the course applies.

APPENDIX I TO PART 141
ADDITIONAL AIRCRAFT CATEGORY OR
CLASS RATING COURSE

1. *Applicability.* This appendix prescribes the minimum curriculum for an additional aircraft category rating course or an additional aircraft class rating course required under this part, for the following ratings:

(a) Airplane single-engine.
(b) Airplane multiengine.
(c) Rotorcraft helicopter.
(d) Rotorcraft gyroplane.
(e) Powered-lift.
(f) Glider.
(g) Lighter-than-air airship.
(h) Lighter-than-air balloon.

2. *Eligibility for enrollment.* A person must hold the level of pilot certificate for the additional aircraft category and class rating for which the course applies prior to enrolling in the flight portion of an additional aircraft category or additional aircraft class rating course.

3. *Aeronautical knowledge training.* Each approved course for an additional aircraft category rating or additional aircraft class rating must include the ground training time requirements and ground training on the aeronautical knowledge areas that are specific to that aircraft category and class rating and pilot certificate level for which the course applies as required in Appendix A, B, D, or E of this part, as appropriate.

4. *Flight training.*

(a) Each approved course for an additional aircraft category rating or additional aircraft class rating must include the flight training time requirements and flight training on the areas of operation that are specific to that aircraft category and class rating and pilot certificate level for which the course applies as required in Appendix A, B, D, or E of this part, as appropriate.

(b) For the use of flight simulators or flight training devices:

(1) The course may include training in a flight simulator or flight training device, provided it is representative of the aircraft for which the course is approved, meets the requirements of this paragraph, and the training is given by an authorized instructor.

(2) Training in a flight simulator that meets the requirements of § 141.41(a) of this part may be credited for a maximum of 30 percent of the total flight training hour requirements of the approved course, or of this section, whichever is less.

(3) Training in a flight training device that meets the requirements of § 141.41(b) of this part may be credited for a maximum of 20 percent of the total flight training hour requirements of the approved course, or of this section, whichever is less.

(4) Training in the flight simulators or flight training devices described in paragraphs (b)(2) and (b)(3) of this section, if used in combination, may be credited for a maximum of 30 percent of the total flight training hour requirements of the approved course, or of this section, whichever is less. However, credit for training in a flight training device that meets the requirements of § 141.41(b) cannot exceed the limitation provided for in paragraph (c)(3) of this section.

5. *Stage checks and end-of-course tests.*

(a) Each student enrolled in an additional aircraft category rating course or an additional aircraft class rating course must satisfactorily accomplish the stage checks and end-of-course tests, in accordance with the school's approved training course, consisting of the approved areas of operation in section No. 4 of this appendix that are appropriate to the aircraft category and class rating for which the course applies at the appropriate pilot certificate level.

(b) Each student must demonstrate satisfactory proficiency prior to receiving an endorsement to operate an aircraft in solo flight.

[Docket No. 25910, 62 FR 16347, April 4, 1997; as amended by Amdt. 141–9, 62 FR 40909, July 30, 1997]

APPENDIX J TO PART 141
AIRCRAFT TYPE RATING COURSE,
FOR OTHER THAN AN
AIRLINE TRANSPORT PILOT CERTIFICATE

1. *Applicability.* This appendix prescribes the minimum curriculum for an aircraft type rating course other than an airline transport pilot certificate, for:

(a) A type rating in an airplane category — single-engine class.

(b) A type rating in an airplane category — multi-engine class.

(c) A type rating in a rotorcraft category — helicopter class.

(d) A type rating in a powered-lift category.

(e) Other aircraft type ratings specified by the Administrator through the aircraft type certificate procedures.

2. *Eligibility for enrollment.* Prior to enrolling in the flight portion of an aircraft type rating course, a person must hold at least a private pilot certificate and:

(a) An instrument rating in the category and class of aircraft that is appropriate to the aircraft type rating for which the course applies, provided the aircraft's type certificate does not have a VFR limitation; or

(b) Be concurrently enrolled in an instrument rating course in the category and class of aircraft that is appropriate to the aircraft type rating for which the course applies, and pass the required instrument rating practical test concurrently with the aircraft type rating practical test.

3. *Aeronautical knowledge training.*

(a) Each approved course must include at least 10 hours of ground training on the aeronautical knowledge areas listed in paragraph (b) of this section, appropriate to the aircraft type rating for which the course applies.

(b) Ground training must include the following aeronautical areas:

(1) Proper control of airspeed, configuration, direction, altitude, and attitude in accordance with procedures and limitations contained in the aircraft's flight manual, checklists, or other approved material appropriate to the aircraft type;

(2) Compliance with approved en route, instrument approach, missed approach, ATC, or other applicable procedures that apply to the aircraft type;

(3) Subjects requiring a practical knowledge of the aircraft type and its powerplant, systems, components, operational, and performance factors;

(4) The aircraft's normal, abnormal, and emergency procedures, and the operations and limitations relating thereto;

(5) Appropriate provisions of the approved aircraft's flight manual;

(6) Location of and purpose for inspecting each item on the aircraft's checklist that relates to the exterior and interior preflight; and

(7) Use of the aircraft's prestart checklist, appropriate control system checks, starting procedures, radio and electronic equipment checks, and the selection of proper navigation and communication radio facilities and frequencies.

4. *Flight training.*

(a) Each approved course must include at least:

(1) Flight training on the approved areas of operation of paragraph (c) of this section in the aircraft type for which the course applies; and

(2) 10 hours of training of which at least 5 hours must be instrument training in the aircraft for which the course applies.

(b) For the use of flight simulators or flight training devices:

(1) The course may include training in a flight simulator or flight training device, provided it is representative of the aircraft for which the course is approved, meets requirements of this paragraph, and the training is given by an authorized instructor.

(2) Training in a flight simulator that meets the requirements of § 141.41(a) of this part, may be credited for a maximum of 50 percent of the total flight training hour requirements of the approved course, or of this section, whichever is less.

(3) Training in a flight training device that meets the requirements of § 141.41(b) of this part, may be credited for a maximum of 25 percent of the total flight training hour requirements of the approved course, or of this section, whichever is less.

(4) Training in the flight simulators or flight training devices described in paragraphs (b)(2) and (b)(3) of this section, if used in combination, may be credited for a maximum of 50 percent of the total flight training hour requirements of the approved course, or of this section, whichever is less. However, credit training in a flight training device that meets the requirements of § 141.41(b) cannot exceed the limitation provided for in paragraph (b)(3) of this section.

(c) Each approved course must include the flight training on the areas of operation listed in this paragraph, that are appropriate to the aircraft category and class rating for which the course applies:

(1) *A type rating for an airplane— single-engine course:*
(i) Preflight preparation;
(ii) Preflight procedures;
(iii) Takeoff and departure phase;
(iv) In-flight maneuvers;
(v) Instrument procedures;
(vi) Landings and approaches to landings;
(vii) Normal and abnormal procedures;
(viii) Emergency procedures; and
(ix) Postflight procedures.

(2) *A type rating for an airplane— multiengine course:*
(i) Preflight preparation;
(ii) Preflight procedures;
(iii) Takeoff and departure phase;
(iv) In-flight maneuvers;
(v) Instrument procedures;
(vi) Landings and approaches to landings;
(vii) Normal and abnormal procedures;
(viii) Emergency procedures; and
(ix) Postflight procedures.

(3) *A type rating for a powered-lift course:*
(i) Preflight preparation;
(ii) Preflight procedures;
(iii) Takeoff and departure phase;
(iv) In-flight maneuvers;
(v) Instrument procedures;
(vi) Landings and approaches to landings;
(vii) Normal and abnormal procedures;
(viii) Emergency procedures; and
(ix) Postflight procedures.

(4) *A type rating for a rotorcraft— helicopter course:*
(i) Preflight preparation;
(ii) Preflight procedures;
(iii) Takeoff and departure phase;
(iv) In-flight maneuvers;
(v) Instrument procedures;
(vi) Landings and approaches to landings;
(vii) Normal and abnormal procedures;
(viii) Emergency procedures; and
(ix) Postflight procedures.

(5) *Other aircraft type ratings specified by the Administrator through aircraft type certificate procedures:*
(i) Preflight preparation;
(ii) Preflight procedures;
(iii) Takeoff and departure phase;
(iv) In-flight maneuvers;
(v) Instrument procedures;
(vi) Landings and approaches to landings;
(vii) Normal and abnormal procedures;
(viii) Emergency procedures; and
(ix) Postflight procedures.

5. *Stage checks and end-of-course tests.*

(a) Each student enrolled in an aircraft type rating course must satisfactorily accomplish the stage checks and end-of-course tests, in accordance with the school's approved training course, consisting of the approved areas of operation that are appropriate to the aircraft type rating for which the course applies at the airline transport pilot certificate level; and

(b) Each student must demonstrate satisfactory proficiency prior to receiving an endorsement to operate an aircraft in solo flight.

[Docket No. 25910, 62 FR 16347, April 4, 1997; as amended by Amdt. 141–9, 62 FR 40910, July 30, 1997]

APPENDIX K TO PART 141

SPECIAL PREPARATION COURSES

1. *Applicability.* This appendix prescribes the minimum curriculum for the special preparation courses that are listed in § 141.11 of this part.

2. *Eligibility for enrollment.* Prior to enrolling in the flight portion of a special preparation course, a person must hold a pilot certificate, flight instructor certificate, or ground instructor certificate that is appropriate for the exercise of the operating privileges or authorizations sought.

3. *General requirements.*

(a) To be approved, a special preparation course must:

(1) Meet the appropriate requirements of this appendix; and

(2) Prepare the graduate with the necessary skills, competency, and proficiency to exercise safely the privileges of the certificate, rating, or authorization for which the course is established.

(b) An approved special preparation course must include ground and flight training on the operating privileges or authorization sought, for developing competency, proficiency, resourcefulness, self-confidence, and self-reliance in the student.

4. *Use of flight simulators or flight training devices.*

(a) The approved special preparation course may include training in a flight simulator or flight training device, provided it is representative of the aircraft for which the course is approved, meets requirements of this paragraph, and the training is given by an authorized instructor.

(b) Training in a flight simulator that meets the requirements of § 141.41(a) of this part, may be credited for a maximum of 10 percent of the total flight training hour requirements of the approved course, or of this section, whichever is less.

(c) Training in a flight training device that meets the requirements of § 141.41(b) of this part, may be credited for a maximum of 5 percent of the total flight training hour requirements of the approved course, or of this section, whichever is less.

(d) Training in the flight simulators or flight training devices described in paragraphs (b) and (c) of this section, if used in combination, may be credited for a maximum of 10 percent of the total flight training hour requirements of the approved course, or of this section, whichever is less. However, credit for training in a flight training device that meets the requirements of § 141.41(b) cannot exceed the limitation provided for in paragraph (c) of this section.

5. *Stage check and end-of-course tests.*

Each person enrolled in a special preparation course must satisfactorily accomplish the stage checks and end-of-course tests, in accordance with the school's approved training course, consisting of the approved areas of operation that are appropriate to the operating privileges or authorization sought, and for which the course applies.

6. *Agricultural aircraft operations course.*

An approved special preparation course for pilots in agricultural aircraft operations must include at least the following—

(a) 25 hours of training on:

(1) Agricultural aircraft operations;

(2) Safe piloting and operating practices and procedures for handling, dispensing, and disposing agricultural and industrial chemicals, including operating in and around congested areas; and

(3) Applicable provisions of part 137 of this chapter.

(b) 15 hours of flight training on agricultural aircraft operations.

7. *Rotorcraft external-load operations course.* An approved special preparation course for pilots of external-load operations must include at least the following—

(a) 10 hours of training on:

(1) Rotorcraft external-load operations;

(2) Safe piloting and operating practices and procedures for external-load operations, including operating in and around congested areas; and

(3) Applicable provisions of part 133 of this chapter.

(b) 15 hours of flight training on external-load operations.

8. *Test pilot course.* An approved special preparation course for pilots in test pilot duties must include at least the following—

(a) Aeronautical knowledge training on:

(1) Performing aircraft maintenance, quality assurance, and certification test flight operations;

(2) Safe piloting and operating practices and procedures for performing aircraft maintenance, quality assurance, and certification test flight operations;

(3) Applicable parts of this chapter that pertain to aircraft maintenance, quality assurance, and certification tests; and

(4) Test pilot duties and responsibilities.

(b) 15 hours of flight training on test pilot duties and responsibilities.

9. *Special operations course.* An approved special preparation course for pilots in special operations that are mission-specific for certain aircraft must include at least the following—

(a) Aeronautical knowledge training on:

(1) Performing that special flight operation;

(2) Safe piloting operating practices and procedures for performing that special flight operation;

(3) Applicable parts of this chapter that pertain to that special flight operation; and

(4) Pilot in command duties and responsibilities for performing that special flight operation.

(b) Flight training:

(1) On that special flight operation; and

(2) To develop skills, competency, proficiency, resourcefulness, self-confidence, and self-reliance in the student for performing that special flight operation in a safe manner.

10. *Pilot refresher course.* An approved special preparation pilot refresher course for a pilot certificate, aircraft category and class rating, or an instrument rating must include at least the following—

(a) 4 hours of aeronautical knowledge training on:

(1) The aeronautical knowledge areas that are applicable to the level of pilot certificate, aircraft category and class rating, or instrument rating, as appropriate, that pertain to that course;

(2) Safe piloting operating practices and procedures; and

(3) Applicable provisions of parts 61 and 91 of this chapter for pilots.

(b) 6 hours of flight training on the approved areas of operation that are applicable to the level of pilot certificate, aircraft category and class rating, or instrument rating, as appropriate, for performing pilot-in-command duties and responsibilities.

11. *Flight instructor refresher course.* An approved special preparation flight instructor refresher course must include at least a combined total of 16 hours of aeronautical knowledge training, flight training, or any combination of ground and flight training on the following—

(a) Aeronautical knowledge training on:

(1) The aeronautical knowledge areas of part 61 of this chapter that apply to student, recreational, private, and commercial pilot certificates and instrument ratings;

(2) The aeronautical knowledge areas of part 61 of this chapter that apply to flight instructor certificates;

(3) Safe piloting operating practices and procedures, including airport operations and operating in the National Airspace System; and

(4) Applicable provisions of parts 61 and 91 of this chapter that apply to pilots and flight instructors.

(b) Flight training to review:

(1) The approved areas of operations applicable to student, recreational, private, and commercial pilot certificates and instrument ratings; and

(2) The skills, competency, and proficiency for performing flight instructor duties and responsibilities.

12. *Ground instructor refresher course.* An approved special preparation ground instructor refresher course must include at least 16 hours of aeronautical knowledge training on:

(a) The aeronautical knowledge areas of part 61 of this chapter that apply to student, recreational, private, and commercial pilots and instrument rated pilots;

(b) The aeronautical knowledge areas of part 61 of this chapter that apply to ground instructors;

(c) Safe piloting operating practices and procedures, including airport operations and operating in the National Airspace System; and

(d) Applicable provisions of parts 61 and 91 of this chapter that apply to pilots and ground instructors.

[Docket No. 25910, 62 FR 16347, April 4, 1997; as amended by Amdt. 141–9, 62 FR 40910, July 30, 1997]

APPENDIX L TO PART 141
PILOT GROUND SCHOOL COURSE

1. *Applicability.* This appendix prescribes the minimum curriculum for a pilot ground school course required under this part.

2. *General requirements.* An approved course of training for a pilot ground school must include training on the aeronautical knowledge areas that are:

(a) Needed to safely exercise the privileges of the certificate, rating, or authority for which the course is established; and

(b) Conducted to develop competency, proficiency, resourcefulness, self-confidence, and self-reliance in each student.

3. *Aeronautical knowledge training requirements.* Each approved pilot ground school course must include:

(a) The aeronautical knowledge training that is appropriate to the aircraft rating and pilot certificate level for which the course applies; and

(b) An adequate number of total aeronautical knowledge training hours appropriate to the aircraft rating and pilot certificate level for which the course applies.

4. *Stage checks and end-of-course tests.* Each person enrolled in a pilot ground school course must satisfactorily accomplish the stage checks and end-of-course tests, in accordance with the school's approved training course, consisting of the approved areas of operation that are appropriate to the operating privileges or authorization that graduation from the course will permit and for which the course applies.

PART 142
TRAINING CENTERS

Subpart A—General

Authority: 49 U.S.C. 106(g), 40113, 40119, 44101, 44701–44703, 44705, 44707, 44709–44711, 45102–45103, 45301–45302.

Source: Docket No. 26933, 61 FR 34562, July 2, 1996, unless otherwise noted.

Subpart A—General

§ 142.1 Applicability.

(a) This subpart prescribes the requirements governing the certification and operation of aviation training centers. Except as provided in paragraph (b) of this section, this part provides an alternative means to accomplish training required by parts 61, 63, 121, 125, 127, 135, or 137 of this chapter.

(b) Certification under this part is not required for training that is—

(1) Approved under the provisions of parts 63, 121, 125, 127, 135, and 137;

(2) Approved under SFAR 58, Advanced Qualification Programs, for the authorization holder's own employees;

(3) Conducted under part 61 unless that part requires certification under this part;

(4) Conducted by a part 121 certificate holder for another part 121 certificate holder; or

(5) Conducted by a part 135 certificate holder for another part 135 certificate holder.

(c) Except as provided in paragraph (b) of this section, after August 3, 1998, no person may conduct training, testing, or checking in advanced flight training devices or flight simulators without, or in violation of, the certificate and training specifications required by this part.

§ 142.3 Definitions.

As used in this part:

Advanced Flight Training Device as used in this part, means a flight training device as defined in part 61 of this chapter that has a cockpit that accurately replicates a specific make, model, and type aircraft cockpit, and handling characteristics that accurately model the aircraft handling characteristics.

Core Curriculum means a set of courses approved by the Administrator, for use by a training center and its satellite training centers. The core curriculum consists of training which is required for certification. It does not include training for tasks and circumstances unique to a particular user.

Course means—

(1) A program of instruction to obtain pilot certification, qualification, authorization, or currency;

(2) A program of instruction to meet a specified number of requirements of a program for pilot training, certification, qualification, authorization, or currency; or

(3) A curriculum, or curriculum segment, as defined in SFAR 58 of part 121 of this chapter.

Courseware means instructional material developed for each course or curriculum, including lesson plans, flight event descriptions, computer software programs, audiovisual programs, workbooks, and handouts.

Evaluator means a person employed by a training center certificate holder who performs tests for certification, added ratings, authorizations, and proficiency checks that are authorized by the certificate holder's training specification, and who is authorized by the Administrator to administer such checks and tests.

Flight training equipment means flight simulators, as defined in § 61.1(b)(5) of this chapter, flight training devices, as defined in § 61.1(b)(7) of this chapter, and aircraft.

Instructor means a person employed by a training center and designated to provide instruction in accordance with subpart C of this part.

Line-Operational Simulation means simulation conducted using operational-oriented flight scenarios that accurately replicate interaction among flightcrew members and between flightcrew members and dispatch facilities, other crewmembers, air traffic control, and ground operations. Line operational simulation simulations are conducted for training and evaluation purposes and include random, abnormal, and emergency occurrences. Line operational simulation specifically includes line-oriented flight training, special purpose operational training, and line operational evaluation.

Specialty Curriculum means a set of courses that is designed to satisfy a requirement of the Federal Aviation Regulations and that is approved by the Administrator for use by a particular training center or satellite training center. The specialty curriculum includes training requirements unique to one or more training center clients.

Training center means an organization governed by the applicable requirements of this part that provides training, testing, and checking under contract or other arrangement to airmen subject to the requirements of this chapter.

Training program consists of courses, courseware, facilities, flight training equipment, and personnel necessary to accomplish a specific training objective. It may include a core curriculum and a specialty curriculum.

Training specifications means a document issued to a training center certificate holder by the Administrator that prescribes that center's training, checking, and testing authorizations and limitations, and specifies training program requirements.

[Docket No. 26933, 61 FR 34562, July 2, 1996; as amended by Amdt. 142–2, 62 FR 68137, Dec. 30, 1997]

§ 142.5 Certificate and training specifications required.

(a) No person may operate a certificated training center without, or in violation of, a training center certificate and training specifications issued under this part.

(b) An applicant will be issued a training center certificate and training specifications with appropriate limitations if the applicant shows that it has adequate facilities, equipment, personnel, and courseware required by § 142.11 to conduct training approved under § 142.37.

§ 142.7 Duration of a certificate.

(a) Except as provided in paragraph (b) of this section, a training center certificate issued under this part is effective until the certificate is surrendered or until the Administrator suspends, revokes, or terminates it.

(b) Unless sooner surrendered, suspended, or revoked, a certificate issued under this part for a training center located outside the United States expires at the end of the twelfth month after the month in which it is issued or renewed.

(c) If the Administrator suspends, revokes, or terminates a training center certificate, the holder of that certificate shall return the certificate to the Administrator within 5 working days after being notified that the certificate is suspended, revoked, or terminated.

§ 142.9 Deviations or waivers.

(a) The Administrator may issue deviations or waivers from any of the requirements of this part.

(b) A training center applicant requesting a deviation or waiver under this section must provide the Administrator with information acceptable to the Administrator that shows—

(1) Justification for the deviation or waiver; and

(2) That the deviation or waiver will not adversely affect the quality of instruction or evaluation.

§ 142.11 Application for issuance or amendment.

(a) An application for a training center certificate and training specifications shall—

(1) Be made on a form and in a manner prescribed by the Administrator;

(2) Be filed with the FAA Flight Standards District Office that has jurisdiction over the area in which the applicant's principal business office is located; and

(3) Be made at least 120 calendar days before the beginning of any proposed training or 60 calendar days before effecting an amendment to any approved training, unless a shorter filing period is approved by the Administrator.

(b) Each application for a training center certificate and training specification shall provide—

(1) A statement showing that the minimum qualification requirements for each management position are met or exceeded;

(2) A statement acknowledging that the applicant shall notify the Administrator within 10 working days of any change made in the assignment of persons in the required management positions;

(3) The proposed training authorizations and training specifications requested by the applicant;

(4) The proposed evaluation authorization;

(5) A description of the flight training equipment that the applicant proposes to use;

(6) A description of the applicant's training facilities, equipment, qualifications of personnel to be used, and proposed evaluation plans;

(7) A training program curriculum, including syllabi, outlines, courseware, procedures, and documentation to support the items required in subpart B of this part, upon request by the Administrator;

(8) A description of a recordkeeping system that will identify and document the details of training, qualification, and certification of students, instructors, and evaluators;

(9) A description of quality control measures proposed; and

(10) A method of demonstrating the applicant's qualification and ability to provide training for a certificate or rating in fewer than the minimum hours prescribed in part 61 of this chapter if the applicant proposes to do so.

(c) The facilities and equipment described in paragraph (b)(6) of this section shall—

(1) Be available for inspection and evaluation prior to approval; and

(2) Be in place and operational at the location of the proposed training center prior to issuance of a certificate under this part.

(d) An applicant who meets the requirements of this part and is approved by the Administrator is entitled to—

(1) A training center certificate containing all business names included on the application under which the certificate holder may conduct operations and the address of each business office used by the certificate holder; and

(2) Training specifications, issued by the Administrator to the certificate holder, containing—

(i) The type of training authorized, including approved courses;

(ii) The category, class, and type of aircraft that may be used for training, testing, and checking;

(iii) For each flight simulator or flight training device, the make, model, and series of airplane or the set of airplanes being simulated and the qualification level assigned, or the make, model, and series of rotorcraft, or set of rotorcraft being simulated and the qualification level assigned;

(iv) For each flight simulator and flight training device subject to qualification evaluation by the Administrator, the identification number assigned by the FAA;

(v) The name and address of all satellite training centers, and the approved courses offered at each satellite training center;

(vi) Authorized deviations or waivers from this part; and

(vii) Any other items the Administrator may require or allow.

(e) The Administrator may deny, suspend, revoke, or terminate a certificate under this part if the Administrator finds that the applicant or the certificate holder—

(1) Held a training center certificate that was revoked, suspended, or terminated within the previous 5 years; or

(2) Employs or proposes to employ a person who—

(i) Was previously employed in a management or supervisory position by the holder of a training center certificate that was revoked, suspended, or terminated within the previous 5 years;

(ii) Exercised control over any certificate holder whose certificate has been revoked, suspended, or terminated within the last 5 years; and

(iii) Contributed materially to the revocation, suspension, or termination of that certificate and who will be employed in a management or supervisory position, or who will be in control of or have a substantial ownership interest in the training center.

(3) Has provided incomplete, inaccurate, fraudulent, or false information for a training center certificate;

(4) Should not be granted a certificate if the grant would not foster aviation safety.

(f) At any time, the Administrator may amend a training center certificate—

(1) On the Administrator's own initiative, under section 609 of the Federal Aviation Act of 1958 (49 U.S.C. 1429), as amended, and part 13 of this chapter; or

(2) Upon timely application by the certificate holder.

(g) The certificate holder must file an application to amend a training center certificate at least 60 calendar days prior to the applicant's proposed effective amendment date unless a different filing period is approved by the Administrator.

[Docket No. 26933, 61 FR 34562, July 2, 1996; as amended by Amdt. No. 142–1, 62 FR 13791, March 21, 1997]

142

§ 142.13 Management and personnel requirements.

An applicant for a training center certificate must show that—

(a) For each proposed curriculum, the training center has, and shall maintain, a sufficient number of instructors who are qualified in accordance with subpart C of this part to perform the duties to which they are assigned;

(b) The training center has designated, and shall maintain, a sufficient number of approved evaluators to provide required checks and tests to graduation candidates within 7 calendar days of training completion for any curriculum leading to airman certificates or ratings, or both;

(c) The training center has, and shall maintain, a sufficient number of management personnel who are qualified and competent to perform required duties; and

(d) A management representative, and all personnel who are designated by the training center to conduct direct student training, are able to understand, read, write, and fluently speak the English language.

§ 142.15 Facilities.

(a) An applicant for, or holder of, a training center certificate shall ensure that—

(1) Each room, training booth, or other space used for instructional purposes is heated, lighted, and ventilated to conform to local building, sanitation, and health codes; and

(2) The facilities used for instruction are not routinely subject to significant distractions caused by flight operations and maintenance operations at the airport.

(b) An applicant for, or holder of, a training center certificate shall establish and maintain a principal business office that is physically located at the address shown on its training center certificate.

(c) The records required to be maintained by this part must be located in facilities adequate for that purpose.

(d) An applicant for, or holder of, a training center certificate must have available exclusively, for adequate periods of time and at a location approved by the Administrator, adequate flight training equipment and courseware, including at least one flight simulator or advanced flight training device.

[Docket No. 26933, 61 FR 34562, July 2, 1996; as amended by Amdt. 142–3, 63 FR 53536, Oct. 5, 1998]

§ 142.17 Satellite training centers.

(a) The holder of a training center certificate may conduct training in accordance with an approved training program at a satellite training center if—

(1) The facilities, equipment, personnel, and course content of the satellite training center meet the applicable requirements of this part;

(2) The instructors and evaluators at the satellite training center are under the direct supervision of management personnel of the principal training center;

(3) The Administrator is notified in writing that a particular satellite is to begin operations at least 60 days prior to proposed commencement of operations at the satellite training center; and

(4) The certificate holder's training specifications reflect the name and address of the satellite training center and the approved courses offered at the satellite training center.

(b) The certificate holder's training specifications shall prescribe the operations required and authorized at each satellite training center.

[Docket No. 26933, 61 FR 34562, July 2, 1996; as amended by Amdt. 142–3, 63 FR 53536, Oct. 5, 1998]

§ 142.21–142.25 [Reserved]

§ 142.27 Display of certificate.

(a) Each holder of a training center certificate must prominently display that certificate in a place accessible to the public in the principal business office of the training center.

(b) A training center certificate and training specifications must be made available for inspection upon request by—

(1) The Administrator;

(2) An authorized representative of the National Transportation Safety Board; or

(3) Any Federal, State, or local law enforcement agency.

§ 142.29 Inspections.

Each certificate holder must allow the Administrator to inspect training center facilities, equipment, and records at any reasonable time and in any reasonable place in order to determine compliance with or to determine initial or continuing eligibility under 49 U.S.C. 44701, 44707, formerly the Federal Aviation Act of 1958, as amended, and the training center's certificate and training specifications.

§ 142.31 Advertising limitations.

(a) A certificate holder may not conduct, and may not advertise to conduct, any training, testing, and checking that is not approved by the Administrator if that training is designed to satisfy any requirement of this chapter.

(b) A certificate holder whose certificate has been surrendered, suspended, revoked, or terminated must—

(1) Promptly remove all indications, including signs, wherever located, that the training center was certificated by the Administrator; and

(2) Promptly notify all advertising agents, or advertising media, or both, employed by the certificate holder to cease all advertising indicating that the training center is certificated by the Administrator.

§ 142.33 Training agreements.

A pilot school certificated under part 141 of this chapter may provide training, testing, and checking for a training center certificated under this part if—

(a) There is a training, testing, and checking agreement between the certificated training center and the pilot school;

(b) The training, testing, and checking provided by the certificated pilot school is approved and conducted in accordance with this part;

(c) The pilot school certificated under part 141 obtains the Administrator's approval for a training course outline that includes the portion of the training, testing, and checking to be conducted under part 141; and

(d) Upon completion of training, testing, and checking conducted under part 141, a copy of each student's training record is forwarded to the part 142 training center and becomes part of the student's permanent training record.

Subpart B— Aircrew Curriculum and Syllabus Requirements

§ 142.35 Applicability.

This subpart prescribes the curriculum and syllabus requirements for the issuance of a training center certificate and training specifications for training, testing, and checking conducted to meet the requirements of part 61 of this chapter.

§ 142.37 Approval of flight aircrew training program.

(a) Except as provided in paragraph (b) of this section, each applicant for, or holder of, a training center certificate must apply to the Administrator for training program approval.

(b) A curriculum approved under SFAR 58 of part 121 of this chapter is approved under this part without modifications.

(c) Application for training program approval shall be made in a form and in a manner acceptable to the Administrator.

(d) Each application for training program approval must indicate—

(1) Which courses are part of the core curriculum and which courses are part of the specialty curriculum;

(2) Which requirements of part 61 of this chapter would be satisfied by the curriculum or curriculums; and

(3) Which requirements of part 61 of this chapter would not be satisfied by the curriculum or curriculums.

(e) If, after a certificate holder begins operations under an approved training program, the Administrator finds that the certificate holder is not meeting the provisions of its approved training program, the Administrator may require the certificate holder to make revisions to that training program.

(f) If the Administrator requires a certificate holder to make revisions to an approved training program and the certificate holder does not make those required revisions, within 30 calendar days, the Administrator may suspend, revoke, or terminate the training center certificate under the provisions of § 142.11(e).

§ 142.39 Training program curriculum requirements.

Each training program curriculum submitted to the Administrator for approval must meet the applicable requirements of this part and must contain—

(a) A syllabus for each proposed curriculum;

(b) Minimum aircraft and flight training equipment requirements for each proposed curriculum;

(c) Minimum instructor and evaluator qualifications for each proposed curriculum;

(d) A curriculum for initial training and continuing training of each instructor or evaluator employed to instruct in a proposed curriculum; and

(e) For each curriculum that provides for the issuance of a certificate or rating in fewer than the minimum hours prescribed by part 61 of this chapter—

(1) A means of demonstrating the ability to accomplish such training in the reduced number of hours; and

(2) A means of tracking student performance.

Subpart C— Personnel and Flight Training Equipment Requirements

§ 142.45 Applicability.

This subpart prescribes the personnel and flight training equipment requirements for a certificate holder that is training to meet the requirements of part 61 of this chapter.

§ 142.47 Training center instructor eligibility requirements.

(a) A certificate holder may not employ a person as an instructor in a flight training course that is subject to approval by the Administrator unless that person—

(1) Is at least 18 years of age;

(2) Is able to read, write, and speak and understand in the English language;

(3) If instructing in an aircraft in flight, is qualified in accordance with subpart H of part 61 of this chapter;

(4) Satisfies the requirements of paragraph (c) of this section; and

(5) Meets at least one of the following requirements—

(i) Except as allowed by paragraph (a)(5)(ii) of this section, meets the aeronautical experience requirements of § 61.129(a), (b), (c), or (e) of this chapter, as applicable, excluding the required hours of instruction in preparation for the commercial pilot practical test;

(ii) If instructing in flight simulator or flight training device that represents an airplane requiring a type rating or if instructing in a curriculum leading to the issuance of an airline transport pilot certificate or an added rating to an airline transport pilot certificate, meets the aeronautical experience requirements of § 61.159, § 61.161, or § 61.163 of this chapter, as applicable; or

(iii) Is employed as a flight simulator instructor or a flight training device instructor for a training center providing instruction and testing to meet the requirements of part 61 of this chapter on August 1, 1996.

(b) A training center must designate each instructor in writing to instruct in each approved course, prior to that person functioning as an instructor in that course.

(c) Prior to initial designation, each instructor shall:

(1) Complete at least 8 hours of ground training on the following subject matter:

(i) Instruction methods and techniques.

(ii) Training policies and procedures.

(iii) The fundamental principles of the learning process.

(iv) Instructor duties, privileges, responsibilities, and limitations.

(v) Proper operation of simulation controls and systems.

(vi) Proper operation of environmental control and warning or caution panels.

(vii) Limitations of simulation.

(viii) Minimum equipment requirements for each curriculum.

(ix) Revisions to the training courses.

(x) Cockpit resource management and crew coordination.

(2) Satisfactorily complete a written test—

(i) On the subjects specified in paragraph (c)(1) of this section; and

(ii) That is accepted by the Administrator as being of equivalent difficulty, complexity, and scope as the tests provided by the Administrator for the flight instructor airplane and instrument flight instructor knowledge tests.

[Docket No. 26933, 61 FR 34562, July 2, 1996; as amended by Amdt. 142–2, 62 FR 68137, Dec. 30, 1997]

§ 142.49 Training center instructor and evaluator privileges and limitations.

(a) A certificate holder may allow an instructor to provide:

(1) Instruction for each curriculum for which that instructor is qualified.

(2) Testing and checking for which that instructor is qualified.

(3) Instruction, testing, and checking intended to satisfy the requirements of any part of this chapter.

(b) A training center whose instructor or evaluator is designated in accordance with the requirements of this subpart to conduct training, testing, or checking in qualified and approved flight training equipment, may allow its instructor or evaluator to give endorsements required by part 61 of this chapter if that instructor or evaluator is authorized by the Administrator to instruct or evaluate in a part 142 curriculum that requires such endorsements.

(c) A training center may not allow an instructor to—

(1) Excluding briefings and debriefings, conduct more than 8 hours of instruction in any 24-consecutive-hour period;

(2) Provide flight training equipment instruction unless that instructor meets the requirements of § 142.53(a)(1) through (a)(4), and § 142.53(b), as applicable; or

(3) Provide flight instruction in an aircraft unless that instructor—

(i) Meets the requirements of § 142.53(a)(1), (a)(2), and (a)(5);

(ii) Is qualified and authorized in accordance with subpart H of part 61 of this chapter;

(iii) Holds certificates and ratings specified by part 61 of this chapter appropriate to the category, class, and type aircraft in which instructing;

(iv) If instructing or evaluating in an aircraft in flight while occupying a required crewmember seat, holds at least a valid second class medical certificate; and

(v) Meets the recency of experience requirements of part 61 of this chapter.

[Docket No. 26933, 61 FR 34562, July 2, 1996; as amended by Amdt. 142–2, 62 FR 68137, Dec. 30, 1997]

§ 142.51 [Reserved]

§ 142.53 Training center instructor training and testing requirements.

(a) Except as provided in paragraph (c) of this section, prior to designation and every 12 calendar months beginning the first day of the month following an instructor's initial designation, a certificate holder must ensure that each of its instructors meets the following requirements:

(1) Each instructor must satisfactorily demonstrate to an authorized evaluator knowledge of, and proficiency in, instructing in a representative segment of each curriculum for which that instructor is designated to instruct under this part.

(2) Each instructor must satisfactorily complete an approved course of ground instruction in at least—

(i) The fundamental principles of the learning process;

(ii) Elements of effective teaching, instruction methods, and techniques;

(iii) Instructor duties, privileges, responsibilities, and limitations;

(iv) Training policies and procedures;

(v) Cockpit resource management and crew coordination; and

(vi) Evaluation.

(3) Each instructor who instructs in a qualified and approved flight simulator or flight training device must satisfactorily complete an approved course of training in the operation of the flight simulator, and an approved course of ground instruction, applicable to the training courses the instructor is designated to instruct.

(4) The flight simulator training course required by paragraph (a)(3) of this section which must include—

(i) Proper operation of flight simulator and flight training device controls and systems;

(ii) Proper operation of environmental and fault panels;

(iii) Limitations of simulation; and

(iv) Minimum equipment requirements for each curriculum.

(5) Each flight instructor who provides training in an aircraft must satisfactorily complete an approved course of ground instruction and flight training in an aircraft, flight simulator, or flight training device.

(6) The approved course of ground instruction and flight training required by paragraph (a)(5) of this section which must include instruction in—

(i) Performance and analysis of flight training procedures and maneuvers applicable to the training courses that the instructor is designated to instruct;

(ii) Technical subjects covering aircraft subsystems and operating rules applicable to the training courses that the instructor is designated to instruct;

(iii) Emergency operations;

(iv) Emergency situations likely to develop during training; and

(v) Appropriate safety measures.

(7) Each instructor who instructs in qualified and approved flight training equipment must pass a written test and annual proficiency check—

(i) In the flight training equipment in which the instructor will be instructing; and

(ii) On the subject matter and maneuvers of a representative segment of each curriculum for which the instructor will be instructing.

(b) In addition to the requirements of paragraphs (a)(1) through (a)(7) of this section, each certificate holder must ensure that each instructor who instructs in a flight simulator that the Administrator has approved for all training and all testing for the airline transport pilot certification test, aircraft type rating test, or both, has met at least one of the following three requirements:

(1) Each instructor must have performed 2 hours in flight, including three takeoffs and three landings as the sole manipulator of the controls of an aircraft of the same category and class, and, if a type rating is required, of the same type replicated by the approved flight simulator in which that instructor is designated to instruct;

(2) Each instructor must have participated in an approved line-observation program under part 121 or part 135 of this chapter, and that—

(i) Was accomplished in the same airplane type as the airplane represented by the flight simulator in which that instructor is designated to instruct; and

(ii) Included line-oriented flight training of at least 1 hour of flight during which the instructor was the sole manipulator of the controls in a flight simulator that replicated the same type aircraft for which that instructor is designated to instruct; or

(3) Each instructor must have participated in an approved in-flight observation training course that—

(i) Consisted of at least 2 hours of flight time in an airplane of the same type as the airplane repli-

142

cated by the flight simulator in which the instructor is designated to instruct; and

(ii) Included line-oriented flight training of at least 1 hour of flight during which the instructor was the sole manipulator of the controls in a flight simulator that replicated the same type aircraft for which that instructor is designated to instruct.

(c) An instructor who satisfactorily completes a curriculum required by paragraph (a) or (b) of this section in the calendar month before or after the month in which it is due is considered to have taken it in the month in which it was due for the purpose of computing when the next training is due.

(d) The Administrator may give credit for the requirements of paragraph (a) or (b) of this section to an instructor who has satisfactorily completed an instructor training course for a part 121 or part 135 certificate holder if the Administrator finds such a course equivalent to the requirements of paragraph (a) or (b) of this section.

[[Docket No. 26933, 61 FR 34562, July 2, 1996; as amended by Amdt. 142–1, 62 FR 13791, March 21, 1997]

§ 142.55 Training center evaluator requirements.

(a) Except as provided by paragraph (d) of this section, a training center must ensure that each person authorized as an evaluator—

(1) Is approved by the Administrator;

(2) Is in compliance with §§ 142.47, 142.49, and 142.53 and applicable sections of part 187 of this chapter; and

(3) Prior to designation, and except as provided in paragraph (b) of this section, every 12-calendar-month period following initial designation, the certificate holder must ensure that the evaluator satisfactorily completes a curriculum that includes the following:

(i) Evaluator duties, functions, and responsibilities;

(ii) Methods, procedures, and techniques for conducting required tests and checks;

(iii) Evaluation of pilot performance; and

(iv) Management of unsatisfactory tests and subsequent corrective action; and

(4) If evaluating in qualified and approved flight training equipment must satisfactorily pass a written test and annual proficiency check in a flight simulator or aircraft in which the evaluator will be evaluating.

(b) An evaluator who satisfactorily completes a curriculum required by paragraph (a) of this section in the calendar month before or the calendar month after the month in which it is due is considered to have taken it in the month is which it was due for the purpose of computing when the next training is due.

(c) The Administrator may give credit for the requirements of paragraph (a)(3) of this section to an evaluator who has satisfactorily completed an evaluator training course for a part 121 or part 135 certificate holder if the Administrator finds such a course equivalent to the requirements of paragraph (a)(3) of this section.

(d) An evaluator who is qualified under SFAR 58 shall be authorized to conduct evaluations under the Advanced Qualification Program without complying with the requirements of this section.

§ 142.57 Aircraft requirements.

(a) An applicant for, or holder of, a training center certificate must ensure that each aircraft used for flight instruction and solo flights meets the following requirements:

(1) Except for flight instruction and solo flights in a curriculum for agricultural aircraft operations, external load operations, and similar aerial work operations, the aircraft must have an FAA standard airworthiness certificate or a foreign equivalent of an FAA standard airworthiness certificate, acceptable to the Administrator.

(2) The aircraft must be maintained and inspected in accordance with—

(i) The requirements of part 91, subpart E, of this chapter; and

(ii) An approved program for maintenance and inspection.

(3) The aircraft must be equipped as provided in the training specifications for the approved course for which it is used.

(b) Except as provided in paragraph (c) of this section, an applicant for, or holder of, a training center certificate must ensure that each aircraft used for flight instruction is at least a two-place aircraft with engine power controls and flight controls that are easily reached and that operate in a conventional manner from both pilot stations.

(c) Airplanes with controls such as nose-wheel steering, switches, fuel selectors, and engine air flow controls that are not easily reached and operated in a conventional manner by both pilots may be used for flight instruction if the certificate holder determines that the flight instruction can be conducted in a safe manner considering the location of controls and their nonconventional operation, or both.

§ 142.59 Flight simulators and flight training devices.

(a) An applicant for, or holder of, a training center certificate must show that each flight simulator and flight training device used for training, testing, and checking (except AQP) will be or is specifically qualified and approved by the Administrator for—

(1) Each maneuver and procedure for the make, model, and series of aircraft, set of aircraft, or aircraft type simulated, as applicable; and

(2) Each curriculum or training course in which the flight simulator or flight training device is used, if that curriculum or course is used to satisfy any requirement of 14 CFR chapter I.

(b) The approval required by paragraph (a)(2) of this section must include—

(1) The set of aircraft, or type aircraft;

(2) If applicable, the particular variation within type, for which the training, testing, or checking is being conducted; and

(3) The particular maneuver, procedure, or crewmember function to be performed.

(c) Each qualified and approved flight simulator or flight training device used by a training center must—

(1) Be maintained to ensure the reliability of the performances, functions, and all other characteristics that were required for qualification;

(2) Be modified to conform with any modification to the aircraft being simulated if the modification results in changes to performance, function, or other characteristics required for qualification;

(3) Be given a functional preflight check each day before being used; and

(4) Have a discrepancy log in which the instructor or evaluator, at the end of each training session, enters each discrepancy.

(d) Unless otherwise authorized by the Administrator, each component on a qualified and approved flight simulator or flight training device used by a training center must be operative if the component is essential to, or involved in, the training, testing, or checking of airmen.

(e) Training centers shall not be restricted to specific—

(1) Route segments during line-oriented flight training scenarios; and

(2) Visual data bases replicating a specific customer's bases of operation.

(f) Training centers may request evaluation, qualification, and continuing evaluation for qualification of flight simulators and flight training devices without—

(1) Holding an air carrier certificate; or

(2) Having a specific relationship to an air carrier certificate holder.

Subpart D—
Operating Rules

§ 142.61 Applicability.

This subpart prescribes the operating rules applicable to a training center certificated under this part and operating a course or training program curriculum approved in accordance with subpart B of this part.

§ 142.63 Privileges.

A certificate holder may allow flight simulator instructors and evaluators to meet recency of experience requirements through the use of a qualified and approved flight simulator or qualified and approved flight training device if that flight simulator or flight training device is—

(a) Used in a course approved in accordance with subpart B of this part; or

(b) Approved under the Advanced Qualification Program for meeting recency of experience requirements.

§ 142.65 Limitations.

(a) A certificate holder shall—

(1) Ensure that a flight simulator or flight training device freeze, slow motion, or repositioning feature is not used during testing or checking; and

(2) Ensure that a repositioning feature is used during line operational simulation for evaluation and line-oriented flight training only to advance along a flight route to the point where the descent and approach phase of the flight begins.

(b) When flight testing, flight checking, or line operational simulation is being conducted, the certificate holder must ensure that one of the following occupies each crewmember position:

(1) A crewmember qualified in the aircraft category, class, and type, if a type rating is required, provided that no flight instructor who is giving instruction may occupy a crewmember position.

(2) A student, provided that no student may be used in a crewmember position with any other student not in the same specific course.

(c) The holder of a training center certificate may not recommend a trainee for a certificate or rating, unless the trainee—

(1) Has satisfactorily completed the training specified in the course approved under § 142.37; and

(2) Has passed the final tests required by § 142.37.

(d) The holder of a training center certificate may not graduate a student from a course unless the student has satisfactorily completed the curriculum requirements of that course.

Subpart E— Recordkeeping

§ 142.71 Applicability.

This subpart prescribes the training center recordkeeping requirements for trainees enrolled in a course, and instructors and evaluators designated to instruct a course, approved in accordance with subpart B of this part.

§ 142.73 Recordkeeping requirements.

(a) A certificate holder must maintain a record for each trainee that contains—

(1) The name of the trainee;

(2) A copy of the trainee's pilot certificate, if any, and medical certificate;

(3) The name of the course and the make and model of flight training equipment used;

(4) The trainee's prerequisite experience and course time completed;

(5) The trainee's performance on each lesson and the name of the instructor providing instruction;

(6) The date and result of each end-of-course practical test and the name of the evaluator conducting the test; and

(7) The number of hours of additional training that was accomplished after any unsatisfactory practical test.

(b) A certificate holder shall maintain a record for each instructor or evaluator designated to instruct a course approved in accordance with subpart B of this part that indicates that the instructor or evaluator has complied with the requirements of §§ 142.13, 142.45, 142.47, 142.49, and 142.53, as applicable.

(c) The certificate holder shall—

(1) Maintain the records required by paragraphs (a) of this section for at least 1 year following the completion of training, testing or checking;

(2) Maintain the qualification records required by paragraph (b) of this section while the instructor or evaluator is in the employ of the certificate holder and for 1 year thereafter; and

(3) Maintain the recurrent demonstration of proficiency records required by paragraph (b) of this section for at least 1 year.

(d) The certificate holder must provide the records required by this section to the Administrator, upon request and at a reasonable time, and shall keep the records required by—

(1) Paragraph (a) of this section at the training center, or satellite training center where the training, testing, or checking, if appropriate, occurred; and

(2) Paragraph (b) of this section at the training center or satellite training center where the instructor or evaluator is primarily employed.

(e) The certificate holder shall provide to a trainee, upon request and at a reasonable time, a copy of his or her training records.

Subpart F— Other Approved Courses

§ 142.81 Conduct of other approved courses.

(a) An applicant for, or holder of, a training center certificate may apply for approval to conduct a course for which a curriculum is not prescribed by this part.

(b) The course for which application is made under paragraph (a) of this section may be for flight crewmembers other than pilots, airmen other than flight crewmembers, material handlers, ground servicing personnel, and security personnel, and others approved by the Administrator.

(c) An applicant for course approval under this subpart must comply with the applicable requirements of subpart A through subpart F of this part.

(d) The Administrator approves the course for which the application is made if the training center or training center applicant shows that the course contains a curriculum that will achieve a level of competency equal to, or greater than, that required by the appropriate part of this chapter.

[Docket No. 26933, 61 FR 34562, July 2, 1996]

PART 830

NOTIFICATION AND REPORTING OF AIRCRAFT ACCIDENTS OR INCIDENTS AND OVERDUE AIRCRAFT, AND PRESERVATION OF AIRCRAFT WRECKAGE, MAIL, CARGO, AND RECORDS

Authority: Federal Aviation Act of 1958, as amended (49 U.S.C. 40101 et seq.), and the Independent Safety Board Act of 1974, as amended (49 U.S.C. 1101 et seq.).

Source: 53 FR 36982, Sept. 23, 1988, unless otherwise noted.

Subpart A — General

§ 830.1 Applicability.

This part contains rules pertaining to:

(a) Initial notification and later reporting of aircraft incidents and accidents and certain other occurrences in the operation of aircraft, wherever they occur, when they involve civil aircraft of the United States; when they involve certain public aircraft, as specified in this part, wherever they occur; and when they involve foreign civil aircraft where the events occur in the United States, its territories, or its possessions.

(b) Preservation of aircraft wreckage, mail, cargo, and records involving all civil and certain public aircraft accidents, as specified in this part, in the United States and its territories or possessions.

[60 FR 40112, Aug. 7, 1995]

§ 830.2 Definitions.

As used in this part the following words or phrases are defined as follows:

Aircraft accident means an occurrence associated with the operation of an aircraft which takes place between the time any person boards the aircraft with the intention of flight and all such persons have disembarked, and in which any person suffers death or serious injury, or in which the aircraft receives substantial damage.

Civil aircraft means any aircraft other than a public aircraft.

Fatal injury means any injury which results in death within 30 days of the accident.

Incident means an occurrence other than an accident, associated with the operation of an aircraft, which affects or could affect the safety of operations.

Operator means any person who causes or authorizes the operation of an aircraft, such as the owner, lessee, or bailee of an aircraft.

Public aircraft means an aircraft used only for the United States Government, or an aircraft owned and operated (except for commercial purposes) or exclusively leased for at least 90 continuous days by a government other than the United States Government, including a State, the District of Columbia, a territory or possession of the United States, or a political subdivision of that government. "Public aircraft" does not include a government-owned aircraft transporting property for commercial purposes and does not include a government-owned aircraft transporting passengers other than: transporting (for other than commercial purposes) crewmembers or other persons aboard the aircraft whose presence is required to perform, or is associated with the performance of, a governmental function such as firefighting, search and rescue, law enforcement, aeronautical research, or biological or geological resource management; or transporting (for other than commercial purposes) persons aboard the aircraft if the aircraft is operated by the Armed Forces or an intelligence agency of the United States. Notwithstanding any limitation relating to use of the aircraft for commercial purposes, an aircraft shall be considered to be a public aircraft without regard to whether it is operated by a unit of government on behalf of another unit of government pursuant to a cost reimbursement agreement, if the unit of government on whose behalf the operation is conducted certifies to the Administrator of the Federal Aviation Administration that the operation was necessary to respond to a significant and imminent threat to life or property (including natural resources) and that no service by a private operator was reasonably available to meet the threat.

830

Serious injury means any injury which: (1) Requires hospitalization for more than 48 hours, commencing within 7 days from the date of the injury was received; (2) results in a fracture of any bone (except simple fractures of fingers, toes, or nose); (3) causes severe hemorrhages, nerve, muscle, or tendon damage; (4) involves any internal organ; or (5) involves second- or third-degree burns, or any burns affecting more than 5 percent of the body surface.

Substantial damage means damage or failure which adversely affects the structural strength, performance, or flight characteristics of the aircraft, and which would normally require major repair or replacement of the affected component. Engine failure or damage limited to an engine if only one engine fails or is damaged, bent fairings or cowling, dented skin, small punctured holes in the skin or fabric, ground damage to rotor or propeller blades, and damage to landing gear, wheels, tires, flaps, engine accessories, brakes, or wingtips are not considered "substantial damage" for the purpose of this part.

[53 FR 36982, Sept. 23, 1988; as amended by 60 FR 40112, Aug. 7, 1995]

Subpart B—
Initial Notification of Aircraft Accidents, Incidents, and Overdue Aircraft

§ 830.5 Immediate notification.

The operator of any civil aircraft, or any public aircraft not operated by the Armed Forces or an intelligence agency of the United States, or any foreign aircraft shall immediately, and by the most expeditious means available, notify the nearest National Transportation Safety Board (Board) field office[1] when:

(a) An aircraft accident or any of the following listed incidents occur:

(1) Flight control system malfunction or failure;

(2) Inability of any required flight crewmember to perform normal flight duties as a result of injury or illness;

(3) Failure of structural components of a turbine engine excluding compressor and turbine blades and vanes;

(4) In-flight fire; or

(5) Aircraft collide in flight.

(6) Damage to property, other than the aircraft, estimated to exceed $25,000 for repair (including materials and labor) or fair market value in the event of total loss, whichever is less.

(7) For large multiengine aircraft (more than 12,500 pounds maximum certificated takeoff weight):

(i) In-flight failure of electrical systems which requires the sustained use of an emergency bus powered by a back-up source such as a battery, auxiliary power unit, or air-driven generator to retain flight control or essential instruments;

(ii) In-flight failure of hydraulic systems that results in sustained reliance on the sole remaining hydraulic or mechanical system for movement of flight control surfaces;

(iii) Sustained loss of the power or thrust produced by two or more engines; and

(iv) An evacuation of an aircraft in which an emergency egress system is utilized.

(b) An aircraft is overdue and is believed to have been involved in an accident.

[53 FR 36982, Sept. 23, 1988; as amended by 60 FR 40113, Aug. 7, 1995]

§ 830.6 Information to be given in notification.

The notification required in § 830.5 shall contain the following information, if available:

(a) Type, nationality, and registration marks of the aircraft;

(b) Name of owner, and operator of the aircraft;

(c) Name of the pilot-in-command;

(d) Date and time of the accident;

(e) Last point of departure and point of intended landing of the aircraft;

(f) Position of the aircraft with reference to some easily defined geographical point;

(g) Number of persons aboard, number killed, and number seriously injured;

(h) Nature of the accident, the weather and the extent of damage to the aircraft, so far as is known; and

(i) A description of any explosives, radioactive materials, or other dangerous articles carried.

1.The Board field offices are listed under U.S. Government in the telephone directories of the following cities: Anchorage, AK; Atlanta, GA; West Chicago, IL; Denver, CO; Arlington, TX; Gardena (Los Angeles), CA; Miami, FL; Parsippany, NJ (metropolitan New York, NY); Seattle, WA; and Washington, DC.

Subpart C— Preservation of Aircraft Wreckage, Mail, Cargo, and Records

§ 830.10 Preservation of aircraft wreckage, mail, cargo, and records.

(a) The operator of an aircraft involved in an accident or incident for which notification must be given is responsible for preserving to the extent possible any aircraft wreckage, cargo, and mail aboard the aircraft, and all records, including all recording mediums of flight, maintenance, and voice recorders, pertaining to the operation and maintenance of the aircraft and to the airmen until the Board takes custody thereof or a release is granted pursuant to § 831.12(b) of this chapter.

(b) Prior to the time the Board or its authorized representative takes custody of aircraft wreckage, mail, or cargo, such wreckage, mail, or cargo may not be disturbed or moved except to the extent necessary:

(1) To remove persons injured or trapped;

(2) To protect the wreckage from further damage; or

(3) To protect the public from injury.

(c) Where it is necessary to move aircraft wreckage, mail or cargo, sketches, descriptive notes, and photographs shall be made, if possible, of the original positions and condition of the wreckage and any significant impact marks.

(d) The operator of an aircraft involved in an accident or incident shall retain all records, reports, internal documents, and memoranda dealing with the accident or incident, until authorized by the Board to the contrary.

Subpart D— Reporting of Aircraft Accidents, Incidents, and Overdue Aircraft

§ 830.15 Reports and statements to be filed.

(a) *Reports.* The operator of a civil, public (as specified in § 830.5), or foreign aircraft shall file a report on Board Form 6120.1/2 (OMB No. 3147–0001)[2] within 10 days after an accident, or after 7 days if an overdue aircraft is still missing. A report on an incident for which immediate notification is required by § 830.5(a) shall be filed only as requested by an authorized representative of the Board.

(b) *Crewmember statement.* Each crewmember, if physically able at the time the report is submitted, shall attach a statement setting forth the facts, conditions, and circumstances relating to the accident or incident as they appear to him. If the crewmember is incapacitated, he shall submit the statement as soon as he is physically able.

(c) *Where to file the reports.* The operator of an aircraft shall file any report with the field office of the Board nearest the accident or incident.

---

2. Forms are available from the Board field offices (see footnote 1), from Board headquarters in Washington, DC, and from the Federal Aviation Administration, Flight Standards District Offices.

830

AIM

Aeronautical Information Manual

FEDERAL AVIATION ADMINISTRATION (FAA)

The Federal Aviation Administration is responsible for insuring the safe, efficient, and secure use of the Nation's airspace, by military as well as civil aviation, for promoting safety in air commerce, for encouraging and developing civil aeronautics, including new aviation technology, and for supporting the requirements of national defense.

The activities required to carry out these responsibilities include: safety regulations; airspace management and the establishment, operation, and maintenance of a civil–military common system of air traffic control (ATC) and navigation facilities; research and development in support of the fostering of a national system of airports, promulgation of standards and specifications for civil airports, and administration of Federal grants–in–aid for developing public airports; various joint and cooperative activities with the Department of Defense; and technical assistance (under State Department auspices) to other countries.

AERONAUTICAL INFORMATION MANUAL (AIM)
BASIC FLIGHT INFORMATION AND ATC PROCEDURES

This manual is designed to provide the aviation community with basic flight information and ATC procedures for use in the National Airspace System (NAS) of the United States. An international version called the Aeronautical Information Publication contains parallel information, as well as specific information on the international airports for use by the international community.

This manual contains the fundamentals required in order to fly in the United States NAS. It also contains items of interest to pilots concerning health and medical facts, factors affecting flight safety, a pilot/controller glossary of terms used in the ATC System, and information on safety, accident, and hazard reporting.

This manual is complemented by other operational publications which are available via separate subscriptions. These publications are:

Notices to Airmen publication - A publication containing current Notices to Airmen (NOTAM's) which are considered essential to the safety of flight as well as supplemental data affecting the other operational publications listed here. It also includes current Flight Data Center NOTAM's, which are regulatory in nature, issued to establish restrictions to flight or to amend charts or published Instrument Approach Procedures. This publication is issued every 28 days and is available through subscription from the Superintendent of Documents.

The Airport/Facility Directory, the Alaska Supplement, and the Pacific Chart Supplement – These publications contain information on airports, communications, navigation aids, instrument landing systems, VOR receiver check points, preferred routes, Flight Service Station/Weather Service telephone numbers, Air Route Traffic Control Center (ARTCC) frequencies, part–time surface areas, and various other pertinent special notices essential to air navigation. These publications are available upon subscription from the NOAA Distribution Branch (N/CG33), National Ocean Service, Riverdale, Maryland 20737.

Publication Schedule		
Basic or Change	Cutoff Date for Submission	Effective Date of Publication
Basic Manual	8/13/97	2/26/98
Change 1	2/26/98	8/13/98
Change 2	8/13/98	1/28/99
Change 3	1/28/99	7/15/99
Basic Manual	7/15/99	2/24/00

FLIGHT INFORMATION PUBLICATION POLICY

The following is in essence, the statement issued by the FAA Administrator and published in the December 10, 1964, issue of the Federal Register, concerning the FAA policy as pertaining to the type of information that will be published as NOTAM's and in the Aeronautical Information Manual.

a. It is a pilot's inherent responsibility to be alert at all times for and in anticipation of all circumstances, situations, and conditions affecting the safe operation of the aircraft. For example, a pilot should expect to find air traffic at any time or place. At or near both civil and military airports and in the vicinity of known training areas, a pilot should expect concentrated air traffic and realize concentrations of air traffic are not limited to these places.

b. It is the general practice of the agency to advertise by NOTAM or other flight information publications such information it may deem appropriate; information which the agency may from time to time make available to pilots is solely for the purpose of assisting them in executing their regulatory responsibilities. Such information serves the aviation community as a whole and not pilots individually.

c. The fact that the agency under one particular situation or another may or may not furnish information does not serve as a precedent of the agency's responsibility to the aviation community; neither does it give assurance that other information of the same or similar nature will be advertised, nor, does it guarantee that any and all information known to the agency will be advertised.

d. This publication, while not regulatory, provides information which reflects examples of operating techniques and procedures which may be requirements in other federal publications or regulations. It is made available solely to assist pilots in executing their responsibilities required by other publications.

Consistent with the foregoing, it shall be the policy of the Federal Aviation Administration to furnish information only when, in the opinion of the agency, a unique situation should be advertised and not to furnish routine information such as concentrations of air traffic, either civil or military. The Aeronautical Information Manual will not contain informative items concerning everyday circumstances that pilots should, either by good practices or regulation, expect to encounter or avoid.

AIM

AERONAUTICAL INFORMATION MANUAL (AIM)
FEDERAL AVIATION REGULATIONS AND
ADVISORY CIRCULARS

ederal Aviation Regulations - The FAA publishes the ederal Aviation Regulations (FAR's) to make readily vailable to the aviation community the regulatory requirements placed upon them. These regulations are ld as individual parts by the Superintendent of Documents.

he more frequently amended parts are sold on subcription service with subscribers receiving changes automatically as issued. Less active parts are sold on a ngle-sale basis. Changes to single-sale parts will be ld separately as issued. Information concerning these anges will be furnished by the FAA through its Status Federal Aviation Regulations, AC 00-44.

dvisory Circulars - The FAA issues advisory circulars C's) to inform the aviation public in a systematic way nonregulatory material. Unless incorporated into a gulation by reference, the contents of an advisory circular are not binding on the public. Advisory Circulars e issued in a numbered subject system corresponding the subject areas of the Federal Aviation Regulations AR's) (Title 14, Code of Federal Regulations, hapter 1, FAA).

C 00-2, Advisory Circular Checklist and Status of ther FAA Publications, contains advisory circulars

that are for sale as well as those distributed free of charge by the FAA.

NOTE-
The above information relating to FAR's and AC's is extracted from AC 00-2. Many of the FAR's and AC's listed in AC 00-2 are cross-referenced in the AIM. These regulatory and nonregulatory references cover a wide range of subjects and are a source of detailed information of value to the aviation community. AC 00-2 is issued annually and can be obtained free-of-charge from:

U.S. Department of Transportation
Distribution Requirements Section
SVC-121.21
Washington, DC 20590

External References - All references to Advisory Circulars and other FAA publications in the Aeronautical Information Manual include the FAA Advisory Circular or Order identification numbers (when available). However due to varied publication dates, the basic publication letter is not included. (Example: Order 7110.65C, Air Traffic Control, is referenced as Order 7110.65).
To insure that you are consulting the latest information when referencing one of these other documents, use AC 00-2.

COMMENTS/CORRECTIONS

Comments, suggested changes, or corrections concerning this publication may be submitted on this form and mailed to:

Federal Aviation Administration,
Air Traffic Publications (ATA–10),
Attn: AIM Editor,
800 Independence Avenue, S.W.,
Washington, DC 20591.

NOTICE TO EDITOR

The following comments/corrections are submitted concerning the information contained in:

Paragraph number_____ Title _____

Page _____ Dated _____

NAME_____

ORGANIZATION_____

STREET_____

CITY_____STATE_____ZIP_____

NOTE:

DO NOT SEND CHANGE OF ADDRESS INFORMATION OR SUBSCRIPTION ORDERS FOR THE AIM TO THE FAA. It will only delay service. These should be directed to:

Superintendent of Documents,
Attn: Chief, Mail List Branch,
Mail Stop: SSOM,
Washington, DC 20402–9373.

AERONAUTICAL INFORMATION MANUAL
EXPLANATION OF CHANGES
Effective: February 26, 1998

a. 1–1–4. VOR Receiver Check.
Updates information.

b. 1–1–9. Marker Beacon.
Removes paragraph.

c. Old 1–1–10 – New 1–1–9. Instrument Landing System (ILS).
Clarifies the text on ILS glide path and inner marker beacon for Category II ILS.

d. Old 1–1–12 – New 1–1–11. Microwave Landing System (MLS).
Updates the text on operation and operational characteristics of the MLS. Deletes Table 1–1–5, MLS Angle and Data Channeling, and Table 1–1–6, MLS DME Channeling.

e. Old 1–1–16 New 1–1–15. LORAN.
Clarifies the text on LORAN signal accuracy and future use of LORAN nonprecision approaches.

f. Old 1–1–17
New 1–1–16. OMEGA and OMEGA/VLF Navigation Systems.
Reflects the termination of OMEGA operations on September 30, 1997.

g. 1–1–22. Global Positioning System (GPS).
Change includes information concerning: GPS instrument procedures design concepts, suggested new transition methods for arriving aircraft equipped with FMS and/or GPS navigational equipment, explains pilot/controller actions for efficient use of Terminal Arrival Area (TAA) procedures, and explains the use of basic "T" legs and/or PT holding as depicted on procedures.

h. 2–1–2. Visual Glideslope Indicators.
Figure 2–1–7, Pulsating Visual Approach Slope Indicator.
Editorial change.

i. 2–1–4. Runway Edge Light Systems.
Editorial change.

j. 2–1–5. In–Runway Lighting.
Reorganizes paragraph for clarity. Updates subsection on land and hold short lights to better describe the operation of the lights.

k. 2–1–9. Taxiway Lights.
Clarifies that a stop bar also includes elevated red lights on each side.

l. 3–4–8. National Security Areas.
Moves paragraph from Section 4. Special Use Airspace, to Section 5. Other Airspace Areas.

a. 3–5–6. Terminal Radar Service Area (TRSA).
Editorial change.

b. 4–1–9. Traffic Advisory Practices at Airports Without Operating Control Towers.
Clarifies action required when airport information is unavailable from FSS or UNICOM.

c. 4–3–26. Operations at Uncontrolled Airports with Automated Surface Observing System (ASOS)/Automated Weather Observing System (AWOS).
Places the responsibility on the pilot to monitor weather at uncontrolled airports with ASOS/AWOS broadcast capability.

d. 4–4–5. Special VFR Clearances.
Places the responsibility on the pilot to monitor the ASOS/AWOS frequency to determine the current weather conditions at the airport and then to advise the controller of his/her intentions. This procedure would apply at all uncontrolled airports that have automated weather reporting and ground–to–air one–minute weather broadcasts.

e. 5–3–7. Holding.
Removes the artificial maximum holding airspeed restriction of 175 KIAS for propeller driven aircraft. Holding patterns are no longer classified into civil, military, propeller–driven or turbojet. There are three recommended maximum holding airspeeds, 200K, 230K and 265K. The other holding airspeeds will be specifically denoted on aeronautical charts.

f. 5-4-4. Advance Information on Instrument Approach.
Places the responsibility on the pilot to monitor the ASOS/AWOS frequency to determine the current weather conditions at the airport and then to advise the controller of his/her intentions. This procedure would apply at all uncontrolled airports that have automated weather reporting and ground-to-air one minute weather broadcasts.

g. 5-4-8. Procedure Turn.
Reduces the maximum airspeed for course reversal maneuvers to 200 knots vice 250 knots and emphasizes to start the maneuver immediately after overheading the fix.

h. 5-4-12. ILS/MLS Approaches to Parallel Runways;
5-4-14. Simultaneous Parallel ILS/MLS Approaches (Independent) and
5-4-15. Simultaneous Close Parallel ILS/MLS Approaches (Independent).
Change includes information concerning design concepts and pilot/controller actions for efficient use of ILS precision runway monitor (PRM) procedures when conducting simultaneous close parallel approaches.

i. 7-1-3. Preflight Briefing.
With this change, the flight service specialist will not have to provide the international cautionary statement if the pilot states having the information.

j. 7-1-12. ATC Inflight Weather Avoidance Assistance.
Provides guidance to air traffic controllers on managing weather deviations and other contingencies.

k. 7-1-13. Runway Visual Range (RVR).
Updates the text on the transmissometer technology RVR and introduces text on the new generation RVR, which is forward scatter technology. The new generation RVR is currently being fielded to replace the existing transmissometers.

l. Chapter 9. Aeronautical Charts and Related Publications.
Revises entire chapter.

m. General: Editorial changes made throughout the manual.

AERONAUTICAL INFORMATION MANUAL
EXPLANATION OF CHANGES
Change 1
Effective: August 13, 1998

a. FIG 2-3-18, Vehicle Roadway Markings - editorial changes.

b. 3-5-5. Published VFR Routes.
FIG 3-5-3, VFR Transition Route - changes Temple Bridge to Tempe Bridge.
Removes **FIG 3-5-4, Terminal Area VFR Routes** - this chart is no longer published.
Updates 3-5-5 and removes subparagraph d. due to the removal of FIG 3-5-4.

c. FIG 4-1-3, Hazardous Area Reporting Service.
Updates graphic - changes Newport News to Leesburg and Elizabeth City to Raleigh-Durham.

d. 7-1-2. FAA Weather Service.
Reorganizes references into their relevant subparagraphs and adds specific information to a general reference to inflight weather information availability.

e. 7-1-3. Preflight Briefing.
Changes ASL to the more commonly understood MSL.

f. 7-1-5. Inflight Weather Advisories.
Adds an explanation of how advisories are described and plotted; adds information to assist pilots in identifying WST's; reorganizes subparagraphs for clarity and removes information no longer current.

g. 7-1-9. Inflight Weather Broadcasts.
Standardizes the phraseology used in the examples in subparagraphs b.1. and b.2. between the AIM and Order 7110.65, Air Traffic Control. Also, adds subparagraph b.3. to provide pilots with information on how to determine local HIWAS availability while in flight.

h. 7-1-10. Weather Observing Programs.
Adds TBL 7-1-1 to provide a quick comparison of the weather observation methods. Adds subparagraph f. and TBL 7-1-2 to provide information concerning the differing levels of detail in ASOS observations.

i. 7-1-19. PIREP's Relating to Airframe Icing.
Adds information on the potential for icing when the temperature is slightly above 0 degrees Celsius.

j. 7-1-28. International Civil Aviation Organization (ICAO) Weather Formats.
Adds diamond dust to clarify term and corrects the order of additive data remarks.

k. 7-5-10. Light Amplification by Stimulated Emission of Radiation (Laser) Operations.
Adds new paragraph.

AERONAUTICAL INFORMATION MANUAL
EXPLANATION OF CHANGES
Change 2
Effective: January 28, 1999

a. Entire manual.
Changes standard instrument departure (SID) to instrument departure procedure (DP) throughout the manual. Editorial changes made where necessary.

b. 1-1-9. Instrument Landing System (ILS).
FIG 1-1-7, FAA Instrument Landing Systems.
Changes megahertz (MHz) to hertz (Hz) in figure.

c. 1-1-14. User Reports on NAVAID Performance.
Removes reference to General Aviation District Offices.

d. 1-1-21. Global Positioning System (GPS).
Reformats subparagraphs.

e. 3-4-1. General.
Removes references to National Security Areas in this paragraph.

f. 4-3-20. Exiting the Runway After Landing.
Adds further direction and guidance to the pilot.

g. 4-3-23. Use of Aircraft Lights.
Removes unnecessary language because the use of anticollision lights is required by 14 CFR Section 91.209(b) for all operations when the aircraft is equipped with an anticollision light system.

h. 4-4-9. Adherence to Clearance.
Provides additional guidance to pilots regarding altitude restrictions and adherence to the last control instruction from ATC.

i. 4-4-11. Speed Adjustments.
Provides additional guidance to pilots regarding advising ATC of current speed restrictions.

j. 4-4-13. Visual Separation.
Clarifies the pilot's responsibility to maintain visual separation during approaches and gives further guidance to the pilot regarding passing other aircraft when on final approach.

k. 5-1-7. Flight Plan - IFR Flights.
TBL 5-1-2 Aircraft Equipment Suffixes.
Updates and reformats table to more clearly depict aircraft suffixes for pilots and controllers. Also, updates paragraph to reflect the new information in the table.

l. 5-3-5. Airway or Route Course Changes.
FIG 5-3-1 Adhering to Airways or Routes.
Revises graphic by depicting a standard rate of turn for both examples.

m. 5-3-7. Holding.
Clarifies the 175 KIAS airspeed restriction.

n. 5-4-1. Standard Terminal Arrival (STAR), Flight Management System Procedures (FMSP) for Arrivals.
Removes the implication that "Expect" altitudes are used for lost communication procedures. Also, updates to indicate military STAR publication and distribution have been accomplished and military aircraft participate and fly these procedures.

o. 5-4-5. Instrument Approach Procedure Charts.
Adds additional types of precision approaches; adds clarification for RNAV systems; adds explanation of the restrictions in the visual segment and explains new depictions on the approach charts.

p. 5-4-17. Side-Step Maneuver.
Clarifies explanation of side-step maneuver.

q. 5-4-18. Approach and Landing Minimums.
Includes decision altitude (DA) as a minimum altitude and adds additional explanation for procedures with stepdown fixes and more than one altimeter source.

r. 7-1-10. Weather Observing Programs.
Changes visibility criteria to conform with standards.

s. 7-1-14. Reporting of Cloud Heights.
Changes contraction to international format.

t. 7-1-15. Reporting Prevailing Visibility.
Incorporates the updated definition of sector visibility.

u. 7-1-17. Estimating Intensity of Snow or Drizzle (Based on Visibility).
Changes wording for clarity.

v. 7-1-18. Pilot Weather Reports (PIREP's).
Changes examples to reflect new format.

w. 7-1-28. International Civil Aviation Organization (ICAO) Weather Formats.
Changes contractions to international standards.

x. 7-5-6. Seaplane Safety
Changes the title of the USCG's navigation rules; updates the CFR cite; updates the mailing address for advisory circulars; and provides users with the correct identification for the USCG navigation rules.

AERONAUTICAL INFORMATION MANUAL
EXPLANATION OF CHANGES
Change 3
Effective: July 15, 1999

a. Entire manual.
Changes Automated Weather Observation System to Automated Weather Observing System. Also, editorial changes made where necessary.

b. 1-1-21. Global Positioning System (GPS).
Adds clarification of the uses of non-IFR GPS receivers. Also, adds an explanation for using IFR certified GPS receivers in place of ADF and DME; and adds a table depicting the authorized uses of GPS receivers.

c. 1-1-22. GNSS Landing System (GLS).
Adds new paragraph describing the use of Global Navigation Satellite System (GNSS) augmentation systems for precision approach operations. This paragraph is largely a placeholder intended for expansion when International Civil Aviation Organization standards for ground based augmentation system and satellite based augmentation system are agreed upon.

d. 1-1-23. Precision Approach Systems Other Than ILS, GLS, and MLS

Adds new paragraph which addresses special instrument approach procedures for nonconforming precision approach systems. This is intended to address systems that require special authorization, like Special Category I Differential Global Positioning System and Transponder Landing System.

e. 3-2-4. Class C Airspace.
Updates Class C airspace list.

f. 5-2-6. Instrument Departures.
Clarifies the combining of standard instrument departures (SID's) and textural instrument departure procedures into instrument departure procedures (DP's). Restructures the paragraph for readability and easier understanding.

g. 5-4-5. Instrument Approach Procedure Charts.
Clarifies determination of the facility the MSA is based on.

h. 6-4-1. Two-Way Radio Communication Failure.
Clarifies note to ensure that the reader understands that this note is directed towards those aircraft flying IFR in the ATC system and not just IFR in VFR conditions.

i. 7-4-3. Reporting Bird Strikes.
Removes references to General Aviation District Office and Air Carrier District Office.

j. 7-5-6. Use of Runway Half-Way Signs at Unimproved Airports.
Adds new paragraph describing the use of the new Runway Half-Way Signs by pilots operating at unimproved runways. Describes the sign's use during takeoff to evaluate acceleration trends, and for situational awareness during landings, thereby increasing safety at unimproved airports.

k. 9-1-5. Where and How to Get Charts of Foreign Areas.
Updates internet address.

TABLE OF CONTENTS

Chapter 1. NAVIGATION AIDS
Section 1. AIR NAVIGATION RADIO AIDS

Chapter 2. AERONAUTICAL LIGHTING AND OTHER AIRPORT VISUAL AIDS
Section 1. AIRPORT LIGHTING AIDS

AIM

Section 2. AIR NAVIGATION AND OBSTRUCTION LIGHTING

Section 3. AIRPORT MARKING AIDS AND SIGNS

Chapter 3. AIRSPACE
Section 1. GENERAL

Section 2. CONTROLLED AIRSPACE

Section 3. CLASS G AIRSPACE

Section 4. SPECIAL USE AIRSPACE

Section 5. OTHER AIRSPACE AREAS

Chapter 4. AIR TRAFFIC CONTROL
Section 1. SERVICES AVAILABLE TO PILOTS

Section 2. RADIO COMMUNICATIONS PHRASEOLOGY
AND TECHNIQUES

Section 3. AIRPORT OPERATIONS

Section 4. ATC CLEARANCES/SEPARATIONS

Chapter 5. AIR TRAFFIC PROCEDURES
Section 1. PREFLIGHT

Section 2. DEPARTURE PROCEDURES

Section 3. EN ROUTE PROCEDURES

Section 4. ARRIVAL PROCEDURES

Section 5. PILOT/CONTROLLER ROLES AND RESPONSIBILITIES

AIM

Appendices

Chapter 1. NAVIGATION AIDS

Section 1. AIR NAVIGATION RADIO AIDS

1-1-1. GENERAL

Various types of air navigation aids are in use today, each serving a special purpose. These aids have varied owners and operators, namely: the Federal Aviation Administration (FAA), the military services, private organizations, individual states and foreign governments. The FAA has the statutory authority to establish, operate, maintain air navigation facilities and to prescribe standards for the operation of any of these aids which are used for instrument flight in federally controlled airspace. These aids are tabulated in the Airport/Facility Directory (A/FD).

1-1-2. NONDIRECTIONAL RADIO BEACON (NDB)

a. A low or medium frequency radio beacon transmits nondirectional signals whereby the pilot of an aircraft properly equipped can determine bearings and "home" on the station. These facilities normally operate in the frequency band of 190 to 535 kHz and transmit a continuous carrier with either 400 or 1020 Hz modulation. All radio beacons except the compass locators transmit a continuous three-letter identification in code except during voice transmissions.

b. When a radio beacon is used in conjunction with the Instrument Landing System markers, it is called a Compass Locator.

c. Voice transmissions are made on radio beacons unless the letter "W" (without voice) is included in the class designator (HW).

d. Radio beacons are subject to disturbances that may result in erroneous bearing information. Such disturbances result from such factors as lightning, precipitation static, etc. At night, radio beacons are vulnerable to interference from distant stations. Nearly all disturbances which affect the ADF bearing also affect the facility's identification. Noisy identification usually occurs when the ADF needle is erratic. Voice, music or erroneous identification may be heard when a steady false bearing is being displayed. Since ADF receivers do not have a "flag" to warn the pilot when erroneous bearing information is being displayed, the pilot should continuously monitor the NDB's identification.

1-1-3. VHF OMNI-DIRECTIONAL RANGE (VOR)

a. VOR's operate within the 108.0 to 117.95 MHz frequency band and have a power output necessary to provide coverage within their assigned operational service volume. They are subject to line–of–sight restrictions, and the range varies proportionally to the altitude of the receiving equipment.

NOTE-
Normal service ranges for the various classes of VOR's are given in AIM, NAVAID SERVICE VOLUMES, paragraph 1-1-8.

b. Most VOR's are equipped for voice transmission on the VOR frequency. VOR's without voice capability are indicated by the letter "W" (without voice) included in the class designator (VORW).

c. The only positive method of identifying a VOR is by its Morse Code identification or by the recorded automatic voice identification which is always indicated by use of the word "VOR" following the range's name. Reliance on determining the identification of an omnirange should never be placed on listening to voice transmissions by the Flight Service Station (FSS) (or approach control facility) involved. Many FSS's remotely operate several omniranges with different names. In some cases, none of the VOR's have the name of the "parent" FSS. During periods of maintenance, the facility may radiate a T–E–S–T code (– •••• –) or the code may be removed.

d. Voice identification has been added to numerous VOR's. The transmission consists of a voice announcement, "AIRVILLE VOR" alternating with the usual Morse Code identification.

e. The effectiveness of the VOR depends upon proper use and adjustment of both ground and airborne equipment.

1. Accuracy: The accuracy of course alignment of the VOR is excellent, being generally plus or minus 1 degree.

2. Roughness: On some VOR's, minor course roughness may be observed, evidenced by course needle or brief flag alarm activity (some receivers are more susceptible to these irregularities than others). At a few stations, usually in mountainous terrain, the pilot may occasionally observe a brief course needle oscillation, similar to the indication of "approaching station."

Pilots flying over unfamiliar routes are cautioned to be on the alert for these vagaries, and in particular, to use the "to/from" indicator to determine positive station passage.

(a) Certain propeller RPM settings or helicopter rotor speeds can cause the VOR Course Deviation Indicator to fluctuate as much as plus or minus six degrees. Slight changes to the RPM setting will normally smooth out this roughness. Pilots are urged to check for this modulation phenomenon prior to reporting a VOR station or aircraft equipment for unsatisfactory operation.

1-1-4. VOR RECEIVER CHECK

a. The FAA VOR test facility (VOT) transmits a test signal which provides users a convenient means to determine the operational status and accuracy of a VOR receiver while on the ground where a VOT is located. The airborne use of VOT is permitted; however, its use is strictly limited to those areas/altitudes specifically authorized in the A/FD or appropriate supplement.

b. To use the VOT service, tune in the VOT frequency on your VOR receiver. With the Course Deviation Indicator (CDI) centered, the omni–bearing selector should read 0 degrees with the to/from indication showing "from" or the omni–bearing selector should read 180 degrees with the to/from indication showing "to." Should the VOR receiver operate an RMI (Radio Magnetic Indicator), it will indicate 180 degrees on any omni–bearing selector (OBS) setting. Two means of identification are used. One is a series of dots and the other is a continuous tone. Information concerning an individual test signal can be obtained from the local FSS.

c. Periodic VOR receiver calibration is most important. If a receiver's Automatic Gain Control or modulation circuit deteriorates, it is possible for it to display acceptable accuracy and sensitivity close into the VOR or VOT and display out–of–tolerance readings when located at greater distances where weaker signal areas exist. The likelihood of this deterioration varies between receivers, and is generally considered a function of time. The best assurance of having an accurate receiver is periodic calibration. Yearly intervals are recommended at which time an authorized repair facility should recalibrate the receiver to the manufacturer's specifications.

d. Federal Aviation Regulations (14 CFR Section 91.171) provides for certain VOR equipment accuracy checks prior to flight under instrument flight rules. T comply with this requirement and to ensure satisfactor operation of the airborne system, the FAA has provide pilots with the following means of checking VOR re ceiver accuracy:

1. VOT or a radiated test signal from an appropri ately rated radio repair station.

2. Certified airborne check points.

3. Certified check points on the airport surface.

e. A radiated VOT from an appropriately rated radi repair station serves the same purpose as an FAA VO signal and the check is made in much the same manne as a VOT with the following differences:

1. The frequency normally approved by the Federal Communications Commission is 108.0 MHz

2. Repair stations are not permitted to radiate th VOR test signal continuously; consequently, the owne or operator must make arrangements with the repair sta tion to have the test signal transmitted. This service i not provided by all radio repair stations. The aircra owner or operator must determine which repair statio in the local area provides this service. A representativ of the repair station must make an entry into the aircra logbook or other permanent record certifying to the ra dial accuracy and the date of transmission. The owne operator or representative of the repair station may ac complish the necessary checks in the aircraft and mak a logbook entry stating the results. It is necessary t verify which test radial is being transmitted and whethe you should get a "to" or "from" indication.

f. Airborne and ground check points consist of certi fied radials that should be received at specific points o the airport surface or over specific landmarks while ai borne in the immediate vicinity of the airport.

1. Should an error in excess of plus or minus 4 de grees be indicated through use of a ground check, c plus or minus 6 degrees using the airborne check, IF flight shall not be attempted without first correcting th source of the error.

CAUTION—
No correction other than the correction card figures
supplied by the manufacturer should be applied in
making these VOR receiver checks.

2. Locations of airborne check points, ground check points and VOT's are published in the A/FD and are depicted on the A/G voice communications panels on the NOS IFR area chart and IFR enroute low altitude chart.

3. If a dual system VOR (units independent of each other except for the antenna) is installed in the aircraft, one system may be checked against the other. Turn both systems to the same VOR ground facility and note the indicated bearing to that station. The maximum permissible variations between the two indicated bearings is 4 degrees.

1–1–5. TACTICAL AIR NAVIGATION (TACAN)

a. For reasons peculiar to military or naval operations (unusual siting conditions, the pitching and rolling of a naval vessel, etc.) the civil VOR/DME system of air navigation was considered unsuitable for military or naval use. A new navigational system, TACAN, was therefore developed by the military and naval forces to more readily lend itself to military and naval requirements. As a result, the FAA has been in the process of integrating TACAN facilities with the civil VOR/DME program. Although the theoretical, or technical principles of operation of TACAN equipment are quite different from those of VOR/DME facilities, the end result, as far as the navigating pilot is concerned, is the same. These integrated facilities are called VORTAC's.

b. TACAN ground equipment consists of either a fixed or mobile transmitting unit. The airborne unit in conjunction with the ground unit reduces the transmitted signal to a visual presentation of both azimuth and distance information. TACAN is a pulse system and operates in the UHF band of frequencies. Its use requires TACAN airborne equipment and does not operate through conventional VOR equipment.

1–1–6. VHF OMNI–DIRECTIONAL RANGE/TACTICAL AIR NAVIGATION (VORTAC)

a. A VORTAC is a facility consisting of two components, VOR and TACAN, which provides three individual services: VOR azimuth, TACAN azimuth and TACAN distance (DME) at one site. Although consisting of more than one component, incorporating more than one operating frequency, and using more than one antenna system, a VORTAC is considered to be a unified navigational aid. Both components of a VORTAC are envisioned as operating simultaneously and providing the three services at all times.

b. Transmitted signals of VOR and TACAN are each identified by three–letter code transmission and are interlocked so that pilots using VOR azimuth with TACAN distance can be assured that both signals being received are definitely from the same ground station. The frequency channels of the VOR and the TACAN at each VORTAC facility are "paired" in accordance with a national plan to simplify airborne operation.

1–1–7. DISTANCE MEASURING EQUIPMENT (DME)

a. In the operation of DME, paired pulses at a specific spacing are sent out from the aircraft (this is the interrogation) and are received at the ground station. The ground station (transponder) then transmits paired pulses back to the aircraft at the same pulse spacing but on a different frequency. The time required for the round trip of this signal exchange is measured in the airborne DME unit and is translated into distance (nautical miles) from the aircraft to the ground station.

b. Operating on the line–of–sight principle, DME furnishes distance information with a very high degree of accuracy. Reliable signals may be received at distances up to 199 NM at line–of–sight altitude with an accuracy of better than $1/2$ mile or 3 percent of the distance, whichever is greater. Distance information received from DME equipment is SLANT RANGE distance and not actual horizontal distance.

c. DME operates on frequencies in the UHF spectrum between 962 MHz and 1213 MHz. Aircraft equipped with TACAN equipment will receive distance information from a VORTAC automatically, while aircraft equipped with VOR must have a separate DME airborne unit.

d. VOR/DME, VORTAC, ILS/DME, and LOC/DME navigation facilities established by the FAA provide course and distance information from collocated components under a frequency pairing plan. Aircraft receiving equipment which provides for automatic DME selection assures reception of azimuth and distance information from a common source when designated VOR/DME, VORTAC, ILS/DME, and LOC/DME are selected.

e. Due to the limited number of available frequencies, assignment of paired frequencies is required for certain military noncollocated VOR and TACAN facilities which serve the same area but which may be separated by distances up to a few miles. The military is presently undergoing a program to collocate

VOR and TACAN facilities or to assign nonpaired frequencies to those that cannot be collocated.

f. VOR/DME, VORTAC, ILS/DME, and LOC/DME facilities are identified by synchronized identifications which are transmitted on a time share basis. The VOR or localizer portion of the facility is identified by a coded tone modulated at 1020 Hz or a combination of code and voice. The TACAN or DME is identified by a coded tone modulated at 1350 Hz. The DME or TACAN coded identification is transmitted one time for each three or four times that the VOR or localizer coded identification is transmitted. When either the VOR or the DME is inoperative, it is important to recognize which identifier is retained for the operative facility. A single coded identification with a repetition interval of approximately 30 seconds indicates that the DME is operative.

g. Aircraft equipment which provides for automatic DME selection assures reception of azimuth and distance information from a common source when designated VOR/DME, VORTAC and ILS/DME navigation facilities are selected. Pilots are cautioned to disregard any distance displays from automatically selected DME equipment when VOR or ILS facilities, which do not have the DME feature installed, are being used for position determination.

1-1-8. NAVAID SERVICE VOLUMES

a. Most air navigation radio aids which provide positive course guidance have a designated standard service volume (SSV). The SSV defines the reception limits of unrestricted NAVAID's which are usable for random/unpublished route navigation.

b. A NAVAID will be classified as restricted if it does not conform to flight inspection signal strength and course quality standards throughout the published SSV. However, the NAVAID should not be considered usable at altitudes below that which could be flown while operating under random route IFR conditions (14 CFR Section 91.177), even though these altitudes may lie within the designated SSV. Service volume restrictions are first published in the Notices to Airman (NOTAM) and then with the alphabetical listing of the NAVAID's in the A/FD.

c. Standard Service Volume limitations do not apply to published IFR routes or procedures.

Standard High Altitude Service Volume
(See FIG 1–1–5 for altitudes below 1,000 feet).

FIG 1–1–1

d. VOR/DME/TACAN Standard Service Volumes (SSV).

1. Standard service volumes (SSV's) are graphically shown in FIG 1–1–1, FIG 1–1–2, FIG 1–1–3, FIG 1–1–4, and FIG 1–1–5. The SSV of a station is indicated by using the class designator as a prefix to the station type designation.

EXAMPLE–
TVOR, LDME, and HVORTAC.

2. Within 25 NM, the bottom of the T service volume is defined by the curve in FIG 1–1–4. Within 40 NM, the bottoms of the L and H service volumes are defined by the curve in FIG 1–1–5. (See TBL 1–1–1.)

e. Nondirectional Radio Beacon (NDB)

1. NDB's are classified according to their intended use.

2. The ranges of NDB service volumes are shown in TBL 1–1–2. The distances (radius) are the same at all altitudes.

Standard Low Altitude Service Volume
(See FIG 1–1–5 for altitudes below 1,000 feet).

NOTE: All elevations shown are with respect to the station's site elevation (AGL). Coverage is not available in a cone of airspace directly above the facility.

FIG 1–1–2

Standard Terminal Service Volume
(See FIG 1–1–4 for altitudes below 1,000 feet).

FIG 1–1–3

VOR/DME/TACAN Standard Service Volumes

SSV CLASS DESIGNATOR	ALTITUDE AND RANGE BOUNDARIES
T (Terminal)	From 1,000 feet above ground level (AGL) up to and including 12,000 feet AGL at radial distances out to 25 NM.
L (Low Altitude)	From 1,000 feet AGL up to and including 18,000 feet AGL at radial distances out to 40 NM.
H (High Altitude)	From 1,000 feet AGL up to and including 14,500 feet AGL at radial distances out to 40 NM. From 14,500 AGL up to and including 60,000 feet at radial distances out to 100 NM. From 18,000 feet AGL up to and including 45,000 feet AGL at radial distances out to 130 NM.

TBL 1–1–1

NDB Service Volumes

CLASS	DISTANCE (RADIUS)
Compass Locator	15 NM
MH	25 NM
H	50 NM*
HH	75 NM

* Service ranges of individual facilities may be less than 50 nautical miles (NM). Restrictions to service volumes are first published as a Notice to Airmen and then with the alphabetical listing of the NAVAID in the A/FD.

TBL 1–1–2

**Service Volume Lower Edge
Terminal**

FIG 1-1-4

**Service Volume Lower Edge
Standard High and Low**

FIG 1-1-5

1-1-9. INSTRUMENT LANDING SYSTEM (ILS)

a. General

1. The ILS is designed to provide an approach path for exact alignment and descent of an aircraft on final approach to a runway.

2. The ground equipment consists of two highly directional transmitting systems and, along the approach, three (or fewer) marker beacons. The directional transmitters are known as the localizer and glide slope transmitters.

3. The system may be divided functionally into three parts:

(a) *Guidance information:* localizer, glide slope,

(b) *Range information:* marker beacon, DME, and

(c) *Visual information:* approach lights, touchdown and centerline lights, runway lights.

4. Compass locators located at the Outer Marker (OM) or Middle Marker (MM) may be substituted for marker beacons. DME, when specified in the procedure, may be substituted for the OM.

5. Where a complete ILS system is installed on each end of a runway; (i.e. the approach end of Runway 4 and the approach end of Runway 22) the ILS systems are not in service simultaneously.

b. Localizer

1. The localizer transmitter operates on one of 40 ILS channels within the frequency range of 108.10 to 111.95 MHz. Signals provide the pilot with course guidance to the runway centerline.

2. The approach course of the localizer is called the front course and is used with other functional parts, e.g., glide slope, marker beacons, etc. The localizer signal is transmitted at the far end of the runway. It is adjusted for a course width of (full scale fly–left to a full scale fly–right) of 700 feet at the runway threshold.

3. The course line along the extended centerline of a runway, in the opposite direction to the front course is called the back course.

CAUTION–
Unless the aircraft's ILS equipment includes reverse sensing capability, when flying inbound on the back course it is necessary to steer the aircraft in the direction opposite the needle deflection when making corrections from off–course to on–course. This "flying away from the needle" is also required when flying outbound on the front course of the localizer. Do not use back course signals for approach unless a back course approach procedure is published for that particular runway and the approach is authorized by ATC.

4. Identification is in International Morse Code and consists of a three–letter identifier preceded by the letter I (●●) transmitted on the localizer frequency.

EXAMPLE–
I–DIA

5. The localizer provides course guidance throughout the descent path to the runway threshold from a distance of 18 NM from the antenna between an altitude of 1,000 feet above the highest terrain along the course line and 4,500 feet above the elevation of the antenna site. Proper off–course indications are provided throughout the following angular areas of the operational service volume:

(a) To 10 degrees either side of the course along a radius of 18 NM from the antenna, and

Limits of Localizer Coverage

FIG 1–1–6

(b) From 10 to 35 degrees either side of the course along a radius of 10 NM. (See FIG 1–1–6.)

6. Unreliable signals may be received outside these areas.

c. Localizer–type Directional Aid

1. The Localizer–type Directional Aid (LDA) is of comparable use and accuracy to a localizer but is not part of a complete ILS. The LDA course usually provides a more precise approach course than the similar Simplified Directional Facility (SDF) installation, which may have a course width of 6 or 12 degrees.

2. The LDA is not aligned with the runway. Straight–in minimums may be published where alignment does not exceed 30 degrees between the course and runway. Circling minimums only are published where this alignment exceeds 30 degrees.

d. Glide Slope/Glide Path

1. The UHF glide slope transmitter, operating on one of the 40 ILS channels within the frequency range 329.15 MHz, to 335.00 MHz radiates its signals in the direction of the localizer front course. The term "glide path" means that portion of the glide slope that intersects the localizer.

CAUTION–
False glide slope signals may exist in the area of the localizer back course approach which can cause the glide slope flag alarm to disappear and present unreliable glide slope information. Disregard all glide slope signal indications when making a localizer back course approach unless a glide slope is specified on the approach and landing chart.

2. The glide slope transmitter is located between 750 feet and 1,250 feet from the approach end of the runway (down the runway) and offset 250 to 650 feet from the runway centerline. It transmits a glide path beam 1.4 degrees wide (vertically). The signal provides descent information for navigation down to the lowest authorized decision height (DH) specified in the approved ILS approach procedure. The glidepath may not be suitable for navigation below the lowest authorized DH and any reference to glidepath indications below that height must be supplemented by visual reference to the runway environment. Glidepaths with no published DH are usable to runway threshold.

3. The glide path projection angle is normally adjusted to 3 degrees above horizontal so that it intersects the MM at about 200 feet and the OM at about 1,400 feet above the runway elevation. The glide slope is normally usable to the distance of 10 NM. However, at some locations, the glide slope has been certified for an extended service volume which exceeds 10 NM.

4. Pilots must be alert when approaching the glidepath interception. False courses and reverse sensing will occur at angles considerably greater than the published path.

5. Make every effort to remain on the indicated glide path.

CAUTION—
Avoid flying below the glide path to assure obstacle/terrain clearance is maintained.

6. The published glide slope threshold crossing height (TCH) DOES NOT represent the height of the actual glide path on–course indication above the runway threshold. It is used as a reference for planning purposes which represents the height above the runway threshold that an aircraft's glide slope antenna should be, if that aircraft remains on a trajectory formed by the four–mile–to–middle marker glidepath segment.

7. Pilots must be aware of the vertical height between the aircraft's glide slope antenna and the main gear in the landing configuration and, at the DH, plan to adjust the descent angle accordingly if the published TCH indicates the wheel crossing height over the runway threshold may not be satisfactory. Tests indicate a comfortable wheel crossing height is approximately 20 to 30 feet, depending on the type of aircraft.

e. Distance Measuring Equipment (DME)

1. When installed with the ILS and specified in the approach procedure, DME may be used:

(a) In lieu of the OM,

(b) As a back course (BC) final approach fix (FAF), and

(c) To establish other fixes on the localizer course.

2. In some cases, DME from a separate facility may be used within Terminal Instrument Procedures (TERPS) limitations:

(a) To provide ARC initial approach segments,

(b) As a FAF for BC approaches, and

(c) As a substitute for the OM.

f. Marker Beacon

1. ILS marker beacons have a rated power output of 3 watts or less and an antenna array designed to produce an elliptical pattern with dimensions, at 1,000 feet above the antenna, of approximately 2,400 feet in width and 4,200 feet in length. Airborne marker beacon receivers with a selective sensitivity feature should always be operated in the "low" sensitivity position for proper reception of ILS marker beacons.

2. Ordinarily, there are two marker beacons associated with an ILS, the OM and MM. Locations with a Category II ILS also have an Inner Marker (IM). When an aircraft passes over a marker, the pilot will receive the indications shown in TBL 1–1–3.

(a) The OM normally indicates a position at which an aircraft at the appropriate altitude on the localizer course will intercept the ILS glide path.

(b) The MM indicates a position approximately 3,500 feet from the landing threshold. This is also the position where an aircraft on the glide path will be at an altitude of approximately 200 feet above the elevation of the touchdown zone.

(c) The inner marker (IM) will indicate a point at which an aircraft is at a designated decision height (DH) on the glide path between the MM and landing threshold.

3. A back course marker normally indicates the ILS back course final approach fix where approach descent is commenced.

Marker Passage Indications

MARKER	CODE	LIGHT
OM	– – –	BLUE
MM	● – ● –	AMBER
IM	● ● ● ●	WHITE
BC	● ● ● ●	WHITE

TBL 1–1–3

g. Compass Locator

1. Compass locator transmitters are often situated at the MM and OM sites. The transmitters have a power of less than 25 watts, a range of at least 15 miles and operate between 190 and 535 kHz. At some locations, higher powered radio beacons, up to 400 watts, are used as OM compass locators. These generally carry Transcribed Weather Broadcast (TWEB) information.

2. Compass locators transmit two letter identification groups. The outer locator transmits the first two letters of the localizer identification group, and the middle locator transmits the last two letters of the localizer identification group.

h. ILS Frequency (See TBL 1–1–4.)

i. ILS Minimums

1. The lowest authorized ILS minimums, with all required ground and airborne systems components operative, are:

   (a) *Category I:* Decision Height (DH) 200 feet and Runway Visual Range (RVR) 2,400 feet (with touchdown zone and centerline lighting, RVR 1,800 feet),

   (b) *Category II:* DH 100 feet and RVR 1,200 feet,

   (c) *Category IIIa:* No DH or DH below 100 feet and RVR not less than 700 feet,

   (d) *Category IIIb:* No DH or DH below 50 feet and RVR less than 700 feet but not less than 150 feet, and

   (e) *Category IIIc:* No DH and no RVR limitation.

NOTE–
Special authorization and equipment required for Categories II and III.

j. Inoperative ILS Components

1. *Inoperative localizer:* When the localizer fails, an ILS approach is not authorized.

2. *Inoperative glide slope:* When the glide slope fails, the ILS reverts to a nonprecision localizer approach.

REFERENCE–
SEE THE INOPERATIVE COMPONENT TABLE IN THE U.S. GOVERNMENT TERMINAL PROCEDURES PUBLICATION (TPP), FOR ADJUSTMENTS TO MINIMUMS DUE TO INOPERATIVE AIRBORNE OR GROUND SYSTEM EQUIPMENT.

Frequency Pairs Allocated for ILS

Localizer MHz	Glide Slope
108.10	334.70
108.15	334.55
108.3	334.10
108.35	333.95
108.5	329.90
108.55	329.75
108.7	330.50
108.75	330.35
108.9	329.30
108.95	329.15
109.1	331.40
109.15	331.25
109.3	332.00
109.35	331.85
109.50	332.60
109.55	332.45
109.70	333.20
109.75	333.05
109.90	333.80
109.95	333.65
110.1	334.40
110.15	334.25
110.3	335.00
110.35	334.85
110.5	329.60
110.55	329.45
110.70	330.20
110.75	330.05
110.90	330.80
110.95	330.65
111.10	331.70
111.15	331.55
111.30	332.30
111.35	332.15
111.50	332.9
111.55	332.75
111.70	333.5
111.75	333.35
111.90	331.1
111.95	330.95

TBL 1–1–4

k. ILS Course Distortion

1. All pilots should be aware that disturbances to ILS localizer and glide slope courses may occur when surface vehicles or aircraft are operated near the localizer or glide slope antennas. Most ILS installations are subject to signal interference by either surface vehicles, aircraft or both. ILS CRITICAL AREAS are established near each localizer and glide slope antenna.

2. ATC issues control instructions to avoid interfering operations within ILS critical areas at controlled airports during the hours the Airport Traffic Control Tower (ATCT) is in operation as follows:

(a) *Weather Conditions:* Less than ceiling 800 feet and/or visibility 2 miles.

(1) **Localizer Critical Area:** Except for aircraft that land, exit a runway, depart or miss approach, vehicles and aircraft are not authorized in or over the critical area when an arriving aircraft is between the ILS final approach fix and the airport. Additionally, when the ceiling is less than 200 feet and/or the visibility is RVR 2,000 or less, vehicle and aircraft operations in or over the area are not authorized when an arriving aircraft is inside the ILS MM.

(2) **Glide Slope Critical Area:** Vehicles and aircraft are not authorized in the area when an arriving aircraft is between the ILS final approach fix and the airport unless the aircraft has reported the airport in sight and is circling or side stepping to land on a runway other than the ILS runway.

(b) *Weather Conditions:* At or above ceiling 800 feet and/or visibility 2 miles.

(1) No critical area protective action is provided under these conditions.

(2) A flight crew, under these conditions, should advise the tower that it will conduct an AUTO-LAND or COUPLED approach to ensure that the ILS critical areas are protected when the aircraft is inside the ILS MM.

EXAMPLE–
Glide slope signal not protected.

3. Aircraft holding below 5,000 feet between the outer marker and the airport may cause localizer signal variations for aircraft conducting the ILS approach. Accordingly, such holding is not authorized when weather or visibility conditions are less than ceiling 800 feet and/or visibility 2 miles.

4. Pilots are cautioned that vehicular traffic not subject to ATC may cause momentary deviation to ILS course or glide slope signals. Also, critical areas are not protected at uncontrolled airports or at airports with an operating control tower when weather or visibility conditions are above those requiring protective measures. Aircraft conducting coupled or autoland operations should be especially alert in monitoring automatic flight control systems. (See FIG 1–1–7.)

NOTE–
Unless otherwise coordinated through Flight Standards, ILS signals to Category I runways are not flight inspected below 100 feet AGL. Guidance signal anomalies may be encountered below this altitude.

1–1–10. SIMPLIFIED DIRECTIONAL FACILITY (SDF)

a. The SDF provides a final approach course similar to that of the ILS localizer. It does not provide glide slope information. A clear understanding of the ILS localizer and the additional factors listed below completely describe the operational characteristics and use of the SDF.

b. The SDF transmits signals within the range of 108.10 to 111.95 MHz.

c. The approach techniques and procedures used in an SDF instrument approach are essentially the same as those employed in executing a standard localizer approach except the SDF course may not be aligned with the runway and the course may be wider, resulting in less precision.

d. Usable off–course indications are limited to 35 degrees either side of the course centerline. Instrument indications received beyond 35 degrees should be disregarded.

e. The SDF antenna may be offset from the runway centerline. Because of this, the angle of convergence between the final approach course and the runway bearing should be determined by reference to the instrument approach procedure chart. This angle is generally not more than 3 degrees. However, it should be noted that inasmuch as the approach course originates at the antenna site, an approach which is continued beyond the runway threshold will lead the aircraft to the SDF offset position rather than along the runway centerline.

f. The SDF signal is fixed at either 6 degrees or 12 degrees as necessary to provide maximum flyability and optimum course quality.

g. Identification consists of a three–letter identifier transmitted in Morse Code on the SDF frequency. The appropriate instrument approach chart will indicate the identifier used at a particular airport.

FAA Instrument Landing Systems

FIG 1-1-7

1-1-11. MICROWAVE LANDING SYSTEM (MLS)

a. General

1. The MLS provides precision navigation guidance for exact alignment and descent of aircraft on approach to a runway. It provides azimuth, elevation, and distance.

2. Both lateral and vertical guidance may be displayed on conventional course deviation indicators or incorporated into multipurpose cockpit displays. Range information can be displayed by conventional DME indicators and also incorporated into multipurpose displays.

3. The MLS supplements the ILS as the standard landing system in the United States for civil, military, and international civil aviation. At international airports, ILS service is protected to 2010.

4. The system may be divided into five functions:

　(a) Approach azimuth,

　(b) Back azimuth,

　(c) Approach elevation,

　(d) Range, and

　(e) Data communications.

5. The standard configuration of MLS ground equipment includes:

　(a) An azimuth station to perform functions (a) and (e) above. In addition to providing azimuth navigation guidance, the station transmits basic data which consists of information associated directly with the operation of the landing system, as well as advisory data on the performance of the ground equipment.

　(b) An elevation station to perform function (c).

　(c) Distance Measuring Equipment (DME) to perform range guidance, both standard DME (DME/N) and precision DME (DME/P).

6. MLS Expansion Capabilities: The standard configuration can be expanded by adding one or more of the following functions or characteristics.

　(a) **Back azimuth:** Provides lateral guidance for missed approach and departure navigation.

　(b) **Auxiliary data transmissions:** Provides additional data, including refined airborne positioning, meteorological information, runway status, and other supplementary information.

　(c) Expanded Service Volume (ESV) proportional guidance to 60 degrees.

7. MLS identification is a four-letter designation starting with the letter M. It is transmitted in International Morse Code at least six times per minute by the approach azimuth (and back azimuth) ground equipment.

b. Approach Azimuth Guidance

1. The azimuth station transmits MLS angle and data on one of 200 channels within the frequency range of 5031 to 5091 MHz.

2. The equipment is normally located about 1,000 feet beyond the stop end of the runway, but there is considerable flexibility in selecting sites. For example, for heliport operations the azimuth transmitter can be collocated with the elevation transmitter.

3. The azimuth coverage extends: (See FIG 1-1-8.)

　(a) Laterally, at least 40 degrees on either side of the runway centerline in a standard configuration,

　(b) In elevation, up to an angle of 15 degrees and to at least 20,000 feet, and

　(c) In range, to at least 20 NM.

Coverage Volume
Azimuth

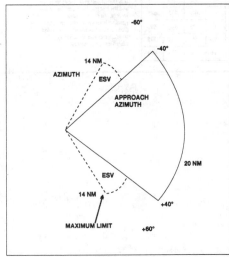

FIG 1-1-8

c. Elevation Guidance

1. The elevation station transmits signals on the same frequency as the azimuth station. A single frequency is time–shared between angle and data functions.

2. The elevation transmitter is normally located about 400 feet from the side of the runway between runway threshold and the touchdown zone.

3. Elevation coverage is provided in the same airspace as the azimuth guidance signals:

   (a) In elevation, to at least +15 degrees,

   (b) Laterally, to fill the Azimuth lateral coverage, and

   (c) In range, to at least 20 NM. (See FIG 1–1–9.)

Coverage Volumes
Elevation

FIG 1–1–9

d. Range Guidance

1. The MLS Precision Distance Measuring Equipment (DME/P) functions the same as the navigation DME described in paragraph 1–1–7, Distance Measuring Equipment (DME), but there are some technical differences. The beacon transponder operates in the frequency band 962 to 1105 MHz and responds to an aircraft interrogator. The MLS DME/P accuracy is improved to be consistent with the accuracy provided by the MLS azimuth and elevation stations.

2. A DME/P channel is paired with the azimuth and elevation channel. A complete listing of the 200 paired channels of the DME/P with the angle functions is contained in FAA Standard 022 (MLS Interoperability and Performance Requirements).

3. The DME/N or DME/P is an integral part of the MLS and is installed at all MLS facilities unless a waiv-

er is obtained. This occurs infrequently and only at outlying, low density airports where marker beacons or compass locators are already in place.

e. Data Communications

1. The data transmission can include both the basic and auxiliary data words. All MLS facilities transmit basic data. Where needed, auxiliary data can be transmitted.

2. Coverage limits: MLS data are transmitted throughout the azimuth (and back azimuth when provided) coverage sectors.

3. Basic data content: Representative data include:

   (a) Station identification,

   (b) Exact locations of azimuth, elevation and DME/P stations (for MLS receiver processing functions),

   (c) Ground equipment performance level, and

   (d) DME/P channel and status.

4. Auxiliary data content: Representative data include:

   (a) 3–D locations of MLS equipment,

   (b) Waypoint coordinates,

   (c) Runway conditions, and

   (d) Weather (e.g., RVR, ceiling, altimeter setting, wind, wake vortex, wind shear).

f. Operational Flexibility

1. The MLS has the capability to fulfill a variety of needs in the approach, landing, missed approach and departure phases of flight. For example:

   (a) Curved and segmented approaches,

   (b) Selectable glide path angles,

   (c) Accurate 3–D positioning of the aircraft in space, and

   (d) The establishment of boundaries to ensure clearance from obstructions in the terminal area.

2. While many of these capabilities are available to any MLS–equipped aircraft, the more sophisticated capabilities (such as curved and segmented approaches) are dependent upon the particular capabilities of the airborne equipment.

g. Summary

1. Accuracy: The MLS provides precision three–dimensional navigation guidance accurate enough for all approach and landing maneuvers.

2. Coverage: Accuracy is consistent throughout the coverage volumes. (See FIG 1–1–10.)

3. Environment: The system has low susceptibility to interference from weather conditions and airport ground traffic.

4. Channels: MLS has 200 channels– enough for any foreseeable need.

5. Data: The MLS transmits ground–air data messages associated with the systems operation.

6. Range information: Continuous range information is provided with an accuracy of about 100 feet.

**Coverage Volumes
3–D Representation**

FIG 1–1–10

■ **1-1-12. NAVAID IDENTIFIER REMOVAL DURING MAINTENANCE**

During periods of routine or emergency maintenance, coded identification (or code and voice, where applicable) is removed from certain FAA NAVAID's.

Removal of identification serves as a warning to pilots that the facility is officially off the air for tune–up or repair and may be unreliable even though intermittent or constant signals are received.

NOTE–
During periods of maintenance VHF ranges may radiate a
T–E–S–T code (– •••• –).

1-1-13. NAVAID'S WITH VOICE

a. Voice equipped en route radio navigational aids are under the operational control of either an FAA AFSS or an approach control facility. The voice communication is available on some facilities. The HIWAS broadcast capability on selected VOR sites is in the process of being implemented throughout the conterminous United States and does not provide voice communication. The availability of two-way voice communication and HIWAS is indicated in the A/FD and aeronautical charts.

b. Unless otherwise noted on the chart, all radio navigation aids operate continuously except during shutdowns for maintenance. Hours of operation of facilities not operating continuously are annotated on charts and in the A/FD.

1-1-14. USER REPORTS ON NAVAID PERFORMANCE

a. Users of the National Airspace System (NAS) can render valuable assistance in the early correction of NAVAID malfunctions by reporting their observations of undesirable NAVAID performance. Although NAVAID's are monitored by electronic detectors, adverse effects of electronic interference, new obstructions or changes in terrain near the NAVAID can exist without detection by the ground monitors. Some of the characteristics of malfunction or deteriorating performance which should be reported are: erratic course or bearing indications; intermittent, or full, flag alarm; garbled, missing or obviously improper coded identification; poor quality communications reception; or, in the case of frequency interference, an audible hum or tone accompanying radio communications or NAVAID identification.

b. Reporters should identify the NAVAID, location of the aircraft, time of the observation, type of aircraft and describe the condition observed; the type of receivers in use is also useful information. Reports can be made in any of the following ways:

1. Immediate report by direct radio communication to the controlling Air Route Traffic Control Center

(ARTCC), Control Tower, or FSS. This method pro-vides the quickest result.

2. By telephone to the nearest FAA facility.

3. By FAA Form 8000-7, Safety Improvement Report, a postage-paid card designed for this purpose. These cards may be obtained at FAA FSS's, Flight Standards District Offices, and General Aviation Fixed Base Operations.

c. In aircraft that have more than one receiver, there are many combinations of possible interference between units. This can cause either erroneous navigation indications or, complete or partial blanking out of the communications. Pilots should be familiar enough with the radio installation of the particular airplanes they fly to recognize this type of interference.

1-1-15. LORAN

a. Introduction

1. LORAN, which uses a network of land-based radio transmitters, was developed to provide an accurate system for LOng RAnge Navigation. The system was configured to provide reliable, all weather navigation for marine users along the U.S. coasts and in the Great Lakes. The current system, known as LORAN-C, was the third version of four developed since World War II.

2. With an expanding user group in the general aviation community, the LORAN coastal facilities were augmented in 1991 to provide signal coverage over the entire continental U.S. The Federal Aviation Administration (FAA) and the United States Coast Guard (USCG) are incorporating LORAN into the National Airspace System (NAS) for supplemental en route and nonprecision approach operations. LORAN-C is also supported in the Canadian airspace system. This guide is intended to provide an introduction to the LORAN system, LORAN avionics, the use of LORAN for aircraft navigation, and to examine the possible future of LORAN in aviation.

b. LORAN Chain

1. The 27 U.S. LORAN transmitters that provide signal coverage for the continental U.S. and the southern half of Alaska are distributed from Caribou, ME, to Attu Island in the Aleutians. Station operations are organized into sub-groups of four to six stations called "chains." One station in the chain is designated the "Master" and the others are "secondary" stations.

2. The LORAN navigation signal is a carefully structured sequence of brief radio frequency pulses centered at 100 kiloHertz. The sequence of signal transmissions consists of a pulse group from the Master (M) station followed at precise time intervals by groups from the secondary stations which are designated by the U.S. Coast Guard with the letters V, W, X, Y and Z. All secondary stations radiate pulses in groups of eight, but the Master signal for identification has an additional ninth pulse.

3. The time interval between the reoccurrence of the Master pulse group is the Group Repetition Interval (GRI). The GRI is the same for all stations in a chain and each LORAN chain has a unique GRI. Since all stations in a particular chain operate on the same radio frequency, the GRI is the key by which a LORAN receiver can identify and isolate signal groups from a specific chain.

EXAMPLE-
Transmitters in the northeast U.S. chain operate with a GRI of 99,600 microseconds which is shortened to 9960 for convenience. The master station (m) at Sseneca, NY, controls: secondary stations (w) at Caribou, ME; (x) at Nantucket, MA; (y) at Carolina Bbeach, NC; and (z) at Dana, IN. In order to keep chain operations precise, the system uses monitor receivers at Cape Elizabeth, ME, Sandy Hook, NJ and Plumbrook, OH. Monitor receivers continuously measure various aspects of the quality and accuracy of LORAN signals and report system status to a control station where chain timing is maintained.

4. The line between the Master and each secondary station is the "baseline" for a pair of stations. Typical baselines are from 600 to 1,000 nautical miles in length. The continuation of the baseline in either direction is a "baseline extension."

LORAN C
Pulse

FIG 1-1-11

LORAN C
Northeast U.S. Chain

FIG 1-1-12

5. LORAN transmitter stations have time and control equipment, a transmitter, auxiliary power equipment, a building about 100 by 30 feet in size and an antenna that is about 700 feet tall. A station generally requires approximately 100 or more acres of land to accommodate guy lines that keep the antenna in position. Each LORAN station transmits from 400 to 1,600 kilowatts of signal power.

6. The USCG operates 27 stations, comprising eight chains, in the U.S. NAS. Four control stations, which monitor chain performance, have personnel on duty full time. The Canadian east and west coast chains also provide signal coverage over small areas of the NAS.

7. When a control station detects a signal problem that could affect navigation accuracy, an alert signal called "Blink" is activated. Blink is a distinctive change in the group of eight pulses that can be recognized automatically by a receiver so the user is notified instantly that the LORAN system should not be used for navigation. In addition, other problems can cause signal transmissions from a station to be halted.

8. Each individual LORAN chain provides navigation-quality signal coverage over an identified area as shown for the West Coast chain, GRI 9940. The chain Master station is at Fallon, NV and secondary stations are at George, WA; Middletown, CA; and Searchlight, NV. In a signal coverage area the signal strength relative to the normal ambient radio noise must be adequate to assure successful reception.

c. The LORAN Receiver

1. Before a LORAN receiver can provide navigation information for a pilot, it must successfully receive, or "acquire", signals from three or more stations in a chain. Acquisition involves the time synchronization of the receiver with the chain GRI, identification of the Master station signals from among those checked, identification of secondary station signals, and the proper selection of the point in each signal at which measurements should be made.

2. Signal reception at any site will require a pilot to provide location information such as approximate latitude and longitude, or the GRI to be used, to the receiver. Once activated, most receivers will store present location information for later use.

3. The basic measurements made by LORAN receivers are the differences in time–of–arrival between the Master signal and the signals from each of the secondary stations of a chain. Each "time difference" (TD) value is measured to a precision of about 0.1 microseconds. As a rule of thumb, 0.1 microsecond is equal to about 100 feet.

4. An aircraft's LORAN receiver must recognize three signal conditions:

  (a) Usable signals,

  (b) Absence of signals, and

  (c) Signal blink.

5. The most critical phase of flight is during the approach to landing at an airport. During the approach phase the receiver must detect a lost signal, or a signal Blink, within 10 seconds of the occurrence and warn the pilot of the event.

6. Most receivers have various internal tests for estimating the probable accuracy of the current TD values and consequent navigation solutions. Tests may include verification of the timing alignment of the receiver clock with the LORAN pulse, or a continuous measurement of the signal–to–noise ratio (SNR). SNR is the relative strength of the LORAN signals compared to the local ambient noise level. If any of the tests fail, or if the quantities measured are out of the limits set for reliable navigation, then an alarm will be activated to alert the pilot.

7. LORAN signals operate in the low frequency band around (100 kHz) that has been reserved for LORAN use. Adjacent to the band, however, are numerous low frequency communications transmitters. Nearby signals can distort the LORAN signals and must be eliminated by the receiver to assure proper operation. To eliminate interfering signals, LORAN receivers have selective internal filters. These filters, commonly known as "notch filters" reduce the effect of interfering signals.

8. Careful installation of antennas, good metal–to–metal electrical bonding, and provisions for precipitation noise discharge on the aircraft are essential for the successful operation of LORAN receivers. A LORAN antenna should be installed on an aircraft in accordance with the manufacturer's instructions. Corroded bonding straps should be replaced, and static discharge devices installed at points indicated by the aircraft manufacturer.

LORAN– C
West Coast Chain

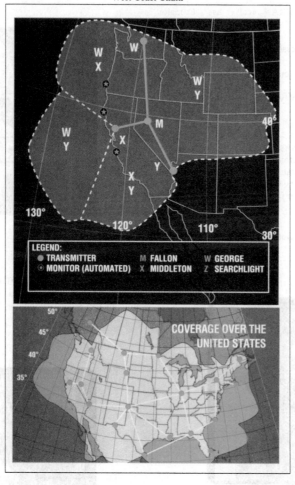

FIG 1–1–13

d. LORAN NAVIGATION

1. An airborne LORAN receiver has four major parts:

    (a) signal processor,

    (b) navigation computer,

    (c) control/display, and

    (d) antenna.

2. The signal processor acquires LORAN signals and measures the difference between the time–of–arrival of each secondary station pulse group and the Master station pulse group. The measured TD's depend on the location of the receiver in relation to the three or more transmitters.

Second Line–of–Position

FIG 1–1–15

    (b) A second LOP is defined by a TD measurement between the Master station signal and the signal from another secondary station.

Intersection of Lines–of–Position

FIG 1–1–16

First Line–of–Position

FIG 1–1–14

    (a) The first TD will locate an aircraft somewhere on a line–of–position (LOP) on which the receiver will measure the same TD value.

(c) The intersection of the measured LOP's is the position of the aircraft.

3. The navigation computer converts TD values to corresponding latitude and longitude. Once the time and position of the aircraft is established at two points, distance to destination, cross track error, ground speed, estimated time of arrival, etc., can be determined. Cross track error can be displayed as the vertical needle of a course deviation indicator, or digitally, as decimal parts of a mile left or right of course. During a nonprecision approach, course guidance must be displayed to the pilot with a full scale deviation of ±0.30 nautical miles or greater.

4. LORAN navigation for nonprecision approaches requires accurate and reliable information. During an approach the occurrence of signal Blink or loss of signal must be detected within 10 seconds and the pilot must be notified. LORAN signal accuracy for approaches is 0.25 nautical miles, well within the required accuracy of 0.30 nautical miles. LORAN signal accuracy can be improved by applying correction values.

5. Flying a LORAN nonprecision approach is different from flying a VOR approach. A VOR approach is on a radial of the VOR station, with guidance sensitivity increasing as the aircraft nears the airport. The LORAN system provides a linear grid, so there is constant guidance sensitivity everywhere in the approach procedure. Consequently, inaccuracies and ambiguities that occur during operations in close proximity to VOR's (station passage, for example) do not occur in LORAN approaches.

6. The navigation computer also provides storage for data entered by pilot or provided by the receiver manufacturer. The receiver's data base is updated at local maintenance facilities every 60 days to include all changes made by the FAA.

7. The FAA is currently canceling all LORAN nonprecision approaches with the advent of GPS.

e. Notices to Airmen (NOTAM's) are issued for LORAN–C chain or station outages. Domestic NOTAM (D)'s are issued under the identifier "LRN." International NOTAM's are issued under the KNMH series. Pilots may obtain these NOTAM's from FSS briefers upon request.

f. LORAN–C status information

Prerecorded telephone answering service messages pertaining to LORAN–C are available in TBL 1–1–5 and TBL 1–1–6.

g. The U.S. plans to terminate LORAN–C operations on December 31, 2000.

North Pacific Chain

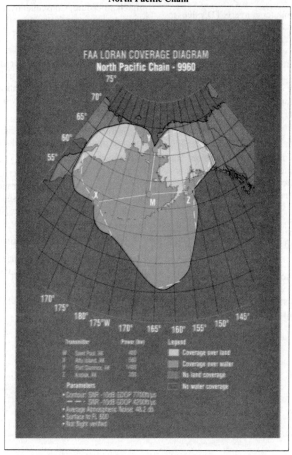

FIG 1-1-17

1-1-22

Air Navigation Radio Aids

Coverage Over Alaska

FIG 1-1-18

Canadian West Coast Chain

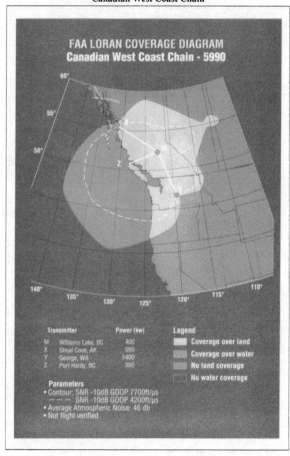

FIG 1-1-19

United States West Coast Chain

FIG 1-1-20

North Central United States Chain

FIG 1-1-21

South Central United States Chain

FIG 1-1-22

United States Great Lakes Chain

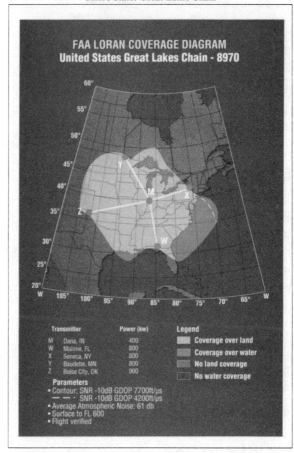

FIG 1–1–23

United States Southeast Chain

FIG 1-1-24

Northeast United States Chain

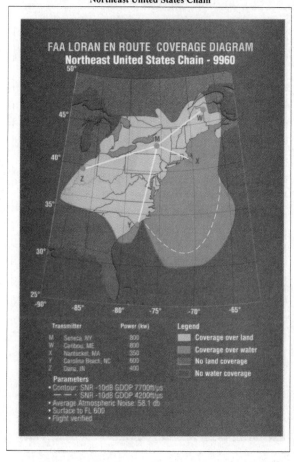

FIG 1-1-25

Canadian East Coast Chain

FIG 1-1-26

Prerecorded LORAN C Status Information

RATE	CHAIN	TELEPHONE
5930	Canadian East Coast	(709) 454–3261*
7980	Southeast U.S.	(904) 569–5241
8970	Great Lakes	(607) 869–5395
9960	Northeast U.S.	(607) 869–5395

*St. Anthony, Newfoundland, Canada.
Information can also be obtained directly from the office of the Coordinator of Chain Operations (COCO) for each chain. The following telephone numbers are for each COCO office:

■   *TBL 1–1–5*

LORAN C Coordinator of Chain Operations Telephone Numbers

RATE	CHAIN	TELEPHONE	LOCATION
4990	Central Pacific	808–247–5591	Kaneohe, HI
5930	Canadian East Coast	709–454–2392	St. Antony, NF
5990	Canadian West Coast	604–666–0472	Vancover, BC
7930	North Atlantic	011–44–1–409–4758	London, UK
7960	Gulf of Alaska	907–487–5583	Kodiak, AK
7970	Norwegian Sea	011–44–1–409–4758	London, UK
7980	Southeast U.S.	205–899–5225	Malone, FL
7990	Mediterranean Sea	011–44–1–409–4758	London, UK
8290	North Central U.S.	707–987–2911	Middletown, CA
8970	Great Lakes	607–869–5393	Seneca, NY
9610	South Central U.S.	205–899–5225	Malone, FL
9940	West Coast U.S.	707–987–2911	Middletown, CA
9960	Northeast U.S.	607–869–5393	Seneca, NY
9970	Northwest Pacific	415–437–3224	San Francisco, CA
9990	North Pacific	907–487–5583	Kodiak, AK

■   *TBL 1–1–6*

1-1-16. OMEGA AND OMEGA/VLF NAVIGATION SYSTEMS

OMEGA operations were terminated on September 30, 1997.

1-1-17. VHF DIRECTION FINDER

a. The VHF Direction Finder (VHF/DF) is one of the common systems that helps pilots without their being aware of its operation. It is a ground based radio receiver used by the operator of the ground station. FAA facilities that provide VHF/DF service are identified in the A/FD.

b. The equipment consists of a directional antenna system and a VHF radio receiver.

c. The VHF/DF receiver display indicates the magnetic direction of the aircraft from the ground station each time the aircraft transmits.

d. DF equipment is of particular value in locating lost aircraft and in helping to identify aircraft on radar.

REFERENCE–
AIM, DIRECTION FINDING INSTRUMENT APPROACH PROCEDURE, PARAGRAPH 6-2-3.

1-1-18. INERTIAL NAVIGATION SYSTEM (INS) ■

The Inertial Navigation System is a totally self–contained navigation system, comprised of gyros, accelerometers, and a navigation computer, which provides aircraft position and navigation information in response to signals resulting from inertial effects on system components, and does not require information from external references. INS is aligned with accurate position information prior to departure, and thereafter calculates its position as it progresses to the destination. By programming a series of waypoints, the system will navigate along a predetermined track. New waypoints can be inserted at any time if a revised routing is desired. INS accuracy is very high initially following alignment, and decays with time at the rate of about 1–2 nautical miles per hour. Position update alignment can be accomplished inflight using ground based references, and many INS systems now have sophisticated automatic update using dual DME and or VOR inputs. INS may be approved as the sole means of navigation or may be used in combination with other systems.

1-1-19. DOPPLER RADAR

Doppler Radar is a semiautomatic self-contained dead reckoning navigation system (radar sensor plus computer) which is not continuously dependent on information derived from ground based or external aids. The system employs radar signals to detect and measure ground speed and drift angle, using the aircraft compass system as its directional reference. Doppler is less accurate than INS or OMEGA however, and the use of an external reference is required for periodic updates if acceptable position accuracy is to be achieved on long range flights.

1-1-20. FLIGHT MANAGEMENT SYSTEM (FMS)

The Flight Management System is a computer system that uses a large database to allow routes to be preprogrammed and fed into the system by means of a data loader. The system is constantly updated with respect to position accuracy by reference to conventional navigation aids. The sophisticated program and its associated database insures that the most appropriate aids are automatically selected during the information update cycle.

1-1-21. GLOBAL POSITIONING SYSTEM (GPS)

a. System Overview

1. GPS is a United States satellite-based radio navigational, positioning, and time transfer system operated by the Department of Defense (DoD). The system provides highly accurate position and velocity information and precise time on a continuous global basis to an unlimited number of properly-equipped users. The system is unaffected by weather and provides a worldwide common grid reference system based on the earth-fixed coordinate system. For its earth model, GPS uses the World Geodetic System of 1984 (WGS-84) datum.

2. GPS provides two levels of service: Standard Positioning Service (SPS) and Precise Positioning Service (PPS). SPS provides, to all users, horizontal positioning accuracy of 100 meters, or less, with a probability of 95 percent and 300 meters with a probability of 99.99 percent. PPS is more accurate than SPS; however, this is limited to authorized U.S. and allied military, federal government, and civil users who can satisfy specific U.S. requirements.

3. GPS operation is based on the concept of ranging and triangulation from a group of satellites in space which act as precise reference points. A GPS receiver measures distance from a satellite using the travel time of a radio signal. Each satellite transmits a specific code, called a course/acquisition (CA) code, which contains information on the satellite's position, the GPS system time, and the health and accuracy of the transmitted data. Knowing the speed at which the signal traveled (approximately 186,000 miles per second) and the exact broadcast time, the distance traveled by the signal can be computed from the arrival time.

4. The GPS receiver matches each satellite's CA code with an identical copy of the code contained in the receiver's database. By shifting its copy of the satellite's code in a matching process, and by comparing this shift with its internal clock, the receiver can calculate how long it took the signal to travel from the satellite to the receiver. The distance derived from this method of computing distance is called a pseudo-range because it is not a direct measurement of distance, but a measurement based on time. Pseudo-range is subject to several error sources; for example: ionospheric and tropospheric delays and multipath.

5. In addition to knowing the distance to a satellite, a receiver needs to know the satellite's exact position in space; this is known as its ephemeris. Each satellite transmits information about its exact orbital location. The GPS receiver uses this information to precisely establish the position of the satellite.

6. Using the calculated pseudo-range and position information supplied by the satellite, the GPS receiver mathematically determines its position by triangulation. The GPS receiver needs at least four satellites to yield a three-dimensional position (latitude, longitude, and altitude) and time solution. The GPS receiver computes navigational values such as distance and bearing to a waypoint, ground speed, etc., by using the aircraft's known latitude/longitude and referencing these to a database built into the receiver.

7. The GPS constellation of 24 satellites is designed so that a minimum of five are always observable by a user anywhere on earth. The receiver uses data from a minimum of four satellites above the mask angle (the lowest angle above the horizon at which it can use a satellite).

8. The GPS receiver verifies the integrity (usability) of the signals received from the GPS constellation through receiver autonomous integrity monitoring (RAIM) to determine if a satellite is providing corrupted information. At least one satellite, in addition to those required for navigation, must be in view for the receiver to perform the RAIM function; thus, RAIM needs a minimum of 5 satellites in view, or 4 satellites and a barometric altimeter (baro-aiding) to detect an integrity anomaly. For receivers capable of doing so, RAIM needs 6 satellites in view (or 5 satellites with baro-aiding) to isolate the corrupt satellite signal and remove it from the navigation solution. Baro-aiding is a method of augmenting the GPS integrity solution by using a nonsatellite input source. GPS derived altitude should not be relied upon to determine aircraft altitude since the vertical error can be quite large. To ensure that baro-aiding is available, the current altimeter setting must be entered into the receiver as described in the operating manual.

9. RAIM messages vary somewhat between receivers; however, generally there are two types. One type indicates that there are not enough satellites available to provide RAIM integrity monitoring and another type indicates that the RAIM integrity monitor has detected a potential error that exceeds the limit for the current phase of flight. **Without RAIM capability, the pilot has no assurance of the accuracy of the GPS position.**

10. The Department of Defense declared initial operational capability (IOC) of the U.S. GPS on December 8, 1993. The Federal Aviation Administration (FAA) has granted approval for U.S. civil operators to use properly certified GPS equipment as a primary means of navigation in oceanic airspace and certain remote areas. Properly certified GPS equipment may be used as a supplemental means of IFR navigation for domestic en route, terminal operations, and certain instrument approach procedures (IAP's). This approval permits the use of GPS in a manner that is consistent with current navigation requirements as well as approved air carrier operations specifications.

b. General Requirements

1. Authorization to conduct any GPS operation under IFR requires that:

(a) GPS navigation equipment used must be approved in accordance with the requirements specified in TSO C-129, or equivalent, and the installation must be done in accordance with Notice 8110.47 or 8110.48, or equivalent. Equipment approved in accordance with

TSO C-115a does not meet the requirements of TSO C-129. VFR and hand-held GPS systems are not authorized for IFR navigation, instrument approaches, or as a principal instrument flight reference. During IFR operations they may be considered only an aid to situational awareness.

(b) Aircraft using GPS navigation equipment under IFR must be equipped with an approved and operational alternate means of navigation appropriate to the flight. Active monitoring of alternative navigation equipment is not required if the GPS receiver uses RAIM for integrity monitoring. Active monitoring of an alternate means of navigation is required when the RAIM capability of the GPS equipment is lost.

(c) Procedures must be established for use in the event that the loss of RAIM capability is predicted to occur. In situations where this is encountered, the flight must rely on other approved equipment, delay departure, or cancel the flight.

(d) The GPS operation must be conducted in accordance with the FAA-approved aircraft flight manual (AFM) or flight manual supplement. Flight crew members must be thoroughly familiar with the particular GPS equipment installed in the aircraft, the receiver operation manual, and the AFM or flight manual supplement. Unlike ILS and VOR, the basic operation, receiver presentation to the pilot, and some capabilities of the equipment can vary greatly. Due to these differences, operation of different brands, or even models of the same brand, of GPS receiver under IFR should not be attempted without thorough study of the operation of that particular receiver and installation. Most receivers have a built-in simulator mode which will allow the pilot to become familiar with operation prior to attempting operation in the aircraft. Using the equipment in flight under VFR conditions prior to attempting IFR operation will allow further familiarization.

(e) Aircraft navigating by IFR approved GPS are considered to be RNAV aircraft and have special equipment suffixes. File the appropriate equipment suffix in accordance with TBL 5-1-2, on the ATC flight plan. If GPS avionics become inoperative, the pilot should advise ATC and amend the equipment suffix.

(f) Prior to any GPS IFR operation, the pilot must review appropriate NOTAM's and aeronautical information. (See GPS NOTAM's/Aeronautical Information.)

(g) Air carrier and commercial operators must meet the appropriate provisions of their approved operations specifications.

c. Use of GPS for IFR Oceanic, Domestic En Route, and Terminal Area Operations

1. GPS IFR operations in oceanic areas can be conducted as soon as the proper avionics systems are installed, provided all general requirements are met. A GPS installation with TSO C-129 authorization in class A1, A2, B1, B2, C1, or C2 may be used to replace one of the other approved means of long-range navigation, such as dual INS or dual Omega. (See TBL 1-1-7 and TBL 1-1-8.) A single GPS installation with these classes of equipment which provide RAIM for integrity monitoring may also be used on short oceanic routes which have only required one means of long-range navigation.

GPS IFR Equipment Classes/Categories

TSO-C129						
EQUIPMENT CLASS	RAIM	INT. NAV SYS. TO PROV. RAIM EQUIV.	OCEANIC	EN ROUTE	TERMINAL	NONPRECISION APPROACH CAPABLE
Class A - GPS sensor and navigation capability.						
A1	yes		yes	yes	yes	yes
A2	yes		yes	yes	yes	no
Class B - GPS sensor data to an integrated navigation system (i.e. FMS, multi-sensor navigation system, etc.).						
B1	yes		yes	yes	yes	yes
B2	yes		yes	yes	yes	no
B3		yes	yes	yes	yes	yes
B4	yes		yes	yes	yes	no
Class C - GPS sensor data to an integrated navigation system (as in Class B) which provides enhanced guidance to an autopilot, or flight director, to reduce flight tech. errors. Limited to 14 CFR Part 121 or equivalent criteria.						
C1	yes		yes	yes	yes	yes
C2	yes		yes	yes	yes	no
C3		yes	yes	yes	yes	yes
C4	yes		yes	yes	yes	no

TBL 1-1-7

GPS Approval Required/Authorized Use

EQUIPMENT TYPE[1]	INSTALLATION APPROVAL REQUIRED	OPERATIONAL APPROVAL REQUIRED	IFR EN ROUTE[2]	IFR TERMINAL[2]	IFR APPROACH[3]	OCEANIC REMOTE	IN LIEU OF ADF AND/OR DME[3]
Hand held[4]	X[5]						
VFR Panel Mount[4]	X						
IFR En Route and Terminal	X	X	X	X			X
IFR Oceanic/ Remote	X	X	X	X		X	X
IFR En Route, Terminal, and Approach	X	X	X	X	X		X

TBL 1-1-8

NOTE-
[1]*To determine equipment approvals and limitations, refer to the AFM, AFM supplements, or pilot guides.*
[2]*Requires verification of data for correctness if database is expired.*
[3]*Requires current database.*
[4]*VFR and hand-held GPS systems are not authorized for IFR navigation, instrument approaches, or as a primary instrument flight reference. During IFR operations they may be considered only an aid to situational awareness.*
[5]*Hand-held receivers require no approval. However, any aircraft modification to support the hand-held receiver; i.e., installation of an external antenna or a permanent mounting bracket, does require approval.*

AIM

2. GPS domestic en route and terminal IFR operations can be conducted as soon as proper avionics systems are installed, provided all general requirements are met. The avionics necessary to receive all of the ground-based facilities appropriate for the route to the destination airport and any required alternate airport must be installed and operational. Ground-based facilities necessary for these routes must also be operational.

3. The GPS Approach Overlay Program is an authorization for pilots to use GPS avionics under IFR for flying designated existing nonprecision instrument approach procedures, except localizer (LOC), localizer directional aid (LDA), and simplified directional facility (SDF) procedures. Only those approaches included in the receiver database are authorized. Overlay approaches are predicated upon the design criteria of the ground-based NAVAID used as the basis of the approach. As such, they do not adhere to the design criteria described later for the stand alone GPS approaches.

4. GPS IFR approach operations can be conducted as soon as proper avionics systems are installed and the following requirements are met:

(a) The authorization to use GPS to fly instrument approaches is limited to U.S. airspace.

(b) The use of GPS in any other airspace must be expressly authorized by the FAA Administrator.

(c) GPS instrument approach operations outside the United States must be authorized by the appropriate sovereign authority.

5. Subject to the restrictions below, operators in the U.S. NAS are authorized to use GPS equipment certified for IFR operations in place of ADF and/or DME equipment for en route and terminal operations. For some operations there is no requirement for the aircraft to be equipped with an ADF or DME receiver, see subparagraphs c. 6. (g) and (h) below. The ground based NDB or DME facility may be temporarily out of service during these operations. Charting will not change to support these operations.

(a) Determining the aircraft position over a DME fix. GPS satisfies the 14 CFR Section 91.205(e) requirement for DME at and above 24,000 feet MSL (FL 240).

(b) Flying a DME arc.

(c) Navigating to/from an NDB/compass locator.

(d) Determining the aircraft position over an NDB/compass locator.

(e) Determining the aircraft position over a fix defined by an NDB/compass locator bearing crossing a VOR/LOC course.

(f) Holding over an NDB/compass locator.

NOTE-
This approval does not alter the conditions and requirements for use of GPS to fly existing nonprecision instrument approach procedures as defined in the GPS approach overlay program.

6. Restrictions

(a) GPS avionics approved for terminal IFR operations may be used in lieu of ADF and/or DME. Included in this approval are both stand-alone and multi-sensor systems actively employing GPS as a sensor. This equipment must be installed in accordance with appropriate airworthiness installation requirements and the provisions of the applicable FAA approved Aircraft Flight Manual (AFM), AFM supplement, or pilot's guide must be met. The required integrity for these operations must be provided by at least en route Receiver Autonomous Integrity Monitoring (RAIM), or an equivalent method; i.e., Wide Area Augmentation System (WAAS).

(b) For air carriers and operators for compensation or hire, POI and operations specification approval is required for any use of GPS.

(c) Waypoints, fixes, intersections, and facility locations to be used for these operations must be retrieved from the GPS airborne database. The database must be current. If the required positions cannot be retrieved from the airborne database, the substitution of GPS for ADF and/or DME is not authorized.

(d) The aircraft GPS system must be operated within the guidelines contained in the AFM, AFM supplement, or pilot's guide.

(e) The Course Deviation Indicator (CDI) must be set to terminal sensitivity (normally 1 or 1 $^1/_4$ NM) when tracking GPS course guidance in the terminal area. This is to ensure that small deviations from course are displayed to the pilot in order to keep the aircraft within the smaller terminal protected areas.

(f) Charted requirements for ADF and/or DME can be met using the GPS system, except for use as the principal instrument approach navigation source.

(g) Procedures must be established for use in the event that GPS integrity outages are predicted or occur (RAIM annunciation). In these situations, the flight must rely on other approved equipment; this may require the aircraft to be equipped with operational NDB and/or DME receivers. Otherwise, the flight must be rerouted, delayed, canceled or conducted VFR.

(h) A non–GPS approach procedure must exist at the alternate airport when one is required. If the non–GPS approaches on which the pilot must rely require DME or ADF, the aircraft must be equipped with DME or ADF avionics as appropriate.

7. Guidance. The following provides general guidance which is not specific to any particular aircraft GPS system. For specific system guidance refer to the AFM, AFM supplement, pilot's guide, or contact the manufacturer of your system.

(a) To determine the aircraft position over a DME fix:

(1) Verify aircraft GPS system integrity monitoring is functioning properly and indicates satisfactory integrity.

(2) If the fix is identified by a five letter name which _is_ contained in the GPS airborne database, you may select either the named fix as the active GPS waypoint (WP) or the facility establishing the DME fix as the active GPS WP.

NOTE-
When using a facility as the active WP, the only acceptable facility is the DME facility which is charted as the one used to establish the DME fix. If this facility is not in your airborne database, you are not authorized to use a facility WP for this operation.

(3) If the fix is identified by a five letter name which _is not_ contained in the GPS airborne database, or if the fix is not named, you must select the facility establishing the DME fix or another named DME fix as the active GPS WP.

NOTE-
An alternative, until all DME sources are in the database, is using a named DME fix as the active waypoint to identify unnamed DME fixes on the same course and from the same DME source as the active waypoint.

CAUTION-
Pilots should be extremely careful to ensure that correct distance measurements are used when utilizing this interim method. It is strongly recommended that pilots review distances for DME fixing during preflight preparation.

(4) If you select the named fix as your active GPS WP, you are over the fix when the GPS system indicates you are at the active WP.

(5) If you select the DME providing facility as the active GPS WP, you are over the fix when the GPS distance from the active WP equals the charted DME value and you are on the appropriate bearing or course.

(b) To fly a DME arc:

(1) Verify aircraft GPS system integrity monitoring is functioning properly and indicates satisfactory integrity.

(2) You must select, from the airborne database, the facility providing the DME arc as the active GPS WP.

NOTE-
The only acceptable facility is the DME facility on which the arc is based. If this facility is not in your airborne database, you are not authorized to perform this operation.

(3) Maintain position on the arc by reference to the GPS distance in lieu of a DME readout.

(c) To navigate to or from an NDB/compass locator:

NOTE-
If the chart depicts the compass locator collocated with a fix of the same name, use of that fix as the active WP in place of the compass locator facility is authorized.

(1) Verify aircraft GPS system integrity monitoring is functioning properly and indicates satisfactory integrity.

(2) Select terminal CDI sensitivity in accordance with the AFM, AFM supplement, or pilot's guide if in the terminal area.

(3) Select the NDB/compass locator facility from the airborne database as the active WP.

(4) Select and navigate on the appropriate course to or from the active WP.

(d) To determine the aircraft position over an NDB/compass locator:

(1) Verify aircraft GPS system integrity monitoring is functioning properly and indicates satisfactory integrity.

(2) Select the NDB/compass locator facility from the airborne database as the active WP.

NOTE-
When using an NDB/compass locator, that facility must be charted and be in the airborne database. If this facility is not in your airborne database, you are not authorized to use a facility WP for this operation.

(3) You are over the NDB/compass locator when the GPS system indicates you are at the active WP.

(e) To determine the aircraft position over a fix made up of an NDB/compass locator bearing crossing a VOR/LOC course:

(1) Verify aircraft GPS system integrity monitoring is functioning properly and indicates satisfactory integrity.

(2) A fix made up by a crossing NDB/compass locator bearing will be identified by a five letter fix name. You may select either the named fix or the NDB/compass locator facility providing the crossing bearing to establish the fix as the active GPS WP.

NOTE-
When using an NDB/compass locator, that facility must be charted and be in the airborne database. If this facility is not in your airborne database, you are not authorized to use a facility WP for this operation.

(3) If you select the named fix as your active GPS WP, you are over the fix when the GPS system indicates you are at the WP as you fly the prescribed track from the non-GPS navigation source.

(4) If you select the NDB/compass locator facility as the active GPS WP, you are over the fix when the GPS bearing to the active WP is the same as the charted NDB/compass locator bearing for the fix as you fly the prescribed track from the non-GPS navigation source.

(f) To hold over an NDB/compass locator:

(1) Verify aircraft GPS system integrity monitoring is functioning properly and indicates satisfactory integrity.

(2) Select terminal CDI sensitivity in accordance with the AFM, AFM supplement, or pilot's guide if in the terminal area.

(3) Select the NDB/compass locator facility from the airborne database as the active WP.

NOTE-
When using a facility as the active WP, the only acceptable facility is the NDB/compass locator facility which is charted. If this facility is not in your airborne database, you are not authorized to use a facility WP for this operation.

(4) Select nonsequencing (e.g. "HOLD" or "OBS") mode and the appropriate course in accordance with the AFM, AFM supplement, or pilot's guide.

(5) Hold using the GPS system in accordance with the AFM, AFM supplement, or pilot's guide.

8. Planning. Good advance planning and intimate knowledge of your navigational systems are vital to safe and successful use of GPS in lieu of ADF and/or DME.

(a) You should plan ahead before using GPS systems as a substitute for ADF and/or DME. You will have several alternatives in selecting waypoints and system configuration. After you are cleared for the approach is not the time to begin programming your GPS. In the flight planning process you should determine whether you will use the equipment in the automatic sequencing mode or in the nonsequencing mode and select the waypoints you will use.

(b) When you are using your aircraft GPS system to supplement other navigation systems, you may need to bring your GPS control panel into your navigation scan to see the GPS information. Some GPS aircraft installations will present localizer information on the CDI whenever a localizer frequency is tuned, removing the GPS information from the CDI display. Good advance planning and intimate knowledge of your navigation systems are vital to safe and successful use of GPS.

(c) The following are some factors to consider when preparing to install a GPS receiver in an aircraft. Installation of the equipment can determine how easy or how difficult it will be to use the system.

(1) Consideration should be given to installing the receiver within the primary instrument scan to facilitate using the GPS in lieu of ADF and/or DME. This will preclude breaking the primary instrument scan while flying the aircraft and tuning, and identifying waypoints. This becomes increasingly important on approaches, and missed approaches.

(2) Many GPS receivers can drive an ADF type bearing pointer. Such an installation will provide the pilot with an enhanced level of situational awareness by providing GPS navigation information while the CDI is set to VOR or ILS.

(3) The GPS receiver may be installed so that when an ILS frequency is tuned, the navigation display defaults to the VOR/ILS mode, preempting the GPS mode. However, if the receiver installation requires a manual selection from GPS to ILS, it allows the ILS to be tuned and identified while navigating on the GPS. Additionally, this prevents the navigation display from automatically switching back to GPS when a VOR frequency is selected. If the navigation display automatically switches to GPS mode when a VOR is selected, the change may go unnoticed and could result in erroneous navigation and departing obstruction protected airspace.

(4) GPS is a supplemental navigation system in part due to signal availability. There will be times when your system will not receive enough satellites with proper geometry to provide accurate positioning or sufficient integrity. Procedures should be established by the pilot in the event that GPS outages occur. In these situations, the pilot should rely on other approved equipment, delay departure, reroute, or discontinue IFR operations.

d. Equipment and Database Requirements

1. Authorization to fly approaches under IFR using GPS avionics systems requires that:

(a) A pilot use GPS avionics with TSO C-129, or equivalent, authorization in class A1, B1, B3, C1, or C3; and

(b) All approach procedures to be flown must be retrievable from the current airborne navigation database supplied by the TSO C-129 equipment manufacturer or other FAA approved source.

e. Phases of the Approach Overlay Program

1. **Phase I:** Phase I has been completed.

2. **Phase II:** Under Phase II, GPS avionics can be used as the IFR flight guidance system for an approach without actively monitoring the ground-based NAVAID('s) which defines the approach. However, the ground-based NAVAID('s) must be operational. In addition, the related avionics must be installed and operational but need not be turned on during the approach (monitoring backup navigation is always recommended when available). Approaches must be requested and approved using the published title of the existing approach procedure, such as "VOR RWY 24."

3. Phase III: In this phase, instrument approach procedures were retitled "or GPS" (e.g., VOR or GPS RWY 24). Ground-based NAVAID's are not required to be operational and associated aircraft avionics need not be installed, operational, turned on or monitored. (Monitoring of the underlying approach is suggested when equipment is available and functional.) GPS approaches are requested and approved using the GPS title, such as "GPS RWY 24."

NOTE-
In each phase, any required alternate airport must have an approved instrument approach procedure other than GPS, which is anticipated to be operational and available at the estimated time of arrival and which the aircraft is equipped to fly.

f. GPS Standard Instrument Approach Procedure (SIAP) Design Concepts

1. The objective of the Terminal Arrival Area (TAA) procedure design is to provide a new transition method for arriving aircraft equipped with FMS and/or GPS navigational equipment. The TAA contains within it a "T" structure that normally provides a NoPT for aircraft using the approach. The TAA provides the pilot and air traffic controller with a very efficient method for routing traffic from en route to terminal structure.

2. The basic "T" that is contained in the TAA normally aligns the procedure on runway centerline, with the missed approach point (MAP) located at the threshold, the final approach fix (FAF) 5 nautical miles from the threshold, and the intermediate fix (IF) 5 nautical miles from the FAF. Two initial approach fixes (IAF's) are located 3 to 6 miles from the center IF(IAF). All of these waypoint fixes will be named with a five character pronounceable name. The length of the initial segment varies with the category of aircraft using the procedure or descent gradient requirements. The minimum length of an initial segment designed for Category A aircraft is 3 nautical miles. The minimum length for an initial segment designed for Category E aircraft is 6 nautical miles. These initial segments are constructed perpendicular (90°) to the intermediate segment. There is a holding pattern at the IF(IAF) for course reversal requirements. For example, some pilots may desire to execute a procedure turn (PT) to meet a descent gradient requirement. The missed approach segment is ideally aligned with the final approach course and terminates in a direct entry into a holding pattern. Conditions may require a different routing. (See FIG 1-1-27 and FIG 1-1-28.)

Basic "T" Design

FIG 1-1-27

Basic "T" Design

FIG 1-1-28

3. In order to accommodate descent from a high en route altitude to the initial segment altitude, the basic "T" configuration may be modified. When this occurs, a PT holding pattern provides aircraft an extended distance for the necessary descent gradient. The holding pattern constructed for this purpose is always established on the IF(IAF) waypoint. (See FIG 1-1-29.)

Modified Basic "T"

FIG 1-1-29

4. Another modification may be required for parallel runways. The normal "T" IAF's serve all parallel runways. However, only one initial, intermediate and final segment combination will be depicted on the approach chart for the landing runway. (See FIG 1-1-30, FIG 1-1-31 and FIG 1-1-32.)

The normal "T" IAF's serve all parallel runways. Each runway will require a separate IF(IAF). Only one initial, intermediate and final segment combination will be depicted on the approach chart.

FIG 1-1-30

Modified Basic "T"

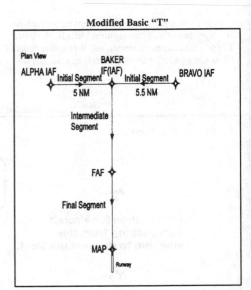

FIG 1-1-31

Modified Basic "T"

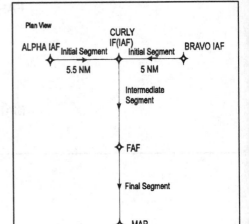

FIG 1-1-32

5. The standard TAA consists of 3 areas that are established by the extension of the legs of the basic "T." These areas are: the straight-in, left base and right base. The 30-nautical-mile arc boundary of each area is equivalent to a feeder fix. When crossing the boundary of each of these areas or when released by ATC, within the area, the pilot is expected to proceed direct to the appropriate waypoint IAF for the approach area being flown. A pilot has the option in all areas to proceed direct to the holding pattern for course reversal. The PT holding pattern at the IF(IAF) is standard. Area boundaries are magnetic course lines to the IF(IAF). The charted altitudes within the TAA are maintained by aircraft that traverse these areas. (See FIG 1-1-33.)

TAA Area

FIG 1-1-33

6. Normally, the minimum altitudes specified in the TAA and PT holding pattern are the same. However, there may be locations where terrain or operational situations require minimum altitudes to maintain within a sector of an area. In FIG 1-1-34, pilots flying into the right or left base areas are expected to maintain a minimum altitude of 6,000 feet MSL until within 17 nautical miles of the appropriate IAF and then descend to the lower charted altitudes. Pilots approaching from the northwest are expected to maintain a minimum altitude of 6,000 feet MSL until within 22 nautical miles of the IF(IAF) then descend to an altitude not lower than 2,000 feet MSL until reaching the IF(IAF).

Sectored TAA Areas

FIG 1-1-34

7. There may be modifications to the area of the standard TAA because of operational requirements. For example, the right or left base areas may be modified or eliminated. A PT holding pattern can be required when approaching from a certain area. FIG 1-1-35 is an example of this situation. Pilots approaching the IF(IAF) within 120° of the final approach course (this is the maximum intercept angle, a smaller angle could be required) are expected to fly a NoPT straight-in approach. If the PT is needed for unusual situations, advise ATC of your intentions. Pilots approaching the IF(IAF) on a course greater than 120° (or a specified smaller angle) from the final approach course are required to execute a procedure turn.

**TAA with Left and Right
Base Areas Eliminated**

FIG 1-1-35

8. FIG 1-1-36 is an example of another modification. The right base is eliminated. Pilots approaching the IF(IAF) from between the courses of 360° clockwise to 060° are required to perform a PT. Pilots are expected to execute a NoPT straight-in approach when approaching the IF(IAF) from between the courses of 060° clockwise to 270°. The left base contains an IAF with an initial leg. NoPT is expected.

TAA with Right Base Eliminated

FIG 1-1-36

Normally an airway will overlie a TAA. FIG 1-1-37 is an example of all airways lying outside of the TAA. The required feeder routes are aligned with the appropriate IAF's of the "T."

Examples of a TAA with Feeders from an Airway

FIG 1-1-37

g. GPS NOTAM's/Aeronautical Information

1. GPS satellite outages are issued as GPS NOTAM's both domestically and internationally. However, the effect of an outage on the intended operation cannot be determined unless the pilot has a RAIM availability prediction program which allows excluding a satellite which is predicted to be out of service based on the NOTAM information.

2. Civilian pilots may obtain GPS RAIM availability information for nonprecision approach procedures by specifically requesting GPS aeronautical information from an Automated Flight Service Station during preflight briefings. GPS RAIM aeronautical information can be obtained for a period of 3 hours (ETA hour and 1 hour before to 1 hour after the ETA hour) or a 24 hour time frame at a particular airport. FAA briefers will provide RAIM information for a period of 1 hour before to 1 hour after the ETA, unless a specific time frame is requested by the pilot. If flying a published GPS departure, a RAIM prediction should also be requested for the departure airport.

3. The military provides airfield specific GPS RAIM NOTAM's for nonprecision approach procedures at military airfields. The RAIM outages are issued as M-series NOTAM's and may be obtained for up to 24 hours from the time of request.

h. Receiver Autonomous Integrity Monitoring (RAIM)

1. RAIM outages may occur due to an insufficient number of satellites or due to unsuitable satellite geometry which causes the error in the position solution to become too large. Loss of satellite reception and RAIM warnings may occur due to aircraft dynamics (changes in pitch or bank angle). Antenna location on the aircraft, satellite position relative to the horizon, and aircraft attitude may affect reception of one or more satellites. Since the relative positions of the satellites are constantly changing, prior experience with the airport does not guarantee reception at all times, and RAIM availability should always be checked.

2. If RAIM is not available, another type of navigation and approach system must be used, another destination selected, or the trip delayed until RAIM is predicted to be available on arrival. On longer flights, pilots should consider rechecking the RAIM prediction for the destination during the flight. This may provide early indications that an unscheduled satellite outage has occurred since takeoff.

3. If a RAIM failure/status annunciation occurs prior to the final approach waypoint (FAWP), the approach should not be completed since GPS may no longer provide the required accuracy. The receiver performs a RAIM prediction by 2 NM prior to the FAWP to ensure that RAIM is available at the FAWP as a condition for entering the approach mode. **The pilot should ensure that the receiver has sequenced from "Armed" to "Approach" prior to the FAWP** (normally occurs 2 NM prior). Failure to sequence may be an indication of the detection of a satellite anomaly, failure to arm the receiver (if required), or other problems which preclude completing the approach.

4. If the receiver does not sequence into the approach mode or a RAIM failure/status annunciation occurs prior to the FAWP, the pilot should not descend to MDA, but should proceed to the missed approach waypoint (MAWP) via the FAWP, perform a missed approach, and contact ATC as soon as practical. Refer to the receiver operating manual for specific indications and instructions associated with loss of RAIM prior to the FAF.

5. If a RAIM failure occurs after the FAWP, the receiver is allowed to continue operating without an annunciation for up to 5 minutes to allow completion of the approach (see receiver operating manual). **If the RAIM flag/status annunciation appears after the FAWP, the missed approach should be executed immediately.**

i. Waypoints

1. GPS approaches make use of both fly-over and fly-by waypoints. Fly-by waypoints are used when an aircraft should begin a turn to the next course prior to reaching the waypoint separating the two route segments. This is known as turn anticipation and is compensated for in the airspace and terrain clearances. Approach waypoints, except for the MAWP and the missed approach holding waypoint (MAHWP), are normally fly-by waypoints. Fly-over waypoints are used when the aircraft must fly over the point prior to starting a turn. New approach charts depict fly-over waypoints as a circled waypoint symbol. Overlay approach charts and some early stand alone GPS approach charts may not reflect this convention.

2. On overlay approaches (titled "or GPS"), if no pronounceable five character name is published for an approach waypoint or fix, it may be given an ARINC database identifier consisting of letters and numbers. These points will appear in the list of waypoints in the approach procedure database, but may not appear on the approach chart. Procedures without a final approach fix (FAF), for instance, have a sensor final approach waypoint (FAWP) added to the database at least 4 NM prior to the MAWP to allow the receiver to transition to the approach mode. Some approaches also contain an additional waypoint in the holding pattern when the MAWP and MAHWP are co-located. Arc and radial approaches have an additional waypoint that is used for turn anticipation computation where the arc joins the final approach course. These coded names will not be used by ATC.

3. Unnamed waypoints in the database will be uniquely identified for each airport but may be repeated for another airport (e.g., RW36 will be used at each airport with a runway 36 but will be at the same location for all approaches at a given airport).

4. The runway threshold waypoint, which is normally the MAWP, may have a five letter identifier (e.g., SNEEZ) or be coded as RW## (e.g., RW36, RW36L). Those thresholds which are coded as five letter identifiers are being changed to the RW## designation. This may cause the approach chart and database to differ until all changes are complete. The runway threshold waypoint is also used as the center of the MSA on most GPS approaches. MAWP's not located at the threshold will have a five letter identifier.

j. Position Orientation

As with most RNAV systems, pilots should pay particular attention to position orientation while using GPS. Distance and track information are provided to the next active waypoint, not to a fixed navigation aid. Receivers may sequence when the pilot is not flying along an active route, such as when being vectored or deviating for weather, due to the proximity to another waypoint in the route. This can be prevented by placing the receiver in the nonsequencing mode. When the receiver is in the nonsequencing mode, bearing and distance are provided to the selected waypoint and the receiver will not sequence to the next waypoint in the route until placed back in the auto sequence mode or the pilot selects a different waypoint. On overlay approaches, the pilot may have to compute the along track distance to stepdown fixes and other points due to the receiver showing along track distance to the next waypoint rather than DME to the VOR or ILS ground station.

k. Conventional Versus GPS Navigation Data

There may be slight differences between the heading information portrayed on navigational charts and the GPS

navigation display when flying an overlay approach or along an airway. All magnetic tracks defined by a VOR radial are determined by the application of magnetic variation at the VOR; however, GPS operations may use an algorithm to apply the magnetic variation at the current position, which may produce small differences in the displayed course. Both operations should produce the same desired ground track. Due to the use of great circle courses, and the variations in magnetic variation, the bearing to the next waypoint and the course from the last waypoint (if available) may not be exactly 180° apart when long distances are involved. Variations in distances will occur since GPS distance-to-waypoint values are along track (straight-line) distances (ATD) computed to the next waypoint and the DME values published on underlying procedures are slant range distances measured to the station. This difference increases with aircraft altitude and proximity to the NAVAID.

l. Departures and Instrument Departure Procedures (DP's)

The GPS receiver must be set to terminal (±1 NM) course deviation indicator (CDI) sensitivity and the navigation routes contained in the database in order to fly published IFR charted departures and DP's. Terminal RAIM should be automatically provided by the receiver. (Terminal RAIM for departure may not be available unless the waypoints are part of the active flight plan rather than proceeding direct to the first destination.) Certain segments of a DP may require some manual intervention by the pilot, especially when radar vectored to a course or required to intercept a specific course to a waypoint. The database may not contain all of the transitions or departures from all runways and some GPS receivers do not contain DP's in the database. It is necessary that helicopter procedures be flown at 70 knots or less since helicopter departure procedures and missed approaches use a 20:1 obstacle clearance surface (OCS), which is double the fixed-wing OCS, and turning areas are based on this speed as well.

m. Flying GPS Approaches

1. Determining which area of the TAA the aircraft will enter when flying a "T" with a TAA must be accomplished using the bearing and distance to the IF(IAF). This is most critical when entering the TAA in the vicinity of the extended runway centerline and determining whether you will be entering the right or left base area. Once inside the TAA, all sectors and stepdowns are based on the bearing and distance to the IAF for that area, which the aircraft should be proceeding direct to at that time, unless on vectors. (See FIG 1-1-29 and FIG 1-1-30.)

2. Pilots should fly the full approach from an Initial Approach Waypoint (IAWP) or feeder fix unless specifically cleared otherwise. Randomly joining an approach at an intermediate fix does not assure terrain clearance.

3. When an approach has been loaded in the flight plan, GPS receivers will give an "arm" annunciation 30 NM straight line distance from the airport/heliport reference point. Pilots should arm the approach mode at this time, if it has not already been armed (some receivers arm automatically). Without arming, the receiver will not change from en route CDI and RAIM sensitivity of ±5 NM either side of centerline to ±1 NM terminal sensitivity. Where the IAWP is inside this 30 mile point, a CDI sensitivity change will occur once the approach mode is armed and the aircraft is inside 30 NM. Where the IAWP is beyond 30 NM from the airport/heliport reference point, CDI sensitivity will not change until the aircraft is within 30 miles of the airport/heliport reference point even if the approach is armed earlier. Feeder route obstacle clearance is predicated on the receiver being in terminal (±1 NM) CDI sensitivity and RAIM within 30 NM of the airport/heliport reference point, therefore, the receiver should always be armed (if required) not later than the 30 NM annunciation.

4. The pilot must be aware of what bank angle/turn rate the particular receiver uses to compute turn anticipation, and whether wind and airspeed are included in the receiver's calculations. This information should be in the receiver operating manual. Over or under banking the turn onto the final approach course may significantly delay getting on course and may result in high descent rates to achieve the next segment altitude.

5. When within 2 NM of the FAWP with the approach mode armed, the approach mode will switch to active, which results in RAIM changing to approach sensitivity and a change in CDI sensitivity. Beginning 2 NM prior to the FAWP, the full scale CDI sensitivity will smoothly change from ±1 NM, to ±0.3 NM at the FAWP. As sensitivity changes from ±1 NM to ±0.3 NM approaching the FAWP, with the CDI not centered, the corresponding increase in CDI displacement may give the impression that the aircraft is moving further

away from the intended course even though it is on an acceptable intercept heading. Referencing the digital track displacement information (cross track error), if it is available in the approach mode, may help the pilot remain position oriented in this situation. Being established on the final approach course prior to the beginning of the sensitivity change at 2 NM will help prevent problems in interpreting the CDI display during ramp down. Therefore, requesting or accepting vectors which will cause the aircraft to intercept the final approach course within 2 NM of the FAWP is not recommended.

6. When receiving vectors to final, most receiver operating manuals suggest placing the receiver in the nonsequencing mode on the FAWP and manually setting the course. This provides an extended final approach course in cases where the aircraft is vectored onto the final approach course outside of any existing segment which is aligned with the runway. Assigned altitudes must be maintained until established on a published segment of the approach. Required altitudes at waypoints outside the FAWP or stepdown fixes must be considered. Calculating the distance to the FAWP may be required in order to descend at the proper location.

7. Overriding an automatically selected sensitivity during an approach will cancel the approach mode annunciation. If the approach mode is not armed by 2 NM prior to the FAWP, the approach mode will not become active at 2 NM prior to the FAWP, and the equipment will flag. In these conditions, the RAIM and CDI sensitivity will not ramp down, and the pilot should not descend to MDA, but fly to the MAWP and execute a missed approach. The approach active annunciator and/or the receiver should be checked to ensure the approach mode is active prior to the FAWP.

8. Do not attempt to fly an approach unless the procedure is contained in the current GPS database. Flying point to point on the approach does not assure compliance with the published approach procedure. The proper RAIM sensitivity will not be available and the CDI sensitivity will not automatically change to ±0.3 NM. Manually setting CDI sensitivity does not automatically change the RAIM sensitivity on some receivers. Some existing nonprecision approach procedures cannot be coded for use with GPS and will not be available as overlays.

9. Pilots should pay particular attention to the exact operation of their GPS receivers for performing holding patterns and in the case of overlay approaches, operations such as procedure turns. These procedures may require manual intervention by the pilot to stop the sequencing of waypoints by the receiver and to resume automatic GPS navigation sequencing once the maneuver is complete. The same waypoint may appear in the route of flight more than once consecutively (e.g., IAWP, FAWP, MAHWP on a procedure turn). Care must be exercised to ensure that the receiver is sequenced to the appropriate waypoint for the segment of the procedure being flown, especially if one or more fly-overs are skipped (e.g., FAWP rather than IAWP if the procedure turn is not flown). The pilot may have to sequence past one or more fly-overs of the same waypoint in order to start GPS automatic sequencing at the proper place in the sequence of waypoints.

10. Incorrect inputs into the GPS receiver are especially critical during approaches. In some cases, an incorrect entry can cause the receiver to leave the approach mode.

11. A fix on an overlay approach identified by a DME fix will not be in the waypoint sequence on the GPS receiver unless there is a published name assigned to it. When a name is assigned, the along track to the waypoint may be zero rather than the DME stated on the approach chart. The pilot should be alert for this on any overlay procedure where the original approach used DME.

12. If a visual descent point (VDP) is published, it will not be included in the sequence of waypoints. Pilots are expected to use normal piloting techniques for beginning the visual descent. In addition, unnamed step-down fixes in the final approach segment will not be coded in the waypoint sequence and must be identified using ATD.

n. Missed Approach

1. A GPS missed approach requires pilot action to sequence the receiver past the MAWP to the missed approach portion of the procedure. The pilot must be thoroughly familiar with the activation procedure for the particular GPS receiver installed in the aircraft and must **initiate appropriate action after the MAWP.** Activating the missed approach prior to the MAWP will cause CDI sensitivity to immediately change to terminal (±1NM) sensitivity and the receiver will continue to navigate to the MAWP. The receiver will not sequence past the MAWP. Turns should not begin prior to the MAWP. If the missed approach is not activated,

the GPS receiver will display an extension of the inbound final approach course and the ATD will increase from the MAWP until it is manually sequenced after crossing the MAWP.

2. Missed approach routings in which the first track is via a course rather than direct to the next waypoint **require additional action by the pilot** to set the course. Being familiar with all of the inputs required is especially critical during this phase of flight.

o. GPS Familiarization

Pilots should practice GPS approaches under visual meteorological conditions (VMC) until thoroughly proficient with all aspects of their equipment (receiver and installation) prior to attempting flight by IFR in instrument meteorological conditions (IMC). Some of the areas which the pilot should practice are:

1. Utilizing the receiver autonomous integrity monitoring (RAIM) prediction function;

2. Inserting a DP into the flight plan, including setting terminal CDI sensitivity, if required, and the conditions under which terminal RAIM is available for departure (some receivers are not DP or STAR capable);

3. Programming the destination airport;

4. Programming and flying the overlay approaches (especially procedure turns and arcs);

5. Changing to another approach after selecting an approach;

6. Programming and flying "direct" missed approaches;

7. Programming and flying "routed" missed approaches;

8. Entering, flying and exiting holding patterns, particularly on overlay approaches with a second waypoint in the holding pattern;

9. Programming and flying a "route" from a holding pattern;

10. Programming and flying an approach with radar vectors to the intermediate segment;

11. Indication of the actions required for RAIM failure both before and after the FAWP; and

12. Programming a radial and distance from a VOR (often used in departure instructions).

1-1-22. GNSS LANDING SYSTEM (GLS)

a. General

1. The GLS provides precision navigation guidance for exact alignment and descent of aircraft on approach to a runway. It provides differential augmentation to the Global Navigation Satellite System (GNSS).

2. The United States plans to provide augmentation services to the GPS for the first phase of GNSS. This section will be revised and updated to reflect international standards and GLS services as they are provided.

1-1-23. PRECISION APPROACH SYSTEMS OTHER THAN ILS, GLS, AND MLS

a. General

Approval and use of precision approach systems other than ILS, GLS and MLS require the issuance of special instrument approach procedures.

b. Special Instrument Approach Procedure

1. Special instrument approach procedures must be issued to the aircraft operator if pilot training, aircraft equipment, and/or aircraft performance is different than published procedures. Special instrument approach procedures are not distributed for general public use. These procedures are issued to an aircraft operator when the conditions for operations approval are satisfied.

2. General aviation operators requesting approval for special procedures should contact the local Flight Standards District Office to obtain a letter of authorization. Air carrier operators requesting approval for use of special procedures should contact their Certificate Holding District Office for authorization through their Operations Specification.

c. Transponder Landing System (TLS)

1. The TLS is designed to provide approach guidance utilizing existing airborne ILS localizer, glide slope, and transponder equipment.

2. TLS special procedures require pilot training and limit operations to a single aircraft on approach.

3. Ground equipment consists of a transponder interrogator, sensor arrays to detect lateral and vertical position, and ILS frequency transmitters. The TLS detects the aircraft's position by interrogating its transponder. It then broadcasts ILS frequency signals to guide the aircraft along the desired approach path.

d. Special Category I Differential GPS (SCAT-I DGPS)

1. The SCAT-I DGPS is designed to provide approach guidance by broadcasting differential correction to GPS.

2. SCAT-I DGPS procedures require aircraft equipment and pilot training.

3. Ground equipment consists of GPS receivers and a VHF digital radio transmitter. The SCAT-I DGPS detects the position of GPS satellites relative to GPS receiver equipment and broadcasts differential corrections over the VHF digital radio.

4. Category I Ground Based Augmentation System (GBAS) will displace SCAT-I DGPS as the public use service.

REFERENCE-
AIM, INSTRUMENT APPROACH PROCEDURES,
PARAGRAPH 5-4-7f.

Section 2. RADAR SERVICES AND PROCEDURES

1-2-1. RADAR

a. Capabilities

1. Radar is a method whereby radio waves are transmitted into the air and are then received when they have been reflected by an object in the path of the beam. Range is determined by measuring the time it takes (at the speed of light) for the radio wave to go out to the object and then return to the receiving antenna. The direction of a detected object from a radar site is determined by the position of the rotating antenna when the reflected portion of the radio wave is received.

2. More reliable maintenance and improved equipment have reduced radar system failures to a negligible factor. Most facilities actually have some components duplicated— one operating and another which immediately takes over when a malfunction occurs to the primary component.

b. Limitations

1. It is very important for the aviation community to recognize the fact that there are limitations to radar service and that ATC controllers may not always be able to issue traffic advisories concerning aircraft which are not under ATC control and cannot be seen on radar. (See FIG 1-2-1.)

(**a**) The characteristics of radio waves are such that they normally travel in a continuous straight line unless they are:

(**1**) "Bent" by abnormal atmospheric phenomena such as temperature inversions;

(**2**) Reflected or attenuated by dense objects such as heavy clouds, precipitation, ground obstacles, mountains, etc.; or

(**3**) Screened by high terrain features.

(**b**) The bending of radar pulses, often called anomalous propagation or ducting, may cause many extraneous blips to appear on the radar operator's display if the beam has been bent toward the ground or may decrease the detection range if the beam is bent upward. It is difficult to solve the effects of anomalous propagation, but using beacon radar and electronically eliminating stationary and slow moving targets by a method called moving target indicator (MTI) usually negate the problem.

Limitations to Radar Service

Precipitation Attenuation

AREA BLACKED OUT BY ATTENUATION

NOT OBSERVED

OBSERVED ECHO

The nearby target absorbs and scatters so much of the out-going and returning energy that the radar does not detect the distant target.

FIG 1-2-1

(**c**) Radar energy that strikes dense objects will be reflected and displayed on the operator's scope thereby blocking out aircraft at the same range and greatly weakening or completely eliminating the display of targets at a greater range. Again, radar beacon and MTI are very effectively used to combat ground clutter and weather phenomena, and a method of circularly polarizing the radar beam will eliminate some weather returns. A negative characteristic of MTI is that an aircraft flying a speed that coincides with the canceling signal of the MTI (tangential or "blind" speed) may not be displayed to the radar controller.

(**d**) Relatively low altitude aircraft will not be seen if they are screened by mountains or are below the radar beam due to earth curvature. The only solution to screening is the installation of strategically placed multiple radars which has been done in some areas.

(**e**) There are several other factors which affect radar control. The amount of reflective surface of an aircraft will determine the size of the radar return. Therefore, a small light airplane or a sleek jet fighter will be more difficult to see on radar than a large commercial jet or military bomber. Here again, the use of radar beacon is invaluable if the aircraft is equipped with an airborne transponder. All ARTCCs' radars in the conterminous U.S. and many airport surveillance radars have the capability to interrogate MODE C and display altitude information to the controller from appropriately equipped aircraft. However, there are a number of airport surveillance radars that don't have Mode C display

AIM

capability and therefore altitude information must be obtained from the pilot.

(f) At some locations within the ATC en route environment, secondary-radar-only (no primary radar) gap filler radar systems are used to give lower altitude radar coverage between two larger radar systems, each of which provides both primary and secondary radar coverage. In those geographical areas served by secondary-radar only, aircraft without transponders cannot be provided with radar service. Additionally, transponder equipped aircraft cannot be provided with radar advisories concerning primary targets and weather.

REFERENCE–
PILOT/CONTROLLER GLOSSARY TERM – RADAR.

(g) The controllers' ability to advise a pilot flying on instruments or in visual conditions of the aircraft's proximity to another aircraft will be limited if the unknown aircraft is not observed on radar, if no flight plan information is available, or if the volume of traffic and workload prevent issuing traffic information. The controller's first priority is given to establishing vertical, lateral, or longitudinal separation between aircraft flying IFR under the control of ATC.

c. FAA radar units operate continuously at the locations shown in the Airport / Facility Directory, and their services are available to all pilots, both civil and military. Contact the associated FAA control tower or ARTCC on any frequency guarded for initial instructions, or in an emergency, any FAA facility for information on the nearest radar service.

1-2-2. AIR TRAFFIC CONTROL RADAR BEACON SYSTEM (ATCRBS)

a. The ATCRBS, sometimes referred to as secondary surveillance radar, consists of three main components:

1. **Interrogator:** Primary radar relies on a signal being transmitted from the radar antenna site and for this signal to be reflected or "bounced back" from an object (such as an aircraft). This reflected signal is then displayed as a "target" on the controller's radarscope. In the ATCRBS, the Interrogator, a ground based radar beacon transmitter-receiver, scans in synchronism with the primary radar and transmits discrete radio signals which repetitiously request all transponders, on the mode being used, to reply. The replies received are then mixed with the primary returns and both are displayed on the same radarscope.

2. **Transponder:** This airborne radar beacon transmitter-receiver automatically receives the signals from the interrogator and selectively replies with a specific pulse group (code) only to those interrogations being received on the mode to which it is set. These replies are independent of, and much stronger than a primary radar return.

3. **Radarscope:** The radarscope used by the controller displays returns from both the primary radar system and the ATCRBS. These returns, called targets, are what the controller refers to in the control and separation of traffic.

b. The job of identifying and maintaining identification of primary radar targets is a long and tedious task for the controller. Some of the advantages of ATCRBS over primary radar are:

1. Reinforcement of radar targets.

2. Rapid target identification.

3. Unique display of selected codes.

c. A part of the ATCRBS ground equipment is the decoder. This equipment enables a controller to assign discrete transponder codes to each aircraft under his/her control. Normally only one code will be assigned for the entire flight. Assignments are made by the ARTCC computer on the basis of the National Beacon Code Allocation Plan. The equipment is also designed to receive MODE C altitude information from the aircraft.

NOTE–
Refer to figures with explanatory legends for an illustration of the target symbology depicted on radar scopes in the NAS Stage A (en route), the ARTS III (terminal) Systems, and other nonautomated (broadband) radar systems. (See FIG 1–2–2 and FIG 1–2–3.)

d. It should be emphasized that aircraft transponders greatly improve the effectiveness of radar systems.

REFERENCE–
AIM, TRANSPONDER OPERATION, PARAGRAPH 4-1-19.

1-2-3. SURVEILLANCE RADAR

a. Surveillance radars are divided into two general categories: Airport Surveillance Radar(ASR) and Air Route Surveillance Radar (ARSR).

1. ASR is designed to provide relatively short-range coverage in the general vicinity of an airport and to serve as an expeditious means of handling terminal area traffic through observation of precise aircraft locations on a radarscope. The ASR can also be used as an instrument approach aid.

2. ARSR is a long-range radar system designed primarily to provide a display of aircraft locations over large areas.

3. Center Radar Automated Radar Terminal Systems (ARTS) Processing (CENRAP) was developed to provide an alternative to a nonradar environment at terminal facilities should an Airport Surveillance Radar (ASR) fail or malfunction. CENRAP sends aircraft radar beacon target information to the ASR terminal facility equipped with ARTS. Procedures used for the separation of aircraft may increase under certain conditions when a facility is utilizing CENRAP because radar target information updates at a slower rate than the normal ASR radar. Radar services for VFR aircraft are also limited during CENRAP operations because of the additional workload required to provide services to IFR aircraft.

b. Surveillance radars scan through 360 degrees of azimuth and present target information on a radar display located in a tower or center. This information is used independently or in conjunction with other navigational aids in the control of air traffic.

1-2-4. PRECISION APPROACH RADAR (PAR)

a. PAR is designed to be used as a landing aid, rather than an aid for sequencing and spacing aircraft. PAR equipment may be used as a primary landing aid, or it may be used to monitor other types of approaches. It is designed to display range, azimuth and elevation information.

b. Two antennas are used in the PAR array, one scanning a vertical plane, and the other scanning horizontally. Since the range is limited to 10 miles, azimuth to 20 degrees, and elevation to 7 degrees, only the final approach area is covered. Each scope is divided into two parts. The upper half presents altitude and distance information, and the lower half presents azimuth and distance.

ARTS III Radar Scope With Alphanumeric Data

FIG 1-2-2

NOTE-

A number of radar terminals do not have ARTS equipment. Those facilities and certain ARTCC's outside the contiguous U.S. would have radar displays similar to the lower right hand subset. ARTS facilities and NAS Stage A ARTCC's, when operating in the nonautomation mode, would also have similar displays and certain services based on automation may not be available.

EXAMPLE–

1. Areas of precipitation (can be reduced by CP)

2. Arrival/departure tabular list

3. Trackball (control) position symbol (A)

4. Airway (lines are sometimes deleted in part)

5. Radar limit line for control

6. Obstruction (video map)

7. Primary radar returns of obstacles or terrain (can be removed by MTI)

8. Satellite airports

9. Runway centerlines (marks and spaces indicate miles)

10. Primary airport with parallel runways

11. Approach gates

12. Tracked target (primary and beacon target)

13. Control position symbol

14. Untracked target select code (monitored) with Mode C readout of 5,000'

15. Untracked target without Mode C

16. Primary target

17. Beacon target only (secondary radar) (transponder)

18. Primary and beacon target

19. Leader line

20. Altitude Mode C readout is 6,000'
(Note: readouts may not be displayed because of nonreceipt of beacon information, garbled beacon signals, and flight plan data which is displayed alternately with the altitude readout)

21. Ground speed readout is 240 knots
(Note: readouts may not be displayed because of a loss of beacon signal, a controller alert that a pilot was squawking emergency, radio failure, etc.)

22. Aircraft ID

23. Asterisk indicates a controller entry in Mode C block. In this case 5,000' is entered and "05" would alternate with Mode C readout.

24. Indicates heavy

25. "Low ALT" flashes to indicate when an aircraft's predicted descent places the aircraft in an unsafe proximity to terrain.
(Note: this feature does not function if the aircraft is not squawking Mode C. When a helicopter or aircraft is known to be operating below the lower safe limit, the "low ALT" can be changed to "inhibit" and flashing ceases.)

26. NAVAID's

27. Airways

28. Primary target only

29. Nonmonitored. No Mode C (an asterisk would indicate nonmonitored with Mode C)

30. Beacon target only (secondary radar based on aircraft transponder)

31. Tracked target (primary and beacon target) control position A

32. Aircraft is squawking emergency code 7700 and is nonmonitored, untracked, Mode C

33. Controller assigned runway 36 right alternates with Mode C readout
(Note: a three letter identifier could also indicate the arrival is at specific airport)

34. Ident flashes

35. Identing target blossoms

36. Untracked target identing on a selected code

37. Range marks (10 and 15 miles) (can be changed/offset)

38. Aircraft controlled by center

39. Targets in suspend status

40. Coast/suspend list (aircraft holding, temporary loss of beacon/target, etc.)

41. Radio failure (emergency information)

42. Select beacon codes (being monitored)

43. General information (ATIS, runway, approach in use)

44. Altimeter setting

45. Time

46. System data area

NAS Stage A Controllers View Plan Display

This figure illustrates the controller's radar scope (PVD) when operating in the full automation (RDP) mode, which is normally 20 hours per day.

(When not in automation mode, the display is similar to the broadband mode shown in the ARTS III radar scope figure. Certain ARTCC's outside the contiguous U.S. also operate in "broadband" mode.)

RADAR SERVICES AND PROCEDURES

FIG 1–2–3

EXAMPLE–
⊡ *Target symbols:*

1. Uncorrelated primary radar target [○] [+]

2. Correlated primary radar target [×]
✳*See note below.*

3. Uncorrelated beacon target [/]

4. Correlated beacon target [\ ]

5. Identing beacon target [≡]

✳*Note: in Number 2. correlated means the association of radar data with the computer projected track of an identified aircraft.*

⊡ *Position symbols:*

6. Free track (no flight plan tracking) [Δ]

7. Flat track (flight plan tracking) [◊]

8. Coast (beacon target lost) [#]

9. Present position hold [X̄]

⊡ *Data block information:*

10. Aircraft ident
✳*See note below.*

11. Assigned altitude FL 280, Mode C altitude same or within ± 200' of assigned altitude.
✳*See note below.*

12. Computer ID #191, handoff is to sector 33 (0–33 would mean handoff accepted)
✳*See note below.*

13. Assigned altitude 17,000', aircraft is climbing, Mode C readout was 14,300 when last beacon interrogation was received.

14. Leader line connecting target symbol and data block.

15. Track velocity and direction vector line (projected ahead of target)

16. Assigned altitude 7,000, aircraft is descending, last Mode C readout (or last reported altitude) was 100' above FL 230

17. Transponder code shows in full data block only when different than assigned code

18. Aircraft is 300' above assigned altitude

19. Reported altitude (no Mode C readout) same as assigned. (An "n" would indicate no reported altitude.)

20. Transponder set on emergency Code 7700 (EMRG flashes to attract attention)

21. Transponder Code 1200 (VFR) with no Mode C

22. Code 1200 (VFR) with Mode C and last altitude readout

23. Transponder set on radio failure Code 7600 (RDOF flashes)

24. Computer ID #228, CST indicates target is in coast status

25. Assigned altitude FL 290, transponder code (these two items constitute a "limited data block")

✳*Note: numbers 10., 11., and 12. constitute a "full data block"*

⊡ *Other symbols:*

26. Navigational aid

27. Airway or jet route

28. Outline of weather returns based on primary radar. "H" represents areas of high density precipitation which might be thunderstorms. Radial lines indicated lower density precipitation.

29. Obstruction

30. Airports
  Major: □
  Small: ⌐

Chapter 2. AERONAUTICAL LIGHTING AND OTHER AIRPORT VISUAL AIDS

Section 1. AIRPORT LIGHTING AIDS

2-1-1. APPROACH LIGHT SYSTEMS (ALS)

a. Approach light systems provide the basic means to transition from instrument flight to visual flight for landing. Operational requirements dictate the sophistication and configuration of the approach light system for a particular runway.

b. Approach light systems are a configuration of signal lights starting at the landing threshold and extending into the approach area a distance of 2400–3000 feet for precision instrument runways and 1400–1500 feet for nonprecision instrument runways. Some systems include sequenced flashing lights which appear to the pilot as a ball of light traveling towards the runway at high speed (twice a second). (See FIG 2–1–1.)

Precision & Nonprecision Configurations

FIG 2-1-1

2-1-2. VISUAL GLIDESLOPE INDICATORS

a. Visual Approach Slope Indicator (VASI)

1. The VASI is a system of lights so arranged to provide visual descent guidance information during the approach to a runway. These lights are visible from 3–5 miles during the day and up to 20 miles or more at night. The visual glide path of the VASI provides safe obstruction clearance within plus or minus 10 degrees of the extended runway centerline and to 4 NM from the runway threshold. Descent, using the VASI, should not be initiated until the aircraft is visually aligned with the runway. Lateral course guidance is provided by the runway or runway lights.

2. VASI installations may consist of either 2, 4, 6, 12, or 16 light units arranged in bars referred to as near, middle, and far bars. Most VASI installations consist of 2 bars, near and far, and may consist of 2, 4, or 12 light units. Some VASI's consist of three bars, near, middle, and far, which provide an additional visual glide path to accommodate high cockpit aircraft. This installation may consist of either 6 or 16 light units. VASI installations consisting of 2, 4, or 6 light units are located on one side of the runway, usually the left. Where the installation consists of 12 or 16 light units, the units are located on both sides of the runway.

3. Two-bar VASI installations provide one visual glide path which is normally set at 3 degrees. Three-bar VASI installations provide two visual glide paths. The lower glide path is provided by the near and middle bar and is normally set at 3 degrees while the upper glide path, provided by the middle and far bars, is normally $1/4$ degree higher. This higher glide path is intended for use only by high cockpit aircraft to provide a sufficient threshold crossing height. Although normal glide path angles are three degrees, angles at some locations may be as high as 4.5 degrees to give proper obstacle clearance. Pilots of high performance aircraft are cautioned that use of VASI angles in excess of 3.5 degrees may cause an increase in runway length required for landing and rollout.

4. The basic principle of the VASI is that of color differentiation between red and white. Each light unit projects a beam of light having a white segment in the upper part of the beam and red segment in the lower part of the beam. The light units are arranged so that the pilot using the VASI's during an approach will see the combination of lights shown below.

5. For 2-bar VASI (4 light units) see FIG 2-1-2.

2-Bar VASI

FIG 2-1-2

6. For 3-bar VASI (6 light units) see FIG 2–1–3.

FIG 2–1–3

7. For other VASI configurations see FIG 2–1–4.

VASI Variations

FIG 2–1–4

b. Precision Approach Path Indicator (PAPI): The precision approach path indicator (PAPI) uses light units similar to the VASI but are installed in a single row of either two or four light units. These systems have an effective visual range of about 5 miles during the day and up to 20 miles at night. The row of light units is normally installed on the left side of the runway and the glide path indications are as depicted. (See FIG 2–1–5.)

Precision Approach Path Indicator (PAPI)

FIG 2–1–5

c. Tri-color Systems: Tri-color visual approach slope indicators normally consist of a single light unit projecting a three-color visual approach path into the final approach area of the runway upon which the indicator is installed. The below glide path indication is red, the above glide path indication is amber, and the on glide path indication is green. These types of indicators have a useful range of approximately one-half to one mile during the day and up to five miles at night depending upon the visibility conditions. (See FIG 2–1–6.)

Tri-Color Visual Approach Slope Indicator

NOTE–
1. *Since the tri-color VASI consists of a single light source which could possibly be confused with other light sources, pilots should exercise care to properly locate and identify the light signal.*
2. *When the aircraft descends from green to red, the pilot may see a dark amber color during the transition from green to red.*

FIG 2–1–6

d. Pulsating Systems: Pulsating visual approach slope indicators normally consist of a single light unit projecting a two-color visual approach path into the final approach area of the runway upon which the indicator is installed. The on glide path indication is a steady white light. The slightly below glide path indication is a steady red light. If the aircraft descends further below the glide path, the red light starts to pulsate. The above glide path indication is a pulsating white light. The pulsating rate increases as the aircraft gets further above or below the desired glide slope. The useful range of the system is about four miles during the day and up to ten miles at night. (See FIG 2–1–7.)

Pulsating Visual Approach Slope Indicator

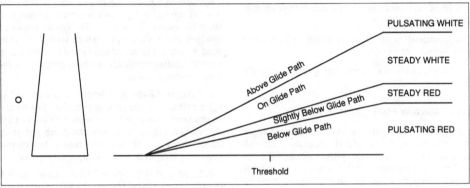

NOTE–
Since the PVASI consists of a single light source which could possibly be confused with other light sources, pilots should exercise care to properly locate and identify the light signal.

FIG 2–1–7

e. Alignment of Elements Systems: Alignment of elements systems are installed on some small general aviation airports and are a low-cost system consisting of painted plywood panels, normally black and white or fluorescent orange. Some of these systems are lighted for night use. The useful range of these systems is approximately three-quarter miles. To use the system the pilot positions the aircraft so the elements are in alignment. The glide path indications are shown in FIG 2–1–8.

Alignment of Elements

FIG 2–1–8

2-1-3. RUNWAY END IDENTIFIER LIGHTS (REIL)

REIL's are installed at many airfields to provide rapid and positive identification of the approach end of a particular runway. The system consists of a pair of synchronized flashing lights located laterally on each side of the runway threshold. REIL's may be either omnidirectional or unidirectional facing the approach area. They are effective for:

a. Identification of a runway surrounded by a preponderance of other lighting.

b. Identification of a runway which lacks contrast with surrounding terrain.

c. Identification of a runway during reduced visibility.

2-1-4. RUNWAY EDGE LIGHT SYSTEMS

a. Runway edge lights are used to outline the edges of runways during periods of darkness or restricted visibility conditions. These light systems are classified according to the intensity or brightness they are capable of producing: they are the High Intensity Runway Lights (HIRL), Medium Intensity Runway Lights (MIRL), and the Low Intensity Runway Lights (LIRL). The HIRL and MIRL systems have variable intensity controls, whereas the LIRL's normally have one intensity setting.

b. The runway edge lights are white, except on instrument runways yellow replaces white on the last 2,000 feet or half the runway length, whichever is less, to form a caution zone for landings.

c. The lights marking the ends of the runway emit red light toward the runway to indicate the end of runway to a departing aircraft and emit green outward from the runway end to indicate the threshold to landing aircraft.

2-1-5. IN-RUNWAY LIGHTING

a. Runway Centerline Lighting System (RCLS): Runway centerline lights are installed on some precision approach runways to facilitate landing under adverse visibility conditions. They are located along the runway centerline and are spaced at 50–foot intervals.

When viewed from the landing threshold, the runway centerline lights are white until the last 3,000 feet of the runway. The white lights begin to alternate with red for the next 2,000 feet, and for the last 1,000 feet of the runway, all centerline lights are red.

b. Touchdown Zone Lights (TDZL): Touchdown zone lights are installed on some precision approach runways to indicate the touchdown zone when landing under adverse visibility conditions. They consist of two rows of transverse light bars disposed symmetrically about the runway centerline. The system consists of steady–burning white lights which start 100 feet beyond the landing threshold and extend to 3,000 feet beyond the landing threshold or to the midpoint of the runway, whichever is less.

c. Taxiway Lead–Off Lights: Taxiway lead–off lights extend from the runway centerline to a point on an exit taxiway to expedite movement of aircraft from the runway. These lights alternate green and yellow from the runway centerline to the runway holding position or the ILS/MLS critical area, as appropriate.

d. Land and Hold Short Lights: Land and hold short lights are used to indicate the hold short point on certain runways which are approved for Land and Hold Short Operations (LAHSO). Land and hold short lights consist of a row of pulsing white lights installed across the runway at the hold short point. Where installed, the lights will be on anytime LAHSO is in effect. These lights will be off when LAHSO is not in effect.

REFERENCE–
AIM, PILOT RESPONSIBILITIES WHEN CONDUCTING LAND AND HOLD SHORT OPERATIONS (LAHSO), PARAGRAPH 4–3–11.

2-1-6. CONTROL OF LIGHTING SYSTEMS

a. Operation of approach light systems and runway lighting is controlled by the control tower (ATCT). At some locations the FSS may control the lights where there is no control tower in operation.

b. Pilots may request that lights be turned on or off. Runway edge lights, in-pavement lights and approach lights also have intensity controls which may be varied to meet the pilots request. Sequenced flashing lights (SFL) may be turned on and off. Some sequenced flashing light systems also have intensity control.

2-1-7. PILOT CONTROL OF AIRPORT LIGHTING

Radio control of lighting is available at selected airports to provide airborne control of lights by keying the aircraft's microphone. Control of lighting systems is often available at locations without specified hours for lighting and where there is no control tower or FSS or when the tower or FSS is closed (locations with a part-time tower or FSS) or specified hours. All lighting systems which are radio controlled at an airport, whether on a single runway or multiple runways, operate on the same radio frequency.
(See TBL 2-1-1 and TBL 2-1-2.)

a. With FAA approved systems, various combinations of medium intensity approach lights, runway lights, taxiway lights, VASI and/or REIL may be activated by radio control. On runways with both approach lighting and runway lighting (runway edge lights, taxiway lights, etc.) systems, the approach lighting system takes precedence for air-to-ground radio control over the runway lighting system which is set at a predetermined intensity step, based on expected visibility conditions. Runways without approach lighting may provide radio controlled intensity adjustments of runway edge lights. Other lighting systems, including VASI, REIL, and taxiway lights may be either controlled with the runway edge lights or controlled independently of the runway edge lights.

Runways With Approach Lights

Lighting System	No. of Int. Steps	Status During Nonuse Period	Intensity Step Selected Per No. of Mike Clicks		
			3 Clicks	5 Clicks	7 Clicks
Approach Lights (Med. Int.)	2	Off	Low	Low	High
Approach Lights (Med. Int.)	3	Off	Low	Med	High
MIRL	3	Off or Low	◆	◆	◆
HIRL	5	Off or Low	◆	◆	◆
VASI	2	Off	★	★	★

NOTES: ◆ Predetermined intensity step.
         ★ Low intensity for night use. High intensity for day use as determined by photocell control.

TBL 2-1-1

Runways Without Approach Lights

Lighting System	No. of Int. Steps	Status During Nonuse Period	Intensity Step Selected Per No. of Mike Clicks		
			3 Clicks	5 Clicks	7 Clicks
MIRL	3	Off or Low	Low	Med.	High
HIRL	5	Off or Low	Step 1 or 2	Step 3	Step 5
LIRL	1	Off	On	On	On
VASI★	2	Off	◆	◆	◆
REIL★	1	Off	Off	On /'Off	On
REIL★	3	Off	Low	Med.	High

NOTES: ◆ Low intensity for night use. High intensity for day use as determined by photocell control.
         ★ The control of VASI and/or REIL may be independent of other lighting systems.

TBL 2-1-2

b. The control system consists of a 3–step control responsive to 7, 5, and/or 3 microphone clicks. This 3–step control will turn on lighting facilities capable of either 3–step, 2–step or 1–step operation. The 3–step and 2–step lighting facilities can be altered in intensity, while the 1–step cannot. All lighting is illuminated for a period of 15 minutes from the most recent time of activation and may not be extinguished prior to end of the 15 minute period (except for 1–step and 2–step REILs which may be turned off when desired by keying the mike 5 or 3 times respectively).

c. Suggested use is to always initially key the mike 7 times; this assures that all controlled lights are turned on to the maximum available intensity. If desired, adjustment can then be made, where the capability is provided, to a lower intensity (or the REIL turned off) by keying 5 and/or 3 times. Due to the close proximity of airports using the same frequency, radio controlled lighting receivers may be set at a low sensitivity requiring the aircraft to be relatively close to activate the system. Consequently, even when lights are on, always key mike as directed when overflying an airport of intended landing or just prior to entering the final segment of an approach. This will assure the aircraft is close enough to activate the system and a full 15 minutes lighting duration is available. Approved lighting systems may be activated by keying the mike (within 5 seconds) as indicated in TBL 2–1–3.

Radio Control System

Key Mike	Function
7 times within 5 seconds	Highest intensity available
5 times within 5 seconds	Medium or lower intensity (Lower REIL or REIL-off)
3 times within 5 seconds	Lowest intensity available (Lower REIL or REIL-off)

TBL 2–1–3

d. For all public use airports with FAA standard systems the Airport/Facility Directory contains the types of lighting, runway and the frequency that is used to activate the system. Airports with IAP's include data on the approach chart identifying the light system, the runway on which they are installed, and the frequency that is used to activate the system.

NOTE–
Although the CTAF is used to activate the lights at many airports, other frequencies may also be used. The appropriate frequency for activating the lights on the airport is provided in the Airport/Facility Directory and the standard instrument approach procedures publications. It is not identified on the sectional charts.

e. Where the airport is not served by an IAP, it may have either the standard FAA approved control system or an independent type system of different specification installed by the airport sponsor. The Airport/Facility Directory contains descriptions of pilot controlled lighting systems for each airport having other than FAA approved systems, and explains the type lights, method of control, and operating frequency in clear text.

2–1–8. AIRPORT/HELIPORT BEACONS

a. Airport and heliport beacons have a vertical light distribution to make them most effective from one to ten degrees above the horizon; however, they can be seen well above and below this peak spread. The beacon may be an omnidirectional capacitor-discharge device, or it may rotate at a constant speed which produces the visual effect of flashes at regular intervals. Flashes may be one or two colors alternately. The total number of flashes are:

1. 24 to 30 per minute for beacons marking airports, landmarks, and points on Federal airways.

2. 30 to 45 per minute for beacons marking heliports.

b. The colors and color combinations of beacons are:

1. White and Green– Lighted land airport

2. *Green alone– Lighted land airport

3. White and Yellow– Lighted water airport

4. *Yellow alone– Lighted water airport

5. Green, Yellow, and White– Lighted heliport

NOTE–
Green alone or yellow alone is used only in connection with a white-and-green or white-and-yellow beacon display, respectively.

c. Military airport beacons flash alternately white and green, but are differentiated from civil beacons by dualpeaked (two quick) white flashes between the green flashes.

d. In Class B, Class C, Class D and Class E surface areas, operation of the airport beacon during the hours of daylight often indicates that the ground visibility is less than 3 miles and/or the ceiling is less than 1,000 feet. ATC clearance in accordance with FAR Part 91 is required for landing, takeoff and flight in the traffic pattern. Pilots should not rely solely on the operation of the airport beacon to indicate if weather conditions are IFR or VFR. At some locations with operating control towers, ATC personnel turn the beacon on or off when controls are in the tower. At many airports the airport beacon is turned on by a photoelectric cell or time clocks and ATC personnel can not control them. There is no regulatory requirement for daylight operation and it is the pilot's responsibility to comply with proper preflight planning as required by FAR Part 91.103.

2-1-9. TAXIWAY LIGHTS

a. Taxiway Edge Lights: Taxiway edge lights are used to outline the edges of taxiways during periods of darkness or restricted visibility conditions. These fixtures emit blue light.

NOTE–
At most major airports these lights have variable intensity settings and may be adjusted at pilot request or when deemed necessary by the controller.

b. Taxiway Centerline Lights: Taxiway centerline lights are used to facilitate ground traffic under low visibility conditions. They are located along the taxiway centerline in a straight line on straight portions, on the centerline of curved portions, and along designated taxiing paths in portions of runways, ramp, and apron areas. Taxiway centerline lights are steady burning and emit green light.

c. Clearance Bar Lights: Clearance bar lights are installed at holding positions on taxiways in order to increase the conspicuity of the holding position in low visibility conditions. They may also be installed to indicate the location of an intersecting taxiway during periods of darkness. Clearance bars consist of three in-pavement steady-burning yellow lights.

d. Runway Guard Lights: Runway guard lights are installed at taxiway/runway intersections. They are primarily used to enhance the conspicuity of taxiway/runway intersections during low visibility conditions, but may be used in all weather conditions. Runway guard lights consist of either a pair of elevated flashing yellow lights installed on either side of the taxiway, or a row of in-pavement yellow lights installed across the entire taxiway, at the runway holding position marking.

NOTE–
Some airports may have a row of three or five in-pavement yellow lights installed at taxiway/runway intersections. They should not be confused with clearance bar lights described in paragraph 2–1–9c, Clearance Bar Lights.

e. Stop Bar Lights: Stop bar lights, when installed, are used to confirm the ATC clearance to enter or cross the active runway in low visibility conditions (below 1,200 ft Runway Visual Range). A stop bar consists of a row of red, unidirectional, steady–burning in-pavement lights installed across the entire taxiway at the runway holding position, and elevated steady–burning red lights on each side. A controlled stop bar is operated in conjunction with the taxiway centerline lead-on lights which extend from the stop bar toward the runway. Following the ATC clearance to proceed, the stop bar is turned off and the lead-on lights are turned on. The stop bar and lead-on lights are automatically reset by a sensor or backup timer.

CAUTION–
Pilots should never cross a red illuminated stop bar, even if an ATC clearance has been given to proceed onto or across the runway.

NOTE–
If after crossing a stop bar, the taxiway centerline lead-on lights inadvertently extinguish, pilots should hold their position and contact ATC for further instructions.

Section 2. AIR NAVIGATION AND OBSTRUCTION LIGHTING

2-2-1. AERONAUTICAL LIGHT BEACONS

a. An aeronautical light beacon is a visual NAVAID displaying flashes of white and/or colored light to indicate the location of an airport, a heliport, a landmark, a certain point of a Federal airway in mountainous terrain, or an obstruction. The light used may be a rotating beacon or one or more flashing lights. The flashing lights may be supplemented by steady burning lights of lesser intensity.

b. The color or color combination displayed by a particular beacon and/or its auxiliary lights tell whether the beacon is indicating a landing place, landmark, point of the Federal airways, or an obstruction. Coded flashes of the auxiliary lights, if employed, further identify the beacon site.

2-2-2. CODE BEACONS AND COURSE LIGHTS

a. Code Beacons: The code beacon, which can be seen from all directions, is used to identify airports and landmarks. The code beacon flashes the three or four character airport identifier in International Morse Code six to eight times per minute. Green flashes are displayed for land airports while yellow flashes indicate water airports.

b. Course Lights: The course light, which can be seen clearly from only one direction, is used only with rotating beacons of the Federal Airway System: two course lights, back to back, direct coded flashing beams of light in either direction along the course of airway.

NOTE–
Airway beacons are remnants of the "lighted" airways which antedated the present electronically equipped federal airways system. Only a few of these beacons exist today to mark airway segments in remote mountain areas. Flashes in morse code identify the beacon site.

2-2-3. OBSTRUCTION LIGHTS

a. Obstructions are marked/lighted to warn airmen of their presence during daytime and nighttime conditions. They may be marked/lighted in any of the following combinations:

1. *Aviation Red Obstruction Lights:* Flashing aviation red beacons (20 to 40 flashes per minute) and steady burning aviation red lights during nighttime operation. Aviation orange and white paint is used for daytime marking.

2. *Medium Intensity Flashing White Obstruction Lights:* Medium intensity flashing white obstruction lights may be used during daytime and twilight with automatically selected reduced intensity for nighttime operation. When this system is used on structures 500 feet (153m) AGL or less in height, other methods of marking and lighting the structure may be omitted. Aviation orange and white paint is always required for daytime marking on structures exceeding 500 feet (153m) AGL. This system is not normally installed on structures less than 200 feet (61m) AGL.

3. *High Intensity White Obstruction Lights:* Flashing high intensity white lights during daytime with reduced intensity for twilight and nighttime operation. When this type system is used, the marking of structures with red obstruction lights and aviation orange and white paint may be omitted.

4. *Dual Lighting:* A combination of flashing aviation red beacons and steady burning aviation red lights for nighttime operation and flashing high intensity white lights for daytime operation. Aviation orange and white paint may be omitted.

5. *Catenary Lighting:* Lighted markers are available for increased night conspicuity of high–voltage (69KV or higher) transmission line catenary wires. Lighted markers provide conspicuity both day and night.

b. Medium intensity omnidirectional flashing white lighting system provides conspicuity both day and night on catenary support structures. The unique sequential/simultaneous flashing light system alerts pilots of the associated catenary wires.

c. High intensity flashing white lights are being used to identify some supporting structures of overhead transmission lines located across rivers, chasms, gorges, etc. These lights flash in a middle, top, lower light sequence at approximately 60 flashes per minute. The top light is normally installed near the top of the supporting structure, while the lower light indicates the approximate lower portion of the wire span. The lights are beamed towards the companion structure and identify the area of the wire span.

AIM

d. High intensity flashing white lights are also employed to identify tall structures, such as chimneys and towers, as obstructions to air navigation. The lights provide a 360 degree coverage about the structure at 40 flashes per minute and consist of from one to seven levels of lights depending upon the height of the structure. Where more than one level is used the vertical banks flash simultaneously.

Section 3. AIRPORT MARKING AIDS AND SIGNS

2-3-1. GENERAL

a. Airport pavement markings and signs provide information that is useful to a pilot during takeoff, landing, and taxiing.

b. Uniformity in airport markings and signs from one airport to another enhances safety and improves efficiency. Pilots are encouraged to work with the operators of the airports they use to achieve the marking and sign standards described in this section.

c. Pilots who encounter ineffective, incorrect, or confusing markings or signs on an airport should make the operator of the airport aware of the problem. These situations may also be reported under the Aviation Safety Reporting Program as described in paragraph 7-6-1, Aviation Safety Reporting Program. Pilots may also report these situations to the FAA regional airports division.

d. The markings and signs described in this section of the AIM reflect the current FAA recommended standards.

REFERENCE-
AC 150/5340-1, STANDARDS FOR AIRPORT MARKINGS.
AC 150/5340-18, STANDARDS FOR AIRPORT SIGN SYSTEMS.

2-3-2. AIRPORT PAVEMENT MARKINGS

a. General: For the purpose of this presentation the Airport Pavement Markings have been grouped into four areas:

1. *Runway Markings.*

2. *Taxiway Markings.*

3. *Holding Position Markings.*

4. *Other Markings.*

b. Marking Colors: Markings for runways are white. Markings defining the landing area on a heliport are also white except for hospital heliports which use a red "H" on a white cross. Markings for taxiways, areas not intended for use by aircraft (closed and hazardous areas), and holding positions (even if they are on a runway) are yellow.

2-3-3. RUNWAY MARKINGS

a. General: There are three types of markings for runways: visual, nonprecision instrument and precision instrument. TBL 2-3-1 identifies the marking elements for each type of runway and TBL 2-3-2 identifies runway threshold markings.

b. Runway Designators: Runway numbers and letters are determined from the approach direction. The runway number is the whole number nearest one-tenth the magnetic azimuth of the centerline of the runway, measured clockwise from the magnetic north. The letters, differentiate between left (L), right (R), or center (C), parallel runways, as applicable:

1. For two parallel runways "L" "R."

2. For three parallel runways "L" "C" "R."

c. Runway Centerline Marking: The runway centerline identifies the center of the runway and provides alignment guidance during takeoff and landings. The centerline consists of a line of uniformly spaced stripes and gaps.

Runway Marking Elements

Marking Element	Visual Runway	Nonprecision Instrument Runway	Precision Instrument Runway
Designation (par. 6)	X	X	X
Centerline (par. 7)	X	X	X
Threshold (par. 8)	X[1]	X	X
Aiming Point (par. 9)	X[2]	X	X
Touchdown Zone (par. 10)			X
Side Stripes (par. 11)			

[1] On runways used, or intended to be used, by international commercial transports.

[2] On runways 4,000 feet (1200 m) or longer used jet aircraft.

TBL 2-3-1

d. Runway Aiming Point Marking: The aiming point marking serves as a visual aiming point for a landing aircraft. These two rectangular markings consist of a broad white stripe located on each side of the runway centerline and approximately 1,000 feet from the landing threshold, as shown in FIG 2–3–1 Precision Instrument Runway Markings.

e. Runway Touchdown Zone Markers: The touchdown zone markings identify the touchdown zone for landing operations and are coded to provide distance information in 500 feet (150m) increments. These markings consist of groups of one, two, and three rectangular bars symmetrically arranged in pairs about the runway centerline, as shown in FIG 2–3–1 Precision Instrument Runway Markings. For runways having touchdown zone markings on both ends, those pairs of markings which extend to within 900 feet (270m) of the midpoint between the thresholds are eliminated.

f. Runway Side Strip Marking: Runway side stripes delineate the edges of the runway. They provide a visual contrast between runway and the abutting terrain or shoulders. Side stripes consist of continuous white stripes located, on each side of the runway as shown in FIG 2–3–5.

g. Runway Shoulder Markings: Runway shoulder stripes may be used to supplement runway side stripes to identify pavement areas contiguous to the runway sides that are not intended for use by aircraft. Runway Shoulder stripes are Yellow. (See FIG 2–3–3.)

h. Runway Threshold Markings: Runway threshold markings come in two configurations. They either consist of eight longitudinal stripes of uniform dimensions disposed symmetrically about the runway centerline, as shown in FIG 2–3–1, or the number of stripes is related to the runway width as indicated in TBL 2–3–2. A threshold marking helps identify the beginning of the runway that is available for landing. In some instances the landing threshold may be relocated or displaced.

Precision Instrument Runway Markings

FIG 2–3–1

Nonprecision Instrument Runway and Visual Runway Markings

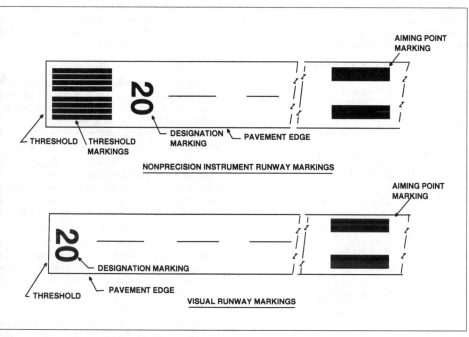

FIG 2–3–2

1. Relocation of a Threshold: Sometimes construction, maintenance, or other activities require the threshold to be relocated towards the rollout end of the runway. (See Figure 2–3–4.) When a threshold is relocated, it closes not only a set portion of the approach end of a runway, but also shortens the length of the opposite direction runway. In these cases, a NOTAM should be issued by the airport operator identifying the portion of the runway that is closed, e.g., 10/28 W 900 CLSD. Because the duration of the relocation can vary from a few hours to several months, methods identifying the new threshold may vary. One common practice is to use a ten feet wide white threshold bar across the width of the runway. Although the runway lights in the area between the old threshold and new threshold will not be illuminated, the runway markings in this area may or may not be obliterated, removed, or covered.

2. Displaced Threshold: A displaced threshold is a threshold located at a point on the runway other than the designated beginning of the runway. Displacement of a threshold reduces the length of runway available for landings. The portion of runway behind a displaced threshold is available for takeoffs in either direction and landings from the opposite direction. A ten feet wide white threshold bar is located across the width of the runway at the displaced threshold. White arrows are located along the centerline in the area between the beginning of the runway and displaced threshold. White arrow heads are located across the width of the runway just prior to the threshold bar, as shown in FIG 2–3–5.

NOTE–
Airport operator. When reporting the relocation or displacement of a threshold, the airport operator should avoid language which confuses the two.

Number of Runway Threshold Stripes

Runway Width	Number of Stripes
60 feet (18 m)	4
75 feet (23 m)	6
100 feet (30 m)	8
150 feet (45 m)	12
200 feet (60 m)	16

TBL 2–3–2

i. Demarcation Bar: A demarcation bar delineates a runway with a displaced threshold from a blast pad, stopway or taxiway that precedes the runway. A demarcation bar is 3 feet (1m) wide and yellow, since it is not located on the runway as shown in FIG 2-3-6.

Runway Shoulder Markings

SHOULDER   RUNWAY   SHOULDER

MIDPOINT OF RUNWAY

RUNWAY THRESHOLD

FIG 2-3-3

1. Chevrons: These markings are used to show pavement areas aligned with the runway that are unusable for landing, takeoff, and taxiing. Chevrons are yellow. (See FIG 2-3-7.)

j. Runway Threshold BAR: A threshold bar delineates the beginning of the runway that is available for landing when the threshold has been relocated or displaced. A threshold bar is 10 feet (3m) in width and extends across the width of the runway, as shown in FIG 2-3-5.

2-3-4. TAXIWAY MARKINGS

a. General: All taxiways should have centerline markings and runway holding position markings whenever they intersect a runway. Taxiway edge markings are present whenever there is a need to separate the taxiway from a pavement that is not intended for aircraft use

or to delineate the edge of the taxiway. Taxiways may also have shoulder markings and holding position markings for Instrument Landing System/Microwave Landing System (ILS/MLS) critical areas, and taxiway/taxiway intersection markings.

REFERENCE–
AIM, HOLDING POSITION MARKINGS, PARAGRAPH 2-3-5.

b. Taxiway Centerline: The taxiway centerline is single continuous yellow line, 6 inches (15 cm) to 1: inches (30 cm) in width. This provides a visual cue t permit taxiing along a designated path. Ideally the aircraft should be kept centered over this line during taxi to ensure wing-tip clearance. (See FIG 2-3-8.)

c. Taxiway Edge Markings: Taxiway edge markings are used to define the edge of the taxiway. They are primarily used when the taxiway edge does not correspond with the edge of the pavement. There are two types of markings depending upon whether the aircraft is suppose to cross the taxiway edge:

1. *Continuous Markings:* These consist of a continuous double yellow line, with each line being at least 6 inches (15 cm) in width spaced 6 inches (15 cm) apart They are used to define the taxiway edge from the shoulder or some other abutting paved surface not intended for use by aircraft.

2. *Dashed Markings:* These markings are used when there is an operational need to define the edge of a taxiway or taxilane on a paved surface where the adjoining pavement to the taxiway edge is intended for use by aircraft. e.g., an apron. Dashed taxiway edge markings consist of a broken double yellow line, with each line being at least 6 inches (15 cm) in width, spaced inches (15 cm) apart (edge to edge). These lines are 1 feet (4.5 m) in length with 25 foot (7.5 m) gaps. (See FIG 2-3-9.)

d. Taxi Shoulder Markings: Taxiways, holding bays, and aprons are sometimes provided with paved shoulders to prevent blast and water erosion. Although shoulders may have the appearance of full strength pavement they are not intended for use by aircraft, and may be unable to support an aircraft. Usually the taxiway edge marking will define this area. Where conditions exist such as islands or taxiway curves that may cause confusion as to which side of the edge stripe is for use by aircraft, taxiway shoulder markings may be used to indicate the pavement is unusable. Taxiway shoulder markings are yellow. (See FIG 2-3-10.)

Relocation of a Threshold with Markings for Taxiway Aligned with Runway

FIG 2-3-4

Airport Marking Aids and Signs

2-3-5

Displaced Threshold Markings

FIG 2–3–5

Markings for Blast Pad or Stopway or Taxiway Preceding a Displaced Threshold

DEMARCATION BAR, YELLOW, 3' (1 m) WIDE, PAINTED ON BLAST PAD OR STOPWAY

BLAST PAD OR STOPWAY AND DISPLACED THRESHOLD PRECEDING A RUNWAY

DEMARCATION BAR, YELLOW, 3' (1m) WIDE, PAINTED ON TAXIWAY

TAXIWAY AND DISPLACED THRESHOLD PRECEDING A RUNWAY

FIG 2-3-6

Markings for Blast Pads and Stopways

FIG 2–3–7

2-3-8   Airport Marking Aids and Signs

Taxiway Centerline

FIG 2-3-8

Taxi Shoulder Markings

FIG 2-3-10

Dashed Markings

FIG 2-3-9

e. Surface Painted Taxiway Direction Signs: Surface painted taxiway direction signs have a yellow background with a black inscription, and are provided when it is not possible to provide taxiway direction signs at intersections, or when necessary to supplement such signs. These markings are located adjacent to the centerline with signs indicating turns to the left being on the left side of the taxiway centerline and signs indicating turns to the right being on the right side of the centerline. (See FIG 2-3-11.)

f. Surface Painted Location Signs: Surface painted location signs have a black background with a yellow inscription. When necessary, these markings are used to supplement location signs located along side the taxiway and assist the pilot in confirming the designation of the taxiway on which the aircraft is located. These markings are located on the right side of the centerline. (See FIG 2-3-11.)

g. Geographic Position Markings: These markings are located at points along low visibility taxi routes designated in the airport's Surface Movement Guidance Control System (SMGCS) plan. They are used to identify the location of taxiing aircraft during low visibility operations. Low visibility operations are those that occur when the runway visible range (RVR) is below 1200 feet(360m). They are positioned to the left of the taxiway centerline in the direction of taxiing. (See FIG 2-3-12.) The geographic position marking is a circle comprised of an outer black ring contiguous to a white ring with a pink circle in the middle. When installed on asphalt or other dark-colored pavements, the white ring and the black ring are reversed, i.e., the white ring becomes the outer ring and the black ring becomes the inner ring. It is designated with either a number or a number and letter. The number corresponds to the consecutive position of the marking on the route.

Surface Painted Signs

FIG 2-3-11

2-3-5. HOLDING POSITION MARKINGS

a. Runway Holding Position Markings: For runways these markings indicate where an aircraft is supposed to stop. They consist of four yellow lines two solid and two dashed, spaced six inches apart and extending across the width of the taxiway or runway. The solid lines are always on the side where the aircraft is to hold. There are three locations where runway holding position markings are encountered.

1. Runway Holding Position Markings on Taxiways: These markings identify the locations on a taxiway where an aircraft is supposed to stop when it does not have clearance to proceed onto the runway. The runway holding position markings are shown in FIG 2–3–13. When instructed by ATC "Hold short of (runway "xx")" the pilot should stop so no part of the aircraft extends beyond the holding position marking. When approaching the holding position marking, a pilot should not cross the marking without ATC clearance at a controlled airport or without making sure of adequate separation from other aircraft at uncontrolled airports. An aircraft exiting a runway is not clear of the runway until all parts of the aircraft have crossed the applicable holding position marking.

2. Runway Holding Position Markings on Runways: These markings are installed on runways only if the runway is normally used by air traffic control for "land, hold short" operations or taxiing operations and have operational significance only for those two types of operations. A sign with a white inscription on a red background is installed adjacent to these holding position markings. (See FIG 2–3–14.) The holding position markings are placed on runways prior to the intersection with another runway, or some designated point. Pilots receiving instructions "cleared to land, runway "xx"" from air traffic control are authorized to use the entire landing length of the runway and should disregard any holding position markings located on the runway. Pilots receiving and accepting instructions "cleared to land runway "xx," hold short of runway "yy"" from air traffic control must either exit runway "xx," or stop at the holding position prior to runway "yy."

3. Taxiways Located in Runway Approach Areas: These markings are used at some airports where it is necessary to hold an aircraft on a taxiway located in the approach or departure area of a runway so that the aircraft does not interfere with the operations on that runway. This marking is collocated with the runway approach area holding position sign. (See subparagraph 2–3–8b. 2. Runway Approach Area Holding Position Sign, and FIG 2–3–14 and FIG 2–3–15.)

b. Holding Position Markings for Instrument Landing System (ILS): Holding position markings for ILS/MLS critical areas consist of two yellow solid lines spaced two feet apart connected by pairs of solid lines spaced ten feet apart extending across the width of the taxiway as shown. (See FIG 2–3–16.) A sign with an inscription in white on a red background is installed adjacent to these hold position markings. When the ILS critical area is being protected, the pilot should stop so no part of the aircraft extends beyond the holding position marking. When approaching the holding position marking, a pilot should not cross the marking without ATC clearance. ILS critical area is not clear until all parts of the aircraft have crossed the applicable holding position marking.

REFERENCE–
AIM, MARKER BEACON, PARAGRAPH 1–1–9.

c. Holding Position Markings for Taxiway/ Taxiway Intersections: Holding position markings for taxiway/taxiway intersections consist of a single dashed line extending across the width of the taxiway as shown. (See FIG 2–3–17.) They are installed on taxiways where air traffic control normally holds aircraft short of a taxiway intersection. When instructed by ATC "hold short of (taxiway)" the pilot should stop so no part of the aircraft extends beyond the holding position marking. When the marking is not present the pilot should stop the aircraft at a point which provides adequate clearance from an aircraft on the intersecting taxiway.

d. Surface Painted Holding Position Signs: Surface painted holding position signs have a red background with a white inscription and supplement the signs located at the holding position. This type of marking is normally used where the width of the holding position on the taxiway is greater than 200 feet(60m). It is located to the left side of the taxiway centerline on the holding side and prior to the holding position marking. (See FIG 2–3–11.)

Geographic Position Markings

YELLOW HOLD
POSITION MARKING

STANDARD TAXIWAY/TAXIWAY
HOLDING POSITION MARKINGS,
BLACK BORDER AND BLACK
SPACES

MARKING CONSISTS OF A
BLACK INSCRIPTION,
CENTERED ON A PINK CIRCLE
WITH A WHITE INNER RING AND BLACK BORDER*

EDGE OF YELLOW →
TAXIWAY CENTERLINE
MARKING

TAXIWAY CENTERLINE MARKING
ASSOCIATED WITH GEOGRAPHIC
POSITION MARKINGS ON LIGHT
COLORED PAVEMENT OUTLINED
WITH BLACK FOR INCREASED
CONSPICUITY

DIRECTION
OF TRAVEL

* When installed on asphalt or other dark colored pavements, the white ring and the
black ring are reversed, i.e., the white ring becomes the outer ring and the black ring
becomes the inner ring.

FIG 2-3-12

Runway Holding Position Markings on Taxiway

RUNWAY

15

TAXIWAY/RUNWAY
HOLDING POSITION
MARKINGS

HOLDING
BAY

TAXIWAY

EXAMPLE OF HOLDING POSITION MARKINGS

EXTENDED ACROSS HOLDING BAY

FIG 2-3-13

Runway Holding Position Markings on Runways

FIG 2-3-14

Taxiways Located in Runway Approach Area

FIG 2-3-15

Holding Position Markings: ILS Critical Area

FIG 2-3-16

2-3-6. OTHER MARKINGS

a. Vehicle Roadway Markings: The vehicle roadway markings are used when necessary to define a pathway for vehicle operations on or crossing areas that are also intended for aircraft. These markings consist of a white solid line to delineate each edge of the roadway and a dashed line to separate lanes within the edges of the roadway. In lieu of the solid lines, zipper markings may be used to delineate the edges of the vehicle roadway. (See FIG 2-3-18.) Details of the zipper markings are shown in FIG 2-3-19.

b. VOR Receiver Checkpoint Markings: The VOR receiver checkpoint marking allows the pilot to check aircraft instruments with navigational aid signals. It consists of a painted circle with an arrow in the middle; the arrow is aligned in the direction of the checkpoint azimuth. This marking, and an associated sign, is located on the airport apron or taxiway at a point selected for easy access by aircraft but where other airport traffic is not to be unduly obstructed. (See FIG 2-3-20.)

NOTE-
The associated sign contains the VOR station identification letter and course selected (published) for the check, the words "VOR check course," and DME data (when applicable). The color of the letters and numerals are black on a yellow background.

Holding Position Markings: Taxiway/Taxiway Intersections

TAXIWAY HOLDING
POSITION MARKINGS,
YELLOW, SEE
DETAIL 1

DETAIL 1

FIG 2-3-17

Vehicle Roadway Markings

ROADWAY EDGE
STRIPES, WHITE,
CONTINUOUS
6" (15 cm) WIDE

ROADWAY STOP LINE,
WHITE 2' (.67 m)
WIDE ACROSS THE
APPROACH LANE - SEE
TEXT FOR ADDITIONAL
REQUIREMENTS

TAXIWAY CENTERLINE
MARKING

TAXIWAY EDGE MARKINGS
(DASHED)

APRON

ROADWAY LANE LINE
WHITE, 6" (15 cm) WIDE,
DASHES 15' (4.5 m) LONG
WITH SPACES BETWEEN
DASHES 25' (7.5 m) LONG

ROADWAY EDGE
STRIPES (SEE TEXT)
WHITE, ZIPPER STYLE

NOT TO SCALE
WHITE ROADWAY MARKINGS
SHOWN IN BLACK

FIG 2-3-18

Roadway Edge Stripes, White, Zipper Style

FIG 2-3-19

Ground Receiver Checkpoint Markings

1. WHITE
2. YELLOW
3. YELLOW ARROW ALIGNED TOWARD THE FACILITY
4. INTERIOR OF CIRCLE BLACK (CONCRETE SURFACE ONLY)
5. CIRCLE MAY BE BORDERED ON INSIDE AND OUTSIDE WITH 6" BLACK BAND IF NECESSARY FOR CONTRAST

FIG 2-3-20

Nonmovement Area Boundary Markings

DASHED LINE ON MOVEMENT SIDE

BOTH LINES ARE YELLOW

SOLID LINE ON NONMOVEMENT SIDE

FIG 2-3-21

Closed or Temporarily Closed Runway and Taxiway Markings

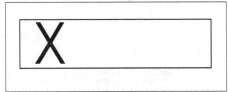

FIG 2-3-22

c. Nonmovement Area Boundary Markings: These markings delineate the movement area, i.e., area under air traffic control. These markings are yellow and located on the boundary between the movement and nonmovement area. The nonmovement area boundary markings consist of two yellow lines (one solid and one dashed) 6 inches(15cm) in width. The solid line is located on the nonmovement area side while the dashed yellow line is located on the movement area side. The nonmovement boundary marking area is shown in FIG 2-3-21.

EXAMPLE-
DCA 176-356
VOR check course
DME XXX

d. Marking and Lighting of Permanently Closed Runways and Taxiways: For runways and taxiways which are permanently closed, the lighting circuits will be disconnected. The runway threshold, runway designation, and touchdown markings are obliterated and yellow crosses are placed at each end of the runway and at 1,000 foot intervals. (See FIG 2-3-22.)

e. Temporarily Closed Runways and Taxiways:
To provide a visual indication to pilots that a runway is temporarily closed, crosses are placed on the runway only at each end of the runway. The crosses are yellow in color. (See FIG 2–3–22.)

1. A raised lighted yellow cross may be placed on each runway end in lieu of the markings described in subparagraph e. Temporarily Closed Runways and Taxiways, to indicate the runway is closed.

2. A visual indication may not be present depending on the reason for the closure, duration of the closure, airfield configuration and the existence and the hours of operation of an airport traffic control tower. Pilots should check NOTAM's and the Automated Terminal Information System (ATIS) for local runway and taxiway closure information.

3. Temporarily closed taxiways are usually treated as hazardous areas, in which no part of an aircraft may enter, and are blocked with barricades. However, as an alternative a yellow cross may be installed at each entrance to the taxiway.

f. Helicopter Landing Areas: The markings illustrated in FIG 2–3–23 are used to identify the landing and takeoff area at a public use heliport and hospital heliport. The letter "H" in the markings is oriented to align with the intended direction of approach. FIG 2–3–23 also depicts the markings for a closed airport.

2–3–7. AIRPORT SIGNS

There are six types of signs installed on airfields: mandatory instruction signs, location signs, direction signs, destination signs, information signs, and runway distance remaining signs. The characteristics and use of these signs are discussed in paragraph 2–3–8, Mandatory Instruction Signs, through paragraph 2–3–13, Runway Distance Remaining Signs.

REFERENCE–
AC150/5340–18, STANDARDS FOR AIRPORT SIGN SYSTEMS FOR DETAILED INFORMATION ON AIRPORT SIGNS.

2–3–8. MANDATORY INSTRUCTION SIGNS

a. These signs have a red background with a white inscription and are used to denote:

1. An entrance to a runway or critical area and;

2. Areas where an aircraft is prohibited from entering.

b. Typical mandatory signs and applications are:

1. *Runway Holding Position Sign:* This sign is located at the holding position on taxiways that intersect a runway or on runways that intersect other runways. The inscription on the sign contains the designation of the intersecting runway as shown in FIG 2–3–24. The runway numbers on the sign are arranged to correspond to the respective runway threshold. For example, "15–33" indicates that the threshold for Runway 15 is to the left and the threshold for Runway 33 is to the right.

Helicopter Landing Areas

Runway Holding Position Sign

FIG 2-3-24

Holding Position Sign at Beginning of Takeoff Runway

FIG 2-3-25

(a) On taxiways that intersect the beginning of the takeoff runway, only the designation of the takeoff runway may appear on the sign as shown in FIG 2-3-25, while all other signs will have the designation of both runway directions.

(b) If the sign is located on a taxiway that intersects the intersection of two runways, the designations for both runways will be shown on the sign along with arrows showing the approximate alignment of each runway as shown in FIG 2-3-26. In addition to showing the approximate runway alignment, the arrow indicates the direction to the threshold of the runway whose designation is immediately next to the arrow.

(c) A runway holding position sign on a taxiway will be installed adjacent to holding position markings on the taxiway pavement. On runways, holding position markings will be located only on the runway pavement adjacent to the sign, if the runway is normally used

by air traffic control for "Land, Hold Short" operations or as a taxiway. The holding position markings are described in paragraph 2-3-5, Holding Position Markings.

2. *Runway Approach Area Holding Position Sign:* At some airports, it is necessary to hold an aircraft on a taxiway located in the approach or departure area for a runway so that the aircraft does not interfere with operations on that runway. In these situations, a sign with the designation of the approach end of the runway followed by a "dash" (–) and letters "APCH" will be located at the holding position on the taxiway. Holding position markings in accordance with paragraph 2-3-5, Holding Position Markings will be located on the taxiway pavement. An example of this sign is shown in FIG 2-3-27. In this example, the sign may protect the approach to Runway 15 and/or the departure for Runway 33.

Holding Position Sign for a Taxiway that Intersects the Intersection of Two Runways

↙5-23↗   ↖9-27↘

FIG 2–3–26

Holding Position Sign for a Runway Approach Area

15-APCH

FIG 2–3–27

Holding Position Sign for ILS Critical Area

ILS

FIG 2–3–28

3. *ILS Critical Area Holding Position Sign:* At some airports, when the instrument landing system is being used, it is necessary to hold an aircraft on a taxiway at a location other than the holding position described in paragraph 2–3–5, Holding Position Markings. In these situations the holding position sign for these operations will have the inscription "ILS" and be located adjacent to the holding position marking on the taxiway described in paragraph 2–3–5. An example of this sign is shown in FIG 2–3–28.

4. *No Entry Sign:* This sign, shown in FIG 2–3–29, prohibits an aircraft from entering an area. Typically, this sign would be located on a taxiway intended to be used in only one direction or at the intersection of vehicle roadways with runways, taxiways or aprons where the roadway may be mistaken as a taxiway or other aircraft movement surface.

NOTE–
The holding position sign provides the pilot with a visual cue as to the location of the holding position marking. The operational significance of holding position markings are described in the notes for paragraph 2–3–5, Holding Position Markings.

Sign Prohibiting Aircraft Entry into an Area

FIG 2–3–29

Taxiway Location Sign

FIG 2–3–30

2-3-9. LOCATION SIGNS

a. Location signs are used to identify either a taxiway or runway on which the aircraft is located. Other location signs provide a visual cue to pilots to assist them in determining when they have exited an area. The various location signs are described below.

1. *Taxiway Location Sign:* This sign has a black background with a yellow inscription and yellow border as shown in FIG 2–3–30. The inscription is the designation of the taxiway on which the aircraft is located. These signs are installed along taxiways either by themselves or in conjunction with direction signs (See FIG 2–3–35, or runway holding position signs, FIG 2–3–31.)

2. *Runway Location Sign:* This sign has a black background with a yellow inscription and yellow bor-

der as shown in FIG 2–3–32. The inscription is the designation of the runway on which the aircraft is located. These signs are intended to complement the information available to pilots through their magnetic compass and typically are installed where the proximity of two or more runways to one another could cause pilots to be confused as to which runway they are on.

3. *Runway Boundary Sign:* This sign has a yellow background with a black inscription with a graphic depicting the pavement holding position marking as shown in FIG 2–3–33. This sign, which faces the runway and is visible to the pilot exiting the runway, is located adjacent to the holding position marking on the pavement. The sign is intended to provide pilots with another visual cue which they can use as a guide in deciding when they are "clear of the runway."

Taxiway Location Sign Collocated with Runway Holding Position Sign

FIG 2-3-31

Runway Location Sign

FIG 2-3-32

4. ILS Critical Area Boundary Sign: This sign has a yellow background with a black inscription with a graphic depicting the ILS pavement holding position marking as shown in FIG 2–3–34. This sign is located adjacent to the ILS holding position marking on the pavement and can be seen by pilots leaving the critical area. The sign is intended to provide pilots with another visual cue which they can use as a guide in deciding when they are "clear of the ILS critical area."

Runway Boundary Sign

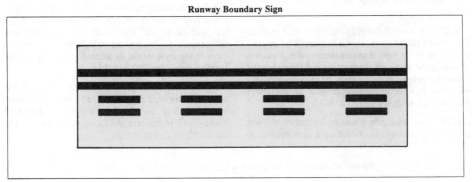

FIG 2–3–33

ILS Critical Area Boundary Sign

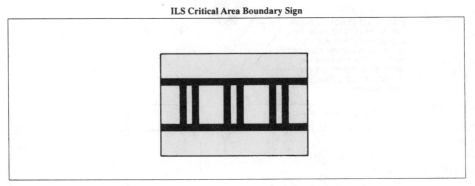

FIG 2–3–34

2-3-10. DIRECTION SIGNS

a. Direction signs have a yellow background with a black inscription. The inscription identifies the designation(s) of the intersecting taxiway(s) leading out of the intersection that a pilot would normally be expected to turn onto or hold short of. Each designation is accompanied by an arrow indicating the direction of the turn.

b. Except as noted in subparagraph e, each taxiway designation shown on the sign is accompanied by only one arrow. When more than one taxiway designation is shown on the sign each designation and its associated arrow is separated from the other taxiway designations by either a vertical message divider or a taxiway location sign as shown in FIG 2-3-35.

c. Direction signs are normally located on the left prior to the intersection. When used on a runway to

indicate an exit, the sign is located on the same side of the runway as the exit. FIG 2-3-36 shows a direction sign used to indicate a runway exit.

d. The taxiway designations and their associated arrows on the sign are arranged clockwise starting from the first taxiway on the pilot's left. (See FIG 2-3-35.)

e. If a location sign is located with the direction signs, it is placed so that the designations for all turns to the left will be to the left of the location sign; the designations for continuing straight ahead or for all turns to the right would be located to the right of the location sign. (See FIG 2-3-35.)

f. When the intersection is comprised of only one crossing taxiway, it is permissible to have two arrows associated with the crossing taxiway as shown in FIG 2-3-37. In this case, the location sign is located to the left of the direction sign.

Direction Sign Array with Location Sign on Far Side of Intersection

NOTE: ORIENTATION OF SIGNS ARE FROM LEFT TO RIGHT IN A CLOCKWISE MANNER. LEFT TURN SIGNS ARE ON THE LEFT OF THE LOCATION SIGN AND RIGHT TURN SIGNS ARE ON THE RIGHT SIDE OF THE LOCATION SIGN.

ALTERNATE ARRAY OF SIGNS SHOWN TO ILLUSTRATE SIGN ORIENTATION WHEN LOCATION SIGN NOT INSTALLED.

FIG 2-3-35

Direction Sign for Runway Exit

FIG 2-3-36

Direction Sign Array for Simple Intersection

FIG 2-3-37

2-3-11. DESTINATION SIGNS

a. Destination signs also have a yellow background with a black inscription indicating a destination on the airport. These signs always have an arrow showing the direction of the taxiing route to that destination. FIG 2–3–38 is an example of a typical destination sign. When the arrow on the destination sign indicates a turn, the sign is located prior to the intersection.

b. Destinations commonly shown on these types of signs include runways, aprons, terminals, military areas, civil aviation areas, cargo areas, international areas, and fixed base operators. An abbreviation may be used as the inscription on the sign for some of these destinations.

c. When the inscription for two or more destinations having a common taxiing route are placed on a sign, the destinations are separated by a "dot" (●) and one arrow would be used as shown in FIG 2–3–39. When the inscription on a sign contains two or more destinations having different taxiing routes, each destination will be accompanied by an arrow and will be separated from the other destinations on the sign with a vertical black message divider as shown in FIG 2–3–40.

Destination Sign for Military Area

FIG 2-3-38

Destination Sign for Common Taxiing Route to Two Runways

FIG 2-3-39

Destination Sign for Different Taxiing Routes to Two Runways

FIG 2–3–40

2–3–12. INFORMATION SIGNS

Information signs have a yellow background with a black inscription. They are used to provide the pilot with information on such things as areas that cannot be seen from the control tower, applicable radio frequencies, and noise abatement procedures. The airport operator determines the need, size, and location for these signs.

2–3–13. RUNWAY DISTANCE REMAINING SIGNS

Runway distance remaining signs have a black background with a white numeral inscription and may be installed along one or both side(s) of the runway. The number on the signs indicates the distance (in thousands of feet) of landing runway remaining. The last sign, i.e., the sign with the numeral "1," will be located at least 950 feet from the runway end. FIG 2–3–41 shows an example of a runway distance remaining sign.

Runway Distance Remaining Sign Indicating 3,000 feet of Runway Remaining

FIG 2–3–41

2-3-14. AIRCRAFT ARRESTING DEVICES

a. Certain airports are equipped with a means of rapidly stopping military aircraft on a runway. This equipment, normally referred to as EMERGENCY ARRESTING GEAR, generally consists of pendant cables supported over the runway surface by rubber "donuts." Although most devices are located in the overrun areas, a few of these arresting systems have cables stretched over the operational areas near the ends of a runway.

b. Arresting cables which cross over a runway require special markings on the runway to identify the cable location. These markings consist of 10 feet diameter solid circles painted "identification yellow," 30 feet on center, perpendicular to the runway centerline across the entire runway width. Additional details are contained in AC 150/5220-9, Aircraft Arresting Systems for Joint Civil/Military Airports.

NOTE-
Aircraft operations on the runway are not restricted by the installation of aircraft arresting devices.

Chapter 3. AIRSPACE

Section 1. GENERAL

3-1-1. GENERAL

a. There are two categories of airspace or airspace areas:

    1. regulatory, and

    2. nonregulatory.

b. Within these two categories, there are four types:

    1. controlled,

    2. uncontrolled,

    3. special use, and

    4. other airspace.

c. The categories and types of airspace are dictated by:

    1. the complexity or density of aircraft movements;

    2. the nature of the operations conducted within the airspace;

    3. the level of safety required; and

    4. the national and public interest.

d. It is important that pilots be familiar with the operational requirements for each of the various types or classes of airspace. Subsequent sections will cover each category and class in sufficient detail to facilitate understanding.

3-1-2. GENERAL DIMENSIONS OF AIRSPACE SEGMENTS

Refer to Federal Aviation Regulations (FAR) for specific dimensions, exceptions, geographical areas covered, exclusions, specific transponder or equipment requirements, and flight operations.

3-1-3. BASIC VFR WEATHER MINIMUMS

a. No person may operate an aircraft under basic VFR when the flight visibility is less, or at a distance from clouds that is less, than that prescribed for the corresponding altitude and class of airspace. (See TBL 3-1-1.)

NOTE–
Student pilots must comply with FAR Part 61.89(A) (6) and (7).

b. Except as provided in FAR Part 91.157, Special VFR Weather Minimums, no person may operate an aircraft beneath the ceiling under VFR within the lateral boundaries of controlled airspace designated to the surface for an airport when the ceiling is less than 1,000 feet. (See FAR Part 91.155(c).)

Basic VFR Weather Minimums

Airspace	Flight Visibility	Distance from Clouds
Class A	Not Applicable	Not Applicable
Class B	3 statute miles	Clear of Clouds
Class C	3 statute miles	500 feet below 1,000 feet above 2,000 feet horizontal
Class D	3 statute miles	500 feet below 1,000 feet above 2,000 feet horizontal
Class E Less than 10,000 feet MSL	3 statute miles	500 feet below 1,000 feet above 2,000 feet horizontal
At or above 10,000 feet MSL	5 statute miles	1,000 feet below 1,000 feet above 1 statute mile horizontal
Class G 1,200 feet or less above the surface (regardless of MSL altitude). Day, except as provided in section 91.155(b)	1 statute mile	Clear of clouds
Night, except as provided in section 91.155(b)	3 statute miles	500 feet below 1,000 feet above 2,000 feet horizontal
More than 1,200 feet above the surface but less than 10,000 feet MSL. Day..	1 statute mile	500 feet below 1,000 feet above 2,000 feet horizontal
Night	3 statute miles	500 feet below 1,000 feet above 2,000 feet horizontal
More than 1,200 feet above the surface and at or above 10,000 feet MSL...............................	5 statute miles	1,000 feet below 1,000 feet above 1 statute mile horizontal

TBL 3-1-1

3-1-4. VFR CRUISING ALTITUDES AND FLIGHT LEVELS

(See TBL 3-1-2.)

VFR Cruising Altitudes and Flight Levels

If your magnetic course (ground track) is:	And you are more than 3,000 feet above the surface but below 18,000 feet MSL, fly:	And you are above 18,000 feet MSL to FL 290, fly:
0° to 179°	Odd thousands MSL, plus 500 feet (3,500; 5,500; 7,500; etc.)	Odd Flight Levels plus 500 feet (FL 195; FL 215; FL 235; etc.)
180° to 359°	Even thousands MSL, plus 500 feet (4,500; 6,500; 8,500; etc.)	Even Flight Levels plus 500 feet (FL 185; FL 205; FL 225; etc.)

TBL 3-1-2

Section 2. CONTROLLED AIRSPACE

-2-1. GENERAL

a. Controlled Airspace: A generic term that covers he different classification of airspace (Class A, Class 3, Class C, Class D, and Class E airspace) and defined limensions within which air traffic control service is rovided to IFR flights and to VFR flights in accordance with the airspace classification.
See FIG 3–2–1.)

b. IFR Requirements: IFR operations in any class of controlled airspace requires that a pilot must file an FR flight plan and receive an appropriate ATC clearance.

c. IFR Separation: Standard IFR separation is provided to all aircraft operating under IFR in controlled airspace.

d. VFR Requirements: It is the responsibility of the pilot to insure that ATC clearance or radio communication requirements are met prior to entry into Class B, Class C, or Class D airspace. The pilot retains this responsibility when receiving ATC radar advisories.
See FAR Part 91.)

e. Traffic Advisories: Traffic advisories will be provided to all aircraft as the controller's work situation permits.

f. Safety Alerts: Safety Alerts are mandatory services and are provided to ALL aircraft. There are two types of Safety Alerts, Terrain/Obstruction Alert and Aircraft Conflict/Mode C Intruder Alert.

1. *Terrain/Obstruction Alert:*
A Terrain/Obstruction Alert is issued when, in the controller's judgment, an aircraft's altitude places it in unsafe proximity to terrain and/or obstructions.

2. *Aircraft Conflict/Mode C Intruder Alert:* An Aircraft Conflict/Mode C Intruder Alert is issued if the controller observes another aircraft which places it in an unsafe proximity. When feasible, the controller will offer the pilot an alternative course of action.

g. Ultralight Vehicles: No person may operate an ultralight vehicle within Class A, Class B, Class C, or Class D airspace or within the lateral boundaries of the surface area of Class E airspace designated for an airport unless that person has prior authorization from the ATC facility having jurisdiction over that airspace.
(See FAR Part 103.)

Airspace Classes

MSL - mean sea level
AGL - above ground level
FL - flight level

FIG 3–2–1

h. Unmanned Free Balloons: Unless otherwise authorized by ATC, no person may operate an unmanned free balloon below 2,000 feet above the surface within the lateral boundaries of Class B, Class C, Class D, or Class E airspace designated for an airport.
(See FAR Part 101.)

i. Parachute Jumps: No person may make a parachute jump, and no pilot in command may allow a parachute jump to be made from that aircraft, in or into Class A, Class B, Class C, or Class D airspace without, or in violation of, the terms of an ATC authorization issued by the ATC facility having jurisdiction over the airspace. (See FAR Part 105.)

3-2-2. CLASS A AIRSPACE

a. Definition: Generally, that airspace from 18,000 feet MSL up to and including FL 600, including the airspace overlying the waters within 12 nautical miles of the coast of the 48 contiguous States and Alaska; and designated international airspace beyond 12 nautical miles of the coast of the 48 contiguous States and Alaska within areas of domestic radio navigational signal or ATC radar coverage, and within which domestic procedures are applied.

b. Operating Rules and Pilot/Equipment Requirements: Unless otherwise authorized, all persons must operate their aircraft under IFR.
(See FAR Part 71.33 and FAR Part 91.167 through FAR Part 91.193.)

c. Charts: Class A airspace is not specifically charted.

3-2-3. CLASS B AIRSPACE

a. Definition: Generally, that airspace from the surface to 10,000 feet MSL surrounding the nation's busiest airports in terms of IFR operations or passenger enplanements. The configuration of each Class B airspace area is individually tailored and consists of a surface area and two or more layers (some Class B airspace areas resemble upside-down wedding cakes), and is designed to contain all published instrument procedures once an aircraft enters the airspace. An ATC clearance is required for all aircraft to operate in the area, and all aircraft that are so cleared receive separation services within the airspace. The cloud clearance requirement for VFR operations is "clear of clouds."

b. Operating Rules and Pilot/Equipment Requirements for VFR Operations: Regardless of weather conditions, an ATC clearance is required prior to operating within Class B airspace. Pilots should not request a clearance to operate within Class B airspace unless the requirements of FAR Part 91.215 and FAR Part 91.131 are met. Included among these requirements are:

1. Unless otherwise authorized by ATC, aircraft must be equipped with an operable two-way radio capable of communicating with ATC on appropriate frequencies for that Class B airspace.

2. No person may take off or land a civil aircraft at the following primary airports within Class B airspace unless the pilot in command holds at least a private pilot certificate:

    (a) Andrews Air Force Base, MD

    (b) Atlanta Hartsfield Airport, GA

    (c) Boston Logan Airport, MA

    (d) Chicago O'Hare Intl. Airport, IL

    (e) Los Angeles Intl. Airport, CA

    (f) Miami Intl. Airport, FL

    (g) Newark Intl. Airport, NJ

    (h) New York Kennedy Airport, NY

    (i) New York La Guardia Airport, NY

    (j) San Francisco Intl. Airport, CA

    (k) Washington National Airport, DC

    (l) Dallas/Fort Worth Intl. Airport, TX

3. No person may take off or land a civil aircraft at an airport within Class B airspace or operate a civil aircraft within Class B airspace unless:

    (a) The pilot in command holds at least a private pilot certificate; or,

    (b) The aircraft is operated by a student pilot or recreational pilot who seeks private pilot certification and has met the requirements of FAR Part 61.95.

4. Unless otherwise authorized by ATC, each person operating a large turbine engine-powered airplane to or from a primary airport shall operate at or above the designated floors while within the lateral limits of Class B airspace.

5. Unless otherwise authorized by ATC, each aircraft must be equipped as follows:

(a) For IFR operations, an operable VOR or TACAN receiver; and

(b) For all operations, a two-way radio capable of communications with ATC on appropriate frequencies for that area; and

(c) Unless otherwise authorized by ATC, an operable radar beacon transponder with automatic altitude reporting equipment.

NOTE–
ATC may, upon notification, immediately authorize a deviation from the altitude reporting equipment requirement; however, a request for a deviation from the 4096 transponder equipment requirement must be submitted to the controlling ATC facility at least one hour before the proposed operation.

REFERENCE–
AIM, TRANSPONDER OPERATION, PARAGRAPH 4-1-19.

6. Mode C Veil: The airspace within 30 nautical miles of an airport listed in Appendix D, Section 1 of FAR Part 91 (generally primary airports within Class B airspace areas), from the surface upward to 10,000 feet MSL. Unless otherwise authorized by air traffic control, aircraft operating within this airspace must be equipped with automatic pressure altitude reporting equipment having Mode C capability.

However, an aircraft that was not originally certificated with an engine–driven electrical system or which has not subsequently been certified with a system installed may conduct operations within a Mode C veil provided the aircraft remains outside Class A, B or C airspace; and below the altitude of the ceiling of a Class B or Class C airspace area designated for an airport or 10,000 feet MSL, whichever is lower.

c. Charts: Class B airspace is charted on Sectional Charts, IFR En Route Low Altitude, and Terminal Area Charts.

d. Flight Procedures:

1. *Flights:* Aircraft within Class B airspace are required to operate in accordance with current IFR procedures. A clearance for a visual approach to a primary airport is not authorization for turbine powered airplanes to operate below the designated floors of the Class B airspace.

2. *VFR Flights:*

(a) Arriving aircraft must obtain an ATC clearance prior to entering Class B airspace and must contact ATC on the appropriate frequency, and in relation to geographical fixes shown on local charts. Although a pilot may be operating beneath the floor of the Class B airspace on initial contact, communications with ATC should be established in relation to the points indicated for spacing and sequencing purposes.

(b) Departing aircraft require a clearance to depart Class B airspace and should advise the clearance delivery position of their intended altitude and route of flight. ATC will normally advise VFR aircraft when leaving the geographical limits of the Class B airspace. Radar service is not automatically terminated with this advisory unless specifically stated by the controller.

(c) Aircraft not landing or departing the primary airport may obtain an ATC clearance to transit the Class B airspace when traffic conditions permit and provided the requirements of FAR Part 91.131 are met. Such VFR aircraft are encouraged, to the extent possible, to operate at altitudes above or below the Class B airspace or transit through established VFR corridors. Pilots operating in VFR corridors are urged to use frequency 122.750 MHz for the exchange of aircraft position information.

e. ATC Clearances and Separation: An ATC clearance is required to enter and operate within Class B airspace. VFR pilots are provided sequencing and separation from other aircraft while operating within Class B airspace.

REFERENCE–
AIM, TERMINAL RADAR SERVICES FOR VFR AIRCRAFT, PARAGRAPH 4-1-17.

NOTE–
[1] Separation and sequencing of VFR aircraft will be suspended in the event of a radar outage as this service is dependent on radar. The pilot will be advised that the service is not available and issued wind, runway information and the time or place to contact the tower.

[2] Separation of VFR aircraft will be suspended during CENRAP operations. Traffic advisories and sequencing to the primary airport will be provided on a workload permitting basis. The pilot will be advised when center radar presentation (CENRAP) is in use.

1. VFR aircraft are separated from all VFR/IFR aircraft which weigh 19,000 pounds or less by a minimum of:

(a) Target resolution, or

(b) 500 feet vertical separation, or

(c) Visual separation

2. VFR aircraft are separated from all VFR/IFR aircraft which weigh more than 19,000 and turbojets by no less than:

(a) 1 $^1/_2$ miles lateral separation, or

(b) 500 feet vertical separation, or

(c) Visual separation.

3. This program is not to be interpreted as relieving pilots of their responsibilities to see and avoid other traffic operating in basic VFR weather conditions, to adjust their operations and flight path as necessary to preclude serious wake encounters, to maintain appropriate terrain and obstruction clearance or to remain in weather conditions equal to or better than the minimums required by FAR Part 91.155. Approach control should be advised and a revised clearance or instruction obtained when compliance with an assigned route, heading and/or altitude is likely to compromise pilot responsibility with respect to terrain and obstruction clearance, vortex exposure, and weather minimums.

4. ATC may assign altitudes to VFR aircraft that do not conform to FAR Part 91.159. **"RESUME APPROPRIATE VFR ALTITUDES"** will be broadcast when the altitude assignment is no longer needed for separation or when leaving Class B airspace. Pilots must return to an altitude that conforms to FAR Part 91.159.

f. Proximity operations: VFR aircraft operating in proximity to Class B airspace are cautioned against operating too closely to the boundaries, especially where the floor of the Class B airspace is 3,000 feet or less or where VFR cruise altitudes are at or near the floor of higher levels. Observance of this precaution will reduce the potential for encountering an aircraft operating at the altitudes of Class B floors. Additionally, VFR aircraft are encouraged to utilize the VFR Planning Chart as a tool for planning flight in proximity to Class B airspace. Charted VFR Flyway Planning Charts are published on the back of the existing VFR Terminal Area Charts.

3-2-4. CLASS C AIRSPACE

a. Definition: Generally, that airspace from the surface to 4,000 feet above the airport elevation (charted in MSL) surrounding those airports that have an operational control tower, are serviced by a radar approach control, and that have a certain number of IFR operations or passenger enplanements. Although the configuration of each Class C airspace area is individually tai-

lored, the airspace usually consists of a 5 NM radius core surface area that extends from the surface up to 4,000 feet above the airport elevation, and a 10 NM radius shelf area that extends from 1,200 feet to 4,000 feet above the airport elevation.

b. Outer Area: The normal radius will be 20NM, with some variations based on site specific requirements. The outer area extends outward from the primary airport and extends from the lower limits of radar/radio coverage up to the ceiling of the approach control's delegated airspace, excluding the Class C airspace and other airspace as appropriate.

c. Charts: Class C airspace is charted on Sectional Charts, IFR En Route Low Altitude, and Terminal Area Charts where appropriate.

d. Operating Rules and Pilot/Equipment Requirements:

1. *Pilot Certification:* No specific certification required.

2. *Equipment:*

(a) Two-way radio, and

(b) Unless otherwise authorized by ATC, an operable radar beacon transponder with automatic altitude reporting equipment.

3. *Arrival or Through Flight Entry Requirements:* Two-way radio communication must be established with the ATC facility providing ATC services prior to entry and thereafter maintain those communications while in Class C airspace. Pilots of arriving aircraft should contact the Class C airspace ATC facility on the publicized frequency and give their position, altitude, radar beacon code, destination, and request Class C service. Radio contact should be initiated far enough from the Class C airspace boundary to preclude entering Class C airspace before two-way radio communications are established.

NOTE–

[1] *If the controller responds to a radio call with, "(aircraft callsign) standby," radio communications have been established and the pilot can enter the Class C airspace.*

[2] *If workload or traffic conditions prevent immediate provision of Class C services, the controller will inform the pilot to remain outside the Class C airspace until conditions permit the services to be provided.*

[3] *It is important to understand that if the controller responds to the initial radio call without using the aircraft identification, radio communications have not been established and the pilot may not enter the Class C airspace.*

EXAMPLE-
1 *[Aircraft callsign] "remain outside the Class Charlie airspace and standby."*

2 *"Aircraft calling Dulles approach control, standby."*

4. Departures from:

(a) A primary or satellite airport with an operating control tower: Two-way radio communications must be established and maintained with the control tower, and thereafter as instructed by ATC while operating in Class C airspace.

(b) A satellite airport without an operating control tower: Two-way radio communications must be established as soon as practicable after departing with the ATC facility having jurisdiction over the Class C airspace.

5. Aircraft Speed: Unless otherwise authorized or required by ATC, no person may operate an aircraft at or below 2,500 feet above the surface within 4 nautical miles of the primary airport of a Class C airspace area at an indicated airspeed of more than 200 knots (230 mph).

e. Air Traffic Services: When two-way radio communications and radar contact are established, all participating VFR aircraft are:

1. Sequenced to the primary airport.

2. Provided Class C services within the Class C airspace and the outer area.

3. Provided basic radar services beyond the outer area on a workload permitting basis. This can be terminated by the controller if workload dictates.

f. Aircraft Separation: Separation is provided within the Class C airspace and the outer area after two-way radio communications and radar contact are established. VFR aircraft are separated from IFR aircraft within the Class C airspace by any of the following:

1. Visual separation.

2. 500 feet vertical; except when operating beneath a heavy jet.

3. Target resolution.

NOTE-

1 *Separation and sequencing of VFR aircraft will be suspended in the event of a radar outage as this service is dependent on radar. The pilot will be advised that the service is not available and issued wind, runway information and the time or place to contact the tower.*

2 *Separation of VFR aircraft will be suspended during CENRAP operations. Traffic advisories and sequencing to the primary airport will be provided on a workload permitting basis. The pilot will be advised when CENRAP is in use.*

3 *Pilot participation is voluntary within the outer area and can be discontinued, within the outer area, at the pilot's request. Class C services will be provided in the outer area unless the pilot requests termination of the service.*

4 *Some facilities provide Class C services only during published hours. At other times, terminal IFR radar service will be provided. It is important to note that the communications and transponder requirements are dependent of the class of airspace established outside of the published hours.*

g. Secondary Airports:

1. In some locations Class C airspace may overlie the Class D surface area of a secondary airport. In order to allow that control tower to provide service to aircraft, portions of the overlapping Class C airspace may be procedurally excluded when the secondary airport tower is in operation. Aircraft operating in these procedurally excluded areas will only be provided airport traffic control services when in communication with the secondary airport tower.

2. Aircraft proceeding inbound to a satellite airport will be terminated at a sufficient distance to allow time to change to the appropriate tower or advisory frequency. Class C services to these aircraft will be discontinued when the aircraft is instructed to contact the tower or change to advisory frequency.

3. Aircraft departing secondary controlled airports will not receive Class C services until they have been radar identified and two-way communications have been established with the Class C airspace facility.

4. This program is not to be interpreted as relieving pilots of their responsibilities to see and avoid other traffic operating in basic VFR weather conditions, to adjust their operations and flight path as necessary to preclude serious wake encounters, to maintain appropriate terrain and obstruction clearance or to remain in weather conditions equal to or better than the minimums required by 14 CFR Section 91.155.

Approach control should be advised and a revised clearance or instruction obtained when compliance with an assigned route, heading and/or altitude is likely to compromise pilot responsibility with respect to terrain and obstruction clearance, vortex exposure, and weather minimums. (See TBL 3-2-1.)

Class C Airspace Areas by State

These states currently have designated Class C airspace areas that are depicted on sectional charts. Pilots should consult current sectional charts and NOTAM's for the latest information on services available. Pilots should be aware that some Class C airspace underlies or is adjacent to Class B airspace.

STATE/CITY	AIRPORT
ALABAMA	
Birmingham	International
Huntsville	International-Carl T Jones Fld
Mobile	Regional
ALASKA	
Anchorage	International
ARIZONA	
Davis-Monthan	AFB
Tucson	International
ARKANSAS	
Little Rock	Adams Field
CALIFORNIA	
Beale	AFB
Burbank	Burbank-Glendale-Pasadena
Fresno	Air Terminal
Monterey	Peninsula
Oakland	Metropolitan Oakland International
Ontario	International
Riverside	March AFB
Sacramento	International
Sacramento	McClellan AFB
San Jose	International
Santa Ana	El Toro MCAS, John Wayne/Orange County
Santa Barbara	Municipal
COLORADO	
Colorado Springs	Municipal
CONNECTICUT	
Windsor Locks	Bradley International
FLORIDA	
Daytona Beach	Regional
Fort Lauderdale	Hollywood International
Fort Myers	SW Florida Regional
Jacksonville	International
Palm Beach	International
Pensacola	NAS
Pensacola	Regional
Sarasota	Bradenton
Tallahassee	Regional
Whiting	NAS

STATE/CITY	AIRPORT
GEORGIA	
Columbus	Metropolitan
Savannah	International
HAWAII	
Kahului	Kahului
IDAHO	
Boise	Air Terminal
ILLINOIS	
Champaign	U of Illinois-Willard
Chicago	Midway
Moline	Quad City
Peoria	Greater Peoria
Springfield	Capital
INDIANA	
Evansville	Regional
Fort Wayne	International
Indianapolis	International
South Bend	Michiana Regional
IOWA	
Cedar Rapids	The Eastern Iowa
Des Moines	International
KANSAS	
Wichita	Mid-Continent
KENTUCKY	
Lexington	Blue Grass
Louisville	Standiford Field
LOUISIANA	
Baton Rouge	BTR Metro, Ryan Field
Lafayette	Regional
Shreveport	Barksdale AFB
Shreveport	Regional
MAINE	
Bangor	International
Portland	International Jetport
MICHIGAN	
Flint	Bishop International
Grand Rapids	Kent County International
Lansing	Capital City
MISSISSIPPI	
Columbus	AFB
Jackson	International
MISSOURI	
Springfield	Springfield-Branson Regional
MONTANA	
Billings	Logan International
NEBRASKA	
Lincoln	Municipal
Omaha	Eppley Airfield
Offutt	AFB
NEVADA	
Reno	Cannon International
NEW HAMPSHIRE	
Manchester	Manchester
NEW JERSEY	
Atlantic City	International
NEW MEXICO	
Albuquerque	International

STATE/CITY	AIRPORT
NEW YORK	
Albany	County
Buffalo	Greater Buffalo International
Islip	Long Island MacArthur
Rochester	Greater Rochester International
Syracuse	Hancock International
NORTH CAROLINA	
Asheville	Regional
Fayetteville	Regional/Grannis Field
Greensboro	Piedmont Triad International
Pope	AFB
Raleigh	Raleigh-Durham International
OHIO	
Akron	Akron-Canton Regional
Columbus	Port Columbus International
Dayton	James M. Cox International
Toledo	Express
OKLAHOMA	
Oklahoma City	Will Rogers World
Tinker	AFB
Tulsa	International
OREGON	
Portland	International
PENNSYLVANIA	
Allentown	Allentown Bethlehem-Easton
PUERTO RICO	
San Juan	Luis Munoz Marin International
RHODE ISLAND	
Providence	Theodore Francis Green State
SOUTH CAROLINA	
Charleston	AFB/International
Columbia	Metropolitan
Greer	Greenville-Spartanburg
Myrtle Beach	Myrtle Beach International
Shaw	AFB
TENNESSEE	
Chattanooga	Lovell Field
Knoxville	McGhee Tyson
Nashville	International
TEXAS	
Abilene	Regional
Amarillo	International
Austin	Robert Mueller Municipal
Corpus Christi	International
Dyess	AFB
El Paso	International
Harlingen	Rio Grande Valley International
Laughlin	AFB
Lubbock	International
Midland	International
San Antonio	International

STATE/CITY	AIRPORT
VERMONT	
Burlington	International
VIRGIN ISLANDS	
St. Thomas	Charlotte Amalie Cyril E. King
VIRGINIA	
Richmond	Richard Evelyn Byrd International
Norfolk	International
Roanoke	Regional/Woodrum Field
WASHINGTON	
Point Roberts	Vancouver International
Spokane	Fairchild AFB
Spokane	International
Whidbey Island	NAS, Ault Field
WEST VIRGINIA	
Charleston	Yeager
WISCONSIN	
Green Bay	Austin Straubel International
Madison	Dane County Regional-Traux Field
Milwaukee	General Mitchell International

TBL 3-2-1

3-2-5. CLASS D AIRSPACE

a. Definition: Generally, that airspace from the surface to 2,500 feet above the airport elevation (charted in MSL) surrounding those airports that have an operational control tower. The configuration of each Class D airspace area is individually tailored and when instrument procedures are published, the airspace will normally be designed to contain the procedures.

b. Operating Rules and Pilot/Equipment Requirements:

1. *Pilot Certification:* No specific certification required.

2. *Equipment:* Unless otherwise authorized by ATC, an operable two-way radio is required.

3. *Arrival or Through Flight Entry Requirements:* Two-way radio communication must be established with the ATC facility providing ATC services prior to entry and thereafter maintain those communications while in the Class D airspace. Pilots of arriving aircraft should contact the control tower on the publicized frequency and give their position, altitude, destination, and any request(s). Radio contact should be initiated far enough from the Class D airspace boundary to preclude entering the Class D airspace before two-way radio communications are established.

NOTE-

1. *If the controller responds to a radio call with, "[aircraft callsign] standby," radio communications have been established and the pilot can enter the Class D airspace.*

2. *If workload or traffic conditions prevent immediate entry into Class D airspace, the controller will inform the pilot to remain outside the Class D airspace until conditions permit entry.*

EXAMPLE-

1. *"[Aircraft callsign] remain outside the Class Delta airspace and standby."*
It is important to understand that if the controller responds to the initial radio call without using the aircraft callsign, radio communications have not been established and the pilot may not enter the Class D airspace.

2. *"Aircraft calling Manassas tower standby."*

At those airports where the control tower does not operate 24 hours a day, the operating hours of the tower will be listed on the appropriate charts and in the A/FD. During the hours the tower is not in operation, the Class E surface area rules or a combination of Class E rules to 700 feet above ground level and Class G rules to the surface will become applicable. Check the A/FD for specifics.

   4. *Departures from:*

      (a) A primary or satellite airport with an operating control tower: two-way radio communications must be established and maintained with the control tower, and thereafter as instructed by ATC while operating in the Class D airspace.

      (b) A satellite airport without an operating control tower: two-way radio communications must be established as soon as practicable after departing with the ATC facility having jurisdiction over the Class D airspace as soon as practicable after departing.

   5. *Aircraft Speed:* Unless otherwise authorized or required by ATC, no person may operate an aircraft at or below 2,500 feet above the surface within 4 nautical miles of the primary airport of a Class D airspace area at an indicated airspeed of more than 200 knots (230 mph).

   c. Class D airspace areas are depicted on Sectional and Terminal charts with blue segmented lines, and on IFR En Route Lows with a boxed [D].

   d. Arrival extensions for instrument approach procedures may be Class D or Class E airspace. As a general rule, if all extensions are 2 miles or less, they remain part of the Class D surface area. However, if any one extension is greater than 2 miles, then all extensions become Class E.

   e. Separation for VFR Aircraft: No separation services are provided to VFR aircraft.

3-2-6. CLASS E AIRSPACE

   a. Definition: Generally, if the airspace is not Class A, Class B, Class C, or Class D, and it is controlled airspace, it is Class E airspace.

   b. Operating Rules and Pilot/Equipment Requirements:

      1. *Pilot Certification:* No specific certification required.

      2. *Equipment:* No specific equipment required by the airspace.

      3. *Arrival or Through Flight Entry Requirements:* No specific requirements.

   c. Charts: Class E airspace below 14,500 feet MSL is charted on Sectional, Terminal, World, and IFR En Route Low Altitude charts.

   d. Vertical limits: Except for 18,000 feet MSL, Class E airspace has no defined vertical limit but rather it extends upward from either the surface or a designated altitude to the overlying or adjacent controlled airspace.

   e. Types of Class E Airspace:

      1. *Surface area designated for an airport:* When designated as a surface area for an airport, the airspace will be configured to contain all instrument procedures.

      2. *Extension to a surface area:* There are Class E airspace areas that serve as extensions to Class B, Class C, and Class D surface areas designated for an airport. Such airspace provides controlled airspace to contain standard instrument approach procedures without imposing a communications requirement on pilots operating under VFR.

      3. *Airspace used for transition:* There are Class E airspace areas beginning at either 700 or 1,200 feet AGL used to transition to/from the terminal or en route environment.

4. *En Route Domestic Areas:* There are Class E airspace areas that extend upward from a specified altitude and are en route domestic airspace areas that provide controlled airspace in those areas where there is a requirement to provide IFR en route ATC services but the Federal airway system is inadequate.

5. *Federal Airways:* The Federal airways are Class E airspace areas and, unless otherwise specified, extend upward from 1,200 feet to, but not including, 18,000 feet MSL. The colored airways are green, red, amber, and blue. The VOR airways are classified as Domestic, Alaskan, and Hawaiian.

6. *Offshore Airspace Areas:* There are Class E airspace areas that extend upward from a specified altitude to, but not including, 18,000 feet MSL and are designated as offshore airspace areas. These areas provide controlled airspace beyond 12 miles from the coast of

the United States in those areas where there is a requirement to provide IFR en route ATC services and within which the United States is applying domestic procedures.

7. Unless designated at a lower altitude, Class E airspace begins at 14,500 feet MSL to, but not including 18,000 feet MSL overlying: the 48 contiguous States including the waters within 12 miles from the coast of the 48 contiguous States; the District of Columbia; Alaska, including the waters within 12 miles from the coast of Alaska, and that airspace above FL 600; excluding the Alaska peninsula west of long. 160°00'00"W, and the airspace below 1,500 feet above the surface of the earth unless specifically so designated.

f. Separation for VFR Aircraft: No separation services are provided to VFR aircraft.

Section 3. CLASS G AIRSPACE

3-3-1. GENERAL

Class G airspace (uncontrolled) is that portion of the airspace that has not been designated as Class A, Class B, Class C, Class D or Class E airspace.

3-3-2. VFR REQUIREMENTS

Rules governing VFR flight have been adopted to assist the pilot in meeting the responsibility to see and avoid other aircraft. Minimum flight visibility and distance from clouds required for VFR flight are contained in FAR Part 91.155. (See TBL 3-1-1.)

3-3-3. IFR REQUIREMENTS

a. The FAR's specify the pilot and aircraft equipment requirements for IFR flight. Pilots are reminded that in addition to altitude or flight level requirements, FAR Part 91.177 includes a requirement to remain at least 1,000 feet (2,000 feet in designated mountainous terrain) above the highest obstacle within a horizontal distance of 4 nautical miles from the course to be flown.

b. IFR Altitudes and Flight Levels. (See TBL 3-3-1.)

IFR Altitudes and Flight Levels
Class G Airspace

If your magnetic course (ground track) is:	And you are below 18,000 feet MSL, fly:	And you are at or above 18,000 feet MSL but below FL 290, fly:	And you are at or above FL 290, fly 4,000 foot intervals:
0° to 179°	Odd thousands MSL, (3,000; 5,000; 7,000, etc.)	Odd Flight Levels, FL 190; 210; 230, etc.)	Beginning at FL 290; (FL 290; 330; 370, etc.)
180° to 359°	Even thousands MSL, (2,000; 4,000; 6,000, etc.)	Even Flight Levels (FL 180; 200; 220, etc.)	Beginning at FL 310; (FL 310; 350; 390, etc.)

TBL 3-3-1

Section 4. SPECIAL USE AIRSPACE

3-4-1. GENERAL

a. Special use airspace consists of that airspace wherein activities must be confined because of their nature, or wherein limitations are imposed upon aircraft operations that are not a part of those activities, or both. Except for controlled firing areas, special use airspace areas are depicted on aeronautical charts.

b. Prohibited and restricted areas are regulatory special use airspace and are established in 14 CFR Part 73 through the rulemaking process.

c. Warning areas, military operations areas (MOA's), alert areas, and controlled firing areas (CFA's) are nonregulatory special use airspace.

d. Special use airspace descriptions (except CFA's) are contained in FAA Order 7400.8, Special Use Airspace.

e. Special use airspace (except CFA's) are charted on IFR or visual charts and include the hours of operation, altitudes, and the controlling agency.

3-4-2. PROHIBITED AREAS

Prohibited areas contain airspace of defined dimensions identified by an area on the surface of the earth within which the flight of aircraft is prohibited. Such areas are established for security or other reasons associated with the national welfare. These areas are published in the Federal Register and are depicted on aeronautical charts.

3-4-3. RESTRICTED AREAS

a. Restricted areas contain airspace identified by an area on the surface of the earth within which the flight of aircraft, while not wholly prohibited, is subject to restrictions. Activities within these areas must be confined because of their nature or limitations imposed upon aircraft operations that are not a part of those activities or both. Restricted areas denote the existence of unusual, often invisible, hazards to aircraft such as artillery firing, aerial gunnery, or guided missiles. Penetration of restricted areas without authorization from the using or controlling agency may be extremely hazardous to the aircraft and its occupants. Restricted areas are published in the Federal Register and constitute 14 CFR Part 73.

b. ATC facilities apply the following procedures when aircraft are operating on an IFR clearance (includ-

ing those cleared by ATC to maintain VFR-on-top) via a route which lies within joint-use restricted airspace.

1. If the restricted area is not active and has been released to the controlling agency (FAA), the ATC facility will allow the aircraft to operate in the restricted airspace without issuing specific clearance for it to do so.

2. If the restricted area is active and has not been released to the controlling agency (FAA), the ATC facility will issue a clearance which will ensure the aircraft avoids the restricted airspace unless it is on an approved altitude reservation mission or has obtained its own permission to operate in the airspace and so informs the controlling facility.

NOTE-
The above apply only to joint-use restricted airspace and not to prohibited and nonjoint-use airspace. For the latter categories, the ATC facility will issue a clearance so the aircraft will avoid the restricted airspace unless it is on an approved altitude reservation mission or has obtained its own permission to operate in the airspace and so informs the controlling facility.

c. Restricted airspace is depicted on the en route chart appropriate for use at the altitude or flight level being flown. For joint-use restricted areas, the name of the controlling agency is shown on these charts. For all prohibited areas and nonjoint-use restricted areas, unless otherwise requested by the using agency, the phrase "NO A/G" is shown.

3-4-4. WARNING AREAS

A warning area is airspace of defined dimensions, extending from three nautical miles outward from the coast of the United States, that contains activity that may be hazardous to nonparticipating aircraft. The purpose of such warning areas is to warn nonparticipating pilots of the potential danger. A warning area may be located over domestic or international waters or both.

3-4-5. MILITARY OPERATIONS AREAS

a. MOA's consist of airspace of defined vertical and lateral limits established for the purpose of separating certain military training activities from IFR traffic. Whenever a MOA is being used, nonparticipating IFR traffic may be cleared through a MOA if IFR separation can be provided by ATC. Otherwise, ATC will reroute or restrict nonparticipating IFR traffic.

b. Most training activities necessitate acrobatic or abrupt flight maneuvers. Military pilots conducting flight in Department of Defense aircraft within a designated and active MOA are exempted from the provisions of 14 CFR Part 91.303(c) and (d) which prohibit acrobatic flight within Federal airways and Class B, Class C, Class D, and Class E surface areas.

c. Pilots operating under VFR should exercise extreme caution while flying within a MOA when military activity is being conducted. The activity status (active/inactive) of MOA's may change frequently. Therefore, pilots should contact any FSS within 100 miles of the area to obtain accurate real-time information concerning the MOA hours of operation. Prior to entering an active MOA, pilots should contact the controlling agency for traffic advisories.

d. MOA's are depicted on sectional, VFR terminal area, and enroute low altitude charts.

3-4-6. ALERT AREAS

Alert areas are depicted on aeronautical charts to inform nonparticipating pilots of areas that may contain a high volume of pilot training or an unusual type of aerial activity. Pilots should be particularly alert when flying in these areas. All activity within an alert area shall be conducted in accordance with CFR's, without waiver, and pilots of participating aircraft as well as pilots transiting the area shall be equally responsible for collision avoidance.

3-4-7. CONTROLLED FIRING AREAS

CFA's contain activities which, if not conducted in a controlled environment, could be hazardous to nonparticipating aircraft. The distinguishing feature of the CFA, as compared to other special use airspace, is that its activities are suspended immediately when spotter aircraft, radar, or ground lookout positions indicate an aircraft might be approaching the area. There is no need to chart CFA's since they do not cause a nonparticipating aircraft to change its flight path.

Section 5. OTHER AIRSPACE AREAS

3-5-1. AIRPORT ADVISORY AREA

a. The airport advisory area is the area within 10 statute miles of an airport where a control tower is not operating but where a FSS is located. At such locations, the FSS provides advisory service to arriving and departing aircraft.

REFERENCE-
AIM, TRAFFIC ADVISORY PRACTICES AT AIRPORTS WITHOUT OP-
ERATING CONTROL TOWERS, PARAGRAPH 4-1-9.

b. It is not mandatory that pilots participate in the Local Airport Advisory program, but it is strongly recommended that they do.

3-5-2. MILITARY TRAINING ROUTES

a. National security depends largely on the deterrent effect of our airborne military forces. To be proficient, the military services must train in a wide range of airborne tactics. One phase of this training involves "low level" combat tactics. The required maneuvers and high speeds are such that they may occasionally make the see-and-avoid aspect of VFR flight more difficult without increased vigilance in areas containing such operations. In an effort to ensure the greatest practical level of safety for all flight operations, the Military Training Route (MTR) program was conceived.

b. The MTR program is a joint venture by the FAA and the Department of Defense (DOD). MTR's are mutually developed for use by the military for the purpose of conducting low-altitude, high-speed training. The routes above 1,500 feet AGL are developed to be flown, to the maximum extent possible, under IFR. The routes at 1,500 feet AGL and below are generally developed to be flown under VFR.

c. Generally, MTR's are established below 10,000 feet MSL for operations at speeds in excess of 250 knots. However, route segments may be defined at higher altitudes for purposes of route continuity. For example, route segments may be defined for descent, climbout, and mountainous terrain. There are IFR and VFR routes as follows:

1. *IFR Military Training Routes-(IR):* Operations on these routes are conducted in accordance with IFR regardless of weather conditions.

2. *VFR Military Training Routes-(VR):* Operations on these routes are conducted in accordance with VFR except flight visibility shall be 5 miles or more;

and flights shall not be conducted below a ceiling of less than 3,000 feet AGL.

d. Military training routes will be identified and charted as follows:

1. *Route identification.*

(a) MTR's with no segment above 1,500 feet AGL shall be identified by four number characters; e.g., IR1206, VR1207.

(b) MTR's that include one or more segments above 1,500 feet AGL shall be identified by three number characters; e.g., IR206, VR207.

(c) Alternate IR/VR routes or route segments are identified by using the basic/principal route designation followed by a letter suffix, e.g., IR008A, VR1007B, etc.

2. *Route charting.*

(a) *IFR Low Altitude En Route Chart:* This chart will depict all IR routes and all VR routes that accommodate operations above 1,500 feet AGL.

(b) *VFR Sectional Charts:* These charts will depict military training activities such as IR, VR, MOA, Restricted Area, Warning Area, and Alert Area information.

(c) *Area Planning (AP/1B) Chart (DOD Flight Information Publication-FLIP):* This chart is published by the DOD primarily for military users and contains detailed information on both IR and VR routes.

REFERENCE-
AIM, PARAGRAPH 9-1-5, SUBPARAGRAPH A, NATIONAL IMAGERY
AND MAPPING AGENCY (NIMA).

e. The FLIP contains charts and narrative descriptions of these routes. This publication is available to the general public by single copy or annual subscription from the DIRECTOR, DMACSC, Attention: DOCP, Washington, DC 20315-0020. This DOD FLIP is available for pilot briefings at FSS and many airports.

f. Nonparticipating aircraft are not prohibited from flying within an MTR; however, extreme vigilance should be exercised when conducting flight through or near these routes. Pilots should contact FSS's within 100 NM of a particular MTR to obtain current information or route usage in their vicinity. Information available includes times of scheduled activity, altitudes in use on each route segment, and actual route width. Route width varies for each MTR and can extend several miles on either side of the charted MTR centerline. Route width information for IR and VR MTR's is also available in the FLIP AP/1B along with additional MTR (SR/AR) information. When requesting MTR information, pilots should give the FSS their position, route of flight, and destination in order to reduce frequency congestion and permit the FSS specialist to identify the MTR which could be a factor.

3-5-3. TEMPORARY FLIGHT RESTRICTIONS

a. **General:** This paragraph describes the types of conditions under which the FAA may impose temporary flight restrictions. It also explains which FAA elements have been delegated authority to issue a temporary flight restrictions NOTAM and lists the types of responsible agencies/offices from which the FAA will accept requests to establish temporary flight restrictions. The 14 CFR is explicit as to what operations are prohibited, restricted, or allowed in a temporary flight restrictions area. Pilots are responsible to comply with 14 CFR Sections 91.137, 91.138, 91.141 and 91.143 when conducting flight in an area where a temporary flight restrictions area is in effect, and should check appropriate NOTAM's during flight planning.

b. **The purpose for establishing a temporary flight restrictions area is to:**

1. Protect persons and property in the air or on the surface from an existing or imminent hazard associated with an incident on the surface when the presence of low flying aircraft would magnify, alter, spread, or compound that hazard (14 CFR Section 91.137(a)(1));

2. Provide a safe environment for the operation of disaster relief aircraft (14 CFR Section 91.137(a)(2)); or

3. Prevent an unsafe congestion of sightseeing aircraft above an incident or event which may generate a high degree of public interest (14 CFR Section 91.137(a)(3)).

4. Protect declared national disasters for humanitarian reasons in the State of Hawaii (14 CFR Section 91.138).

5. Protect the President, Vice President, or other public figures (14 CFR Section 91.141).

6. Provide a safe environment for space agency operations (14 CFR Section 91.143).

c. Except for hijacking situations, when the provisions of 14 CFR Section 91.137(a)(1) or (a)(2) are necessary, a temporary flight restrictions area will only be established by or through the area manager at the Air Route Traffic Control Center (ARTCC) having jurisdiction over the area concerned. A temporary flight restrictions NOTAM involving the conditions of 14 CFR Section 91.137(a)(3) will be issued at the direction of the regional air traffic division manager having oversight of the airspace concerned. When hijacking situations are involved, a temporary flight restrictions area will be implemented through the FAA Washington Headquarters Office of Civil Aviation Security. The appropriate FAA air traffic element, upon receipt of such a request, will establish a temporary flight restrictions area under 14 CFR Section 91.137(a)(1).

d. The FAA accepts recommendations for the establishment of a temporary flight restrictions area under 14 CFR Section 91.137(a)(1) from military major command headquarters, regional directors of the Office of Emergency Planning, Civil Defense State Directors, State Governors, or other similar authority. For the situations involving 14 CFR Section 91.137(a)(2), the FAA accepts recommendations from military commanders serving as regional, subregional, or Search and Rescue (SAR) coordinators; by military commanders directing or coordinating air operations associated with disaster relief; or by civil authorities directing or coordinating organized relief air operations (includes representatives of the Office of Emergency Planning, U.S. Forest Service, and State aeronautical agencies). Appropriate authorities for a temporary flight restrictions establishment under 14 CFR Section 91.137(a)(3) are any of those listed above or by State, county, or city government entities.

e. The type of restrictions issued will be kept to a minimum by the FAA consistent with achievement of the necessary objective. Situations which warrant the extreme restrictions of 14 CFR Section 91.137(a)(1) include, but are not limited to: toxic gas leaks or spills, flammable agents, or fumes which if fanned by rotor or propeller wash could endanger persons or property on the surface, or if entered by an aircraft could endanger persons or property in the air; imminent volcano eruptions which could endanger airborne aircraft and occupants; nuclear accident or incident; and hijackings. Situations which warrant the restrictions associated with 14 CFR Section 91.137(a)(2) include: forest fires which are being fought by releasing fire retardants from aircraft; and aircraft relief activities following a disaster (earthquake, tidal wave, flood, etc.). 14 CFR Section 91.137(a)(3) restrictions are established for events and incidents that would attract an unsafe congestion of sightseeing aircraft.

f. The amount of airspace needed to protect persons and property or provide a safe environment for rescue/relief aircraft operations is normally limited to within 2,000 feet above the surface and within a 3-nautical-mile radius. Incidents occurring within Class B, Class C, or Class D airspace will normally be handled through existing procedures and should not require the issuance of a temporary flight restrictions NOTAM. Temporary flight restrictions affecting airspace outside of the United States and its territories and possessions are issued with verbiage excluding that airspace outside of the 12-mile coastal limits.

g. The FSS nearest the incident site is normally the "coordination facility." When FAA communications assistance is required, the designated FSS will function as the primary communications facility for coordination between emergency control authorities and affected aircraft. The ARTCC may act as liaison for the emergency control authorities if adequate communications cannot be established between the designated FSS and the relief organization. For example, the coordination facility may relay authorizations from the on-scene emergency response official in cases where news media aircraft operations are approved at the altitudes used by relief aircraft.

h. ATC may authorize operations in a temporary flight restrictions area under its own authority only when flight restrictions are established under 14 CFR Section 91.137(a)(2) and (a)(3). The appropriate ARTCC/airport traffic control tower manager will, however, ensure that such authorized flights do not hamper activities or interfere with the event for which restrictions were implemented. However, ATC will not authorize local IFR flights into the temporary flight restrictions area.

i. To preclude misunderstanding, the implementing NOTAM will contain specific and formatted information. The facility establishing a temporary flight restrictions area will format a NOTAM beginning with the phrase "FLIGHT RESTRICTIONS" followed by: the location of the temporary flight restrictions area; the effective period; the area defined in statute miles; the altitudes affected; the FAA coordination facility and commercial telephone number; the reason for the temporary flight restrictions; the agency directing any relief activities and its commercial telephone number; and other in-

formation considered appropriate by the issuing authority.

EXAMPLE-
[1] *14 CFR Section 91.137(a)(1):*
The following NOTAM prohibits all aircraft operations except those specified in the NOTAM.
Flight restrictions Matthews, Virginia, effective immediately until 9610211200. Pursuant to 14 CFR Section 91.137(a)(1) temporary flight restrictions are in effect. Rescue operations in progress. Only relief aircraft operations under the direction of the Department of Defense are authorized in the airspace at and below 5,000 feet MSL within a 2-nautical-mile radius of Laser AFB, Matthews, Virginia. Commander, Laser AFB, in charge (897) 946-5543 (122.4). Steenson FSS (792) 555-6141 (123.1) is the FAA coordination facility.

[2] *14 CFR Section 91.137(a)(2):·*
The following NOTAM permits flight operations in accordance with 14 CFR Section 91.137(a)(2). The on-site emergency response official to authorize media aircraft operations below the altitudes used by the relief aircraft. Flight restrictions 25 miles east of Bransome, Idaho, effective immediately until 9601202359 UTC. Pursuant to 14 CFR Section 91.137(a)(2) temporary flight restrictions are in effect within a 4-nautical-mile radius of the intersection of county roads 564 and 315 at and below 3,500 feet MSL to provide a safe environment for fire fighting aircraft operations. Davis County sheriff's department (792) 555-8122 (122.9) is in charge of on-scene emergency response activities. Glivings FSS (792) 555-1618 (122.2) is the FAA coordination facility.

[3] *14 CFR Section 91.137(a)(3):*
The following NOTAM prohibits sightseeing aircraft operations.
Flight restrictions Brown, Tennessee, due to olympic activity. Effective 9606181100 UTC until 9607190200 UTC. Pursuant to 14 CFR Section 91.137(a)(3) temporary flight restrictions are in effect within a 3-nautical-mile radius of N355783/W835242 and Volunteer VORTAC 019 degree radial 3.7 DME fix at and below 2,500 feet MSL. Norton FSS (423) 555-6742 (126.6) is the FAA coordination facility.

[4] *14 CFR Section 91.138:*
The following NOTAM prohibits all aircraft except those operating under the authorization of the official in charge of associated emergency or disaster relief response activities, aircraft carrying law enforcement officials, aircraft carrying personnel involved in an emergency or legitimate scientific purposes, carrying properly accredited news media, and aircraft operating in accordance with an ATC clearance or instruction.

Flight restrictions Kapalua, Hawaii, effective 9605101200 UTC until 9605151500 UTC. Pursuant to 14 CFR Section 91.138 temporary flight restrictions are in effect within a 3-nautical-mile radius of N205778/W1564038 and Maui/OGG/VORTAC 275 degree radial at 14.1 nautical miles. John Doe 808-757-4469 or 122.4 is in charge of the operation. Honolulu/HNL 808-757-4470 (123.6) AFSS is the FAA coordination facility.

[5] *14 CFR Section 91.141:*
The following NOTAM prohibits all aircraft.
Flight restrictions Stillwater, Oklahoma, June 21, 1996. Pursuant to 14 CFR Section 91.141 aircraft flight operations are prohibited within a 3-nautical-mile radius, below 2000 feet AGL of N360962/W970515 and the Stillwater/SWO/VOR/DME 176 degree radial 3.8-nautical-mile fix from 1400 local time to 1700 local time June 21, 1996 unless otherwise authorized by ATC.

[6] *14 CFR Section 91.143:*
The following NOTAM prohibits any aircraft of U.S. registry, or pilot any aircraft under the authority of an airman certificate issued by the FAA.
Kennedy space center space operations area effective immediately until 9610152100 UTC. Pursuant to Section 91.143, flight operations conducted by FAA certificated pilots or conducted in aircraft of U.S. registry are prohibited at any altitude from surface to unlimited, within the following area 30-nautical-mile radius of the Melbourne/MLB/VORTAC 010 degree radial 21-nautical-mile fix. St. Petersburg, Florida/PIE/AFSS 813-545-1645 (122.2) is the FAA coordination facility and should be contacted for the current status of any airspace associated with the space shuttle operations. This airspace encompasses R2933, R2932, R2931, R2934, R2935, W497A and W158A. Additional warning and restricted areas will be active in conjunction with the operations. Pilots shall consult all NOTAM's regarding this operation.

3-5-4. PARACHUTE JUMP AIRCRAFT OPERATIONS

a. Procedures relating to parachute jump areas are contained in FAR Part 105. Tabulations of parachute jump areas in the U.S. are contained in the A/FD.

b. Pilots of aircraft engaged in parachute jump operations are reminded that all reported altitudes must be with reference to mean sea level, or flight level, as appropriate, to enable ATC to provide meaningful traffic information.

c. Parachute operations in the vicinity of an airport without an operating control tower - there is no substitute for alertness while in the vicinity of an airport. It is essential that pilots conducting parachute operations be alert, look for other traffic, and exchange traffic information as recommended in paragraph 4-1-9, Traffic Advisory Practices at Airports Without Operating Control Towers. In addition, pilots should avoid releasing parachutes while in an airport traffic pattern when there are other aircraft in that pattern. Pilots should make appropriate broadcasts on the designated Common Traffic Advisory Frequency (CTAF), and monitor that CTAF until all parachute activity has terminated or the aircraft has left the area. Prior to commencing a jump operation, the pilot should broadcast the aircraft's altitude and position in relation to the airport, the approximate relative time when the jump will commence and terminate, and listen to the position reports of other aircraft in the area.

3-5-5. PUBLISHED VFR ROUTES

Published VFR routes for transitioning around, under and through complex airspace such as Class B airspace were developed through a number of FAA and industry initiatives. All of the following terms, i.e., "VFR Flyway" "VFR Corridor" and "Class B Airspace VFR Transition Route" have been used when referring to the same or different types of routes or airspace. The following paragraphs identify and clarify the functionality of each type of route, and specify where and when an ATC clearance is required.

a. VFR Flyways:

1. VFR Flyways and their associated Flyway Planning Charts were developed from the recommendations of a National Airspace Review Task Group. A VFR Flyway is defined as a general flight path not defined as a specific course, for use by pilots in planning flights into, out of, through or near complex terminal airspace to avoid Class B airspace. An ATC clearance is NOT required to fly these routes.

VFR Flyway Planning Chart

FIG 3–5–1

2. VFR Flyways are depicted on the reverse side of some of the VFR Terminal Area Charts (TAC), commonly referred to as Class B airspace charts. (See FIG 3–5–1.) Eventually all TAC's will include a VFR Flyway Planning Chart. These charts identify VFR flyways designed to help VFR pilots avoid major controlled traffic flows. They may further depict multiple VFR routings throughout the area which may be used as an alternative to flight within Class B airspace. The ground references provide a guide for improved visual navigation. These routes are not intended to discourage requests for VFR operations within Class B airspace but are designed solely to assist pilots in planning for flights under and around busy Class B airspace without actually entering Class B airspace.

3. It is very important to remember that these suggested routes are not sterile of other traffic. The entire Class B airspace, and the airspace underneath it, may be heavily congested with many different types of aircraft. Pilot adherence to VFR rules must be exercised at all times. Further, when operating beneath Class B airspace, communications must be established and maintained between your aircraft and any control tower while transiting the Class B, Class C, and Class D surface areas of those airports under Class B Airspace.

b. VFR Corridors:

1. The design of a few of the first Class B airspace areas provided a corridor for the passage of uncontrolled traffic. A VFR corridor is defined as airspace through Class B airspace, with defined vertical and lateral boundaries, in which aircraft may operate without an ATC clearance or communication with air traffic control.

2. These corridors are, in effect, a "hole" through Class B airspace. (See FIG 3–5–2.) A classic example would be the corridor through the Los Angeles Class B airspace, which has been subsequently changed to Special Flight Rules airspace (SFR). A corridor is surrounded on all sides by Class B airspace and does not extend down to the surface like a VFR Flyway. Because of their finite lateral and vertical limits, and the volume of VFR traffic using a corridor, extreme caution and vigilance must be exercised.

Class B Airspace

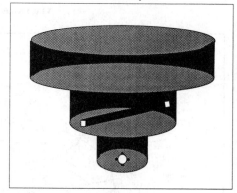

FIG 3–5–2

3. Because of the heavy traffic volume and the procedures necessary to efficiently manage the flow of traffic, it has not been possible to incorporate VFR corridors in the development or modifications of Class B airspace in recent years.

c. Class B Airspace VFR Transition Routes:

1. To accommodate VFR traffic through certain Class B airspace, such as Seattle, Phoenix and Los Angeles, Class B Airspace VFR Transition Routes were developed. A Class B Airspace VFR Transition Route is defined as a specific flight course depicted on a Terminal Area Chart (TAC) for transiting a specific Class B airspace. These routes include specific ATC-assigned altitudes, and pilots must obtain an ATC clearance prior to entering Class B airspace on the route.

2. These routes, as depicted in FIG 3–5–3, are designed to show the pilot where to position the aircraft outside of, or clear of, the Class B airspace where an ATC clearance can normally be expected with minimal or no delay. Until ATC authorization is received, pilots must remain clear of Class B airspace. On initial contact, pilots should advise ATC of their position, altitude, route name desired, and direction of flight. After a clearance is received, pilot must fly the route as depicted and, most importantly, adhere to ATC instructions.

VFR Transition Route

PHOENIX
VFR TRANSITION ROUTE
(ATC CLEARANCE REQUIRED)

ALTITUDE ASSIGNED BY ATC

THIS CHART ALSO IDENTIFIES VFR TRANSITION ROUTES IN THE PHOENIX CLASS B AIRSPACE. OPERATION ON THESE ROUTES REQUIRES ATC AUTHORIZATION FROM PHOENIX APPROACH CONTROL. UNTIL AUTHORIZATION IS RECEIVED, REMAIN OUTSIDE CLASS B AIRSPACE. DEPICTION OF THESE ROUTES IS TO ASSIST PILOTS IN POSITIONING THE AIRCRAFT IN AN AREA OUTSIDE THE CLASS B AIRSPACE WHERE ATC CLEARANCE CAN NORMALLY BE EXPECTED WITH MINIMAL OR NO DELAY. ON INITIAL CONTACT, ADVISE ATC OF POSITION ALTITUDE, ROUTE NAME DESIRED AND DIRECTION OF FLIGHT. REFER TO CURRENT PHOENIX VFR TERMINAL AREA CHART FOR USER REQUIREMENTS.

PARADISE VALLEY MALL

ABOVE 3500

SDL 224

SCOTTSDALE (SDL)

CACTUS RD

BILTMORE TRANSITION ROUTE
3,500' MSL to 5,500' MSL as assigned by ATC
Aircraft should overfly PHX at midfield

RTE 51

CAMELBACK MTN

PIMA RD

PAPAGO AAF (NG)

FAIRGROUNDS

TANK FARM

I-10

PHOENIX SKY HARBOR INTL (PHX)

I-17

MOTOROLA PLANT

TEMPE BRIDGE

RTE 202

PXR 115.6

51ST AVE

SALT RIVER

100
SFC

US-60

THE LAKES

100
30

LAVEEN

GUADALUPE RD

2500

100
40

CHANDLER BLVD

SOUTH MOUNTAIN

2500

FOOTHILLS GC

AHWATUKEE
STELLAR AIRPARK

2500

100
40

FIREBIRD LAKE

MEMORIAL (Pvt)

3500

SIERRA ESTRELLA MTS

ATC CLEARANCE REQUIRED
Contact Approach Control on 123.7 or 363.0 Class B controlled transition route Bitmore (south of airport flying north). Altitudes assigned by ATC. Altitudes available 3500' - 5500'.

RIGGS RD

110

GILA RIVER

BILTMORE TRANSITION ROUTE
3,500' MSL to 5,500' MSL as assigned by ATC
Aircraft should overfly PHX at midfield

5500

(Not to be used for navigation)

FIG 3-5-3

3-5-6. TERMINAL RADAR SERVICE AREA (TRSA)

a. Background: TRSA's were originally established as part of the Terminal Radar Program at selected airports. TRSA's were never controlled airspace from a regulatory standpoint because the establishment of TRSA's was never subject to the rulemaking process; consequently, TRSA's are not contained in FAR Part 71 nor are there any TRSA operating rules in FAR Part 91. Part of the Airport Radar Service Area (ARSA) program was to eventually replace all TRSA's. However, the ARSA requirements became relatively stringent and it was subsequently decided that TRSA's would have to meet ARSA criteria before they would be converted. TRSA's do not fit into any of the U.S. airspace classes; therefore, they will continue to be non-Part 71 airspace areas where participating pilots can receive additional radar services which have been redefined as TRSA Service.

b. TRSA's: The primary airport(s) within the TRSA become(s) Class D airspace. The remaining portion of the TRSA overlies other controlled airspace which is normally Class E airspace beginning at 700 or 1,200 feet and established to transition to/from the en route/ terminal environment.

c. Participation: Pilots operating under VFR are encouraged to contact the radar approach control and avail themselves of the TRSA Services. However, participation is voluntary on the part of the pilot. See Chapter 4. Air Traffic Control for details and procedures.

d. Charts: TRSA's are depicted on VFR sectional and terminal area charts with a solid black line and altitudes for each segment. The Class D portion is charted with a blue segmented line.

3-5-7. NATIONAL SECURITY AREAS

National Security Areas consist of airspace of defined vertical and lateral dimensions established at locations where there is a requirement for increased security and safety of ground facilities. Pilots are requested to voluntarily avoid flying through the depicted NSA. When it is necessary to provide a greater level of security and safety, flight in NSA's may be temporarily prohibited by regulation under the provisions of FAR Part 99.7. Regulatory prohibitions will be issued by ATA-400 and disseminated via NOTAM. Inquiries about NSA's should be directed to the Airspace and Rules Division, ATA-400.

Chapter 4. AIR TRAFFIC CONTROL

Section 1. SERVICES AVAILABLE TO PILOTS

4-1-1. AIR ROUTE TRAFFIC CONTROL CENTERS

Centers are established primarily to provide air traffic service to aircraft operating on IFR flight plans within controlled airspace, and principally during the en route phase of flight.

4-1-2. CONTROL TOWERS

Towers have been established to provide for a safe, orderly and expeditious flow of traffic on and in the vicinity of an airport. When the responsibility has been so delegated, towers also provide for the separation of IFR aircraft in the terminal areas.

REFERENCE-
AIM, APPROACH CONTROL, PARAGRAPH 5-4-3.

4-1-3. FLIGHT SERVICE STATIONS

a. Flight Service Stations (FSS's) are air traffic facilities which provide pilot briefings, en route communications and VFR search and rescue services, assist lost aircraft and aircraft in emergency situations, relay ATC clearances, originate Notices to Airmen, broadcast aviation weather and National Airspace System (NAS) information, receive and process IFR flight plans, and monitor NAVAID's. In addition, at selected locations FSS's provide En Route Flight Advisory Service (Flight Watch), take weather observations, issue airport advisories, and advise Customs and Immigration of transborder flights.

b. Supplemental Weather Service Locations (SWSL's) are airport facilities staffed with contract personnel who take weather observations and provide current local weather to pilots via telephone or radio. All other services are provided by the parent FSS.

4-1-4. RECORDING AND MONITORING

a. Calls to air traffic control (ATC) facilities (ARTCC's, Towers, FSS's, Central Flow, and Operations Centers) over radio and ATC operational telephone lines (lines used for operational purposes such as controller instructions, briefings, opening and closing flight plans, issuance of IFR clearances and amendments, counter hijacking activities, etc.) may be monitored and recorded for operational uses such as accident investigations, accident prevention, search and rescue purposes, specialist training and evaluation, and techni-cal evaluation and repair of control and communications systems.

b. Where the public access telephone is recorded, a beeper tone is not required. In place of the "beep" tone the FCC has substituted a mandatory requirement that persons to be recorded be given notice they are to be recorded and give consent. Notice is given by this entry, consent to record is assumed by the individual placing a call to the operational facility.

4-1-5. COMMUNICATIONS RELEASE OF IFR AIRCRAFT LANDING AT AN AIRPORT WITHOUT AN OPERATING CONTROL TOWER

Aircraft operating on an IFR flight plan, landing at an airport without an operating control tower will be advised to change to the airport advisory frequency when direct communications with ATC are no longer required. Towers and centers do not have nontower airport traffic and runway in use information. The instrument approach may not be aligned with the runway in use; therefore, if the information has not already been obtained, pilots should make an expeditious change to the airport advisory frequency when authorized.

REFERENCE-
AIM, ADVANCE INFORMATION ON INSTRUMENT APPROACH,
PARAGRAPH 5-4-4.

4-1-6. PILOT VISITS TO AIR TRAFFIC FACILITIES

Pilots are encouraged to visit air traffic facilities (Towers, Centers and FSS's) and familiarize themselves with the ATC system. On rare occasions, facilities may not be able to approve a visit because of ATC workload or other reasons. It is therefore requested that pilots contact the facility prior to the visit and advise of the number of persons in the group, the time and date of the proposed visit and the primary interest of the group. With this information available, the facility can prepare an itinerary and have someone available to guide the group through the facility.

4-1-7. OPERATION TAKE-OFF AND OPERATION RAINCHECK

Operation Take-off is a program that educates pilots in how best to utilize the FSS modernization efforts and services available in Automated Flight Service Stations (AFSS), as stated in FAA Order 7230.17, Pilot Education Program - Operation Takeoff. Operation Rain-check is a program designed to familiarize pilots with the ATC system, its functions, responsibilities and benefits.

4-1-8. APPROACH CONTROL SERVICE FOR VFR ARRIVING AIRCRAFT

a. Numerous approach control facilities have established programs for arriving VFR aircraft to contact approach control for landing information. This information includes: wind, runway, and altimeter setting at the airport of intended landing. This information may be omitted if contained in the ATIS broadcast and the pilot states the appropriate ATIS code.

NOTE-
Pilot use of "have numbers" does not indicate receipt of the ATIS broadcast. In addition, the controller will provide traffic advisories on a workload permitting basis.

b. Such information will be furnished upon initial contact with concerned approach control facility. The pilot will be requested to change to the *tower* frequency at a predetermined time or point, to receive further landing information.

c. Where available, use of this procedure will not hinder the operation of VFR flights by requiring excessive spacing between aircraft or devious routing.

d. Compliance with this procedure is not mandatory but pilot participation is encouraged.

REFERENCE-
AIM, TERMINAL RADAR SERVICES FOR VFR AIRCRAFT, PARAGRAPH 4-1-17.

NOTE-
Approach control services for VFR aircraft are normally dependent on air traffic control radar. These services are not available during periods of a radar outage. Approach control services for VFR aircraft are limited when CENRAP is in use.

4-1-9. TRAFFIC ADVISORY PRACTICES AT AIRPORTS WITHOUT OPERATING CONTROL TOWERS

(See TBL 4-1-1.)

a. Airport Operations Without Operating Control Tower:

1. There is no substitute for alertness while in the vicinity of an airport. It is essential that pilots be alert and look for other traffic and exchange traffic informa-tion when approaching or departing an airport without an operating control tower. This is of particular importance since other aircraft may not have communication capability or, in some cases, pilots may not communicate their presence or intentions when operating into or out of such airports. To achieve the greatest degree of safety, it is essential that all radio-equipped aircraft transmit/receive on a common frequency identified for the purpose of airport advisories.

2. An airport may have a full or part-time tower or FSS located on the airport, a full or part-time UNICOM station or no aeronautical station at all. There are three ways for pilots to communicate their intention and obtain airport/traffic information when operating at an airport that does not have an operating tower: by communicating with an FSS, a UNICOM operator, or by making a self-announce broadcast.

b. Communicating on a Common Frequency:

1. The key to communicating at an airport without an operating control tower is selection of the correct common frequency. The acronym CTAF which stands for Common Traffic Advisory Frequency, is synonymous with this program. A CTAF is a frequency designated for the purpose of carrying out airport advisory practices while operating to or from an airport without an operating control tower. The CTAF may be a UNICOM, MULTICOM, FSS, or tower frequency and is identified in appropriate aeronautical publications.

2. The CTAF frequency for a particular airport is contained in the A/FD, Alaska Supplement, Alaska Terminal Publication, Instrument Approach Procedure Charts, and Instrument Departure Procedure (DP) Charts. Also, the CTAF frequency can be obtained by contacting any FSS. Use of the appropriate CTAF, combined with a visual alertness and application of the following recommended good operating practices, will enhance safety of flight into and out of all uncontrolled airports.

c. Recommended Traffic Advisory Practices:

1. Pilots of inbound traffic should monitor and communicate as appropriate on the designated CTAF from 10 miles to landing. Pilots of departing aircraft should monitor/communicate on the appropriate frequency from start-up, during taxi, and until 10 miles from the airport unless the CFR's or local procedures require otherwise.

Summary of Recommended Communication Procedures

	FACILITY AT AIRPORT	FREQUENCY USE	COMMUNICATION/BROADCAST PROCEDURES		
			OUTBOUND	INBOUND	PRACTICE INSTRUMENT APPROACH
1.	UNICOM (No Tower or FSS)	Communicate with UNICOM station on published CTAF frequency (122.7; 122.8; 122.725; 122.975; or 123.0). If unable to contact UNICOM station, use self-announce procedures on CTAF.	Before taxiing and before taxiing on the runway for departure.	10 miles out. Entering downwind, base, and final. Leaving the runway.	
2.	No Tower, FSS, or UNICOM	Self-announce on MULTICOM frequency 122.9.	Before taxiing and before taxiing on the runway for departure.	10 miles out. Entering downwind, base, and final. Leaving the runway.	Departing final approach fix (name) or on final approach segment inbound.
3.	No Tower in operation, FSS open	Communicate with FSS on CTAF frequency.	Before taxiing and before taxiing on the runway for departure.	10 miles out. Entering downwind, base, and final. Leaving the runway.	Approach completed/ terminated.
4.	FSS Closed (No Tower)	Self-announce on CTAF.	Before taxiing and before taxiing on the runway for departure.	10 miles out. Entering downwind, base, and final. Leaving the runway.	
5.	Tower or FSS not in operation	Self-announce on CTAF.	Before taxiing and before taxiing on the runway for departure.	10 miles out. Entering downwind, base, and final. Leaving the runway.	

TBL 4-1-1

2. Pilots of aircraft conducting other than arriving or departing operations at altitudes normally used by arriving and departing aircraft should monitor/communicate on the appropriate frequency while within 10 miles of the airport unless required to do otherwise by the FAR's or local procedures. Such operations include parachute jumping/dropping, en route, practicing maneuvers, etc.

REFERENCE-
AIM, PARACHUTE JUMP AIRCRAFT OPERATIONS, PARAGRAPH 3-5-4.

d. Local Airport Advisory provided by an FSS:

1. Local Airport Advisory (LAA) is a service provided at selected locations by an FSS physically located on an airport which does not have a control tower or where the tower is operated on a part-time basis. The CTAF for FSS's which provide this service will be disseminated in appropriate aeronautical publications.

2. In communicating with a CTAF FSS, establish two-way communications before transmitting outbound/inbound intentions or information. An inbound aircraft should report approximately 10 miles from the airport, reporting altitude and aircraft type, location relative to the airport, state whether landing or overflight, and request airport advisory. Departing aircraft should state the aircraft type, full identification number, type of flight planned, i.e., VFR or IFR and the planned destination or direction of flight. Report before taxiing and before taxiing on the runway for departure. If communications with a UNICOM are necessary after initial report to FSS, return to FSS frequency for traffic update.

(a) Inbound

EXAMPLE-
Vero Beach radio, Centurion Six Niner Delta Delta is ten miles south, two thousand, landing Vero Beach. Request airport advisory.

(b) Outbound

EXAMPLE-
Vero Beach radio, Centurion Six Niner Delta Delta, ready
to taxi, VFR, departing to the southwest. Request airport
advisory.

3. A CTAF FSS provides wind direction and velocity, favored or designated runway, altimeter setting, known traffic, NOTAM's, airport taxi routes, airport traffic pattern information, and instrument approach procedures. These elements are varied so as to best serve the current traffic situation. Some airport managers have specified that under certain wind or other conditions designated runways be used. Pilots should advise the FSS of the runway they intend to use.

CAUTION-
All aircraft in the vicinity of an airport may not be in
communication with the FSS.

e. Information Provided by Aeronautical Advisory Stations (UNICOM):

1. UNICOM is a nongovernment air/ground radio communication station which may provide airport information at public use airports where there is no tower or FSS.

2. On pilot request, UNICOM stations may provide pilots with weather information, wind direction, the recommended runway, or other necessary information. If the UNICOM frequency is designated as the CTAF, it will be identified in appropriate aeronautical publications.

f. Unavailability of Information from FSS or UNICOM:

Should LAA by an FSS or Aeronautical Advisory Station UNICOM be unavailable, wind and weather information may be obtainable from nearby controlled airports via Automatic Terminal Information Service (ATIS) or Automated Weather Observing System (AWOS) frequency.

g. Self-Announce Position and/or Intentions:

1. *General.* Self-announce is a procedure whereby pilots broadcast their position or intended flight activity or ground operation on the designated CTAF. This procedure is used primarily at airports which do not have an FSS on the airport. The self-announce procedure should also be used if a pilot is unable to communicate with the FSS on the designated CTAF.

2. If an airport has a tower and it is temporarily closed, or operated on a part-time basis and there is no

FSS on the airport or the FSS is closed, use the CTAF to self-announce your position or intentions.

3. Where there is no tower, FSS, or UNICOM station on the airport, use MULTICOM frequency 122.9 for self-announce procedures. Such airports will be identified in appropriate aeronautical information publications.

4. *Practice Approaches.* Pilots conducting practice instrument approaches should be particularly alert for other aircraft that may be departing in the opposite direction. When conducting any practice approach, regardless of its direction relative to other airport operations, pilots should make announcements on the CTAF as follows:

(a) departing the final approach fix, inbound (nonprecision approach) or departing the outer marker or fix used in lieu of the outer marker, inbound (precision approach);

(b) established on the final approach segment or immediately upon being released by ATC;

(c) upon completion or termination of the approach; and

(d) upon executing the missed approach procedure.

5. Departing aircraft should always be alert for arrival aircraft coming from the opposite direction.

6. Recommended self-announce phraseologies: It should be noted that aircraft operating to or from another nearby airport may be making self-announce broadcasts on the same UNICOM or MULTICOM frequency. To help identify one airport from another, the airport name should be spoken at the beginning and end of each self-announce transmission.

(a) Inbound

EXAMPLE-
Strawn traffic, Apache Two Two Five Zulu, (position),
(altitude), (descending) or entering downwind/base/final
(as appropriate) runway one seven full stop, touch-and-
go, Strawn.
Strawn traffic Apache Two Two Five Zulu clear of runway
one seven Strawn.

(b) Outbound

EXAMPLE-
Strawn traffic, Queen Air Seven One Five Five Bravo
(location on airport) taxiing to runway two six Strawn.
Strawn traffic, Queen Air Seven One Five Five Bravo de-
parting runway two six. Departing the pattern to the (di-
rection), climbing to (altitude) Strawn.

(c) Practice Instrument Approach

EXAMPLE-
Strawn traffic, Cessna Two One Four Three Quebec (posi-
tion from airport) inbound descending through (altitude)
practice (name of approach) approach runway three five
Strawn.
Strawn traffic, Cessna Two One Four Three Quebec prac-
tice (type) approach completed or terminated runway
three five Strawn.

h. UNICOM Communications Procedures:

1. In communicating with a UNICOM station, the following practices will help reduce frequency congestion, facilitate a better understanding of pilot intentions, help identify the location of aircraft in the traffic pattern, and enhance safety of flight:

(a) Select the correct UNICOM frequency.

(b) State the identification of the UNICOM station you are calling in each transmission.

(c) Speak slowly and distinctly.

(d) Report approximately 10 miles from the airport, reporting altitude, and state your aircraft type, aircraft identification, location relative to the airport, state whether landing or overflight, and request wind information and runway in use.

(e) Report on downwind, base, and final approach.

(f) Report leaving the runway.

2. Recommended UNICOM phraseologies:

(a) Inbound

PHRASEOLOGY-
FREDERICK UNICOM CESSNA EIGHT ZERO ONE
TANGO FOXTROT 10 MILES SOUTHEAST
DESCENDING THROUGH (altitude) LANDING
FREDERICK, REQUEST WIND AND RUNWAY
INFORMATION FREDERICK.
FREDERICK TRAFFIC CESSNA EIGHT ZERO ONE
TANGO FOXTROT ENTERING
DOWNWIND/BASE/FINAL (as appropriate) FOR
RUNWAY ONE NINER (full stop/touch-and-go)
FREDERICK.
FREDERICK TRAFFIC CESSNA EIGHT ZERO ONE
TANGO FOXTROT CLEAR OF RUNWAY ONE NINER
FREDERICK.

(b) Outbound

PHRASEOLOGY-
FREDERICK UNICOM CESSNA EIGHT ZERO ONE
TANGO FOXTROT (location on airport) TAXIING TO
RUNWAY ONE NINER, REQUEST WIND AND TRAFFIC
INFORMATION FREDERICK.
FREDERICK TRAFFIC CESSNA EIGHT ZERO ONE
TANGO FOXTROT DEPARTING RUNWAY ONE NINER.
"REMAINING IN THE PATTERN" OR "DEPARTING
THE PATTERN TO THE (direction) (as appropriate)"
FREDERICK.

4-1-10. IFR APPROACHES/GROUND VEHICLE OPERATIONS

a. IFR Approaches: When operating in accordance with an IFR clearance and ATC approves a change to the advisory frequency, make an expeditious change to the CTAF and employ the recommended traffic advisory procedures.

b. Ground Vehicle Operation: Airport ground vehicles equipped with radios should monitor the CTAF frequency when operating on the airport movement area and remain clear of runways/taxiways being used by aircraft. Radio transmissions from ground vehicles should be confined to safety-related matters.

c. Radio Control of Airport Lighting Systems: Whenever possible, the CTAF will be used to control airport lighting systems at airports without operating control towers. This eliminates the need for pilots to change frequencies to turn the lights on and allows a continuous listening watch on a single frequency. The CTAF is published on the instrument approach chart and in other appropriate aeronautical information publications. For further details concerning radio controlled lights, see AC 150/5340-27.

4-1-11. DESIGNATED UNICOM/MULTICOM FREQUENCIES

a. Communications between aircraft.

CAUTION-
The Federal Communications Commission (FCC) re-
quires an aircraft station license to operate on UNICOM/
MULTICOM frequencies and usage must be in accor-
dance with Part 87 of the FCC rules (see Section 87.29
regarding license applications). Misuse of these frequen-
cies may result in either the imposition of fines and/or
revocation/suspension of FCC aircraft station license.

b. Frequency use.

1. The following listing depicts UNICOM and MULTICOM frequency uses as designated by the Federal Communications Commission (FCC). (See TBL 4–1–2.)

Unicom/Multicom Frequency Usage

USE	FREQUENCY
Airports without an operating control tower.	122.700 122.725 122.800 122.975 123.000 123.050 123.075
(MULTICOM FREQUENCY) Activities of a temporary, seasonal, emergency nature or search and rescue, as well as, airports with no tower, FSS, or UNICOM.	122.900
(MULTICOM FREQUENCY) Forestry management and fire suppression, fish and game management and protection, and environmental monitoring and protection.	122.925
Airports with a control tower or FSS on airport.	122.950

TBL 4–1–2

NOTE–

1 *In some areas of the country, frequency interference may be encountered from nearby airports using the same UNICOM frequency. Where there is a problem, UNICOM operators are encouraged to develop a "least interference" frequency assignment plan for airports concerned using the frequencies designated for airports without operating control towers. UNICOM licensees are encouraged to apply for UNICOM 25 kHz spaced channel frequencies. Due to the extremely limited number of frequencies with 50 kHz channel spacing, 25 kHz channel spacing should be implemented. UNICOM licensees may then request FCC to assign frequencies in accordance with the plan, which FCC will review and consider for approval.*

2 *Wind direction and runway information may not be available on UNICOM frequency 122.950.*

2. The following listing depicts other frequency uses as designated by the Federal Communications Commission (FCC). (See TBL 4–1–3.)

Other Frequency Usage Designated by FCC

USE	FREQUENCY
Air-to-air communications & private airports (not open to the public).	122.750 122.850
Air-to-air communications (general aviation helicopters).	123.025
Aviation instruction, Glider, Hot Air Balloon (**not to be used for advisory service**).	123.300 123.500

TBL 4–1–3

4–1–12. USE OF UNICOM FOR ATC PURPOSES

UNICOM service may be used for air traffic control purposes, only under the following circumstances:

1. Revision to proposed departure time.

2. Takeoff, arrival, or flight plan cancellation time.

3. ATC clearance, provided arrangements are made between the ATC facility and the UNICOM licensee to handle such messages.

4–1–13. AUTOMATIC TERMINAL INFORMATION SERVICE (ATIS)

a. ATIS is the continuous broadcast of recorded non-control information in selected high activity terminal areas. Its purpose is to improve controller effectiveness and to relieve frequency congestion by automating the repetitive transmission of essential but routine information. The information is continuously broadcast over a discrete VHF radio frequency or the voice portion of a local NAVAID. ATIS transmissions on a discrete VHF radio frequency are engineered to be receivable to a maximum of 60 NM from the ATIS site and a maximum altitude of 25,000 feet AGL. At most locations, ATIS signals may be received on the surface of the airport, but local conditions may limit the maximum ATIS reception distance and/or altitude. Pilots are urged to cooperate in the ATIS program as it relieves frequency congestion on approach control, ground control, and local control frequencies. The A/FD indicates airports for which ATIS is provided.

b. ATIS information includes the time of the latest weather sequence, ceiling, visibility, obstructions to visibility, temperature, dew point (if available), wind direction (magnetic), and velocity, altimeter, other pertinent remarks, instrument approach and runway in use. The ceiling/sky condition, visibility, and obstructions to vision may be omitted from the ATIS broadcast if the ceiling is above 5,000 feet and the visibility is more than 5 miles. The departure runway will only be given if different from the landing runway except at locations hav-ng a separate ATIS for departure. The broadcast may nclude the appropriate frequency and instructions for 'FR arrivals to make initial contact with approach conrol. Pilots of aircraft arriving or departing the terminal rea can receive the continuous ATIS broadcast at times vhen cockpit duties are least pressing and listen to as nany repeats as desired. ATIS broadcast shall be upated upon the receipt of any official hourly and special veather. A new recording will also be made when there s a change in other pertinent data such as runway hange, instrument approach in use, etc.

XAMPLE-

)ulles International information Sierra. 1300 zulu weathr. Measured ceiling three thousand overcast. Visibility hree, smoke. Temperature six eight. Wind three five zero t eight. Altimeter two niner niner two. ILS runway one ight approach in use. Landing runway one right and left.)eparture runway three zero. Armel VORTAC out of serice. Advise you have Sierra.

c. Pilots should listen to ATIS broadcasts whenever \TIS is in operation.

d. Pilots should notify controllers on initial contact hat they have received the ATIS broadcast by repeating he alphabetical code word appended to the broadcast.

XAMPLE-

Information Sierra received."

e. When a pilot acknowledges receipt of the ATIS *roadcast, controllers may omit those items contained n the broadcast if they are current. Rapidly changing :onditions will be issued by ATC and the ATIS will ontain words as follows:

XAMPLE-

'Latest ceiling/visibility/altimeter/wind/(other conditions) vill be issued by approach control/tower."

VOTE-

*he absence of a sky condition or ceiling and/or visibility *n ATIS indicates a sky condition or ceiling of 5,000 feet r above and visibility of 5 miles or more. A remark may e made on the broadcast, "the weather is better than `000 and 5," or the existing weather may be broadcast.*

f. Controllers will issue pertinent information to *ilots who do not acknowledge receipt of a broadcast or vho acknowledge receipt of a broadcast which is not :urrent.

g. To serve frequency limited aircraft, FSS's are quipped to transmit on the omnirange frequency at nost en route VOR's used as ATIS voice outlets. Such :ommunication interrupts the ATIS broadcast. Pilots of .ircraft equipped to receive on other FSS frequencies

are encouraged to do so in order that these override transmissions may be kept to an absolute minimum.

h. While it is a good operating practice for pilots to make use of the ATIS broadcast where it is available, some pilots use the phrase "Have Numbers" in communications with the control tower. Use of this phrase means that the pilot has received wind, runway, and altimeter information ONLY and the tower does not have to repeat this information. It does not indicate receipt of the ATIS broadcast and should never be used for this purpose.

4-1-14. RADAR TRAFFIC INFORMATION SERVICE

This is a service provided by radar ATC facilities. Pilots receiving this service are advised of any radar target observed on the radar display which may be in such proximity to the position of their aircraft or its intended route of flight that it warrants their attention. This service is not intended to relieve the pilot of the responsibility for continual vigilance to see and avoid other aircraft.

a. Purpose of the Service:

1. The issuance of traffic information as observed on a radar display is based on the principle of assisting and advising a pilot that a particular radar target's position and track indicates it may intersect or pass in such proximity to that pilot's intended flight path that it warrants attention. This is to alert the pilot to the traffic, to be on the lookout for it, and thereby be in a better position to take appropriate action should the need arise.

2. Pilots are reminded that the surveillance radar used by ATC does not provide altitude information unless the aircraft is equipped with MODE C and the radar facility is capable of displaying altitude information.

b. Provisions of the Service:

1. Many factors, such as limitations of the radar, volume of traffic, controller workload and communications frequency congestion, could prevent the controller from providing this service. Controllers possess complete discretion for determining whether they are able to provide or continue to provide this service in a specific case. The controller's reason against providing or continuing to provide the service in a particular case is not subject to question nor need it be communicated to the pilot. In other words, the provision of this service is entirely dependent upon whether controllers believe they are in a position to provide it. Traffic information is routinely provided to all aircraft operating on IFR flight plans except when the pilot declines the service, or the pilot is operating within Class A airspace. Traffic information may be provided to flights not operating on IFR flight plans when requested by pilots of such flights.

NOTE-
Radar ATC facilities normally display and monitor both primary and secondary radar when it is available, except that secondary radar may be used as the sole display source in Class A airspace, and under some circumstances outside of Class A airspace (beyond primary coverage and in en route areas where only secondary is available). Secondary radar may also be used outside Class A airspace as the sole display source when the primary radar is temporarily unusable or out of service. Pilots in contact with the affected ATC facility are normally advised when a temporary outage occurs; i.e., "primary radar out of service; traffic advisories available on transponder aircraft only." This means simply that only the aircraft which have transponders installed and in use will be depicted on ATC radar indicators when the primary radar is temporarily out of service.

2. When receiving VFR radar advisory service, pilots should monitor the assigned frequency at all times. This is to preclude controllers' concern for radio failure or emergency assistance to aircraft under the controller's jurisdiction. VFR radar advisory service does not include vectors away from conflicting traffic unless requested by the pilot. When advisory service is no longer desired, advise the controller before changing frequencies and then change your transponder code to 1200, if applicable. Pilots should also inform the controller when changing VFR cruising altitude. Except in programs where radar service is automatically terminated, the controller will advise the aircraft when radar is terminated.

NOTE-
Participation by VFR pilots in formal programs implemented at certain terminal locations constitutes pilot request. This also applies to participating pilots at those locations where arriving VFR flights are encouraged to make their first contact with the tower on the approach control frequency.

c. **Issuance of Traffic Information:** Traffic information will include the following concerning a target which may constitute traffic for an aircraft that is:

1. *Radar identified:*

   (a) Azimuth from the aircraft in terms of the 12 hour clock, or

   (b) When rapidly maneuvering civil test or military aircraft prevent accurate issuance of traffic as in (a above, specify the direction from an aircraft's position in terms of the eight cardinal compass points (N, NE, E, SE, S, SW, W, NW). This method shall be terminated at the pilot's request.

   (c) Distance from the aircraft in nautical miles;

   (d) Direction in which the target is proceeding; and

   (e) Type of aircraft and altitude if known.

EXAMPLE-
Traffic 10 o'clock, 3 miles, west-bound (type aircraft and altitude, if known, of the observed traffic). The altitude may be known, by means of Mode C, but not verified with the pilot for accuracy. (To be valid for separation purposes by ATC, the accuracy of Mode C readouts must be verified. This is usually accomplished upon initial entry into the radar system by a comparison of the readout to pilot stated altitude, or the field elevation in the case of continuous readout being received from an aircraft on the airport.) When necessary to issue traffic advisories containing unverified altitude information, the controller will issue the advisory in the same manner as if it were verified due to the accuracy of these readouts. The pilot may upon receipt of traffic information, request a vector (heading) to avoid such traffic. The vector will be provided to the extent possible as determined by the controller provided the aircraft to be vectored is within the airspace under the jurisdiction of the controller.

2. *Not radar identified:*

   (a) Distance and direction with respect to a fix;

   (b) Direction in which the target is proceeding; and

   (c) Type of aircraft and altitude if known.

EXAMPLE-
Traffic 8 miles south of the airport northeastbound, (type aircraft and altitude if known).

d. The examples depicted in the following figures point out the possible error in the position of this traffic when it is necessary for a pilot to apply drift correction to maintain this track. This error could also occur in the event a change in course is made at the time radar traffic information is issued.

Induced Error in Position of Traffic

FIG 4-1-1

EXAMPLE-
*n FIG 4-1-1 traffic information would be issued to the
ilot of aircraft "A" as 12 o'clock. The actual position of
he traffic as seen by the pilot of aircraft "A" would be 2
'clock. Traffic information issued to aircraft "B" would
lso be given as 12 o'clock, but in this case, the pilot of
B" would see the traffic at 10 o'clock.*

Induced Error in Position of Traffic

FIG 4-1-2

EXAMPLE-
*1 FIG 4-1-2 traffic information would be issued to the
ilot of aircraft "C" as 2 o'clock. The actual position of
ie traffic as seen by the pilot of aircraft "C" would be 3
'clock. Traffic information issued to aircraft "D" would
e at an 11 o'clock position. Since it is not necessary for
ie pilot of aircraft "D" to apply wind correction (crab)
remain on track, the actual position of the traffic issued
ould be correct. Since the radar controller can only ob-
erve aircraft track (course) on the radar display, traffic
dvisories are issued accordingly, and pilots should give
ue consideration to this fact when looking for reported
affic.*

-1-15. SAFETY ALERT

safety alert will be issued to pilots of aircraft being
ontrolled by ATC if the controller is aware the aircraft
at an altitude which, in the controller's judgment,
laces the aircraft in unsafe proximity to terrain, ob-
tructions or other aircraft. The provision of this service
contingent upon the capability of the controller to
ave an awareness of a situation involving unsafe prox-
nity to terrain, obstructions and uncontrolled aircraft.
he issuance of a safety alert cannot be mandated, but
can be expected on a reasonable, though intermittent
asis. Once the alert is issued, it is solely the pilot's pre-

rogative to determine what course of action, if any, to
take. This procedure is intended for use in time critical
situations where aircraft safety is in question. Noncriti-
cal situations should be handled via the normal traffic
alert procedures.

a. Terrain or Obstruction Alert:

1. Controllers will immediately issue an alert to the
pilot of an aircraft under their control when they recognize that the aircraft is at an altitude which, in their judgment, may be in an unsafe proximity to terrain/obstruc-
tions. The primary method of detecting unsafe
proximity is through MODE C automatic altitude reports.

EXAMPLE-
*Low altitude alert, check your altitude immediately. The,
as appropriate, MEA/MVA/MOCA in your area is (altitude) or, if past the final approach fix (nonprecision approach) or the outer marker or fix used in lieu of the outer
marker (precision approach), the, as appropriate, MDA/
DH (if known) is (altitude).*

2. Terminal ARTS IIA, III, AND IIIA facilities
have an automated function which, if operating, alerts
controllers when a tracked MODE C equipped aircraft
under their control is below or is predicted to be below
a predetermined minimum safe altitude. This function,
called Minimum Safe Altitude Warning (MSAW), is
designed solely as a controller aid in detecting potentially unsafe aircraft proximity to terrain/obstructions.
The ARTS IIA, III, and IIIA facility will, when MSAW
is operating, provide MSAW monitoring for all aircraft
with an operating MODE C altitude encoding transponder that are tracked by the system and are:

(a) Operating on an IFR flight plan, or

(b) Operating VFR and have requested MSAW
monitoring.

3. Terminal AN/TPX-42A (number beacon decoder system) facilities have an automated function
called Low Altitude Alert System (LAAS). Although
not as sophisticated as MSAW, LAAS alerts the controller when a MODE C transponder equipped aircraft operating on an IFR flight plan is below a predetermined
minimum safe altitude.

NOTE-
*Pilots operating VFR may request MSAW or LAAS moni-
toring if their aircraft are equipped with Mode C transponders.*

EXAMPLE-
Apache Three Three Papa request MSAW/LAAS.

b. Aircraft Conflict Alert:

1. Controllers will immediately issue an alert to the pilot of an aircraft under their control if they are aware of another aircraft which is not under their control, at an altitude which, in the controller's judgment, places both aircraft in unsafe proximity to each other. With the alert, when feasible, the controller will offer the pilot the position of the traffic if time permits and an alternate course(s) of action. Any alternate course(s) of action the controller may recommend to the pilot will be predicated only on other traffic being worked by the controller.

EXAMPLE–
American Three, traffic alert, (position of traffic, if time permits), advise you turn right/left heading (degrees) and/ or climb/descend to (altitude) immediately.

4-1-16. RADAR ASSISTANCE TO VFR AIRCRAFT

a. Radar equipped FAA ATC facilities provide radar assistance and navigation service (vectors) to VFR aircraft provided the aircraft can communicate with the facility, are within radar coverage, and can be radar identified.

b. Pilots should clearly understand that authorization to proceed in accordance with such radar navigational assistance does not constitute authorization for the pilot to violate FARs. In effect, assistance provided is on the basis that navigational guidance information issued is advisory in nature and the job of flying the aircraft safely, remains with the pilot.

c. In many cases, controllers will be unable to determine if flight into instrument conditions will result from their instructions. To avoid possible hazards resulting from being vectored into IFR conditions, pilots should keep controllers advised of the weather conditions in which they are operating and along the course ahead.

d. Radar navigation assistance (vectors) may be initiated by the controller when one of the following conditions exist:

1. The controller suggests the vector and the pilot concurs.

2. A special program has been established and vectoring service has been advertised.

3. In the controller's judgment the vector is necessary for air safety.

e. Radar navigation assistance (vectors) and other radar derived information may be provided in response to pilot requests. Many factors, such as limitations of radar, volume of traffic, communications frequency, congestion, and controller workload could prevent the controller from providing it. Controllers have complete discretion for determining if they are able to provide the service in a particular case. Their decision not to provide the service in a particular case is not subject to question.

4-1-17. TERMINAL RADAR SERVICES FOR VFR AIRCRAFT

a. Basic Radar Service:

1. In addition to the use of radar for the control of IFR aircraft, all commissioned radar facilities provide the following basic radar services for VFR aircraft:

(a) Safety alerts.

(b) Traffic advisories.

(c) Limited radar vectoring (on a workload permitting basis).

(d) Sequencing at locations where procedures have been established for this purpose and/or when covered by a Letter of Agreement.

NOTE–
When the stage services were developed, two basic radar services (traffic advisories and limited vectoring) were identified as "Stage I." This definition became unnecessary and the term "Stage I" was eliminated from use. The term "Stage II" has been eliminated in conjunction with the airspace reclassification, and sequencing services to locations with local procedures and/or letters of agreement to provide this service have been included in basic services to VFR aircraft. These basic services will still be provided by all terminal radar facilities whether they include Class B, Class C, Class D or Class E airspace. "Stage III" services have been replaced with "Class B" and "TRSA" service where applicable.

2. Vectoring service may be provided when requested by the pilot or with pilot concurrence when suggested by ATC.

3. Pilots of arriving aircraft should contact approach control on the publicized frequency and give their position, altitude, aircraft call sign, type aircraft, radar beacon code (if transponder equipped), destination, and request traffic information.

4. Approach control will issue wind and runway except when the pilot states "have numbers" or this information is contained in the ATIS broadcast and the pilot

lot states that the current ATIS information has been received. Traffic information is provided on a workload permitting basis. Approach control will specify the time or place at which the pilot is to contact the tower on local control frequency for further landing information. Radar service is automatically terminated upon being advised to contact the tower.

5. Sequencing for VFR aircraft is available at certain terminal locations (see locations listed in the Airport/Facility Directory). The purpose of the service is to adjust the flow of arriving VFR and IFR aircraft into the traffic pattern in a safe and orderly manner and to provide radar traffic information to departing VFR aircraft. Pilot participation is urged but is not mandatory. Traffic information is provided on a workload permitting basis. Standard radar separation between VFR or between VFR and IFR aircraft is not provided.

(a) Pilots of arriving VFR aircraft should initiate radio contact on the publicized frequency with approach control when approximately 25 miles from the airport at which sequencing services are being provided. On initial contact by VFR aircraft, approach control will assume that sequencing service is requested. After radar contact is established, the pilot may use pilot navigation to enter the traffic pattern or, depending on traffic conditions, approach control may provide the pilot with routings or vectors necessary for proper sequencing with other participating VFR and IFR traffic en route to the airport. When a flight is positioned behind a preceding aircraft and the pilot reports having that aircraft in sight, the pilot will be instructed to follow the preceding aircraft. THE ATC INSTRUCTION TO FOLLOW THE PRECEDING AIRCRAFT DOES NOT AUTHORIZE THE PILOT TO COMPLY WITH ANY ATC CLEARANCE OR INSTRUCTION ISSUED TO THE PRECEDING AIRCRAFT. If other "nonparticipating" or "local" aircraft are in the traffic pattern, the tower will issue a landing sequence. Radar service will be continued to the runway. If an arriving aircraft does not want the service, the pilot should state "NEGATIVE RADAR SERVICE" or make a similar comment, on initial contact with approach control.

(b) Pilots of departing VFR aircraft are encouraged to request radar traffic information by notifying ground control on initial contact with their request and proposed direction of flight.

EXAMPLE–
Xray ground control, November One Eight Six, Cessna One Seventy Two, ready to taxi, VFR southbound at 2,500, have information bravo and request radar traffic information.

NOTE–
Following takeoff, the tower will advise when to contact departure control.

(c) Pilots of aircraft transiting the area and in radar contact/communication with approach control will receive traffic information on a controller workload permitting basis. Pilots of such aircraft should give their position, altitude, aircraft call sign, aircraft type, radar beacon code (if transponder equipped), destination, and/or route of flight.

b. TRSA Service (Radar Sequencing and Separation Service for VFR Aircraft in a TRSA).

1. This service has been implemented at certain terminal locations. The service is advertised in the Airport/Facility Directory. The purpose of this service is to provide separation between all participating VFR aircraft and all IFR aircraft operating within the airspace defined as the Terminal Radar Service Area (TRSA). Pilot participation is urged but is not mandatory.

2. If any aircraft does not want the service, the pilot should state "NEGATIVE TRSA SERVICE" or make a similar comment, on initial contact with approach control or ground control, as appropriate.

3. TRSAs are depicted on sectional aeronautical charts and listed in the Airport/Facility Directory.

4. While operating within a TRSA, pilots are provided TRSA service and separation as prescribed in this paragraph. In the event of a radar outage, separation and sequencing of VFR aircraft will be suspended as this service is dependent on radar. The pilot will be advised that the service is not available and issued wind, runway information, and the time or place to contact the tower. Traffic information will be provided on a workload permitting basis.

5. Visual separation is used when prevailing conditions permit and it will be applied as follows:

(a) When a VFR flight is positioned behind a preceding aircraft and the pilot reports having that aircraft in sight, the pilot will be instructed by ATC to follow the preceding aircraft. Radar service will be continued to the runway. THE ATC INSTRUCTION TO FOLLOW THE PRECEDING AIRCRAFT DOES NOT AUTHORIZE THE PILOT TO COMPLY WITH ANY ATC CLEARANCE OR INSTRUCTION ISSUED TO THE PRECEDING AIRCRAFT.

(b) If other "nonparticipating" or "local" aircraft are in the traffic pattern, the tower will issue a landing sequence.

(c) Departing VFR aircraft may be asked if they can visually follow a preceding departure out of the TRSA. The pilot will be instructed to follow the other aircraft provided that the pilot can maintain visual contact with that aircraft.

6. VFR aircraft will be separated from VFR/IFR aircraft by one of the following:

(a) 500 feet vertical separation.

(b) Visual separation.

(c) Target resolution (a process to ensure that correlated radar targets do not touch) when using broadband radar systems.

7. Participating pilots operating VFR in a TRSA:

(a) Must maintain an altitude when assigned by ATC unless the altitude assignment is to maintain at or below a specified altitude. ATC may assign altitudes for separation that do not conform to FAR Part 91.159. When the altitude assignment is no longer needed for separation or when leaving the TRSA, the instruction will be broadcast, "RESUME APPROPRIATE VFR ALTITUDES." Pilots must then return to an altitude that conforms to FAR Part 91.159 as soon as practicable.

(b) When not assigned an altitude, the pilot should coordinate with ATC prior to any altitude change.

8. Within the TRSA, traffic information on observed but unidentified targets will, to the extent possible, be provided to all IFR and participating VFR aircraft. The pilot will be vectored upon request to avoid the observed traffic, provided the aircraft to be vectored is within the airspace under the jurisdiction of the controller.

9. Departing aircraft should inform ATC of their intended destination and/or route of flight and proposed cruising altitude.

10. ATC will normally advise participating VFR aircraft when leaving the geographical limits of the TRSA. Radar service is not automatically terminated with this advisory unless specifically stated by the controller.

c. Class C Service: This service provides, in addition to basic radar service, approved separation between IFR and VFR aircraft, and sequencing of VFR arrivals to the primary airport.

d. Class B Service: This service provides, in addition to basic radar service, approved separation of aircraft based on IFR, VFR, and/or weight, and sequencing of VFR arrivals to the primary airport(s).

e. PILOT RESPONSIBILITY: THESE SERVICES ARE NOT TO BE INTERPRETED AS RELIEVING PILOTS OF THEIR RESPONSIBILITIES TO SEE AND AVOID OTHER TRAFFIC OPERATING IN BASIC VFR WEATHER CONDITIONS, TO ADJUST THEIR OPERATIONS AND FLIGHT PATH AS NECESSARY TO PRECLUDE SERIOUS WAKE ENCOUNTERS, TO MAINTAIN APPROPRIATE TERRAIN AND OBSTRUCTION CLEARANCE, OR TO REMAIN IN WEATHER CONDITIONS EQUAL TO OR BETTER THAN THE MINIMUMS REQUIRED BY FAR PART 91.155. WHENEVER COMPLIANCE WITH AN ASSIGNED ROUTE, HEADING AND/OR ALTITUDE IS LIKELY TO COMPROMISE PILOT RESPONSIBILITY RESPECTING TERRAIN AND OBSTRUCTION CLEARANCE, VORTEX EXPOSURE, AND WEATHER MINIMUMS, APPROACH CONTROL SHOULD BE SO ADVISED AND A REVISED CLEARANCE OR INSTRUCTION OBTAINED.

f. ATC services for VFR aircraft participating in terminal radar services are dependent on air traffic control radar. Services for VFR aircraft are not available during periods of a radar outage and are limited during CENRAP operations. The pilot will be advised when VFR services are limited or not available.

NOTE–
Class B and Class C airspace are areas of regulated airspace. The absence of ATC radar does not negate the requirement of an ATC clearance to enter Class B airspace or two way radio contact with ATC to enter Class C airspace.

4-1-18. TOWER EN ROUTE CONTROL (TEC)

a. TEC is an ATC program to provide a service to aircraft proceeding to and from metropolitan areas. It links designated Approach Control Areas by a network of identified routes made up of the existing airway structure of the National Airspace System. The FAA initiated an expanded TEC program to include as many facilities as possible. The program's intent is to provide an overflow resource in the low altitude system which would enhance ATC services. A few facilities have historically allowed turbojets to proceed between certain city pairs, such as Milwaukee and Chicago, via tower en route and these locations may continue this service. However, the expanded TEC program will be applied, generally, for nonturbojet aircraft operating at and below 10,000 feet. The program is entirely within the approach control airspace of multiple terminal facilities. Essentially, it is for relatively short flights. Participating pilots are encouraged to use TEC for flights of two hours duration or less. If longer flights are planned, extensive coordination may be required within the multiple complex which could result in unanticipated delays.

b. Pilots requesting TEC are subject to the same delay factor at the destination airport as other aircraft in the ATC system. In addition, departure and en route delays may occur depending upon individual facility workload. When a major metropolitan airport is incurring significant delays, pilots in the TEC program may want to consider an alternative airport experiencing no delay.

c. There are no unique requirements upon pilots to use the TEC program. Normal flight plan filing procedures will ensure proper flight plan processing. Pilots should include the acronym "TEC" in the remarks section of the flight plan when requesting tower en route control.

d. All approach controls in the system may not operate up to the maximum TEC altitude of 10,000 feet. IFR flight may be planned to any satellite airport in proximity to the major primary airport via the same routing.

4-1-19. TRANSPONDER OPERATION

a. General

1. Pilots should be aware that proper application of transponder operating procedures will provide both VFR and IFR aircraft with a higher degree of safety in the environment where high-speed closure rates are possible. Transponders substantially increase the capability of radar to see an aircraft and the MODE C feature enables the controller to quickly determine where potential traffic conflicts may exist. Even VFR pilots who are not in contact with ATC will be afforded greater protection from IFR aircraft and VFR aircraft which are receiving traffic advisories. Nevertheless, pilots should never relax their visual scanning vigilance for other aircraft.

2. Air Traffic Control Radar Beacon System (ATCRBS) is similar to and compatible with military coded radar beacon equipment. Civil MODE A is identical to military MODE 3.

3. Civil and military transponders should be adjusted to the "on" or normal operating position as late as practicable prior to takeoff and to "off" or "standby" as soon as practicable after completing landing roll, unless the change to "standby" has been accomplished previously at the request of ATC. IN ALL CASES, WHILE IN CONTROLLED AIRSPACE EACH PILOT OPERATING AN AIRCRAFT EQUIPPED WITH AN OPERABLE ATC TRANSPONDER MAINTAINED IN ACCORDANCE WITH FAR PART 91.413 SHALL OPERATE THE TRANSPONDER, INCLUDING MODE C IF INSTALLED, ON THE APPROPRIATE CODE OR AS ASSIGNED BY ATC. IN CLASS G AIRSPACE, THE TRANSPONDER SHOULD BE OPERATING WHILE AIRBORNE UNLESS OTHERWISE REQUESTED BY ATC.

4. A pilot on an IFR flight who elects to cancel the IFR flight plan prior to reaching destination, should adjust the transponder according to VFR operations.

5. If entering a U.S. OFFSHORE AIRSPACE AREA from outside the U.S., the pilot should advise on first radio contact with a U.S. radar ATC facility that such equipment is available by adding "transponder" to the aircraft identification.

6. It should be noted by all users of ATC transponders that the coverage they can expect is limited to "line of sight." Low altitude or aircraft antenna shielding by the aircraft itself may result in reduced range. Range can be improved by climbing to a higher altitude. It may be possible to minimize antenna shielding by locating the antenna where dead spots are only noticed during abnormal flight attitudes.

b. Transponder Code Designation

1. For ATC to utilize one or a combination of the 4096 discrete codes FOUR DIGIT CODE DESIGNATION will be used, e.g., code 2100 will be expressed as TWO ONE ZERO ZERO. Due to the operational characteristics of the rapidly expanding automated air traffic control system, THE LAST TWO DIGITS OF THE SELECTED TRANSPONDER CODE SHOULD ALWAYS READ "00" UNLESS SPECIFICALLY REQUESTED BY ATC TO BE OTHERWISE.

c. Automatic Altitude Reporting (MODE C)

1. Some transponders are equipped with a MODE C automatic altitude reporting capability. This system converts aircraft altitude in 100 foot increments to coded digital information which is transmitted together with MODE C framing pulses to the interrogating radar facility. The manner in which transponder panels are designed differs, therefore, a pilot should be thoroughly familiar with the operation of the transponder so that ATC may realize its full capabilities.

2. Adjust transponder to reply on the MODE A/3 code specified by ATC and, if equipped, to reply on MODE C with altitude reporting capability activated unless deactivation is directed by ATC or unless the installed aircraft equipment has not been tested and calibrated as required by FAR Part 91.217. If deactivation is required by ATC, turn off the altitude reporting feature of your transponder. An instruction by ATC to "STOP ALTITUDE SQUAWK, ALTITUDE DIFFERS (number of feet) FEET," may be an indication that your transponder is transmitting incorrect altitude information or that you have an incorrect altimeter setting. While an incorrect altimeter setting has no effect on the MODE C altitude information transmitted by your transponder (transponders are preset at 29.92), it would cause you to fly at an actual altitude different from your assigned altitude. When a controller indicates that an altitude readout is invalid, the pilot should initiate a check to verify that the aircraft altimeter is set correctly.

3. Pilots of aircraft with operating MODE C altitude reporting transponders should report exact altitude or flight level to the nearest hundred foot increment when establishing initial contact with an ATC facility. Exact altitude or flight level reports on initial contact provide ATC with information that is required prior to using MODE C altitude information for separation purposes. This will significantly reduce altitude verification requests.

d. Transponder IDENT Feature

1. The transponder shall be operated only as specified by ATC. Activate the "IDENT" feature only upon request of the ATC controller.

e. Code Changes

1. When making routine code changes, pilots should avoid inadvertent selection of codes 7500, 7600 or 7700 thereby causing momentary false alarms at automated ground facilities. For example, when switching from code 2700 to code 7200, switch first to 2200 then to 7200, NOT to 7700 and then 7200. This procedure applies to nondiscrete code 7500 and all discrete codes in the 7600 and 7700 series (i.e. 7600–7677, 7700–7777) which will trigger special indicators in automated facilities. Only nondiscrete code 7500 will be decoded as the hijack code.

2. Under no circumstances should a pilot of a civil aircraft operate the transponder on Code 7777. This code is reserved for military interceptor operations.

3. Military pilots operating VFR or IFR within restricted/warning areas should adjust their transponders to code 4000 unless another code has been assigned by ATC.

f. Mode C Transponder Requirements

1. Specific details concerning requirements to carry and operate Mode C transponders, as well as exceptions and ATC authorized deviations from the requirements are found in FAR Part 91.215 and FAR Part 99.12.

2. In general, the FAR requires aircraft to be equipped with Mode C transponders when operating:

(a) at or above 10,000 feet MSL over the 48 contiguous states or the District of Columbia, excluding that airspace below 2,500 feet AGL;

(b) within 30 miles of a Class B airspace primary airport, below 10,000 feet MSL. Balloons, gliders, and aircraft not equipped with an engine driven electrical system are excepted from the above requirements when operating below the floor of Class A airspace and/or; outside of a Class B airspace and below the ceiling of the Class B Airspace (or 10,000 feet MSL, whichever is lower);

(c) within and above all Class C airspace, up to 10,000 feet MSL;

(d) within 10 miles of certain designated airports, excluding that airspace which is both outside the Class D surface area and below 1,200 feet AGL. Balloons, gliders and aircraft not equipped with an engine driven electrical system are excepted from this requirement.

3. FAR Part 99.12 requires all aircraft flying into, within, or across the contiguous U.S. ADIZ be equipped with a Mode C or Mode S transponder. Balloons, gliders and aircraft not equipped with an engine driven electrical system are excepted from this requirement.

4. Pilots shall ensure that their aircraft transponder is operating on an appropriate ATC assigned VFR/IFR code and MODE C when operating in such airspace. If in doubt about the operational status of either feature of your transponder while airborne, contact the nearest ATC facility or FSS and they will advise you what facility you should contact for determining the status of your equipment.

5. In-flight requests for "immediate" deviation from the transponder requirement may be approved by controllers only when the flight will continue IFR or when weather conditions prevent VFR descent and continued VFR flight in airspace not affected by the FAR. All other requests for deviation should be made by contacting the nearest Flight Service or Air Traffic facility in person or by telephone. The nearest ARTCC will normally be the controlling agency and is responsible for coordinating requests involving deviations in other ARTCC areas.

g. Transponder Operation Under Visual Flight Rules (VFR)

1. Unless otherwise instructed by an Air Traffic Control Facility, adjust transponder to reply on MODE 3/A code 1200 regardless of altitude.

2. Adjust transponder to reply on MODE C, with altitude reporting *capability activated* if the aircraft is so equipped, unless deactivation is directed by ATC or unless the installed equipment has not been tested and calibrated as required by FAR Part 91.217. If deactivation is required and your transponder is so designed, turn off the altitude reporting switch and continue to transmit MODE C framing pulses. If this capability does not exist, turn off MODE C.

h. Radar Beacon Phraseology

Air traffic controllers, both civil and military, will use the following phraseology when referring to operation of the Air Traffic Control Radar Beacon System (ATCRBS). Instructions by ATC refer only to MODE A/3 or MODE C operation and do not affect the operation of the transponder on other MODE's.

1. *SQUAWK (number):* Operate radar beacon transponder on designated code in MODE A/3.

2. *IDENT:* Engage the "IDENT" feature (military I/P) of the transponder.

3. *SQUAWK (number) and IDENT:* Operate transponder on specified code in MODE A/3 and engage the "IDENT" (military I/P) feature.

4. *SQUAWK STANDBY:* Switch transponder to standby position.

5. *SQUAWK LOW/NORMAL:* Operate transponder on low or normal sensitivity as specified. Transponder is operated in "NORMAL" position unless ATC specifies "LOW" ("ON" is used instead of "NORMAL" as a master control label on some types of transponders.)

6. *SQUAWK ALTITUDE:* Activate MODE C with automatic altitude reporting.

7. *STOP ALTITUDE SQUAWK:* Turn off altitude reporting switch and continue transmitting MODE C framing pulses. If your equipment does not have this capability, turn off MODE C.

8. *STOP SQUAWK (mode in use):* Switch off specified mode. (Used for military aircraft when the controller is unaware of military service requirements for the aircraft to continue operation on another MODE.)

9. *STOP SQUAWK:* Switch off transponder.

10. *SQUAWK MAYDAY:* Operate transponder in the emergency position (MODE A Code 7700 for civil transponder. MODE 3 Code 7700 and emergency feature for military transponder.)

11. *SQUAWK VFR:* Operate radar beacon transponder on code 1200 in the MODE A/3, or other appropriate VFR code.

4-1-20. HAZARDOUS AREA REPORTING SERVICE

a. Selected FSS's provide flight monitoring where regularly traveled VFR routes cross large bodies of water, swamps, and mountains. This service is provided for the purpose of expeditiously alerting Search and Rescue facilities when required. (See FIG 4-1-3.)

1. When requesting the service either in person, by telephone or by radio, pilots should be prepared to give the following information: type of aircraft, altitude, indicated airspeed, present position, route of flight, heading.

2. Radio contacts are desired at least every 10 minutes. If contact is lost for more than 15 minutes, Search and Rescue will be alerted. Pilots are responsible for canceling their request for service when they are outside the service area boundary. Pilots experiencing two-way radio failure are expected to land as soon as practicable and cancel their request for the service. FIG 4-1-3 depicts the areas and the FSS facilities involved in this program.

Hazardous Area Reporting Service

FIG 4-1-.

b. Long Island Sound Reporting Service:

The New York and Bridgeport AFSS's provide Long Island Sound Reporting service on request for aircraft traversing Long Island Sound.

1. When requesting the service pilots should ask for SOUND REPORTING SERVICE and should be prepared to provide the following appropriate information:

(a) type and color of aircraft,

(b) the specific route and altitude across the sound including the shore crossing point,

(c) the overwater crossing time,

(d) number of persons on board, and

(e) true air speed.

2. Radio contacts are desired at least every 10 minutes; however, for flights of shorter duration a mid-sound report is requested. If contact is lost for more than 15 minutes Search and Rescue will be alerted. Pilots are responsible for canceling their request for the Long Island Sound Reporting Service when outside the service area boundary. Aircraft experiencing radio failure will be expected to land as soon as practicable and cancel their request for the service.

3. *Communications:* Primary communications - pilots are to transmit on 122.1 MHz and listen on one of the following VOR frequencies:

(a) New York AFSS Controls:

(1) Hampton RCO (FSS transmits and receives on 122.6 MHz).

(2) Calverton VORTAC (FSS transmits on 117.2 and receives on standard FSS frequencies).

(3) Kennedy VORTAC (FSS transmits on 115.9 and receives on 122.1 MHz).

(b) Bridgeport AFSS Controls:

(1) Madison VORTAC (FSS transmits on 110.4 and receives on 122.1 MHz).

(2) Groton VOR (FSS transmits on 111.8 and receives on 122.1 MHz).

(3) Bridgeport VOR (FSS transmits on 108.8 and receives on 122.1 MHz).

c. Block Island Reporting Service:

Within the Long Island Reporting Service, the New York FSS also provides an additional service for aircraft operating between Montauk Point and Block Island. When requesting this service, pilots should ask for BLOCK ISLAND REPORTING SERVICE and should be prepared to provide the same flight information as required for the Long Island Sound Reporting Service.

1. A minimum of three position reports are mandatory for this service; these are:

(a) Reporting leaving either Montauk Point or Block Island.

(b) Midway report.

(c) Report when over either Montauk Point or Block Island. At this time, the overwater service is canceled.

2. COMMUNICATIONS: Pilots are to transmit and receive on 122.6 MHz.

NOTE—
Pilots are advised that 122.6 MHz is a remote receiver located at the Hampton VORTAC site and designed to provide radio coverage between Hampton and Block Island. Flights proceeding beyond Block Island may contact the Bridgeport AFSS by transmitting on 122.1 MHz and listening on Groton VOR (TMU) frequency 111.8 MHz.

d. Cape Cod and Islands Radar Overwater Flight Following:

In addition to normal VFR radar advisory services, traffic permitting, Cape Approach Control provides a radar overwater flight following service for aircraft traversing the Cape Cod and adjacent Island area. Pilots desiring this service may contact Cape RAPCON on 118.2 MHz.

1. Pilots requesting this service should be prepared to give the following information:

(a) type and color of aircraft,

(b) altitude,

(c) position and heading,

(d) route of flight, and

(e) true airspeed.

2. For best radar coverage, pilots are encouraged to fly at 1,500 feet MSL or above.

3. Pilots are responsible for canceling their request for overwater flight following when they are over the mainland and/or outside the service area boundary.

e. Lake Reporting Service:

Cleveland and Lansing AFSS's provide Lake Reporting Service on request for aircraft traversing the western half of Lake Erie; Green Bay, Kankakee, Lansing, and Terre Haute AFSS's provide Lake Reporting Service on request for aircraft traversing Lake Michigan.

1. When requesting the service, pilots should ask for LAKE REPORTING SERVICE.

2. Pilots *not* on a VFR flight plan should be prepared to provide all information that is normally provided for a complete VFR flight plan.

3. Pilots already on a VFR flight plan should be prepared to provide the following information:

(a) Aircraft or flight identification.

(b) Type of aircraft.

(c) Near–shore crossing point or last fix before crossing.

(d) Proposed time over near–shore crossing point or last fix before crossing.

(e) Proposed altitude.

(f) Proposed route of flight.

(g) Estimated time over water.

(h) Next landing point.

(i) AFSS/FSS having complete VFR flight plan information.

4. Radio contacts must not exceed 10 minutes when pilots fly at an altitude that affords continuous communications. If radio contact is lost for more than 15 minutes (5 minutes after a scheduled reporting time), Search and Rescue (SAR) will be alerted.

5. The estimated time for crossing the far shore will be the scheduled reporting time for aircraft that fly at an altitude that does not afford continuous communication coverage while crossing the lake. If radio contact is not established within 5 minutes of that time, SAR will be alerted.

6. Pilots are responsible for canceling their request for Lake Reporting Service when outside the service area boundary. Aircraft experiencing radio failure will be expected to land as soon as practicable and cancel their Lake Reporting Service flight plan.

7. Communications: Primary communications – Pilots should communicate with the following facilities on the indicated frequencies:

(a) **Cleveland AFSS Controls:**

(1) Cleveland RCO (FSS transmits and receives on 122.35 or 122.55 MHz).

(2) Sandusky VOR (FSS transmits on 109.2 and receives on 122.1 MHz).

(b) **Green Bay AFSS Controls:**

(1) Escanaba VORTAC (FSS transmits on 110.8 and receives on 122.1 MHz).

(2) Green Bay RCO (FSS transmits and receives on 122.55 MHz).

(3) Manistique RCO (FSS transmits and receives on 122.25 MHz).

(4) Manitowoc VOR (FSS transmits on 111.0 and receives on 122.1 MHz).

(5) Menominee VOR (FSS transmits on 109.6 and receives on 122.1 MHz).

(6) Milwaukee RCO (FSS transmits and receives on 122.65 MHz).

(7) Falls VOR (FSS transmits on 110.0 and receives on 122.1 MHz).

(c) **Kankakee AFSS Controls:**

(1) Northbrook VORTAC (FSS transmits on 113.0 and receives on 122.1 MHz).

(2) Chicago Heights VORTAC (FSS transmits on 114.2 and receives on 122.1 MHz).

(3) Meigs RCO (FSS transmits and receives on 122.15 MHz).

(d) **Lansing Afss Controls:**

(1) **Lake Erie:** Detroit City RCO (FSS transmits and receives on 122.55 MHz).

(2) **Lake Michigan:**

[a] Keeler VORTAC (FSS transmits on 116.6 and receives on 122.1 MHz).

[b] Ludington RCO (FSS transmits and receives on 122.45 MHz).

[c] Manistee VORTAC (FSS transmits on 111.4 and receives on 122.1 MHz).

[d] Muskegon RCO (FSS transmits and receives on 122.5 MHz).

[e] Pellston RCO (FSS transmits and receives on 122.3 MHz).

[f] Pullman VORTAC (FSS transmits on 112.1 and receives on 122.1 MHz).

[g] Traverse City RCO (FSS transmits and receives on 122.65 MHz).

(e) **Terre Haute AFSS Controls:** South Bend RCOs (FSS transmits and receives on 123.65/primary and 122.6/secondary MHz).

4-1-21. AIRPORT RESERVATIONS OPERATIONS AND PROCEDURES

a. FAA operates the Computerized Voice Reservation System (CVRS) which is used to make arrival and/or departure reservations at airports designated by FAR Part 93 Subpart K as High Density Traffic Airports (HDTA). The system may also be used to make arrival and/or departure reservations at airports which are part of a Special Traffic Management Program (STMP). Some STMPs may require users to contact the controlling ARTCC to make reservations, while others will use the CVRS to make reservations. Pilots should check current Notices to Airmen (NOTAM) to determine airports included in a special traffic management program and reservations procedures.

b. High Density Traffic Airports (HDTA):

1. The FAA, by FAR Part 93, Subpart K, as amended, has designated the John F. Kennedy (JFK), LaGuardia (LGA), Chicago O'Hare (ORD), Washington National (DCA), and Newark (EWR) Airports as high density airports and has prescribed air traffic rules and requirements for operating aircraft to and from these airports. (The quota for EWR has been suspended indefinitely.) Reservations for JFK are required between 3:00 p.m. and 7:59 p.m. local time. Reservations at ORD are required between 6:45 a.m. and 9:15 p.m. local time. Reservations for LGA and DCA are required between 6:00 a.m. and 11:59 p.m. local time. Helicopter operations are excluded from the requirement for a reservation.

NOTE–
Time periods for ORD are in 30–minute increments.

2. The FAA has established an Airport Reservations Office (ARO) to receive and process all Instrument Flight Rules (IFR) requests for operations at the designated HDTA's. This office monitors operation of the high density rule and allots reservations on a "first-come-first-served" basis determined by the time the request is received at the reservation office. Standby lists are not maintained. The ARO utilizes the CVRS to make all reservations. Users may access the computer system using a touch tone telephone, rotary dial telephone, or a personal computer equipped with a modem. Requests for IFR reservations will be accepted starting 48 hours prior to the proposed time of operation at the affected airport. For example, a request for an 11:00 a.m. reservation on a Thursday will be accepted beginning at 11:00 a.m. on the preceding Tuesday. An exception to the 48 hour limitation is made for weekends to recognize normal business hours. Consequently, a reservation request for an IFR operation on Monday would be accepted on the previous Thursday, starting at the proposed hour of operation. Similarly, requests for IFR operations on Tuesday would be accepted on the previous Friday, starting at the proposed hour of operation. For example, a request for an 11:00 a.m. reservation on Tuesday would be accepted beginning at 11:00 a.m. on Friday. Another exception to the 48 hour time limit is made for users who make both an arrival and departure reservation provided they both fall on the same calendar day and they are both made during the same phone call. For example, a reservation request for an 11:00 a.m. arrival on Friday and a 4:00 p.m. departure on Friday may be made beginning at 11:00 a.m. Wednesday.

3. A maximum of two transactions per phone call will be accepted.

4. The ARO will not provide scheduling according to planned departure/arrival time. Assignments will be made on an hourly or 30–minute basis, e.g., an approved reservation for 1300 covers an operation any time between 1300 and 1359 and an approved reservation for 0845 at O'Hare covers an operation between 0845 and 0914.

5. An approved reservation does not constitute a warranty against traffic delays nor does it guarantee arrival and/or departure within such allocated hours.

Also, a reservation does not constitute an Air Traffic Control (ATC) clearance.

6. The filing of a request for an IFR reservation does not constitute the filing of an IFR flight plan as required by regulation. The IFR flight plan should be filed only after the reservation is obtained and should be filed through normal channels. The ARO is not equipped to accept or process IFR flight plans.

c. IFR Reservations:

1. If operating IFR, an IFR reservation is required prior to takeoff for any operation to or from a high density airport. Users may obtain IFR reservations in either of two ways. They may file their request with the nearest Flight Service Station (FSS) by any available means or call the AROs interactive computer system via touch-tone telephone, rotary dial telephone, or personal computer modem. The telephone numbers for the ARO computer are: Using touch-tone or rotary phone: 1–800–875–9694. For Personal Computer and Modem: 1–800–875–9759.

(a) Users may contact the ARO at 703–904–4452 if they have a problem making a reservation or have a question concerning the HDTA regulations. (Being unable to make a reservation due to the fact that all the slots have been allocated is not considered as having a problem making a reservation).

2. When filing a request for an IFR reservation, the pilot should be prepared to provide the following information:

(a) Name(s) of high density traffic airport(s) for which the pilot wishes reservation(s).

(b) Date(s) and hour(s) (UTC) of proposed operation(s).

(c) Aircraft identification/tail number(s).

3. Should the requested time not be available, the user will be offered the closest time before or after the requested time. If an alternate time is accepted, this will be considered as an assigned allocation unless subsequently cancelled by the user.

4. Users are encouraged to advise the ARO whenever they need to change their reservation or to cancel their IFR reservation when it is known that the reservation will not be used. For other than scheduled air carriers/commuters, a cancellation should be made directly to the ARO computer system or an FSS.

5. The following information should be available when cancelling a reservation:

(a) Aircraft identification/tail number.

(b) Airport for which reservation was made.

(c) Date and Time (UTC) of reservation.

(d) Reservation number.

6. To ensure retention of a reservation, a pilot holding an IFR arrival reservation must retain IFR status until in contact with the terminal ATC facility.

7. Reservations are required when filing one of the HDTA's as an alternate airport. Pilots are encouraged to file airports other than the high density as alternate airports.

d. Additional IFR Reservations:

1. If favorable conditions in the system and at the HDTA indicate a significant delay is not likely in the short term, the ARO may coordinate with the HDTA tower to determine that additional IFR reservations may be accommodated for a specific time period. This is an additional IFR reservation as described in FAR Part 93. If additional IFR reservations can be accommodated, they are administered by the ARO under the procedures described above.

2. An operator of an IFR unscheduled operation may take off or land an aircraft without regard to the maximum allocation if a reservation is obtained from ATC in accordance with the procedures above. A reservation is granted for an additional IFR operation only if it can be accommodated by ATC without significant additional delay to operations already allocated. The granting of an additional IFR reservation is contingent upon dynamic, short-term traffic and weather conditions. Generally, availability of additionals will not be known more than 8 hours in advance of the current time. If available, IFR additionals will be granted on a first-come-first-served basis.

3. An operator who has been unable to obtain a reservation under the normal 48 hour in advance procedure may find they are able to obtain a reservation on the scheduled day of operation when additionals can be authorized.

e. Visual Flight Rules (VFR) Reservations:

1. The operator of a VFR unscheduled operation may take off or land an aircraft under VFR at an HDTA if a departure or arrival reservation is obtained from the FAA ATC facility serving the HDTA.

2. Under FAR Part 93, a VFR operation is considered to be an additional operation. VFR additional operations may be granted by ATC if they can be accommodated without significant delay to operations already allocated. In addition, the reported ceiling at the HDTA must be at least 1,000 feet and the reported ground visibility at least 3 miles.

3. Each HDTA lies within Class B airspace. A clearance from ATC to enter the airspace or depart the airport under VFR constitutes an approval for a VFR additional reservation.

4. Any time an HDTA is not authorizing VFR operations, a NOTAM to that effect will be issued by the controlling ATC facility and a recording placed on the Automated Terminal Information Service. This information can be obtained from any FSS or by referring to the HDTA teletype weather report. The code "VNA" at the end of the weather report indicates VFR arrival reservations are not authorized. The indication will not be made when IFR weather conditions exist.

5. The requirements for obtaining reservations pursuant to FAR Part 93, Subpart K, are mandatory. Failure to operate in accordance with the FAR may be grounds for enforcement action.

f. Special Traffic Management Programs (STMP):

1. Special procedures may be established when a location requires special traffic handling to accommodate above normal traffic demand (e.g., the Indianapolis 500, Super Bowl, etc.) or reduced airport capacity (e.g., airport runway/taxiway closures for airport construction). The special procedures may remain in effect until the problem has been resolved or until local traffic management procedures can handle the situation and a need for special handling no longer exists.

2. CVRS may be used to allocate the reservations during an STMP. If CVRS is being used, the toll-free telephone numbers will be advertised by NOTAM. Be sure to check current NOTAM's to determine what airports are included in an STMP, days and times reservations are required, time limits for reservations requests, and who to contact for reservations.

g. Making HDTA/STMP Reservations Using The CVRS:

1. *Computer Modem Users:* A Personal Computer (PC) may be used to make reservations on the CVRS. Equipment required is a computer with a modem capable of a 300 to 9600 baud rate and a communications software program. There are several communications software programs available from many computer stores. The type program required is one which is used to connect with a Bulletin Board System (BBS). The CVRS modem data is transmitted using No Parity, 8 data bits, and 1 stop bit (N,8,1). Be sure your computer software is set to these parameters.

2. When your computer connects with CVRS, you will be presented with a screen that will ask you to log on. If this is the first time you have logged onto the CVRS, you will be asked for your name, the city you are calling from, and a password. (Be sure to record your password for future use). CVRS uses your name and password to save your computer "set-up" so that the next time you call you will have the same display. After you have logged on, every thing you need to do involving a reservation is menu driven. There are also several files you can download which explain CVRS operations in greater detail.

3. *Telephone users:* When using the telephone to make a reservation, you are prompted for input of information about what you wish to do. All input is accomplished using the keypad or rotary dial on the telephone. The only problem with a telephone is that most

keys have a letter and number associated with them. When the system asks for a date or time, it is expecting an input of numbers. A problem arises when entering a tail number. The system does not detect if you are entering a letter (alpha character) or a number. Therefore, when entering a tail number two keys are used to represent each letter or number. When entering a number, precede the number you wish by the number 0 (zero) i.e. 01, 02, 03, 04, ... If you wish to enter a letter, first press the key on which the letter appears and then press 1, 2, or 3, depending upon whether the letter you desire is the first, second, or third letter on that key. For example to enter the letter "N" first press the "6" key because "N" is on that key, then press the "2" key because the letter "N" is the second letter on the "6" key. Since there are no keys for the letters "Q" and "Z" CVRS pretends they are on the number "1" key. Therefore, to enter the letter "Q", press 11, and to enter the letter "Z" press 12.

NOTE-
Users are reminded to enter the "N" character with their tail numbers. (See TBL 4-1-4.)

4. Additional helpful key entries:
(See TBL 4-1-5.)

Codes for Tail Number Input

CODES FOR TAIL NUMBER INPUT ONLY			
A–21	J–51	S–73	1-01
B–22	K–52	T–81	2–02
C–23	L–53	U–82	3–03
D–31	M–61	V–83	4–04
E–32	N–62	W–91	5–05
F–33	O–63	X–92	6–06
G–11	P–71	Y–93	7–07
H–42	Q–11	Z–12	8–08
I–43	R–72	0–00	9–09

TBL 4-1-4

Helpful Key Entries

#	After entering a tail number, depressing the "pound key" (#) twice will indicate the end of the tail number.
*2	Will take the user back to the start of the process.
*3	Will repeat the tail number used in a previous reservation.
*5	Will repeat the previous question.
*8	Tutorial Mode: In the tutorial mode each prompt for input includes a more detailed description of what is expected as input. *8 is a toggle on/off switch. If you are in tutorial mode and enter *8, you will return to the normal mode.
*0	Expert Mode: In the expert mode each prompt for input is brief with little or no explanation. Expert mode is also on/off toggle.

TBL 4-1-5

4-1-22. REQUESTS FOR WAIVERS AND AUTHORIZATIONS FROM TITLE 14, CODE OF FEDERAL REGULATIONS (14 CFR)

a. Requests for a Certificate of Waiver or Authorization (FAA Form 7711-2), or requests for renewal of a waiver or authorization, may be accepted by any FAA facility and will be forwarded, if necessary, to the appropriate office having waiver authority.

b. The grant of a Certificate of Waiver or Authorization from 14 CFR constitutes relief from specific regulations, to the degree and for the period of time specified in the certificate, and does not waive any state law or local ordinance. Should the proposed operations conflict with any state law or local ordinance, or require permission of local authorities or property owners, it is the applicant's responsibility to resolve the matter. The holder of a waiver is responsible for compliance with the terms of the waiver and its provisions.

c. A waiver may be canceled at any time by the Administrator, the person authorized to grant the waiver, or the representative designated to monitor a specific operation. In such case either written notice of cancellation, or written confirmation of a verbal cancellation will be provided to the holder.

Section 2. RADIO COMMUNICATIONS PHRASEOLOGY AND TECHNIQUES

4-2-1. GENERAL

a. Radio communications are a critical link in the ATC system. The link can be a strong bond between pilot and controller or it can be broken with surprising speed and disastrous results. Discussion herein provides basic procedures for new pilots and also highlights safe operating concepts for all pilots.

b. The single, most important thought in pilot-controller communications is understanding. It is essential, therefore, that pilots acknowledge each radio communication with ATC by using the appropriate aircraft call sign. Brevity is important, and contacts should be kept as brief as possible, but controllers must know what you want to do before they can properly carry out their control duties. And you, the pilot, must know exactly what the controller wants you to do. Since concise phraseology may not always be adequate, use whatever words are necessary to get your message across. Pilots are to maintain vigilance in monitoring air traffic control radio communications frequencies for potential traffic conflicts with their aircraft especially when operating on an active runway and/or when conducting a final approach to landing.

c. All pilots will find the *Pilot/Controller Glossary* very helpful in learning what certain words or phrases mean. Good phraseology enhances safety and is the mark of a professional pilot. Jargon, chatter, and "CB" slang have no place in ATC communications. The *Pilot/Controller Glossary* is the same glossary used in FAA Order 7110.65, *Air Traffic Control*. We recommend that it be studied and reviewed from time to time to sharpen your communication skills.

4-2-2. RADIO TECHNIQUE

a. Listen before you transmit. Many times you can get the information you want through ATIS or by monitoring the frequency. Except for a few situations where some frequency overlap occurs, if you hear someone else talking, the keying of your transmitter will be futile and you will probably jam their receivers causing them to repeat their call. If you have just changed frequencies, pause, listen, and make sure the frequency is clear.

b. Think before keying your transmitter. Know what you want to say and if it is lengthy; e.g., a flight plan or IFR position report, jot it down.

c. The microphone should be very close to your lips and after pressing the mike button, a slight pause may be necessary to be sure the first word is transmitted. Speak in a normal, conversational tone.

d. When you release the button, wait a few seconds before calling again. The controller or FSS specialist may be jotting down your number, looking for your flight plan, transmitting on a different frequency, or selecting the transmitter for your frequency.

e. Be alert to the sounds *or the lack of sounds* in your receiver. Check your volume, recheck your frequency, and *make sure that your microphone is not stuck* in the transmit position. Frequency blockage can, and has, occurred for extended periods of time due to unintentional transmitter operation. This type of interference is commonly referred to as a "stuck mike," and controllers may refer to it in this manner when attempting to assign an alternate frequency. If the assigned frequency is completely blocked by this type of interference, use the procedures described for en route IFR radio frequency outage to establish or reestablish communications with ATC.

f. Be sure that you are within the performance range of your radio equipment and the ground station equipment. Remote radio sites do not always transmit and receive on all of a facility's available frequencies, particularly with regard to VOR sites where you can hear but not reach a ground station's receiver. Remember that higher altitudes increase the range of VHF "line of sight" communications.

4-2-3. CONTACT PROCEDURES

a. Initial Contact:

1. The terms *initial contact* or *initial callup* means the first radio call you make to a given facility or the first call to a different controller or FSS specialist within a facility. Use the following format:

(a) Name of the facility being called;

(b) Your *full* aircraft identification as filed in the flight plan or as discussed under Aircraft Call Signs below;

(c) The type of message to follow or your request if it is short, and

(d) The word "Over" if required.

EXAMPLE—
☐1 *"New York radio, Mooney Three One One Echo."*
☐2 *"Columbia ground, Cessna Three One Six Zero Foxtrot, I–F–R Memphis."*
☐3 *"Miami center, Baron Five Six Three Hotel, request
V–F–R traffic advisories."*

2. Many FSS's are equipped with RCO's and can
transmit on the same frequency at more than one location. The frequencies available at specific locations are
indicated on charts above FSS communications boxes.
To enable the specialist to utilize the correct transmitter,
advise the location and the frequency on which you expect a reply.

EXAMPLE—
*St. Louis FSS can transmit on frequency 122.3 at either
Farmington, Missouri, or Decatur, Illinois, if you are in
the vicinity of Decatur, your callup should be "Saint Louis
radio, Piper Six Niner Six Yankee, receiving Decatur One
Two Two Point Three."*

3. If radio reception is reasonably assured, inclusion of your request, your position or altitude, and the
phrase "(ATIS) Information Charlie received" in the
initial contact helps decrease radio frequency congestion. Use discretion; do not overload the controller with
information unneeded or superfluous. If you do not get
a response from the ground station, recheck your radios
or use another transmitter, but keep the next contact
short.

EXAMPLE—
*"Atlanta center, Duke Four One Romeo, request V–F–R
traffic advisories, Twenty Northwest Rome, seven thousand five hundred, over."*

**b. Initial Contact When your Transmitting and
Receiving Frequencies are Different:**

1. If you are attempting to establish contact with a
ground station and you are receiving on a different frequency than that transmitted, indicate the VOR name or
the frequency on which you expect a reply. Most FSS's
and control facilities can transmit on several VOR stations in the area. Use the appropriate FSS call-sign as
indicated on charts.

EXAMPLE—
*New York FSS transmits on the Kennedy, the Hampton,
and the Calverton VORTAC's. If you are in the Calverton
area, your callup should be "New York radio, Cessna
Three One Six Zero Foxtrot, receiving Calverton V–O–R,
over."*

2. If the chart indicates FSS frequencies above the
VORTAC or in the FSS communications boxes, trans-

mit or receive on those frequencies nearest your location.

3. When unable to establish contact and you wish
to call *any* ground station, use the phrase "ANY RA-
DIO (tower) (station), GIVE CESSNA THREE ONE
SIX ZERO FOXTROT A CALL ON (frequency) OR
(V–O–R)." If an emergency exists or you need assis-
tance, so state.

**c. Subsequent Contacts and Responses to Callup
from a Ground Facility:**

Use the same format as used for the initial contact except you should state your message or request with the
callup in one transmission. The ground station name
and the word "Over" may be omitted if the message requires an obvious reply and there is no possibility for
misunderstandings. *You should acknowledge all cal-
lups or clearances* unless the controller or FSS specialist advises otherwise. There are some occasions when
controllers must issue time-critical instructions to other
aircraft, and they may be in a position to observe your
response, either visually or on radar. If the situation de
mands your response, take appropriate action or immediately advise the facility of any problem. Acknowledge with your aircraft identification, either at the
beginning or at the end of your transmission, and one
of the words "Wilco," "Roger," "Affirmative,"
"Negative," or other appropriate remarks; e.g., "PIP
ER TWO ONE FOUR LIMA, ROGER." If you have
been receiving services; e.g., VFR traffic advisories and
you are leaving the area or changing frequencies, advise
the ATC facility and terminate contact.

d. Acknowledgement of Frequency Changes:

1. When advised by ATC to change frequencies
acknowledge the instruction. If you select the new fre
quency without an acknowledgement, the controller's
workload is increased because there is no way of knowing whether you received the instruction or have had ra
dio communications failure.

2. At times, a controller/specialist may be working
a sector with multiple frequency assignments. In order
to eliminate unnecessary verbiage and to free the con
troller/specialist for higher priority transmissions, the
controller/specialist may request the pilot "(Identifica
tion), change to my frequency 123.4." This phrase
should alert the pilot that the controller/specialist is
only changing frequencies, not controller/specialist
and that initial callup phraseology may be abbreviated

EXAMPLE—
*"United Two Twenty–Two on one two three point four" or
"one two three point four, United Two Twenty–Two."*

e. Compliance with Frequency Changes:

When instructed by ATC to change frequencies, select the new frequency as soon as possible unless instructed to make the change at a specific time, fix, or altitude. A delay in making the change could result in an untimely receipt of important information. If you are instructed to make the frequency change at a specific time, fix, or altitude, monitor the frequency you are on until reaching the specified time, fix, or altitudes unless instructed otherwise by ATC.

REFERENCE-
AIM, ARTCC COMMUNICATIONS, PARAGRAPH 5-3-1.

4-2-4. AIRCRAFT CALL SIGNS

a. Precautions in the Use of Call Signs:

1. Improper use of call signs can result in pilots executing a clearance intended for another aircraft. Call signs should never be abbreviated on an initial contact or at any time when other aircraft call signs have similar numbers/sounds or identical letters/number; e.g., Cessna 6132F, Cessna 1622F, Baron 123F, Cherokee 732F, etc.

EXAMPLE-
Assume that a controller issues an approach clearance to an aircraft at the bottom of a holding stack and an aircraft with a similar call sign (at the top of the stack) acknowledges the clearance with the last two or three numbers of the aircraft's call sign. If the aircraft at the bottom of the stack did not hear the clearance and intervene, flight safety would be affected, and there would be no reason for either the controller or pilot to suspect that anything is wrong. This kind of "human factors" error can strike swiftly and is extremely difficult to rectify.

2. Pilots, therefore, must be certain that aircraft identification is complete and clearly identified before taking action on an ATC clearance. ATC specialists will not abbreviate call signs of air carrier or other civil aircraft having authorized call signs. ATC specialists may initiate abbreviated call signs of other aircraft by using the prefix and the last three digits/letters of the aircraft identification after communications are established. The pilot may use the abbreviated call sign in subsequent contacts with the ATC specialist. When aware of similar/identical call signs, ATC specialists will take action to minimize errors by emphasizing certain numbers/letters, by repeating the entire call sign, by repeating the prefix, or by asking pilots to use a different call sign temporarily. Pilots should use the phrase "VERIFY CLEARANCE FOR (your complete call sign)" if doubt exists concerning proper identity.

3. Civil aircraft pilots should state the aircraft type, model or manufacturer's name, followed by the digits/letters of the registration number. When the aircraft manufacturer's name or model is stated, the prefix "N" is dropped; e.g., Aztec Two Four Six Four Alpha.

EXAMPLE-
1 Bonanza Six Five Five Golf.

2 Breezy Six One Three Romeo Experimental (omit "Experimental" after initial contact).

4. Air Taxi or other commercial operators not having FAA authorized call signs should prefix their normal identification with the phonetic word "Tango."

EXAMPLE-
Tango Aztec Two Four Six Four Alpha.

5. Air carriers and commuter air carriers having FAA authorized call signs should identify themselves by stating the complete call sign (using group form for the numbers) and the word "heavy" if appropriate.

EXAMPLE-
1 United Twenty-Five Heavy.

2 Midwest Commuter Seven Eleven.

6. Military aircraft use a variety of systems including serial numbers, word call signs, and combinations of letters/numbers. Examples include Army Copter 48931; Air Force 61782; REACH 31792; Pat 157; Air Evac 17652; Navy Golf Alfa Kilo 21; Marine 4 Charlie 36, etc.

b. Air Ambulance Flights:

Because of the priority afforded air ambulance flights in the ATC system, extreme discretion is necessary when using the term "LIFEGUARD." It is only intended for those missions of an urgent medical nature and to be utilized only for that portion of the flight requiring expeditious handling. When requested by the pilot, necessary notification to expedite ground handling of patients, etc., is provided by ATC; however, when possible, this information should be passed in advance through non-ATC communications systems.

1. Civilian air ambulance flights responding to medical emergencies (first call to an accident scene, carrying patients, organ donors, organs, or other urgently needed lifesaving medical material) will be expedited by ATC when necessary. When expeditious handling is necessary, add the word "LIFEGUARD" in the remarks section of the flight plan. In radio communications, use the call sign "LIFEGUARD" followed by the aircraft registration letters/numbers.

2. Similar provisions have been made for the use of "AIR EVAC" and "MED EVAC" by military air ambulance flights, except that these military flights will receive priority handling only when specifically requested.

EXAMPLE–
Lifeguard Two Six Four Six.

3. Air carrier and Air Taxi flights responding to medical emergencies will also be expedited by ATC when necessary. The nature of these medical emergency flights usually concerns the transportation of urgently needed lifesaving medical materials or vital organs. IT IS IMPERATIVE THAT THE COMPANY/PILOT DETERMINE, BY THE NATURE/URGENCY OF THE SPECIFIC MEDICAL CARGO, IF PRIORITY ATC ASSISTANCE IS REQUIRED. Pilots shall ensure that the word "LIFEGUARD" is included in the remarks section of the flight plan and use the call sign "LIFEGUARD" followed by the company name and flight number for all transmissions when expeditious handling is required. It is important for ATC to be aware of "LIFEGUARD" status, and it is the pilot's responsibility to ensure that this information is provided to ATC.

EXAMPLE–
Lifeguard Delta Thirty–Seven.

c. Student Pilots Radio Identification:

1. The FAA desires to help student pilots in acquiring sufficient practical experience in the environment in which they will be required to operate. To receive additional assistance while operating in areas of concentrated air traffic, student pilots need only identify themselves as a student pilot during their initial call to an FAA radio facility.

EXAMPLE–
Dayton tower, this is Fleetwing One Two Three Four, student pilot.

2. This special identification will alert FAA ATC personnel and enable them to provide student pilots with such extra assistance and consideration as they may need. This procedure is not mandatory.

4-2-5. DESCRIPTION OF INTERCHANGE OR LEASED AIRCRAFT

a. Controllers issue traffic information based on familiarity with airline equipment and color/markings. When an air carrier dispatches a flight using another company's equipment and the pilot does not advise the

terminal ATC facility, the possible confusion in aircraft identification can compromise safety.

b. Pilots flying an "interchange" or "leased" aircraft not bearing the colors/markings of the company operating the aircraft should inform the terminal ATC facility on first contact the name of the operating company and trip number, followed by the company name as displayed on the aircraft, and aircraft type.

EXAMPLE–
Air Cal Three Eleven, United (interchange/lease), Boeing Seven Two Seven.

4-2-6. GROUND STATION CALL SIGNS

Pilots, when calling a ground station, should begin with the name of the facility being called followed by the type of the facility being called as indicated in TBL 4–2–1.

Calling a Ground Station

Facility	Call Sign
Airport UNICOM	"Shannon UNICOM"
FAA Flight Service Station	"Chicago Radio"
FAA Flight Service Station (En Route Flight Advisory Service (Weather))	"Seattle Flight Watch"
Airport Traffic Control Tower	"Augusta Tower"
Clearance Delivery Position (IFR)	"Dallas Clearance Delivery"
Ground Control Position in Tower	"Miami Ground"
Radar or Nonradar Approach Control Position	"Oklahoma City Approach"
Radar Departure Control Position	"St. Louis Departure"
FAA Air Route Traffic Control Center	"Washington Center"

TBL 4–2–1

4-2-7. PHONETIC ALPHABET

The International Civil Aviation Organization (ICAO) phonetic alphabet is used by FAA personnel when communications conditions are such that the information cannot be readily received without their use. ATC facilities may also request pilots to use phonetic letter equivalents when aircraft with similar sounding identifications are receiving communications on the same frequency. Pilots should use the phonetic alphabet when identifying their aircraft during initial contact with air traffic control facilities. Additionally, use the phonetic equivalents for single letters and to spell out groups of letters or difficult words during adverse communications conditions. (See TBL 4–2–2.)

Phonetic Alphabet/Morse Code

CHARACTER	MORSE CODE	TELEPHONY	PHONIC (PRONUNCIATION)
A	• —	Alfa	(AL–FAH)
B	— • • •	Bravo	(BRAH–VOH)
C	— • — •	Charlie	(CHAR–LEE) or (SHAR–LEE)
D	— • •	Delta	(DELL–TAH)
E	•	Echo	(ECK–OH)
F	• • — •	Foxtrot	(FOKS–TROT)
G	— — •	Golf	(GOLF)
H	• • • •	Hotel	(HOH–TEL)
I	• •	India	(IN–DEE–AH)
J	• — — —	Juliett	(JEW–LEE–ETT)
K	— • —	Kilo	(KEY–LOH)
L	• — • •	Lima	(LEE–MAH)
M	— —	Mike	(MIKE)
N	— •	November	(NO–VEM–BER)
O	— — —	Oscar	(OSS–CAH)
P	• — — •	Papa	(PAH–PAH)
Q	— — • —	Quebec	(KEH–BECK)
R	• — •	Romeo	(ROW–ME–OH)
S	• • •	Sierra	(SEE–AIR–RAH)
T	—	Tango	(TANG–GO)
U	• • —	Uniform	(YOU–NEE–FORM) or (OO–NEE–FORM)
V	• • • —	Victor	(VIK–TAH)
W	• — —	Whiskey	(WISS–KEY)
X	— • • —	Xray	(ECKS–RAY)
Y	— • — —	Yankee	(YANG–KEY)
Z	— — • •	Zulu	(ZOO–LOO)
1	• — — — —	One	(WUN)
2	• • — — —	Two	(TOO)
3	• • • — —	Three	(TREE)
4	• • • • —	Four	(FOW–ER)
5	• • • • •	Five	(FIFE)
6	— • • • •	Six	(SIX)
7	— — • • •	Seven	(SEV–EN)
8	— — — • •	Eight	(AIT)
9	— — — — •	Nine	(NIN–ER)
0	— — — — —	Zero	(ZEE–RO)

TBL 4–2–2

4-2-8. FIGURES

a. Figures indicating hundreds and thousands in round number, as for ceiling heights, and upper wind levels up to 9,900 shall be spoken in accordance with the following.

EXAMPLE–
1 500 .... five hundred

2 4,500 ..... four thousand five hundred

b. Numbers above 9,900 shall be spoken by separating the digits preceding the word "thousand."

EXAMPLE–
1 10,000 ... one zero thousand

2 13,500 ... one three thousand five hundred

c. Transmit airway or jet route numbers as follows.

EXAMPLE–
1 V12 ...... Victor Twelve

2 J533 ..... J Five Thirty–Three

d. All other numbers shall be transmitted by pronouncing each digit.

EXAMPLE–
10 .... one zero

e. When a radio frequency contains a decimal point, the decimal point is spoken as "POINT."

EXAMPLE–
122.1 .... one two two point one

NOTE–
ICAO procedures require the decimal point be spoken as "DECIMAL." The FAA will honor such usage by military aircraft and all other aircraft required to use ICAO procedures.

4-2-9. ALTITUDES AND FLIGHT LEVELS

a. Up to but not including 18,000 feet MSL, state the separate digits of the thousands plus the hundreds if appropriate.

EXAMPLE–
1 12,000 .... one two thousand
2 12,500 .... one two thousand five hundred

b. At and above 18,000 feet MSL (FL 180), state the words "flight level" followed by the separate digits of the flight level.

EXAMPLE–
1 190 .... Flight Level One Niner Zero
2 275 .... Flight Level Two Seven Five

4-2-10. DIRECTIONS

The three digits of bearing, course, heading, or wind direction should always be magnetic. The word "true" must be added when it applies.

EXAMPLE-

1	*(Magnetic course) 005*	*zero zero five*
2	*(True course) 050*	*zero five zero true*
3	*(Magnetic bearing) 360*	*three six zero*
4	*(Magnetic heading) 100* ...	*heading one zero zero*
5	*(Wind direction) 220*	*wind two two zero*

4-2-11. SPEEDS

The separate digits of the speed followed by the word "KNOTS." Except, controllers may omit the word "KNOTS" when using speed adjustment procedures; e.g., "REDUCE/INCREASE SPEED TO TWO FIVE ZERO."

EXAMPLE-
(Speed) 250 .... *two five zero knots*
(Speed) 190 .... *one niner zero knots*

The separate digits of the Mach Number preceded by "Mach."

EXAMPLE-
(Mach number) 1.5 .... *Mach one point five*
(Mach number) 0.64 .... *Mach point six four*
(Mach number) 0.7 .... *Mach point seven*

4-2-12. TIME

a. FAA uses Coordinated Universal Time (UTC) for all operations. The word "local" or the time zone equivalent shall be used to denote local when local time is given during radio and telephone communications. The term "Zulu" may be used to denote UTC.

EXAMPLE-
0920 UTC ..... *zero niner two zero,*
zero one two zero pacific or local,
or one twenty AM

b. To convert from Standard Time to Coordinated Universal Time:

Standard Time to Coordinated Universal Time

Eastern Standard Time	Add 5 hours
Central Standard Time	Add 6 hours
Mountain Standard Time	Add 7 hours
Pacific Standard Time.........	Add 8 hours
Alaska Standard Time.........	Add 9 hours
Hawaii Standard Time	Add 10 hours

TBL 4-2-3

NOTE-
For daylight time, subtract 1 hour.

c. A reference may be made to local daylight or standard time utilizing the 24-hour clock system. The hour is indicated by the first two figures and the minutes by the last two figures.

EXAMPLE-
0000 .... *zero zero zero zero*
0920 .... *zero niner two zero*

d. Time may be stated in minutes only (two figures) in radiotelephone communications when no misunderstanding is likely to occur.

e. Current time in use at a station is stated in the nearest quarter minute in order that pilots may use this information for time checks. Fractions of a quarter minute less than 8 seconds are stated as the preceding quarter minute; fractions of a quarter minute of 8 seconds or more are stated as the succeeding quarter minute.

EXAMPLE-
0929:05 ...... *time, zero niner two niner*
0929:10 ...... *time, zero niner two niner and*
one-quarter

4-2-13. COMMUNICATIONS WITH TOWER WHEN AIRCRAFT TRANSMITTER OR RECEIVER OR BOTH ARE INOPERATIVE

a. Arriving Aircraft:

1. *Receiver inoperative:*

(a) If you have reason to believe your receiver is inoperative, remain outside or above the Class D surface area until the direction and flow of traffic has been determined; then, advise the tower of your type aircraft, position, altitude, intention to land, and request that you be controlled with light signals.

REFERENCE-
AIM, TRAFFIC CONTROL LIGHT SIGNALS, PARAGRAPH 4-3-13.

(b) When you are approximately 3 to 5 miles from the airport, advise the tower of your position and join the airport traffic pattern. From this point on, watch the tower for light signals. Thereafter, if a complete pattern is made, transmit your position downwind and/or turning base leg.

2. *Transmitter inoperative:* Remain outside or above the Class D surface area until the direction and flow of traffic has been determined; then, join the airport traffic pattern. Monitor the primary local control frequency as depicted on Sectional Charts for landing or traffic information, and look for a light signal which may be addressed to your aircraft. During hours of daylight, acknowledge tower transmissions or light signals by rocking your wings. At night, acknowledge by blinking the landing or navigation lights. To acknowledge

tower transmissions during daylight hours, hovering helicopters will turn in the direction of the controlling facility and flash the landing light. While in flight, helicopters should show their acknowledgement of receiving a transmission by making shallow banks in opposite directions. At night, helicopters will acknowledge receipt of transmissions by flashing either the landing or the search light.

3. Transmitter and receiver inoperative: Remain outside or above the Class D surface area until the direction and flow of traffic has been determined; then, join the airport traffic pattern and maintain visual contact with the tower to receive light signals. Acknowledge light signals as noted above.

b. Departing Aircraft: If you experience radio failure prior to leaving the parking area, make every effort to have the equipment repaired. If you are unable to have the malfunction repaired, call the tower by telephone and request authorization to depart without two-way radio communications. If tower authorization is granted, you will be given departure information and requested to monitor the tower frequency or watch for light signals as appropriate. During daylight hours, acknowledge tower transmissions or light signals by moving the ailerons or rudder. At night, acknowledge by blinking the landing or navigation lights. If radio malfunction occurs after departing the parking area,

watch the tower for light signals or monitor tower frequency.

REFERENCE-
FAR PART 91.125 AND FAR PART 91.129.

4-2-14. COMMUNICATIONS FOR VFR FLIGHTS

a. FSS's and Supplemental Weather Service Locations (SWSL's) are allocated frequencies for different functions; for example, 122.0 MHz is assigned as the En Route Flight Advisory Service frequency at selected FSS's. In addition, certain FSS's provide Local Airport Advisory on 123.6 MHz. Frequencies are listed in the A/FD. If you are in doubt as to what frequency to use, 122.2 MHz is assigned to the majority of FSS's as a common en route simplex frequency.

NOTE-
In order to expedite communications, state the frequency being used and the aircraft location during initial callup.

EXAMPLE-
Dayton radio, this is November One Two Three Four Five on one two two point two, over Springfield V-O-R, over.

b. Certain VOR voice channels are being utilized for recorded broadcasts; i.e., ATIS, HIWAS, etc. These services and appropriate frequencies are listed in the A/FD. On VFR flights, pilots are urged to monitor these frequencies. When in contact with a control facility, notify the controller if you plan to leave the frequency to monitor these broadcasts.

Section 3. AIRPORT OPERATIONS

4-3-1. GENERAL

Increased traffic congestion, aircraft in climb and descent attitudes, and pilot preoccupation with cockpit duties are some factors that increase the hazardous accident potential near the airport. The situation is further compounded when the weather is marginal–that is, just meeting VFR requirements. Pilots must be particularly alert when operating in the vicinity of an airport. This section defines some rules, practices, and procedures that pilots should be familiar with and adhere to for safe airport operations.

4-3-2. AIRPORTS WITH AN OPERATING CONTROL TOWER

a. When operating at an airport where traffic control is being exercised by a control tower, pilots are required to maintain two-way radio contact with the tower while operating within the Class B, Class C, and Class D surface area unless the tower authorizes otherwise. Initial callup should be made about 15 miles from the airport. Unless there is a good reason to leave the tower frequency before exiting the Class B, Class C, and Class D surface areas, it is a good operating practice to remain on the tower frequency for the purpose of receiving traffic information. In the interest of reducing tower frequency congestion, pilots are reminded that it is not necessary to request permission to leave the tower frequency once outside of Class B, Class C, and Class D surface areas. Not all airports with an operating control tower will have Class D airspace. These airports do not have weather reporting which is a requirement for surface based controlled airspace, previously known as a control zone. The controlled airspace over these airports will normally begin at 700 feet or 1,200 feet above ground level and can be determined from the visual aeronautical charts. Pilots are expected to use good operating practices and communicate with the control tower as described in this section.

b. When necessary, the tower controller will issue clearances or other information for aircraft to generally follow the desired flight path (traffic patterns) when flying in Class B, Class C, and Class D surface areas and the proper taxi routes when operating on the ground. If not otherwise authorized or directed by the tower, pilots of fixed-wing aircraft approaching to land must circle the airport to the left. Pilots approaching to land in a helicopter must avoid the flow of fixed-wing traffic.

However, in all instances, an appropriate clearance must be received from the tower before landing.

Components of a Traffic Pattern

FIG 4-3-1

NOTE–
This diagram is intended only to illustrate terminology used in identifying various components of a traffic pattern. It should not be used as a reference or guide on how to enter a traffic pattern.

c. The following terminology for the various components of a traffic pattern has been adopted as standard for use by control towers and pilots (See FIG 4-3-1):

1. *Upwind leg:* A flight path parallel to the landing runway in the direction of landing.

2. *Crosswind leg:* A flight path at right angles to the landing runway off its takeoff end.

3. *Downwind leg:* A flight path parallel to the landing runway in the opposite direction of landing.

4. *Base leg:* A flight path at right angles to the landing runway off its approach end and extending from the downwind leg to the intersection of the extended runway centerline.

5. *Final approach:* A flight path in the direction of landing along the extended runway centerline from the base leg to the runway.

6. *Departure leg:* The flight path which begins after takeoff and continues straight ahead along the extended runway centerline. The departure climb continues until reaching a point at least $1/2$ mile beyond the departure end of the runway and within 300 feet of the traffic pattern altitude.

d. Many towers are equipped with a tower radar display. The radar uses are intended to enhance the effectiveness and efficiency of the local control, or tower, position. They are not intended to provide radar services or benefits to pilots except as they may accrue through a more efficient tower operation. The four basic uses are:

1. To determine an aircraft's exact location: This is accomplished by radar identifying the VFR aircraft through any of the techniques available to a radar position, such as having the aircraft *squawk ident.* Once identified, the aircraft's position and spatial relationship to other aircraft can be quickly determined, and standard instructions regarding VFR operation in Class B, Class C, and Class D surface areas will be issued. Once initial radar identification of a VFR aircraft has been established and the appropriate instructions have been issued, radar monitoring may be discontinued; the reason being that the local controller's primary means of surveillance in VFR conditions is visually scanning the airport and local area.

2. To provide radar traffic advisories: Radar traffic advisories may be provided to the extent that the local controller is able to monitor the radar display. Local control has primary control responsibilities to the aircraft operating on the runways, which will normally supersede radar monitoring duties.

3. To provide a direction or suggested heading: The local controller may provide pilots flying VFR with generalized instructions which will facilitate operations; e.g., "PROCEED SOUTHWEST BOUND, ENTER A RIGHT DOWNWIND RUNWAY THREE ZERO," or provide a suggested heading to establish radar identification or as an advisory aid to navigation; e.g., "SUGGESTED HEADING TWO TWO ZERO, FOR RADAR IDENTIFICATION." In both cases, the instructions are advisory aids to the pilot flying VFR and are not radar vectors.

NOTE–
Pilots have complete discretion regarding acceptance of the suggested headings or directions and have sole responsibility for seeing and avoiding other aircraft.

4. To provide information and instructions to aircraft operating within Class B, Class C, and Class D surface areas: In an example of this situation, the local controller would use the radar to advise a pilot on an extended downwind when to turn base leg.

NOTE–
The above tower radar applications are intended to augment the standard functions of the local control position. There is no controller requirement to maintain constant radar identification. In fact, such a requirement could compromise the local controller's ability to visually scan the airport and local area to meet FAA responsibilities to

the aircraft operating on the runways and within the Class B, Class C, and Class D surface areas. Normally, pilots will not be advised of being in radar contact since that continued status cannot be guaranteed and since the purpose of the radar identification is not to establish a link for the provision of radar services.

e. A few of the radar equipped towers are authorize to use the radar to ensure separation between aircraft specific situations, while still others may function a limited radar approach controls. The various radar use are strictly a function of FAA operational need. The facilities may be indistinguishable to pilots since they ar all referred to as tower and no publication lists the degree of radar use. THEREFORE, WHEN IN COMMUNICATION WITH A TOWER CONTROLLER WHO MAY HAVE RADAR AVAILABLE, DO NOT ASSUME THAT CONSTANT RADAR MONITORING AND COMPLETE ATC RADAR SERVICES ARE BEING PROVIDED.

4-3-3. VISUAL INDICATORS AT AIRPORTS WITHOUT AN OPERATING CONTROL TOWER

a. At those airports *without an operating control tower,* a segmented circle visual indicator system, i installed, is designed to provide traffic pattern information.

REFERENCE–
AIM, TRAFFIC ADVISORY PRACTICES AT AIRPORTS WITHOUT OPERATING CONTROL TOWERS, PARAGRAPH 4-1-9.

b. The segmented circle system consists of the following components:

1. The segmented circle: Located in a position affording maximum visibility to pilots in the air and on the ground and providing a centralized location for other elements of the system.

2. The wind direction indicator: A wind cone wind sock, or wind tee installed near the operationa runway to indicate wind direction. The large end of the wind cone/wind sock points into the wind as does the large end (cross bar) of the wind tee. In lieu of a tetrahedron and where a wind sock or wind cone is collocated with a wind tee, the wind tee may be manually aligned with the runway in use to indicate landing direction These signaling devices may be located in the center of the segmented circle and may be lighted for night use Pilots are cautioned against using a tetrahedron to indicate wind direction.

3. The landing direction indicator: A tetrahedron is installed when conditions at the airport warrant it use. It may be used to indicate the direction of landing and takeoffs. A tetrahedron may be located at the center of a segmented circle and may be lighted for night op erations. The small end of the tetrahedron points in the direction of landing. Pilots are cautioned against using a tetrahedron for any purpose other than as an indicator of landing direction. Further, pilots should use extreme caution when making runway selection by use of a tetrahedron in very light or calm wind conditions as the tetrahedron may not be aligned with the designated calm-wind runway. At airports with control towers, the tetrahedron should only be referenced when the control tower is not in operation. Tower instructions supersede tetrahedron indications.

4. Landing strip indicators: Installed in pairs as shown in the segmented circle diagram and used to show the alignment of landing strips.

5. Traffic pattern indicators: Arranged in pairs in conjunction with landing strip indicators and used to indicate the direction of turns when there is a variation from the normal left traffic pattern. (If there is no segmented circle installed at the airport, traffic pattern indicators may be installed on or near the end of the runway.)

c. Preparatory to landing at an airport without a control tower, or when the control tower is not in operation, pilots should concern themselves with the indicator for the approach end of the runway to be used. When approaching for landing, all turns must be made to the left unless a traffic pattern indicator indicates that turns should be made to the right. If the pilot will mentally enlarge the indicator for the runway to be used, the base and final approach legs of the traffic pattern to be flown immediately become apparent. Similar treatment of the indicator at the departure end of the runway will clearly indicate the direction of turn after takeoff.

d. When two or more aircraft are approaching an airport for the purpose of landing, the aircraft at the lower altitude has the right of way, but it shall not take advantage of this rule to cut in front of another which is on final approach to land, or to overtake that aircraft (FAR Part 91.113(f)).

Traffic Pattern Operations
Single Runway

FIG 4-3-2 See Key to Traffic Pattern Operations under FIG 4-3-3.

Traffic Pattern Operations
Parallel Runways

FIG 4-3-3 *See Key to Traffic Pattern Operations below*

EXAMPLE-

Key to traffic pattern operations

1 *Enter pattern in level flight, abeam the midpoint of the runway, at pattern altitude. (1,000' AGL is recommended pattern altitude unless established otherwise...)*

2 *Maintain pattern altitude until abeam approach end of the landing runway on downwind leg.*

3 *Complete turn to final at least $^1/_4$ mile from the runway.*

4 *Continue straight ahead until beyond departure end of runway.*

5 *If remaining in the traffic pattern, commence turn to crosswind leg beyond the departure end of the runway within 300 feet of pattern altitude.*

6 *If departing the traffic pattern, continue straight out, or exit with a 45 degree turn (to the left when in a left–hand traffic pattern; to the right when in a right–hand traffic pattern) beyond the departure end of the runway, after reaching pattern altitude.*

7 *Do not overshoot final or continue on a track which will penetrate the final approach of the parallel runway.*

8 *Do not continue on a track which will penetrate the departure path of the parallel runway.*

4-3-4. TRAFFIC PATTERNS

At most airports and military air bases, traffic pattern altitudes for propeller-driven aircraft generally extend from 600 feet to as high as 1,500 feet above the ground. Also, traffic pattern altitudes for military turbojet aircraft sometimes extend up to 2,500 feet above the ground. Therefore, pilots of en route aircraft should be constantly on the alert for other aircraft in traffic patterns and avoid these areas whenever possible. Traffic pattern altitudes should be maintained unless otherwise required by the applicable distance from cloud criteria (FAR Part 91.155). (See FIG 4-3-2 and FIG 4-3-3.)

4-3-5. UNEXPECTED MANEUVERS IN THE AIRPORT TRAFFIC PATTERN

There have been several incidents in the vicinity of controlled airports that were caused primarily by aircraft executing unexpected maneuvers. ATC service is based upon observed or known traffic and airport conditions. Controllers establish the sequence of arriving and departing aircraft by requiring them to adjust flight as necessary to achieve proper spacing. These adjustments can only be based on observed traffic, accurate pilot reports, and anticipated aircraft maneuvers. Pilots are expected to cooperate so as to preclude disrupting traffic flows or creating conflicting patterns. The pilot-in-command of an aircraft is directly responsible for and is the final authority as to the operation of the aircraft. On occasion it may be necessary for pilots to maneuver their aircraft to maintain spacing with the traffic they have been sequenced to follow. The controller can anticipate minor maneuvering such as shallow "S" turns. The controller cannot, however, anticipate a major maneuver such as a 360 degree turn. If a pilot makes a 360 degree turn after obtaining a landing sequence, the result is usually a gap in the landing interval and, more importantly, it causes a chain reaction which may result in a conflict with following traffic and an interruption of the sequence established by the tower or approach controller. Should a pilot decide to make maneuvering turns to maintain spacing behind a preceding aircraft, the pilot should always advise the controller if at all possible. Except when requested by the controller or in emergency situations, a 360 degree turn should never be executed in the traffic pattern or when receiving radar service without first advising the controller.

4-3-6. USE OF RUNWAYS/DECLARED DISTANCES

a. Runways are identified by numbers which indicate the nearest 10-degree increment of the azimuth of the runway centerline. For example, where the magnetic azimuth is 183 degrees, the runway designation would be 18; for a magnetic azimuth of 87 degrees, the runway designation would be 9. For a magnetic azimuth ending in the number 5, such as 185, the runway designation could be either 18 or 19. Wind direction issued by the tower is also magnetic and wind velocity is in knots.

b. Airport proprietors are responsible for taking the lead in local aviation noise control. Accordingly, they may propose specific noise abatement plans to the FAA. If approved, these plans are applied in the form of Formal or Informal Runway Use Programs for noise abatement purposes.

REFERENCE-
PILOT/CONTROLLER GLOSSARY TERM- RUNWAY USE PROGRAM.

1. At airports where no runway use program is established, ATC clearances may specify:

(a) the runway most nearly aligned with the wind when it is 5 knots or more;

(b) the "calm wind" runway when wind is less than 5 knots; or

(c) another runway if operationally advantageous.

NOTE-
It is not necessary for a controller to specifically inquire if the pilot will use a specific runway or to offer a choice of runways. If a pilot prefers to use a different runway from that specified or the one most nearly aligned with the wind, the pilot is expected to inform ATC accordingly.

2. At airports where a runway use program is established, ATC will assign runways deemed to have the least noise impact. If in the interest of safety a runway different from that specified is preferred, the pilot is expected to advise ATC accordingly. ATC will honor such requests and advise pilots when the requested runway is noise sensitive. When use of a runway other than the one assigned is requested, pilot cooperation is encouraged to preclude disruption of traffic flows or the creation of conflicting patterns.

c. At some airports, the airport proprietor may declare that sections of a runway at one or both ends are not available for landing or takeoff. For these airports, the declared distance of runway length available for a particular operation is published in the *Airport/Facility Directory*. Declared distances (*TORA, TODA, ASDA,* and *LDA*) are defined in the *Pilot/Controller Glossary*. These distances are calculated by adding to the full length of paved runway any applicable clearway or stopway and subtracting from that sum the sections of the runway unsuitable for satisfying the required take-off run, takeoff, accelerate/stop, or landing distance.

4-3-7. LOW LEVEL WIND SHEAR ALERT SYSTEM (LLWAS) AND TERMINAL DOPPLER WEATHER RADAR (TDWR)

LLWAS and TDWR are systems designed to provide pilots with information on hazardous wind shear and microburst activity in the vicinity of an airport. Not all airports will have this capability, but more than half of the towered airports will have the capability to provide some level of alert.

a. At airports equipped with LLWAS, controllers are provided with gust front wind shear information. Controllers will provide this information to pilots by giving the pilot the centerfield wind followed by the boundary wind.

EXAMPLE-
Wind shear alert, Centerfield wind 230 at 8, south boundary wind 170 at 20.

NOTE-
The LLWAS is designed to detect low level wind shear conditions around the periphery of an airport. It does not detect wind shear beyond that limitation.

b. Airports equipped with LLWAS "network expansion," LLWAS systems integrated with TDWR and TDWR systems provide the capability of detecting microburst alerts and wind shear alerts. Controllers will issue the appropriate wind shear alerts or microburst alerts. In some of these systems controllers also have the ability to issue wind information oriented to the threshold or departure end of the runway.

EXAMPLE-
Runway 17 arrival microburst alert, 40 knot loss 3 mile final.

REFERENCE-
AIM, MICROBURSTS, PARAGRAPH 7-1-23.

c. An airport equipped with the LLWAS is so indicated in the *Airport/Facility Directory* under *Weather Data Sources* for that particular airport.

4-3-8. BRAKING ACTION REPORTS AND ADVISORIES

a. When available, ATC furnishes pilots the quality of braking action received from pilots or airport man-

agement. The quality of braking action is described k the terms "good," "fair," "poor," and "nil," or a co bination of these terms. When pilots report the quali of braking action by using the terms noted above, the should use descriptive terms that are easily understoo such as, "braking action poor the first/last half of tł runway," together with the particular type of aircraf

b. For NOTAM purposes, braking action reports a classified according to the most critical term ("fair "poor," or "nil") used and issued as a NOTAM(D).

c. When tower controllers have received runwa braking action reports which include the terms *poor c nil,* or whenever weather conditions are conducive t deteriorating or rapidly changing runway brakin conditions, the tower will include on the ATIS broac cast the statement, *"BRAKING ACTION ADVISORIE ARE IN EFFECT."*

d. During the time that braking action advisories a in effect, ATC will issue the latest braking action repo for the runway in use to each arriving and departin aircraft. Pilots should be prepared for deterioratir braking conditions and should request current runwa condition information if not volunteered by controller Pilots should also be prepared to provide a descriptiv runway condition report to controllers after landing.

4-3-9. RUNWAY FRICTION REPORTS AND ADVISORIES

a. Friction is defined as the ratio of the tangentia force needed to maintain uniform relative motion be tween two contacting surfaces (aircraft tires to the pave ment surface) to the perpendicular force holding ther in contact (distributed aircraft weight to the aircraft ti area). Simply stated, friction quantifies slipperiness c pavement surfaces.

b. The greek letter MU (pronounced "myew"), i used to designate a friction value representing runwa surface conditions.

c. MU (friction) values range from 0 to 100 wher zero is the lowest friction value and 100 is the maximum friction value obtainable. For frozen contaminants o runway surfaces, a MU value of 40 or less is the leve when the aircraft braking performance starts to deterio rate and directional control begins to be less responsive The lower the MU value, the less effective braking per formance becomes and the more difficult directiona control becomes.

d. At airports with friction measuring devices, airport management should conduct friction measurements on runways covered with compacted snow and/or ice.

1. Numerical readings may be obtained by using any FAA approved friction measuring device. It is not necessary to designate the type of friction measuring device since they provide essentially the same numerical reading when the values are 40 or less.

2. When the MU value for any one-third zone of an active runway is 40 or less, a report should be given to ATC by airport management for dissemination to pilots. The report will identify the runway, the time of measurement, MU values for each zone, and the contaminant conditions, e.g., wet snow, dry snow, slush, deicing chemicals, etc. Measurements for each one-third zone will be given in the direction of takeoff and landing on the runway. A report should also be given when MU values rise above 40 in all zones of a runway previously reporting a MU below 40.

3. Airport management should initiate a NOTAM(D) when the friction measuring device is out of service.

e. When MU reports are provided by airport management, the ATC facility providing approach control or local airport advisory will provide the report to any pilot upon request.

f. Pilots should use MU information with other knowledge including aircraft performance characteristics, type, and weight, previous experience, wind conditions, and aircraft tire type (i.e., bias ply vs. radial constructed) to determine runway suitability.

g. No correlation has been established between MU values and the descriptive terms "good," "fair," "poor," and "nil" used in braking action reports.

4-3-10. INTERSECTION TAKEOFFS

a. In order to enhance airport capacities, reduce taxiing distances, minimize departure delays, and provide for more efficient movement of air traffic, controllers may initiate intersection takeoffs as well as approve them when the pilot requests. If for ANY reason a pilot prefers to use a different intersection or the full length of the runway or desires to obtain the distance between the intersection and the runway end, THE PILOT IS EXPECTED TO INFORM ATC ACCORDINGLY.

b. An aircraft is expected to taxi to (but not onto) the end of the assigned runway unless prior approval for an intersection departure is received from ground control.

c. Pilots should state their position on the airport when calling the tower for takeoff from a runway intersection.

EXAMPLE-
Cleveland tower, Apache Three Seven Two Two Papa, at the intersection of taxiway oscar and runway two three right, ready for departure.

d. Controllers are required to separate small aircraft (12,500 pounds or less, maximum certificated takeoff weight) departing (same or opposite direction) from an intersection behind a large nonheavy aircraft on the same runway, by ensuring that at least a 3-minute interval exists between the time the preceding large aircraft has taken off and the succeeding small aircraft begins takeoff roll. To inform the pilot of the required 3-minute hold, the controller will state, "Hold for wake turbulence." If after considering wake turbulence hazards, the pilot feels that a lesser time interval is appropriate, the pilot may request a waiver to the 3-minute interval. To initiate such a request, simply say "Request waiver to 3-minute interval," or a similar statement. Controllers may then issue a takeoff clearance if other traffic permits, since the pilot has accepted the responsibility for wake turbulence separation.

e. The 3-minute interval is not required when the intersection is 500 feet or less from the departure point of the preceding aircraft and both aircraft are taking off in the same direction. Controllers may permit the small aircraft to alter course after takeoff to avoid the flight path of the preceding departure.

f. The 3-minute interval is mandatory behind a heavy aircraft in all cases.

4-3-11. PILOT RESPONSIBILITIES WHEN CONDUCTING LAND AND HOLD SHORT OPERATIONS (LAHSO)

a. LAHSO is an acronym for "Land And Hold Short Operations." These operations include landing and holding short of an **intersecting runway**, an **intersecting taxiway**, or some other designated **point on a runway** other than an intersecting runway or taxiway. (See FIG 4-3-4, FIG 4-3-5, FIG 4-3-6)

b. Pilot Responsibilities and Basic Procedures:

1. LAHSO is an air traffic control procedure that requires pilot participation to balance the needs for increased airport capacity and system efficiency, consistent with safety. This procedure can be done safely **provided** pilots and controllers are knowledgeable and understand their responsibilities. The following paragraphs outline specific pilot/operator responsibilities when conducting LAHSO.

2. At controlled airports, air traffic may clear a pilot to land and hold short. Pilots may accept such a clearance provided that the pilot–in–command determines that the aircraft can safely land and stop within the Available Landing Distance (ALD). ALD data are published in the special notices section of the Airport/Facility Directory (A/FD) and in the U.S. Terminal Procedures Publications. Controllers will also provide ALD data upon request. Student pilots or pilots not familiar with LAHSO should **not** participate in the program.

3. The pilot–in–command has the final authority to accept or decline any land and hold short clearance. The safety and operation of the aircraft remain the responsibility of the pilot. Pilots are expected to decline a LAHSO clearance if they determine it will compromise safety.

4. To conduct LAHSO, pilots should become familiar with all available information concerning LAHSO at their destination airport. Pilots should have, *readily available,* the **published ALD** and runway **slope information** for **all** LAHSO runway combinations at **each** airport of intended landing. Additionally, knowledge about landing performance data permits the pilot to *readily* determine that the ALD for the assigned runway is sufficient for safe LAHSO. As part of a pilot's preflight planning process, pilots should determine if their destination airport has LAHSO. If so, their preflight planning process should include an assessment of which LAHSO combinations would work for them given their aircraft's required landing distance. Good pilot decision making is knowing in advance whether one can accept a LAHSO clearance if offered.

Land and Hold Short of an Intersecting Runway

FIG 4–3–

EXAMPLE–
FIG 4–3–6 – holding short at a designated point may be required to avoid conflicts with the runway safety area/flight path of a nearby runway.

NOTE–
Each figure shows the approximate location of LAHSO markings, signage, and in–pavement lighting when installed.

REFERENCE–
AIM, CHAPTER 2, AERONAUTICAL LIGHTING AND OTHER AIRPOR VISUAL AIDS.

Land and Hold Short of an Intersecting Taxiway

FIG 4-3-5

Land and Hold Short of a Designated Point on a Runway Other Than an Intersecting Runway or Taxiway

FIG 4-3-6

5. If, for any reason, such as difficulty in discerning the location of a LAHSO intersection, wind conditions, aircraft condition, etc., the pilot elects to request to land on the full length of the runway, to land on another runway, or to decline LAHSO, a pilot is expected to promptly inform air traffic, ideally even before the clearance is issued. **A LAHSO clearance, once accepted, must be adhered to, just as any other ATC clearance, unless an amended clearance is obtained or an emergency occurs. A LAHSO clearance does not preclude a rejected landing.**

6. A pilot who accepts a LAHSO clearance should land and exit the runway at the first convenient taxiway (unless directed otherwise) before reaching the hold short point. Otherwise, the pilot must stop and hold at the hold short point. **If a rejected landing becomes necessary after accepting a LAHSO clearance, the pilot should maintain safe separation from other aircraft or vehicles, and should promptly notify the controller.**

7. Controllers need a full read back of all LAHSO clearances. Pilots should read back their LAHSO clearance and include the words, "HOLD SHORT OF (RUNWAY/TAXIWAY/OR POINT)" in their acknowledgment of all LAHSO clearances. In order to reduce frequency congestion, pilots are encouraged to read back the LAHSO clearance without prompting. Don't make the controller have to ask for a read back!

c. LAHSO Situational Awareness

1. Situational awareness is **vital** to the success of LAHSO. Situational awareness starts with having current airport information in the cockpit, readily accessible to the pilot. (An airport diagram assists pilots in identifying their location on the airport, thus reducing requests for "progressive taxi instructions" from controllers.)

2. Situational awareness includes effective pilot–controller radio communication. ATC expects pilots to specifically acknowledge and read back all LAHSO clearances as follows:

EXAMPLE–
ATC: "(Aircraft ID) cleared to land runway six right, hold short of taxiway bravo for crossing traffic (type aircraft)."
Aircraft: "(Aircraft ID), wilco, cleared to land runway six right to hold short of taxiway bravo."
ATC: "(Aircraft ID) cross runway six right at taxiway bravo, landing aircraft will hold short."
Aircraft: "(Aircraft ID), wilco, cross runway six right at bravo, landing traffic (type aircraft) to hold."

3. For those airplanes flown with two crewmembers, effective **intra–cockpit** communication between cockpit crewmembers is also critical. There have been several instances where the pilot working the radios accepted a LAHSO clearance but then simply forgot to tell the pilot flying the aircraft.

4. Situational awareness also includes a thorough understanding of the airport markings, signage, and lighting associated with LAHSO. These visual aids consist of a three–part system of **yellow hold–short markings, red and white signage** and, in certain cases,

in–pavement lighting. Visual aids assist the pilot in determining where to hold short.

FIG 4–3–4, FIG 4–3–5, FIG 4–3–6 depict how these markings, signage, and lighting combinations will appear once installed. Pilots are cautioned that not all airports conducting LAHSO have installed any or all of the above markings, signage, or lighting.

5. Pilots should only receive a LAHSO clearance when there is a minimum ceiling of 1,000 feet and 3 statute miles visibility. The intent of having "basic" VFR weather conditions is to allow pilots to maintain visual contact with other aircraft and ground vehicle operations. Pilots should consider the effects of prevailing inflight visibility (such as landing into the sun) and how it may affect overall situational awareness. Additionally, surface vehicles and aircraft being taxied by maintenance personnel may also be participating in LAHSO, especially in those operations that involve crossing an active runway.

4–3–12. LOW APPROACH

a. A low approach (sometimes referred to as a low pass) is the go-around maneuver following an approach. Instead of landing or making a touch-and-go, a pilot may wish to go around (low approach) in order to expedite a particular operation (a series of practice instrument approaches is an example of such an operation). Unless otherwise authorized by ATC, the low approach should be made straight ahead, with no turns or climb made until the pilot has made a thorough visual check for other aircraft in the area.

b. When operating within a Class B, Class C, and Class D surface area, a pilot intending to make a low approach should contact the tower for approval. This request should be made prior to starting the final approach.

c. When operating to an airport, not within a Class B, Class C, and Class D surface area, a pilot intending to make a low approach should, prior to leaving the final

approach fix inbound (nonprecision approach) or ↑ outer marker or fix used in lieu of the outer mar▶ inbound (precision approach), so advise the FS UNICOM, or make a broadcast as appropriate.

REFERENCE-
AIM, TRAFFIC ADVISORY PRACTICES AT AIRPORTS WITHOUT O. ERATING CONTROL TOWERS, PARAGRAPH 4–1–9.

4–3–13. TRAFFIC CONTROL LIGHT SIGNALS

a. The following procedures are used by ATCT's the control of aircraft, ground vehicles, equipment, a personnel not equipped with radio. These same proc dures will be used to control aircraft, ground vehicle equipment, and personnel equipped with radio if rad contact cannot be established. ATC personnel use a ◀ rective traffic control signal which emits an intense n row light beam of a selected color (either red, white, green) when controlling traffic by light signals.

b. Although the traffic signal light offers the adva tage that some control may be exercised over nonrad equipped aircraft, pilots should be cognizant of the di advantages which are:

1. Pilots may not be looking at the control tower the time a signal is directed toward their aircraft.

2. The directions transmitted by a light signal a very limited since only approval or disapproval of a p lot's anticipated actions may be transmitted. No suppl ment or explanatory information may be transmitte except by the use of the "General Warning Signa which advises the pilot to be on the alert.

c. Between sunset and sunrise, a pilot wishing ↑ attract the attention of the control tower should turn c a landing light and taxi the aircraft into a position, cle of the active runway, so that light is visible to the towe The landing light should remain on until appropria signals are received from the tower.

d. Air Traffic Control Tower Light Gun Signals (See TBL 4–3–1.)

Air Traffic Control Tower Light Gun Signals

COLOR AND TYPE OF SIGNAL	MEANING		
	MOVEMENT OF VEHICLES, EQUIPMENT AND PERSONNEL	AIRCRAFT ON THE GROUND	AIRCRAFT IN FLIGHT
Steady green	Cleared to cross, proceed or go	Cleared for takeoff	Cleared to land
Flashing green	Not applicable	Cleared for taxi	Return for landing (to be followed by steady green at the proper time)
Steady red	STOP	STOP	Give way to other aircraft and continue circling
Flashing red	Clear the taxiway/runway	Taxi clear of the runway in use	Airport unsafe, do not land
Flashing white	Return to starting point on airport	Return to starting point on airport	Not applicable
Alternating red and green	Exercise extreme caution	Exercise extreme caution	Exercise extreme caution

TBL 4-3-1

e. During daylight hours, acknowledge tower transmissions or light signals by moving the ailerons or rudder. At night, acknowledge by blinking the landing or navigation lights. If radio malfunction occurs after departing the parking area, watch the tower for light signals or monitor tower frequency.

4-3-14. COMMUNICATIONS

a. Pilots of departing aircraft should communicate with the control tower on the appropriate ground control/clearance delivery frequency prior to starting engines to receive engine start time, taxi and/or clearance information. Unless otherwise advised by the tower, remain on that frequency during taxiing and runup, then change to local control frequency when ready to request takeoff clearance.

REFERENCE-
AIM, AUTOMATIC TERMINAL INFORMATION SERVICE (ATIS) FOR CONTINUOUS BROADCAST OF TERMINAL INFORMATION, PARAGRAPH 4-1-13.

b. The majority of ground control frequencies are in the 121.6–121.9 MHz bandwidth. Ground control frequencies are provided to eliminate frequency congestion on the tower (local control) frequency and are limited to communications between the tower and aircraft on the ground and between the tower and utility vehicles on the airport, provide a clear VHF channel for arriving and departing aircraft. They are used for issuance of taxi information, clearances, and other necessary contacts between the tower and aircraft or other vehicles operated on the airport. A pilot who has just landed should not change from the tower frequency to the ground control frequency until directed to do so by the controller. Normally, only one ground control frequency is assigned at an airport; however, at locations where the amount of traffic so warrants, a second ground control frequency and/or another frequency designated as a clearance delivery frequency, may be assigned.

c. A controller may omit the ground or local control frequency if the controller believes the pilot knows which frequency is in use. If the ground control frequency is in the 121 MHz bandwidth the controller may omit the numbers preceding the decimal point; e.g., 121.7, "CONTACT GROUND POINT SEVEN." However, if any doubt exists as to what frequency is in use, the pilot should promptly request the controller to provide that information.

d. Controllers will normally avoid issuing a radio frequency change to helicopters, known to be single-piloted, which are hovering, air taxiing, or flying near the ground. At times, it may be necessary for pilots to alert ATC regarding single pilot operations to minimize delay of essential ATC communications. Whenever possible, ATC instructions will be relayed through the frequency being monitored until a frequency change can be accomplished. You must promptly advise ATC if you are unable to comply with a frequency change. Also, you should advise ATC if you must land to accomplish the frequency change unless it is clear the landing will have no impact on other air traffic; e.g., on a taxiway or in a helicopter operating area.

4-3-15. GATE HOLDING DUE TO DEPARTURE DELAYS

a. Pilots should contact ground control or clearance delivery prior to starting engines as gate hold procedures will be in effect whenever departure delays exceed or are anticipated to exceed 15 minutes. The sequence for departure will be maintained in accordance with initial call up unless modified by flow control restrictions. Pilots should monitor the ground control or clearance delivery frequency for engine startup advisories or new proposed start time if the delay changes.

b. The tower controller will consider that pilots of turbine-powered aircraft are ready for takeoff when they reach the runway or warm-up block unless advised otherwise.

4-3-16. VFR FLIGHTS IN TERMINAL AREAS

Use reasonable restraint in exercising the prerogative of VFR flight, especially in terminal areas. The weather minimums and distances from clouds are minimums. Giving yourself a greater margin in specific instances is just good judgment.

a. Approach Area: Conducting a VFR operation in a Class B, Class C, Class D and Class E surface area when the official visibility is 3 or 4 miles is not prohibited, but good judgment would dictate that you keep out of the approach area.

b. Reduced Visibility: It has always been recognized that precipitation reduces forward visibility. Consequently, although again it may be perfectly legal to cancel your IFR flight plan at any time you can proceed VFR, it is good practice, when precipitation is occurring, to continue IFR operation into a terminal area until you are reasonably close to your destination.

c. Simulated Instrument Flights: In conducting simulated instrument flights, be sure that the weather is good enough to compensate for the restricted visibility of the safety pilot and your greater concentration on your flight instruments. Give yourself a little greater margin when your flight plan lies in or near a busy airway or close to an airport.

4-3-17. VFR HELICOPTER OPERATIONS AT CONTROLLED AIRPORTS

a. General:

1. The following ATC procedures and phraseologies recognize the unique capabilities of helicopters and were developed to improve service to all users. Helicopter design characteristics and user needs often require operations from movement areas and nonmovement areas within the airport boundary. In order for ATC to properly apply these procedures, it is essential that pilots familiarize themselves with the local operations and make it known to controllers when additional instructions are necessary.

2. Insofar as possible, helicopter operations will be instructed to avoid the flow of fixed-wing aircraft to minimize overall delays; however, there will be many situations where faster/larger helicopters may be inte-

grated with fixed-wing aircraft for the benefit of all co cerned. Examples would include IFR flights, avoidan of noise sensitive areas, or use of runways/taxiways minimize the hazardous effects of rotor downwash congested areas.

3. Because helicopter pilots are intimately famili with the effects of rotor downwash, they are best qua fied to determine if a given operation can be conduct safely. Accordingly, the pilot has the final authori with respect to the specific airspeed/altitude combin tions. ATC clearances are in no way intended to pla the helicopter in a hazardous position. It is expected th pilots will advise ATC if a specific clearance will cau undue hazards to persons or property.

b. Controllers normally limit ATC ground servic and instruction to *movement* areas; therefore, oper tions from *nonmovement* areas are conducted at pil discretion and should be based on local policies, proce dures, or letters of agreement. In order to maximize th flexibility of helicopter operations, it is necessary t rely heavily on sound pilot judgment. For example, haz ards such as debris, obstructions, vehicles, or personne must be recognized by the pilot, and action should b taken as necessary to avoid such hazards. Taxi, hove taxi, and air taxi operations are considered to be groun movements. Helicopters conducting such operation are expected to adhere to the same conditions, require ments, and practices as apply to other ground taxiin and ATC procedures in the AIM.

1. The phraseology *taxi* is used when it is intended or expected that the helicopter will taxi on the airpor surface, either via taxiways or other prescribed route *Taxi* is used primarily for helicopters equipped wit wheels or in response to a pilot request. Preferenc should be given to this procedure whenever it is neces sary to minimize effects of rotor downwash.

2. Pilots may request a *hover taxi* when slow for ward movement is desired or when it may be appropri ate to move very short distances. Pilots should avoid this procedure if rotor downwash is likely to cause dam age to parked aircraft or if blowing dust/snow could ob scure visibility. If it is necessary to operate above 25 fee AGL when hover taxiing, the pilot should initiate a re quest to ATC.

3. *Air taxi* is the preferred method for helicopter ground movements on airports provided ground opera tions and conditions permit. Unless otherwise re quested or instructed, pilots are expected to remain be low 100 feet AGL. However, if a higher than normal airspeed or altitude is desired, the request should be made prior to lift-off. The pilot is solely responsible for selecting a safe airspeed for the altitude/operation being conducted. Use of *air taxi* enables the pilot to proceed at an optimum airspeed/altitude, minimize downwash effect, conserve fuel, and expedite movement from one point to another. Helicopters should avoid overflight of other aircraft, vehicles, and personnel during air-taxi operations. Caution must be exercised concerning active runways and pilots must be certain that air taxi instructions are understood. Special precautions may be necessary at unfamiliar airports or airports with multiple/intersecting active runways. The taxi procedures given in paragraph 4–3–18, Taxiing, paragraph 4–3–19, Taxi During Low Visibility, and paragraph 4–3–20, Exiting the Runway After Landing, also apply.

REFERENCE–
PILOT/CONTROLLER GLOSSARY TERM–TAXI.
PILOT/CONTROLLER GLOSSARY TERM–HOVER TAXI.
PILOT/CONTROLLER GLOSSARY TERM–AIR TAXI.

c. Takeoff and Landing Procedures:

1. Helicopter operations may be conducted from a runway, taxiway, portion of a landing strip, or any clear area which could be used as a landing site such as the scene of an accident, a construction site, or the roof of a building. The terms used to describe designated areas from which helicopters operate are: movement area, landing/takeoff area, apron/ramp, heliport and helipad (See *Pilot/Controller Glossary*). These areas may be improved or unimproved and may be separate from or located on an airport/heliport. ATC will issue takeoff clearances from *movement* areas other than active runways, or in diverse directions from active runways, with additional instructions as necessary. Whenever possible, takeoff clearance will be issued in lieu of extended hover/air taxi operations. Phraseology will be "CLEARED FOR TAKEOFF FROM (taxiway, helipad, runway number, etc.), MAKE RIGHT/LEFT TURN FOR (direction, heading, NAVAID radial) DEPARTURE/DEPARTURE ROUTE (number, name, etc.)." Unless requested by the pilot, downwind takeoffs will not be issued if the tailwind exceeds 5 knots.

2. Pilots should be alert to wind information as well as to wind indications in the vicinity of the helicopter. ATC should be advised of the intended method of departing. A pilot request to takeoff in a given direction indicates that the pilot is willing to accept the wind condition and controllers will honor the request if traffic permits. Departure points could be a significant distance from the control tower and it may be difficult or impossible for the controller to determine the helicopter's relative position to the wind.

3. If takeoff is requested from *nonmovement* areas, the phraseology "PROCEED AS REQUESTED" will be used. Additional instructions will be issued as necessary. The pilot is responsible for operating in a safe manner and should exercise due caution. When other known traffic is not a factor and takeoff is requested from an area not visible from the tower, an area not authorized for helicopter use, an unlighted area at night, or an area not on the airport, the phraseology "DEPARTURE FROM (location) WILL BE AT YOUR OWN RISK (with reason, and additional instructions as necessary)."

4. Similar phraseology is used for helicopter landing operations. Every effort will be made to permit helicopters to proceed direct and land as near as possible to their final destination on the airport. Traffic density, the need for detailed taxiing instructions, frequency congestion, or other factors may affect the extent to which service can be expedited. As with ground movement operations, a high degree of pilot/controller cooperation and communication is necessary to achieve safe and efficient operations.

4–3–18. TAXIING

a. General: Approval must be obtained prior to moving an aircraft or vehicle onto the movement area during the hours an Airport Traffic Control Tower is in operation.

1. Always state your position on the airport when calling the tower for taxi instructions.

2. The movement area is normally described in local bulletins issued by the airport manager or control tower. These bulletins may be found in FSS's, fixed base operators offices, air carrier offices, and operations offices.

3. The control tower also issues bulletins describing areas where they cannot provide ATC service due to nonvisibility or other reasons.

4. A clearance must be obtained prior to taxiing on a runway, taking off, or landing during the hours an Airport Traffic Control Tower is in operation.

5. When ATC clears an aircraft to "taxi to" an assigned takeoff runway, the absence of holding instructions authorizes the aircraft to "cross" all runways which the taxi route intersects except the assigned takeoff runway. It does not include authorization to "taxi onto" or "cross" the assigned takeoff runway at any point. In order to preclude misunderstandings in radio communications, ATC will not use the word "cleared" in conjunction with authorization for aircraft to taxi.

6. In the absence of holding instructions, a clearance to "taxi to" any point other than an assigned takeoff runway is a clearance to cross all runways that intersect the taxi route to that point.

7. Air traffic control will first specify the runway, issue taxi instructions, and then state any required hold short instructions, when authorizing an aircraft to taxi for departure. This does not authorize the aircraft to "enter" or "cross" the assigned departure runway at any point.

NOTE–
Air traffic controllers are required to obtain from the pilot a readback of all runway hold short instructions.

8. Pilots should always read back the runway assignment when taxi instructions are received from the controller. Controllers are required to confirm the runway hold–short assignment when they issue taxi instructions.

b. ATC clearances or instructions pertaining to taxiing are predicated on known traffic and known physical airport conditions. Therefore, it is important that pilots clearly understand the clearance or instruction. Although an ATC clearance is issued for taxiing purposes, when operating in accordance with the FAR's, it is the responsibility of the pilot to avoid collision with other aircraft. Since "the pilot-in-command of an aircraft is directly responsible for, and is the final authority as to, the operation of that aircraft" the pilot should obtain clarification of any clearance or instruction which is not understood.

REFERENCE–
AIM, GENERAL, PARAGRAPH 7-3-1.

1. Good operating practice dictates that pilots acknowledge all runway crossing, hold short, or takeoff clearances unless there is some misunderstanding, at which time the pilot should query the controller until the clearance is understood.

NOTE–
Air traffic controllers are required to obtain from the pilot a readback of all runway hold short instructions.

2. Pilots operating a single pilot aircraft should monitor only assigned ATC communications after being cleared onto the active runway for departure. Single pilot aircraft should not monitor other than ATC communications until flight from Class B, Class C, or Class

D surface area is completed. This same procedu should be practiced from after receipt of the clearan for landing until the landing and taxi activities are con plete. Proper effective scanning for other aircraft, su face vehicles, or other objects should be continuousl exercised in all cases.

3. If the pilot is unfamiliar with the airport or fo any reason confusion exists as to the correct taxi rou ing, a request may be made for progressive taxi instruc tions which include step-by-step routing directions Progressive instructions may also be issued if the con troller deems it necessary due to traffic or field cond tions; i.e., construction or closed taxiways.

c. At those airports where the U.S. Government oper ates the control tower and ATC has authorized noncom pliance with the requirement for two-way radio com munications while operating within the Class B, Class C, or Class D surface area, or at those airports where th U.S. Government does not operate the control towe and radio communications cannot be established, pilots shall obtain a clearance by visual light signal prior to taxiing on a runway and prior to takeoff and landing.

d. The following phraseologies and procedures are used in radiotelephone communications with aeronautical ground stations.

1. *Request for taxi instructions prior to departure:* State your aircraft identification, location, type o operation planned (VFR or IFR), and the point of first intended landing.

EXAMPLE–
Aircraft: "Washington ground, Beechcraft One Three One Five Niner at hangar eight, ready to taxi, I–F–R to Chicago."

Tower: "Beechcraft One Three One Five Niner, Washington ground, taxi to runway three six, wind zero three zero at two five, altimeter three zero zero four."

or

Tower: "Beechcraft one three one five niner, Washington ground, runway two seven, taxi via taxiways charlie and delta, hold short of runway three three left."

Aircraft: "Beechcraft One Three One Five Niner, hold short of runway three three left."

2. Receipt of ATC clearance: ARTCC clearances are relayed to pilots by airport traffic controllers in the following manner.

EXAMPLE-
Tower: "Beechcraft One Three One Five Niner, cleared to the Chicago Midway Airport via Victor Eight, maintain eight thousand."

Aircraft: "Beechcraft One Three One Five Niner, cleared to the Chicago Midway Airport via Victor Eight, maintain eight thousand."

NOTE-
Normally, an ATC IFR clearance is relayed to a pilot by the ground controller. At busy locations, however, pilots may be instructed by the ground controller to "contact clearance delivery" on a frequency designated for this purpose. No surveillance or control over the movement of traffic is exercised by this position of operation.

3. Request for taxi instructions after landing: State your aircraft identification, location, and that you request taxi instructions.

EXAMPLE-
Aircraft: "Dulles ground, Beechcraft One Four Two Six One clearing runway one right on taxiway echo three, request clearance to Page."

Tower: "Beechcraft One Four Two Six One, Dulles ground, taxi to Page via taxiways echo three, echo one, and echo niner."

or

Aircraft: "Orlando ground, Beechcraft One Four Two Six One clearing runway one eight left at taxiway bravo three, request clearance to Page."

Tower: "Beechcraft One Four Two Six One, Orlando ground, hold short of runway one eight right."

Aircraft: "Beechcraft One Four Two Six One, hold short of runway one eight right."

4-3-19. TAXI DURING LOW VISIBILITY

a. Pilots and aircraft operators should be constantly aware that during certain low visibility conditions the movement of aircraft and vehicles on airports may not be visible to the tower controller. This may prevent visual confirmation of an aircraft's adherence to taxi instructions. Pilots should, therefore, exercise extreme vigilance and proceed cautiously under such conditions.

b. Of vital importance is the need for pilots to notify the controller when difficulties are encountered or at the first indication of becoming disoriented. Pilots should proceed with extreme caution when taxiing toward the sun. When vision difficulties are encountered pilots should immediately inform the controller.

c. Advisory Circular 120-57, Surface Movement Guidance and Control System, commonly known as SMGCS (pronounced "SMIGS") requires a low visibility taxi plan for any airport which has takeoff or landing operations in less than 1,200 feet runway visual range (RVR) visibility conditions. These plans, which affect aircrew and vehicle operators, may incorporate additional lighting, markings, and procedures to control airport surface traffic. They will be addressed at two levels; operations less than 1,200 feet RVR to 600 feet RVR and operations less than 600 feet RVR.

NOTE-
Specific lighting systems and surface markings may be found in paragraph 2-1-9, Taxiway Lights, and paragraph 2-3-4, Taxiway Markings.

4-3-20. EXITING THE RUNWAY AFTER LANDING

The following procedures should be followed after landing and reaching taxi speed.

a. Exit the runway without delay at the first available taxiway or on a taxiway as instructed by ATC. Pilots shall not exit the landing runway onto another runway unless authorized by ATC. At airports with an operating control tower, pilots should not stop or reverse course on the runway without first obtaining ATC approval.

b. Taxi clear of the runway unless otherwise directed by ATC. In the absence of ATC instructions the pilot is expected to taxi clear of the landing runway even if that requires the aircraft to protrude into or cross another taxiway, runway, or ramp area. This does not authorize an aircraft to cross a subsequent taxiway/runway/ramp after clearing the landing runway.

NOTE-
The tower will issue the pilot with instructions which will normally permit the aircraft to enter another taxiway, runway, or ramp area when required to taxi clear of the runway.

c. Stop the aircraft after clearing the runway if instructions have not been received from ATC.

d. Immediately change to ground control frequency when advised by the tower and obtain a taxi clearance.

AIM

NOTE-
[1] *The tower will issue instructions required to resolve any potential conflictions with other ground traffic prior to advising the pilot to contact ground control.*

[2] *A clearance from ATC to taxi to the ramp authorizes the aircraft to cross all runways and taxiway intersections. Pilots not familiar with the taxi route should request specific taxi instructions from ATC.*

4-3-21. PRACTICE INSTRUMENT APPROACHES

a. Various air traffic incidents have indicated the necessity for adoption of measures to achieve more organized and controlled operations where practice instrument approaches are conducted. Practice instrument approaches are considered to be instrument approaches made by either a VFR aircraft not on an IFR flight plan or an aircraft on an IFR flight plan. To achieve this and thereby enhance air safety, it is Air Traffic's policy to provide for separation of such operations at locations where approach control facilities are located and, as resources permit, at certain other locations served by ARTCC's or parent approach control facilities. Pilot requests to practice instrument approaches may be approved by ATC subject to traffic and workload conditions. Pilots should anticipate that in some instances the controller may find it necessary to deny approval or withdraw previous approval when traffic conditions warrant. It must be clearly understood, however, that even though the controller may be providing separation, pilots on VFR flight plans are required to comply with basic VFR weather minimums (14 CFR Section 91.155). Application of ATC procedures or any action taken by the controller to avoid traffic conflictions does not relieve IFR and VFR pilots of their responsibility to see-and-avoid other traffic while operating in VFR conditions (14 CFR Section 91.113). In addition to the normal IFR separation minimums (which includes visual separation) during VFR conditions, 500 feet vertical separation may be applied between VFR aircraft and between a VFR aircraft and the IFR aircraft. Pilots not on IFR flight plans desiring practice instrument approaches should always state 'practice' when making requests to ATC. Controllers will instruct VFR aircraft requesting an instrument approach to maintain VFR. This is to preclude misunderstandings between the pilot and controller as to the status of the aircraft. If pilots wish to proceed in accordance with instrument flight rules, they must specifically request and obtain, an IFR clearance.

b. Before practicing an instrument approach, pilots should inform the approach control facility or the tower of the type of practice approach they desire to make and how they intend to terminate it, i.e., full-stop landing, touch-and-go, or missed or low approach maneuver. This information may be furnished progressively when conducting a series of approaches. Pilots on an IFR flight plan, who have made a series of instrument approaches to full stop landings should inform ATC when they make their final landing. The controller will control flights practicing instrument approaches so as to ensure that they do not disrupt the flow of arriving and departing itinerant IFR or VFR aircraft. The priority afforded itinerant aircraft over practice instrument approaches is not intended to be so rigidly applied that it causes grossly inefficient application of services. A minimum delay to itinerant traffic may be appropriate to allow an aircraft practicing an approach to complete that approach.

NOTE-
A clearance to land means that appropriate separation on the landing runway will be ensured. A landing clearance does not relieve the pilot from compliance with any previously issued restriction.

c. At airports without a tower, pilots wishing to make practice instrument approaches should notify the facility having control jurisdiction of the desired approach as indicated on the approach chart. All approach control facilities and ARTCC's are required to publish a Letter to Airmen depicting those airports where they provide standard separation to both VFR and IFR aircraft conducting practice instrument approaches.

d. The controller will provide approved separation between both VFR and IFR aircraft when authorization is granted to make practice approaches to airports where an approach control facility is located and to certain other airports served by approach control or an ARTCC. Controller responsibility for separation of VFR aircraft begins at the point where the approach clearance becomes effective, or when the aircraft enters Class B or Class C airspace, or a TRSA, whichever comes first.

e. VFR aircraft practicing instrument approaches are not automatically authorized to execute the missed approach procedure. This authorization must be specifically requested by the pilot and approved by the controller. Separation will not be provided unless the missed approach has been approved by ATC.

f. Except in an emergency, aircraft cleared to practice instrument approaches must not deviate from the approved procedure until cleared to do so by the controller.

g. At radar approach control locations when a full approach procedure (procedure turn, etc.,) cannot be approved, pilots should expect to be vectored to a final approach course for a practice instrument approach which is compatible with the general direction of traffic at that airport.

h. When granting approval for a practice instrument approach, the controller will usually ask the pilot to report to the tower prior to or over the final approach fix inbound (nonprecision approaches) or over the outer marker or fix used in lieu of the outer marker inbound (precision approaches).

i. When authorization is granted to conduct practice instrument approaches to an airport with a tower, but where approved standard separation is not provided to aircraft conducting practice instrument approaches, the tower will approve the practice approach, instruct the aircraft to maintain VFR and issue traffic information, as required.

j. When an aircraft notifies a FSS providing Local Airport Advisory to the airport concerned of the intent to conduct a practice instrument approach and whether or not separation is to be provided, the pilot will be instructed to contact the appropriate facility on a specified frequency prior to initiating the approach. At airports where separation is not provided, the FSS will acknowledge the message and issue known traffic information but will neither approve or disapprove the approach.

k. Pilots conducting practice instrument approaches should be particularly alert for other aircraft operating in the local traffic pattern or in proximity to the airport.

4-3-22. OPTION APPROACH

The "Cleared for the Option" procedure will permit an instructor, flight examiner or pilot the option to make a touch-and-go, low approach, missed approach, stop-and-go, or full stop landing. This procedure can be very beneficial in a training situation in that neither the student pilot nor examinee would know what maneuver would be accomplished. The pilot should make a request for this procedure passing the final approach fix inbound on an instrument approach or entering down-

wind for a VFR traffic pattern. The advantages of this procedure as a training aid are that it enables an instructor or examiner to obtain the reaction of a trainee or examinee under changing conditions, the pilot would not have to discontinue an approach in the middle of the procedure due to student error or pilot proficiency requirements, and finally it allows more flexibility and economy in training programs. This procedure will only be used at those locations with an operational control tower and will be subject to ATC approval.

4-3-23. USE OF AIRCRAFT LIGHTS

a. Aircraft position lights are required to be lighted on aircraft operated on the surface and in flight from sunset to sunrise. In addition, aircraft equipped with an anti-collision light system are required to be operated during all types of operations (day and night) except when the pilot-in-command determines that the anti-collision lights should be turned off when their light output during adverse meteorological conditions would constitute a hazard to safety (14 CFR Section 91.209). Supplementary strobe lights should be turned off on the ground when they adversely affect ground personnel or other pilots, and in flight when there are adverse reflection from clouds.

b. An aircraft anti-collision light system can use one or more rotating beacons and/or strobe lights, be colored either red or white, and have different (higher than minimum) intensities when compared to other aircraft. Many aircraft have both a rotating beacon and a strobe light system.

c. The FAA has a voluntary pilot safety program, *Operation Lights On*, to enhance the *see-and-avoid* concept. Pilots are encouraged to turn on their landing lights during takeoff; i.e., either after takeoff clearance has been received or when beginning takeoff roll. Pilots are further encouraged to turn on their landing lights when operating below 10,000 feet, day or night, especially when operating within 10 miles of any airport, or in conditions of reduced visibility and in areas where flocks of birds may be expected, i.e., coastal areas, lake areas, around refuse dumps, etc. Although turning on aircraft lights does enhance the *see-and-avoid* concept, pilots should not become complacent about keeping a sharp lookout for other aircraft. Not all aircraft are equipped with lights and some pilots may not have their lights turned on. Aircraft manufacturer's recommendations for operation of landing lights and electrical systems should be observed.

d. Prop and jet blast forces generated by large aircraft have overturned or damaged several smaller aircraft taxiing behind them. To avoid similar results, and in the interest of preventing upsets and injuries to ground personnel from such forces, the FAA recommends that air carriers and commercial operators turn on their rotating beacons anytime their aircraft engines are in operation. General aviation pilots using rotating beacon equipped aircraft are also encouraged to participate in this program which is designed to alert others to the potential hazard. Since this is a voluntary program, exercise caution and do not rely solely on the rotating beacon as an indication that aircraft engines are in operation.

e. At the sole discretion of the pilot in command, if aircraft equipment permits, at least one landing light may be turned on when holding in position on the runway. This increases the conspicuity of the holding aircraft to aircraft approaching to land, aircraft taxiing, and/or aircraft crossing the runway. When appropriate, or cleared for takeoff, pilots should turn on all remaining exterior lights. Pilots should be aware of and respect any operating limitations on aircraft systems or other limitations, and the effect of landing lights to other aircraft in the immediate vicinity.

4-3-24. FLIGHT INSPECTION/'FLIGHT CHECK' AIRCRAFT IN TERMINAL AREAS

a. *Flight check* is a call sign used to alert pilots and air traffic controllers when a FAA aircraft is engaged in flight inspection/certification of NAVAID's and flight procedures. Flight check aircraft fly preplanned high/low altitude flight patterns such as grids, orbits, DME arcs, and tracks, including low passes along the full length of the runway to verify NAVAID performance. In most instances, these flight checks are being automatically recorded and/or flown in an automated mode.

b. Pilots should be especially watchful and avoid the flight paths of any aircraft using the call sign "Flight Check" or "Flight Check Recorded." The latter call sign; e.g. "Flight Check 47 Recorded" indicates that automated flight inspections are in progress in terminal areas. These flights will normally receive special handling from ATC. Pilot patience and cooperation in allowing uninterrupted recordings can significantly help expedite flight inspections, minimize costly, repetitive runs, and reduce the burden on the U.S. taxpayer.

4-3-25. HAND SIGNALS

Signalman Directs Towing

FIG 4-3-7

Signalman's Position

FIG 4-3-8

Flagman Directs Pilot

FIG 4-3-9

All Clear
(O.K.)

FIG 4-3-10

Start Engine

FIG 4-3-11

Pull Chocks

FIG 4-3-12

Come Ahead

FIG 4-3-13

Left Turn

FIG 4-3-14

Right Turn

FIG 4-3-15

Stop

FIG 4-3-17

Slow Down

FIG 4-3-16

Insert Chocks

FIG 4-3-18

Cut Engines

FIG 4-3-19

Emergency Stop

FIG 4-3-21

Night Operation

Use same hand movements
as day operation

FIG 4-3-20

4-3-26. OPERATIONS AT UNCONTROLLED AIRPORTS WITH AUTOMATED SURFACE OBSERVING SYSTEM (ASOS)/AUTOMATED WEATHER OBSERVING SYSTEM (AWOS)

a. Many airports throughout the National Airspace System are equipped with either ASOS or AWOS. At most airports with an operating control tower or human observer, the weather will be available to you in a METAR hourly or special observation format on the Automatic Terminal Information Service (ATIS) or directly transmitted from the controller/observer.

b. At uncontrolled airports that are equipped with ASOS/AWOS with ground-to-air broadcast capability, the one-minute updated airport weather should be available to you within approximately 25 NM of the airport below 10,000 feet. The frequency for the weather broadcast will be published on sectional charts and in the Airport/Facility Directory. Some part-time towered airports may also broadcast the automated weather on their ATIS frequency during the hours that the tower is closed.

c. Controllers issue SVFR or IFR clearances based on pilot request, known traffic and reported weather, i.e., METAR/SPECI observations, when they are available. Pilots have access to more current weather at uncontrolled ASOS/AWOS airports than do the controllers who may be located several miles away. Controllers will rely on the pilot to determine the current airport weather from the ASOS/AWOS. All aircraft arriving or departing an ASOS/AWOS equipped uncontrolled airport should monitor the airport weather frequency to ascertain the status of the airspace. Pilots in Class E airspace must be alert for changing weather conditions which may effect the status of the airspace from IFR/VFR. If ATC service is required for IFR/SVFR approach/departure or requested for VFR service, the pilot should advise the controller that he/she has received the one-minute weather and state his/her intentions.

EXAMPLE-
"I have the (airport) one-minute weather, request an ILS Runway 14 approach."

REFERENCE-
AIM, WEATHER OBSERVING PROGRAMS, PARAGRAPH 7-1-10.

Section 4. ATC CLEARANCES/SEPARATIONS

4-4-1. CLEARANCE

a. A clearance issued by ATC is predicated on known traffic and known physical airport conditions. An ATC clearance means an authorization by ATC, for the purpose of preventing collision between known aircraft, for an aircraft to proceed under specified conditions within controlled airspace. IT IS NOT AUTHORIZATION FOR A PILOT TO DEVIATE FROM ANY RULE, REGULATION, OR MINIMUM ALTITUDE NOR TO CONDUCT UNSAFE OPERATION OF THE AIRCRAFT.

b. 14 CFR Section 91.3(a) states: "The pilot-in-command of an aircraft is directly responsible for, and is the final authority as to, the operation of that aircraft." If ATC issues a clearance that would cause a pilot to deviate from a rule or regulation, or in the pilot's opinion, would place the aircraft in jeopardy, IT IS THE PILOT'S RESPONSIBILITY TO REQUEST AN AMENDED CLEARANCE. Similarly, if a pilot prefers to follow a different course of action, such as make a 360 degree turn for spacing to follow traffic when established in a landing or approach sequence, land on a different runway, takeoff from a different intersection, takeoff from the threshold instead of an intersection, or delay operation, THE PILOT IS EXPECTED TO INFORM ATC ACCORDINGLY. When the pilot requests a different course of action, however, the pilot is expected to cooperate so as to preclude disruption of traffic flow or creation of conflicting patterns. The pilot is also expected to use the appropriate aircraft call sign to acknowledge all ATC clearances, frequency changes, or advisory information.

c. Each pilot who deviates from an ATC clearance in response to a Traffic Alert and Collision Avoidance System resolution advisory shall notify ATC of that deviation as soon as possible.

REFERENCE-
PILOT/CONTROLLER GLOSSARY TERM- TRAFFIC ALERT AND COLLISION AVOIDANCE SYSTEM.

d. When weather conditions permit, during the time an IFR flight is operating, it is the direct responsibility of the pilot to avoid other aircraft since VFR flights may be operating in the same area without the knowledge of ATC. Traffic clearances provide standard separation only between IFR flights.

4-4-2. CLEARANCE PREFIX

A clearance, control information, or a response to a request for information originated by an ATC facility and relayed to the pilot through an air-to-ground communication station will be prefixed by "ATC clears," "ATC advises," or "ATC requests."

4-4-3. CLEARANCE ITEMS

ATC clearances normally contain the following:

a. Clearance Limit: The traffic clearance issued prior to departure will normally authorize flight to the airport of intended landing. Under certain conditions, at some locations a short-range clearance procedure is utilized whereby a clearance is issued to a fix within or just outside of the terminal area and pilots are advised of the frequency on which they will receive the long-range clearance direct from the center controller.

b. Departure Procedure: Headings to fly and altitude restrictions may be issued to separate a departure from other air traffic in the terminal area. Where the volume of traffic warrants, DP's have been developed. ▮

REFERENCE-
AIM, ABBREVIATED IFR DEPARTURE CLEARANCE (CLEARED...AS FILED) PROCEDURES, PARAGRAPH 5-2-3.
AIM, INSTRUMENT DEPARTURES, PARAGRAPH 5-2-6.

c. Route of Flight:

1. Clearances are normally issued for the altitude or flight level and route filed by the pilot. However, due to traffic conditions, it is frequently necessary for ATC to specify an altitude or flight level or route different from that requested by the pilot. In addition, flow patterns have been established in certain congested areas or between congested areas whereby traffic capacity is increased by routing all traffic on preferred routes. Information on these flow patterns is available in offices where preflight briefing is furnished or where flight plans are accepted.

2. When required, air traffic clearances include data to assist pilots in identifying radio reporting points. It is the responsibility of pilots to notify ATC immediately if their radio equipment cannot receive the type of signals they must utilize to comply with their clearance.

d. Altitude Data:

1. The altitude or flight level instructions in an ATC clearance normally require that a pilot "MAINTAIN" the altitude or flight level at which the flight will operate when in controlled airspace. Altitude or flight level changes while en route should be requested prior to the time the change is desired.

2. When possible, if the altitude assigned is different from the altitude requested by the pilot, ATC will inform the pilot when to expect climb or descent clearance or to request altitude change from another facility. If this has not been received prior to crossing the boundary of the ATC facility's area and assignment at a different altitude is still desired, the pilot should reinitiate the request with the next facility.

3. The term "cruise" may be used instead of "MAINTAIN" to assign a block of airspace to a pilot from the minimum IFR altitude up to and including the altitude specified in the cruise clearance. The pilot may level off at any intermediate altitude within this block of airspace. Climb/descent within the block is to be made at the discretion of the pilot. However, once the pilot starts descent and verbally reports leaving an altitude in the block, the pilot may not return to that altitude without additional ATC clearance.

REFERENCE-
PILOT/CONTROLLER GLOSSARY TERM- CRUISE.

e. Holding Instructions:

1. Whenever an aircraft has been cleared to a fix other than the destination airport and delay is expected, it is the responsibility of the ATC controller to issue complete holding instructions (unless the pattern is charted), an EFC time, and a best estimate of any additional en route/terminal delay.

2. If the holding pattern is charted and the controller doesn't issue complete holding instructions, the pilot is expected to hold as depicted on the appropriate chart. When the pattern is charted, the controller may omit all holding instructions except the charted holding direction and the statement *AS PUBLISHED*, e.g., *"HOLD EAST AS PUBLISHED."* Controllers shall always issue complete holding instructions when pilots request them.

NOTE-
Only those holding patterns depicted on U.S. government or commercially produced charts which meet FAA requirements should be used.

3. If no holding pattern is charted and holding instructions have not been issued, the pilot should ask ATC for holding instructions prior to reaching the fix. This procedure will eliminate the possibility of an aircraft entering a holding pattern other than that desired by ATC. If unable to obtain holding instructions prior to reaching the fix (due to frequency congestion, stuck

microphone, etc.), hold in a standard pattern on the course on which you approached the fix and request further clearance as soon as possible. In this event, the altitude/flight level of the aircraft at the clearance limit will be protected so that separation will be provided as required.

4. When an aircraft is 3 minutes or less from a clearance limit and a clearance beyond the fix has not been received, the pilot is expected to start a speed reduction so that the aircraft will cross the fix, initially, at or below the maximum holding airspeed.

5. When no delay is expected, the controller should issue a clearance beyond the fix as soon as possible and, whenever possible, at least 5 minutes before the aircraft reaches the clearance limit.

6. Pilots should report to ATC the time and altitude/flight level at which the aircraft reaches the clearance limit and report leaving the clearance limit.

NOTE-
In the event of two-way communications failure, pilots are required to comply with 14 CFR Section 91.185.

4-4-4. AMENDED CLEARANCES

a. Amendments to the initial clearance will be issued at any time an air traffic controller deems such action necessary to avoid possible confliction between aircraft. Clearances will require that a flight "hold" or change altitude prior to reaching the point where standard separation from other IFR traffic would no longer exist.

NOTE-
Some pilots have questioned this action and requested "traffic information" and were at a loss when the reply indicated "no traffic report." In such cases the controller has taken action to prevent a traffic confliction which would have occurred at a distant point.

b. A pilot may wish an explanation of the handling of the flight at the time of occurrence; however, controllers are not able to take time from their immediate control duties nor can they afford to overload the ATC communications channels to furnish explanations. Pilots may obtain an explanation by directing a letter or telephone call to the chief controller of the facility involved.

c. Pilots have the privilege of requesting a different clearance from that which has been issued by ATC if they feel that they have information which would make another course of action more practicable or if aircraft equipment limitations or company procedures forbid compliance with the clearance issued.

4-4-5. SPECIAL VFR CLEARANCES

a. An ATC clearance must be obtained *prior* to operating within a Class B, Class C, Class D or Class E surface area when the weather is less than that required for VFR flight. A VFR pilot may request and be given a clearance to enter, leave, or operate within most Class D and Class E surface areas and some Class B and Class C surface areas in special VFR conditions, traffic permitting, and providing such flight will not delay IFR operations. All special VFR flights must remain clear of clouds. The visibility requirements for special VFR aircraft (other than helicopters) are:

1. At least 1 statute mile flight visibility for operations within Class B, Class C, Class D and Class E surface areas.

2. At least 1 statute mile ground visibility if taking off or landing. If ground visibility is not reported at that airport, the flight visibility must be at least 1 statute mile.

3. The restrictions in subparagraphs 1. and 2. do not apply to helicopters. Helicopters must remain clear of clouds and may operate in Class B, Class C, Class D and Class E surface areas with less than 1 statute mile visibility.

b. When a control tower is located within the Class B, Class C, or Class D surface area, requests for clearances should be to the tower. In a Class E surface area, a clearance may be obtained from the nearest tower, FSS, or center.

c. It is not necessary to file a complete flight plan with the request for clearance, but pilots should state their intentions in sufficient detail to permit ATC to fit their flight into the traffic flow. The clearance will not contain a specific altitude as the pilot must remain clear of clouds. The controller may require the pilot to fly at or below a certain altitude due to other traffic, but the altitude specified will permit flight at or above the minimum safe altitude. In addition, at radar locations, flights may be vectored if necessary for control purposes or on pilot request.

NOTE-
The pilot is responsible for obstacle or terrain clearance.

REFERENCE-
14 CFR SECTION 91.119.

d. Special VFR clearances are effective within Class B, Class C, Class D and Class E surface areas only. ATC does not provide separation after an aircraft

leaves the Class B, Class C, Class D or Class E surface area on a special VFR clearance.

e. Special VFR operations by fixed-wing aircraft are prohibited in some Class B and Class C surface areas due to the volume of IFR traffic. A list of these Class B and Class C surface areas is contained in 14 CFR Part 91, Appendix D, Section 3. They are also depicted on sectional aeronautical charts.

f. ATC provides separation between Special VFR flights and between these flights and other IFR flights.

g. Special VFR operations by fixed-wing aircraft are prohibited between sunset and sunrise unless the pilot is instrument rated and the aircraft is equipped for IFR flight.

h. Pilots arriving or departing an uncontrolled airport that has automated weather broadcast capability (ASOS/AWOS) should monitor the broadcast frequency, advise the controller that they have the "one-minute weather" and state intentions prior to operating within the Class B, Class C, Class D or Class E surface areas.

REFERENCE-
PILOT/CONTROLLER GLOSSARY TERM- ONE-MINUTE WEATHER.

4-4-6. PILOT RESPONSIBILITY UPON CLEARANCE ISSUANCE

a. Record ATC clearance: When conducting an IFR operation, make a written record of your clearance. The specified conditions which are a part of your air traffic clearance may be somewhat different from those included in your flight plan. Additionally, ATC may find it necessary to ADD conditions, such as particular departure route. The very fact that ATC specifies different or additional conditions means that other aircraft are involved in the traffic situation.

b. ATC Clearance/Instruction Readback: Pilots of airborne aircraft should read back *those parts* of ATC clearances and instructions containing altitude assignments or vectors as a means of mutual verification. The readback of the "numbers" serves as a double check between pilots and controllers and reduces the kinds of communications errors that occur when a number is either "misheard" or is incorrect.

1. Include the aircraft identification in all readbacks and acknowledgments. This aids controllers in determining that the correct aircraft received the clearance or instruction. The requirement to include aircraft identification in all readbacks and acknowledgements becomes more important as frequency congestion increases and when aircraft with similar call signs are on the same frequency.

EXAMPLE-
*"Climbing to Flight Level three three zero, United Twelve"
or "November Five Charlie Tango, roger, cleared to land."*

2. Read back altitudes, altitude restrictions, and vectors in the same sequence as they are given in the clearance or instruction.

3. Altitudes contained in charted procedures, such as DP's, instrument approaches, etc., should not be read back unless they are specifically stated by the controller.

c. It is the responsibility of the pilot to accept or refuse the clearance issued.

4-4-7. IFR CLEARANCE VFR-ON-TOP

a. A pilot on an IFR flight plan operating in VFR weather conditions, may request VFR-on-top in lieu of an assigned altitude. This permits a pilot to select an altitude or flight level of their choice (subject to any ATC restrictions.)

b. Pilots desiring to climb through a cloud, haze, smoke, or other meteorological formation and then either cancel their IFR flight plan or operate VFR-on-top may request a climb to VFR-on-top. The ATC authorization shall contain either a top report or a statement that no top report is available, and a request to report reaching VFR-on-top. Additionally, the ATC authorization may contain a clearance limit, routing and an alternative clearance if VFR-on-top is not reached by a specified altitude.

c. A pilot on an IFR flight plan, operating in VFR conditions, may request to climb/descend in VFR conditions.

d. ATC may not authorize VFR-on-top/VFR conditions operations unless the pilot requests the VFR operation or a clearance to operate in VFR conditions will result in noise abatement benefits where part of the IFR departure route does not conform to an FAA approved noise abatement route or altitude.

e. When operating in VFR conditions with an ATC authorization to "maintain VFR-on-top /maintain VFR conditions" pilots on IFR flight plans must:

1. Fly at the appropriate VFR altitude as prescribed in 14 CFR Section 91.159.

2. Comply with the VFR visibility and distance from cloud criteria in 14 CFR Section 91.155 (Basic VFR Weather Minimums).

3. Comply with instrument flight rules that are applicable to this flight; i.e., minimum IFR altitudes, position reporting, radio communications, course to be flown, adherence to ATC clearance, etc.

NOTE-
Pilots should advise ATC prior to any altitude change to insure the exchange of accurate traffic information.

f. ATC authorization to "maintain VFR-on-top" is not intended to restrict pilots so that they must operate only *above* an obscuring meteorological formation (layer). Instead, it permits operation above, below, between layers, or in areas where there is no meteorological obscuration. It is imperative, however, that pilots understand that clearance to operate "VFR-on-top/VFR conditions" does not imply cancellation of the IFR flight plan.

g. Pilots operating VFR-on-top/VFR conditions may receive traffic information from ATC on other pertinent IFR or VFR aircraft. However, aircraft operating in Class B airspace/TRSA's shall be separated as required by FAA Order 7110.65, Air Traffic Control.

NOTE-
When operating in VFR weather conditions, it is the pilot's responsibility to be vigilant so as to see-and-avoid other aircraft.

h. ATC will not authorize VFR or VFR-on-top operations in Class A airspace.

REFERENCE-
AIM, CLASS A AIRSPACE, PARAGRAPH 3-2-2.

4-4-8. VFR/IFR FLIGHTS

A pilot departing VFR, either intending to or needing to obtain an IFR clearance en route, must be aware of the position of the aircraft and the relative terrain/obstructions. When accepting a clearance below the MEA/MIA/MVA/OROCA, pilots are responsible for their own terrain/obstruction clearance until reaching the MEA/MIA/MVA/OROCA. If pilots are unable to maintain terrain/obstruction clearance, the controller should be advised and pilots should state their intentions.

NOTE-
OROCA is an off-route altitude which provides obstruction clearance with a 1,000 foot buffer in nonmountainous terrain areas and a 2,000 foot buffer in designated mountainous areas within the U.S. This altitude may not provide signal coverage from ground-based navigational aids, air traffic control radar, or communications coverage.

4-4-9. ADHERENCE TO CLEARANCE

a. When air traffic clearance has been obtained under either visual or instrument flight rules, the pilot-in-command of the aircraft shall not deviate from the provisions thereof unless an amended clearance is obtained. When ATC issues a clearance or instruction, pilots are expected to execute its provisions upon receipt. ATC, in certain situations, will include the word "IMMEDIATELY" in a clearance or instruction to impress urgency of an imminent situation and expeditious compliance by the pilot is expected and necessary for safety. The addition of a VFR or other restriction; i.e., climb or descent point or time, crossing altitude, etc., does not authorize a pilot to deviate from the route of flight or any other provision of the ATC clearance.

b. When a heading is assigned or a turn is requested by ATC, pilots are expected to promptly initiate the turn, to complete the turn, and maintain the new heading unless issued additional instructions.

c. The term "AT PILOT'S DISCRETION" included in the altitude information of an ATC clearance means that ATC has offered the pilot the option to start climb or descent when the pilot wishes, is authorized to conduct the climb or descent at any rate, and to temporarily level off at any intermediate altitude as desired. However, once the aircraft has vacated an altitude, it may not return to that altitude.

d. When ATC has not used the term "AT PILOT'S DISCRETION" nor imposed any climb or descent restrictions, pilots should initiate climb or descent promptly on acknowledgement of the clearance. Descend or climb at an optimum rate consistent with the operating characteristics of the aircraft to 1,000 feet above or below the assigned altitude, and then attempt to descend or climb at a rate of between 500 and 1,500 fpm until the assigned altitude is reached. If at anytime the pilot is unable to climb or descend at a rate of at least 500 feet a minute, advise ATC. If it is necessary to level off at an intermediate altitude during climb or descent, advise ATC, except when leveling off at 10,000 feet MSL on descent, or 2,500 feet above airport elevation (prior to entering a Class B, Class C, or Class D surface area), when required for speed reduction.

REFERENCE-
14 CFR SECTION 91.117.

NOTE-
Leveling off at 10,000 feet MSL on descent or 2,500 feet above airport elevation (prior to entering a Class B, Class C, or Class D surface area) to comply with 14 CFR Section 91.117 airspeed restrictions is commonplace. Controllers anticipate this action and plan accordingly. Leveling off at any other time on climb or descent may seriously affect air traffic handling by ATC. Consequently, it is imperative that pilots make every effort to fulfill the above expected actions to aid ATC in safely handling and expediting traffic.

e. If the altitude information of an ATC DESCENT clearance includes a provision to "CROSS (fix) AT" or "AT OR ABOVE/BELOW (altitude)," the manner in which the descent is executed to comply with the crossing altitude is at the pilot's discretion. This authorization to descend at pilot's discretion is only applicable to that portion of the flight to which the crossing altitude restriction applies, and the pilot is expected to comply with the crossing altitude as a provision of the clearance. Any other clearance in which pilot execution is optional will so state "AT PILOT'S DISCRETION."

EXAMPLE-
1 *"United Four Seventeen, descend and maintain six thousand."*

NOTE-
1 *The pilot is expected to commence descent upon receipt of the clearance and to descend at the suggested rates until reaching the assigned altitude of 6,000 feet.*

EXAMPLE-
2 *"United Four Seventeen, descend at pilot's discretion, maintain six thousand."*

NOTE-
2 *The pilot is authorized to conduct descent within the context of the term at pilot's discretion as described above.*

EXAMPLE-
3 *"United Four Seventeen, cross Lakeview V-O-R at or above Flight Level two zero zero, descend and maintain six thousand."*

NOTE-
3 *The pilot is authorized to conduct descent at pilot's discretion until reaching Lakeview VOR and must comply with the clearance provision to cross the Lakeview VOR at or above FL 200. After passing Lakeview VOR, the pilot is expected to descend at the suggested rates until reaching the assigned altitude of 6,000 feet.*

EXAMPLE-
4 *"United Four Seventeen, cross Lakeview V-O-R at six thousand, maintain six thousand."*

NOTE-

4 *The pilot is authorized to conduct descent at pilot's discretion, however, must comply with the clearance provision to cross the Lakeview VOR at 6,000 feet.*

EXAMPLE-

5 *"United Four Seventeen, descend now to Flight Level two seven zero, cross Lakeview V-O-R at or below one zero thousand, descend and maintain six thousand."*

NOTE-

5 *The pilot is expected to promptly execute and complete descent to FL 270 upon receipt of the clearance. After reaching FL 270 the pilot is authorized to descend "at pilot's discretion" until reaching Lakeview VOR. The pilot must comply with the clearance provision to cross Lakeview VOR at or below 10,000 feet. After Lakeview VOR the pilot is expected to descend at the suggested rates until reaching 6,000 feet.*

EXAMPLE-

6 *"United Three Ten, descend now and maintain Flight Level two four zero, pilot's discretion after reaching Flight Level two eight zero."*

NOTE-

6 *The pilot is expected to commence descent upon receipt of the clearance and to descend at the suggested rates until reaching FL 280. At that point, the pilot is authorized to continue descent to FL 240 within the context of the term "at pilot's discretion" as described above.*

f. In case emergency authority is used to deviate from provisions of an ATC clearance, the pilot-in-command shall notify ATC as soon as possible and obtain an amended clearance. In an emergency situation which does not result in a deviation from the rules prescribed in 14 CFR Part 91 but which requires ATC to give priority to an aircraft, the pilot of such aircraft shall, when requested by ATC, make a report within 48 hours of such emergency situation to the manager of that ATC facility.

g. The guiding principle is that the last ATC clearance has precedence over the previous ATC clearance. When the route or altitude in a previously issued clearance is amended, the controller will restate applicable altitude restrictions. If altitude to maintain is changed or restated, whether prior to departure or while airborne, and previously issued altitude restrictions are omitted, those altitude restrictions are canceled, including departure procedures and STAR altitude restrictions.

EXAMPLE-

1 *A departure flight receives a clearance to destination airport to maintain FL 290. The clearance incorporates a DP which has certain altitude crossing restrictions. Shortly after takeoff, the flight receives a new clearance changing the maintaining FL from 290 to 250. If the altitude restrictions are still applicable, the controller restates them.*

2 *A departing aircraft is cleared to cross Fluky Intersection at or above 3,000 feet, Gordonville VOR at or above 12,000 feet, maintain FL 200. Shortly after departure, the altitude to be maintained is changed to FL 240. If the altitude restrictions are still applicable, the controller issues an amended clearance as follows: "cross Fluky Intersection at or above three thousand, cross Gordonville V-O-R at or above one two thousand, maintain Flight Level two four zero."*

3 *An arriving aircraft is cleared to the destination airport via V45 Delta VOR direct; the aircraft is cleared to cross Delta VOR at 10,000 feet, and then to maintain 6,000 feet. Prior to Delta VOR, the controller issues an amended clearance as follows: "turn right heading one eight zero for vector to runway three six I-L-S approach, maintain six thousand."*

NOTE-

Because the altitude restriction "cross Delta V-O-R at 10,000 feet" was omitted from the amended clearance, it is no longer in effect.

h. Pilots of turbojet aircraft equipped with afterburner engines should advise ATC prior to takeoff if they intend to use afterburning during their climb to the en route altitude. Often, the controller may be able to plan traffic to accommodate a high performance climb and allow the aircraft to climb to the planned altitude without restriction.

4-4-10. IFR SEPARATION STANDARDS

a. ATC effects separation of aircraft vertically by assigning different altitudes; longitudinally by providing an interval expressed in time or distance between aircraft on the same, converging, or crossing courses, and laterally by assigning different flight paths.

b. Separation will be provided between all aircraft operating on IFR flight plans except during that part of the flight (outside Class B airspace or a TRSA) being conducted on a VFR-on-top/VFR conditions clearance. Under these conditions, ATC may issue traffic advisories, but it is the sole responsibility of the pilot to be vigilant so as to see and avoid other aircraft.

c. When radar is employed in the separation of aircraft at the same altitude, a minimum of 3 miles separation is provided between aircraft operating within 40 miles of the radar antenna site, and 5 miles between aircraft operating beyond 40 miles from the antenna site.

These minima may be increased or decreased in certain specific situations.

NOTE-
Certain separation standards are increased in the terminal environment when CENRAP is being utilized.

4-4-11. SPEED ADJUSTMENTS

a. ATC will issue speed adjustments to pilots of radar-controlled aircraft to achieve or maintain required or desire spacing.

b. ATC will express all speed adjustments in terms of knots based on indicated airspeed (IAS) in 10 knot increments except that at or above FL 240 speeds may be expressed in terms of Mach numbers in 0.01 increments. The use of Mach numbers is restricted to turbojet aircraft with Mach meters.

c. Pilots complying with speed adjustments are expected to maintain a speed within plus or minus 10 knots or 0.02 Mach number of the specified speed.

d. Unless pilot concurrence is obtained, ATC requests for speed adjustments will be in accordance with the following minimums:

1. To aircraft operating between FL 280 and 10,000 feet, a speed not less than 250 knots or the equivalent Mach number.

2. To turbine-powered aircraft operating below 10,000 feet:

    (a) A speed not less than 210 knots, except;

    (b) Within 20 flying miles of the airport of intended landing, a speed not less than 170 knots.

3. Reciprocating engine or turboprop aircraft within 20 flying miles of the runway threshold of the airport of intended landing, a speed not less than 150 knots.

4. To departing aircraft:

    (a) Turbine-powered aircraft, a speed not less than 230 knots.

    (b) Reciprocating engine aircraft, a speed not less than 150 knots.

e. When ATC combines a speed adjustment with a descent clearance, the sequence of delivery, with the word "then" between, indicates the expected order of execution.

EXAMPLE-
1 Descend and maintain (altitude); then, reduce speed to (speed).
2 Reduce speed to (speed); then, descend and maintain (altitude).

NOTE-
The maximum speeds below 10,000 feet as established in 14 CFR Section 91.117 still apply. If there is any doubt concerning the manner in which such a clearance is to be executed, request clarification from ATC.

f. If ATC determines (before an approach clearance is issued) that it is no longer necessary to apply speed adjustment procedures, they will inform the pilot to resume normal speed. Approach clearances supersede any prior speed adjustment assignments, and pilots are expected to make their own speed adjustments, as necessary, to complete the approach. Under certain circumstances however, it may be necessary for ATC to issue further speed adjustments after approach clearance is issued to maintain separation between successive arrivals. Under such circumstances, previously issued speed adjustments will be restated if that speed is to be maintained or additional speed adjustments are requested. ATC must obtain pilot concurrence for speed adjustments after approach clearances are issued. Speed adjustments should not be assigned inside the final approach fix on final or a point 5 miles from the runway, whichever is closer to the runway.

g. The pilots retain the prerogative of rejecting the application of speed adjustment by ATC if the minimum safe airspeed for any particular operation is greater than the speed adjustment.

NOTE-
In such cases, pilots are expected to advise ATC of the speed that will be used.

h. Pilots are reminded that they are responsible for rejecting the application of speed adjustment by ATC if, in their opinion, it will cause them to exceed the maximum indicated airspeed prescribed by 14 CFR Section 91.117(a), (c) and (d). *IN SUCH CASES, THE PILOT IS EXPECTED TO SO INFORM ATC.* Pilots operating at or above 10,000 feet MSL who are issued speed adjustments which exceed 250 knots IAS and are subsequently cleared below 10,000 feet MSL are expected to comply with 14 CFR Section 91.117(a).

i. For operations conducted below 10,000 feet MSL when outside the U.S. and beneath Class B airspace, airspeed restrictions apply to all U.S. registered aircraft. For operations conducted below 10,000 feet MSL when outside the U.S. within a Class B airspace, there are no speed restrictions.

j. For operations in a Class B, Class C, and Class D surface area, ATC is authorized to request or approve a speed greater than the maximum indicated airspeeds prescribed for operation within that airspace (14 CFR Section 91.117(b)).

NOTE-
Pilots are expected to comply with the maximum speed of 200 knots when operating beneath Class B airspace or in a Class B VFR corridor (14 CFR Section 91.117(c) and (d)).

k. When in communications with the ARTCC or approach control facility, pilots should, as a good operating practice, state any ATC assigned speed restriction on initial radio contact associated with an ATC communications frequency change.

4-4-12. RUNWAY SEPARATION

Tower controllers establish the sequence of arriving and departing aircraft by requiring them to adjust flight or ground operation as necessary to achieve proper spacing. They may "HOLD" an aircraft short of the runway to achieve spacing between it and an arriving aircraft; the controller may instruct a pilot to "EXTEND DOWNWIND" in order to establish spacing from an arriving or departing aircraft. At times a clearance may include the word "IMMEDIATE." For example: "CLEARED FOR IMMEDIATE TAKEOFF." In such cases "IMMEDIATE" is used for purposes of *air traffic separation.* It is up to the pilot to refuse the clearance if, in the pilot's opinion, compliance would adversely affect the operation.

REFERENCE-
AIM, GATE HOLDING DUE TO DEPARTURE DELAYS,
PARAGRAPH 4-3-15.

4-4-13. VISUAL SEPARATION

a. Visual separation is a means employed by ATC to separate aircraft in terminal areas and en route airspace in the NAS. There are two methods employed to effect this separation:

1. The tower controller sees the aircraft involved and issues instructions, as necessary, to ensure that the aircraft avoid each other.

2. A pilot sees the other aircraft involved and upon instructions from the controller provides separation by maneuvering the aircraft to avoid it. When pilots accept responsibility to maintain visual separation, they must maintain constant visual surveillance and not pass the other aircraft until it is no longer a factor.

NOTE-
Traffic is no longer a factor when during approach phase the other aircraft is in the landing phase of flight or executes a missed approach; and during departure or en route, when the other aircraft turns away or is on a diverging course.

b. A pilot's acceptance of instructions to follow another aircraft or provide visual separation from it is an acknowledgment that the pilot will maneuver the aircraft as necessary to avoid the other aircraft or to maintain in-trail ·separation. In operations conducted behind heavy jet aircraft, it is also an acknowledgment that the pilot accepts the responsibility for wake turbulence separation.

NOTE-
When a pilot has been told to follow another aircraft or to provide visual separation from it, the pilot should promptly notify the controller if visual contact with the other aircraft is lost or cannot be maintained or if the pilot cannot accept the responsibility for the separation for any reason.

c. Scanning the sky for other aircraft is a key factor in collision avoidance. Pilots and copilots (or the right seat passenger) should continuously scan to cover all areas of the sky visible from the cockpit. Pilots must develop an effective scanning technique which maximizes one's visual capabilities. Spotting a potential collision threat increases directly as more time is spent looking outside the aircraft. One must use timesharing techniques to effectively scan the surrounding airspace while monitoring instruments as well.

d. Since the eye can focus only on a narrow viewing area, effective scanning is accomplished with a series of short, regularly spaced eye movements that bring successive areas of the sky into the central visual field. Each movement should not exceed ten degrees, and each area should be observed for at least one second to enable collision detection. Although many pilots seem to prefer the method of horizontal back-and-forth scanning every pilot should develop a scanning pattern that is not only comfortable but assures optimum effectiveness. Pilots should remember, however, that they have a regulatory responsibility (14 CFR Section 91.113(a)) to see and avoid other aircraft when weather conditions permit.

4-4-14. USE OF VISUAL CLEARING PROCEDURES

a. Before Takeoff: Prior to taxiing onto a runway or landing area in preparation for takeoff, pilots should scan the approach areas for possible landing traffic and execute the appropriate clearing maneuvers to provide them a clear view of the approach areas.

b. Climbs and Descents: During climbs and descents in flight conditions which permit visual detection of other traffic, pilots should execute gentle banks, left and right at a frequency which permits continuous visual scanning of the airspace about them.

c. Straight and Level: Sustained periods of straight and level flight in conditions which permit visual detection of other traffic should be broken at intervals with appropriate clearing procedures to provide effective visual scanning.

d. Traffic Pattern: Entries into traffic patterns while descending create specific collision hazards and should be avoided.

e. Traffic at VOR Sites: All operators should emphasize the need for sustained vigilance in the vicinity of VOR's and airway intersections due to the convergence of traffic.

f. Training Operations: Operators of pilot training programs are urged to adopt the following practices:

1. Pilots undergoing flight instruction at all levels should be requested to verbalize clearing procedures (call out "clear" left, right, above, or below) to instill and sustain the habit of vigilance during maneuvering.

2. *High-wing airplane:* momentarily raise the wing in the direction of the intended turn and look.

3. *Low-wing airplane:* momentarily lower the wing in the direction of the intended turn and look.

4. Appropriate clearing procedures should precede the execution of all turns including chandelles, lazy eights, stalls, slow flight, climbs, straight and level, spins, and other combination maneuvers.

4-4-15. TRAFFIC ALERT AND COLLISION AVOIDANCE SYSTEM (TCAS I & II)

a. TCAS I provides proximity warning only, to assist the pilot in the visual acquisition of intruder aircraft. No recommended avoidance maneuvers are provided nor authorized as a direct result of a TCAS I warning. It is intended for use by smaller commuter aircraft holding 10 to 30 passenger seats, and general aviation aircraft.

b. TCAS II provides traffic advisories (TA's) and resolution advisories (RA's). Resolution advisories provide recommended maneuvers in a vertical direction (climb or descend only) to avoid conflicting traffic. Airline aircraft, and larger commuter and business aircraft holding 31 passenger seats or more, use TCAS II equipment.

1. Each pilot who deviates from an ATC clearance in response to a TCAS II RA shall notify ATC of that deviation as soon as practicable and expeditiously return to the current ATC clearance when the traffic conflict is resolved.

2. Deviations from rules, policies, or clearances should be kept to the minimum necessary to satisfy a TCAS II RA.

3. The serving IFR air traffic facility is not responsible to provide approved standard IFR separation to an aircraft after a TCAS II RA maneuver until one of the following conditions exists:

(a) The aircraft has returned to its assigned altitude and course.

(b) Alternate ATC instructions have been issued.

c. TCAS does not alter or diminish the pilot's basic authority and responsibility to ensure safe flight. Since TCAS does not respond to aircraft which are not transponder equipped or aircraft with a transponder failure, TCAS alone does not ensure safe separation in every case.

d. At this time, no air traffic service nor handling is predicated on the availability of TCAS equipment in the aircraft.

Chapter 5. AIR TRAFFIC PROCEDURES

Section 1. PREFLIGHT

5-1-1. PREFLIGHT PREPARATION

a. Every pilot is urged to receive a preflight briefing and to file a flight plan. This briefing should consist of the latest or most current weather, airport, and en route NAVAID information. Briefing service may be obtained from an FSS either by telephone or interphone, by radio when airborne, or by a personal visit to the station. Pilots with a current medical certificate in the 48 contiguous States may access toll-free the Direct User Access Terminal System (DUATS) through a personal computer. DUATS will provide alpha-numeric preflight weather data and allow pilots to file domestic VFR or IFR flight plans.

REFERENCE-
AIM, FAA WEATHER SERVICES, PARAGRAPH 7-1-2, LISTS DUATS VENDORS.

NOTE-
Pilots filing flight plans via "fast file" who desire to have their briefing recorded, should include a statement at the end of the recording as to the source of their weather briefing.

b. The information required by the FAA to process flight plans is contained on FAA Form 7233-1, Flight Plan. The forms are available at all flight service stations. Additional copies will be provided on request.

REFERENCE-
AIM, FLIGHT PLAN-VFR FLIGHTS, PARAGRAPH 5-1-4.
AIM, FLIGHT PLAN-IFR FLIGHTS, PARAGRAPH 5-1-7.

c. Consult an FSS or a Weather Service Office (WSO) for preflight weather briefing. Supplemental Weather Service Locations (SWSL's) do not provide weather briefings.

d. FSS's are required to advise of pertinent NOTAM's if a *standard* briefing is requested, but if they are overlooked, don't hesitate to remind the specialist that you have not received NOTAM information.

NOTE-
NOTAM's which are known in sufficient time for publication and are of 7 days duration or longer are normally incorporated into the Notices to Airmen Publication and carried there until cancellation time. FDC NOTAM's, which apply to instrument flight procedures, are also included in the Notices to Airmen Publication up to and including the number indicated in the FDC NOTAM legend. Printed NOTAM's are not provided during a briefing unless specifically requested by the pilot since the FSS specialist has no way of knowing whether the pilot has
already checked the Notices to Airmen Publication prior to calling. Remember to ask for NOTAM's in the Notices to Airmen Publication. This information is not normally furnished during your briefing.

REFERENCE-
AIM, NOTICE TO AIRMEN (NOTAM) SYSTEM, PARAGRAPH 5-1-3.

e. Pilots are urged to use only the latest issue of aeronautical charts in planning and conducting flight operations. Aeronautical charts are revised and reissued on a regular scheduled basis to ensure that depicted data are current and reliable. In the conterminous U.S., Sectional Charts are updated every 6 months, IFR En Route Charts every 56 days, and amendments to civil IFR Approach Charts are accomplished on a 56-day cycle with a change notice volume issued on the 28-day midcycle. Charts that have been superseded by those of a more recent date may contain obsolete or incomplete flight information.

REFERENCE-
AIM, GENERAL DESCRIPTION OF EACH CHART SERIES, PARAGRAPH 9-1-4.

f. When requesting a preflight briefing, identify yourself as a pilot and provide the following:

1. *Type of flight planned; e.g., VFR or IFR.*

2. *Aircraft's number or pilot's name.*

3. *Aircraft type.*

4. *Departure Airport.*

5. *Route of flight.*

6. *Destination.*

7. *Flight altitude(s).*

8. *ETD and ETE.*

g. Prior to conducting a briefing, briefers are required to have the background information listed above so that they may tailor the briefing to the needs of the proposed flight. The objective is to communicate a "picture" of meteorological and aeronautical information necessary for the conduct of a safe and efficient flight. Briefers use all available weather and aeronautical information to summarize data applicable to the proposed flight. They do not read weather reports and forecasts verbatim unless specifically requested by the pilot.

REFERENCE-
AIM, PREFLIGHT BRIEFINGS, PARAGRAPH 7-1-3, CONTAINS THOSE ITEMS OF A WEATHER BRIEFING THAT SHOULD BE EXPECTED OR REQUESTED.

h. FAA by FAR Part 93, Subpart K, has designated High Density Traffic Airports (HDTA's) and has prescribed air traffic rules and requirements for operating aircraft (excluding helicopter operations) to and from these airports.

REFERENCE–
AIRPORT/FACILITY DIRECTORY, SPECIAL NOTICES SECTION.
AIM, AIRPORT RESERVATIONS OPERATIONS AND PROCEDURES,
PARAGRAPH 4–1–21.

i. In addition to the filing of a flight plan, if the flight will traverse or land in one or more foreign countries, it is particularly important that pilots leave a complete itinerary with someone directly concerned and keep that person advised of the flight's progress. If serious doubt arises as to the safety of the flight, that person should first contact the FSS.

REFERENCE–
AIM, FLIGHTS OUTSIDE THE UNITED STATES AND U.S. TERRITO-
RIES, PARAGRAPH 5–1–9.

j. Pilots operating under provisions of FAR Part 135 and not having an FAA assigned 3–letter designator, are urged to prefix the normal registration (N) number with the letter "T" on flight plan filing; e.g., TN1234B.

REFERENCE–
AIM, AIRCRAFT CALL SIGNS, PARAGRAPH 4–2–4.

5–1–2. FOLLOW IFR PROCEDURES EVEN WHEN OPERATING VFR

a. To maintain IFR proficiency, pilots are urged to practice IFR procedures whenever possible, even when operating VFR. Some suggested practices include:

1. Obtain a complete preflight and weather briefing. Check the NOTAM's.

2. File a flight plan. This is an excellent low cost insurance policy. The cost is the time it takes to fill it out. The insurance includes the knowledge that someone will be looking for you if you become overdue at your destination.

3. Use current charts.

4. Use the navigation aids. Practice maintaining a good course–keep the needle centered.

5. Maintain a constant altitude which is appropriate for the direction of flight.

6. Estimate en route position times.

7. Make accurate and frequent position reports to the FSS's along your route of flight.

b. Simulated IFR flight is recommended (under the hood); however, pilots are cautioned to review and adhere to the requirements specified in FAR Part 91.109 before and during such flight.

c. When flying VFR at night, in addition to the altitude appropriate for the direction of flight, pilots should maintain an altitude which is at or above the minimum en route altitude as shown on charts. This is especially true in mountainous terrain, where there is usually very little ground reference. Do not depend on your eyes alone to avoid rising unlighted terrain, or even lighted obstructions such as TV towers.

5–1–3. NOTICE TO AIRMEN (NOTAM) SYSTEM

a. Time-critical aeronautical information which is of either a temporary nature or not sufficiently known in advance to permit publication on aeronautical charts or in other operational publications receives immediate dissemination via the National NOTAM System.

NOTE–
1 *NOTAM information is that aeronautical information that could affect a pilot's decision to make a flight. It includes such information as airport or primary runway closures, changes in the status of navigational aids, ILS's, radar service availability, and other information essential to planned en route, terminal, or landing operations.*

2 *NOTAM information is transmitted using standard contractions to reduce transmission time. See TBL 5–1–1 for a listing of the most commonly used contractions.*

b. NOTAM information is classified into three categories. These are NOTAM (D) or distant, NOTAM (L) or local, and Flight Data Center (FDC) NOTAM's.

1. *NOTAM (D)* information is disseminated for all navigational facilities that are part of the National Airspace System (NAS), all public use airports, seaplane bases, and heliports listed in the Airport/Facility Directory (AFD). The complete file of all NOTAM (D) information is maintained in a computer data base at the Weather Message Switching Center (WMSC), located in Atlanta, Georgia. This category of information is distributed automatically via Service A telecommunications system. Air traffic facilities, primarily FSS's, with Service A capability have access to the entire WMSC data base of NOTAM's. These NOTAM's remain available via Service A for the duration of their validity or until published. Once published, the NOTAM data is deleted from the system.

2. *NOTAM (L)*
(a) NOTAM (L) information includes such data as taxiway closures, personnel and equipment near or crossing runways, airport rotating beacon outages and

airport lighting aids that do not affect instrument approach criteria, such as VASI.

(b) NOTAM (L) information is distributed locally only and is not attached to the hourly weather reports. A separate file of local NOTAM's is maintained at each FSS for facilities in their area only. NOTAM (L) information for other FSS areas must be specifically requested directly from the FSS that has responsibility for the airport concerned.

3. FDC NOTAM's

(a) On those occasions when it becomes necessary to disseminate information which is regulatory in nature, the National Flight Data Center (NFDC), in Washington, DC, will issue an FDC NOTAM. FDC NOTAM's contain such things as amendments to published IAP's and other current aeronautical charts. They are also used to advertise temporary flight restrictions caused by such things as natural disasters or large-scale public events that may generate a congestion of air traffic over a site.

(b) FDC NOTAM's are transmitted via Service A only once and are kept on file at the FSS until published or canceled. FSS's are responsible for maintaining a file of current, unpublished FDC NOTAM's concerning conditions within 400 miles of their facilities. FDC information concerning conditions that are more than 400 miles from the FSS, or that is already published, is given to a pilot only on request.

NOTE-
[1] *DUATS vendors will provide FDC NOTAM's only upon site-specific requests using a location identifier.*

[2] *NOTAM data may not always be current due to the changeable nature of national airspace system components, delays inherent in processing information, and occasional temporary outages of the United States NOTAM system. While en route, pilots should contact FSS's and obtain updated information for their route of flight and destination.*

c. An integral part of the NOTAM System is the biweekly Notices to Airmen Publication (NTAP). Data is included in this publication to reduce congestion on the telecommunications circuits and, therefore, is not available via Service A. Once published, the information is not provided during pilot weather briefings unless specifically requested by the pilot. This publication contains two sections.

1. The first section consists of notices that meet the criteria for NOTAM (D) and are expected to remain in effect for an extended period and FDC NOTAM's that are current at the time of publication. Occasionally, some NOTAM (L) and other unique information is included in this section when it will contribute to flight safety.

2. The second section contains special notices that are either too long or concern a wide or unspecified geographic area and are not suitable for inclusion in the first section. The content of these notices vary widely and there are no specific criteria for their inclusion, other than their enhancement of flight safety.

3. The number of the last FDC NOTAM included in the publication is noted on the first page to aid the user in updating the listing with any FDC NOTAM's which may have been issued between the cut-off date and the date the publication is received. All information contained will be carried until the information expires, is canceled, or in the case of permanent conditions, is published in other publications, such as the A/FD.

4. All new notices entered, excluding FDC NOTAM's, will be published only if the information is expected to remain in effect for at least 7 days after the effective date of the publication.

d. NOTAM information is not available from a Supplemental Weather Service Location (SWSL).

NOTAM CONTRACTIONS

	A
AADC	Approach and Departure Control
ABV	Above
A/C	Approach Control
ACCUM	Accumulate
ACFT	Aircraft
ACR	Air Carrier
ACTV/ACTVT ..	Active/Activate
ADF	Automatic Direction Finder
AFSS	Automated Flight Service Station
ADJ	Adjacent
ADZ/ADZD	Advise/Advised
AFD	Airport/Facility Directory
ALS	Approach Light System
ALTM	Altimeter
ALTN/ALTNLY .	Alternate/Alternately
ALSTG	Altimeter Setting
AMDT	Amendment
APCH	Approach
APL	Airport Lights
ARFF	Aircraft Rescue & Fire Fighting
ARPT	Airport
ARSR	Air Route Surveillance Radar
ASDE	Airport Surface Detection Equipment
ASOS	Automated Surface Observing System
ASPH	Asphalt
ASR	Airport Surveillance Radar
ATC	Air Traffic Control
ATCT	Airport Traffic Control Tower

ATIS	Automated Terminal Information Service
AVBL	Available
AWOS	Automatic Weather Observing System
AZM	Azimuth

B

BC	Back Course
BCN	Beacon
BERM	Snowbank/s Containing Earth/Gravel
BLO	Below
BND	Bound
BRAF	Braking Action Fair
BRAG	Braking Action Good
BRAN	Braking Action Nil
BRAP	Braking Action Poor
BYD	Beyond

C

CAAS	Class A Airspace
CAT	Category
CBAS	Class B Airspace
CBSA	Class B Surface Area
CCAS	Class C Airspace
CCLKWS	Counterclockwise
CCSA	Class C Surface Area
CD	Clearance Delivery
CDAS	Class D Airspace
CDSA	Class D Surface Area
CEAS	Class E Airspace
CESA	Class E Surface Area
CFA	Controlled Firing Area
CGAS	Class G Airspace
CHG	Change
CLKWS	Clockwise
CLNC	Clearance
CLSD	Closed
CMSN/CMSND	Commission/Commissioned
CNCL/CNCLD/ CNL	Cancel/Canceled/Cancel
CNTRLN	Centerline
CONC	Concrete
CONT	Continue/Continuously
CRS	Course
CTAF	Common Traffic Advisory Frequency
CTLZ	Control Zone

D

DALGT	Daylight
DCMS/DCMSND	Decommission/Decommissioned
DCT	Direct
DEP	Depart/Departure
DEPT	Department
DH	Decision Height
DISABLD	Disabled
DLA/DLAD	Delay/Delayed
DLT/DLTD	Delete/Deleted
DLY	Daily
DME	Distance Measuring Equipment
DMSTN	Demonstration
DP	Instrument Departure Procedure
DPCR	Departure Procedure
DRCT	Direct
DRFT/DRFTD	Drift/Drifted Snowbank/s Caused By Wind Action
DSPLCD	Displaced
DSTC	Distance
DWPNT	Dew Point

E

E	East
EBND	Eastbound
EFAS	En Route Flight Advisory Service
EFF	Effective
ELEV	Elevate/Elevation
ENG	Engine
ENTR	Entire
EXCP	Except

F

FA	Final Approach
FAC	Facility
FAF	Final Approach Fix
FDC	Flight Data Center
FM	Fan Marker
FREQ	Frequency
FRH	Fly Runway Heading
FRZN	Frozen
FRNZ SLR	Frozen Slush on Runway/s
FSS	Flight Service Station

G

GC	Ground Control
GCA	Ground Controlled Approach
GOVT	Government
GP	Glide Path
GPS	Global Positioning System
GRVL	Gravel
GS	Glide Slope

H

HAA	Height Above Airport
HAT	Height Above Touchdown
HAZ	Hazard
HEL	Helicopter
HELI	Heliport
HF	High Frequency
HIRL	High Intensity Runway Lights
HIWAS	Hazardous Inflight Weather Advisory Service
HOL	Holiday
HP	Holding Pattern

I

IAP	Instrument Approach Procedure
IBND	Inbound
ID	Identification
IDENT	Identify/Identifier/Identification
IFR	Instrument Flight Rules
ILS	Instrument Landing System
IM	Inner Marker
IN	Inch/Inches
INDEFLY	Indefinitely
INOP	Inoperative
INST	Instrument
INT	Intersection
INTST	Intensity
IR	Ice On Runway/s

L

L	Left
LAA	Local Airport Advisory
LAT	Latitude
LAWRS	Limited Aviation Weather Reporting Station
LB	Pound/Pounds

LC	Local Control
LCL	Local
LCTD	Located
LDA	Localizer Type Directional Aid
LDIN	Lead In Lighting System
LGT/LGTD/LGTS	Light/Lighted/Lights
LIRL	Low Intensity Runway Edge Lights
LLWAS	Low Level Wind Shear Alert System
LMM	Compass Locator at ILS Middle Marker
LNDG	Landing
LOC	Localizer
LOM	Compass Locator at ILS Outer Marker
LONG	Longitude
LRN	Loran
LSR	Loose Snow on Runway/s
LT	Left Turn After Take-off
M	
MALS	Medium Intensity Approach Lighting System
MALSF	Medium Intensity Approach Lighting System with Sequenced Flashers
MALSR	Medium Intensity Approach Lighting System with Runway Alignment Indicator Lights
MAP	Missed Approach Point
MCA	Minimum Crossing Altitude
MDA..........	Minimum Descent Altitude
MEA	Minimum En route Altitude
MED	Medium
MIN	Minute
MIRL	Medium Intensity Runway Edge Lights
MLS	Microwave Landing System
MM...........	Middle Marker
MNM	Minimum
MOCA	Minimum Obstruction Clearance Altitude
MONTR	Monitor
MSA	Minimum Safe Altitude/Minimum Sector Altitude
MSAW	Minimum Safe Altitude Warning
MSL	Mean Sea Level
MU	Designate a Friction Value Representing Runway Surface Conditions
MUD..........	Mud
MUNI	Municipal
N	
N	North
NA	Not Authorized
NBND.........	Northbound
NDB	Nondirectional Radio Beacon
NE	Northeast
NGT	Night
NM	Nautical Mile/s
NMR	Nautical Mile Radius
NOPT	No Procedure Turn Required
NTAP	Notice To Airmen Publication
NW	Northwest
O	
OBSC	Obscured
OBSTN	Obstruction
OM	Outer Marker
OPER	Operate
OPN	Operation
ORIG	Original
OTS	Out of Service

OVR	Over
P	
PAEW	Personnel and Equipment Working
PAJA	Parachute Jumping Activities
PAPI	Precision Approach Path Indicator
PAR	Precision Approach Radar
PARL	Parallel
PAT	Pattern
PCL...........	Pilot Controlled Lighting
PERM/PERMLY	Permanent/Permanently
PLA	Practice Low Approach
PLW	Plow/Plowed
PN	Prior Notice Required
PPR...........	Prior Permission Required
PREV	Previous
PRIRA	Primary Radar
PROC	Procedure
PROP	Propeller
PSGR	Passenger/s
PSR..........	Packed Snow on Runway/s
PT/PTN	Procedure Turn
PVT	Private
R	
RAIL.........	Runway Alignment Indicator Lights
RCAG	Remote Communication Air/Ground Facility
RCL	Runway Centerline
RCLS	Runway Centerline Light System
RCO	Remote Communication Outlet
RCV/RCVR	Receive/Receiver
REF..........	Reference
REIL.........	Runway End Identifier Lights
RELCTD	Relocated
RMDR	Remainder
RNAV	Area Navigation
RPRT	Report
RQRD	Required
RRL	Runway Remaining Lights
RSVN	Reservation
RT	Right Turn after Take-off
RTE	Route
RTR	Remote Transmitter/Receiver
RTS	Return to Service
RUF	Rough
RVR	Runway Visual Range
RVRM........	RVR Midpoint
RVRR	RVR Rollout
RVRT	RVR Touchdown
RVV	Runway Visibility Value
RY/RWY	Runway
S	
S	South
SBND	Southbound
SDF...........	Simplified Directional Facility
SE	Southeast
SECRA	Secondary Radar
SFL	Sequenced Flashing Lights
SI	Straight-In Approach
SIR	Packed or Compacted Snow and Ice on Runway/s
SKED	Scheduled
SLR...........	Slush on Runway/s
SNBNK	Snowbank/s Caused by Plowing

AIM

SND	Sand/Sanded
SNGL	Single
SNW	Snow
SPD	Speed
SR	Sunrise
SS	Sunset
SSALF	Simplified Short Approach Lighting System with Sequenced Flashers
SSALR	Simplified Short Approach Lighting System with Runway Alignment Indicator Lights
SSALS	Simplified Short Approach Lighting System
STAR	Standard Terminal Arrival
SVC	Service
SW	Southwest
SWEPT	Swept or Broom/Broomed
T	
TACAN	Tactical Air Navigational Aid
TDZ/TDZL	Touchdown Zone/Touchdown Zone Lights
TFC..........	Traffic
TFR	Temporary Flight Restriction
TGL	Touch and Go Landings
THN	Thin
THR	Threshold
THRU	Through
TIL	Until
TKOF	Takeoff
TMPRY	Temporary
TRML	Terminal
TRNG	Training
TRSA	Terminal Radar Service Area
TRSN	Transition
TSNT	Transient
TWEB	Transcribed Weather Broadcast
TWR	Tower
TWY	Taxiway
U	
UNAVBL	Unavailable
UNLGTD	Unlighted
UNMKD	Unmarked
UNMON	Unmonitored
UNRELBL	Unreliable
UNUSBL	Unusable
V	
VASI	Visual Approach Slope Indicator
VDP	Visual Descent Point
VFR	Visual Flight Rules
VIA..........	By Way Of
VICE..........	Instead/Versus
VIS/VSBY	Visibility
VMC..........	Visual Meteorological Conditions
VOL	Volume
VOLMET	Meteorlogical Information for Aircraft in Flight
VOR	VHF Omni-Directional Radio Range
VORTAC	VOR and TACAN (collocated)
VOT	VOR Test Signal
W	
W	West
WBND	Westbound
WEA/WX	Weather

WI	Within
WKDAYS	Monday through Friday
WKEND	Saturday and Sunday
WND	Wind
WP	Waypoint
WSR	Wet Snow on Runway/s
WTR	Water on Runway/s
WX	Weather
/	And
+	In Addition/Also

TBL 5-1-1

5-1-4. FLIGHT PLAN - VFR FLIGHTS

a. Except for operations in or penetrating a Coastal or Domestic ADIZ or DEWIZ a flight plan is not required for VFR flight.

REFERENCE-
AIM, NATIONAL SECURITY, PARAGRAPH 5-6-1.

b. It is strongly recommended that a flight plan (for a VFR flight) be filed with an FAA FSS. This will ensure that you receive VFR Search and Rescue Protection.

REFERENCE-
AIM, SEARCH AND RESCUE, PARAGRAPH 6-2-7 GIVES THE PROPER METHOD OF FILING A VFR FLIGHT PLAN.

c. To obtain maximum benefits from the flight plan program, flight plans should be filed directly with the nearest FSS. For your convenience, FSS's provide aeronautical and meteorological briefings while accepting flight plans. Radio may be used to file if no other means are available.

NOTE-
Some states operate aeronautical communications facilities which will accept and forward flight plans to the FSS for further handling.

d. When a "stopover" flight is anticipated, it is recommended that a separate flight plan be filed for each "leg" when the stop is expected to be more than 1 hour duration.

e. Pilots are encouraged to give their departure times directly to the FSS serving the departure airport or as otherwise indicated by the FSS when the flight plan is filed. This will ensure more efficient flight plan service and permit the FSS to advise you of significant changes in aeronautical facilities or meteorological conditions. When a VFR flight plan is filed, it will be held by the FSS until 1 hour after the proposed departure time unless:

1. The actual departure time is received.

2. A revised proposed departure time is received.

3. At a time of filing, the FSS is informed that the proposed departure time will be met, but actual time cannot be given because of inadequate communications (assumed departures).

f. On pilot's request, at a location having an active tower, the aircraft identification will be forwarded by the tower to the FSS for reporting the actual departure time. This procedure should be avoided at busy airports.

g. Although position reports are not required for VFR flight plans, periodic reports to FAA FSS's along the route are good practice. Such contacts permit significant information to be passed to the transiting aircraft and also serve to check the progress of the flight should it be necessary for any reason to locate the aircraft.

EXAMPLE-
1 *Bonanza 314K, over Kingfisher at (time), VFR flight plan, Tulsa to Amarillo.*

2 *Cherokee 5133J, over Oklahoma City at (time), Shreveport to Denver, no flight plan.*

h. Pilots not operating on an IFR flight plan and when in level cruising flight, are cautioned to conform with VFR cruising altitudes appropriate to the direction of flight.

i. When filing VFR flight plans, indicate aircraft equipment capabilities by appending the appropriate suffix to aircraft type in the same manner as that prescribed for IFR flight.

REFERENCE-
AIM, FLIGHT PLAN IFR FLIGHTS, PARAGRAPH 5-1-7.

j. Under some circumstances, ATC computer tapes can be useful in constructing the radar history of a downed or crashed aircraft. In each case, knowledge of the aircraft's transponder equipment is necessary in determining whether or not such computer tapes might prove effective.

k. Flight Plan Form - (See FIG 5-1-1).

FAA Flight Plan
Form 7233-1 (8-82)

FIG 5-1-1

l. Explanation of VFR Flight Plan Items:

1. *Block 1.* Check the type flight plan. Check both the VFR and IFR blocks if composite VFR/IFR.

2. *Block 2.* Enter your complete aircraft identification including the prefix "N" if applicable.

3. *Block 3.* Enter the designator for the aircraft, or if unknown, consult an FSS briefer.

4. *Block 4.* Enter your true airspeed (TAS).

5. *Block 5.* Enter the departure airport identifier code, or if unknown, the name of the airport.

6. *Block 6.* Enter the proposed departure time in Coordinated Universal Time (UTC) (Z). If airborne, specify the actual or proposed departure time as appropriate.

7. *Block 7.* Enter the appropriate VFR altitude (to assist the briefer in providing weather and wind information).

8. *Block 8.* Define the route of flight by using NAVAID identifier codes and airways.

9. *Block 9.* Enter the destination airport identifier code, or if unknown, the airport name.

NOTE-
Include the city name (or even the state name) if needed for clarity.

10. *Block 10.* Enter your estimated time en route in hours and minutes.

11. *Block 11.* Enter only those remarks pertinent to ATC or to the clarification of other flight plan information, such as the appropriate radiotelephony (call sign) associated with the designator filed in Block 2. Items of a personal nature are not accepted.

12. *Block 12.* Specify the fuel on board in hours and minutes.

13. *Block 13.* Specify an alternate airport if desired.

14. *Block 14.* Enter your complete name, address, and telephone number. Enter sufficient information to identify home base, airport, or operator.

NOTE-
This information is essential in the event of search and rescue operations.

15. *Block 15.* Enter total number of persons on board (POB) including crew.

16. *Block 16.* Enter the predominant colors.

17. *Block 17.* Record the FSS name for closing the flight plan. If the flight plan is closed with a different FSS or facility, state the recorded FSS name that would normally have closed your flight plan.

NOTE-
① Optional- record a destination telephone number to assist search and rescue contact should you fail to report or cancel your flight plan within 1/2 hour after your estimated time of arrival (ETA).

② The information transmitted to the destination FSS will consist only of flight plan blocks 2, 3, 9, and 10. estimated time en route (ETE) will be converted to the correct ETA.

5-1-5. FLIGHT PLAN- DEFENSE VFR (DVFR) FLIGHTS

VFR flights into a Coastal or Domestic ADIZ/DEWIZ are required to file DVFR flight plans for security purposes. Detailed ADIZ procedures are found in the National Security and Interception Procedures in Section 6 of this chapter. (See 14 CFR Part 99.)

5-1-6. COMPOSITE FLIGHT PLAN (VFR/IFR FLIGHTS)

a. Flight plans which specify VFR operation for one portion of a flight, and IFR for another portion, will be accepted by the FSS at the point of departure. If VFR flight is conducted for the first portion of the flight, pilots should report their departure time to the FSS with whom the VFR/IFR flight plan was filed; and, subsequently, close the VFR portion and request ATC clearance from the FSS nearest the point at which change from VFR to IFR is proposed. Regardless of the type facility you are communicating with (FSS, center, or tower), it is the pilot's responsibility to request that facility to "CLOSE VFR FLIGHT PLAN." The pilot must remain in VFR weather conditions until operating in accordance with the IFR clearance.

b. When a flight plan indicates IFR for the first portion of flight and VFR for the latter portion, the pilot will normally be cleared to the point at which the change is proposed. After reporting over the clearance limit and not desiring further IFR clearance, the pilot should advise ATC to cancel the IFR portion of the flight plan. Then, the pilot should contact the nearest FSS to activate the VFR portion of the flight plan. If the pilot desires to continue the IFR flight plan beyond the clearance limit, the pilot should contact ATC at least 5 minutes prior to the clearance limit and request further IFR clearance. If the requested clearance is not received prior to reaching the clearance limit fix, the pilot will be expected to enter into a standard holding pattern on the radial or course to the fix unless a holding pattern for the clearance limit fix is depicted on a U.S. Government or commercially produced (meeting FAA requirements) low or high altitude enroute, area or STAR chart. In this case the pilot will hold according to the depicted pattern.

5-1-7. FLIGHT PLAN- IFR FLIGHTS

a. General:

1. Prior to departure from within, or prior to entering controlled airspace, a pilot must submit a complete flight plan and receive an air traffic clearance, if weather conditions are below VFR minimums. Instrument flight plans may be submitted to the nearest FSS or ATCT either in person or by telephone (or by radio if no other means are available). Pilots should file IFR flight plans at least 30 minutes prior to estimated time of departure to preclude possible delay in receiving a departure clearance from ATC. In order to provide FAA traffic management units strategic route planning capabilities, nonscheduled operators conducting IFR operations above FL 230 are requested to voluntarily file IFR flight plans at least 4 hours prior to estimated time of departure (ETD). To minimize your delay in entering Class B, Class C, Class D and Class E surface areas at destination when IFR weather conditions exist or are forecast at that airport, an IFR flight plan should be filed before departure. Otherwise, a 30 minute delay

is not unusual in receiving an ATC clearance because of time spent in processing flight plan data. Traffic saturation frequently prevents control personnel from accepting flight plans by radio. In such cases, the pilot is advised to contact the nearest FSS for the purpose of filing the flight plan.

NOTE-
There are several methods of obtaining IFR clearances at nontower, non-FSS, and outlying airports. The procedure may vary due to geographical features, weather conditions, and the complexity of the ATC system. To determine the most effective means of receiving an IFR clearance, pilots should ask the nearest FSS the most appropriate means of obtaining the IFR clearance.

2. When filing an IFR flight plan for a Traffic Alert and Collision Avoidance System (TCAS)/heavy equipped aircraft, add the prefix T for TCAS, H for heavy, or B for both TCAS and heavy to the aircraft type.

EXAMPLE-
T/B727/A
H/DC10/U
B/B747/R

3. When filing an IFR flight plan for flight in an aircraft equipped with a radar beacon transponder, DME equipment, TACAN-only equipment, Global Navigation Satellite System (GNSS), or a combination of any of these types of equipment, identify the equipment capability by adding a suffix, preceded by a slant, to the AIRCRAFT TYPE, as shown in TBL 5-1-2.

AIM

AIRCRAFT EQUIPMENT SUFFIXES

SUFFIX	AIRCRAFT EQUIPMENT SUFFIXES
	NO DME
/X	No transponder
/T	Transponder with no Mode C
/U	Transponder with Mode C
	DME
/D	No transponder
/B	Transponder with no Mode C
/A	Transponder with Mode C
	TACAN ONLY
/M	No transponder
/N	Transponder with no Mode C
/P	Transponder with Mode C
	AREA NAVIGATION (RNAV)
/Y	LORAN, VOR/DME, or INS with no transponder
/C	LORAN, VOR/DME, or INS, transponder with no Mode C
/I	LORAN, VOR/DME, or INS, transponder with Mode C
	ADVANCED RNAV WITH TRANSPONDER AND MODE C (If an aircraft is unable to operate with a transponder and/or Mode C, it will revert to the appropriate code listed above under Area Navigation.)
/E	Flight Management System (FMS) with en route, terminal, and approach capability. Equipment requirements are: (a) Dual FMS which meets the specifications of AC 25-15, Approval of Flight Management Systems in Transport Category Airplanes; AC 20-129, Airworthiness Approval of Vertical Navigation (VNAV) Systems for use in the U.S. NAS and Alaska; AC 20-130A, Airworthiness Approval of Navigation or Flight Management Systems Integrating Multiple Navigation Sensors; or equivalent criteria as approved by Flight Standards. (b) A flight director and autopilot control system capable of following the lateral and vertical FMS flight path. (c) At least dual inertial reference units (IRU's). (d) A database containing the waypoints and speed/altitude constraints for the route and/or procedure to be flown that is automatically loaded into the FMS flight plan. (e) An electronic map. (U.S. and U.S. territories only unless otherwise authorized.)
/F	A single FMS with en route, terminal, and approach capability that meets the equipment requirements of /E, (a) through (d), above. (U.S. and U.S. territories only unless otherwise authorized.)
/G	Global Positioning System (GPS)/Global Navigation Satellite System (GNSS) equipped aircraft with en route, terminal, and GPS approach capability
/R	Required Navigational Performance (Denotes capability to operate in RNP designated airspace and routes)
/W	Reduced Vertical Separation Minima (RVSM)

TBL 5-1-2

4. It is recommended that pilots file the maximum transponder or navigation capability of their aircraft in the equipment suffix. This will provide ATC with the necessary information to utilize all facets of navigational equipment and transponder capabilities available.

NOTE-
The suffix is not to be added to the aircraft identification or be transmitted by radio as part of the aircraft identification.

b. Airways and Jet Routes Depiction on Flight Plan:

1. It is vitally important that the route of flight be accurately and completely described in the flight plan. To simplify definition of the proposed route, and to fa-

cilitate ATC, pilots are requested to file via airways or jet routes established for use at the altitude or flight level planned.

2. If flight is to be conducted via designated airways or jet routes, describe the route by indicating the type and number designators of the airway(s) or jet route(s) requested. If more than one airway or jet route is to be used, clearly indicate points of transition. If the transition is made at an unnamed intersection, show the next succeeding NAVAID or named intersection on the intended route and the complete route from that point. Reporting points may be identified by using authorized name/code as depicted on appropriate aeronautical charts. The following two examples illustrate the need to specify the transition point when two routes share more than one transition fix.

EXAMPLE-
☐ *ALB J37 BUMPY J14 BHM*
Spelled out: From Albany, New York, via Jet Route 37 transitioning to Jet Route 14 at BUMPY intersection, thence via Jet Route 14 to Birmingham, Alabama.
② *ALB J37 ENO J14 BHM*
Spelled out: from Albany, New York, via Jet Route 37 transitioning to Jet Route 14 at Kenton VORTAC (ENO) thence via Jet Route 14 to Birmingham, Alabama.

3. The route of flight may also be described by naming the reporting points or NAVAID's over which the flight will pass, provided the points named are established for use at the altitude or flight level planned.

EXAMPLE-
BWI V44 SWANN V433 DQO
Spelled out: from Baltimore-Washington International, via Victor 44 to Swann intersection, transitioning to Victor 433 at Swann, thence via Victor 433 to Dupont.

4. When the route of flight is defined by named reporting points, whether alone or in combination with airways or jet routes, and the navigational aids (VOR, VORTAC, TACAN, NDB) to be used for the flight are a combination of different types of aids, enough information should be included to clearly indicate the route requested.

EXAMPLE-
LAX J5 LKV J3 GEG YXC FL 330 J500 VLR J515 YWG
Spelled out: from Los Angeles International via Jet Route 5 Lakeview, Jet Route 3 Spokane, direct Cranbrook, British Columbia VOR/DME, Flight Level 330 Jet Route 500 to Langruth, Manitoba VORTAC, Jet Route 515 to Winnepeg, Manitoba.

5. When filing IFR, it is to the pilot's advantage to file a preferred route.

REFERENCE-
PREFERRED IFR ROUTES ARE DESCRIBED AND TABULATED IN THE AIRPORT/FACILITY DIRECTORY.

6. ATC may issue a DP or a STAR, as appropriate.

REFERENCE-
AIM, INSTRUMENT DEPARTURES, PARAGRAPH 5-2-6 .
AIM, STANDARD TERMINAL ARRIVAL (STAR), FLIGHT MANAGEMENT SYSTEM PROCEDURES (FMSP) FOR ARRIVALS, PARAGRAPH 5-4-1.

NOTE-
Pilots not desiring a DP or STAR should so indicate in the remarks section of the flight plan as "no DP" or "no STAR."

c. Direct Flights:

1. All or any portions of the route which will not be flown on the radials or courses of established airways or routes, such as direct route flights, must be defined by indicating the radio fixes over which the flight will pass. Fixes selected to define the route shall be those over which the position of the aircraft can be accurately determined. Such fixes automatically become compulsory reporting points for the flight, unless advised otherwise by ATC. Only those navigational aids established for use in a particular structure; i.e., in the low or high structures, may be used to define the en route phase of a direct flight within that altitude structure.

2. The azimuth feature of VOR aids and that azimuth and distance (DME) features of VORTAC and TACAN aids are assigned certain frequency protected areas of airspace which are intended for application to established airway and route use, and to provide guidance for planning flights outside of established airways or routes. These areas of airspace are expressed in terms of cylindrical service volumes of specified dimensions called "class limits" or "categories."

REFERENCE-
AIM, NAVAID SERVICE VOLUMES, PARAGRAPH 1-1-8.

3. An operational service volume has been established for each class in which adequate signal coverage and frequency protection can be assured. To facilitate use of VOR, VORTAC, or TACAN aids, consistent with their operational service volume limits, pilot use of such aids for defining a direct route of flight in controlled airspace should not exceed the following:

(a) Operations above FL 450 - Use aids not more than 200 NM apart. These aids are depicted on enroute high altitude charts.

(b) Operation off established routes from 18,000 feet MSL to FL 450 - Use aids not more than 260 NM apart. These aids are depicted on enroute high altitude charts.

(c) Operation off established airways below 18,000 feet MSL - Use aids not more than 80 NM apart. These aids are depicted on enroute low altitude charts.

(d) Operation off established airways between 14,500 feet MSL and 17,999 feet MSL in the conterminous U.S. - (H) facilities not more than 200 NM apart may be used.

4. Increasing use of self-contained airborne navigational systems which do not rely on the VOR/VORTAC/TACAN system has resulted in pilot requests for direct routes which exceed NAVAID service volume limits. These direct route requests will be approved only in a radar environment, with approval based on pilot responsibility for navigation on the authorized direct route. Radar flight following will be provided by ATC for ATC purposes.

5. At times, ATC will initiate a direct route in a radar environment which exceeds NAVAID service volume limits. In such cases ATC will provide radar monitoring and navigational assistance as necessary.

6. Airway or jet route numbers, appropriate to the stratum in which operation will be conducted, may also be included to describe portions of the route to be flown.

EXAMPLE-
MDW V262 BDF V10 BRL STJ SLN GCK
Spelled out: from Chicago Midway Airport via Victor 262 to Bradford, Victor 10 to Burlington, Iowa, direct St. Joseph, Missouri, direct Salina, Kansas, direct Garden City, Kansas.

NOTE-
When route of flight is described by radio fixes, the pilot will be expected to fly a direct course between the points named.

7. Pilots are reminded that they are responsible for adhering to obstruction clearance requirements on those segments of direct routes that are outside of controlled airspace. The MEA's and other altitudes shown on low altitude IFR enroute charts pertain to those route segments within controlled airspace, and those altitudes may not meet obstruction clearance criteria when operating off those routes.

d. Area Navigation (RNAV):

1. Random RNAV routes can only be approved in a radar environment. Factors that will be considered by ATC in approving random RNAV routes include the capability to provide radar monitoring and compatibility with traffic volume and flow. ATC will radar monitor each flight, however, navigation on the random RNAV route is the responsibility of the pilot.

2. To be certified for use in the National Airspace System, RNAV equipment must meet the specifications outlined in AC 90-45. The pilot is responsible for variations in equipment capability and must advise ATC if a RNAV clearance cannot be accepted as specified. The controller need only be concerned that the aircraft is RNAV equipped; if the flight plan equipment suffix denotes RNAV capability, the RNAV routing can be applied.

3. Pilots of aircraft equipped with operational area navigation equipment may file for random RNAV routes throughout the National Airspace System, where radar monitoring by ATC is available, in accordance with the following procedures.

(a) File airport-to-airport flight plans prior to departure.

(b) File the appropriate RNAV capability certification suffix in the flight plan.

(c) Plan the random route portion of the flight plan to begin and end over appropriate arrival and departure transition fixes or appropriate navigation aids for the altitude stratum within which the flight will be conducted. The use of normal preferred departure and arrival routes (DP/STAR), where established, is recommended.

(d) File route structure transitions to and from the random route portion of the flight.

(e) Define the random route by waypoints. File route description waypoints by using degree-distance fixes based on navigational aids which are appropriate for the altitude stratum.

(f) File a minimum of one route description waypoint for each ARTCC through whose area the random route will be flown. These waypoints must be located within 200 NM of the preceding center's boundary.

(g) File an additional route description waypoint for each turnpoint in the route.

(h) Plan additional route description waypoints as required to ensure accurate navigation via the filed route of flight. Navigation is the pilot's responsibility unless ATC assistance is requested.

(i) Plan the route of flight so as to avoid prohibited and restricted airspace by 3 NM unless permission has been obtained to operate in that airspace and the appropriate ATC facilities are advised.

4. Pilots of aircraft equipped with latitude/longitude coordinate navigation capability, independent of VOR/TACAN references, may file for random RNAV routes at and above FL 390 within the conterminous U.S. using the following procedures.

(a) File airport-to-airport flight plans prior to departure.

(b) File the appropriate RNAV capability certification suffix in the flight plan.

(c) Plan the random route portion of the flight to begin and end over published departure/arrival transition fixes or appropriate navigation aids for airports without published transition procedures. The use of preferred departure and arrival routes, such as DP and STAR where established, is recommended.

(d) Plan the route of flight so as to avoid prohibited and restricted airspace by 3 NM unless permission has been obtained to operate in that airspace and the appropriate ATC facility is advised.

(e) Define the route of flight after the departure fix, including each intermediate fix (turnpoint) and the arrival fix for the destination airport in terms of latitude/longitude coordinates plotted to the nearest minute. The arrival fix must be identified by both the latitude/longitude coordinates and a fix identifier.

EXAMPLE-
MIA[1] SRQ[2] 3407/10615[3] 3407/11546 TNP[4] LAX [5]

[1] *Departure airport.*
[2] *Departure fix.*
[3] *Intermediate fix (turning point).*
[4] *Arrival fix.*
[5] *Destination airport.*

(f) Record latitude/longitude coordinates by four figures describing latitude in degrees and minutes followed by a solidus and five figures describing longitude in degrees and minutes.

(g) File at FL 390 or above for the random RNAV portion of the flight.

(h) Fly all routes/route segments on Great Circle tracks.

(i) Make any inflight requests for random RNAV clearances or route amendments to an en route ATC facility.

e. **Flight Plan Form-** See FIG 5-1-2.

f. **Explanation of IFR Flight Plan Items:**

1. *Block 1.* Check the type flight plan. Check both the VFR and IFR blocks if composite VFR/IFR.

2. *Block 2.* Enter your complete aircraft identification including the prefix "N" if applicable.

3. *Block 3.* Enter the designator for the aircraft, followed by a slant(/), and the transponder or DME equip-

ment code letter; e.g., C-182/U. Heavy aircraft, add prefix "H" to aircraft type; example: H/DC10/U. Consult an FSS briefer for any unknown elements.

4. *Block 4.* Enter your computed true airspeed (TAS).

NOTE-
If the average TAS changes plus or minus 5 percent or 10 knots, whichever is greater, advise ATC.

5. *Block 5.* Enter the departure airport identifier code (or the name if the identifier is unknown).

NOTE-
Use of identifier codes will expedite the processing of your flight plan.

6. *Block 6.* Enter the proposed departure time in Coordinated Universal Time (UTC) (Z). If airborne, specify the actual or proposed departure time as appropriate.

7. *Block 7.* Enter the requested en route altitude or flight level.

NOTE-
Enter only the initial requested altitude in this block. When more than one IFR altitude or flight level is desired along the route of flight, it is best to make a subsequent request direct to the controller.

8. *Block 8.* Define the route of flight by using NAVAID identifier codes (or names if the code is unknown), airways, jet routes, and waypoints (for RNAV).

NOTE-
Use NAVAID's or waypoint's to define direct routes and radials/bearings to define other unpublished routes.

9. *Block 9.* Enter the destination airport identifier code (or name if the identifier is unknown).

10. *Block 10.* Enter your estimated time en route based on latest forecast winds.

11. *Block 11.* Enter only those remarks pertinent to ATC or to the clarification of other flight plan information, such as the appropriate radiotelephony (call sign) associated with the designator filed in Block 2. Items of a personal nature are not accepted. Do not assume that remarks will be automatically transmitted to every controller. Specific ATC or en route requests should be made directly to the appropriate controller.

FAA Flight Plan
Form 7233-1 (8-82)

U.S. DEPARTMENT OF TRANSPORTATION FEDERAL AVIATION ADMINISTRATION **FLIGHT PLAN**	(FAA USE ONLY) □ PILOT BRIEFING □ VNR □ STOPOVER		TIME STARTED	SPECIALIST INITIALS

1. TYPE VFR IFR DVFR	2. AIRCRAFT IDENTIFICATION	3. AIRCRAFT TYPE/ SPECIAL EQUIPMENT	4. TRUE AIRSPEED KTS	5. DEPARTURE POINT	6. DEPARTURE TIME PROPOSED (Z) ACTUAL (Z)	7. CRUISING ALTITUDE

8. ROUTE OF FLIGHT

9. DESTINATION (Name of airport and city)	10. EST. TIME ENROUTE HOURS MINUTES	11. REMARKS

12. FUEL ON BOARD HOURS MINUTES	13. ALTERNATE AIRPORT(S)	14. PILOT'S NAME, ADDRESS & TELEPHONE NUMBER & AIRCRAFT HOME BASE 17. DESTINATION CONTACT/TELEPHONE (OPTIONAL)	15. NUMBER ABOARD

16. COLOR OF AIRCRAFT	CIVIL AIRCRAFT PILOTS, FAR 91 requires you file an IFR flight plan to operate under instrument flight rules in controlled airspace. Failure to file could result in a civil penalty not to exceed $1,000 for each violation (Section 901 of the Federal Aviation Act of 1958, as amended). Filing of a VFR flight plan is recommended as a good operating practice. See also Part 99 for requirements concerning DVFR flight plans.

FAA Form 7233-1 (8-82)   **CLOSE VFR FLIGHT PLAN WITH _____ FSS ON ARRIVAL**

FIG 5-1-2

12. *Block 12.* Specify the fuel on board, computed from the departure point.

13. *Block 13.* Specify an alternate airport if desired or required, but do not include routing to the alternate airport.

14. *Block 14.* Enter the complete name, address, and telephone number of pilot-in-command, or in the case of a formation flight, the formation commander. Enter sufficient information to identify home base, airport, or operator.

NOTE-
This information would be essential in the event of search and rescue operation.

15. *Block 15.* Enter the total number of persons on board including crew.

16. *Block 16.* Enter the predominant colors.

NOTE-
Close IFR flight plans with tower, approach control, or ARTCC, or if unable, with FSS. When landing at an airport with a functioning control tower, IFR flight plans are automatically canceled.

g. The information transmitted to the ARTCC for IFR flight plans will consist of only flight plan blocks 2, 3, 4, 5, 6, 7, 8, 9, 10, and 11.

h. A description of the International Flight Plan Form is contained in the International Flight Information Manual (IFIM).

5-1-8. IFR OPERATIONS TO HIGH ALTITUDE DESTINATIONS

a. Pilots planning IFR flights to airports located in mountainous terrain are cautioned to consider the necessity for an alternate airport even when the forecast weather conditions would technically relieve them from the requirement to file one.

REFERENCE-
14 CFR SECTION 91.167.
AIM, TOWER EN ROUTE CONTROL (TEC), PARAGRAPH 4-1-18.

b. The FAA has identified three possible situations where the failure to plan for an alternate airport when flying IFR to such a destination airport could result in a critical situation if the weather is less than forecast and sufficient fuel is not available to proceed to a suitable airport.

1. An IFR flight to an airport where the MDA's or landing visibility minimums for *all instrument approaches* are higher than the forecast weather minimums specified in FAR Part 91.167(b). For example, there are 11 high altitude airports in the United States with approved instrument approach procedures where all of the Minimum Descent Altitudes (MDA's) are greater than 2,000 feet and/or the landing visibility minimums are greater than 3 miles (Bishop, California; South Lake Tahoe, California; Ukiah, California; Aspen–Pitkin Co./Sardy Field, Colorado; Butte, Montana; Helena, Montana; Missoula, Montana; Chadron, Nebraska; Ely, Nevada; Klamath Falls, Oregon; and Omak, Washington). In the case of these 11 airports, it is possible for a pilot to elect, on the basis of forecasts, not to carry sufficient fuel to get to an alternate when the ceiling and/or visibility is actually lower than that necessary to complete the approach.

2. A small number of other airports in mountainous terrain have MDA's which are slightly (100 to 300 feet) below 2,000 feet AGL. In situations where there is an option as to whether to plan for an alternate, pilots should bear in mind that just a slight worsening of the weather conditions from those forecast could place the airport below the published IFR landing minimums.

3. An IFR flight to an airport which requires special equipment; i.e., DME, glide slope, etc., in order to make the available approaches to the lowest minimums. Pilots should be aware that all other minimums on the approach charts may require weather conditions better than those specified in FAR Part 91.167(b). An inflight equipment malfunction could result in the inability to comply with the published approach procedures or, again, in the position of having the airport below the published IFR landing minimums for all remaining instrument approach alternatives.

5-1-9. FLIGHTS OUTSIDE THE UNITED STATES AND U.S. TERRITORIES

a. When conducting flights, particularly extended flights, outside the U.S. and its territories, full account should be taken of the amount and quality of air navigation services available in the airspace to be traversed. Every effort should be made to secure information on the location and range of navigational aids, availability of communications and meteorological services, the provision of air traffic services, including alerting service, and the existence of search and rescue services.

b. Pilots should remember that there is a need to continuously guard the VHF emergency frequency 121.5 MHz when on long over-water flights, except when communications on other VHF channels, equipment limitations, or cockpit duties prevent simultaneous guarding of two channels. Guarding of 121.5 MHz is particularly critical when operating in proximity to Flight Information Region (FIR) boundaries, for example, operations on Route R220 between Anchorage and Tokyo, since it serves to facilitate communications with regard to aircraft which may experience in-flight emergencies, communications, or navigational difficulties.

REFERENCE–
ICAO ANNEX 10, VOL II PARAS 5.2.2.1.1.1 AND 5.2.2.1.1.2.

c. The filing of a flight plan, always good practice, takes on added significance for extended flights outside U.S. airspace and is, in fact, usually required by the laws of the countries being visited or overflown. It is also particularly important in the case of such flights that pilots leave a complete itinerary and schedule of the flight with someone directly concerned and keep that person advised of the flight's progress. If serious doubt arises as to the safety of the flight, that person should first contact the appropriate FSS. Round Robin Flight Plans to Mexico are not accepted.

d. All pilots should review the foreign airspace and entry restrictions published in the IFIM during the flight planning process. Foreign airspace penetration without official authorization can involve both danger to the aircraft and the imposition of severe penalties and inconvenience to both passengers and crew. A flight plan on file with ATC authorities does not necessarily constitute the prior permission required by certain other authorities. The possibility of fatal consequences cannot be ignored in some areas of the world.

e. Current NOTAM's for foreign locations must also be reviewed. The publication International Notices to Airmen, published biweekly, contains considerable information pertinent to foreign flight. Current foreign NOTAM's are also available from the U.S. International NOTAM Office in Washington, D.C., through any local FSS.

f. When customs notification is required, it is the responsibility of the pilot to arrange for customs notification in a timely manner. The following guidelines are applicable:

1. When customs notification is required on flights to Canada and Mexico and a predeparture flight plan cannot be filed or an advise customs message (ADCUS) cannot be included in a predeparture flight plan, call the nearest en route domestic or International FSS as soon as radio communication can be established and file a

VFR or DVFR flight plan, as required, and include as the last item the advise customs information. The station with which such a flight plan is filed will forward it to the appropriate FSS who will notify the customs office responsible for the destination airport.

2. If the pilot fails to include ADCUS in the radioed flight plan, it will be assumed that other arrangements have been made and FAA will not advise customs.

3. The FAA assumes no responsibility for any delays in advising customs if the flight plan is given too late for delivery to customs before arrival of the aircraft. **It is still the pilot's responsibility to give timely notice even though a flight plan is given to FAA.**

4. Air Commerce Regulations of the Treasury Department's Customs Service require all private aircraft arriving in the United States via:

(a) the United States/Mexican border or the Pacific Coast from a foreign place in the Western Hemisphere south of 33 degrees north latitude and between 97 degrees and 120 degrees west longitude; or

(b) the Gulf of Mexico and Atlantic Coasts from a foreign place in the Western Hemisphere south of 30 degrees north latitude, shall furnish a notice of arrival to the Customs service at the nearest designated airport. This notice may be furnished directly to Customs by:

(1) radio through the appropriate FAA Flight Service Station;

(2) normal FAA flight plan notification procedures (a flight plan filed in Mexico does not meet this requirement due to unreliable relay of data), or

(3) directly to the district Director of Customs or other Customs officer at place of first intended landing but must be furnished at least 1 hour prior to crossing the U.S./Mexican border or the United States coastline.

(c) This notice will be valid as long as actual arrival is within 15 minutes of the original ETA, otherwise a new notice must be given to Customs. Notices will be accepted up to 23 hours in advance. Unless an exemption has been granted by Customs, private aircraft are required to make first landing in the U.S. at one of the following designated airports nearest to the point of border of coastline crossing:

Designated Airports

ARIZONA
Bisbee Douglas Intl Airport
Nogales Intl Airport
Tucson Intl Airport
Yuma MCAS–Yuma Intl Airport

CALIFORNIA
Calexico Intl Airport
Brown Field Municipal Airport (San Diego)

FLORIDA
Fort Lauderdale Executive Airport
Fort Lauderdale/Hollywood Intl Airport
Key West Intl Airport (Miami Intl Airport)
Opa Locka Airport (Miami)
Kendall–Tamiami Executive Airport (Miami)
St. Lucie County Intl Airport (Fort Pierce)
Tampa Intl Airport
Palm Beach Intl Airport (West Palm Beach)

LOUISANA
New Orleans Intl Airport (Moisant Field)
New Orleans Lakefront Airport

NEW MEXICO
Las Cruces Intl Airport

NORTH CAROLINA
New Hanover Intl Airport (Wilmington)

TEXAS
Brownsville/South Padre Island Intl Airport
Corpus Christi Intl Airport
Del Rio Intl Airport
Eagle Pass Municipal Airport
El Paso Intl Airport
William P. Hobby Airport (Houston)
Laredo Intl Airport
McAllen Miller Intl Airport
Presidio Lely Intl Airport

5-1-10. CHANGE IN FLIGHT PLAN

In addition to altitude or flight level, destination and/o route changes, increasing or decreasing the speed of a aircraft constitutes a change in a flight plan. Therefor at any time the average true airspeed at cruising altitud between reporting points varies or is expected to var from that given in the flight plan by *plus or minus 5 percent, or 10 knots, whichever is greater,* ATC shoul be advised.

5-1-11. CHANGE IN PROPOSED DEPARTURE TIME

a. To prevent computer saturation in the en route environment, parameters have been established to delete proposed departure flight plans which have not been activated. Most centers have this parameter set so as to delete these flight plans a minimum of 1 hour after the proposed departure time. To ensure that a flight plan remains active, pilots whose actual departure time will be delayed 1 hour or more beyond their filed departure time, are requested to notify ATC of their departure time.

b. Due to traffic saturation, control personnel frequently will be unable to accept these revisions via radio. It is recommended that you forward these revisions to the nearest FSS.

5-1-12. CLOSING VFR/DVFR FLIGHT PLANS

Pilots are responsible for ensuring that their VFR or DVFR flight plan is canceled. You should close your flight plan with the nearest FSS, or if one is not available, you may request any ATC facility to relay your cancellation to the FSS. Control towers do not automatically close VFR or DVFR flight plans since they do not know if a particular VFR aircraft is on a flight plan. If you fail to report or cancel your flight plan within $1/2$ hour after your ETA, search and rescue procedures are started.

REFERENCE—
FAR PART 91.153.
FAR PART 91.169.

5-1-13. CANCELING IFR FLIGHT PLAN

a. FAR Part 91.153 and FAR Part 91.169 include the statement "When a flight plan has been activated, the pilot-in-command, upon canceling or completing the flight under the flight plan, shall notify an FAA Flight Service Station or ATC facility."

b. An IFR flight plan may be canceled at any time the flight is operating in VFR conditions outside Class A airspace by pilots stating "CANCEL MY IFR FLIGHT PLAN" to the controller or air/ground station with which they are communicating. Immediately after canceling an IFR flight plan, a pilot should take the necessary action to change to the appropriate air/ground frequency, VFR radar beacon code and VFR altitude or flight level.

c. ATC separation and information services will be discontinued, including radar services (where applicable). Consequently, if the canceling flight desires VFR radar advisory service, the pilot must specifically request it.

NOTE—
Pilots must be aware that other procedures may be applicable to a flight that cancels an IFR flight plan within an area where a special program, such as a designated TRSA, Class C airspace, or Class B airspace, has been established.

d. If a DVFR flight plan requirement exists, the pilot is responsible for filing this flight plan to replace the canceled IFR flight plan. If a subsequent IFR operation becomes necessary, a new IFR flight plan must be filed and an ATC clearance obtained before operating in IFR conditions.

e. If operating on an IFR flight plan to an airport with a functioning control tower, the flight plan is automatically closed upon landing.

f. If operating on an IFR flight plan to an airport where there is no functioning control tower, the pilot must initiate cancellation of the IFR flight plan. This can be done after landing if there is a functioning FSS or other means of direct communications with ATC. In the event there is no FSS and/or air/ground communications with ATC is not possible below a certain altitude, the pilot should, weather conditions permitting, cancel the IFR flight plan while still airborne and able to communicate with ATC by radio. This will not only save the time and expense of canceling the flight plan by telephone but will quickly release the airspace for use by other aircraft.

AIM

Section 2. DEPARTURE PROCEDURES

5-2-1. PRE-TAXI CLEARANCE PROCEDURES

a. Certain airports have established pre-taxi clearance programs whereby pilots of departing IFR aircraft may elect to receive their IFR clearances before they start taxiing for takeoff. The following provisions are included in such procedures:

1. Pilot participation is not mandatory.

2. Participating pilots call clearance delivery or ground control not more than 10 minutes before proposed taxi time.

3. IFR clearance (or delay information, if clearance cannot be obtained) is issued at the time of this initial call-up.

4. When the IFR clearance is received on clearance delivery frequency, pilots call ground control when ready to taxi.

5. Normally, pilots need not inform ground control that they have received IFR clearance on clearance delivery frequency. Certain locations may, however, require that the pilot inform ground control of a portion of the routing or that the IFR clearance has been received.

6. If a pilot cannot establish contact on clearance delivery frequency or has not received an IFR clearance before ready to taxi, the pilot should contact ground control and inform the controller accordingly.

b. Locations where these procedures are in effect are indicated in the *Airport/Facility Directory*.

5-2-2. TAXI CLEARANCE

Pilots on IFR flight plans should communicate with the control tower on the appropriate ground control or clearance delivery frequency, prior to starting engines, to receive engine start time, taxi and/or clearance information.

5-2-3. ABBREVIATED IFR DEPARTURE CLEARANCE (CLEARED...AS FILED) PROCEDURES

a. ATC facilities will issue an abbreviated IFR departure clearance based on the ROUTE of flight filed in the IFR flight plan, provided the filed route can be approved with little or no revision. These abbreviated clearance procedures are based on the following conditions:

1. The aircraft is on the ground or it has departed VFR and the pilot is requesting IFR clearance while airborne.

2. That a pilot will not accept an abbreviated clearance if the route or destination of a flight plan filed with ATC has been changed by the pilot or the company or the operations officer before departure.

3. That it is the responsibility of the company or operations office to inform the pilot when they make a change to the filed flight plan.

4. That it is the responsibility of the pilot to inform ATC in the initial call-up (for clearance) when the filed flight plan has been either:

(a) amended, or

(b) canceled and replaced with a new filed flight plan.

NOTE-
The facility issuing a clearance may not have received the revised route or the revised flight plan by the time a pilot requests clearance.

b. Controllers will issue a detailed clearance when they know that the original filed flight plan has been changed or when the pilot requests a full route clearance.

c. The clearance as issued will include the destination airport filed in the flight plan.

d. ATC procedures now require the controller to state the DP name, the current number and the DP transition name after the phrase "Cleared to (destination) airport" and prior to the phrase, "then as filed," for ALL departure clearances when the DP or DP transition is to be flown. The procedures apply whether or not the DP is filed in the flight plan.

e. STAR's, when filed in a flight plan, are considered a part of the filed route of flight and will not normally be stated in an initial departure clearance. If the ARTCC's jurisdictional airspace includes both the departure airport and the fix where a STAR or STAR transition begins, the STAR name, the current number and the STAR transition name MAY be stated in the initial clearance.

f. "Cleared to (destination) airport as filed" does NOT include the en route altitude filed in a flight plan. An en route altitude will be stated in the clearance or the pilot will be advised to expect an assigned or filed altitude within a given time frame or at a certain point after departure. This may be done verbally in the departure instructions or stated in the DP.

g. In both radar and nonradar environments, the controller will state "Cleared to (destination) airport as filed" or:

1. If a DP or DP transition is to be flown, specify the DP name, the current DP number, the DP transition name, the assigned altitude/flight level, and any additional instructions (departure control frequency, beacon code assignment, etc.) necessary to clear a departing aircraft via the DP or DP transition and the route filed.

EXAMPLE-
National Seven Twenty cleared to Miami Airport Intercontinental one departure, Lake Charles transition then as filed, maintain Flight Level two seven zero.

2. When there is no DP or when the pilot cannot accept a DP, the controller will specify the assigned altitude or flight level, and any additional instructions necessary to clear a departing aircraft via an appropriate departure routing and the route filed.

NOTE-
A detailed departure route description or a radar vector may be used to achieve the desired departure routing.

3. If it is necessary to make a minor revision to the filed route, the controller will specify the assigned DP or DP transition (or departure routing), the revision to the filed route, the assigned altitude or flight level and any additional instructions necessary to clear a departing aircraft.

EXAMPLE-
Jet Star One Four Two Four cleared to Atlanta Airport, South Boston two departure then as filed except change route to read South Boston Victor 20 Greensboro, maintain one seven thousand.

4. Additionally, in a nonradar environment, the controller will specify one or more fixes, as necessary, to identify the initial route of flight.

EXAMPLE-
Cessna Three One Six Zero Foxtrot cleared to Charlotte Airport as filed via Brooke, maintain seven thousand.

h. To ensure success of the program, pilots should:

1. Avoid making changes to a filed flight plan just prior to departure.

2. State the following information in the initial call-up to the facility when no change has been made to

the filed flight plan: Aircraft call sign, location, type operation (IFR) and the name of the airport (or fix) to which you expect clearance.

EXAMPLE-
"Washington clearance delivery (or ground control i, appropriate) American Seventy Six at gate one, IFR Los Angeles."

3. If the flight plan has been changed, state the change and request a full route clearance.

EXAMPLE-
"Washington clearance delivery, American Seventy Six at gate one. IFR San Francisco. My flight plan route has been amended (or destination changed). Request full route clearance."

4. Request verification or clarification from ATC if ANY portion of the clearance is not clearly understood.

5. When requesting clearance for the IFR portion of a VFR/IFR flight, request such clearance prior to the fix where IFR operation is proposed to commence in sufficient time to avoid delay. Use the following phraseology:

EXAMPLE-
"Los Angeles center, Apache Six One Papa, VFR estimating Paso Robles VOR at three two, one thousand five hundred, request IFR to Bakersfield."

5-2-4. DEPARTURE RESTRICTIONS, CLEARANCE VOID TIMES, HOLD FOR RELEASE, AND RELEASE TIMES

a. ATC may assign departure restrictions, clearance void times, hold for release, and release times, when necessary, to separate departures from other traffic or to restrict or regulate the departure flow.

1. *CLEARANCE VOID TIMES:* A pilot may receive a clearance, when operating from an airport without a control tower, which contains a provision for the clearance to be void if not airborne by a specific time. A pilot who does not depart prior to the clearance void time must advise ATC as soon as possible of their intentions. ATC will normally advise the pilot of the time allotted to notify ATC that the aircraft did not depart prior to the clearance void time. This time cannot exceed 30 minutes. Failure of an aircraft to contact ATC within 30 minutes after the clearance void time will result in the aircraft being considered overdue and search and rescue procedures initiated.

NOTE-

1 *Other IFR traffic for the airport where the clearance is issued is suspended until the aircraft has contacted ATC or until 30 minutes after the clearance void time or 30 minutes after the clearance release time if no clearance void time is issued.*

2 *Pilots who depart at or after their clearance void time are not afforded IFR separation and may be in violation of 14 CFR Part 91.173 which requires that pilots receive an appropriate ATC clearance before operating IFR in controlled airspace.*

EXAMPLE-
Clearance void if not off by (clearance void time) and, if required, if not off by (clearance void time) advise (facility) not later than (time) of intentions.

2. HOLD FOR RELEASE: ATC may issue "hold for release" instructions in a clearance to delay an aircraft's departure for traffic management reasons (i.e., weather, traffic volume, etc.). When ATC states in the clearance, "hold for release," the pilot may not depart utilizing that instrument flight rules (IFR) clearance until a release time or additional instructions are issued by ATC. In addition, ATC will include departure delay information in conjunction with "hold for release" instructions. The ATC instruction, "hold for release," applies to the IFR clearance and does not prevent the pilot from departing under visual flight rules (VFR). However, prior to takeoff the pilot should cancel the IFR flight plan and operate the transponder on the appropriate VFR code. An IFR clearance may not be available after departure.

EXAMPLE-
(Aircraft identification) cleared to (destination) airport as filed, maintain (altitude), and, if required (additional instructions or information), hold for release, expect (time in hours and/or minutes) departure delay.

3. RELEASE TIMES: A "release time" is a departure restriction issued to a pilot by ATC, specifying the earliest time an aircraft may depart. ATC will use "release times" in conjunction with traffic management procedures and/or to separate a departing aircraft from other traffic.

EXAMPLE-
(Aircraft identification) released for departure at (time in hours and/or minutes).

b. If practical, pilots departing uncontrolled airports should obtain IFR clearances prior to becoming airborne when two-way communications with the controlling ATC facility is available.

5-2-5. DEPARTURE CONTROL

a. Departure Control is an approach control function responsible for ensuring separation between departures. So as to expedite the handling of departures, Departure Control may suggest a take off direction other than that which may normally have been used under VFR handling. Many times it is preferred to offer the pilot a runway that will require the fewest turns after take off to place the pilot on course or selected departure route as quickly as possible. At many locations particular attention is paid to the use of preferential runways for local noise abatement programs, and route departures away from congested areas.

b. Departure Control utilizing radar will normally clear aircraft out of the terminal area using DP's via radio navigation aids. When a departure is to be vectored immediately following take off, the pilot will be advised prior to take off of the initial heading to be flown but may not be advised of the purpose of the heading. Pilots operating in a radar environment are expected to associate departure headings with vectors to their planned route or flight. When given a vector taking the aircraft off a previously assigned nonradar route, the pilot will be advised briefly what the vector is to achieve. Thereafter, radar service will be provided until the aircraft has been reestablished "on-course" using an appropriate navigation aid and the pilot has been advised of the aircraft's position or a handoff is made to another radar controller with further surveillance capabilities.

c. Controllers will inform pilots of the departure control frequencies and, if appropriate, the transponder code before takeoff. Pilots should not operate their transponder until ready to start the takeoff roll or change to the departure control frequency until requested. Controllers may omit the departure control frequency if a DP has or will be assigned and the departure control frequency is published on the DP.

5-2-6. INSTRUMENT DEPARTURES

The FAA has combined the former standard instrument departures (SID's) and textual IFR departure procedures into a single entity called an instrument departure procedure (DP). DP's will be published in either text form, like the former IFR departure procedures, or in charted graphic form like the former SID's. Regardless of the format, all DP's provide the pilot with a way to depart the airport and transition to the en route structure safely. All DP's provide obstacle clearance and any DP may be filed for and flown. Pilots operating under

14 CFR Part 91 are strongly encouraged to file and fly a DP at night, during marginal visual meteorological conditions (VMC) and instrument meteorological conditions (IMC), when one is available. The following paragraphs will provide an overview of the DP program, why DP's are developed, what criteria are used, where to find them, how they are to be flown, and finally pilot and ATC responsibilities.

a. Why are DP's necessary? The primary reason is to provide obstacle clearance protection to aircraft in IMC. A secondary reason, at busier airports, is to increase efficiency and reduce communications and departure delays. When an instrument approach is initially developed for an airport, the procedure designer also does an assessment for departures. If an aircraft may turn in any direction from a runway, and be clear of obstacles, that runway meets what is called diverse departure criteria and no DP will be published unless needed for air traffic purposes. However, if there is an obstacle penetration of what is called the 40:1 slope, then the procedure designer chooses whether to:

1. Increase the climb gradient; or

2. Increase the standard takeoff minima to allow the pilot to visually remain clear of the obstacle(s); or

3. Design and publish a specific departure route; or

4. A combination or all of the above.

b. What criteria is used to provide obstruction clearance during departure?

1. Obstacle clearance for all departures, including diverse, is based on the pilot crossing the end of the runway at least 35 feet AGL, climbing to 400 feet above airport elevation before turning, and climbing at least 200 feet per nautical mile (FPNM), unless a higher climb gradient is specified in the DP, or unless required to level off by a crossing restriction.

2. The 40:1 slope begins at 35 feet above the departure end of the runway and slopes upward at 152 FPNM until reaching the minimum IFR altitude or entering the en route structure.

3. Climb gradients greater than 200 FPNM are specified when required for obstacle clearance and/or ATC required crossing restrictions.

EXAMPLE-
"Cross ALPHA intersection at or below 4000; maintain 6000." The pilot climbs at least 200 FPNM to 6000. If 4000 is reached before ALPHA, the pilot levels off at 4000 until passing ALPHA; then immediately resumes at least 200 FPNM climb.

4. Climb gradients may be specified only to an altitude/fix, above which the normal gradient applies.

EXAMPLE-
"Minimum climb 340 FPNM to ALPHA." The pilot climbs at least 340 FPNM to ALPHA, then at least 200 FPNM to MIA.

5. Some DP's established solely for obstacle avoidance require a climb in visual conditions to cross the airport or an on-airport NAVAID in a specified direction, at or above a specified altitude.

EXAMPLE-
"Climb in visual conditions so as to cross the McElory Airport southbound, at or above 6000, then climb via Keemmling radial zero three three to Keemmling VORTAC."

c. Who is responsible for obstacle clearance? DP's are designed so that adherence to the procedure by the pilot will ensure obstacle protection. Additionally:

1. Obstacle clearance responsibility also rests with the pilot when he/she chooses to climb in visual conditions in lieu of flying a DP and/or depart under increased takeoff minima rather than fly the DP. Standard takeoff minima are one statute mile for aircraft having two engines or less and one-half statute mile for aircraft having more than two engines. Specified ceiling and visibility minima will allow visual avoidance of obstacles until the pilot enters the standard obstacle protection area. Obstacle avoidance is not guaranteed if the pilot maneuvers farther from the airport than the specified visibility minimum. That segment of the procedure which requires the pilot to see and avoid obstacles ends when the aircraft crosses the specified point at the required altitude. Thereafter, standard obstacle protection is provided and the standard climb gradient is required unless specified otherwise.

2. ATC may assume responsibility for obstacle clearance by vectoring the aircraft prior to minimum vectoring altitude by using a diverse vector area (DVA). The DVA has been assessed for departures which do not follow a specific ground track. ATC may also vector an aircraft off a previously assigned DP. In all cases, the 200 FPNM climb gradient is assumed and obstacle clearance is not provided by ATC until the controller begins to provide navigational guidance in the form of radar vectors.

NOTE-
When used by the controller during departure, the term radar contact should not be interpreted as relieving pilots of their responsibility to maintain appropriate terrain and obstruction clearance.

d. Where are DP's located? DP's will be listed by airport in the IFR Take-Off Minimums and Departure Procedures Section, Section C, of the Terminal Procedures Publications (TPP's). If the DP is textual, it will be described in TPP Section C as previously done. Complex non-RNAV and all RNAV DP's will be published graphically and named. The name will be listed by airport name and runway in Section C. Graphic DP's developed solely for obstacle clearance will also have the term "(OBSTACLE)" printed on the charted procedure.

NOTE-
Existing textual and RNAV DP's will be reviewed individually by the FAA and, where appropriate, processed for graphic depiction.

1. A DP that has been developed solely for obstacle avoidance will be indicated with the symbol "T" on appropriate Instrument Approach Procedure (IAP) charts and DP charts for that airport. The "T" symbol will continue to refer users to TPP Section C. In the case of a graphic DP, the TPP Section C will only contain the name of the DP. Since there may be both a textual and a graphic DP, Section C should still be checked for additional information. All information on new graphic DP's will be printed on the graphic depiction. If not assigned a DP by ATC, any published DP may be filed and flown. As a general rule, ATC will only assign a DP from a nontowered airport when compliance with the DP is necessary for aircraft to aircraft separation.

2. All charted graphic DP's will be listed by name in the index in the front of the TPP volume.

e. Responsibilities.

1. Each pilot, prior to departing an airport on an IFR flight should consider the type of terrain and other obstacles on or in the vicinity of the departure airport; and:

2. Determine whether a DP is available; and

3. Determine if obstacle avoidance can be maintained visually or if the DP should be flown; and

4. Consider the effect of degraded climb performance and the actions to take in the event of an engine loss during the departure.

5. After an aircraft is established on a DP and subsequently vectored or cleared off of the DP or DP transition, pilots shall consider the DP canceled, unless the controller adds "expect to resume DP."

6. Aircraft instructed to resume a procedure which contains restrictions, such as a DP, shall be issued/reissued all applicable restrictions or shall be advised to comply with those restrictions.

7. If an altitude to "maintain" is restated, whether prior to departure or while airborne, previously issued altitude restrictions are canceled, including any DP altitude restrictions if any.

8. Pilots of civil aircraft operating from locations where DP's are effective may expect ATC clearances containing a DP. Use of a DP requires pilot possession of the textual description or graphic depiction of the approved current DP, as appropriate. ATC must be immediately advised if the pilot does not possess a charted DP or a preprinted DP description, or the aircraft is not capable of flying the DP. Notification may be accomplished by filing "NO DP" in the remarks section of the filed flight plan or by the less desirable method of verbally advising ATC. Adherence to all restrictions on the DP is required unless clearance to deviate is received.

9. Controllers may omit the departure control frequency if a DP clearance is issued and the departure control frequency is published on the graphic DP.

Section 3. EN ROUTE PROCEDURES

5-3-1. ARTCC COMMUNICATIONS

a. Direct Communications, Controllers and Pilots:

1. ARTCC's are capable of direct communications with IFR air traffic on certain frequencies. Maximum communications coverage is possible through the use of Remote Center Air/Ground (RCAG) sites comprised of both VHF and UHF transmitters and receivers. These sites are located throughout the U.S. Although they may be several hundred miles away from the ARTCC, they are remoted to the various ARTCC's by land lines or microwave links. Since IFR operations are expedited through the use of direct communications, pilots are requested to use these frequencies strictly for communications pertinent to the control of IFR aircraft. Flight plan filing, en route weather, weather forecasts, and similar data should be requested through FSS's, company radio, or appropriate military facilities capable of performing these services.

2. An ARTCC is divided into sectors. Each sector is handled by one or a team of controllers and has its own sector discrete frequency. As a flight progresses from one sector to another, the pilot is requested to change to the appropriate sector discrete frequency.

b. ATC Frequency Change Procedures:

1. The following phraseology will be used by controllers to effect a frequency change:

EXAMPLE-
(Aircraft identification) contact (facility name or location name and terminal function) (frequency) at (time, fix, or altitude).

NOTE-
Pilots are expected to maintain a listening watch on the transferring controller's frequency until the time, fix, or altitude specified. ATC will omit frequency change restrictions whenever pilot compliance is expected upon receipt.

2. The following phraseology should be utilized by pilots for establishing contact with the designated facility:

(a) When operating in a radar environment: On initial contact, the pilot should inform the controller of the aircraft's assigned altitude preceded by the words "level," or "climbing to," or "descending to," as appropriate; and the aircraft's present vacating altitude, if applicable.

EXAMPLE-
1 *(Name) CENTER, (aircraft identification), LEVEL (altitude or flight level).*
2 *(Name) CENTER, (aircraft identification), LEAVING (exact altitude or flight level), CLIMBING TO OR DESCENDING TO (altitude of flight level).*

NOTE-
Exact altitude or flight level means to the nearest 100 foot increment. Exact altitude or flight level reports on initial contact provide ATC with information required prior to using Mode C altitude information for separation purposes.

(b) When operating in a nonradar environment:

(1) On initial contact, the pilot should inform the controller of the aircraft's present position, altitude and time estimate for the next reporting point.

EXAMPLE-
(Name) CENTER, (aircraft identification), (position), (altitude), ESTIMATING (reporting point) AT (time).

(2) After initial contact, when a position report will be made, the pilot should give the controller a complete position report.

EXAMPLE-
(Name) CENTER, (aircraft identification), (position), (time), (altitude), (type of flight plan), (ETA and name of next reporting point), (the name of the next succeeding reporting point), AND (remarks).

REFERENCE-
AIM, POSITION REPORTING, PARAGRAPH 5-3-2.

3. At times controllers will ask pilots to verify that they are at a particular altitude. The phraseology used will be: "VERIFY AT (altitude)." In climbing or descending situations, controllers may ask pilots to "VERIFY ASSIGNED ALTITUDE AS (altitude)." Pilots should confirm that they are at the altitude stated by the controller or that the assigned altitude is correct as stated. If this is not the case, they should inform the controller of the actual altitude being maintained or the different assigned altitude.

CAUTION-
Pilots should not take action to change their actual altitude or different assigned altitude to the altitude stated in the controllers verification request unless the controller specifically authorizes a change.

c. ARTCC Radio Frequency Outage:
ARTCC's normally have at least one back-up radio receiver and transmitter system for each frequency, which can usually be placed into service quickly with little or no disruption of ATC service. Occasionally, technical problems

may cause a delay but switchover seldom takes more than 60 seconds. When it appears that the outage will not be quickly remedied, the ARTCC will usually request a nearby aircraft, if there is one, to switch to the affected frequency to broadcast communications instructions. It is important, therefore, that the pilot wait at least 1 minute before deciding that the ARTCC has actually experienced a radio frequency failure. When such an outage does occur, the pilot should, if workload and equipment capability permit, maintain a listening watch on the affected frequency while attempting to comply with the following recommended communications procedures:

1. If two-way communications cannot be established with the ARTCC after changing frequencies, a pilot should attempt to recontact the transferring controller for the assignment of an alternative frequency or other instructions.

2. When an ARTCC radio frequency failure occurs after two-way communications have been established, the pilot should attempt to reestablish contact with the center on any other known ARTCC frequency, preferably that of the next responsible sector when practicable, and ask for instructions. However, when the next normal frequency change along the route is known to involve another ATC facility, the pilot should contact that facility, if feasible, for instructions. If communications cannot be reestablished by either method, the pilot is expected to request communications instructions from the FSS appropriate to the route of flight.

NOTE-
The exchange of information between an aircraft and an ARTCC through an FSS is quicker than relay via company radio because the FSS has direct interphone lines to the responsible ARTCC sector. Accordingly, when circumstances dictate a choice between the two, during an ARTCC frequency outage, relay via FSS radio is recommended.

5-3-2. POSITION REPORTING

The safety and effectiveness of traffic control depends to a large extent on accurate position reporting. In order to provide the proper separation and expedite aircraft movements, ATC must be able to make accurate estimates of the progress of every aircraft operating on an IFR flight plan.

a. Position Identification:

1. When a position report is to be made passing a VOR radio facility, the time reported should be the time

at which the first complete reversal of the "to/from" dicator is accomplished.

2. When a position report is made passing a facili by means of an airborne ADF, the time reported shou be the time at which the indicator makes a complete versal.

3. When an aural or a light panel indication is us to determine the time passing a reporting point, such a fan marker, Z marker, cone of silence or intersecti of range courses, the time should be noted when the si nal is first received and again when it ceases. The me: of these two times should then be taken as the actu time over the fix.

4. If a position is given with respect to distance ar direction from a reporting point, the distance and dire tion should be computed as accurately as possible.

5. Except for terminal area transition purpose position reports or navigation with reference to aids n established for use in the structure in which flight is b ing conducted will not normally be required by ATC

b. Position Reporting Points: FAR's require pilo to maintain a listening watch on the appropriate fr quency and, unless operating under the provisions c subparagraph c. , to furnish position reports passin certain reporting points. Reporting points are indicate by symbols on en route charts. The designated compu sory reporting point symbol is a solid triangle▲ an the "on request" reporting point symbol is the ope triangle△. Reports passing an "on request" reportin point are only necessary when requested by ATC.

c. Position Reporting Requirements:

1. *Flights along airways or routes:* A position re port is required by all flights regardless of altitude, in cluding those operating in accordance with an ATC clearance specifying "*VFR-on-top,*" over each desig nated compulsory reporting point along the route being flown.

2. *Flights Along a Direct Route:* Regardless of the altitude or flight level being flown, including flights op erating in accordance with an ATC clearance specifyin "*VFR-on-top,*" pilots shall report over each reportin point used in the flight plan to define the route of flight

3. *Flights in a Radar Environment:* When in formed by ATC that their aircraft are in "Radar Con tact," pilots should discontinue position reports ove designated reporting points. They should resume nor mal position reporting when ATC advises "*RADAR CONTACT LOST*" or "*RADAR SERVICE TERMI NATED.*"

NOTE—
ATC will inform pilots that they are in "radar contact"
  (a) when their aircraft is initially identified in the ATC system; and
  (b) when radar identification is reestablished after radar service has been terminated or radar contact lost. Subsequent to being advised that the controller has established radar contact, this fact will not be repeated to the pilot when handed off to another controller. At times, the aircraft identity will be confirmed by the receiving controller; however, this should not be construed to mean that radar contact has been lost. The identity of transponder equipped aircraft will be confirmed by asking the pilot to "ident," "squawk standby," or to change codes. Aircraft without transponders will be advised of their position to confirm identity. In this case, the pilot is expected to advise the controller if in disagreement with the position given. Any pilot who cannot confirm the accuracy of the position given because of not being tuned to the NAVAID referenced by the controller, should ask for another radar position relative to the tuned in NAVAID.

d. Position Report Items:

1. *Position reports should include the following items:*

(a) Identification.

(b) Position.

(c) Time.

(d) Altitude or flight level (include actual altitude or flight level when operating on a clearance specifying VFR–on–top.)

(e) Type of flight plan (not required in IFR position reports made directly to ARTCC's or approach control),

(f) ETA and name of next reporting point.

(g) The name only of the next succeeding reporting point along the route of flight, and

(h) Pertinent remarks.

5-3-3. ADDITIONAL REPORTS

a. The following reports should be made to ATC or FSS facilities without a specific ATC request:

1. *At all times:*

(a) When vacating any previously assigned altitude or flight level for a newly assigned altitude or flight level.

(b) When an altitude change will be made if operating on a clearance specifying VFR–on–top.

(c) When *unable* to climb/descend at a rate of a least 500 feet per minute.

(d) When approach has been missed. (Request clearance for specific action; i.e., to alternative airport, another approach, etc.)

(e) Change in the average true airspeed (at cruising altitude) when it varies by 5 percent or 10 knots (whichever is greater) from that filed in the flight plan.

(f) The time and altitude or flight level upon reaching a holding fix or point to which cleared.

(g) When leaving any assigned holding fix or point.

NOTE—
The reports in subparagraphs (f) and (g) may be omitted by pilots of aircraft involved in instrument training at military terminal area facilities when radar service is being provided.

(h) Any loss, in controlled airspace, of VOR, TACAN, ADF, low frequency navigation receiver capability, complete or partial loss of ILS receiver capability or impairment of air/ground communications capability. Reports should include aircraft identification, equipment affected, degree to which the capability to operate under IFR in the ATC system is impaired, and the nature and extent of assistance desired from ATC.

NOTE—
Other equipment installed in an aircraft may effectively impair safety and/or the ability to operate under IFR. If such equipment (e.g. airborne weather radar) malfunctions and in the pilot's judgment either safety or IFR capabilities are affected, reports should be made as above.

(i) Any information relating to the safety of flight.

2. *When not in radar contact:*

(a) When leaving final approach fix inbound on final approach (nonprecision approach) or when leaving the outer marker or fix used in lieu of the outer marker inbound on final approach (precision approach).

(b) A corrected estimate at anytime it becomes apparent that an estimate as previously submitted is in error in excess of 3 minutes.

b. Pilots encountering weather conditions which have not been forecast, or hazardous conditions which have been forecast, are expected to forward a report of such weather to ATC.

REFERENCE-
AIM, PILOT WEATHER REPORTS (PIREPS), PARAGRAPH 7-1-18.
FAR PART 91.183(B) AND (C).

5-3-4. AIRWAYS AND ROUTE SYSTEMS

a. Two fixed route systems are established for air navigation purposes. They are the VOR and L/MF system, and the jet route system. To the extent possible, these route systems are aligned in an overlying manner to facilitate transition between each.

1. The VOR and L/MF Airway System consists of airways designated from 1,200 feet above the surface (or in some instances higher) up to but not including 18,000 feet MSL. These airways are depicted on Enroute Low Altitude Charts.

NOTE-
The altitude limits of a victor airway should not be exceeded except to effect transition within or between route structures.

(a) Except in Alaska and coastal North Carolina, the VOR airways are predicated solely on VOR or VORTAC navigation aids; are depicted in blue on aeronautical charts; and are identified by a "V" (Victor) followed by the airway number (e.g., V12).

NOTE-
Segments of VOR airways in Alaska and North Carolina (V56, V290) are based on L/MF navigation aids and charted in brown instead of blue on en route charts.

(1) A segment of an airway which is common to two or more routes carries the numbers of all the airways which coincide for that segment. When such is the case, pilots filing a flight plan need to indicate only that airway number for the route filed.

NOTE-
A pilot who intends to make an airway flight, using VOR facilities, will simply specify the appropriate "victor" airways(s) in the flight plan. For example, if a flight is to be made from Chicago to New Orleans at 8,000 feet, using omniranges only, the route may be indicated as "departing from Chicago–Midway, cruising 8,000 feet via Victor 9 to Moisant International." If flight is to be conducted in part by means of L/MF navigation aids and in part on omniranges, specifications of the appropriate airways in the flight plan will indicate which types of facilities will be used along the described routes, and, for IFR flight, permit ATC to issue a traffic clearance accordingly. A route may also be described by specifying the station over which the flight will pass, but in this case since many VOR's and L/MF aids have the same name, the pilot must be careful to indicate which aid will be used at a particular location. This will be indicated in the route of flight

portion of the flight plan by specifying the type of facility to be used after the location name in the following manner: Newark L/MF, Allentown VOR.

(2) With respect to position reporting, reporting points are designated for VOR Airway System Flights using Victor Airways will report over the points unless advised otherwise by ATC.

(b) The L/MF airways (colored airways) are predicated solely on L/MF navigation aids and are depicted in brown on aeronautical charts and are identified by color name and number (e.g., Amber One). Green and Red airways are plotted east and west. Amber and Blue airways are plotted north and south.

NOTE-
Except for G13 in North Carolina, the colored airway system exists only in the state of Alaska. All other such airways formerly so designated in the conterminous U.S. have been rescinded.

2. The jet route system consists of jet routes established from 18,000 feet MSL to FL 450 inclusive.

(a) These routes are depicted on Enroute High Altitude Charts. Jet routes are depicted in black on aeronautical charts and are identified by a "J" (Jet) followed by the airway number (e.g., J12). Jet routes, as VOR airways, are predicated solely on VOR or VORTAC navigation facilities (except in Alaska).

NOTE-
Segments of jet routes in Alaska are based on L/MF navigation aids and are charted in brown color instead of black on en route charts.

(b) With respect to position reporting, reporting points are designated for jet route systems. Flights using jet routes will report over these points unless otherwise advised by ATC.

3. Area Navigation (RNAV) Routes:

(a) RNAV is a method of navigation that permits aircraft operations on any desired course within the coverage of station referenced navigation signals or within the limits of a self-contained system capability or combination of these.

(b) Fixed RNAV routes are permanent, published routes which can be flight planned for use by aircraft with RNAV capability. A previously established fixed RNAV route system has been terminated except for a few high altitude routes in Alaska.

(c) Random RNAV routes are direct routes based on area navigation capability, between waypoints defined in terms of latitude/longitude coordinates, degree-distance fixes, or offsets from established routes/ airways at a specified distance and direction. Radar monitoring by ATC is required on all random RNAV routes.

b. Operation above FL 450 may be conducted on a point-to-point basis. Navigational guidance is provided on an area basis utilizing those facilities depicted on the enroute high altitude charts.

c. *Radar Vectors:* Controllers may vector aircraft within controlled airspace for separation purposes, noise abatement considerations, when an operational advantage will be realized by the pilot or the controller, or when requested by the pilot. Vectors outside of controlled airspace will be provided only on pilot request. Pilots will be advised as to what the vector is to achieve when the vector is controller initiated and will take the aircraft off a previously assigned nonradar route. To the extent possible, aircraft operating on RNAV routes will be allowed to remain on their own navigation.

d. When flying in Canadian airspace, pilots are cautioned to review Canadian Air Regulations.

1. Special attention should be given to the parts which differ from U.S. CFR's.

(a) The Canadian Airways Class B airspace restriction is an example. Class B airspace is all controlled low level airspace above 12,500 feet MSL or the MEA, whichever is higher, within which only IFR and controlled VFR flights are permitted. (Low level airspace means an airspace designated and defined as such in the *Designated Airspace Handbook*.)

(b) Regardless of the weather conditions or the height of the terrain, no person shall operate an aircraft under VFR conditions within Class B airspace except in accordance with a clearance for VFR flight issued by ATC.

(c) The requirement for entry into Class B airspace is a student pilot permit (under the guidance or control of a flight instructor).

(d) VFR flight requires visual contact with the ground or water at all times.

2. Segments of VOR airways and high level routes in Canada are based on L/MF navigation aids and are charted in brown color instead of blue on en route charts.

5-3-5. AIRWAY OR ROUTE COURSE CHANGES

a. Pilots of aircraft are required to adhere to airways or routes being flown. Special attention must be given to this requirement during course changes. Each course change consists of variables that make the technique applicable in each case a matter only the pilot can resolve. Some variables which must be considered are turn radius, wind effect, airspeed, degree of turn, and cockpit instrumentation. An early turn, as illustrated below, is one method of adhering to airways or routes. The use of any available cockpit instrumentation, such as Distance Measuring Equipment, may be used by the pilot to lead the turn when making course changes. This *is consistent* with the intent of 14 CFR Part 91.181, which requires pilots to operate along the centerline of an airway and along the direct course between navigational aids or fixes.

b. Turns which begin at or after fix passage may exceed airway or route boundaries. FIG 5-3-1 contains an example flight track depicting this, together with an example of an early turn.

c. Without such actions as leading a turn, aircraft operating in excess of 290 knots true air speed (TAS) can exceed the normal airway or route boundaries depending on the amount of course change required, wind direction and velocity, the character of the turn fix (DME, overhead navigation aid, or intersection), and the pilot's technique in making a course change. For example, a flight operating at 17,000 feet MSL with a TAS of 400 knots, a 25 degree bank, and a course change of more than 40 degrees would exceed the width of the airway or route; i.e., 4 nautical miles each side of centerline. However, in the airspace below 18,000 feet MSL, operations in excess of 290 knots TAS are not prevalent and the provision of additional IFR separation in all course change situations for the occasional aircraft making a turn in excess of 290 knots TAS creates an unacceptable waste of airspace and imposes a penalty upon the preponderance of traffic which operate at low speeds. Consequently, the FAA expects pilots to lead turns and take other actions they consider necessary during course changes to adhere as closely as possible to the airways or route being flown.

d. Due to the high airspeeds used at 18,000 feet MSL and above, FAA provides additional IFR separation protection for course changes made at such altitude levels.

Adhering to Airways or Routes

EARLY TURN

TURN AT OR AFTER
FIX PASSAGE

Boundary

Airway/Route

Airway/Route Boundary

Turning Fix

FIG 5-3-1

5-3-6. CHANGEOVER POINTS (COP'S)

a. COP's are prescribed for Federal airways, jet routes, area navigation routes, or other direct routes for which an MEA is designated under 14 CFR Part 95. The COP is a point along the route or airway segment between two adjacent navigation facilities or waypoints where changeover in navigation guidance should occur. At this point, the pilot should change navigation receiver frequency from the station behind the aircraft to the station ahead.

b. The COP is normally located midway between the navigation facilities for straight route segments, or at the intersection of radials or courses forming a dogleg in the case of dogleg route segments. When the COP is NOT located at the midway point, aeronautical charts will depict the COP location and give the mileage to the radio aids.

c. COP's are established for the purpose of preventing loss of navigation guidance, to prevent frequency interference from other facilities, and to prevent use of different facilities by different aircraft in the same airspace. Pilots are urged to observe COP's to the fullest extent.

5-3-7. HOLDING

a. Whenever an aircraft is cleared to a fix other than the destination airport and delay is expected, it is the responsibility of the ATC controller to issue complete holding instructions (unless the pattern is charted), an EFC time and best estimate of any additional en route/terminal delay.

NOTE-
Only those holding patterns depicted on U.S. government or commercially produced (meeting FAA requirements) low/high altitude enroute, and area or STAR charts should be used.

b. If the holding pattern is charted and the controller doesn't issue complete holding instructions, the pilot is expected to hold as depicted on the appropriate chart. When the pattern is charted, the controller may omit all holding instructions except the charted holding direction and the statement *AS PUBLISHED; e.g., HOLD EAST AS PUBLISHED.* Controllers shall always issue complete holding instructions when pilots request them.

c. If no holding pattern is charted and holding instructions have not been issued, the pilot should ask ATC for holding instructions prior to reaching the fix. This procedure will eliminate the possibility of an aircraft entering a holding pattern other than that desired by ATC. If unable to obtain holding instructions prior to reaching the fix (due to frequency congestion, stuck microphone, etc.), then enter a standard pattern on the course on which the aircraft approached the fix and request further clearance as soon as possible. In this event, the altitude/flight level of the aircraft at the clearance limit will be protected so that separation will be provided as required.

d. When an aircraft is 3 minutes or less from a clearance limit and a clearance beyond the fix has not been received, the pilot is expected to start a speed reduction so that the aircraft will cross the fix, initially, at or below the maximum holding airspeed.

e. When no delay is expected, the controller should issue a clearance beyond the fix as soon as possible and, whenever possible, at least 5 minutes before the aircraft reaches the clearance limit.

f. Pilots should report to ATC the time and altitude/flight level at which the aircraft reaches the clearance limit and report leaving the clearance limit.

NOTE–
In the event of two-way communications failure, pilots are required to comply with FAR Part 91.185.

g. When holding at a VOR station, pilots should begin the turn to the outbound leg at the time of the first complete reversal of the to/from indicator.

h. Patterns at the most generally used holding fixes are depicted (charted) on U.S. Government or commercially produced (meeting FAA requirements) Low or High Altitude Enroute, Area and STAR Charts. Pilots

are expected to hold in the pattern depicted unless specifically advised otherwise by ATC.

NOTE–
Holding patterns that protect for a maximum holding airspeed other than the standard may be depicted by an icon, unless otherwise depicted. The icon is a standard holding pattern symbol (racetrack) with the airspeed restriction shown in the center. In other cases, the airspeed restriction will be depicted next to the standard holding pattern symbol.

REFERENCE–
AIM, HOLDING, PARAGRAPH 5–3–7j2.

i. An ATC clearance requiring an aircraft to hold at a fix where the pattern is not charted will include the following information: (See FIG 5–3–2.)

1. Direction of holding from the fix in terms of the eight cardinal compass points (i.e., N, NE, E, SE, etc.).

2. Holding fix (the fix may be omitted if included at the beginning of the transmission as the clearance limit).

3. Radial, course, bearing, airway or route on which the aircraft is to hold.

4. Leg length in miles if DME or RNAV is to be used (leg length will be specified in minutes on pilot request or if the controller considers it necessary).

5. Direction of turn if left turns are to be made, the pilot requests, or the controller considers it necessary.

6. Time to expect further clearance and any pertinent additional delay information.

EXAMPLES OF HOLDING

TYPICAL PROCEDURE ON AN ILS OUTER MARKER

TYPICAL PROCEDURE AT INTERSECTION OF VOR RADIALS

TYPICAL PROCEDURE AT DME FIX

FIG 5-3-2

j. Holding pattern airspace protection is based on the following procedures.

   1. *Descriptive Terms:*

   (a) *Standard Pattern:* Right turns
(See FIG 5-3-3.)

   (b) *Nonstandard Pattern:* Left turns

   2. *Airspeeds:*

   (a) All aircraft may hold at the following altitudes and maximum holding airspeeds:

Altitude (MSL)	Airspeed (KIAS)
MHA - 6,000'	200
6,001' - 14,000'	230
14,001' and above	265

TBL 5-3-1

   (b) The following are exceptions to the maximum holding airspeeds:

   (1) Holding patterns from 6,001' to 14,000' may be restricted to a maximum airspeed of 210 KIAS. This nonstandard pattern will be depicted by an icon.

   (2) Holding patterns may be restricted to a maximum airspeed of 175 KIAS. This nonstandard pattern will be depicted by an icon. Holding patterns restricted to 175 KIAS will generally be found on instrument approach procedures applicable to Category A and B aircraft only.

   (3) Holding patterns at USAF airfields only - 310 KIAS maximum, unless otherwise depicted.

   (4) Holding patterns at Navy fields only - 230 KIAS maximum, unless otherwise depicted.

   (c) The following phraseology may be used by an ATCS to advise a pilot of the maximum holding airspeed for a holding pattern airspace area.

PHRASEOLOGY-
(AIRCRAFT IDENTIFICATION) (holding instructions, when needed) MAXIMUM HOLDING AIRSPEED IS (speed in knots).

   3. *Entry Procedures:*
(See FIG 5-3-4.)

   (a) *Parallel Procedure:* When approaching the holding fix from anywhere in sector (a), the parallel entry procedure would be to turn to a heading to parallel the holding course outbound on the nonholding side for one minute, turn in the direction of the holding pattern through more than 180 degrees, and return to the holding fix or intercept the holding course inbound.

   (b) *Teardrop Procedure:* When approaching the holding fix from anywhere in sector (b), the teardrop entry procedure would be to fly to the fix, turn outbound to a heading for a 30 degree teardrop entry within the pattern (on the holding side) for a period of one minute, then turn in the direction of the holding pattern to intercept the inbound holding course.

   (c) *Direct Entry Procedure:* When approaching the holding fix from anywhere in sector (c), the direct entry procedure would be to fly directly to the fix and turn to follow the holding pattern.

   (d) While other entry procedures may enable the aircraft to enter the holding pattern and remain within protected airspace, the parallel, teardrop and direct entries are the procedures for entry and holding recommended by the FAA.

   4. *Timing:*

   (a) *Inbound Leg:*

   (1) At or below 14,000 feet MSL: 1 minute.

   (2) Above 14,000 feet MSL: $1^1/_2$ minutes.

NOTE-
The initial outbound leg should be flown for 1 minute or 1 $^1/_2$ minutes (appropriate to altitude). Timing for subsequent outbound legs should be adjusted, as necessary, to achieve proper inbound leg time. Pilots may use any navigational means available; i.e. DME, RNAV, etc., to insure the appropriate inbound leg times.

   (b) *Outbound leg* timing begins *over/abeam* the fix, whichever occurs later. If the abeam position cannot be determined, start timing when turn to outbound is completed.

Holding Pattern Descriptive Terms

FIG 5-3-3

Holding Pattern Entry Procedures

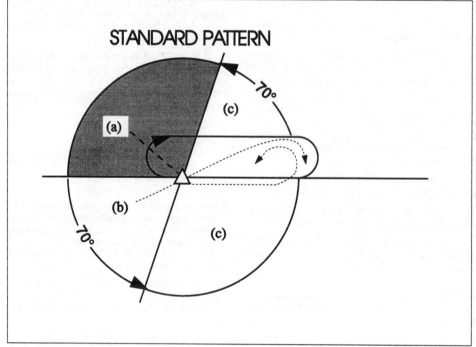

FIG 5-3-4

5. Distance Measuring Equipment (DME): DME holding is subject to the same entry and holding procedures except that distances (nautical miles) are used in lieu of time values. The *outbound course* of a DME holding pattern is called the outbound leg of the pattern. The length of the outbound leg will be specified by the controller. The end of the outbound leg is determined by the odometer reading. (See FIG 5–3–5 and FIG 5–3–6.)

Inbound Leg Toward NAVAID

FIG 5–3–5

NOTE–
When the inbound course is toward the NAVAID and the fix distance is 10 NM, and the leg length is 5 NM, then the end of the outbound leg will be reached when the DME reads 15 NM.

Inbound Leg Away from NAVAID

FIG 5–3–6

NOTE–
When the inbound course is away from the NAVAID and the fix distance is 28 NM, and the leg length is 8 NM, then the end of the outbound leg will be reached when the DME reads 20 NM.

6. *Pilot Action:*

(a) Start speed reduction when 3 minutes or less from the holding fix. Cross the holding fix, initially, at or below the maximum holding airspeed.

(b) *Make all turns during entry and while holding at:*

(1) 3 degrees per second, or

(2) 30 degree bank angle, or

(3) 25 degree bank provided a flight director system is used.

NOTE–
Use whichever requires the least bank angle.

(c) Compensate for wind effect primarily by drift correction on the inbound and outbound legs. When outbound, triple the inbound drift correction to avoid major turning adjustments; e.g., if correcting left by 8 degrees when inbound, correct right by 24 degrees when outbound.

(d) Determine entry turn from aircraft heading upon arrival at the holding fix; +/_5 degrees in heading is considered to be within allowable good operating limits for determining entry.

(e) Advise ATC immediately what increased airspeed is necessary, if any, due to turbulence, icing, etc., or if unable to accomplish any part of the holding procedures. When such higher speeds become no longer necessary, operate according to the appropriate published holding speed and notify ATC.

7. *Nonstandard Holding Pattern:* Fix end and outbound end turns are made to the left. Entry procedures to a nonstandard pattern are oriented in relation to the 70 degree line on the holding side just as in the standard pattern.

k. When holding at a fix and instructions are received specifying the time of departure from the fix, the pilot should adjust the aircraft's flight path within the limits of the established holding pattern in order to leave the fix at the exact time specified. After departing the holding fix, normal speed is to be resumed with respect to other governing speed requirements, such as terminal area speed limits, specific ATC requests, etc. Where the

fix is associated with an instrument approach and timed approaches are in effect, a procedure turn shall not be executed unless the pilot advises ATC, since aircraft holding are expected to proceed inbound on final approach directly from the holding pattern when approach clearance is received.

l. Radar surveillance of outer fix holding pattern airspace areas.

1. Whenever aircraft are holding at an outer fix, ATC will usually provide radar surveillance of the outer fix holding pattern airspace area, or any portion of it, if it is shown on the controller's radar scope.

2. The controller will attempt to detect any holding aircraft that stray outside the holding pattern airspace area and will assist any detected aircraft to return to the assigned airspace area.

NOTE–
Many factors could prevent ATC from providing this additional service, such as workload, number of targets, precipitation, ground clutter, and radar system capability. These circumstances may make it unfeasible to maintain radar identification of aircraft to detect aircraft straying from the holding pattern. The provision of this service depends entirely upon whether controllers believe they are in a position to provide it and does not relieve a pilot of their responsibility to adhere to an accepted ATC clearance.

3. If an aircraft is established in a published holding pattern at an assigned altitude above the published minimum holding altitude and subsequently cleared for the approach, the pilot may descend to the published minimum holding altitude. The holding pattern would only be a segment of the IAP *if* it is published on the instrument procedure chart and is used in lieu of a procedure turn.

m. For those holding patterns where there are no published minimum holding altitudes, the pilot, upon receiving an approach clearance, must maintain the last assigned altitude until leaving the holding pattern and established on the inbound course. Thereafter, the published minimum altitude of the route segment being flown will apply. It is expected that the pilot will be assigned a holding altitude that will permit a normal descent on the inbound course.

Section 4. ARRIVAL PROCEDURES

5-4-1. STANDARD TERMINAL ARRIVAL (STAR), FLIGHT MANAGEMENT SYSTEM PROCEDURES (FMSP) FOR ARRIVALS

a. A STAR is an ATC coded IFR arrival route established for application to arriving IFR aircraft destined for certain airports. FMSP's for arrivals serve the same purpose but are only used by aircraft equipped with FMS. The purpose of both is to simplify clearance delivery procedures and facilitate transition between en route and instrument approach procedures.

1. STAR's/FMSP's may have mandatory speeds and/or crossing altitudes published. Other STAR's may have planning information depicted to inform pilots what clearances or restrictions to "expect." "Expect" altitudes/speeds are not considered STAR/FMSP crossing restrictions until verbally issued by ATC.

NOTE-
The "expect" altitudes/speeds are published so that pilots may have the information for planning purposes. These altitudes/speeds should not be used in the event of lost communications unless ATC has specifically advised the pilot to expect these altitudes/speeds as part of a further clearance.

REFERENCE-
14 CFR SECTION 91.185(c)(2)(iii).

2. Pilots shall maintain last assigned altitude until receiving authorization/clearance to change altitude. At that time, pilots are expected to comply with all published/issued restrictions. The authorization may be via a normal descent clearance or the phraseology "**DESCEND VIA.**"

(a) A "descend via" clearance authorizes pilots to vertically and laterally navigate, in accordance with the depicted procedure, to meet published restrictions. Vertical navigation is at pilot's discretion, however, adherence to published altitude crossing restrictions and speeds is mandatory unless otherwise cleared. (MEA's are not considered restrictions, however, pilots are expected to remain above MEA's).

EXAMPLE-
① *Lateral/routing clearance only:*
"Cleared Hadly One arrival."
② *Routing with assigned altitude:*
"Cleared Hadly One arrival, descend and maintain Flight Level two four zero."
"Cleared Hadly One arrival, descend at pilot's discretion, maintain Flight Level two four zero."
③ *Lateral/routing and vertical navigation clearance:*
"Descend via the Civit One arrival."

"Descend via the Civit One arrival, except, cross Arnes at or above one one thousand."

NOTE-
Procedures for subsequent revisions to speed and/or altitudes after a "descend via" clearance has been issued and accepted may be found in the U.S. Terminal Procedures, General Information Section.

(b) Pilots cleared for vertical navigation using the phraseology "descend via" shall inform ATC upon initial contact with a new frequency.

EXAMPLE-
"Delta One Twenty One descending via the Civit One arrival."

b. Pilots of IFR aircraft destined to locations for which STAR's have been published may be issued a clearance containing a STAR whenever ATC deems it appropriate.

c. Use of STAR's requires pilot possession of at least the approved textual description. As with any ATC clearance or portion thereof, it is the responsibility of each pilot to accept or refuse an issued STAR. Pilots should notify ATC if they do not wish to use a STAR by placing "NO STAR" in the remarks section of the flight plan or by the less desirable method of verbally stating the same to ATC.

d. STAR charts are published in the *Terminal Procedures Publication (TPP)* and are available on subscription from the National Ocean Service.

5-4-2. LOCAL FLOW TRAFFIC MANAGEMENT PROGRAM

a. This program is a continuing effort by the FAA to enhance safety, minimize the impact of aircraft noise and conserve aviation fuel. The enhancement of safety and reduction of noise is achieved in this program by minimizing low altitude maneuvering of arriving turbojet and turboprop aircraft weighing more than 12,500 pounds and, by permitting departure aircraft to climb to higher altitudes sooner, as arrivals are operating at higher altitudes at the points where their flight paths cross. The application of these procedures also reduces exposure time between controlled aircraft and uncontrolled aircraft at the lower altitudes in and around the terminal environment. Fuel conservation is accomplished by absorbing any necessary arrival delays for aircraft included in this program operating at the higher and more fuel efficient altitudes.

b. A fuel efficient descent is basically an uninterrupted descent (except where level flight is required for speed adjustment) from cruising altitude to the point when level flight is necessary for the pilot to stabilize the aircraft on final approach. The procedure for a fuel efficient descent is based on an altitude loss which is most efficient for the majority of aircraft being served. This will generally result in a descent gradient window of 250–350 feet per nautical mile.

c. When crossing altitudes and speed restrictions are issued verbally or are depicted on a chart, ATC will expect the pilot to descend first to the crossing altitude and then reduce speed. Verbal clearances for descent will normally permit an uninterrupted descent in accordance with the procedure as described in paragraph b. above. Acceptance of a charted fuel efficient descent (Runway Profile Descent) clearance requires the pilot to adhere to the altitudes, speeds, and headings depicted on the charts unless otherwise instructed by ATC. PILOTS RECEIVING A CLEARANCE FOR A FUEL EFFICIENT DESCENT ARE EXPECTED TO ADVISE ATC IF THEY DO NOT HAVE RUNWAY PROFILE DESCENT CHARTS PUBLISHED FOR THAT AIRPORT OR ARE UNABLE TO COMPLY WITH THE CLEARANCE.

5-4-3. APPROACH CONTROL

a. Approach control is responsible for controlling all instrument flight operating within its area of responsibility. Approach control may serve one or more airfields, and control is exercised primarily by direct pilot and controller communications. Prior to arriving at the destination radio facility, instructions will be received from ARTCC to contact approach control on a specified frequency.

b. **Radar Approach Control:**

1. Where radar is approved for approach control service, it is used not only for radar approaches (ASR and PAR) but is also used to provide vectors in conjunction with published nonradar approaches based on radio NAVAID's (ILS, MLS, VOR, NDB, TACAN). Radar vectors can provide course guidance and expedite traffic to the final approach course of any established IAP or to the traffic pattern for a visual approach. Approach control facilities that provide this radar service will operate in the following manner:

(a) Arriving aircraft are either cleared to an outer fix most appropriate to the route being flown with vertical separation and, if required, given holding information or, when radar handoffs are effected between the ARTCC and approach control, or between two approach control facilities, aircraft are cleared to the airport or to a fix so located that the handoff will be completed prior to the time the aircraft reaches the fix. When radar handoffs are utilized, successive arriving flights

may be handed off to approach control with radar separation in lieu of vertical separation.

(b) After release to approach control, aircraft are vectored to the final approach course (ILS, MLS, VOR, ADF, etc.). Radar vectors and altitude or flight levels will be issued as required for spacing and separating aircraft. *Therefore, pilots must not deviate from the headings issued by approach control.* Aircraft will normally be informed when it is necessary to vector across the final approach course for spacing or other reasons. If approach course crossing is imminent and the pilot has not been informed that the aircraft will be vectored across the final approach course, the pilot should query the controller.

(c) The pilot is not expected to turn inbound on the final approach course unless an approach clearance has been issued. This clearance will normally be issued with the final vector for interception of the final approach course, and the vector will be such as to enable the pilot to establish the aircraft on the final approach course prior to reaching the final approach fix.

(d) In the case of aircraft already inbound on the final approach course, approach clearance will be issued prior to the aircraft reaching the final approach fix. When established inbound on the final approach course, radar separation will be maintained and the pilot will be expected to complete the approach utilizing the approach aid designated in the clearance (ILS, MLS, VOR, radio beacons, etc.) as the primary means of navigation. Therefore, once established on the final approach course, pilots must not deviate from it unless a clearance to do so is received from ATC.

(e) After passing the final approach fix on final approach, aircraft are expected to continue inbound on the final approach course and complete the approach or effect the missed approach procedure published for that airport.

2. ARTCC's are approved for and may provide approach control services to specific airports. The radar systems used by these centers do not provide the same precision as an airport surveillance radar (ASR)/precision approach radar (PAR) used by approach control facilities and towers, and the update rate is not as fast. Therefore, pilots may be requested to report established on the final approach course.

3. Whether aircraft are vectored to the appropriate final approach course or provide their own navigation on published routes to it, radar service is automatically terminated when the landing is completed or when instructed to change to advisory frequency at uncontrolled airports, whichever occurs first.

5-4-4. ADVANCE INFORMATION ON INSTRUMENT APPROACH

a. When landing at airports with approach control services and where two or more IAP's are published, pilots will be provided in advance of their arrival with the type of approach to expect or that they may be vectored for a visual approach. This information will be broadcast either by a controller or on ATIS. It will not be furnished when the visibility is three miles or better and the ceiling is at or above the highest initial approach altitude established for any low altitude IAP for the airport.

b. The purpose of this information is to aid the pilot in planning arrival actions; however, it is not an ATC clearance or commitment and is subject to change. Pilots should bear in mind that fluctuating weather, shifting winds, blocked runway, etc., are conditions which may result in changes to approach information previously received. It is important that pilots advise ATC immediately they are unable to execute the approach ATC advised will be used, or if they prefer another type of approach.

c. Aircraft destined to uncontrolled airports, which have automated weather data with broadcast capability, should monitor the ASOS/AWOS frequency to ascertain the current weather for the airport. The pilot shall advise ATC when he/she has received the broadcast weather and state his/her intentions.

NOTE-

☐ *ASOS/AWOS should be set to provide one-minute broadcast weather updates at uncontrolled airports that are without weather broadcast capability by a human observer.*

② *Controllers will consider the long line disseminated weather from an automated weather system at an uncontrolled airport as trend and planning information only and will rely on the pilot for current weather information for the airport. If the pilot is unable to receive the current broadcast weather, the last long line disseminated weather will be issued to the pilot. When receiving IFR services, the pilot/aircraft operator is responsible for determining if weather/visibility is adequate for approach/landing.*

d. When making an IFR approach to an airport not served by a tower or FSS, after ATC advises "CHANGE TO ADVISORY FREQUENCY APPROVED" you should broadcast your intentions, including the type of approach being executed, your position, and when over the final approach fix inbound (nonprecision approach) or when over the outer marker or fix used in lieu of the outer marker inbound (precision approach). Continue to monitor the appropriate frequency (UNICOM, etc.) for reports from other pilots.

5-4-5. INSTRUMENT APPROACH PROCEDURE CHARTS

a. 14 CFR Section 91.175(a), *Instrument approaches to civil airports*, requires the use of SIAP's prescribed for the airport in 14 CFR Part 97 unless otherwise authorized by the Administrator (including ATC). 14 CFR Section 91.175(g), *Military airports*, requires civil pilots flying into or out of military airports to comply with the IAP's and takeoff and landing minimums prescribed by the authority having jurisdiction at those airports.

1. All IAP's (standard and special, civil and military) are based on joint civil and military criteria contained in the U.S. Standard for TERPS. The design of IAP's based on criteria contained in TERPS, takes into account the interrelationship between airports, facilities, and the surrounding environment, terrain, obstacles, noise sensitivity, etc.. Appropriate altitudes, courses, headings, distances, and other limitations are specified and, once approved, the procedures are published and distributed by government and commercial cartographers as instrument approach charts.

2. Not all IAP's are published in chart form. Radar IAP's are established where requirements and facilities exist but they are printed in tabular form in appropriate U.S. Government Flight Information Publications.

3. A pilot adhering to the altitudes, flight paths, and weather minimums depicted on the IAP chart or vectors and altitudes issued by the radar controller, is assured of terrain and obstruction clearance and runway or airport alignment during approach for landing.

4. IAP's are designed to provide an IFR descent from the en route environment to a point where a safe landing can be made. They are prescribed and approved by appropriate civil or military authority to ensure a safe descent during instrument flight conditions at a specific airport. It is important that pilots understand these procedures and their use prior to attempting to fly instrument approaches.

5. TERPS criteria are provided for the following type of instrument approach procedures:

(a) Precision approaches where an electronic glide slope is provided (PAR, ILS, MLS, TLS, WAAS, LAAS, GLS, and SCAT-1).

(b) Nonprecision approaches where glide slope information is not provided (all except for subparagraph a. above).

b. The method used to depict prescribed altitudes on instrument approach charts differs according to techniques employed by different chart publishers. Prescribed altitudes may be depicted in three different configurations: minimum, maximum, and mandatory. The U.S. Government distributes charts produced by National Imagery and Mapping Agency (NIMA) and National Ocean Service (NOS). Altitudes are depicted on these charts in the profile view with underscore, overscore, or both to identify them as minimum, maximum, or mandatory.

1. Minimum altitude will be depicted with the altitude value underscored. Aircraft are required to maintain altitude at or above the depicted value.

2. Maximum altitude will be depicted with the altitude value overscored. Aircraft are required to maintain altitude at or below the depicted value.

3. Mandatory altitude will be depicted with the altitude value both underscored and overscored. Aircraft are required to maintain altitude at the depicted value.

NOTE-
The underscore and overscore to identify mandatory altitudes and the overscore to identify maximum altitudes are used almost exclusively by DMA for military charts. With very few exceptions, civil approach charts produced by NOS utilize only the underscore to identify minimum altitudes. Pilots are cautioned to adhere to altitudes as prescribed because, in certain instances, they may be used as the basis for vertical separation of aircraft by ATC. When a depicted altitude is specified in the ATC clearance, that altitude becomes mandatory as defined above.

c. Minimum Safe/Sector Altitudes (MSA) are published for emergency use on IAP charts. For conventional navigation systems, the MSA is normally based on the primary omnidirectional facility on which the IAP is predicated. The MSA depiction on the approach chart contains the facility identifier of the NAVAID used to determine the MSA altitudes. For RNAV approaches, the MSA is based on the runway waypoint (RWY WP) for straight-in approaches, or the airport waypoint (APT WP) for circling approaches. For GPS approaches, the MSA center will be the missed approach waypoint (MAWP). MSA's are expressed in feet above mean sea level and normally have a 25 NM radius; however, this radius may be expanded to 30 NM if necessary to encompass the airport landing surfaces.

Ideally, a single sector altitude is established and depicted on the plan view of approach charts; however, when necessary to obtain relief from obstructions, the area may be sectored and as many as four MSA's established. When established, sectors may be no less than 90° in spread. MSA's provide 1,000 feet clearance over all obstructions but do not necessarily assure acceptable navigation signal coverage.

d. Minimum Vectoring Altitudes (MVA) are established for use by ATC when radar ATC is exercised. MVA charts are prepared by air traffic facilities at locations where there are numerous different minimum IFR altitudes. Each MVA chart has sectors large enough to accommodate vectoring of aircraft within the sector at the MVA. Each sector boundary is at least 3 miles from the obstruction determining the MVA. To avoid a large sector with an excessively high MVA due to an isolated prominent obstruction, the obstruction may be enclosed in a buffer area whose boundaries are at least 3 miles from the obstruction. This is done to facilitate vectoring around the obstruction. (See FIG 5-4-1.)

1. The minimum vectoring altitude in each sector provides 1,000 feet above the highest obstacle in nonmountainous areas and 2,000 feet above the highest obstacle in designated mountainous areas. Where lower MVA's are required in designated mountainous areas to achieve compatibility with terminal routes or to permit vectoring to an IAP, 1,000 feet of obstacle clearance may be authorized with the use of Airport Surveillance Radar (ASR). The minimum vectoring altitude will provide at least 300 feet above the floor of controlled airspace.

NOTE-
OROCA is an off-route altitude which provides obstruction clearance with a 1,000 foot buffer in nonmountainous terrain areas and a 2,000 foot buffer in designated mountainous areas within the United States. This altitude may not provide signal coverage from ground-based navigational aids, air traffic control radar, or communications coverage.

2. Because of differences in the areas considered for MVA, and those applied to other minimum altitudes, and the ability to isolate specific obstacles, some MVA's may be lower than the nonradar Minimum En Route Altitudes (MEA), Minimum Obstruction Clearance Altitudes (MOCA) or other minimum altitudes depicted on charts for a given location. While being radar vectored, IFR altitude assignments by ATC will be at or above MVA.

Minimum Vectoring Altitude Charts

FIG 5-4-1

e. Visual Descent Points (VDP's) are being incorporated in selected nonprecision approach procedures. The VDP is a defined point on the final approach course of a nonprecision straight-in approach procedure from which normal descent from the MDA to the runway touchdown point may be commenced, provided visual reference required by 14 CFR Section 91.175(c)(3) is established. The VDP will normally be identified by DME on VOR and LOC procedures and by along track distance to the next waypoint for RNAV procedures. The VDP is identified on the profile view of the approach chart by the symbol: V.

1. VDP's are intended to provide additional guidance where they are implemented. No special technique is required to fly a procedure with a VDP. The pilot should not descend below the MDA prior to reaching the VDP and acquiring the necessary visual reference.

2. Pilots not equipped to receive the VDP should fly the approach procedure as though no VDP had been provided.

f. Visual Portion of the Final Segment. Instrument procedures designers perform a visual area obstruction evaluation off the approach end of each runway authorized for instrument landing, straight-in, or circling. Restrictions to instrument operations are imposed if penetrations of the obstruction clearance surfaces exist. These restrictions vary based on the severity of the pen-

etrations, and may include increasing required visibility, denying VDP's and prohibiting night instrument operations to the runway.

g. Final Approach Descent Angles. Gradients and threshold crossing heights (TCH) will now be depicted on all nonprecision instrument approach procedures which meet straight in alignment to a runway, except those charted on a precision approach chart. The descent gradient will be expressed in feet per nautical mile and the angle will be expressed in degrees. Both values will be computed from the FAF at the minimum charted FAF altitude to the runway threshold at the charted TCH. When the final segment contains a stepdown fix with a minimum charted altitude which is above the angle from the FAF to the threshold, the published angle and gradient will be computed from the stepdown fix at the minimum charted fix altitude to the threshold at the charted TCH.

5-4-6. APPROACH CLEARANCE

a. An aircraft which has been cleared to a holding fix and subsequently "cleared . . . approach" has not received new routing. Even though clearance for the approach may have been issued prior to the aircraft reaching the holding fix, ATC would expect the pilot to proceed via the holding fix (his last assigned route), and the feeder route associated with that fix (if a feeder route is published on the approach chart) to the initial approach fix (IAF) to commence the approach. *WHEN CLEARED FOR THE APPROACH, THE PUBLISHED OFF AIRWAY (FEEDER) ROUTES THAT LEAD FROM THE EN ROUTE STRUCTURE TO THE IAF ARE PART OF THE APPROACH CLEARANCE.*

b. If a feeder route to an IAF begins at a fix located along the route of flight prior to reaching the holding fix, and clearance for an approach is issued, a pilot should commence the approach via the published feeder route; i.e., the aircraft would not be expected to overfly the feeder route and return to it. The pilot is expected to commence the approach in a similar manner at the IAF, if the IAF for the procedure is located along the route of flight to the holding fix.

c. If a route of flight directly to the initial approach fix is desired, it should be so stated by the controller with phraseology to include the words "direct . . . ," "proceed direct" or a similar phrase which the pilot can interpret without question. When uncertain of the clearance, immediately query ATC as to what route of flight is desired.

d. The name of an instrument approach, as published, is used to identify the approach, even though a component of the approach aid, such as the glideslope on an Instrument Landing System, is inoperative or unreliable. The controller will use the name of the approach as published, but must advise the aircraft at the time an approach clearance is issued that the inoperative or unreliable approach aid component is unusable.

5-4-7. INSTRUMENT APPROACH PROCEDURES

a. Minimums are specified for various aircraft approach categories based upon a value 1.3 times the stalling speed of the aircraft in the landing configuration at maximum certificated gross landing weight. (See 14 CFR Section 97.3(b).) If it is necessary, while circling-to-land, to maneuver at speeds in excess of the upper limit of the speed range for each category, due to the possibility of extending the circling maneuver beyond the area for which obstruction clearance is provided, the circling minimum for the next higher approach category should be used. For example, an aircraft which falls in Category C, but is circling to land at a speed of 141 knots or higher should use the approach category "D" minimum when circling to land.

b. When operating on an unpublished route or while being radar vectored, the pilot, when an approach clearance is received, shall, in addition to complying with the minimum altitudes for IFR operations (14 CFR

Section 91.177), maintain the last assigned altitude unless a different altitude is assigned by ATC, or until the aircraft is established on a segment of a published route or IAP. After the aircraft is so established, published altitudes apply to descent within each succeeding route or approach segment unless a different altitude is assigned by ATC. Notwithstanding this pilot responsibility, for aircraft operating on unpublished routes or while being radar vectored, ATC will, except when conducting a radar approach, issue an IFR approach clearance only after the aircraft is established on a segment of a published route or IAP, or assign an altitude to maintain until the aircraft is established on a segment of a published route or instrument approach procedure. For this purpose, the procedure turn of a published IAP shall not be considered a segment of that IAP until the aircraft reaches the initial fix or navigation facility upon which the procedure turn is predicated.

EXAMPLE-
Cross Redding VOR at or above five thousand, cleared VOR runway three four approach.
or
Five miles from outer marker, turn right heading three three zero, maintain two thousand until established on the localizer, cleared ILS runway three six approach.

NOTE-
The altitude assigned will assure IFR obstruction clearance from the point at which the approach clearance is issued until established on a segment of a published route or IAP. If uncertain of the meaning of the clearance, immediately request clarification from ATC.

c. Several IAP's, using various navigation and approach aids may be authorized for an airport. ATC may advise that a particular approach procedure is being used, primarily to expedite traffic. If issued a clearance that specifies a particular approach procedure, notify ATC immediately if a different one is desired. In this event it may be necessary for ATC to withhold clearance for the different approach until such time as traffic conditions permit. However, a pilot involved in an emergency situation will be given priority. If the pilot is not familiar with the specific approach procedure, ATC should be advised and they will provide detailed information on the execution of the procedure.

REFERENCE-
AIM, ADVANCE INFORMATION ON INSTRUMENT APPROACH, PARAGRAPH 5-4-4.

d. At times ATC may not specify a particular approach procedure in the clearance, but will state "CLEARED APPROACH." Such clearance indicates that the pilot may execute any one of the authorized IAP's for that airport. This clearance does not constitute approval for the pilot to execute a contact approach or a visual approach.

e. Except when being radar vectored to the final approach course, when cleared for a specifically prescribed IAP; i.e., "cleared ILS runway one niner approach" or when "cleared approach" i.e., execution of any procedure prescribed for the airport, pilots shall execute the entire procedure commencing at an IAF or an associated feeder route as described on the IAP chart unless an appropriate new or revised ATC clearance is received, or the IFR flight plan is canceled.

f. Pilots planning flights to locations served by special IAP's should obtain advance approval from the owner of the procedure. Approval by the owner is necessary because special procedures are for the exclusive use of the single interest unless otherwise authorized by the owner. Additionally, some special approach procedures require certain crew qualifications training, or other special considerations in order to execute the approach. Also, some of these approach procedures are based on privately owned navigational aids. Owners of aids that are not for public use may elect to turn off the aid for whatever reason they may have; i.e., maintenance, conservation, etc. Air traffic controllers are not required to question pilots to determine if they have permission to use the procedure. Controllers presume a pilot has obtained approval and is aware of any details of the procedure if an IFR flight plan was filed to that airport.

g. When executing an instrument approach and in radio contact with an FAA facility, unless in "radar contact," report passing the final approach fix inbound (nonprecision approach) or the outer marker or fix used in lieu of the outer marker inbound (precision approach).

h. If a missed approach is required, advise ATC and include the reason (unless initiated by ATC). Comply with the missed approach instructions for the instrument approach procedure being executed, unless otherwise directed by ATC.

REFERENCE-
AIM, MISSED APPROACH, PARAGRAPH 5-4-19.
AIM, MISSED APPROACH, PARAGRAPH 5-5-5.

5-4-8. PROCEDURE TURN

a. A procedure turn is the maneuver prescribed when it is necessary to reverse direction to establish the aircraft inbound on an intermediate or final approach course. It is a required maneuver except when the symbol NoPT is shown, when RADAR VECTORING is provided, when a holding pattern is published in lieu of procedure turn, when conducting a timed approach, or when the procedure turn is not authorized. The altitude prescribed for the procedure turn is a *minimum* altitude until the aircraft is established on the inbound course. The maneuver must be completed within the distance specified in the profile view.

1. On U.S. Government charts, a barbed arrow indicates the direction or side of the outbound course on which the procedure turn is made. Headings are provided for course reversal using the 45 degree type procedure turn. However, the point at which the turn may be commenced and the type and rate of turn is left to the discretion of the pilot. Some of the options are the 45 degree procedure turn, the racetrack pattern, the teardrop procedure turn, or the 80 degree ↔ 260 degree course reversal. Some procedure turns are specified by procedural track. These turns must be flown exactly as depicted.

2. When the approach procedure involves a procedure turn, a maximum speed of not greater than 200 knots (IAS) should be observed from first overheading the course reversal IAF through the procedure turn maneuver to ensure containment within the obstruction clearance area. Pilots should begin the outbound turn immediately after passing the procedure turn fix. The procedure turn maneuver must be executed within the distance specified in the profile view. The normal procedure turn distance is 10 miles. This may be reduced to a minimum of 5 miles where only Category A or helicopter aircraft are to be operated or increased to as much as 15 miles to accommodate high performance aircraft.

3. A teardrop procedure or penetration turn may be specified in some procedures for a required course reversal. The teardrop procedure consists of departure from an initial approach fix on an outbound course followed by a turn toward and intercepting the inbound course at or prior to the intermediate fix or point. Its purpose is to permit an aircraft to reverse direction and lose considerable altitude within reasonably limited airspace. Where no fix is available to mark the beginning of the intermediate segment, it shall be assumed to commence at a point 10 miles prior to the final approach fix. When the facility is located on the airport, an aircraft is considered to be on final approach upon completion of the penetration turn. However, the final approach segment begins on the final approach course 10 miles from the facility.

4. A holding pattern in lieu of procedure turn may be specified for course reversal in some procedures. In such cases, the holding pattern is established over an intermediate fix or a final approach fix. The holding pattern distance or time specified in the profile view must be observed. Maximum holding airspeed limitations as set forth for all holding patterns apply. The holding pattern maneuver is completed when the aircraft is established on the inbound course after executing the appropriate entry. If cleared for the approach prior to returning to the holding fix, and the aircraft is at the prescribed altitude, additional circuits of the holding pattern are not necessary nor expected by ATC. If pilots elect to make additional circuits to lose excessive altitude or to become better established on course, it is their responsibility to so advise ATC upon receipt of their approach clearance.

5. A procedure turn is not required when an approach can be made directly from a specified intermediate fix to the final approach fix. In such cases, the term "NoPT" is used with the appropriate course and altitude to denote that the procedure turn is not required. If a procedure turn is desired, and when cleared to do so by ATC, descent below the procedure turn altitude should not be made until the aircraft is established on the inbound course, since some NoPT altitudes may be lower than the procedure turn altitudes.

b. Limitations on Procedure Turns:

1. In the case of a radar initial approach to a final approach fix or position, or a timed approach from a holding fix, or where the procedure specifies NoPT, no pilot may make a procedure turn unless, when final approach clearance is received, the pilot so advises ATC and a clearance is received to execute a procedure turn.

2. When a teardrop procedure turn is depicted and a course reversal is required, this type turn must be executed.

3. When a holding pattern replaces a procedure turn, the holding pattern must be followed, except when RADAR VECTORING is provided or when NoPT is shown on the approach course. The recommended entry procedures will ensure the aircraft remains within the holding pattern's protected airspace. As in the procedure turn, the descent from the minimum holding pattern altitude to the final approach fix altitude (when lower) may not commence until the aircraft is established on the inbound course. Where a holding pattern

is established in-lieu-of a procedure turn, the maximum holding pattern airspeeds apply.

REFERENCE-
AIM, HOLDING, PARAGRAPH 5-3-7j2.

4. The absence of the procedure turn barb in the plan view indicates that a procedure turn is not authorized for that procedure.

5-4-9. TIMED APPROACHES FROM A HOLDING FIX

a. TIMED APPROACHES may be conducted when the following conditions are met:

1. A control tower is in operation at the airport where the approaches are conducted.

2. Direct communications are maintained between the pilot and the center or approach controller until the pilot is instructed to contact the tower.

3. If more than one missed approach procedure is available, none require a course reversal.

4. If only one missed approach procedure is available, the following conditions are met:

(a) Course reversal is not required; and,

(b) Reported ceiling and visibility are equal to or greater than the highest prescribed circling minimums for the IAP.

5. When cleared for the approach, pilots shall not execute a procedure turn. (14 CFR Section 91.175.)

b. Although the controller will not specifically state that "timed approaches are in progress," the assigning of a time to depart the final approach fix inbound (nonprecision approach) or the outer marker or fix used in lieu of the outer marker inbound (precision approach) is indicative that timed approach procedures are being utilized, or in lieu of holding, the controller may use radar vectors to the Final Approach Course to establish a mileage interval between aircraft that will insure the appropriate time sequence between the final approach fix/outer marker or fix used in lieu of the outer marker and the airport.

c. Each pilot in an approach sequence will be given advance notice as to the time they should leave the holding point on approach to the airport. When a time to leave the holding point has been received, the pilot should adjust the flight path to leave the fix as closely as possible to the designated time. (See FIG 5-4-2.)

Timed Approaches from a Holding Fix

FIG 5-4-2

AIM

EXAMPLE-

At 12:03 local time, in the example shown, a pilot holding, receives instructions to leave the fix inbound at 12:07. These instructions are received just as the pilot has completed turn at the outbound end of the holding pattern and is proceeding inbound towards the fix. Arriving back over the fix, the pilot notes that the time is 12:04 and that there are 3 minutes to lose in order to leave the fix at the assigned time. Since the time remaining is more than two minutes, the pilot plans to fly a race track pattern rather than a 360 degree turn, which would use up 2 minutes. The turns at the ends of the race track pattern will consume approximately 2 minutes. Three minutes to go, minus 2 minutes required for the turns, leaves 1 minute for level flight. Since two portions of level flight will be required to get back to the fix inbound, the pilot halves the 1 minute remaining and plans to fly level for 30 seconds outbound before starting the turn back to the fix on final approach.

If the winds were negligible at flight altitude, this procedure would bring the pilot inbound across the fix precisely at the specified time of 12:07. However, if expecting headwind on final approach, the pilot should shorten the 30 second outbound course somewhat, knowing that the wind will carry the aircraft away from the fix faster while outbound and decrease the ground speed while returning to the fix. On the other hand, compensating for a tailwind on final approach, the pilot should lengthen the calculated 30 second outbound heading somewhat, knowing that the wind would tend to hold the aircraft closer to the fix while outbound and increase the ground speed while returning to the fix.

5-4-10. RADAR APPROACHES

a. The only airborne radio equipment required for radar approaches is a functioning radio transmitter and receiver. The radar controller vectors the aircraft to align it with the runway centerline. The controller continues the vectors to keep the aircraft on course until the pilot can complete the approach and landing by visual reference to the surface. There are two types of radar approaches: Precision (PAR) and Surveillance (ASR).

b. A radar approach may be given to any aircraft upon request and may be offered to pilots of aircraft in distress or to expedite traffic, however, an ASR might not be approved unless there is an ATC operational requirement, or in an unusual or emergency situation. Acceptance of a PAR or ASR by a pilot does not waive the prescribed weather minimums for the airport or for the particular aircraft operator concerned. The decision to make a radar approach when the reported weather is below the established minimums rests with the pilot.

c. PAR and ASR minimums are published on separate pages in the NOS Terminal Procedures Publication (TPP).

1. A PRECISION APPROACH (PAR) is one in which a controller provides highly accurate navigational guidance in azimuth and elevation to a pilot. Pilots are given headings to fly, to direct them to, and keep their aircraft aligned with the extended centerline of the landing runway. They are told to anticipate glide path interception approximately 10 to 30 seconds before it occurs and when to start descent. The published Decision Height will be given only if the pilot requests it. If the aircraft is observed to deviate above or below the glide path, the pilot is given the relative amount of deviation by use of terms "slightly" or "well" and is expected to adjust the aircraft's rate of descent/ascent to return to the glide path. Trend information is also issued with respect to the elevation of the aircraft and may be modified by the terms "rapidly" and "slowly"; e.g., "well above glide path, coming down rapidly." Range from touchdown is given at least once each mile. If an aircraft is observed by the controller to proceed outside of specified safety zone limits in azimuth and/or elevation and continue to operate outside these prescribed

limits, the pilot will be directed to execute a missed approach or to fly a specified course unless the pilot has the runway environment (runway, approach lights, etc.) in sight. Navigational guidance in azimuth and elevation is provided the pilot until the aircraft reaches the published Decision Height (DH). Advisory course and glidepath information is furnished by the controller until the aircraft passes over the landing threshold, at which point the pilot is advised of any deviation from the runway centerline. Radar service is automatically terminated upon completion of the approach.

2. A SURVEILLANCE APPROACH (ASR) is one in which a controller provides navigational guidance in azimuth only. The pilot is furnished headings to fly to align the aircraft with the extended centerline of the landing runway. Since the radar information used for a surveillance approach is considerably less precise than that used for a precision approach, the accuracy of the approach will not be as great and higher minimums will apply. Guidance in elevation is not possible but the pilot will be advised when to commence descent to the Minimum Descent Altitude (MDA) or, if appropriate, to an intermediate step-down fix Minimum Crossing Altitude and subsequently to the prescribed MDA. In addition, the pilot will be advised of the location of the Missed Approach Point (MAP) prescribed for the procedure and the aircraft's position each mile on final from the runway, airport or heliport or MAP, as appropriate. If requested by the pilot, recommended altitudes will be issued at each mile, based on the descent gradient established for the procedure, down to the last mile that is at or above the MDA. Normally, navigational guidance will be provided until the aircraft reaches the MAP. Controllers will terminate guidance and instruct the pilot to execute a missed approach unless at the MAP the pilot has the runway, airport or heliport in sight or, for a helicopter point-in-space approach, the prescribed visual reference with the surface is established. Also, if, at any time during the approach the controller considers that safe guidance for the remainder of the approach cannot be provided, the controller will terminate guidance and instruct the pilot to execute a missed approach. Similarly, guidance termination and missed approach will be effected upon pilot request and for civil aircraft only, controllers may terminate guidance when the pilot reports the runway, airport/heliport or visual surface route (point-in-space approach) in sight or otherwise indicates that continued guidance is not required. Radar service is automatically terminated at the completion of a radar approach.

NOTE–
1 *The published MDA for straight–in approaches will be issued to the pilot before beginning descent. When a surveillance approach will terminate in a circle–to–land maneuver, the pilot must furnish the aircraft approach category to the controller. The controller will then provide the pilot with the appropriate MDA.*

2 *ASR APPROACHES ARE NOT AVAILABLE WHEN AN ATC FACILITY IS USING CENRAP.*

3. A NO-GYRO APPROACH is available to a pilot under radar control who experiences circumstances wherein the directional gyro or other stabilized compass is inoperative or inaccurate. When this occurs, the pilot should so advise ATC and request a No-Gyro vector or approach. Pilots of aircraft not equipped with a directional gyro or other stabilized compass who desire radar handling may also request a No-Gyro vector or approach. The pilot should make all turns at standard rate and should execute the turn immediately upon receipt of instructions. For example, "TURN RIGHT," "STOP TURN." When a surveillance or precision approach is made, the pilot will be advised after the aircraft has been turned onto final approach to make turns at half standard rate.

5–4–11. RADAR MONITORING OF INSTRUMENT APPROACHES

a. PAR facilities operated by the FAA and the military services at some joint-use (civil and military) and military installations monitor aircraft on instrument approaches and issue radar advisories to the pilot when weather is below VFR minimums (1,000 and 3), at night, or when requested by a pilot. This service is provided only when the PAR Final Approach Course coincides with the final approach of the navigational aid and only during the operational hours of the PAR. The radar advisories serve only as a secondary aid since the pilot has selected the navigational aid as the primary aid for the approach.

b. Prior to starting final approach, the pilot will be advised of the frequency on which the advisories will be transmitted. If, for any reason, radar advisories cannot be furnished, the pilot will be so advised.

c. Advisory information, derived from radar observations, includes information on:

1. Passing the final approach fix inbound (nonprecision approach) or passing the outer marker or fix used in lieu of the outer marker inbound (precision approach).

NOTE–
At this point, the pilot may be requested to report sighting the approach lights or the runway.

2. Trend advisories with respect to elevation and/or azimuth radar position and movement will be provided.

NOTE–
Whenever the aircraft nears the PAR safety limit, the pilot will be advised that the aircraft is well above or below the glidepath or well left or right of course. Glidepath information is given only to those aircraft executing a precision approach, such as ILS or MLS. Altitude information is not transmitted to aircraft executing other than precision approaches because the descent portions of these approaches generally do not coincide with the depicted PAR glidepath. At locations where the MLS glidepath and PAR glidepath are not coincidental, only azimuth monitoring will be provided.

3. If, after repeated advisories, the aircraft proceeds outside the PAR safety limit or if a radical deviation is observed, the pilot will be advised to execute a missed approach unless the prescribed visual reference with the surface is established.

d. Radar service is automatically terminated upon completion of the approach.

5–4–12. ILS/MLS APPROACHES TO PARALLEL RUNWAYS

a. ATC procedures permit ILS instrument approach operations to dual or triple parallel runway configurations. ILS/MLS approaches to parallel runways are grouped into three classes: Parallel (dependent) ILS/MLS Approaches; Simultaneous Parallel (independent) ILS/MLS Approaches; and Simultaneous Close Parallel (independent) ILS Precision Runway Monitor (PRM) Approaches. (See FIG 5–4–3.) The classification of a parallel runway approach procedure is dependent on adjacent parallel runway centerline separation, ATC procedures, and airport ATC radar monitoring and communications capabilities. At some airports one or more parallel localizer courses may be offset up to 3 degrees. Offset localizer configurations result in loss of Category II capabilities and an increase in decision height (50').

b. Parallel approach operations demand heightened pilot situational awareness. A thorough Approach Procedure Chart review should be conducted with, as a minimum, emphasis on the following approach chart information: name and number of the approach, localizer frequency, inbound localizer/azimuth course, glide slope intercept altitude, decision height, missed approach instructions, special notes/procedures, and the assigned runway location/proximity to adjacent runways. Pilots will be advised that simultaneous ILS/MLS or simultaneous close parallel ILS PRM approaches are in use. This information may be provided through the ATIS.

c. The close proximity of adjacent aircraft conducting simultaneous parallel ILS/MLS and simultaneous close parallel ILS PRM approaches mandates strict pilot compliance with all ATC clearances. ATC assigned airspeeds, altitudes, and headings must be complied with in a timely manner. Autopilot coupled ILS/MLS approaches require pilot knowledge of procedures necessary to comply with ATC instructions. Simultaneous parallel ILS/MLS and simultaneous close parallel ILS PRM approaches necessitate precise localizer tracking to minimize final monitor controller intervention, and unwanted No Transgression Zone (NTZ) penetration. In the unlikely event of a breakout, ATC will not assign altitudes lower than the minimum vectoring altitude. Pilots should notify ATC immediately if there is a degradation of aircraft or navigation systems.

d. Strict radio discipline is mandatory during parallel ILS/MLS approach operations. This includes an alert listening watch and the avoidance of lengthy, unnecessary radio transmissions. Attention must be given to proper call sign usage to prevent the inadvertent execution of clearances intended for another aircraft. Use of abbreviated call signs must be avoided to preclude confusion of aircraft with similar sounding call signs. Pilots must be alert to unusually long periods of silence or any unusual background sounds in their radio receiver. A stuck microphone may block the issuance of ATC instructions by the final monitor controller during simultaneous parallel ILS/MLS and simultaneous close parallel ILS PRM approaches.

REFERENCE-
AIM, CHAPTER 4, SECTION 2. RADIO COMMUNICATIONS PHRASEOLOGY AND TECHNIQUES, GIVES ADDITIONAL COMMUNICATIONS INFORMATION.

e. Use of Traffic Collision Avoidance System (TCAS) provides an additional element of safety to parallel approach operations. Pilots should follow recommended TCAS operating procedures presented in approved flight manuals, original equipment manufacturer recommendations, professional newsletters, and FAA publications.

Parallel ILS Approaches

DEPENDENT PARALLEL ILS APPROACHES
-RUNWAY CENTERLINES SPACE 2500' OR greater
-STAGGERED Approaches
-Final Monitor Controller NOT required

INDEPENDENT PARALLEL ILS APPROACHES

SIMULTANEOUS PARALLEL ILS APPROACHES
-Runway centerlines spaced 4300' or greater (Duals & Trips)
-Final Monitor Controllers required

ILS PRM APPROACHES (SIMULTANEOUS CLOSE PARALLEL)
-Runway centerlines spaced less than 4300'. (Duals & Trips)
-Final Monitor Controllers required
-PRM required

NO TRANSGRESSION ZONE

NO TRANSGRESSION ZONE

FIG 5-4-3

5-4-13. PARALLEL ILS/MLS APPROACHES (DEPENDENT)

(See FIG 5-4-4.)

Staggered ILS Approaches

DIAGONAL
SEPARATION

Parallel ILS Approaches
Runway centerlines spaced 2500' or greater.
Radar monitoring not required.
Staggered Approaches.

FIG 5-4-4

a. Parallel approaches are an ATC procedure permitting parallel ILS/MLS approaches to airports having parallel runways separated by at least 2,500 feet between centerlines. Integral parts of a total system are ILS/MLS, radar, communications, ATC procedures, and required airborne equipment.

b. A parallel (dependent) approach differs from a simultaneous (independent) approach in that, the minimum distance between parallel runway centerlines is reduced; there is no requirement for radar monitoring or advisories; and a staggered separation of aircraft on the adjacent localizer/azimuth course is required.

c. Aircraft are afforded a minimum of 1.5 miles radar separation diagonally between successive aircraft on the adjacent localizer/azimuth course when runway centerlines are at least 2,500 feet but no more than 4,300 feet apart. When runway centerlines are more than 4,300 feet but no more than 9,000 feet apart a minimum of 2 miles diagonal radar separation is provided. Aircraft on the same localizer/azimuth course within 10 miles of the runway end are provided a minimum of 2.5 miles radar separation. In addition, a minimum of 1,000 feet vertical or a minimum of three miles radar separation is provided between aircraft during turn on to the parallel final approach course.

d. Whenever parallel ILS/MLS approaches are in progress, pilots are informed that approaches to both runways are in use. In addition, the radar controller will have the interphone capability of communicating with the tower controller where separation responsibility has not been delegated to the tower.

5-4-14. SIMULTANEOUS PARALLEL ILS/MLS APPROACHES (INDEPENDENT)

(See FIG 5-4-5.)

Simultaneous Parallel ILS Approaches

FIG 5-4-5

a. System: An approach system permitting simultaneous ILS/MLS approaches to parallel runways with centerlines separated by 4,300 to 9,000 feet, and equipped with final monitor controllers. Simultaneous parallel ILS/MLS approaches require radar monitoring to ensure separation between aircraft on the adjacent parallel approach course. Aircraft position is tracked by final monitor controllers who will issue instructions to aircraft observed deviating from the assigned localizer course. Staggered radar separation procedures are not utilized. Integral parts of a total system are ILS/MLS, radar, communications, ATC procedures, and required airborne equipment. The Approach Procedure Chart permitting simultaneous parallel ILS/MLS approaches will contain the note "simultaneous approaches authorized RWYS 14L and 14R," identifying the appropriate

runways as the case may be. When advised that simultaneous parallel ILS/MLS approaches are in progress, pilots shall advise approach control immediately of malfunctioning or inoperative receivers, or if a simultaneous parallel ILS/MLS approach is not desired.

b. Radar Monitoring: This service is provided for each simultaneous parallel ILS/MLS approach to ensure aircraft do not deviate from the final approach course. Radar monitoring includes instructions if an aircraft nears or penetrates the prescribed NTZ (an area 2,000 feet wide located equidistant between parallel final approach courses). This service will be provided as follows:

1. During turn on to parallel final approach aircraft will be provided 3 miles radar separation or a minimum of 1,000 feet vertical separation. Aircraft will not be vectored to intercept the final approach course at an angle greater than thirty degrees.

2. The final monitor controller will have the capability of overriding the tower controller on the tower frequency.

3. Pilots will be instructed to monitor the tower frequency to receive advisories and instructions.

4. Aircraft observed to overshoot the turn-on or to continue on a track which will penetrate the NTZ will be instructed to return to the correct final approach course immediately. The final monitor controller may also issue missed approach or breakout instructions to the deviating aircraft.

PHRASEOLOGY–
"(Aircraft call sign) YOU HAVE CROSSED THE FINAL APPROACH COURSE. TURN (left/right) IMMEDIATELY AND RETURN TO THE LOCALIZER/AZIMUTH COURSE,"

or

"(aircraft call sign) TURN (left/right) AND RETURN TO THE LOCALIZER/AZIMUTH COURSE."

5. If a deviating aircraft fails to respond to such instructions or is observed penetrating the NTZ, the aircraft on the adjacent final approach course may be instructed to alter course.

PHRASEOLOGY–
"TRAFFIC ALERT (aircraft call sign) TURN (left/right) IMMEDIATELY HEADING (degrees), (climb/descend) AND MAINTAIN (altitude)."

6. Radar monitoring will automatically be terminated when visual separation is applied, the aircraft reports the approach lights or runway in sight, or the aircraft is 1 mile or less from the runway threshold (for runway centerlines spaced 4,300 feet or greater). Final monitor controllers will **not** advise pilots when radar monitoring is terminated.

5-4-15. SIMULTANEOUS CLOSE PARALLEL ILS PRM APPROACHES (INDEPENDENT) ▮

(See FIG 5-4-6.)

ILS PRM Approaches
(Simultaneous Close Parallel)

FIG 5-4-6

a. System: An approach system permitting simultaneous ILS PRM approaches to dual runways with centerlines separated by **less** than 4,300 feet, and equipped with final monitor controllers. To qualify for reduced lateral runway separation, final monitor controllers must be equipped with high update radar and high resolution ATC radar displays, collectively called a PRM system. The PRM system displays almost instantaneous radar information. Automated tracking software provides monitor controllers with aircraft identification, position, a ten-second projected position, as well as visual and aural controller alerts. The PRM system is a supplemental requirement for simultaneous close parallel approaches in addition to the system requirements for simultaneous parallel ILS/MLS approaches described in paragraph 5-4-14, Simultaneous Parallel ILS/MLS Approaches (Independent). Simultaneous close parallel ILS PRM approaches are identified by a separate Approach Procedure Chart named ILS PRM (Simultaneous Close Parallel). The name ILS PRM is derived from the Precision Runway Monitor System which provides a means for simplifying the name of the simultaneous close parallel ILS approach.

b. Requirements: The following requirements must be met in order to fly an ILS PRM approach:

1. Air carrier pilots (including Part 121 and Part 135) must complete ILS PRM training which includes viewing one of the FAA videos, *RDU Precision Runway Monitor: A Pilot's Approach* or *ILS PRM Approaches, Information for Pilots.* Watching one of these videos is strongly recommended for all pilots who wish to fly these approaches.

2. All ATC directed "breakouts," a vector off the ILS prior to the decision altitude (DA), must be hand-flown.

3. If the airport has two tower frequencies operating for each runway, the aircraft flying the ILS PRM approach must have the capability of enabling the pilot/s to listen to two frequencies simultaneously.

Pilots shall advise air traffic control within 200 miles of the airport of intended landing if the pilot(s) are not qualified and/or the aircraft is not equipped to fly the approach.

c. Radar Monitoring: Simultaneous close parallel ILS/MLS approaches require final monitor controllers utilize the Precision Runway Monitor system to ensure prescribed separation standards are met. Procedures and communications phraseology are described in paragraph 5–4–14, Simultaneous Parallel ILS/MLS Approaches (Independent). To ensure separation is maintained, and in order to avoid an imminent situation during simultaneous close parallel ILS/MLS approaches, pilots must immediately comply with final monitor controller instructions to avoid an imminent situation. A minimum of 3 miles radar separation or 1,000 feet vertical separation will be provided during the turn on to close parallel final approach courses. In the event of a missed approach, radar monitoring is provided to one-half mile beyond the departure end of the runway. Final monitor controllers will **not** notify pilots when radar monitoring is terminated.

d. Differences between ILS and ILS PRM approaches of importance to the pilot:

1. Runway Spacing – Prior to ILS PRM approaches, most ATC directed breakouts were the result of two aircraft in trail getting too close together. Two aircraft going in the same direction did not mandate quick reaction times, but two aircraft along side each other separated by less than 4,300 feet and closing at 135 feet per second, does constitute the need for quick action. A blunder has to be recognized by one controller, the information passed on to another controller and breakout instructions issued to the endangered aircraft. The pilot will not have any warning that a breakout is eminent because the blundering aircraft will probably be on another frequency. It is important that when a pilot receives breakout instructions, he/she assumes that a blundering aircraft is heading into his/her approach course and begins the breakout as soon as safety allows.

2. Communications – To help in avoiding communication problems caused by stuck mikes and two parties talking at the same time, two tower frequencies for each runway will be in use during ILS PRM approach operations. The tower controller and the monitor controller will be broadcasting on both of the assigned frequencies. The monitor controller has the capability of overriding the tower controller. The pilots flying the approach will listen to both frequencies and only broadcast on the primary tower frequency. If a breakout is initiated by the monitor controller and the primary frequency is blocked by another transmission, the breakout instruction will be able to be heard on the second frequency. Anti–blocking technology installed in VHF radios might remove the requirement for the second VHF communications frequency in the near future.

3. Hand–flown Breakouts –The use of the autopilot is encouraged while flying an ILS PRM approach, but the autopilot must be disengaged in the rare event that a breakout is issued. Simulation studies of breakouts have shown that a handflown breakout is initiated consistently faster than a breakout performed using the autopilot.

4. TCAS – TCAS II equipped aircraft will fly the ILS PRM approach with the TCAS set to the Traffic Advisory (TA) only mode. If the TCAS is set to the TA/Resolution Advisory (RA) mode there is a chance that the TCAS resolution advisory will be in conflict with the breakout instruction and result in a confusing situation during a critical time. Pilots must remember to switch back to the TA/RA mode after completing the breakout maneuver.

5. Descending Breakouts – In the past, breakout descents were rarely given to pilots when flying on the ILS localizer and glideslope. A greater chance exists for the controller to issue a descending breakout when there is a blundering aircraft from an adjacent approach course crossing an aircraft's path. Pilots must be aware that a descending breakout is a possibility. In no case will the controller descend an aircraft below the minimum vectoring altitude (MVA) which will provide at least 1,000 feet clearance above obstacles. The pilot is not expected to exceed 1,000 feet per minute rate of descent in the event a descending breakout is issued.

5–4–16. SIMULTANEOUS CONVERGING INSTRUMENT APPROACHES

a. ATC may conduct instrument approaches simultaneously to converging runways; i.e., runways having an included angle from 15 to 100 degrees, at airports where a program has been specifically approved to do so.

b. The basic concept requires that dedicated, separate standard instrument approach procedures be developed for each converging runway included. Missed Approach Points must be at least 3 miles apart and missed approach procedures ensure that missed approach protected airspace does not overlap.

c. Other requirements are: radar availability, nonintersecting final approach courses, precision (ILS/MLS) approach systems on each runway and, if runways intersect, controllers must be able to apply visual separation as well as intersecting runway separation criteria. Intersecting runways also require minimums of at least 700 foot ceilings and 2 miles visibility. Straight in approaches and landings must be made.

d. Whenever simultaneous converging approaches are in progress, aircraft will be informed by the controller as soon as feasible after initial contact or via ATIS. Additionally, the radar controller will have direct communications capability with the tower controller where separation responsibility has not been delegated to the tower.

5-4-17. SIDE-STEP MANEUVER

a. ATC may authorize a nonprecision approach procedure which serves either one of parallel runways that are separated by 1,200 feet or less followed by a straight-in landing on the adjacent runway.

b. Aircraft that will execute a side-step maneuver will be cleared for a specified nonprecision approach and landing on the adjacent parallel runway. Example, "cleared ILS runway 7 left approach, side-step to runway 7 right." Pilots are expected to commence the side-step maneuver as soon as possible after the runway or runway environment is in sight.

c. Landing minimums to the adjacent runway will be based on nonprecision criteria and therefore higher than the precision minimums to the primary runway, but will normally be lower than the published circling minimums.

5-4-18. APPROACH AND LANDING MINIMUMS

a. Landing Minimums: The rules applicable to landing minimums are contained in 14 CFR Section 91.175.

b. Published Approach Minimums: Approach minimums are published for different aircraft categories and consist of a minimum altitude (DA, DH, MDA) and required visibility. These minimums are determined by applying the appropriate TERPS criteria. When a fix is incorporated in a nonprecision final segment, two sets of minimums may be published: one for the pilot that is able to identify the fix, and a second for the pilot that cannot. Two sets of minimums may also be published when a second altimeter source is used in the procedure. When a nonprecision procedure incorporates both a stepdown fix in the final segment and a second altimeter source, two sets of minimums are published to account for the stepdown fix and a note addresses minimums for the second altimeter source.

Final Approach Obstacle Clearance

CIRCLING APPROACH AREA RADII	
Approach Category	**Radius (Miles)**
A	1.3
B	1.5
C	1.7
D	2.3
E	4.5

RADI (r) DEFINING SIZE
OF AREAS, VARY WITH THE
APPROACH CATEGORY

CIRCLING APPROACH AREA

FIG 5-4-7

c. Obstacle Clearance: Final approach obstacle clearance is provided from the start of the final segment to the runway or missed approach point, whichever occurs last. Side-step obstacle protection is provided by increasing the width of the final approach obstacle clearance area. Circling approach protected areas are defined by the tangential connection of arcs drawn from each runway end. The arc radii distance differs by aircraft approach category. Because of obstacles near the airport, a portion of the circling area may be restricted by a procedural note: e.g., "Circling NA E of RWY 17-35." Obstacle clearance is provided at the published minimums for the pilot that makes a straight-in approach, side-steps, circles, or executes the missed approach. Missed approach obstacle clearance requirements may dictate the published minimums for the approach. (See FIG 5-4-7.)

d. Straight-in Minimums are shown on the IAP when the final approach course is within 30 degrees of the runway alignment (15 degrees for GPS IAP's) and a normal descent can be made from the IFR altitude shown on the IAP to the runway surface. When either the normal rate of descent or the runway alignment factor of 30 degrees (15 degrees for GPS IAP's) is exceeded, a straight-in minimum is not published and a circling minimum applies. The fact that a straight-in minimum is not published does not preclude pilots from landing straight-in if they have the active runway in sight and have sufficient time to make a normal approach for landing. Under such conditions and when ATC has cleared them for landing on that runway, pilots are not expected to circle even though only circling minimums are published. If they desire to circle, they should advise ATC.

e. Side-Step Maneuver Minimums: Landing minimums for a side-step maneuver to the adjacent runway will normally be higher than the minimums to the primary runway.

f. Circling Minimums: In some busy terminal areas, ATC may not allow circling and circling minimums will not be published. Published circling minimums provide obstacle clearance when pilots remain within the appropriate area of protection. Pilots should remain at or above the circling altitude until the aircraft is continuously in a position from which a descent to a landing on the intended runway can be made at a normal rate of descent using normal maneuvers. Circling may require maneuvers at low altitude, at low airspeed, and in marginal weather conditions. Pilots must use sound judgment, have an indepth knowledge of their capabilities, and fully understand the aircraft performance to determine the exact circling maneuver since weather, unique airport design, and the aircraft position, altitude, and airspeed must all be considered. The following basic rules apply:

1. Maneuver the shortest path to the base or downwind leg, as appropriate, considering existing weather conditions. There is no restriction from passing over the airport or other runways.

2. It should be recognized that circling maneuvers may be made while VFR or other flying is in progress at the airport. Standard left turns or specific instruction from the controller for maneuvering must be considered when circling to land.

3. At airports without a control tower, it may be desirable to fly over the airport to observe wind and turn indicators and other traffic which may be on the runway or flying in the vicinity of the airport.

g. Instrument Approach at a Military Field: When instrument approaches are conducted by civil aircraft at military airports, they shall be conducted in accordance with the procedures and minimums approved by the military agency having jurisdiction over the airport.

5-4-19. MISSED APPROACH

a. When a landing cannot be accomplished, advise ATC and, upon reaching the missed approach point defined on the approach procedure chart, the pilot must comply with the missed approach instructions for the procedure being used or with an alternate missed approach procedure specified by ATC.

b. Protected obstacle clearance areas for missed approach are predicated on the assumption that the abort is initiated at the missed approach point not lower than the MDA or DH. Reasonable buffers are provided for normal maneuvers. However, no consideration is given to an abnormally early turn. Therefore, when an early missed approach is executed, pilots should, unless otherwise cleared by ATC, fly the IAP as specified on the approach plate to the missed approach point at or above the MDA or DH before executing a turning maneuver.

c. If visual reference is lost while circling-to-land from an instrument approach, the missed approach specified for that particular procedure must be followed (unless an alternate missed approach procedure is specified by ATC). To become established on the prescribed missed approach course, the pilot should make an initial climbing turn toward the landing runway and continue the turn until established on the missed approach course. Inasmuch as the circling maneuver may be accomplished in more than one direction, different patterns will be required to become established on the prescribed missed approach course, depending on the aircraft position at the time visual reference is lost. Adherence to the procedure will assure that an aircraft will remain within the circling and missed approach obstruction clearance areas. (See FIG 5-4-8.)

d. At locations where ATC radar service is provided, the pilot should conform to radar vectors when provided by ATC in lieu of the published missed approach procedure. (See FIG 5-4-9.)

e. When approach has been missed, request clearance for specific action; i.e., to alternative airport, another approach, etc.

Circling and Missed Approach Obstruction Clearance Areas

FIG 5-4-8

Missed Approach

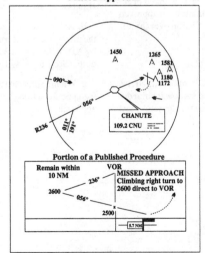

FIG 5-4-9

["

are recommended only. Pilots are not prohibited from flying other than recommended altitudes if operational requirements dictate.

e. When landmarks used for navigation are not visible at night, the approach will be annotated *"PROCEDURE NOT AUTHORIZED AT NIGHT."*

f. CVFP's usually begin within 20 flying miles from the airport.

g. Published weather minimums for CVFP's are based on minimum vectoring altitudes rather than the recommended altitudes depicted on charts.

h. CVFP's are not instrument approaches and do not have missed approach segments.

i. ATC will not issue clearances for CVFP's when the weather is less than the published minimum.

j. ATC will clear aircraft for a CVFP after the pilot reports siting a charted landmark or a preceding aircraft. If instructed to follow a preceding aircraft, pilots are responsible for maintaining a safe approach interval and wake turbulence separation.

k. Pilots should advise ATC if at any point they are unable to continue an approach or lose sight of a preceding aircraft. Missed approaches will be handled as a go-around.

5-4-22. CONTACT APPROACH

a. Pilots operating in accordance with an IFR flight plan, provided they are clear of clouds and have at least 1 mile flight visibility and can reasonably expect to continue to the destination airport in those conditions, may request ATC authorization for a contact approach.

b. Controllers may authorize a contact approach provided:

1. The contact approach is specifically requested by the pilot. ATC cannot initiate this approach.

EXAMPLE-
Request contact approach.

2. The reported ground visibility at the destinatio airport is at least 1 statute mile.

3. The contact approach will be made to an airpo having a standard or special instrument approach proce dure.

4. Approved separation is applied between aircra so cleared and between these aircraft and other IFR special VFR aircraft.

EXAMPLE-
Cleared contact approach (and, if required) at or below (altitude) (routing) if not possible (alternative procedures) and advise.

c. A contact approach is an approach procedure th: may be used by a pilot (with prior authorization fror ATC) in lieu of conducting a standard or special IAP t an airport. It is not intended for use by a pilot on an IF flight clearance to operate to an airport not having published and functioning IAP. Nor is it intended fc an aircraft to conduct an instrument approach to one ai port and then, when "in the clear," discontinue that ap proach and proceed to another airport. In the executio of a contact approach, the pilot assumes the responsibil ity for obstruction clearance. If radar service is being r ceived, it will automatically terminate when the pilot i instructed to change to advisory frequency.

5-4-23. LANDING PRIORITY

A clearance for a specific type of approach (ILS, ML' ADF, VOR or Straight-in Approach) to an aircraft ope ating on an IFR flight plan does not mean that landing priority will be given over other traffic. ATCT's handl all aircraft, regardless of the type of flight plan, on "first-come, first-served" basis. Therefore, because c local traffic or runway in use, it may be necessary for th controller in the interest of safety, to provide a differer landing sequence. In any case, a landing sequence wil be issued to each aircraft as soon as possible to enabl the pilot to properly adjust the aircraft's flight path.

5-4-24. OVERHEAD APPROACH MANEUVER

a. Pilots operating in accordance with an IFR flight plan in visual meteorological conditions (VMC) may request ATC authorization for an overhead maneuver. An overhead maneuver is not an instrument approach procedure. Overhead maneuver patterns are developed at airports where aircraft have an operational need to conduct the maneuver. An aircraft conducting an overhead maneuver is considered to be VFR and the IFR flight plan is cancelled when the aircraft crosses the landing threshold on the initial approach portion of the maneuver. (See FIG 5-4-10.) The existence of a standard overhead maneuver pattern does not eliminate the possible requirement for an aircraft to conform to conventional rectangular patterns if an overhead maneuver cannot be approved. Aircraft operating to an airport without a functioning control tower must initiate cancellation of an IFR flight plan prior to executing the overhead maneuver. Cancellation of the IFR flight plan must be accomplished after crossing the landing threshold on the initial portion of the maneuver or after landing. Controllers may authorize an overhead maneuver and issue the following to arriving aircraft:

1. Pattern altitude and direction of traffic. This information may be omitted if either is standard.

PHRASEOLOGY-
PATTERN ALTITUDE (altitude). RIGHT TURNS.

2. Request for a report on initial approach.

PHRASEOLOGY-
REPORT INITIAL.

3. "Break" information and a request for the pilot to report. The "Break Point" will be specified if nonstandard. Pilots may be requested to report "break" if required for traffic or other reasons.

PHRASEOLOGY-
BREAK AT (specified point).
REPORT BREAK.

Overhead Maneuver

FIG 5-4-10

Section 5. PILOT/CONTROLLER ROLES
AND RESPONSIBILITIES

5-5-1. GENERAL

a. The roles and responsibilities of the pilot and controller for effective participation in the ATC system are contained in several documents. Pilot responsibilities are in the FAR's and the air traffic controller's are in the FAA Order 7110.65, Air Traffic Control, and supplemental FAA directives. Additional and supplemental information for pilots can be found in the current Aeronautical Information Manual (AIM), Notices to Airmen, Advisory Circulars and aeronautical charts. Since there are many other excellent publications produced by nongovernment organizations, as well as other government organizations, with various updating cycles, questions concerning the latest or most current material can be resolved by cross-checking with the above mentioned documents.

b. The pilot in command of an aircraft is directly responsible for, and is the final authority as to the safe operation of that aircraft. In an emergency requiring immediate action, the pilot in command may deviate from any rule in the General Subpart A and Flight Rules Subpart B in accordance with FAR Part 91.3.

c. The air traffic controller is responsible to give first priority to the separation of aircraft and to the issuance of radar safety alerts, second priority to other services that are required, but do not involve separation of aircraft and third priority to additional services to the extent possible.

d. In order to maintain a safe and efficient air traffic system, it is necessary that each party fulfill their responsibilities to the fullest.

e. The responsibilities of the pilot and the controller intentionally overlap in many areas providing a degree of redundancy. Should one or the other fail in any manner, this overlapping responsibility is expected to compensate, in many cases, for failures that may affect safety.

f. The following, while not intended to be all inclusive, is a brief listing of pilot and controller responsibilities for some commonly used procedures or phases of flight. More detailed explanations are contained in other portions of this publication, the appropriate FARs', AC's and similar publications. The information provided is an overview of the principles involved and is not meant as an interpretation of the rules nor is it intended to extend or diminish responsibilities.

5-5-2. AIR TRAFFIC CLEARANCE

a. Pilot:

1. Acknowledges receipt and understanding of an ATC clearance.

2. Readbacks any hold short of runway instructions issued by ATC.

3. Requests clarification or amendment, as appropriate, any time a clearance is not fully understood or considered unacceptable from a safety standpoint.

4. Promptly complies with an air traffic clearance upon receipt except as necessary to cope with an emergency. Advises ATC as soon as possible and obtains an amended clearance, if deviation is necessary.

NOTE–
A clearance to land means that appropriate separation on the landing runway will be ensured. A landing clearance does not relieve the pilot from compliance with any previously issued altitude crossing restriction.

b. Controller:

1. Issues appropriate clearances for the operation to be conducted, or being conducted, in accordance with established criteria.

2. Assigns altitudes in IFR clearances that are at or above the minimum IFR altitudes in controlled airspace.

3. Ensures acknowledgement by the pilot for issued information, clearances, or instructions.

4. Ensures that readbacks by the pilot of altitude, heading, or other items are correct. If incorrect, distorted, or incomplete, makes corrections as appropriate.

5-5-3. CONTACT APPROACH

a. Pilot:

1. Must request a contact approach and makes it in lieu of a standard or special instrument approach.

2. By requesting the contact approach, indicates that the flight is operating clear of clouds, has at least one mile flight visibility, and reasonably expects to continue to the destination airport in those conditions.

3. Assumes responsibility for obstruction clearance while conducting a contact approach.

4. Advises ATC immediately if unable to continue the contact approach or if encounters less than 1 mile flight visibility.

5. Is aware that if radar service is being received, it may be automatically terminated when told to contact the tower.

REFERENCE-
PILOT/CONTROLLER GLOSSARY TERM- RADAR SERVICE TERMI-
NATED.

b. Controller:

1. Issues clearance for a contact approach only when requested by the pilot. Does not solicit the use of this procedure.

2. Before issuing the clearance, ascertains that reported ground visibility at destination airport is at least 1 mile.

3. Provides approved separation between the aircraft cleared for a contact approach and other IFR or special VFR aircraft. When using vertical separation, does not assign a fixed altitude, but clears the aircraft at or below an altitude which is at least 1,000 feet below any IFR traffic but not below Minimum Safe Altitudes prescribed in FAR Part 91.119.

4. Issues alternative instructions if, in their judgment, weather conditions may make completion of the approach impracticable.

5-5-4. INSTRUMENT APPROACH

a. Pilot:

1. Be aware that the controller issues clearance for approach based only on known traffic.

2. Follows the procedure as shown on the IAP, including all restrictive notations, such as:

(a) Procedure not authorized at night;

(b) Approach not authorized when local area altimeter not available;

(c) Procedure not authorized when control tower not in operation;

(d) Procedure not authorized when glide slope not used;

(e) Straight-in minimums not authorized at night; etc.

(f) Radar required; or

(g) The circling minimums published on the instrument approach chart provide adequate obstruction clearance and pilots should not descend below the circling altitude until the aircraft is in a position to make final descent for landing. Sound judgment and knowledge of the pilot's and the aircraft's capabilities are the criteria for determining the exact maneuver in each instance since airport design and the aircraft position, altitude and airspeed must all be considered.

REFERENCE-
AIM, APPROACH AND LANDING MINIMUMS, PARAGRAPH 5-4-18.

3. Upon receipt of an approach clearance while on an unpublished route or being radar vectored:

(a) Complies with the minimum altitude for IFR, and

(b) Maintains the last assigned altitude until established on a segment of a published route or IAP, at which time published altitudes apply.

b. Controller:

1. Issues an approach clearance based on known traffic.

2. Issues an IFR approach clearance only after the aircraft is established on a segment of published route or IAP, or assigns an appropriate altitude for the aircraft to maintain until so established.

5-5-5. MISSED APPROACH

a. Pilot:

1. Executes a missed approach when one of the following conditions exist:

(a) Arrival at the Missed Approach Point (MAP) or the Decision Height (DH) and visual reference to the runway environment is insufficient to complete the landing.

(b) Determined that a safe landing is not possible.

(c) Instructed to do so by ATC.

2. Advises ATC that a missed approach will be made. Include the reason for the missed approach unless the missed approach is initiated by ATC.

3. Complies with the missed approach instructions for the IAP being executed unless other missed approach instructions are specified by ATC.

4. If executing a missed approach prior to reaching the MAP or DH, flies the instrument procedure to the

MAP at an altitude at or above the Minimum Descent Altitude (MDA) or DH before executing a turning maneuver.

5. Radar vectors issued by ATC when informed that a missed approach is being executed supersedes the previous missed approach procedure.

6. If making a missed approach from a radar approach, executes the missed approach procedure previously given or climbs to the altitude and flies the heading specified by the controller.

7. Following a missed approach, requests clearance for specific action; i.e., another approach, hold for improved conditions, proceed to an alternate airport, etc.

b. Controller:

1. Issues an approved alternate missed approach procedure if it is desired that the pilot execute a procedure other than as depicted on the instrument approach chart.

2. May vector a radar identified aircraft executing a missed approach when operationally advantageous to the pilot or the controller.

3. In response to the pilot's stated intentions, issues a clearance to an alternate airport, to a holding fix, or for reentry into the approach sequence, as traffic conditions permit.

5-5-6. RADAR VECTORS

a. Pilot:

1. Promptly complies with headings and altitudes assigned to you by the controller.

2. Questions any assigned heading or altitude believed to be incorrect.

3. If operating VFR and compliance with any radar vector or altitude would cause a violation of any FAR, advises ATC and obtains a revised clearance or instructions.

b. Controller:

1. Vectors aircraft in Class A, Class B, Class C, Class D and Class E airspace:

(a) For separation.

(b) For noise abatement.

(c) To obtain an operational advantage for the pilot or controller.

2. Vectors aircraft in Class A, Class B, Class C, Class D, Class E and Class G airspace when requested by the pilot.

3. Vectors IFR aircraft at or above minimum vectoring altitudes.

4. May vector VFR aircraft, not at an ATC assigned altitude, at any altitude. In these cases, terrain separation is the pilot's responsibility.

5-5-7. SAFETY ALERT

a. Pilot:

1. Initiates appropriate action if a safety alert is received from ATC.

2. Be aware that this service is not always available and that many factors affect the ability of the controller to be aware of a situation in which unsafe proximity to terrain, obstructions, or another aircraft may be developing.

b. Controller:

1. Issues a safety alert if aware an aircraft under their control is at an altitude which, in the controller's judgment, places the aircraft in unsafe proximity to terrain, obstructions or another aircraft. Types of safety alerts are:

(a) *Terrain or Obstruction Alert:* Immediately issued to an aircraft under their control if aware the aircraft is at an altitude believed to place the aircraft in unsafe proximity to terrain or obstructions.

(b) *Aircraft Conflict Alert:* Immediately issued to an aircraft under their control if aware of an aircraft not under their control at an altitude believed to place the aircraft in unsafe proximity to each other. With the alert, they offer the pilot an alternative, if feasible.

2. Discontinue further alerts if informed by the pilot action is being taken to correct the situation or that the other aircraft is in sight.

5-5-8. SEE AND AVOID

a. Pilot: When meteorological conditions permit, regardless of type of flight plan or whether or not under control of a radar facility, the pilot is responsible to see and avoid other traffic, terrain, or obstacles.

b. Controller:

1. Provides radar traffic information to radar identified aircraft operating outside positive control airspace on a workload permitting basis.

2. Issues safety alerts to aircraft under their control if aware the aircraft is at an altitude believed to place the aircraft in unsafe proximity to terrain, obstructions, or other aircraft.

5-5-9. SPEED ADJUSTMENTS

a. Pilot:

1. Advises ATC any time cruising airspeed varies plus or minus 5 percent or 10 knots, whichever is greater, from that given in the flight plan.

2. Complies with speed adjustments from ATC unless:

(a) The minimum or maximum safe airspeed for any particular operation is greater or less than the requested airspeed. In such cases, advises ATC.

NOTE-
It is the pilot's responsibility and prerogative to refuse speed adjustments considered excessive or contrary to the aircraft's operating specifications.

(b) Operating at or above 10,000 feet MSL on an ATC assigned SPEED ADJUSTMENT of more than 250 knots IAS and subsequent clearance is received for descent below 10,000 feet MSL. In such cases, pilots are expected to comply with FAR Part 91.117(a).

3. When complying with speed adjustment assignments, maintains an indicated airspeed within plus or minus 10 knots or 0.02 Mach number of the specified speed.

b. Controller:

1. Assigns speed adjustments to aircraft when necessary but not as a substitute for good vectoring technique.

2. Adheres to the restrictions published in the FAA Order 7110.65, Air Traffic Control, as to when speed adjustment procedures may be applied.

3. Avoids speed adjustments requiring alternate decreases and increases.

4. Assigns speed adjustments to a specified IAS (KNOTS)/Mach number or to increase or decrease speed using increments of 10 knots or multiples thereof.

5. Advises pilots to resume normal speed when speed adjustments are no longer required.

6. Gives due consideration to aircraft capabilities to reduce speed while descending.

7. Does not assign speed adjustments to aircraft at or above FL 390 without pilot consent.

5-5-10. TRAFFIC ADVISORIES (TRAFFIC INFORMATION)

a. Pilot:

1. Acknowledges receipt of traffic advisories.

2. Informs controller if traffic in sight.

3. Advises ATC if a vector to avoid traffic is desired.

4. Does not expect to receive radar traffic advisories on all traffic. Some aircraft may not appear on the radar display. Be aware that the controller may be occupied with higher priority duties and unable to issue traffic information for a variety of reasons.

5. Advises controller if service not desired.

b. Controller:

1. Issues radar traffic to the maximum extent consistent with higher priority duties except in Class A airspace.

2. Provides vectors to assist aircraft to avoid observed traffic when requested by the pilot.

3. Issues traffic information to aircraft in the Class B, Class C, and Class D surface areas for sequencing purposes.

5-5-11. VISUAL APPROACH

a. Pilot:

1. If a visual approach is not desired, advises ATC.

2. Complies with controller's instructions for vectors toward the airport of intended landing or to a visual position behind a preceding aircraft.

3. The pilot must, at all times, have either the airport or the preceding aircraft in sight. After being cleared for a visual approach, proceed to the airport in a normal manner or follow the preceding aircraft. Remain clear of clouds while conducting a visual approach.

4. If the pilot accepts a visual approach clearance to visually follow a preceding aircraft, you are required to establish a safe landing interval behind the aircraft you were instructed to follow. You are responsible for wake turbulence separation.

5. Advise ATC immediately if the pilot is unable to continue following the preceding aircraft, cannot remain clear of clouds, or lose sight of the airport.

6. Be aware that radar service is automatically terminated, without being advised by ATC, when the pilot is instructed to change to advisory frequency.

7. Be aware that there may be other traffic in the traffic pattern and the landing sequence may differ from the traffic sequence assigned by approach control or ARTCC.

b. Controller:

1. Do not clear an aircraft for a visual approach unless reported weather at the airport is ceiling at or above 1,000 feet and visibility is 3 miles or greater. When weather is not available for the destination airport, inform the pilot and do not initiate a visual approach to that airport unless there is reasonable assurance that descent and flight to the airport can be made visually.

2. Issue visual approach clearance when the pilot reports sighting either the airport or a preceding aircraft which is to be followed.

3. Provide separation except when visual separation is being applied by the pilot.

4. Continue flight following and traffic information until the aircraft has landed or has been instructed to change to advisory frequency.

5. Inform the pilot when the preceding aircraft is a heavy.

6. When weather is available for the destination airport, do not initiate a vector for a visual approach unless the reported ceiling at the airport is 500 feet or more above the MVA and visibility is 3 miles or more. If vectoring weather minima are not available but weather at the airport is ceiling at or above 1,000 feet and visibility of 3 miles or greater, visual approaches may still be conducted.

7. Informs the pilot conducting the visual approach of the aircraft class when pertinent traffic is known to be a heavy aircraft.

5-5-12. VISUAL SEPARATION

a. Pilot:

1. Acceptance of instructions to follow another aircraft or to provide visual separation from it is an acknowledgment that the pilot will maneuver the aircraft as necessary to avoid the other aircraft or to maintain intrail separation. Pilots are responsible to maintain visual separation until flight paths (altitudes and/or courses) diverge.

2. If instructed by ATC to follow another aircraft or to provide visual separation from it, promptly notify the controller if you lose sight of that aircraft, are unable to maintain continued visual contact with it, or cannot accept the responsibility for your own separation for any reason.

3. The pilot also accepts responsibility for wake turbulence separation under these conditions.

b. Controller: Applies visual separation only:

1. Within the terminal area when a controller has both aircraft in sight or by instructing a pilot who sees the other aircraft to maintain visual separation from it.

2. Pilots are responsible to maintain visual separation until flight paths (altitudes and/or courses) diverge.

3. Within en route airspace when aircraft are on opposite courses and one pilot reports having seen the other aircraft and that the aircraft have passed each other.

5-5-13. VFR-ON-TOP

a. Pilot:

1. This clearance must be requested by the pilot on an IFR flight plan, and if approved, allows the pilot the choice (subject to any ATC restrictions) to select an altitude or flight level in lieu of an assigned altitude.

NOTE-
VFR-on-top is not permitted in certain airspace areas, such as Class A airspace, certain restricted areas, etc. Consequently, IFR flights operating VFR-on-top will avoid such airspace.

REFERENCE-
AIM, IFR CLEARANCE VFR-ON-TOP, PARAGRAPH 4-4-7.
AIM, IFR SEPARATION STANDARDS, PARAGRAPH 4-4-10.
AIM, POSITION REPORTING, PARAGRAPH 5-3-2.
AIM, ADDITIONAL REPORTS, PARAGRAPH 5-3-3.

2. By requesting a VFR-on-top clearance, the pilot assumes the sole responsibility to be vigilant so as to see and avoid other aircraft and to:

(a) Fly at the appropriate VFR altitude as prescribed in 14 CFR Section 91.159.

(b) Comply with the VFR visibility and distance from clouds criteria in 14 CFR Section 91.155, *Basic VFR Weather minimums.*

(c) Comply with instrument flight rules that are applicable to this flight; i.e., minimum IFR altitudes, position reporting, radio communications, course to be flown, adherence to ATC clearance, etc.

3. Should advise ATC prior to any altitude change to ensure the exchange of accurate traffic information.

b. Controller:

1. May clear an aircraft to maintain VFR-on-top if the pilot of an aircraft on an IFR flight plan requests the clearance.

2. Informs the pilot of an aircraft cleared to climb to VFR-on-top the reported height of the tops or that no top report is available; issues an alternate clearance if necessary; and once the aircraft reports reaching VFR-on-top, reclears the aircraft to maintain VFR-on-top.

3. Before issuing clearance, ascertain that the aircraft is not in or will not enter Class A airspace.

5-5-14. INSTRUMENT DEPARTURES

a. Pilot:

1. Prior to departure considers the type of terrain and other obstructions on or in the vicinity of the departure airport.

2. Determines if obstruction avoidance can be maintained visually or that the departure procedure should be followed.

3. Determines whether a departure procedure and/ or DP is available for obstruction avoidance.

4. At airports where IAP's have not been published, hence to published departure procedure, determines what action will be necessary and takes such action that will assure a safe departure.

b. Controller:

1. At locations with airport traffic control service, when necessary, specifies direction of takeoff, turn, or initial heading to be flown after takeoff.

2. At locations without airport traffic control service but within Class E surface area when necessary to specify direction of takeoff, turn, or initial heading to be flown, obtains pilot's concurrence that the procedure will allow the pilot to comply with local traffic patterns, terrain, and obstruction avoidance.

3. Includes established departure procedures as part of the ATC clearance when pilot compliance is necessary to ensure separation.

5-5-15. MINIMUM FUEL ADVISORY

a. Pilot:

1. Advise ATC of your minimum fuel status when your fuel supply has reached a state where, upon reaching destination, you cannot accept any undue delay.

2. Be aware this is not an emergency situation, but merely an advisory that indicates an emergency situation is possible should any undue delay occur.

3. On initial contact the term "minimum fuel" should be used after stating call sign.

EXAMPLE-
Salt Lake Approach, United 621, "minimum fuel."

4. Be aware a minimum fuel advisory does not imply a need for traffic priority.

5. If the remaining usable fuel supply suggests the need for traffic priority to ensure a safe landing, you should declare an emergency due to low fuel and report fuel remaining in minutes.

REFERENCE-
PILOT/CONTROLLER GLOSSARY ITEM – FUEL REMAINING

b. Controller:

1. When an aircraft declares a state of minimum fuel, relay this information to the facility to whom control jurisdiction is transferred.

2. Be alert for any occurrence which might delay the aircraft.

Section 6. NATIONAL SECURITY AND INTERCEPTION PROCEDURES

5-6-1. NATIONAL SECURITY

a. National security in the control of air traffic is governed by (FAR Part 99).

b. All aircraft entering domestic U.S. airspace from points outside must provide for identification prior to entry. To facilitate early aircraft identification of all aircraft in the vicinity of U.S. and international airspace boundaries, Air Defense Identification Zones (ADIZ) have been established.

REFERENCE-
AIM, ADIZ BOUNDARIES AND DESIGNATED MOUNTAINOUS AREAS, PARAGRAPH 5-6-5.

c. Operational requirements for aircraft operations associated with an ADIZ are as follows:

1. *Flight Plan:* Except as specified in subparagraphs d. and e. below, an IFR or DVFR flight plan must be filed with an appropriate aeronautical facility as follows:

(a) Generally, for all operations that enter an ADIZ.

(b) For operations that will enter or exit the United States and which will operate into, within or across the Contiguous U.S. ADIZ regardless of true airspeed.

(c) The flight plan must be filed before departure except for operations associated with the Alaskan ADIZ when the airport of departure has no facility for filing a flight plan, in which case the flight plan may be filed immediately after takeoff or when within range of the aeronautical facility.

2. *Two-way Radio:* For the majority of operations associated with an ADIZ, an operating two-way radio is required. See FAR Part 99.1 for exceptions.

3. *Transponder Requirements:* Unless otherwise authorized by ATC, each aircraft conducting operations into, within, or across the Contiguous U.S. ADIZ must be equipped with an operable radar beacon transponder having altitude reporting capability (Mode C), and that transponder must be turned on and set to reply on the appropriate code or as assigned by ATC.

4. *Position Reporting:*

(a) **For IFR flight:** Normal IFR position reporting.

(b) **For DVFR flights:** The estimated time of ADIZ penetration must be filed with the aeronautical facility at least 15 minutes prior to penetration except for flight in the Alaskan ADIZ, in which case report prior to penetration.

(c) **For inbound aircraft of foreign registry:** The pilot must report to the aeronautical facility at least one hour prior to ADIZ penetration.

5. *Aircraft Position Tolerances:*

(a) Over land, the tolerance is within plus or minus five minutes from the estimated time over a reporting point or point of penetration and within 10 NM from the centerline of an intended track over an estimated reporting point or penetration point.

(b) Over water, the tolerance is plus or minus five minutes from the estimated time over a reporting point or point of penetration and within 20 NM from the centerline of the intended track over an estimated reporting point or point of penetration (to include the Aleutian Islands).

d. Except when applicable under FAR Part 99.7, FAR Part 99 does not apply to aircraft operations:

1. Within the 48 contiguous states and the District of Columbia, or within the State of Alaska, and remains within 10 miles of the point of departure;

2. Over any island, or within three nautical miles of the coastline of any island, in the Hawaii ADIZ; or

3. Associated with any ADIZ other than the Contiguous U.S. ADIZ, when the aircraft true airspeed is less than 180 knots.

e. Authorizations to deviate from the requirements of Part 99 may also be granted by the ARTCC, on a local basis, for some operations associated with an ADIZ.

f. An Airfiled VFR Flight Plan makes an aircraft subject to interception for positive identification when entering an ADIZ. Pilots are therefore urged to file the required DVFR flight plan either in person or by telephone prior to departure.

g. Special Security Instructions:

1. During defense emergency or air defense emergency conditions, additional special security instructions may be issued in accordance with the Security Control of Air Traffic and Air Navigation Aids (SCATANA) Plan.

AIM

2. Under the provisions of the SCATANA Plan, the military will direct the action to be taken-in regard to landing, grounding, diversion, or dispersal of aircraft and the control of air navigation aids in the defense of the U.S. during emergency conditions.

3. At the time a portion or all of SCATANA is implemented, ATC facilities will broadcast appropriate instructions received from the military over available ATC frequencies. Depending on instructions received from the military, VFR flights may be directed to land at the nearest available airport, and IFR flights will be expected to proceed as directed by ATC.

4. Pilots on the ground may be required to file a flight plan and obtain an approval (through FAA) prior to conducting flight operation.

5. In view of the above, all pilots should guard an ATC or FSS frequency at all times while conducting flight operations.

5-6-2. INTERCEPTION PROCEDURES

a. General

1. Identification intercepts during peacetime operations are vastly different than those conducted under increased states of readiness. Unless otherwise directed by the control agency, intercepted aircraft will be identified by type only. When specific information is required (i.e. markings, serial numbers, etc.) the interceptor aircrew will respond only if the request can be conducted in a safe manner. During hours of darkness or Instrument Meteorological Conditions (IMC), identification of unknown aircraft will be by type only. The interception pattern described below is the typical peacetime method used by air interceptor aircrews. In all situations, the interceptor aircrew will use caution to avoid startling the intercepted aircrew and/or passengers.

b. Intercept phases (See FIG 5-6-1).

1. *Phase One– Approach Phase:*
During peacetime, intercepted aircraft will be approached from the stern. Generally two interceptor aircraft will be employed to accomplish the identification. The flight leader and wingman will coordinate their individual positions in conjunction with the ground controlling agency. Their relationship will resemble a line abreast formation. At night or in IMC, a comfortable radar trail tactic will be used. Safe vertical separation between interceptor aircraft and unknown aircraft will be maintained at all times.

2. *Phase Two– Identification Phase:*
The intercepted aircraft should expect to visually a quire the lead interceptor and possibly the wingm during this phase in visual meteorological conditio (VMC). The wingman will assume a surveillance pos tion while the flight leader approaches the unknown a craft. Intercepted aircraft personnel may observe the u of different drag devices to allow for speed and positi stabilization during this phase. The flight leader w then initiate a gentle closure toward the intercepted a craft, stopping at a distance no closer than absolute necessary to obtain the information needed. The inte ceptor aircraft will use every possible precaution avoid startling intercepted aircrew or passengers. Add tionally, the interceptor aircrews will constantly keep mind that maneuvers considered normal to a fighter a craft may be considered hazardous to passengers a crews of nonfighter aircraft. When interceptor aircre know or believe that an unsafe condition exists, th identification phase will be terminated. As previous stated, during darkness or IMC identification of u known aircraft will be by type only. Positive vertic separation will be maintained by interceptor aircra throughout this phase.

3. *Phase Three– Post Intercept Phase:*
Upon identification phase completion, the flight lead will turn away from the intercepted aircraft. The win man will remain well clear and accomplish a rejoin wi the leader.

c. Communication interface between intercept aircrews and the ground controlling agency is essenti to ensure successful intercept completion. Flight Safe is paramount. An aircraft which is intercepted b another aircraft shall immediately:

1. Follow the instructions given by the interceptin aircraft, interpreting and responding to the visual si nals.

2. Notify, if possible, the appropriate air traffic se vices unit.

3. Attempt to establish radio communication wit the intercepting aircraft or with the appropriate inte cept control unit, by making a general call on the eme gency frequency 243.0 MHz and repeating this call o the emergency frequency 121.5 MHz, if practicabl giving the identity and position of the aircraft and th nature of the flight.

INTERCEPTION PATTERNS
FOR IDENTIFICATION OF
INTERCEPTED AIRCRAFT
(TYPICAL)

APPROACH   IDENTIFICATION PHASE   POST INTERCEPT PHASE
PHASE (DAY)

TRANSPORT

INTERCEPTORS   WINGMAN

FLIGHT LEAD

Note: During Night/IMC,
approach will be from
below flight path.

FIG 5–6–1

4. If equipped with SSR transponder, select MODE 3/A Code 7700, unless otherwise instructed by the appropriate air traffic services unit. If any instructions received by radio from any sources conflict with those given by the intercepting aircraft by visual or radio signals, the intercepted aircraft shall request immediate clarification while continuing to comply with the instructions given by the intercepting aircraft.

5–6–3. LAW ENFORCEMENT OPERATIONS BY CIVIL AND MILITARY ORGANIZATIONS

a. Special law enforcement operations.

1. Special law enforcement operations include inflight identification, surveillance, interdiction, and pursuit activities performed in accordance with official civil and/or military mission responsibilities.

2. To facilitate accomplishment of these special missions, exemptions from specified sections of the FAR have been granted to designated departments and agencies. However, it is each organization's responsibility to apprise ATC of their intent to operate under an authorized exemption before initiating actual operations.

3. Additionally, some departments and agencies that perform special missions have been assigned coded identifiers to permit them to apprise ATC of ongoing mission activities and solicit special air traffic assistance.

5-6-4. INTERCEPTION SIGNALS

TBL 5-6-1 and TBL 5-6-2.

	INTERCEPTING SIGNALS Signals initiated by intercepting aircraft and responses by intercepted aircraft (as set forth in ICAO Annex 2-Appendix A, 2.1)			
Series	**INTERCEPTING Aircraft Signals**	**Meaning**	**INTERCEPTED Aircraft Responds**	**Meaning**
1	DAY–Rocking wings from a position slightly above and ahead of, and normally to the left of, the intercepted aircraft and, after acknowledgement, a slow level turn, normally to the left, on to the desired heading. NIGHT–Same and, in addition, flashing navigational lights at irregular intervals. *NOTE 1–Meteorological conditions or terrain may require the intercepting aircraft to take up a position slightly above and ahead of, and to the right of, the intercepted aircraft and to make the subsequent turn to the right.* *NOTE 2–If the intercepted aircraft is not able to keep pace with the intercepting aircraft, the latter is expected to fly a series of race-track patterns and to rock its wings each time it passes the intercepted aircraft.*	You have been intercepted. Follow me.	AEROPLANES: DAY–Rocking wings and following. NIGHT–Same and, in addition, flashing navigational lights at irregular intervals. HELICOPTERS: DAY or NIGHT–Rocking aircraft, flashing navigational lights at irregular intervals and following.	Understood, will comply.
2	DAY or NIGHT–An abrupt break-away maneuver from the intercepted aircraft consisting of a climbing turn of 90 degrees or more without crossing the line of flight of the intercepted aircraft.	You may proceed.	AEROPLANES: DAY or NIGHT–Rocking wings. HELICOPTERS: DAY or NIGHT–Rocking aircraft.	Understood, will comply.
3	DAY–Circling aerodrome, lowering landing gear and overflying runway in direction of landing or, if the intercepted aircraft is a helicopter, overflying the helicopter landing area. NIGHT–Same and, in addition, showing steady landing lights.	Land at this aerodrome.	AEROPLANES: DAY–Lowering landing gear, following the intercepting aircraft and, if after overflying the runway landing is considered safe, proceeding to land. NIGHT–Same and, in addition, showing steady landing lights (if carried). HELICOPTERS: DAY or NIGHT-Following the intercepting aircraft and proceeding to land, showing a steady landing light (if carried).	Understood, will comply.

TBL 5-6-1

INTERCEPTING SIGNALS
Signals and Responses During Aircraft Intercept
Signals initiated by intercepting aircraft and responses by intercepted aircraft
(as set forth in ICAO Annex 2-Appendix A, 2.2)

Series	INTERCEPTING Aircraft Signals	Meaning	INTERCEPTED Aircraft Responds	Meaning
4	AEROPLANES: DAY–Raising landing gear while passing over landing runway at a height exceeding 300m (1,000 ft) but not exceeding 600m (2,000 ft) above the aerodrome level, and continuing to circle the aerodrome. NIGHT–Flashing landing lights while passing over landing runway at a height exceeding 300m (1,000 ft) but not exceeding 600m (2,000 ft) above the aerodrome level, and continuing to circle the aerodrome. If unable to flash landing lights, flash any other lights available.	Aerodrome you have designated is inadequate.	DAY or NIGHT–If it is desired that the intercepted aircraft follow the intercepting aircraft to an alternate aerodrome, the intercepting aircraft raises its landing gear and uses the Series 1 signals prescribed for intercepting aircraft. If it is decided to release the intercepted aircraft, the intercepting aircraft uses the Series 2 signals prescribed for intercepting aircraft.	Understood, follow me. Understood, you may proceed.
5	AEROPLANES: DAY or NIGHT–Regular switching on and off of all available lights but in such a manner as to be distinct from flashing lights.	Cannot comply.	DAY or NIGHT-Use Series 2 signals prescribed for intercepting aircraft.	Understood.
6	AEROPLANES: DAY or NIGHT–Irregular flashing of all available lights. HELICOPTERS: DAY or NIGHT–Irregular flashing of all available lights.	In distress.	DAY or NIGHT-Use Series 2 signals prescribed for intercepting aircraft.	Understood.

TBL 5–6–2

AIM

5-6-5. ADIZ BOUNDARIES AND DESIGNATED MOUNTAINOUS AREAS

(See FIG 5-6-2.)

Air Defense Identification Zone Boundaries
Designated Mountainous Areas

FIG 5-6-2

Chapter 6. EMERGENCY PROCEDURES

Section 1. GENERAL

6-1-1. PILOT RESPONSIBILITY AND AUTHORITY

a. The pilot in command of an aircraft is directly responsible for and is the final authority as to the operation of that aircraft. In an emergency requiring immediate action, the pilot in command may deviate from any rule in the FAR, Subpart A, General, and Subpart B, Flight Rules, to the extent required to meet that emergency.

REFERENCE-
FAR PART 91.3(B).

b. If the emergency authority of FAR Part 91.3.(b) is used to deviate from the provisions of an ATC clearance, the pilot in command must notify ATC as soon as possible and obtain an amended clearance.

c. Unless deviation is necessary under the emergency authority of FAR Part 91.3, pilots of IFR flights experiencing two-way radio communications failure are expected to adhere to the procedures prescribed under "IFR operations, two-way radio communications failure."

REFERENCE-
FAR PART 91.185.

6-1-2. EMERGENCY CONDITION- REQUEST ASSISTANCE IMMEDIATELY

a. An emergency can be either a *distress* or *urgency* condition as defined in the *Pilot/Controller Glossary*. Pilots do not hesitate to declare an emergency when they are faced with *distress* conditions such as fire, mechanical failure, or structural damage. However, some are reluctant to report an *urgency* condition when they encounter situations which may not be immediately perilous, but are potentially catastrophic. An aircraft is in at least an *urgency* condition the moment the pilot becomes doubtful about position, fuel endurance, weather, or any other condition that could adversely affect flight safety. This is the time to ask for help, not after the situation has developed into a *distress* condition.

b. Pilots who become apprehensive for their safety for any reason should *request assistance immediately.* Ready and willing help is available in the form of radio, radar, direction finding stations and other aircraft. Delay has caused accidents and cost lives. *Safety is not a luxury! Take action!*

Section 2. EMERGENCY SERVICES AVAILABLE TO PILOTS

6-2-1. RADAR SERVICE FOR VFR AIRCRAFT IN DIFFICULTY

a. Radar equipped ATC facilities can provide radar assistance and navigation service (vectors) to VFR aircraft in difficulty when the pilot can talk with the controller, and the aircraft is within radar coverage. Pilots should clearly understand that authorization to proceed in accordance with such radar navigational assistance does not constitute authorization for the pilot to violate FARs. In effect, assistance is provided on the basis that navigational guidance information is advisory in nature, and the responsibility for flying the aircraft safely remains with the pilot.

b. Experience has shown that many pilots who are not qualified for instrument flight cannot maintain control of their aircraft when they encounter clouds or other reduced visibility conditions. In many cases, the controller will not know whether flight into instrument conditions will result from ATC instructions. To avoid possible hazards resulting from being vectored into IFR conditions, a pilot in difficulty should keep the controller advised of the current weather conditions being encountered and the weather along the course ahead and observe the following:

1. If a course of action is available which will permit flight and a safe landing in VFR weather conditions, noninstrument rated pilots should choose the VFR condition rather than requesting a vector or approach that will take them into IFR weather conditions; or

2. If continued flight in VFR conditions is not possible, the noninstrument rated pilot should so advise the controller and indicating the lack of an instrument rating, declare a *distress* condition, or

3. If the pilot is instrument rated and current, and the aircraft is instrument equipped, the pilot should so indicate by requesting an IFR flight clearance. Assistance will then be provided on the basis that the aircraft can operate safely in IFR weather conditions.

6-2-2. TRANSPONDER EMERGENCY OPERATION

a. When a *distress* or *urgency* condition is encountered, the pilot of an aircraft with a coded radar beacon transponder, who desires to alert a ground radar facility, should squawk MODE 3/A, Code 7700/Emergency and MODE C altitude reporting and then immediately establish communications with the ATC facility.

b. Radar facilities are equipped so that Code 7700 normally triggers an alarm or special indicator at all control positions. Pilots should understand that they might not be within a radar coverage area. Therefore, they should continue squawking Code 7700 and establish radio communications as soon as possible.

6-2-3. DIRECTION FINDING INSTRUMENT APPROACH PROCEDURE

a. Direction Finder (DF) equipment has long been used to locate lost aircraft and to guide aircraft to areas of good weather or to airports. Now at most DF equipped airports, DF instrument approaches may be given to aircraft in a *distress* or *urgency* condition.

b. Experience has shown that most emergencies requiring DF assistance involve pilots with little flight experience. With this in mind, DF approach procedures provide maximum flight stability in the approach by using small turns, and wings-level descents. The DF specialist will give the pilot headings to fly and tell the pilot when to begin descent.

c. DF IAP's are for emergency use only and will not be used in IFR weather conditions unless the pilot has declared a *distress* or *urgency* condition.

d. To become familiar with the procedures and other benefits of DF, pilots are urged to request practice DF guidance and approaches in VFR weather conditions. DF specialists welcome the practice and will honor such requests, workload permitting.

6-2-4. INTERCEPT AND ESCORT

a. The concept of airborne intercept and escort is based on the Search and Rescue (SAR) aircraft establishing visual and/or electronic contact with an aircraft in difficulty, providing in-flight assistance, and escorting it to a safe landing. If bailout, crash landing or ditching becomes necessary, SAR operations can be conducted without delay. For most incidents, particularly those occurring at night and/or during instrument flight conditions, the availability of intercept and escort services will depend on the proximity of SAR units with suitable aircraft on alert for immediate dispatch. In limited circumstances, other aircraft flying in the vicinity of an aircraft in difficulty can provide these services.

b. If specifically requested by a pilot in difficulty or if a *distress* condition is declared, SAR coordinators *will* take steps to intercept and escort an aircraft. Steps may be initiated for intercept and escort if an *urgency* condition is declared and unusual circumstances make such action advisable.

c. It is the pilot's prerogative to refuse intercept and escort services. Escort services will normally be provided to the nearest adequate airport. Should the pilot receiving escort services continue onto another location after reaching a safe airport, or decide not to divert to the nearest safe airport, the escort aircraft is not obligated to continue and further escort is discretionary. The decision will depend on the circumstances of the individual incident.

6-2-5. EMERGENCY LOCATOR TRANSMITTERS

a. General:

1. Emergency Locator Transmitters (ELT) are required for most General Aviation airplanes.

REFERENCE–
FAR PART 91.207.

2. ELT's of various types have been developed as a means of locating downed aircraft. These electronic, battery operated transmitters emit a distinctive downward swept audio tone on 121.5 MHz and 243.0 MHz. If "armed" and when subject to crash generated forces they are designed to automatically activate and continuously emit these signals. The transmitters will operate continuously for at least 48 hours over a wide temperature range. A properly installed and maintained ELT can expedite search and rescue operations and save lives.

b. Testing:

1. ELT's should be tested in accordance with the manufacturer's instructions, preferably in a shielded or screened room to prevent the broadcast of signals which could trigger a false alert.

2. When this cannot be done, aircraft operational testing is authorized on 121.5 MHz and 243.0 MHz as follows:

(a) Tests should be conducted only during the first 5 minutes after any hour. If operational tests must be made outside of this time-frame, they should be coordinated with the nearest FAA Control Tower or FSS.

(b) Tests should be no longer than three audible sweeps.

(c) If the antenna is removable, a dummy loa should be substituted during test procedures.

(d) Airborne tests are not authorized.

c. False Alarms:

1. Caution should be exercised to prevent the inac vertent activation of ELT's in the air or while they a being handled on the ground. Accidental or unautho rized activation will generate an emergency signal th cannot be distinguished from the real thing, leading t expensive and frustrating searches. A false ELT signa could also interfere with genuine emergency transmi sions and hinder or prevent the timely location of cras sites. Frequent false alarms could also result in compla cency and decrease the vigorous reaction that must b attached to all ELT signals.

2. Numerous cases of inadvertent activation hav occurred as a result of aerobatics, hard landings, move ment by ground crews and aircraft maintenance. Thes false alarms can be minimized by monitoring 121.. MHz and/or 243.0 MHz as follows:

(a) In flight when a receiver is available.

(b) Prior to engine shut down at the end of eac flight.

(c) When the ELT is handled during installatio or maintenance.

(d) When maintenance is being performed in th vicinity of the ELT.

(e) When the aircraft is moved by a ground crew

(f) If an ELT signal is heard, turn off the ELT t determine if it is transmitting. If it has been activated maintenance might be required before the unit is re turned to the "ARMED" position.

d. In-flight Monitoring And Reporting:

1. Pilots are encouraged to monitor 121.5 MHz and/or 243.0 MHz while in-flight to assist in identifying possible emergency ELT transmissions. On receiving a signal, report the following information to the neares air traffic facility:

(a) Your position at the time the signal was first heard.

(b) Your position at the time the signal was last heard.

(c) Your position at maximum signal strength.

(d) Your flight altitudes and frequency on which the emergency signal was heard–121.5 MHz or 243.0

MHz. If possible, positions should be given relative to a navigation aid. If the aircraft has homing equipment, provide the bearing to the emergency signal with each reported position.

6-2-6. FAA K-9 EXPLOSIVES DETECTION TEAM PROGRAM

a. The FAA's Office of Civil Aviation Security Operations manages the FAA K-9 Explosives Detection Team Program which was established in 1972. Through a unique agreement with law enforcement agencies and airport authorities, the FAA has strategically placed FAA-certified K-9 teams (a team is one handler and one dog) at airports throughout the country. If a bomb threat is received while an aircraft is in flight, the aircraft can be directed to an airport with this capability.

The FAA provides initial and refresher training for all handlers, provides single purpose explosive detector dogs, and requires that each team is annually evaluated in five areas for FAA certification: aircraft (widebody and narrowbody), vehicles, terminal, freight (cargo), and luggage. **If you desire this service, notify your company or an FAA air traffic control facility.**

b. The following list shows the locations of current FAA K-9 teams:

FAA Sponsored Explosives Detection Dog/Handler Team Locations

AIRPORT SYMBOL	LOCATION
ATL	Atlanta, Georgia
BHM	Birmingham, Alabama
BOS	Boston, Massachusetts
BUF	Buffalo, New York
CLT	Charlotte, North Carolina
ORD	Chicago, Illinois
CVG	Cincinnati, Ohio
DFW	Dallas, Texas
DEN	Denver, Colorado
DTW	Detroit, Michigan
IAH	Houston, Texas
JAX	Jacksonville, Florida
MCI	Kansas City, Missouri
LAX	Los Angeles, California
MEM	Memphis, Tennessee
MIA	Miami, Florida
MKE	Milwaukee, Wisconsin
MSY	New Orleans, Louisiana
MCO	Orlando, Florida
PHX	Phoenix, Arizona
PIT	Pittsburgh, Pennsylvania
PDX	Portland, Oregon
SLC	Salt Lake City, Utah
SFO	San Francisco, California
SJU	San Juan, Puerto Rico
SEA	Seattle, Washington
STL	St. Louis, Missouri
TUS	Tucson, Arizona
TUL	Tulsa, Oklahoma

TBL 6-2-1

c. If due to weather or other considerations an aircraft with a suspected hidden explosive problem were to land or intended to land at an airport other than those listed in b. above, it is recommended that they call the FAA's Washington Operations Center (telephone 202-267-3333, if appropriate) or have an air traffic facility with which you can communicate contact the above center requesting assistance.

6-2-7. SEARCH AND RESCUE

a. General: SAR is a lifesaving service provided through the combined efforts of the federal agencies signatory to the National SAR Plan, and the agencies responsible for SAR within each state. Operational resources are provided by the U.S. Coast Guard, DOD components, the Civil Air Patrol, the Coast Guard Auxiliary, state, county and local law enforcement and other public safety agencies, and private volunteer organizations. Services include search for missing aircraft, survival aid, rescue, and emergency medical help for the occupants after an accident site is located.

b. National Search and Rescue Plan: By federal interagency agreement, the National Search and Rescue Plan provides for the effective use of all available facilities in all types of SAR missions. These facilities include aircraft, vessels, pararescue and ground rescue teams, and emergency radio fixing. Under the Plan, the U.S. Coast Guard is responsible for the coordination of SAR in the Maritime Region, and the USAF is responsible in the Inland Region. To carry out these responsibilities, the Coast Guard and the Air Force have established Rescue Coordination Centers (RCC's) to direct SAR activities within their regions. For aircraft emergencies, distress, and urgency, information normally will be passed to the appropriate RCC through an ARTCC or FSS.

c. Coast Guard Rescue Coordination Centers. (See TBL 6-2-2.)

Coast Guard Rescue Coordination Centers	
Boston, MA 617-223-8555	Long Beach, CA 213-590-2225 310-499-5380
New York, NY 212-668-7055	San Francisco, CA 415-437-3700
Portsmouth, VA 804-398-6231	Seattle, WA 206-553-5886
Miami, FL 305-536-5611	Juneau, AK 907-463-2000
New Orleans, LA 504-589-6225	Honolulu, HI 808-541-2500
Cleveland, OH 216-522-3984	San Juan, Puerto Rico 809-729-6770
St. Louis, MO 314-262-3706	

TBL 6-2-2

d. Air Force Rescue Coordination Centers. (See TBL 6-2-3 and TBL 6-2-4.)

Air Force Rescue Coordination Center 48 Contiguous States

Air Force Rescue Coordination Center	
Langley AFB, Virginia	*Phone*
Commercial	804-764-8112
WATS	800-851-3051
DSN	574-8112

TBL 6-2-3

Air Command Rescue Coordination Center Alaska

Alaskan Air Command Rescue Coordination Center	
Elmendorf AFB, Alaska	*Phone*
Commercial	907-552-5375
DSN	317-552-2426

TBL 6-2-4

e. Joint Rescue Coordination Center. (See TBL 6-2-5.)

Joint Rescue Coordination Center Hawaii

Honolulu Joint Rescue Coordination Center	
HQ 14th CG District Honolulu	*Phone*
Commercial	808-541-2500
DSN	448-0301

TBL 6-2-5

f. Emergency and Overdue Aircraft:

1. ARTCC's and FSS's will alert the SAR system when information is received from any source that an aircraft is in difficulty, overdue, or missing.

(a) Radar facilities providing radar flight following or advisories consider the loss of radar and radios, without service termination notice, to be a possible emergency. Pilots receiving VFR services from radar facilities should be aware that SAR may be initiated under these circumstances.

(b) A filed flight plan is the most timely and effective indicator that an aircraft is overdue. Flight plan information is invaluable to SAR forces for search planning and executing search efforts.

2. Prior to departure on every flight, local or otherwise, someone at the departure point should be advised of your destination and route of flight if other than direct. Search efforts are often wasted and rescue is often delayed because of pilots who thoughtlessly takeoff without telling anyone where they are going. File a flight plan for *your* safety.

3. According to the National Search and Rescue Plan, "The life expectancy of an injured survivor decreases as much as 80 percent during the first 24 hours, while the chances of survival of uninjured survivors rapidly diminishes after the first 3 days."

4. An Air Force Review of 325 SAR missions conducted during a 23–month period revealed that "Time works against people who experience a *distress* but are not on a flight plan, since 36 hours normally pass before family concern initiates an (alert)."

g. VFR Search and Rescue Protection:

1. To receive this valuable protection, *file a VFR or DVFR Flight Plan* with an FAA FSS. For maximum protection, file only to the point of first intended landing, and refile for each leg to final destination. When a lengthy flight plan is filed, with several stops en route and an ETE to final destination, a mishap could occur on any leg, and unless other information is received, it is probable that no one would start looking for you until 30 minutes after your ETA at your final destination.

2. If you land at a location other than the intended destination, report the landing to the nearest FAA FSS and advise them of your original destination.

3. If you land en route and are delayed more than 30 minutes, report this information to the nearest FSS and give them your original destination.

4. If your ETE changes by 30 minutes or more, report a new ETA to the nearest FSS and give them your original destination. Remember that if you fail to respond within one-half hour after your ETA at final destination, a search will be started to locate you.

5. It is important that you *close your flight plan IMMEDIATELY AFTER ARRIVAL AT YOUR FINAL DESTINATION WITH THE FSS DESIGNATED WHEN YOUR FLIGHT PLAN WAS FILED. The pilot is responsible for closure of a VFR or DVFR flight plan; they are not closed automatically.* This will prevent needless search efforts.

6. The rapidity of rescue on land or water will depend on how accurately your position may be deter-

mined. If a flight plan has been followed and your position is on course, rescue will be expedited.

h. Survival Equipment:

1. For flight over uninhabited land areas, it is wise to take and know how to use survival equipment for the type of climate and terrain.

2. If a forced landing occurs at sea, chances for survival are governed by the degree of crew proficiency in emergency procedures and by the availability and effectiveness of water survival equipment.

i. Body Signal Illustrations:

1. If you are forced down and are able to attract the attention of the pilot of a rescue airplane, the body signals illustrated on these pages can be used to transmit messages to the pilot circling over your location.

2. Stand in the open when you make the signals.

3. Be sure the background, as seen from the air, is not confusing.

4. Go through the motions slowly and repeat each signal until you are positive that the pilot understands you.

j. Observance of Downed Aircraft:

1. Determine if crash is marked with a yellow cross; if so, the crash has already been reported and identified.

2. If possible, determine type and number of aircraft and whether there is evidence of survivors.

3. Fix the position of the crash as accurately as possible with reference to a navigational aid. If possible, provide geographic or physical description of the area to aid ground search parties.

4. Transmit the information to the nearest FAA or other appropriate radio facility.

5. If circumstances permit, orbit the scene to guide in other assisting units until their arrival or until you are relieved by another aircraft.

6. Immediately after landing, make a complete report to the nearest FAA facility, or Air Force or Coast Guard Rescue Coordination Center. The report can be made by a long distance collect telephone call.

Ground–Air Visual Code for Use by Survivors

NO.	MESSAGE	CODE SYMBOL
1	Require assistance	V
2	Require medical assistance	X
3	No or Negative	N
4	Yes or Affirmative	Y
5	Proceeding in this direction	↑

IF IN DOUBT, USE INTERNATIONAL SYMBOL   S O S

INSTRUCTIONS

1. Lay out symbols by using strips of fabric or parachutes, pieces of wood, stones, or any available material.
2. Provide as much color contrast as possible between material used for symbols and background against which symbols are exposed.
3. Symbols should be at least 10 feet high or larger. Care should be taken to lay out symbols exactly as shown.
4. In addition to using symbols, every effort is to be made to attract attention by means of radio, flares, smoke, or other available means.
5. On snow covered ground, signals can be made by dragging, shoveling or tramping. Depressed areas forming symbols will appear black from the air.
6. Pilot should acknowledge message by rocking wings from side to side.

FIG 6–2–

Ground–Air Visual Code for use by Ground Search Parties

NO.	MESSAGE	CODE SYMBOL
1	Operation completed.	L L L
2	We have found all personnel.	L L
3	We have found only some personnel.	╫
4	We are not able to continue. Returning to base.	X X
5	Have divided into two groups. Each proceeding in direction indicated.	⚡
6	Information received that aircraft is in this direction.	➝ ➝
7	Nothing found. Will continue search.	N N

Note: These visual signals have been accepted for international use and appear in Annex 12 to the Convention on International Civil Aviation.

FIG 6–2–

Urgent Medical Assistance

FIG 6–2–3

Short Delay

FIG 6–2–5

All OK

FIG 6–2–4

Long Delay

FIG 6–2–6

Drop Message

Make throwing motion

FIG 6–2–7

Do Not Land Here

DO NOT ATTEMPT
TO LAND HERE
Both arms waved across face

FIG 6–2–9

Receiver Operates

OUR RECEIVER IS
OPERATING
Cup hands over ears

FIG 6–2–8

Land Here

LAND HERE

Both arms forward horizontally,
squatting and point in direction
of landing - Repeat

FIG 6–2–10

Negative (Ground)

NEGATIVE (NO)

White cloth waved horizontally

FIG 6–2–11

Pick Us Up

PICK US UP-
PLANE ABANDONED
Both arms vertical

FIG 6–2–13

Affirmative (Ground)

AFFIRMATIVE (YES)

White cloth waved vertically

FIG 6–2–12

Affirmative (Aircraft)

Affirmative reply from aircraft:

AFFIRMATIVE (YES)

Dip nose of plane several times

FIG 6–2–14

Negative (Aircraft)

Negative reply from aircraft:

NEGATIVE (NO)

Fishtail plane

FIG 6–2–15

Message received and understood (Aircraft)

Message received and understood by aircraft:
Day or moonlight - Rocking wings
Night - Green flashed from signal lamp

FIG 6–2–16

Message received and NOT understood (Aircraft)

Message received and NOT understood by aircraft:
Day or moonlight - Making a complete right-hand circle
Night-Red flashes from signal lamp.

FIG 6–2–17

Section 3. DISTRESS AND URGENCY PROCEDURES

6-3-1. DISTRESS AND URGENCY COMMUNICATIONS

a. A pilot who encounters a *distress* or *urgency* condition can obtain assistance simply by contacting the air traffic facility or other agency in whose area of responsibility the aircraft is operating, stating the nature of the difficulty, pilot's intentions and assistance desired. *Distress* and *urgency* communications procedures are prescribed by the International Civil Aviation Organization (ICAO), however, and have decided advantages over the informal procedure described above.

b. *Distress* and *urgency* communications procedures discussed in the following paragraphs relate to the use of air ground voice communications.

c. The initial communication, and if considered necessary, any subsequent transmissions by an aircraft in *distress* should begin with the signal MAYDAY, preferably repeated three times. The signal PAN–PAN should be used in the same manner for an *urgency* condition.

d. *Distress* communications have absolute priority over all other communications, and the word MAYDAY commands radio silence on the frequency in use. *Urgency* communications have priority over all other communications except *distress,* and the word PAN–PAN warns other stations not to interfere with *urgency* transmissions.

e. Normally, the station addressed will be the air traffic facility or other agency providing air traffic services, on the frequency in use at the time. If the pilot is not communicating and receiving services, the station to be called will normally be the air traffic facility or other agency in whose area of responsibility the aircraft is operating, on the appropriate assigned frequency. If the station addressed does not respond, or if time or the situation dictates, the *distress* or *urgency* message may be broadcast, or a collect call may be used, addressing "Any Station (Tower)(Radio)(Radar)."

f. The station addressed should immediately acknowledge a *distress* or *urgency* message, provide assistance, coordinate and direct the activities of assisting facilities, and alert the appropriate search and rescue coordinator if warranted. Responsibility will be transferred to another station only if better handling will result.

g. All other stations, aircraft and ground, will continue to listen until it is evident that assistance is being provided. If any station becomes aware that the station being called either has not received a *distress* or *urgency* message, or cannot communicate with the aircraft in difficulty, it will attempt to contact the aircraft and provide assistance.

h. Although the frequency in use or other frequencies assigned by ATC are preferable, the following emergency frequencies can be used for distress or urgency communications, if necessary or desirable:

1. *121.5 MHz and 243.0 MHz:* Both have a range generally limited to line of sight. 121.5 MHz is guarded by direction finding stations and some military and civil aircraft. 243.0 MHz is guarded by military aircraft. Both 121.5 MHz and 243.0 MHz are guarded by military towers, most civil towers, FSS's, and radar facilities. Normally ARTCC emergency frequency capability does not extend to radar coverage limits. If an ARTCC does not respond when called on 121.5 MHz or 243.0 MHz, call the nearest tower or FSS.

2. *2182 kHz:* The range is generally less than 300 miles for the average aircraft installation. It can be used to request assistance from stations in the maritime service. 2182 kHz is guarded by major radio stations serving Coast Guard Rescue Coordination Centers, and Coast Guard units along the sea coasts of the U.S. and shores of the Great Lakes. The call "Coast Guard" will alert all Coast Guard Radio Stations within range. 2182 kHz is also guarded by most commercial coast stations and some ships and boats.

6-3-2. OBTAINING EMERGENCY ASSISTANCE

a. A pilot in any *distress* or *urgency* condition should *immediately* take the following action, not necessarily in the order listed, to obtain assistance:

1. Climb, if possible, for improved communications, and better radar and direction finding detection. However, it must be understood that unauthorized climb or descent under IFR conditions within controlled airspace is prohibited, except as permitted by FAR Part 91.3(b).

2. If equipped with a radar beacon transponder (civil) or IFF/SIF (military):

(a) Continue squawking assigned MODE A/3 discrete code/VFR code and MODE C altitude encoding when in radio contact with an air traffic facility or other agency providing air traffic services, unless instructed to do otherwise.

(b) If unable to immediately establish communications with an air traffic facility/agency, squawk MODE A/3, Code 7700/Emergency and MODE C.

3. Transmit a *distress* or *urgency* message consisting of *as many* as necessary of the following elements, preferably in the order listed:

(a) If distress, MAYDAY, MAYDAY, MAYDAY; if *urgency*, PAN–PAN, PAN–PAN, PAN–PAN.

(b) Name of station addressed.

(c) Aircraft identification and type.

(d) Nature of *distress* or *urgency*.

(e) Weather.

(f) Pilots intentions and request.

(g) Present position, and heading; or if *lost*, last known position, time, and heading since that position.

(h) Altitude or flight level.

(i) Fuel remaining in minutes.

(j) Number of people on board.

(k) Any other useful information.

REFERENCE–
PILOT/CONTROLLER GLOSSARY TERM–FUEL REMAINING.

b. After establishing radio contact, comply with advice and instructions received. Cooperate. Do not hesitate to ask questions or clarify instructions when you do not understand or if you cannot comply with clearance. Assist the ground station to control communications on the frequency in use. Silence interfering radio stations. Do not change frequency or change to another ground station unless absolutely necessary. If you do, advise the ground station of the new frequency and station name prior to the change, transmitting in the blind if necessary. If two-way communications cannot be established on the new frequency, return immediately to the frequency or station where two-way communications last existed.

c. When in a distress condition with bailout, crash landing or ditching imminent, take the following additional actions to assist search and rescue units:

1. Time and circumstances permitting, transmit as many as necessary of the message elements in subparagraph a. 3. above, and any of the following that you think might be helpful:

(a) ELT status.

(b) Visible landmarks.

(c) Aircraft color.

(d) Number of persons on board.

(e) Emergency equipment on board.

2. Actuate your ELT if the installation permits.

3. For bailout, and for crash landing or ditching if risk of fire is not a consideration, set your radio for continuous transmission.

4. If it becomes necessary to ditch, make every effort to ditch near a surface vessel. If time permits, an FAA facility should be able to get the position of the nearest commercial or Coast Guard vessel from a Coast Guard Rescue Coordination Center.

5. After a crash landing, unless you have good reason to believe that you will not be located by search aircraft or ground teams, it is best to remain with your aircraft and prepare means for signaling search aircraft.

6-3-3. DITCHING PROCEDURES

Single Swell (15 knot wind)

FIG 6-3-1

Double Swell (30 knot wind)

FIG 6-3-3

Double Swell (15 knot wind)

FIG 6-3-2

(50 knot wind)

Aircraft with low landing speeds - land into the wind.

Aircraft with high landing speeds - choose compromise heading between wind and swell.

Both - land on back side of swell.

FIG 6-3-4

Wind–Swell–Ditch Heading

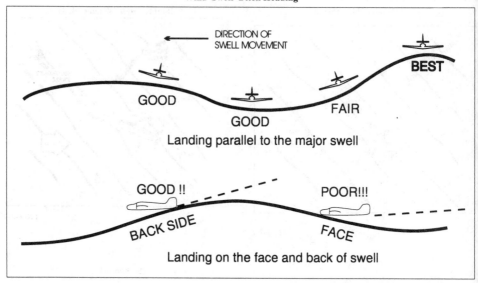

FIG 6–3–5

a. A successful aircraft ditching is dependent on three primary factors. In order of importance they are:

1. *Sea conditions and wind.*

2. *Type of aircraft.*

3. *Skill and technique of pilot.*

b. Common oceanographic terminology:

1. *Sea.* The condition of the surface that is the result of both waves and swells.

2. *Wave (or Chop).* The condition of the surface caused by the local winds.

3. *Swell.* The condition of the surface which has been caused by a distance disturbance.

4. *Swell Face.* The side of the swell toward the observer. The backside is the side away from the observer. These definitions apply regardless of the direction of swell movement.

5. *Primary Swell.* The swell system having the greatest height from trough to crest.

6. *Secondary Swells.* Those swell systems of less height than the primary swell.

7. *Fetch.* The distance the waves have been driven by a wind blowing in a constant direction, without obstruction.

8. *Swell Period.* The time interval between the passage of two successive crests at the same spot in the water, measured in seconds.

9. *Swell Velocity.* The speed and direction of the swell with relation to a fixed reference point, measured in knots. There is little movement of water in the horizontal direction. Swells move primarily in a vertical motion, similar to the motion observed when shaking out a carpet.

10. *Swell Direction.* The direction *from* which a swell is moving. This direction is not necessarily the result of the wind present at the scene. The swell may be moving into or across the local wind. Swells, once set in motion, tend to maintain their original direction for as long as they continue in deep water, regardless of changes in wind direction.

11. *Swell Height.* The height between crest and trough, measured in feet. The vast majority of ocean swells are lower than 12 to 15 feet, and swells over 25 feet are not common at any spot on the oceans. Successive swells may differ considerably in height.

c. In order to select a good heading when ditching an aircraft, a basic evaluation of the sea is required. Selection of a good ditching heading may well minimize damage and could save your life. It can be extremely dangerous to land into the wind without regard to sea conditions; the swell system, or systems, must be taken into consideration. Remember one axiom– *AVOID THE FACE OF A SWELL.*

1. In ditching parallel to the swell, it makes little difference whether touchdown is on the top of the crest or in the trough. It is preferable, however, to land on the top or back side of the swell, if possible. After determining which heading (and its reciprocal) will parallel the swell, select the heading with the most into the wind component.

2. If only one swell system exists, the problem is relatively simple–even with a high, fast system. Unfortunately, most cases involve two or more swell systems running in different directions. With more than one system present, the sea presents a confused appearance. One of the most difficult situations occurs when two swell systems are at right angles. For example, if one system is eight feet high, and the other three feet, plan to land parallel to the primary system, and on the down swell of the secondary system. If both systems are of equal height, a compromise may be advisable–select an intermediate heading at 45 degrees down swell to both systems. When landing down a secondary swell, attempt to touch down on the back side, not on the face of the swell.

3. If the swell system is formidable, it is considered advisable, in landplanes, to accept more crosswind in order to avoid landing directly into the swell.

4. The secondary swell system is often from the same direction as the wind. Here, the landing may be made parallel to the primary system, with the wind and secondary system at an angle. There is a choice to two directions paralleling the primary system. One direction is downwind and down the secondary swell, and the other is into the wind and into the secondary swell, the choice will depend on the velocity of the wind versus the velocity and height of the secondary swell.

d. The simplest method of estimating the wind direction and velocity is to examine the windstreaks on the water. These appear as long streaks up and down wind. Some persons may have difficulty determining wind direction after seeing the streaks on the water. Whitecaps fall forward with the wind but are overrun by the waves thus producing the illusion that the foam is

sliding backward. Knowing this, and by observing the direction of the streaks, the wind direction is easily determined. Wind velocity can be estimated by noting the appearance of the whitecaps, foam and wind streaks.

1. The behavior of the aircraft on making contact with the water will vary within wide limits according to the state of the sea. If landed parallel to a single swell system, the behavior of the aircraft may approximate that to be expected on a smooth sea. If landed into a heavy swell or into a confused sea, the deceleration forces may be extremely great–resulting in breaking up of the aircraft. Within certain limits, the pilot is able to minimize these forces by proper sea evaluation and selection of ditching heading.

2. When on final approach the pilot should look ahead and observe the surface of the sea. There may be shadows and whitecaps–signs of large seas. Shadows and whitecaps close together indicate short and rough seas. Touchdown in these areas is to be avoided. Select and touchdown in any area (only about 500 feet is needed) where the shadows and whitecaps are not so numerous.

3. Touchdown should be at the *lowest* speed and rate of descent which permit safe handling and optimum nose up attitude on impact. Once first impact has been made, there is often little the pilot can do to control a landplane.

e. Once preditching preparations are completed, the pilot should turn to the ditching heading and commence let-down. The aircraft should be flown low over the water, and slowed down until ten knots or so above stall. At this point, additional power should be used to overcome the increased drag caused by the nose up attitude. When a smooth stretch of water appears ahead, cut power, and touchdown at the best recommended speed as fully stalled as possible. By cutting power when approaching a relatively smooth area, the pilot will prevent overshooting and will touchdown with less chance of planing off into a second uncontrolled landing. Most experienced seaplane pilots prefer to make contact with the water in a semi-stalled attitude, cutting power as the tail makes contact. This technique eliminates the chance of misjudging altitude with a resultant heavy drop in a fully stalled condition. Care must be taken not to drop the aircraft from too high altitude or to balloon due to excessive speed. The altitude above water depends on the aircraft. Over glassy smooth water, or at night without sufficient light, it is very easy, for even the most experienced pilots to misjudge altitude by 50 feet or more. Under such conditions, carry enough power to maintain nine to twelve degrees nose up attitude, and 10 to 20 percent over stalling speed until contact is made with the water. The proper use of power on the approach is of great importance. If power is available on one side only, a little power should be used to flatten the approach; however, the engine should not be used to such an extent that the aircraft cannot be turned against the good engines right down to the stall with a margin of rudder movement available. When near the stall, sudden application of excessive unbalanced power may result in loss of directional control. If power is available on one side only, a slightly higher than normal glide approach speed should be used. This will insure good control and some margin of speed after leveling off without excessive use of power. The use of power in ditching is so important that when it is certain that the coast cannot be reached, the pilot should, if possible, ditch before fuel is exhausted. The use of power in a night or instrument ditching is far more essential than under daylight contact conditions.

1. If no power is available, a greater than normal approach speed should be used down to the flare-out. This speed margin will allow the glide to be broken early and more gradually, thereby giving the pilot time and distance to feel for the surface– decreasing the possibility of stalling high or flying into the water. When landing parallel to a swell system, little difference is noted between landing on top of a crest or in the trough. If the wings of aircraft are trimmed to the surface of the sea rather than the horizon, there is little need to worry about a wing hitting a swell crest. The actual slope of a swell is very gradual. If forced to land into a swell, touchdown should be made just after passage of the crest. If contact is made on the face of the swell, the aircraft may be swamped or thrown violently into the air, dropping heavily into the next swell. If control surfaces remain intact, the pilot should attempt to maintain the proper nose above the horizon attitude by rapid and positive use of the controls.

f. After Touchdown: In most cases drift, caused by crosswind can be ignored; the forces acting on the aircraft after touchdown are of such magnitude that drift will be only a secondary consideration. If the aircraft is under good control, the "crab" may be kicked out with rudder just prior to touchdown. This is more important with high wing aircraft, for they are laterally unstable on the water in a crosswind and may roll to the side in ditching.

REFERENCE–
THIS INFORMATION HAS BEEN EXTRACTED FROM APPENDIX H OF THE "NATIONAL SEARCH AND RESCUE MANUAL."

6–3–4. SPECIAL EMERGENCY (AIR PIRACY)

a. A special emergency is a condition of air piracy, or other hostile act by a person(s) aboard an aircraft, which threatens the safety of the aircraft or its passengers.

b. The pilot of an aircraft reporting a special emergency condition should:

1. If circumstances permit, apply *distress* or *urgency* radio-telephony procedures. Include the details of the special emergency.

REFERENCE–
AIM, DISTRESS AND URGENCY COMMUNICATIONS, PARAGRAPH 6–3–1.

2. If circumstances do not permit the use of prescribed *distress* or *urgency* procedures, transmit:

(a) On the air/ground frequency in use at the time.

(b) As many as possible of the following elements spoken distinctly and in the following order:

(1) Name of the station addressed (time and circumstances permitting).

(2) The identification of the aircraft and present position.

(3) The nature of the special emergency condition and pilot intentions (circumstances permitting).

(4) If unable to provide this information, use code words and/or transponder as follows: state "TRANSPONDER SEVEN FIVE ZERO ZERO." Meaning: "I am being hijacked/forced to a new destination;" and/or use Transponder Setting MODE 3/A, Code 7500.

NOTE–
Code 7500 will never be assigned by ATC without prior notification from the pilot that the aircraft is being subjected to unlawful interference. The pilot should refuse the assignment of Code 7500 in any other situation and inform the controller accordingly. Code 7500 will trigger the special emergency indicator in all radar ATC facilities.

c. Air traffic controllers will acknowledge and confirm receipt of transponder Code 7500 by asking the pilot to verify it. If the aircraft is not being subjected to unlawful interference, the pilot should respond to the query by broadcasting in the clear that the aircraft is not being subjected to unlawful interference. Upon receipt of this information, the controller will request the pilot to verify the code selection depicted in the code selector windows in the transponder control panel and change the code to the appropriate setting. If the pilot replies in the affirmative or does not reply, the controller will not ask further questions but will flight follow, respond to pilot requests and notify appropriate authorities.

d. If it is possible to do so without jeopardizing the safety of the flight, the pilot of a hijacked passenger aircraft, after departing from the cleared routing over which the aircraft was operating, will attempt to do one or more of the following things, insofar as circumstances may permit:

1. Maintain a true airspeed of no more than 400 knots, and preferably an altitude of between 10,000 and 25,000 feet.

2. Fly a course toward the destination which the hijacker has announced.

e. If these procedures result in either radio contact or air intercept, the pilot will attempt to comply with any instructions received which may direct the aircraft to an appropriate landing field.

6-3-5. FUEL DUMPING

a. Should it become necessary to dump fuel, the pilot should immediately advise ATC. Upon receipt of information that an aircraft will dump fuel, ATC will broadcast or cause to be broadcast immediately and every 3 minutes thereafter the following on appropriate ATC and FSS radio frequencies:

EXAMPLE-
Attention all aircraft—fuel dumping in progress over—(location) at (altitude) by (type aircraft) (flight direction).

b. Upon receipt of such a broadcast, pilots of aircraft affected, which are not on IFR flight plans or special VFR clearances, should clear the area specified in the advisory. Aircraft on IFR flight plans or special VFR clearances will be provided specific separation by ATC. At the termination of the fuel dumping operation, pilots should advise ATC. Upon receipt of such information, ATC will issue, on the appropriate frequencies, the following:

EXAMPLE-
ATTENTION ALL AIRCRAFT—FUEL DUMPING BY—(type aircraft)—TERMINATED.

Section 4. TWO-WAY RADIO COMMUNICATIONS FAILURE

5-4-1. TWO-WAY RADIO COMMUNICATIONS FAILURE

a. It is virtually impossible to provide regulations and procedures applicable to all possible situations associated with two-way radio communications failure. During two-way radio communications failure, when confronted by a situation not covered in the regulation, pilots are expected to exercise good judgment in whatever action they elect to take. Should the situation so dictate they should not be reluctant to use the emergency action contained in 14 CFR Section 91.3(b).

b. Whether two-way communications failure constitutes an emergency depends on the circumstances, and in any event, it is a determination made by the pilot. 14 CFR Section 91.3(b) authorizes a pilot to deviate from any rule in Subparts A and B to the extent required to meet an emergency.

c. In the event of two-way radio communications failure, ATC service will be provided on the basis that the pilot is operating in accordance with 14 CFR Section 91.185. A pilot experiencing two-way communications failure should (unless emergency authority is exercised) comply with 14 CFR Section 91.185 quoted below:

NOTE-
Capitalization, print and examples changed/added for emphasis.

1. General. Unless otherwise authorized by ATC, each pilot who has two-way radio communications failure when operating under IFR shall comply with the rules of this section.

2. VFR conditions. If the failure occurs in VFR conditions, or if VFR conditions are encountered after the failure, each pilot shall continue the flight under VFR and land as soon as practicable.

NOTE-
This procedure also applies when two-way radio failure occurs while operating in Class A airspace. The primary objective of this provision in 14 CFR Section 91.185 is to preclude extended IFR operation by these aircraft within the ATC system. Pilots should recognize that operation under these conditions may unnecessarily as well as adversely affect other users of the airspace, since ATC may be required to reroute or delay other users in order to protect the failure aircraft. However, it is not intended that the requirement to "land as soon as practicable" be construed to mean "as soon as possible." Pilots retain the prerogative of exercising their best judgment and are not required to land at an unauthorized airport, at an airport unsuitable for the type of aircraft flown, or to land only minutes short of their intended destination.

3. IFR conditions. If the failure occurs in IFR conditions, or if subparagraph 2. above cannot be complied with, each pilot shall continue the flight according to the following:

(a) *Route:*

(1) By the route assigned in the last ATC clearance received;

(2) If being radar vectored, by the direct route from the point of radio failure to the fix, route, or airway specified in the vector clearance;

(3) In the absence of an assigned route, by the route that ATC has advised may be expected in a further clearance; or

(4) In the absence of an assigned route or a route that ATC has advised may be expected in a further clearance by the route filed in the flight plan.

(b) *Altitude:* At the HIGHEST of the following altitudes or flight levels FOR THE ROUTE SEGMENT BEING FLOWN:

(1) The altitude or flight level assigned in the last ATC clearance received;

(2) The minimum altitude (converted, if appropriate, to minimum flight level as prescribed in 14 CFR Section 91.121(c)) for IFR operations; or

(3) The altitude or flight level ATC has advised may be expected in a further clearance.

NOTE-
The intent of the rule is that a pilot who has experienced two-way radio failure should select the appropriate altitude for the particular route segment being flown and make the necessary altitude adjustments for subsequent route segments. If the pilot received an "expect further clearance" containing a higher altitude to expect at a specified time or fix, maintain the highest of the following altitudes until that time/fix:
(1) the last assigned altitude, or
(2) the minimum altitude/flight level for IFR operations.

Upon reaching the time/fix specified, the pilot should commence climbing to the altitude advised to expect. If the radio failure occurs after the time/fix specified, the altitude to be expected is not applicable and the pilot should maintain an altitude consistent with 1 or 2 above.
If the pilot receives an "expect further clearance"

containing a lower altitude, the pilot should maintain the highest of 1 or 2 above until that time/fix specified in subparagraph (c) Leave clearance limit, below.

EXAMPLE-

1 *A pilot experiencing two-way radio failure at an assigned altitude of 7,000 feet is cleared along a direct route which will require a climb to a minimum IFR altitude of 9,000 feet, should climb to reach 9,000 feet at the time or place where it becomes necessary (see 14 CFR Section 91.177(b)). Later while proceeding along an airway with an MEA of 5,000 feet, the pilot would descend to 7,000 feet (the last assigned altitude), because that altitude is higher than the MEA.*

2 *A pilot experiencing two-way radio failure while being progressively descended to lower altitudes to begin an approach is assigned 2,700 feet until crossing the VOR and then cleared for the approach. The MOCA along the airway is 2,700 feet and MEA is 4,000 feet. The aircraft is within 22 NM of the VOR. The pilot should remain at 2,700 feet until crossing the VOR because that altitude is the minimum IFR altitude for the route segment being flown.*

3 *The MEA between a and b - 5,000 feet. The MEA between b and c - 5,000 feet. The MEA between c and d - 11,000 feet. The MEA between d and e - 7,000 feet. A pilot had been cleared via a, b, c, d, to e. while flying between a and b the assigned altitude was 6,000 feet and the pilot was told to expect a clearance to 8,000 feet at b. Prior to receiving the higher altitude assignment, the pilot experienced two-way failure. The pilot would maintain 6,000 to b, then climb to 8,000 feet (the altitude advised to expect). The pilot would maintain 8,000 feet, then climb to 11,000 at c, or prior to c if necessary to comply with an MCA at c. (14 CFR Section 91.177(b).) Upon reaching d, the pilot would descend to 8,000 feet (even though the MEA was 7,000 feet), as 8,000 was the highest of the altitude situations stated in the rule (14 CFR Section 91.185).*

(c) *Leave clearance limit:*

(1) When the clearance limit is a fix from which an approach begins, commence descent or descent and approach as close as possible to the expect further clearance time if one has been received, or if one has not been received, as close as possible to the Estimated Time of Arrival (ETA) as calculated from the filed or amended (with ATC) Estimated Time En Route (ETE).

(2) If the clearance limit is not a fix from which an approach begins, leave the clearance limit at the expect further clearance time if one has been received, or if none has been received, upon arrival over the clearance limit, and proceed to a fix from which an approach begins and commence descent or descent and approach as close as possible to the estimated time of arrival as calculated from the filed or amended (with ATC) estimated time en route.

6-4-2. TRANSPONDER OPERATION DURING TWO-WAY COMMUNICATIONS FAILURE

a. If an aircraft with a coded radar beacon transponder experiences a loss of two-way radio capability, the pilot should adjust the transponder to reply on MODE A/3, Code 7600.

b. The pilot should understand that the aircraft may not be in an area of radar coverage.

6-4-3. REESTABLISHING RADIO CONTACT

a. In addition to monitoring the NAVAID voice feature, the pilot should attempt to reestablish communications by attempting contact:

1. on the previously assigned frequency, or

2. with an FSS or *ARINC.

b. If communications are established with an FSS or ARINC, the pilot should advise that radio communications on the previously assigned frequency has been lost giving the aircraft's position, altitude, last assigned frequency and then request further clearance from the controlling facility. The preceding does not preclude the use of 121.5 MHz. There is no priority on which action should be attempted first. If the capability exists, do all at the same time.

NOTE-

*Aeronautical Radio/Incorporated (ARINC)- is a commercial communications corporation which designs, constructs, operates, leases or otherwise engages in radio activities serving the aviation community. ARINC has the capability of relaying information to/from ATC facilities throughout the country.

Chapter 7. SAFETY OF FLIGHT

Section 1. METEOROLOGY

7-1-1. NATIONAL WEATHER SERVICE AVIATION PRODUCTS

a. Weather service to aviation is a joint effort of the National Weather Service (NWS), the Federal Aviation Administration (FAA), the military weather services, and other aviation oriented groups and individuals. The NWS maintains an extensive surface, upper air, and radar weather observing program; a nationwide aviation weather forecasting service; and provides limited pilot briefing service (interpretational). The majority of pilot weather briefings are provided by FAA personnel at Flight Service Stations (AFSS's/FSS's). Aviation routine weather reports (METAR) are taken manually by NWS, FAA, contractors, or supplemental observers. METAR reports are also provided by Automated Weather Observing System (AWOS) and Automated Surface Observing System (ASOS).

REFERENCE-
AIM, WEATHER OBSERVING PROGRAMS, PARAGRAPH 7-1-10.

b. Aerodrome forecasts are prepared by approximately 100 Weather Forecast Offices (WFO's). These offices prepare and distribute approximately 525 aerodrome forecasts 4 times daily for specific airports in the 50 States, Puerto Rico, the Caribbean and Pacific Islands. These forecasts are valid for 24 hours and amended as required. WFO's prepare over 300 route forecasts and 39 synopses for Transcribed Weather Broadcasts (TWEB), and briefing purposes. The route forecasts are issued 3 times daily, each forecast is valid for 15 hours. A centralized aviation forecast program originating from the Aviation Weather Center (AWC) in Kansas City was implemented in October 1995. In the conterminous U.S., all Inflight Advisories Significant Meteorological Information (SIGMET's), Convective SIGMET's, and Airmen's Meteorological Information (AIRMET's) and all Area Forecasts (FA's) (6 areas) are now issued by AWC. FA's are prepared 3 times a day in the conterminous U.S. and Alaska (4 times in Hawaii), and amended as required. Inflight Advisories are issued only when conditions warrant. Winds aloft forecasts are provided for 176 locations in the 48 contiguous States and 21 locations in Alaska for flight planning purposes. (Winds aloft forecasts for Hawaii are prepared locally.)

All the aviation weather forecasts are given wide distribution through the Weather Message Switching Center Replacement (WMSCR) in Atlanta, Georgia, and Salt Lake City, Utah.

REFERENCE-
AIM, INFLIGHT WEATHER ADVISORIES, PARAGRAPH 7-1-5.

c. Weather element values may be expressed by using different measurement systems depending on several factors, such as whether the weather products will be used by the general public, aviation interests, international services, or a combination of these users. FIG 7-1-1 provides conversion tables for the most used weather elements that will be encountered by pilots.

7-1-2. FAA WEATHER SERVICES

a. The FAA maintains a nationwide network of Automated Flight Service Stations (AFSS's/FSS's) to serve the weather needs of pilots. In addition, NWS meteorologists are assigned to most ARTCC's as part of the Center Weather Service Unit (CWSU). They provide Center Weather Advisories (CWA) and gather weather information to support the needs of the FAA and other users of the system.

b. The primary source of preflight weather briefings is an individual briefing obtained from a briefer at the AFSS/FSS. These briefings, which are tailored to your specific flight, are available 24 hours a day through the use of the toll free number (1-800-WX BRIEF). Numbers for these services can be found in the Airport/Facility Directory (A/FD) under "FAA and NWS Telephone Numbers" section. They may also be listed in the U.S. Government section of your local telephone directory under Department of Transportation, Federal Aviation Administration, or Department of Commerce, National Weather Service. NWS pilot weather briefers do not provide aeronautical information (NOTAM's, flow control advisories, etc.) nor do they accept flight plans.

REFERENCE-
AIM, PREFLIGHT BRIEFING, PARAGRAPH 7-1-3, EXPLAINS THE TYPES OF PREFLIGHT BRIEFINGS AVAILABLE AND THE INFORMATION CONTAINED IN EACH.

Weather Elements Conversion Tables

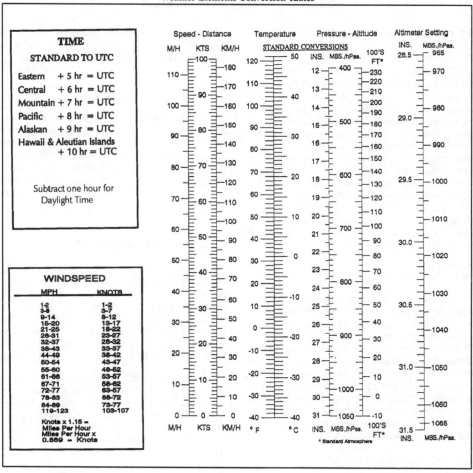

FIG 7-1-1

c. Other sources of weather information are as follows:

1. Telephone Information Briefing Service (TIBS) (AFSS), a small number of Transcribed Weather Broadcast (TWEB) locations, and telephone access to the TWEB (TEL-TWEB) provide continuously updated recorded weather information for short or local flights. Separate paragraphs in this section give additional information regarding these services.

REFERENCE-
AIM, TELEPHONE INFORMATION BRIEFING SERVICE (TIBS),
PARAGRAPH 7-1-7.
AIM, TRANSCRIBED WEATHER BROADCAST (TWEB),
PARAGRAPH 7-1-8.

2. Weather and aeronautical information are also available from numerous private industry sources on an individual or contract pay basis. Information on how to obtain this service should be available from local pilot organizations.

3. The Direct User Access System (DUATS) can be accessed by pilots with a current medical certificate toll-free in the 48 contiguous States via personal computer. Pilots can receive alpha-numeric preflight weather data and file domestic VFR and IFR flight plans. The following are the contract DUATS vendors:

GTE Federal Systems
15000 Conference Center Drive
Chantilly, VA 22021-3808
Computer Modem Access Number: For filing flight plans and obtaining weather briefings: (800) 767-9989
For customer service: (800) 345-3828

Data Transformation Corporation
108-D Greentree Road
Turnersville, NJ 08012
Computer Modem Access Number: For filing flight plans and obtaining weather briefings: (800) 245-3828
For customer service: (800) 243-3828

d. Inflight weather information is available from any FSS within radio range. The common frequency for all AFSS's is 122.2. Discrete frequencies for individual stations are listed in the Airport/Facility Directory.

1. Information on In-Flight Weather broadcasts.

REFERENCE-
AIM, INFLIGHT WEATHER BROADCASTS, PARAGRAPH 7-1-9.

2. En Route Flight Advisory Service (EFAS) is provided to serve the nonroutine weather needs of pilots in flight.

REFERENCE-
AIM, EN ROUTE FLIGHT ADVISORY SERVICE (EFAS),
PARAGRAPH 7-1-4 GIVES DETAILS ON THIS SERVICE.

7-1-3. PREFLIGHT BRIEFING

a. Flight Service Stations (AFSS's/FSS's) are the primary source for obtaining preflight briefings and inflight weather information. Flight Service Specialists are qualified and certificated by the NWS as Pilot Weather Briefers. They are not authorized to make original forecasts, but are authorized to translate and interpret available forecasts and reports directly into terms describing the weather conditions which you can expect along your flight route and at your destination. Available aviation weather reports, forecasts and aviation weather charts are displayed at each AFSS/FSS, for pilot use. Pilots should feel free to use these self briefing displays where available, or to ask for a briefing or assistance from the specialist on duty. Three basic types of preflight briefings are available to serve your specific needs. These are: Standard Briefing, Abbreviated Briefing, and Outlook Briefing. You should specify to the briefer the type of briefing you want, along with your appropriate background information. This will enable the briefer to tailor the information to your intended flight. The following paragraphs describe the types of briefings available and the information provided in each briefing.

REFERENCE-
AIM, PREFLIGHT PREPARATION, PARAGRAPH 5-1-1 FOR ITEMS
THAT ARE REQUIRED.

b. Standard Briefing: You should request a Standard Briefing any time you are planning a flight and you have not received a previous briefing or have not received preliminary information through mass dissemination media; e.g., TIBS, TWEB, etc. International data may be inaccurate or incomplete. If you are planning a flight outside of United States controlled airspace, the briefer will advise you to check data as soon as practical after entering foreign airspace, unless you advise that you have the international cautionary advisory. The briefer will automatically provide the following information in the sequence listed, except as noted, when it is applicable to your proposed flight.

1. *Adverse Conditions:* Significant meteorological and aeronautical information that might influence the pilot to alter the proposed flight; e.g., hazardous weather conditions, airport closures, air traffic delays, etc.

2. VFR Flight Not Recommended: When VFR flight is proposed and sky conditions or visibilities are present or forecast, surface or aloft, that in the briefer's judgment would make flight under visual flight rules doubtful, the briefer will describe the conditions, affected locations, and use the phrase *"VFR flight not recommended."* This recommendation is advisory in nature. The final decision as to whether the flight can be conducted safely rests solely with the pilot.

3. Synopsis: A brief statement describing the type, location and movement of weather systems and/or air masses which might affect the proposed flight.

NOTE-
These first 3 elements of a briefing may be combined in any order when the briefer believes it will help to more clearly describe conditions.

4. Current Conditions: Reported weather conditions applicable to the flight will be summarized from all available sources; e.g., METAR's/SPECI's, PIREP's, RAREP's. This element will be omitted if the proposed time of departure is beyond 2 hours, unless the information is specifically requested by the pilot.

5. En Route Forecast: Forecast en route conditions for the proposed route are summarized in logical order; i.e., departure/climbout, en route, and descent. (Heights are MSL, unless the contractions "AGL" or "CIG" are denoted indicating that heights are above ground.)

6. Destination Forecast: The destination forecast for the planned ETA. Any significant changes within 1 hour before and after the planned arrival are included.

7. Winds Aloft: Forecast winds aloft will be provided using degrees of the compass. The briefer will interpolate wind directions and speeds between levels and stations as necessary to provide expected conditions at planned altitudes. (Heights are MSL.) Temperature information will be provided on request.

8. Notices to Airmen (NOTAM's):

(a) Available NOTAM (D) information pertinent to the proposed flight.

(b) NOTAM (L) information pertinent to the departure and/or local area, if available, and pertinent FDC NOTAM's within approximately 400 miles of the FSS providing the briefing. AFSS facilities will provide FDC NOTAM's for the entire route of flight.

NOTE-
NOTAM information may be combined with current conditions when the briefer believes it is logical to do so.

NOTE-
NOTAM (D) information and FDC NOTAM's which have been published in the Notices to Airmen Publication are not included in pilot briefings unless a review of this publication is specifically requested by the pilot. For complete flight information you are urged to review the printed NOTAM's in the Notices to Airmen Publication and the A/FD in addition to obtaining a briefing.

9. ATC Delays: Any known ATC delays and flow control advisories which might affect the proposed flight.

10. Pilots may obtain the following from AFSS/FSS briefers upon request:

(a) Information on military training routes (MTR) and military operations area (MOA) activity within the flight plan area and a 100 NM extension around the flight plan area.

NOTE-
Pilots are encouraged to request updated information from en route AFSS's.

(b) A review of the Notices to Airmen Publication for pertinent NOTAM's and Special Notices.

(c) Approximate density altitude data.

(d) Information regarding such items as air traffic services and rules, customs/immigration procedures, ADIZ rules, search and rescue, etc.

(e) LORAN-C NOTAM's, available military NOTAM's, and runway friction measurement value NOTAM's.

(f) GPS RAIM availability for 1 hour before to 1 hour after ETA or a time specified by the pilot.

(g) Other assistance as required.

c. Abbreviated Briefing: Request an Abbreviated Briefing when you need information to supplement mass disseminated data, update a previous briefing, or when you need only one or two specific items. Provide the briefer with appropriate background information, the time you received the previous information, and/or the specific items needed. You should indicate the source of the information already received so that the briefer can limit the briefing to the information that you have not received, and/or appreciable changes in meteorological/aeronautical conditions since your previous briefing. To the extent possible, the briefer will provide the information in the sequence shown for a Standard Briefing. If you request only one or two specific items, the briefer will advise you if adverse conditions are present or forecast. (Adverse conditions contain both meteorological and/or aeronautical information.) Details on these conditions will be provided at your request. International data may be inaccurate or incomplete. If you are planning a flight outside of United States controlled airspace, the briefer will advise you to check data as soon as practical after entering foreign airspace, unless you advise that you have the international cautionary advisory.

d. Outlook Briefing: You should request an Outlook Briefing whenever your proposed time of departure is six or more hours from the time of the briefing. The briefer will provide available forecast data applicable to the proposed flight. This type of briefing is provided for planning purposes only. You should obtain a Standard or Abbreviated Briefing prior to departure in order to obtain such items as adverse conditions, current conditions, updated forecasts, winds aloft and NOTAM's, etc.

e. When filing a flight plan only, you will be asked if you require the latest information on adverse conditions pertinent to the route of flight.

f. Inflight Briefing: You are encouraged to obtain your preflight briefing by telephone or in person before departure. In those cases where you need to obtain a preflight briefing or an update to a previous briefing by radio, you should contact the nearest AFSS/FSS to obtain this information. After communications have been established, advise the specialist of the type briefing you require and provide appropriate background information. You will be provided information as specified in the above paragraphs, depending on the type briefing requested. In addition, the specialist will recommend shifting to the Flight Watch frequency when conditions along the intended route indicate that it would be advantageous to do so.

g. Following any briefing, feel free to ask for any information that you or the briefer may have missed or are not understood. This way, the briefer is able to present the information in a logical sequence, and lessens the chance of important items being overlooked.

7-1-4. EN ROUTE FLIGHT ADVISORY SERVICE (EFAS)

a. EFAS is a service specifically designed to provide en route aircraft with timely and meaningful weather advisories pertinent to the type of flight intended, route of flight, and altitude. In conjunction with this service, EFAS is also a central collection and distribution point for pilot reported weather information. EFAS is provided by specially trained specialists in selected AFSS's controlling multiple Remote Communications Outlets covering a large geographical area and is normally available throughout the conterminous U.S. and Puerto Rico from 6 a.m. to 10 p.m. EFAS provides communications capabilities for aircraft flying at 5,000 feet above ground level to 17,500 feet MSL on a common frequency of 122.0 MHz. Discrete EFAS frequencies have been established to ensure communications coverage from 18,000 through 45,000 MSL serving in each specific ARTCC area. These discrete frequencies may be used below 18,000 feet when coverage permits reliable communication.

NOTE-
When an EFAS outlet is located in a time zone different from the zone in which the flight watch control station is located, the availability of service may be plus or minus one hour from the normal operating hours.

b. Contact flight watch by using the name of the ARTCC facility identification serving the area of your location, followed by your aircraft identification, and the name of the nearest VOR to your position. The specialist needs to know this approximate location to select the most appropriate transmitter/receiver outlet for communications coverage.

EXAMPLE-
Cleveland Flight Watch, Cessna One Two Three Four Kilo, Mansfield V-O-R, over.

c. Charts depicting the location of the flight watch control stations (parent facility) and the outlets they use are contained in the A/FD. If you do not know in which flight watch area you are flying, initiate contact by using the words "Flight Watch," your aircraft identification, and the name of the nearest VOR. The facility will respond using the name of the flight watch facility.

EXAMPLE-
Flight Watch, Cessna One Two Three Four Kilo, Mansfield V-O-R, over.

d. AFSS's that provide En Route Flight Advisory Service are listed regionally in the A/FD's.

e. EFAS is not intended to be used for filing or closing flight plans, position reporting, getting complete preflight briefings, or obtaining random weather reports and forecasts. En route flight advisories are tailored to the phase of flight that begins after climb-out and ends with descent to land. Immediate destination weather and terminal aerodrome forecasts will be provided on request. Pilots requesting information not within the scope of flight watch will be advised of the appropriate AFSS/FSS frequency to obtain the information. Pilot participation is essential to the success of EFAS by providing a continuous exchange of information on weather, winds, turbulence, flight visibility, icing, etc., between pilots and flight watch specialists. Pilots are encouraged to report good weather as well as bad, and to confirm expected conditions as well as unexpected to EFAS facilities.

7-1-5. INFLIGHT WEATHER ADVISORIES

a. The NWS issues inflight weather advisories designated as Severe Weather Forecast Alerts (AWW's), Convective SIGMET's (WST's), SIGMET's (WS's), Center Weather Advisories (CWA's), and AIRMET's (WA's). Inflight advisories serve to notify en route pilots of the possibility of encountering hazardous flying conditions which may not have been forecast at the time of the preflight briefing. Whether or not the condition described is potentially hazardous to a particular flight is for the pilot and/or aircraft dispatcher in a FAR Part 121 operation to evaluate on the basis of experience and the operational limits of the aircraft. Inflight weather advisories in the contiguous United States are described and plotted primarily using high altitude VOR's as reference points. In Alaska and Hawaii, advisories are described and plotted using either geographic references or latitude/longitude coordinates.

b. Severe Weather Forecast Alerts (AWW's) are preliminary messages issued in order to alert users that a Severe Weather Bulletin (WW) is being issued. These messages define areas of possible severe thunderstorms or tornado activity. The messages are unscheduled and issued as required by the Aviation Weather Center at Kansas City, Missouri.

1. Each AWW is numbered sequentially beginning January 1 of each year.

EXAMPLE-
MKC AWW 161755
WW 279 SEVERE TSTM NY PA NJ
161830Z-170000Z
AXIS..70 STATUTE MILES EITHER SIDE OF LINE..10W
KMSS TO 20E KABE..AVIATION COORDS..60NM
EITHER SIDE/60NW KSLK - 35W KEWR..HAIL
SURFACE AND ALOFT..2 INCHES. SURFACE WIND
GUSTS..65 KNOTS. MAX TOPS TO 540. MEAN WIND
VECTOR 19020.
REPLACES WW 278..OH PA NY

2. Status reports are issued as needed on Severe Weather Watch Bulletins to show progress of storms and to delineate areas no longer under the threat of severe storm activity. Cancellation bulletins are issued

when it becomes evident that no severe weather will develop or that storms have subsided and are no longer severe.

c. Convective SIGMET's (WST's) in the Conterminous United States: WST's concern only thunderstorms and related phenomena (tornadoes, heavy precipitation, hail, and high surface winds) over the conterminous United States and imply the associated occurrence of turbulence, icing, and convective low level wind shear. Individual WST's for each day are numbered sequentially (00-1-99), beginning at 00Z. The affected geographic area is contained in the number; i.e., the first WST issued each day in the eastern U.S. is Convective SIGMET 1E, the second is Convective SIGMET 2E, and so forth. WST's are issued on a scheduled basis, hourly at 55 minutes past the hour (H+55), and are valid for two hours or until superseded by the next hourly update. WST's are issued for any of the following phenomena:

1. Severe thunderstorm due to:

(a) surface winds greater than or equal to 50 knots.

(b) hail at the surface greater than or equal to $3/4$ inches in diameter.

(c) tornadoes.

2. Embedded thunderstorms.

3. A line of thunderstorms.

4. Thunderstorms greater than or equal to VIP level 4 affecting 40% or more of an area at least 3,000 square miles.

REFERENCE-
PILOT/CONTROLLER GLOSSARY TERM- RADAR WEATHER ECHO INTENSITY LEVELS.
NOTE-
Since thunderstorms are the reason for issuing the WST, severe or greater turbulence, severe icing, and low-level wind shear (gust fronts, downbursts, microbursts, etc.) are implied and will not be specified in the advisory.

d. Convective SIGMET Bulletins:

1. Three Convective SIGMET bulletins, each covering a specified geographic area, are issued. These areas are the Eastern (E), Central (C), and Western (W) U.S. The boundaries that separate the Eastern from the Central and the Central from the Western U.S. are 87 and 107 degrees West, respectively. These bulletins are issued on a scheduled basis, hourly at 55 minutes past the hour (H+55), and as special bulletins on an unscheduled basis.

2. Each of the Convective SIGMET bulletins will be:

(a) Made up of one or more individually numbered Convective SIGMET's,

(b) Valid for two hours or until superseded by the next hourly issuance.

(c) The text of the bulletin consists of either an observation and a forecast or just a forecast.

3. On an hourly basis, an outlook is made for each of the three Convective SIGMET regions. The outlook for a particular region is appended to the Convective SIGMET bulletin for the same region. The convective outlook is also appended to special Convective SIGMET's. The outlook is reviewed each hour and revised when necessary. The outlook is a forecast and meteorological discussion for thunderstorm systems that are expected to require Convective SIGMET issuances during a time period 2-6 hours into the future. Furthermore, an outlook will always be made for each of the three regions, even if it is a negative statement.

e. SIGMET's (WS's) within the conterminous U.S. are issued by the Aviation Weather Center (AWC) when the following phenomena occur or are expected to occur:

1. Severe or extreme turbulence or clear air turbulence (CAT) not associated with thunderstorms.

2. Severe icing not associated with thunderstorms.

3. Duststorms, sandstorms, or volcanic ash lowering surface or inflight visibilities to below three miles.

4. Volcanic eruption.

f. Volcanic eruption SIGMET's are identified by an alphanumeric designator which consists of an alphabetic identifier and issuance number. The first time an advisory is issued for a phenomenon associated with a particular weather system, it will be given the next alphabetic designator in the series and will be numbered as the first for that designator. Subsequent advisories will retain the same alphabetic designator until the phenomenon ends. In the conterminous U.S., this means that a phenomenon that is assigned an alphabetic designator in one area will retain that designator as it moves within the area or into one or more other areas. Issuances for the same phenomenon will be sequentially numbered, using the same alphabetic designator until the phenomenon no longer exists. Alphabetic designators NOVEMBER through YANKEE, except SIERRA and TANGO are only used for SIGMET's, while

designators SIERRA, TANGO and ZULU are used for AIRMET's.

g. Center Weather Advisories (CWA's):

1. CWA's are unscheduled inflight, flow control, air traffic, and air crew advisory. By nature of its short lead time, the CWA is not a flight planning product. It is generally a Nowcast for conditions beginning within the next two hours. CWA's will be issued:

(a) As a supplement to an existing SIGMET, Convective SIGMET or AIRMET.

(b) When an Inflight Advisory has not been issued but observed or expected weather conditions meet SIGMET/AIRMET criteria based on current pilot reports and reinforced by other sources of information about existing meteorological conditions.

(c) When observed or developing weather conditions do not meet SIGMET, Convective SIGMET, or AIRMET criteria; e.g., in terms of intensity or area coverage, but current pilot reports or other weather information sources indicate that existing or anticipated meteorological phenomena will adversely affect the safe flow of air traffic within the ARTCC area of responsibility.

2. The following example is a CWA issued from the Kansas City, Missouri, ARTCC. The "3" after ZKC in the first line denotes this CWA has been issued for the third weather phenomena to occur for the day. The "301" in the second line denotes the phenomena number again (3) and the issuance number (01) for this phenomena. The CWA was issued at 2140Z and is valid until 2340Z.

EXAMPLE-
ZKC3 CWA 032140
ZKC CWA 301 VALID UNTIL 032340
ISOLD SVR TSTM over KCOU MOVG SWWD 10 KTS ETC.

h. AIRMET's (WA's) may be of significance to any pilot or aircraft operator and are issued for all domestic airspace. They are of particular concern to operators and pilots of aircraft sensitive to the phenomena described and to pilots without instrument ratings and are issued by the AWC for the following weather phenomena which are potentially hazardous to aircraft:

1. Moderate icing.

2. Moderate turbulence.

3. Sustained winds of 30 knots or more at the surface.

4. Widespread area of ceilings less than 1,000 feet and/or visibility less than three miles.

5. Extensive mountain obscurement.

i. AIRMET's are issued on a scheduled basis every six hours, with unscheduled amendments issued as required. AIRMET's have fixed alphanumeric designator with ZULU for icing and freezing level data, TANGO for turbulence, strong surface winds, and wind shear, and SIERRA for instrument flight rules and mountain obscuration.

7-1-6. CATEGORICAL OUTLOOKS

a. Categorical outlook terms, describing general ceiling and visibility conditions for advanced planning purposes are used only in area forecasts and are defined as follows:

1. *LIFR (Low IFR):* Ceiling less than 500 feet and/or visibility less than 1 mile.

2. *IFR:* Ceiling 500 to less than 1,000 feet and/or visibility 1 to less than 3 miles.

3. *MVFR (Marginal VFR):* Ceiling 1,000 to 3,000 feet and/or visibility 3 to 5 miles inclusive.

4. *VFR:* Ceiling greater than 3,000 feet and visibility greater than 5 miles; includes sky clear.

b. The cause of LIFR, IFR, or MVFR is indicated by either ceiling or visibility restrictions or both. The contraction "CIG" and/or weather and obstruction to vision symbols are used. If winds or gusts of 25 knots or greater are forecast for the outlook period, the word "WIND" is also included for all categories including VFR.

EXAMPLE-
1 *LIFR CIG-low IFR due to low ceiling.*
2 *IFR FG-IFR due to visibility restricted by fog.*
3 *MVFR CIG HZ FU-marginal VFR due to both ceiling and visibility restricted by haze and smoke.*
4 *IFR CIG RA WIND-IFR due to both low ceiling and visibility restricted by rain; wind expected to be 25 knots or greater.*

7-1-7. TELEPHONE INFORMATION BRIEFING SERVICE (TIBS)

a. TIBS, provided by automated flight service stations (AFSS's) is a continuous recording of meteorological and aeronautical information, available by telephone. Each AFSS provides at least four route and/or area briefings. In addition, airspace procedures and special announcements (if applicable) concerning aviation interests may also be available. Depending on user demand, other items may be provided; i.e.,

METAR observations, terminal aerodrome forecasts, wind/temperatures aloft forecasts, etc.

b. TIBS is not intended to substitute for specialist-provided preflight briefings. It is, however, recommended for use as a preliminary briefing, and often will be valuable in helping you to make a "go or no go" decision.

c. TIBS is provided by Automated Flight Service Stations (AFSS's) and provides continuous telephone recordings of meteorological and/or aeronautical information. Specifically, TIBS provides area and/or route briefings, airspace procedures, and special announcements (if applicable) concerning aviation interests.

d. Depending on user demand, other items may be provided; i.e., surface observations, terminal forecasts, winds/temperatures aloft forecasts, etc. A TOUCH-TONE™ telephone is necessary to fully utilize the TIBS program.

e. Pilots are encouraged to avail themselves of this service. TIBS locations are found at AFSS sites and can be accessed by use of 1-800-WX BRIEF toll free number.

7-1-8. TRANSCRIBED WEATHER BROADCAST (TWEB)

Equipment is provided at three AFSS/FSS locations in the lower 48 States (Arcata, California; Kankakee, Illinois; Princeton, Minnesota) and all of Alaska, by which meteorological and aeronautical data are recorded on tapes and broadcast continuously over selected low-frequency (190–535 kHz) navigational aids (L/MF ranges or H facilities) and/or VOR's. Broadcasts are made from a series of individual tape recordings, and changes, as they occur, are transcribed onto the tapes. The information provided varies depending on the type equipment available. Generally, the broadcast contains route-oriented data with specially prepared NWS forecasts, Inflight Advisories, and winds aloft plus preselected current information, such as weather reports (METAR/SPECI), NOTAM's, and special notices. In some locations, the information is broadcast over the local VOR only and is limited to such items as the hourly weather for the parent station and up to 5 immediately adjacent stations, local NOTAM information, aerodrome forecast (TAF) for the parent station, adverse conditions extracted from Inflight Advisories, and other potentially hazardous conditions. At selected locations, telephone access to the TWEB has been provided (TEL-TWEB). Telephone numbers for this service are found in the FSS and National Weather Service Telephone Numbers section of the A/FD. These broadcasts are made available primarily for preflight and inflight planning, and as such, should not be considered as a substitute for specialist-provided preflight briefings.

7-1-9. INFLIGHT WEATHER BROADCASTS

a. Weather Advisory Broadcasts: ARTCC's broadcast a Severe Weather Forecast Alert (AWW), Convective SIGMET, SIGMET, or CWA alert once on all frequencies, except emergency, when any part of the area described is within 150 miles of the airspace under their jurisdiction. These broadcasts contain SIGMET or CWA (identification) and a brief description of the weather activity and general area affected.

EXAMPLE-
[1] *Attention all aircraft, SIGMET Delta Three, from Myton to Tuba City to Milford, severe turbulence and severe clear icing below one zero thousand feet. Expected to continue beyond zero three zero zero zulu.*
[2] *Attention all aircraft, convective SIGMET Two Seven Eastern. From the vicinity of Elmira to Phillipsburg. Scattered embedded thunderstorms moving east at one zero knots. A few intense level five cells, maximum tops four five zero.*
[3] *Attention all aircraft, Kansas City Center weather advisory one zero three. Numerous reports of moderate to severe icing from eight to niner thousand feet in a three zero mile radius of St. Louis. Light or negative icing reported from four thousand to one two thousand feet remainder of Kansas City Center area.*

NOTE-
Terminal control facilities have the option to limit the AWW, convective SIGMET, SIGMET, or CWA broadcast as follows: local control and approach control positions may opt to broadcast SIGMET or CWA alerts only when any part of the area described is within 50 miles of the airspace under their jurisdiction.

b. Hazardous InFlight Weather Advisory Service (HIWAS): This is a continuous broadcast of inflight weather advisories including summarized AWW, SIGMET's, Convective SIGMET's, CWA's, AIRMET's, and urgent PIREP's. HIWAS has been adopted as a national program and will be implemented throughout the conterminous U.S. as resources permit. In those areas where HIWAS is commissioned, ARTCC, Terminal ATC, and AFSS/FSS facilities have discontinued the broadcast of inflight advisories as described in the preceding paragraph. HIWAS is an additional source of hazardous weather information which makes these data available on a continuous basis. It is not, however, a replacement for preflight or inflight briefings or

real-time weather updates from Flight Watch (EFAS). As HIWAS is implemented in individual center areas, the commissioning will be advertised in the Notices to Airmen Publication.

1. Where HIWAS has been implemented, a HIWAS alert will be broadcast on all except emergency frequencies once upon receipt by ARTCC and terminal facilities, which will include an alert announcement, frequency instruction, number, and type of advisory updated; e.g., AWW, SIGMET, Convective SIGMET, or CWA.

EXAMPLE-
Attention all aircraft. Hazardous weather information (SIGMET, Convective SIGMET, AIRMET, Urgent Pilot Weather Report (UUA), or Center Weather Advisory (CWA), Number or Numbers) for (geographical area) available on HIWAS, Flight Watch, or Flight Service frequencies.

2. In HIWAS ARTCC areas, AFSS/FSS's will broadcast a HIWAS update announcement once on all except emergency frequencies upon completion of recording an update to the HIWAS broadcast. Included in the broadcast will be the type of advisory updated; e.g. AWW, SIGMET, Convective SIGMET, CWA, etc..

EXAMPLE-
Attention all aircraft. Hazardous weather information for (geographical area) available from Flight Watch or Flight Service.

3. HIWAS availability is shown on IFR Enroute Low Altitude Charts and VFR Sectional Charts. The symbol depiction is identified in the chart legend.

7-1-10. WEATHER OBSERVING PROGRAMS

a. Manual Observations: With only a few exceptions, these reports are from airport locations staffed by FAA or NWS personnel who manually observe, perform calculations, and enter these observations into the (WMSCR) communication system. The format and coding of these observations are contained in paragraph 7-1-27, Key to Aviation Routine Weather Report (METAR) and Aerodrome Forecasts (TAF).

b. Automated Weather Observing System (AWOS):

1. Automated weather reporting systems are increasingly being installed at airports. These systems consist of various sensors, a processor, a computer-generated voice subsystem, and a transmitter to broadcast local, minute-by-minute weather data directly to the pilot.

NOTE-
When the barometric pressure exceeds 31.00 inches Hg., see paragraph 7-2-2, Procedures, for the altimeter setting procedures.

2. The AWOS observations will include the prefix "AUTO" to indicate that the data are derived from an automated system. Some AWOS locations will be augmented by certified observers who will provide weather and obstruction to vision information in the remarks of the report when the reported visibility is less than 7 miles. These sites, along with the hours of augmentation, are to be published in the A/FD. Augmentation is identified in the observation as "OBSERVER WEATHER." The AWOS wind speed, direction and gusts, temperature, dew point, and altimeter setting are exactly the same as for manual observations. The AWOS will also report density altitude when it exceeds the field elevation by more than 1,000 feet. The reported visibility is derived from a sensor near the touchdown of the primary instrument runway. The visibility sensor output is converted to a visibility value using a 10-minute harmonic average. The reported sky condition/ceiling is derived from the ceilometer located next to the visibility sensor. The AWOS algorithm integrates the last 30 minutes of ceilometer data to derive cloud layers and heights. This output may also differ from the observer sky condition in that the AWOS is totally dependent upon the cloud advection over the sensor site.

3. These real-time systems are operationally classified into four basic levels:

(a) *AWOS-A:* only reports altimeter setting,

(b) *AWOS-1:* usually reports altimeter setting, wind data, temperature, dew point, and density altitude,

(c) *AWOS-2:* provides the information provided by AWOS-1 plus visibility, and

(d) *AWOS-3:* provides the information provided by AWOS-2 plus cloud/ceiling data.

4. The information is transmitted over a discrete VHF radio frequency or the voice portion of a local NAVAID. AWOS transmissions on a discrete VHF radio frequency are engineered to be receivable to a maximum of 25 NM from the AWOS site and a maximum altitude of 10,000 feet AGL. At many locations, AWOS signals may be received on the surface of the airport, but local conditions may limit the maximum AWOS reception distance and/or altitude.

The system transmits a 20 to 30 second weather message updated each minute. Pilots should monitor the designated frequency for the automated weather broadcast. A description of the broadcast is contained in subparagraph c. There is no two-way communication capability. Most AWOS sites also have a dial-up capability so that the minute-by-minute weather messages can be accessed via telephone.

5. AWOS information (system level, frequency, phone number, etc.) concerning specific locations is published, as the systems become operational, in the A/FD, and where applicable, on published Instrument Approach Procedures. Selected individual systems may be incorporated into nationwide data collection and dissemination networks in the future.

c. AWOS Broadcasts: Computer-generated voice is used in AWOS to automate the broadcast of the minute-by-minute weather observations. In addition, some systems are configured to permit the addition of an operator-generated voice message; e.g., weather remarks following the automated parameters. The phraseology used generally follows that used for other weather broadcasts. Following are explanations and examples of the exceptions.

1. *Location and Time:* The location/name and the phrase "AUTOMATED WEATHER OBSERVATION," followed by the time are announced.

(a) If the airport's specific location is included in the airport's name, the airport's name is announced.

EXAMPLE-
"Bremerton National Airport automated weather observation, one four five six zulu;"
"Ravenswood Jackson County Airport automated weather observation, one four five six zulu."

(b) If the airport's specific location is not included in the airport's name, the location is announced followed by the airport's name.

EXAMPLE-
"Sault Ste. Marie, Chippewa County International Airport automated weather observation;"
"Sandusky, Cowley Field automated weather observation."

(c) The word "TEST" is added following "OBSERVATION" when the system is not in commissioned status.

EXAMPLE-
"Bremerton National Airport automated weather observation test, one four five six zulu."

(d) The phrase "TEMPORARILY INOPERATIVE" is added when the system is inoperative.

EXAMPLE-
"Bremerton National Airport automated weather observing system temporarily inoperative."

2. Visibility:

(a) The lowest reportable visibility value in AWOS is "less than $1/4$." It is announced as "VISIBILITY LESS THAN ONE QUARTER."

(b) A sensor for determining visibility is not included in some AWOS. In these systems, visibility is not announced. "VISIBILITY MISSING" is announced only if the system is configured with a visibility sensor and visibility information is not available.

3. Weather: In the future, some AWOS's are to be configured to determine the occurrence of precipitation. However, the type and intensity may not always be determined. In these systems, the word "PRECIPITATION" will be announced if precipitation is occurring, but the type and intensity are not determined.

4. Ceiling and Sky Cover:

(a) Ceiling is announced as either "CEILING" or "INDEFINITE CEILING." With the exception of indefinite ceilings, all automated ceiling heights are measured.

EXAMPLE-
"Bremerton National Airport automated weather observation, one four five six zulu. Ceiling two thousand overcast;"

"Bremerton National Airport automated weather observation, one four five six zulu. Indefinite ceiling two hundred, sky obscured."

(b) The word "Clear" is not used in AWOS due to limitations in the height ranges of the sensors. No clouds detected is announced as "NO CLOUDS BELOW XXX" or, in newer systems as "CLEAR BELOW XXX" (where XXX is the range limit of the sensor).

EXAMPLE-
"No clouds below one two thousand."
"Clear below one two thousand."

(c) A sensor for determining ceiling and sky cover is not included in some AWOS. In these systems, ceiling and sky cover are not announced. "SKY CONDITION MISSING" is announced only if the system is configured with a ceilometer and the ceiling and sky cover information is not available.

5. Remarks: If remarks are included in the observation, the word "REMARKS" is announced following the altimeter setting.

(a) Automated "Remarks."

(1) Density Altitude.

(2) Variable Visibility.

(3) Variable Wind Direction.

(b) Manual Input Remarks: Manual input remarks are prefaced with the phrase "OBSERVER WEATHER." As a general rule the manual remarks are limited to:

(1) Type and intensity of precipitation,

(2) Thunderstorms and direction, and

(3) Obstructions to vision when the visibility is 3 miles or less.

EXAMPLE-
"Remarks ... density altitude, two thousand five hundred ... visibility variable between one and two ... wind direction variable between two four zero and three one zero ...observed weather ... thunderstorm moderate rain showers and fog ... thunderstorm overhead."

(c) If an automated parameter is "missing" and no manual input for that parameter is available, the parameter is announced as "MISSING." For example, a report with the dew point "missing" and no manual input available, would be announced as follows:

EXAMPLE-
"Ceiling one thousand overcast ... visibility three ... precipitation ... temperature three zero, dew point missing ... wind calm ... altimeter three zero zero one."

(d) "REMARKS" are announced in the following order of priority:

(1) Automated "REMARKS."

[a] Density Altitude.

[b] Variable Visibility.

[c] Variable Wind Direction.

(2) Manual Input "REMARKS."

[a] Sky Condition,

[b] Visibility,

[c] Weather and Obstructions to Vision,

[d] Temperature,

[e] Dew Point,

[f] Wind, and

[g] Altimeter Setting.

EXAMPLE-
"Remarks ... density altitude, two thousand five hundred ... visibility variable between one and two ... wind direction variable between two four zero and three one zero ... observer ceiling estimated two thousand broken ... observer temperature two, dew point minus five."

d. Automated Surface Observing System (ASOS): The ASOS is the primary surface weather observing system of the United States. (See Key to Decode an ASOS (METAR) Observation: FIG 7-1-2 and FIG 7-1-3.) The program to install and operate up to 1,700 systems throughout the United States is a joint effort of the NWS, the FAA and the Department of Defense. ASOS is designed to support aviation operations and weather forecast activities. The ASOS will provide continuous minute-by-minute observations and perform the basic observing functions necessary to generate an aviation routine weather report (METAR) and other aviation weather information. The information may be transmitted over a discrete VHF radio frequency or the voice portion of a local NAVAID. ASOS transmissions on a discrete VHF radio frequency are engineered to be receivable to a maximum of 25 NM from the ASOS site and a maximum altitude of 10,000 feet AGL. At many locations, ASOS signals may be received on the surface of the airport, but local conditions may limit the maximum reception distance and/or altitude. While the automated system and the human may differ in their methods of data collection and interpretation, both produce an observation quite similar in form and content. For the "objective" elements such as pressure, ambient temperature, dew point temperature, wind, and precipitation accumulation, both the automated system and the observer use a fixed location and time-averaging technique. The quantitative differences between the observer and the automated observation of these elements are negligible. For the "subjective" elements, however, observers use a fixed time, spatial averaging technique to describe the visual elements (sky condition, visibility and present weather), while the automated systems use a fixed location, time averaging technique. Although this is a fundamental change, the manual and automated techniques yield remarkably similar results within the limits of their respective capabilities.

1. *System Description:*

(a) The ASOS at each airport location consists of four main components:

(1) Individual weather sensors.

(2) Data collection package(s) (DCP).

(3) The acquisition control unit.

(4) Peripherals and displays.

(b) The ASOS sensors perform the basic function of data acquisition. They continuously sample and measure the ambient environment, derive raw sensor data and make them available to the collocated DCP.

2. *Every ASOS will contain the following basic set of sensors:*

(a) Cloud height indicator (one or possibly three).

(b) Visibility sensor (one or possibly three).

(c) Precipitation identification sensor.

(d) Freezing rain sensor (at select sites).

(e) Pressure sensors (two sensors at small airports; three sensors at large airports).

(f) Ambient temperature/Dew point temperature sensor.

(g) Anemometer (wind direction and speed sensor).

(h) Rainfall accumulation sensor.

3. *The ASOS data outlets include:*

(a) Those necessary for on-site airport users.

(b) National communications networks.

(c) Computer-generated voice (available through FAA radio broadcast to pilots, and dial-in telephone line).

4. An ASOS/AWOS report without human intervention will contain only that weather data capable of being reported automatically. The modifier for this METAR report is "AUTO." When an observer augments or backs-up an ASOS/AWOS site, the "AUTO" modifier disappears.

5. There are two types of automated stations, AO1 for automated weather reporting stations without a precipitation discriminator, and AO2 for automated stations with a precipitation discriminator. As appropriate, "AO1" and "AO2" shall appear in remarks. (A precipitation discriminator can determine the difference between liquid and frozen/freezing precipitation).

NOTE-
To decode an ASOS report, refer to FIG 7-1-2 and FIG 7-1-3.

REFERENCE-
A COMPLETE EXPLANATION OF METAR TERMINOLOGY IS LOCATED IN AIM, PARAGRAPH 7-1-27, KEY TO AVIATION ROUTINE WEATHER REPORT (METAR) AND AERODROME FORECASTS.

Key to Decode an ASOS (METAR) Observation (Front)

KEY TO DECODE AN ASOS (METAR) OBSERVATION

```
METAR KABC 121755Z AUTO 21016G24KT 180V240 1SM R11/P6000FT -RA BR BKN015 OVC025 06/04 A2990
RMK AO2 PK WND 20032/25 WSHFT 1715 VIS 3/4V1 1/2 VIS 3/4 RWY11 RAB07 CIG 013V017 CIG 017 RWY11 PRESFR
SLP125 P0003 60009 T00640036 10066 21012 58033 TSNO $
```

TYPE OF REPORT	METAR: hourly (scheduled) report; SPECI: special (unscheduled) report.	METAR
STATION IDENTIFIER	Four alphabetic characters; ICAO location identifier.	KABC
DATE/TIME	All dates and times in UTC using a 24-hour clock; two-digit date and four-digit time; always appended with Z to indicate UTC.	121755Z
REPORT MODIFIER	Fully automated report, no human intervention; removed when observer signed-on.	AUTO
WIND DIRECTION AND SPEED	Direction in tens of degrees from true north (first three digits); next two digits: speed in whole knots; as needed Gusts (character) followed by maximum observed speed; always appended with KT to indicate knots; 00000KT for calm; if direction varies by 60° or more a Variable wind direction group is reported.	21016G24KT 180V240
VISIBILITY	Prevailing visibility in statute miles and fractions (space between whole miles and fractions); always appended with SM to indicate statute miles; values <1/4 reported as M1/4.	1SM
RUNWAY VISUAL RANGE	10-minute RVR value in hundreds of feet; reported if prevailing visibility is ≤ one mile or RVR ≤ 6000 feet; always appended with FT to indicate feet; value prefixed with M or P to indicate value is lower or higher than the reportable RVR value .	R11/P6000FT
WEATHER PHENOMENA	RA: liquid precipitation that does not freeze; SN: frozen precipitation other than hail; UP: precipitation of unknown type; intensity prefixed to precipitation: light (-), moderate (no sign), heavy (+); FG: fog; FZFG: freezing fog (temperature below 0°C); BR: mist; HZ: haze; SQ: squall; maximum of three groups reported; augmented by observer: FC (funnel cloud/tornado/waterspout); TS (thunderstorm); GR (hail); GS (small hail; <1/4 inch); FZRA (intensity; freezing rain); VA (volcanic ash).	-RA BR
SKY CONDITION	Cloud amount and height: CLR (no clouds detected below 12000 feet); FEW (few); SCT (scattered); BKN (broken); OVC (overcast); followed by 3-digit height in hundreds of feet; or vertical visibility (VV) followed by height for indefinite ceiling.	BKN015 OVC025
TEMPERATURE/DEW POINT	Each is reported in whole degrees Celsius using two digits; values are separated by a solidus; sub-zero values are prefixed with an M (minus).	06/04
ALTIMETER	Altimeter always prefixed with an A indicating inches of mercury; reported using four digits: tens, units, tenths, and hundredths.	A2990

FIG 7-1-2

Key to Decode an ASOS (METAR) Observation (Back)

REMARKS IDENTIFIER: RMK	RMK
TORNADIC ACTIVITY: Augmented; report should include TORNADO, FUNNEL CLOUD, or WATERSPOUT; time begin/end, location, movement; e.g., TORNADO B25 N MOV E.	
TYPE OF AUTOMATED STATION: AO2; automated station with precipitation discriminator.	AO2
PEAK WIND: PK WND dddff(f)/(hh)mm; direction in tens of degrees, speed in whole knots, and time.	PK WND 20032/25
WIND SHIFT: WSHFT (hh)mm	WSHFT 1715
TOWER OR SURFACE VISIBILITY: TWR VIS vvvvv: visibility reported by tower personnel, e.g., TWR VIS 2; SFC VIS vvvvv: visibility reported by ASOS; e.g., SFC VIS 2.	
VARIABLE PREVAILING VISIBILITY: VIS $v_nv_nv_nv_nV v_xv_xv_xv_x$; reported if prevailing visibility is < 3 miles and variable.	VIS 3/4V1 1/2
VISIBILITY AT SECOND LOCATION: VIS vvvvv [LOC]; reported if different than the reported prevailing visibility in body of report.	VIS 3/4 RWY11
LIGHTNING: [FREQ] LTG [LOC]; when detected the frequency and location is reported, e.g., FRQ LTG NE.	
BEGINNING AND ENDING OF PRECIPITATION AND THUNDERSTORMS: w'w'B(hh)mmE(hh)mm; TSB(hh)mmE(hh)mm	RAB07
VIRGA: Augmented; precipitation not reaching the ground, e.g., VIRGA.	
VARIABLE CEILING HEIGHT: CIG $h_nh_nh_nVh_xh_xh_x$; reported if ceiling in body of report is < 3000 feet and variable.	CIG 013V017
CEILING HEIGHT AT SECOND LOCATION: CIG hhh [LOC]; Ceiling height reported if secondary ceilometer site is different than the ceiling height in the body of the report.	CIG 017 RWY11
PRESSURE RISING OR FALLING RAPIDLY: PRESRR or PRESFR; pressure rising or falling rapidly at time of observation.	PRESFR
SEA-LEVEL PRESSURE: SLPppp: tens, units, and tenths of SLP in hPa.	SLP125
HOURLY PRECIPITATION AMOUNT: Prrrr; in .01 inches since last METAR; a trace is P0000.	P0003
3- AND 6-HOUR PRECIPITATION AMOUNT: 6RRRR; precipitation amount in .01 inches for past 6 hours reported in 00, 06, 12, and 18 UTC observations and for past 3 hours in 03, 09, 15, and 21 UTC observations; a trace is 60000.	60009
24-HOUR PRECIPITATION AMOUNT: $7R_{24}R_{24}R_{24}R_{24}$; precipitation amount in .01 inches for past 24 hours reported in 12 UTC observation, e.g., 70015.	
HOURLY TEMPERATURE AND DEW POINT: $Ts_nT_nT_nT_nS_nT'_dT'_dT'_d$; tenth of degree Celsius; s_n: 1 if temperature below 0°C and 0 if temperature 0°C or higher.	T00640036
6-HOUR MAXIMUM TEMPERATURE: $1s_nT_xT_xT_x$; tenth of degree Celsius; 00, 06, 12, 18 UTC; s_n: 1 if temperature below 0°C and 0 if temperature 0°C or higher.	10066
6-HOUR MINIMUM TEMPERATURE: $2s_nT_nT_nT_n$; tenth of degree Celsius; 00, 06, 12, 18 UTC; s_n: 1 if temperature below 0°C and 0 if temperature 0°C or higher.	21012
24-HOUR MAXIMUM AND MINIMUM TEMPERATURE: $4s_nT_xT_xT_xs_nT_nT_nT_n$; tenth of degree Celsius; reported at midnight local standard time; 1 if temperature below 0°C and 0 if temperature 0°C or higher, e.g., 400461006.	
PRESSURE TENDENCY: 5appp; the character (a) and change in pressure (ppp; tenths of hPa) the past 3 hours.	58033
SENSOR STATUS INDICATORS: RVRNO: RVR missing; PWINO: precipitation identifier information not available; PNO: precipitation amount not available; FZRANO: freezing rain information not available; TSNO: thunderstorm information not available; VISNO [LOC]: visibility at secondary location not available, e.g. VISNO RWY06; CHINO [LOC]: (cloud-height-indicator) sky condition at secondary location not available, e.g., CHINO RWY06.	TSNO
MAINTENANCE CHECK INDICATOR: $; Maintenance needed on the system.	$

If an element or phenomena does not occur, is missing or cannot be observed, the corresponding group and space are omitted (body and/or remarks) from that particular report, except for Sea-Level Pressure (SLPppp). SLPNO shall be reported in a METAR when the SLP is not available.

U.S. DEPARTMENT OF COMMERCE - NATIONAL OCEANIC AND ATMOSPHERIC ADMINISTRATION - National Weather Service - Observing Systems Branch. 1325 East-West Highway, Silver Spring, Maryland 20910

METAR/TA2/2-8-96

FIG 7-1-3

e. TBL 7-1-1 contains a comparison of weather observing programs and the elements reported.

f. Service Standards: During 1995, a government/industry team worked to comprehensively reassess the requirements for surface observations at the nation's airports. That work resulted in agreement on a set of service standards, and the FAA and NWS ASOS sites to which the standards would apply. The term "Service Standards" refers to the level of detail in weather observation. The service standards consist of four different levels of service (A, B, C and D) as described below. Specific observational elements included in each service level are listed in TBL 7-1-2.

1. Service Level D defines the minimum acceptable level of service. It is a completely automated service in which the ASOS observation will constitute the entire observation, i.e., no additional weather information is added by a human observer. This service is referred to as a stand alone D site.

2. Service Level C is a service in which the human observer, usually an air traffic controller, augments or adds information to the automated observation. Service Level C also includes backup of ASOS elements in the event of an ASOS malfunction or an unrepresentative ASOS report. In backup, the human observer inserts the correct or missing value for the automated ASOS elements. This service is provided by air traffic controllers under the Limited Aviation Weather Reporting Station (LAWRS) process, FSS and NWS observers, and, at selected sites, Non-Federal Observation Program observers.

Two categories of airports require detail beyond Service Level C in order to enhance air traffic control efficiency and increase system capacity. Services at these airports are typically provided by contract weather observers, NWS observers, and, at some locations, FSS observers.

3. Service Level B is a service in which weather observations consist of all elements provided under Service Level C, plus augmentation of additional data beyond the capability of the ASOS. This category of airports includes smaller hubs or special airports in other ways that have worse than average bad weather operations for thunderstorms and/or freezing/frozen precipitation, and/or that are remote airports.

4. Service Level A, the highest and most demanding category, includes all the data reported in Service Standard B, plus additional requirements as specified. Service Level A covers major aviation hubs and/or high volume traffic airports with average or worse weather.

WEATHER OBSERVING PROGRAMS						
Element Reported	AWOS-A	AWOS-1	AWOS-2	AWOS-3	ASOS	Manual
Altimeter	X	X	X	X	X	X
Wind		X	X	X	X	X
Temperature/ Dew Point		X	X	X	X	X
Density Altitude		X	X	X	X	
Visibility			X	X	X	X
Clouds/Ceiling				X	X	X
Precipitation					X	X
Remarks					X	X

TBL 7-1-1

SERVICE LEVEL A	
Service Level A consists of all the elements of Service Levels B, C and D plus the elements listed to the right, if observed.	10 minute longline RVR at precedented sites or additional visibility increments of 1/8, 1/16 and 0 Sector visibility Variable sky condition Cloud layers above 12,000 feet and cloud types Widespread dust, sand and other obscurations Volcanic eruptions
SERVICE LEVEL B	
Service Level B consists of all the elements of Service Levels C and D plus the elements listed to the right, if observed.	Longline RVR at precedented sites (may be instantaneous readout) Freezing drizzle versus freezing rain Ice pellets Snow depth & snow increasing rapidly remarks Thunderstorm and lightning location remarks Observed significant weather not at the station remarks
SERVICE LEVEL C	
Service Level C consists of all the elements of Service Level D plus augmentation and backup by a human observer or an air traffic control specialist on location nearby. Backup consists of inserting the correct value if the system malfunctions or is unrepresentative. Augmentation consists of adding the elements listed to the right, if observed. During hours that the observing facility is closed, the site reverts to Service Level D.	Thunderstorms Tornadoes Hail Virga Volcanic ash Tower visibility Operationally significant remarks as deemed appropriate by the observer
SERVICE LEVEL D	
This level of service consists of an ASOS continually measuring the atmosphere at a point near the runway. The ASOS senses and measures the weather parameters listed to the right.	Wind Visibility Precipitation/Obstruction to vision Cloud height Sky cover Temperature Dew point Altimeter

TBL 7-1-2

7-1-11. WEATHER RADAR SERVICES

a. The National Weather Service operates a network of radar sites for detecting coverage, intensity, and movement of precipitation. The network is supplemented by FAA and DOD radar sites in the western sections of the country. Local warning radar sites augment the network by operating on an as needed basis to support warning and forecast programs.

b. Scheduled radar observations are taken hourly and transmitted in alpha-numeric format on weather telecommunications circuits for flight planning purposes. Under certain conditions, special radar reports are issued in addition to the hourly transmittals. Data con-

tained in the reports are also collected by the National Center for Environmental Prediction and used to prepare national radar summary charts for dissemination on facsimile circuits.

c. A clear radar display (no echoes) does not mean that there is no significant weather within the coverage of the radar site. Clouds and fog are not detected by the radar. However, when echoes are present, turbulence can be implied by the intensity of the precipitation, and icing is implied by the presence of the precipitation at temperatures at or below zero degrees Celsius. Used in conjunction with other weather products, radar provides invaluable information for weather avoidance and flight planning.

NEXRAD Coverage

COMPOSITE CONUS NEXRAD COVERAGE
DELIVERIES AS OF AUGUST 20, 1996

+   EQUIPMENT DELIVERY DATE OF 8-20-96 OR EARLIER

+   EQUIPMENT DELIVERY DATE OF 8-21-96 OR LATER

    AREAS NOT COVERED BELOW
    10,000 ft ABOVE SITE LEVEL

FIG 7-1-4

NEXRAD Coverage

FIG 7-1-5

NEXRAD Coverage

FIG 7-1-6

d. All En Route Flight Advisory Service facilities and AFSS's have equipment to directly access the radar displays from the individual weather radar sites. Specialists at these locations are trained to interpret the display for pilot briefing and inflight advisory services. The Center Weather Service Units located in ARTCC's also have access to weather radar displays and provide support to all air traffic facilities within their center's area.

e. Additional information on weather radar products and services can be found in AC 00-45, AVIATION WEATHER SERVICES.

REFERENCE-
PILOT/CONTROLLER GLOSSARY, RADAR WEATHER ECHO INTENSITY LEVELS.
AIM, THUNDERSTORMS, PARAGRAPH 7-1-25.
A/FD, CHARTS, NWS UPPER AIR OBSERVING STATIONS AND WEATHER NETWORK FOR THE LOCATION OF SPECIFIC RADAR SITES.

7-1-12. ATC INFLIGHT WEATHER AVOIDANCE ASSISTANCE

a. ATC Radar Weather Display:

1. Areas of radar weather clutter result from rain or moisture. *Radars cannot detect turbulence.* The determination of the intensity of the weather displayed is based on its precipitation density. Generally, the turbulence associated with a very heavy rate of rainfall will normally be more severe than any associated with a very light rainfall rate.

2. ARTCC's use Narrowband Radar which provides the controller with two distinct levels of weather intensity by assigning radar display symbols for specific precipitation densities measured by the narrowband system.

b. Weather Avoidance Assistance:

1. To the extent possible, controllers will issue pertinent information on weather or chaff areas and assist pilots in avoiding such areas when requested. Pilots should respond to a weather advisory by either acknowledging the advisory or by acknowledging the advisory and requesting an alternative course of action as follows:

(a) Request to deviate off course by stating the number of miles and the direction of the requested deviation. In this case, when the requested deviation is approved, navigation is at the pilot's prerogative, but must maintain the altitude assigned by ATC and to remain within the specified mileage of the original course.

(b) Request a new route to avoid the affected area.

(c) Request a change of altitude.

(d) Request radar vectors around the affected areas.

2. For obvious reasons of safety, an IFR pilot must not deviate from the course or altitude or flight level without a proper ATC clearance. When weather conditions encountered are so severe that an immediate deviation is determined to be necessary and time will not permit approval by ATC, the pilot's emergency authority may be exercised.

3. When the pilot requests clearance for a route deviation or for an ATC radar vector, the controller must evaluate the air traffic picture in the affected area, and coordinate with other controllers (if ATC jurisdictional boundaries may be crossed) before replying to the request.

4. It should be remembered that the controller's primary function is to provide safe separation between aircraft. Any additional service, such as weather avoidance assistance, can only be provided to the extent that it does not derogate the primary function. It's also worth noting that the separation workload is generally greater than normal when weather disrupts the usual flow of traffic. ATC radar limitations and frequency congestion may also be a factor in limiting the controller's capability to provide additional service.

5. It is very important, therefore, that the request for deviation or radar vector be forwarded to ATC as far in advance as possible. Delay in submitting it may delay or even preclude ATC approval or require that additional restrictions be placed on the clearance. Insofar as possible the following information should be furnished to ATC when requesting clearance to detour around weather activity:

(a) Proposed point where detour will commence.

(b) Proposed route and extent of detour (direction and distance).

(c) Point where original route will be resumed.

(d) Flight conditions (IFR or VFR).

(e) Any further deviation that may become necessary as the flight progresses.

(f) Advise if the aircraft is equipped with functioning airborne radar.

6. To a large degree, the assistance that might be rendered by ATC will depend upon the weather information available to controllers. Due to the extremely transitory nature of severe weather situations, the controller's weather information may be of only limited value if based on weather observed on radar only. Frequent updates by pilots giving specific information as to the area affected, altitudes, intensity and nature of the severe weather can be of considerable value. Such reports are relayed by radio or phone to other pilots and controllers and also receive widespread teletypewriter dissemination.

7. Obtaining IFR clearance or an ATC radar vector to circumnavigate severe weather can often be accommodated more readily in the en route areas away from terminals because there is usually less congestion and, therefore, offer greater freedom of action. In terminal areas, the problem is more acute because of traffic density, ATC coordination requirements, complex departure and arrival routes, adjacent airports, etc. As a consequence, controllers are less likely to be able to accommodate all requests for weather detours in a terminal area or be in a position to volunteer such routing to the pilot. Nevertheless, pilots should not hesitate to advise controllers of any observed severe weather and should specifically advise controllers if they desire circumnavigation of observed weather.

c. Procedures for Weather Deviations and Other Contingencies in Oceanic Controlled Airspace:

1. When the pilot initiates communications with ATC, rapid response may be obtained by stating "WEATHER DEVIATION REQUIRED" to indicate priority is desired on the frequency and for ATC response.

2. The pilot still retains the option of initiating the communications using the urgency call "PAN-PAN" 3 times to alert all listening parties of a special handling condition which will receive ATC priority for issuance of a clearance or assistance.

3. ATC will:

(a) Approve the deviation,

(b) Provide vertical separation and then approve the deviation, or

(c) If ATC is unable to establish vertical separation, ATC shall advise the pilot that standard separation cannot be applied; provide essential traffic information for all affected aircraft, to the extent practicable; and if possible, suggest a course of action. ATC may suggest

that the pilot climb or descend to a contingency altitude (1,000 feet above or below that assigned if operating above FL 290; 500 feet above or below that assigned if operating at or below FL 290).

PHRASEOLOGY-
STANDARD SEPARATION NOT AVAILABLE, DEVIATE AT PILOT'S DISCRETION; SUGGEST CLIMB (or descent) TO (appropriate altitude); TRAFFIC (position and altitude); REPORT DEVIATION COMPLETE.

4. The pilot will follow the ATC advisory altitude when approximately 10 NM from track as well as execute the procedures detailed in paragraph 7-1-12c.5.

5. If contact cannot be established or revised ATC clearance or advisory is not available and deviation from track is required, the pilot shall take the following actions:

(a) If possible, deviate away from an organized track or route system.

(b) Broadcast aircraft position and intentions on the frequency in use, as well as on frequency 121.5 MHz at suitable intervals stating: flight identification (operator call sign), flight level, track code or ATS route designator, and extent of deviation expected.

(c) Watch for conflicting traffic both visually and by reference to TCAS (if equipped).

(d) Turn on aircraft exterior lights.

(e) Deviations of less than 10 NM or operations within COMPOSITE (NOPAC and CEPAC) Airspace, should REMAIN at ASSIGNED altitude. Otherwise, when the aircraft is approximately 10 NM from track, initiate an altitude change based on the following criteria:

Route Centerline/Track	Deviations >10 NM	Altitude Change
EAST 000 - 179°M	LEFT	DESCEND 500 FEET
	RIGHT	CLIMB 500 FEET
WEST 180-359°M	LEFT	CLIMB 500 FEET
	RIGHT	DESCEND 500 FEET
Pilot Memory Slogan: "East right up, West right down."		

TBL 7-1-3

(f) When returning to track, be at assigned flight level when the aircraft is within approximately 10 NM of centerline.

(g) If contact was not established prior to deviating, continue to attempt to contact ATC to obtain a clearance. If contact was established, continue to keep ATC advised of intentions and obtain essential traffic information.

7-1-13. RUNWAY VISUAL RANGE (RVR)

There are currently two configurations of RVR in the NAS commonly identified as Taskers and New Generation RVR. The Taskers are the existing configuration which uses transmissometer technology. The New Generation RVR's were deployed in November 1994 and use forward scatter technology. The New Generation RVR's are currently being deployed in the NAS to replace the existing Taskers.

a. RVR values are measured by transmissometers mounted on 14-foot towers along the runway. A full RVR system consists of:

1. Transmissometer projector and related items.

2. Transmissometer receiver (detector) and related items.

3. Analogue recorder.

4. Signal data converter and related items.

5. Remote digital or remote display programmer.

b. The transmissometer projector and receiver are mounted on towers 250 feet apart. A known intensity of light is emitted from the projector and is measured by the receiver. Any obscuring matter such as rain, snow, dust, fog, haze or smoke reduces the light intensity arriving at the receiver. The resultant intensity measurement is then converted to an RVR value by the signal data converter. These values are displayed by readout equipment in the associated air traffic facility and updated approximately once every minute for controller issuance to pilots.

c. The signal data converter receives information on the high intensity runway edge light setting in use (step 3, 4, or 5); transmission values from the transmissometer and the sensing of day or night conditions. From the three data sources, the system will compute appropriate RVR values.

d. An RVR transmissometer established on a 250 foot baseline provides digital readouts to a minimum of 600 feet, which are displayed in 200 foot increments to 3,000 feet and in 500 foot increments from 3,000 feet to a maximum value of 6,000 feet.

e. RVR values for Category IIIa operations extend down to 700 feet RVR; however, only 600 and 800 feet are reportable RVR increments. The 800 RVR reportable value covers a range of 701 feet to 900 feet and is therefore a valid minimum indication of Category IIIa operations.

f. Approach categories with the corresponding minimum RVR values: (See TBL 7-1-4.)

Approach Category/Minimum RVR Table

Category	Visibility (RVR)
Nonprecision	2,400 feet
Category I	1,800 feet
Category II	1,200 feet
Category IIIa	700 feet
Category IIIb	150 feet
Category IIIc	0 feet

TBL 7-1-4

g. Ten minute maximum and minimum RVR values for the designated RVR runway are reported in the body of the aviation weather report when the prevailing visibility is less than one mile and/or the RVR is 6,000 feet or less. ATCT's report RVR when the prevailing visibility is 1 mile or less and/or the RVR is 6,000 feet or less.

h. Details on the requirements for the operational use of RVR are contained in FAA AC 97-1, "Runway Visual Range (RVR)." Pilots are responsible for compliance with minimums prescribed for their class of operations in the appropriate FAR's and/or operations specifications.

i. RVR values are also measured by forward scatter meters mounted on 14-foot frangible fiberglass poles. A full RVR system consists of:

1. Forward scatter meter with a transmitter, receiver and associated items.

2. A runway light intensity monitor (RLIM).

3. An ambient light sensor (ALS).

4. A data processor unit (DPU).

5. Controller display (CD).

j. The forward scatter meter is mounted on a 14-foot frangible pole. Infrared light is emitted from the transmitter and received by the receiver. Any obscuring matter such as rain, snow, dust, fog, haze or smoke increases the amount of scattered light reaching the receiver. The resulting measurement along with inputs from the runway light intensity monitor and the ambient light sensor are forwarded to the DPU which calculates the proper RVR value. The RVR values are displayed locally and remotely on controller displays.

k. The runway light intensity monitors both the runway edge and centerline light step settings (steps 1 through 5). Centerline light step settings are used for CAT IIIb operations. Edge Light step settings are used for CAT I, II, and IIIa operations.

l. New Generation RVR's can measure and display RVR values down to the lowest limits of Category IIIb operations (150 feet RVR). RVR values are displayed in 100 feet increments and are reported as follows:

1. 100-feet increments for products below 800 feet.

2. 200-feet increments for products between 800 feet and 3,000 feet.

3. 500-feet increments for products between 3,000 feet and 6,500 feet.

4. 25-meter increments for products below 150 meters.

5. 50-meter increments for products between 150 meters and 800 meters.

6. 100-meter increments for products between 800 meters and 1,200 meters.

7. 200-meter increments for products between 1,200 meters and 2,000 meters.

7-1-14. REPORTING OF CLOUD HEIGHTS

a. Ceiling, by definition in the CFR's and as used in aviation weather reports and forecasts, is the height above ground (or water) level of the lowest layer of clouds or obscuring phenomenon that is reported as "broken," "overcast," or "obscuration," e.g., an aerodrome forecast (TAF) which reads "BKN030" refers to height above ground level. An area forecast which reads "BKN030" indicates that the height is above mean sea level.

REFERENCE-
AIM, KEY TO ROUTINE WEATHER REPORT (METAR) AND AERODROME FORECASTS (TAF), PARAGRAPH 7-1-27, DEFINES "BROKEN," "OVERCAST," AND "OBSCURATION."

b. Pilots usually report height values above MSL, since they determine heights by the altimeter. This is taken in account when disseminating and otherwise applying information received from pilots. ("Ceiling" heights are always above ground level.) In reports disseminated as PIREP's, height references are given the same as received from pilots, that is, above MSL.

c. In area forecasts or inflight advisories, ceilings are denoted by the contraction "CIG" when used with sky cover symbols as in "LWRG TO CIG OVC005," or the contraction "AGL" after, the forecast cloud height value. When the cloud base is given in height above MSL, it is so indicated by the contraction "MSL" or "ASL" following the height value. The heights of clouds tops, freezing level, icing, and turbulence are always given in heights above ASL or MSL.

7-1-15. REPORTING PREVAILING VISIBILITY

a. Surface (horizontal) visibility is reported in METAR reports in terms of statute miles and increments thereof; e.g., $1/16$, $1/8$, $3/16$, $1/4$, $5/16$, $3/8$, $1/2$, $5/8$, $3/4$, $7/8$, 1, 1 $1/8$, etc. (Visibility reported by an unaugmented automated site is reported differently than in a manual report, i.e., $M1/4$, $1/4$, $1/2$, $3/4$, 1, 1 $1/4$, 1 $1/2$, 1 $3/4$, 2, 2 $1/2$, 3, 4, 5, etc.) Visibility is determined through the ability to see and identify preselected and prominent objects at a known distance from the usual point of observation. Visibilities which are determined to be less than 7 miles, identify the obscuring atmospheric condition; e.g., fog, haze, smoke, etc., or combinations thereof.

b. Prevailing visibility is the greatest visibility equalled or exceeded throughout at least one half of the horizon circle, not necessarily contiguous. Segments of the horizon circle which may have a significantly different visibility may be reported in the remarks section of the weather report; i.e., the southeastern quadrant of the horizon circle may be determined to be 2 miles in mist while the remaining quadrants are determined to be 3 miles in mist.

c. When the prevailing visibility at the usual point of observation, or at the tower level, is less than 4 miles, certificated tower personnel will take visibility observations in addition to those taken at the usual point of observation. The lower of these two values will be used as the prevailing visibility for aircraft operations.

7-1-16. ESTIMATING INTENSITY OF RAIN AND ICE PELLETS

a. RAIN:

1. Light: From scattered drops that, regardless of duration, do not completely wet an exposed surface up to a condition where individual drops are easily seen.

2. Moderate: Individual drops are not clearly identifiable; spray is observable just above pavements and other hard surfaces.

3. Heavy: Rain seemingly falls in sheets; individual drops are not identifiable; heavy spray to height of several inches is observed over hard surfaces.

b. ICE PELLETS:

1. Light: Scattered pellets that do not completely cover an exposed surface regardless of duration. Visibility is not affected.

2. Moderate: Slow accumulation on ground. Visibility reduced by ice pellets to less than 7 statute miles.

3. Heavy: Rapid accumulation on ground. Visibility reduced by ice pellets to less than 3 statute miles.

7-1-17. ESTIMATING INTENSITY OF SNOW OR DRIZZLE (BASED ON VISIBILITY)

a. Light: Visibility more than $1/2$ statute mile.

b. Moderate: Visibility from more than $1/4$ statute mile to $1/2$ statute mile.

c. Heavy: Visibility $1/4$ statute mile or less.

7-1-18. PILOT WEATHER REPORTS (PIREP'S)

a. FAA air traffic facilities are required to solicit PIREP's when the following conditions are reported or forecast: ceilings at or below 5,000 feet; visibility at or below 5 miles (surface or aloft); thunderstorms and related phenomena; icing of light degree or greater; turbulence of moderate degree or greater; wind shear and reported or forecast volcanic ash clouds.

b. Pilots are urged to cooperate and promptly volunteer reports of these conditions and other atmospheric data such as: cloud bases, tops and layers; flight visibility; precipitation; visibility restrictions such as haze, smoke and dust; wind at altitude; and temperature aloft.

c. PIREP's should be given to the ground facility with which communications are established; i.e., EFAS, AFSS/FSS, ARTCC, or terminal ATC. One of the primary duties of EFAS facilities, radio call "FLIGHT WATCH," is to serve as a collection point for the exchange of PIREP's with en route aircraft.

d. If pilots are not able to make PIREP's by radio, reporting upon landing of the inflight conditions encountered to the nearest AFSS/FSS or Weather Forecast Office will be helpful. Some of the uses made of the reports are:

1. The ATCT uses the reports to expedite the flow of air traffic in the vicinity of the field and for hazardous weather avoidance procedures.

2. The AFSS/FSS uses the reports to brief other pilots, to provide inflight advisories, and weather avoidance information to en route aircraft.

3. The ARTCC uses the reports to expedite the flow of en route traffic, to determine most favorable altitudes, and to issue hazardous weather information within the center's area.

4. The NWS uses the reports to verify or amend conditions contained in aviation forecast and advisories. In some cases, pilot reports of hazardous conditions are the triggering mechanism for the issuance of advisories. They also use the reports for pilot weather briefings.

5. The NWS, other government organizations, the military, and private industry groups use PIREP's for research activities in the study of meteorological phenomena.

6. All air traffic facilities and the NWS forward the reports received from pilots into the weather distribution system to assure the information is made available to all pilots and other interested parties.

e. The FAA, NWS, and other organizations that enter PIREP's into the weather reporting system use the format listed in TBL 7-1-5. Items 1 through 6 are included in all transmitted PIREP's along with one or more of items 7 through 13. Although the PIREP should be as complete and concise as possible, pilots should not be overly concerned with strict format or phraseology. The important thing is that the information is relayed so other pilots may benefit from your observation. If a portion of the report needs clarification, the ground station will request the information. Completed PIREP's will be transmitted to weather circuits as in the following examples:

EXAMPLE-
1 *KCMH UA /OV APE 230010/TM 1516/FL085/TP BE20/SK BKN065/WX FV03SM HZ FU/TA 20/TB LGT*

NOTE-
1 *One zero miles southwest of Appleton VOR; time 1516 UTC; altitude eight thousand five hundred; aircraft type BE200; bases of the broken cloud layer is six thousand five hundred; flight visibility 3 miles with haze and smoke; air temperature 20 degrees Celsius; light turbulence.*

EXAMPLE-
2 *KCRW UV /OV KBKW 360015-KCRW/TM 1815/FL120//TP BE99/SK IMC/WX RA/TA M08 /WV 290030/TB LGT-MDT/IC LGT RIME/RM MDT MXD ICG DURGC KROA NWBND FL080-100 1750Z*

NOTE-
2 *From 15 miles north of Beckley VOR to Charleston VOR; time 1815 UTC; altitude 12,000 feet; type aircraft, BE-99; in clouds; rain; temperature minus 8 Celsius; wind 290 degrees true at 30 knots; light to moderate turbulence; light rime icing; encountered moderate mixed icing during climb northwestbound from Roanoke, VA, between 8,000 and 10,000 feet at 1750 UTC.*

PIREP ELEMENT CODE CHART

	PIREP ELEMENT	PIREP CODE	CONTENTS
1.	3-letter station identifier	XXX	Nearest weather reporting location to the reported phenomenon
2.	Report type	UA or UUA	Routine or Urgent PIREP
3.	Location	/OV	In relation to a VOR
4.	Time	/TM	Coordinated Universal Time
5.	Altitude	/FL	Essential for turbulence and icing reports
6.	Type Aircraft	/TP	Essential for turbulence and icing reports
7.	Sky cover	/SK	Cloud height and coverage (sky clear, few, scattered, broken, or overcast)
8.	Weather	/WX	Flight visibility, precipitation, restrictions to visibility, etc.
9.	Temperature	/TA	Degrees Celsius
10.	Wind	/WV	Direction in degrees true north and speed in knots
11.	Turbulence	/TB	See AIM paragraph 7-1-20
12.	Icing	/IC	See AIM paragraph 7-1-19
13.	Remarks	/RM	For reporting elements not included or to clarify previously reported items

TBL 7-1-5 ■

7-1-19. PIREP'S RELATING TO AIRFRAME ICING

a. The effects of ice on aircraft are cumulative-thrust is reduced, drag increases, lift lessens, and weight increases. The results are an increase in stall speed and a deterioration of aircraft performance. In extreme cases, 2 to 3 inches of ice can form on the leading edge of the airfoil in less than 5 minutes. It takes but $1/2$ inch of ice to reduce the lifting power of some aircraft by 50 percent and increases the frictional drag by an equal percentage.

b. A pilot can expect icing when flying in visible precipitation, such as rain or cloud droplets, and the temperature is between +02 and -10 degrees Celsius. When icing is detected, a pilot should do one of two things, particularly if the aircraft is not equipped with deicing equipment; get out of the area of precipitation; or go to an altitude where the temperature is above freezing. This "warmer" altitude may not always be a lower altitude. Proper preflight action includes obtaining information on the freezing level and the above freezing levels in precipitation areas. Report icing to ATC, and if operating IFR, request new routing or altitude if icing will be a hazard. Be sure to give the type of aircraft to ATC when reporting icing. The following describes how to report icing conditions.

1. *Trace:* Ice becomes perceptible. Rate of accumulation is slightly greater than the rate of sublimation.

It is not hazardous even though deicing/anti-icing equipment is not utilized unless encountered for an extended period of time (over 1 hour).

2. *Light:* The rate of accumulation may create a problem if flight is prolonged in this environment (over 1 hour). Occasional use of deicing/anti-icing equipment removes/prevents accumulation. It does not present a problem if the deicing/anti-icing equipment is used.

3. *Moderate:* The rate of accumulation is such that even short encounters become potentially hazardous and use of deicing/anti-icing equipment or flight diversion is necessary.

4. *Severe:* The rate of accumulation is such that deicing/anti-icing equipment fails to reduce or control the hazard. Immediate flight diversion is necessary.

EXAMPLE-
Pilot report: give aircraft identification, location, time (UTC), intensity of type, altitude/FL, aircraft type, indicated air speed (IAS), and outside air temperature (OAT).

NOTE-
1 *Rime ice: rough, milky, opaque ice formed by the instantaneous freezing of small supercooled water droplets.*
2 *Clear ice: a glossy, clear, or translucent ice formed by the relatively slow freezing of large supercooled water droplets.*
3 *The OAT should be requested by the AFSS/FSS or ATC if not included in the PIREP.*

AIM

Turbulence Reporting Criteria Table

Intensity	Aircraft Reaction	Reaction Inside Aircraft	Reporting Term-Definition
Light	Turbulence that momentarily causes slight, erratic changes in altitude and/or attitude (pitch, roll, yaw). Report as **Light Turbulence;** [1] or Turbulence that causes slight, rapid and somewhat rhythmic bumpiness without appreciable changes in altitude or attitude. Report as **Light Chop.**	Occupants may feel a slight strain against seat belts or shoulder straps. Unsecured objects may be displaced slightly. Food service may be conducted and little or no difficulty is encountered in walking.	Occasional–Less than $1/3$ of the time. Intermittent–$1/3$ to $2/3$. Continuous–More than $2/3$.
Moderate	Turbulence that is similar to Light Turbulence but of greater intensity. Changes in altitude and/or attitude occur but the aircraft remains in positive control at all times. It usually causes variations in indicated airspeed. Report as **Moderate Turbulence;** [1] or Turbulence that is similar to Light Chop but of greater intensity. It causes rapid bumps or jolts without appreciable changes in aircraft altitude or attitude. Report as **Moderate Chop.** [1]	Occupants feel definite strains against seat belts or shoulder straps. Unsecured objects are dislodged. Food service and walking are difficult.	**NOTE** 1. Pilots should report location(s), time (UTC), intensity, whether in or near clouds, altitude, type of aircraft and, when applicable, duration of turbulence. 2. Duration may be based on time between two locations or over a single location. All locations should be readily identifiable.
Severe	Turbulence that causes large, abrupt changes in altitude and/or attitude. It usually causes large variations in indicated airspeed. Aircraft may be momentarily out of control. Report **as Severe Turbulence.** [1]	Occupants are forced violently against seat belts or shoulder straps. Unsecured objects are tossed about. Food Service and walking are impossible.	**EXAMPLES:** a. Over Omaha. 1232Z, Moderate Turbulence, in cloud, Flight Level 310, B707.
Extreme	Turbulence in which the aircraft is violently tossed about and is practically impossible to control. It may cause structural damage. Report as **Extreme Turbulence.** [1]		b. From 50 miles south of Albuquerque to 30 miles north of Phoenix, 1210Z to 1250Z, occasional Moderate Chop, Flight Level 330, DC8.

[1] High level turbulence (normally above 15,000 feet ASL) not associated with cumuliform cloudiness, including thunderstorms, should be reported as CAT (clear air turbulence) preceded by the appropriate intensity, or light or moderate chop.

TBL 7-1-6

7-1-20. PIREP'S RELATING TO TURBULENCE

a. When encountering turbulence, pilots are urgently requested to report such conditions to ATC as soon as practicable. PIREP's relating to turbulence should state:

1. Aircraft location.

2. Time of occurrence in UTC.

3. Turbulence intensity.

4. Whether the turbulence occurred in or near clouds.

5. Aircraft altitude or flight level.

6. Type of Aircraft.

7. Duration of turbulence.

EXAMPLE-
[1] *Over Omaha, 1232Z, moderate turbulence in clouds at Flight Level three one zero, Boeing 707.*
[2] *From five zero miles south of Albuquerque to three zero miles north of Phoenix, 1250Z, occasional moderate chop at Flight Level three three zero, DC8.*

b. Duration and classification of intensity should be made using TBL 7-1-6.

7-1-21. WIND SHEAR PIREP'S

a. Because unexpected changes in wind speed and direction can be hazardous to aircraft operations at low altitudes on approach to and departing from airports, pilots are urged to promptly volunteer reports to controllers of wind shear conditions they encounter. An advance warning of this information will assist other pilots in avoiding or coping with a wind shear on approach or departure.

b. When describing conditions, use of the terms "negative" or "positive" wind shear should be avoided. PIREP's of "negative wind shear on final," intended to describe loss of airspeed and lift, have been interpreted to mean that no wind shear was encountered. The recommended method for wind shear reporting is to state the loss or gain of airspeed and the altitudes at which it was encountered.

EXAMPLE-

1 *Denver Tower, Cessna 1234 encountered wind shear, loss of 20 knots at 400.*

2 *Tulsa Tower, American 721 encountered wind shear on final, gained 25 knots between 600 and 400 feet followed by loss of 40 knots between 400 feet and surface.*

1. Pilots who are not able to report wind shear in these specific terms are encouraged to make reports in terms of the effect upon their aircraft.

EXAMPLE-

Miami Tower, Gulfstream 403 Charlie encountered an abrupt wind shear at 800 feet on final, max thrust required.

2. Pilots using Inertial Navigation Systems (INS) should report the wind and altitude both above and below the shear level.

7-1-22. CLEAR AIR TURBULENCE (CAT) PIREP'S

CAT has become a very serious operational factor to flight operations at all levels and especially to jet traffic flying in excess of 15,000 feet. The best available information on this phenomenon must come from pilots via the PIREP reporting procedures. All pilots encountering CAT conditions are urgently requested to report time, location, and intensity (light, moderate, severe, or extreme) of the element to the FAA facility with which they are maintaining radio contact. If time and conditions permit, elements should be reported according to the standards for other PIREP's and position reports.

REFERENCE-
AIM, PIREP'S RELATING TO TURBULENCE, PARAGRAPH 7-1-20.

7-1-23. MICROBURSTS

a. Relatively recent meteorological studies have confirmed the existence of microburst phenomenon. Microbursts are small scale intense downdrafts which, on reaching the surface, spread outward in all directions from the downdraft center. This causes the presence of both vertical and horizontal wind shears that can be extremely hazardous to all types and categories of aircraft, especially at low altitudes. Due to their small size, short life span, and the fact that they can occur over areas without surface precipitation, microbursts are not easily detectable using conventional weather radar or wind shear alert systems.

b. Parent clouds producing microburst activity can be any of the low or middle layer convective cloud types. Note, however, that microbursts commonly occur within the heavy rain portion of thunderstorms, and in much weaker, benign appearing convective cells that have little or no precipitation reaching the ground.

Evolution of a Microburst

Vertical cross section of the evolution of a microburst wind field. T is the time of initial divergence at the surface. The shading refers to the vector wind speeds. Figure adapted from Wilson et al., 1984, Microburst Wind Structure and Evaluation of Doppler Radar for Wind Shear Detection, DOT/FAA Report No. DOT/FAA/PM-84/29, National Technical Information Service, Springfield, VA 37 pp.

FIG 7-1-7

c. The life cycle of a microburst as it descends in a convective rain shaft is seen in FIG 7-1-7. An important consideration for pilots is the fact that the microburst intensifies for about 5 minutes after it strikes the ground.

d. Characteristics of microbursts include:

1. *Size:* The microburst downdraft is typically less than 1 mile in diameter as it descends from the cloud base to about 1,000-3,000 feet above the ground. In the transition zone near the ground, the downdraft changes to a horizontal outflow that can extend to approximately 2 1/2 miles in diameter.

2. *Intensity:* The downdrafts can be as strong as 6,000 feet per minute. Horizontal winds near the surface can be as strong as 45 knots resulting in a 90 knot shear (headwind to tailwind change for a traversing aircraft) across the microburst. These strong horizontal winds occur within a few hundred feet of the ground.

3. *Visual Signs:* Microbursts can be found almost anywhere that there is convective activity. They may be embedded in heavy rain associated with a thunderstorm or in light rain in benign appearing virga. When there is little or no precipitation at the surface accompanying the microburst, a ring of blowing dust may be the only visual clue of its existence.

4. *Duration:* An individual microburst will seldom last longer than 15 minutes from the time it strikes the ground until dissipation. The horizontal winds continue to increase during the first 5 minutes with the maximum intensity winds lasting approximately 2-4 minutes. Sometimes microbursts are concentrated into a line structure, and under these conditions, activity may continue for as long as an hour. Once microburst activity starts, multiple microbursts in the same general area are not uncommon and should be expected.

Microburst Encounter During Takeoff

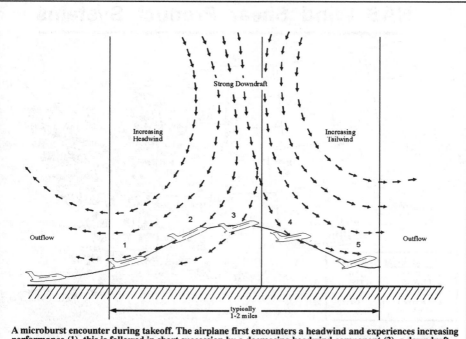

A microburst encounter during takeoff. The airplane first encounters a headwind and experiences increasing performance (1), this is followed in short succession by a decreasing headwind component (2), a downdraft (3), and finally a strong tailwind (4), where 2 through 5 all result in decreasing performance of the airplane. Position (5) represents an extreme situation just prior to impact. Figure courtesy of Walter Frost, FWG Associates, Inc., Tullahoma, Tennessee.

FIG 7-1-8

e. Microburst wind shear may create a severe hazard for aircraft within 1,000 feet of the ground, particularly during the approach to landing and landing and take-off phases. The impact of a microburst on aircraft which have the unfortunate experience of penetrating one is characterized in FIG 7-1-8. The aircraft may encounter a headwind (performance increasing) followed by a downdraft and tailwind (both performance decreasing), possibly resulting in terrain impact.

FIG 7-1-9

f. Detection of Microbursts, Wind Shear and Gust Fronts

1. FAA's Integrated Wind Shear Detection Plan

(a) The FAA currently employs an integrated plan for wind shear detection that will significantly improve both the safety and capacity of the majority of the airports currently served by the air carriers. This plan integrates several programs, such as the Integrated Terminal Weather System (ITWS), Terminal Doppler Weather Radar (TDWR), Weather System Processor (WSP), and Low Level Wind Shear Alert Systems (LLWAS) into a single strategic concept that significantly improves the aviation weather information in the terminal area. (See FIG 7-1-9.)

(b) The wind shear/microburst information and warnings are displayed on the ribbon display terminals (RBDT) located in the tower cabs. They are identical (and standardized) in the LLWAS, TDWR and WSP

systems, and so designed that the controller does not need to interpret the data, but simply read the displayed information to the pilot. The RBDT's are constantly monitored by the controller to ensure the rapid and timely dissemination of any hazardous event(s) to the pilot.

(c) The early detection of a wind shear/microburst event, and the subsequent warning(s) issued to an aircraft on approach or departure, will alert the pilot/crew to the potential of, and to be prepared for, a situation that could become very dangerous! Without these warnings, the aircraft may NOT be able to climb out of, or safely transition, the event, resulting in a catastrophe. The air carriers, working with the FAA, have developed specialized training programs using their simulators to train and prepare their pilots on the demanding aircraft procedures required to escape these very dangerous wind shear and/or microburst encounters.

LLWAS SITING CRITERIA

FIG 7-1-10

2. Low Level Wind Shear Alert System (LLWAS)

(a) The LLWAS provides wind data and software processes to detect the presence of hazardous wind shear and microbursts in the vicinity of an airport. Wind sensors, mounted on poles sometimes as high as 150 feet, are (ideally) located 2,000 - 3,500 feet, but not more than 5,000 feet, from the centerline of the runway. (See FIG 7-1-10.)

(b) LLWAS was fielded in 1988 at 110 airports across the nation. Many of these systems have been replaced by new TDWR and WSP technology. Eventually all LLWAS systems will be phased out; however, 39 airports will be upgraded to the LLWAS-NE (Network Expansion) system, which employs the very latest software and sensor technology. The new LLWAS-NE systems will not only provide the controller with wind shear warnings and alerts, including wind shear/microburst detection at the centerfield wind sensor location, but will also provide the location of the hazards relative to the airport runway(s). It will also have the flexibility and capability to grow with the airport as new runways are built. As many as 32 sensors, strategically located around the airport and in relationship to its runway configuration, can be accommodated by the LLWAS-NE network.

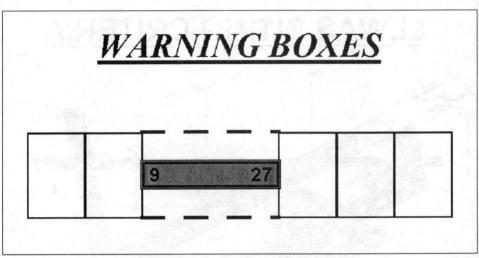

FIG 7-1-11

3. Terminal Doppler Weather Radar (TDWR)

(a) TDWR's are being deployed at 45 locations across the United States. Optimum locations for TDWR's are 8 to 12 miles off of the airport proper, and designed to look at the airspace around and over the airport to detect microbursts, gust fronts, wind shifts and precipitation intensities. TDWR products advise the controller of wind shear and microburst events impacting all runways and the areas $1/2$ mile on either side of the extended centerline of the runways out to 3 miles on final approach and 2 miles out on departure. (FIG 7-1-11 is a theoretical view of the warning boxes, including the runway, that the software uses in determining the location(s) of wind shear or microbursts). These warnings are displayed (as depicted in the examples in subparagraph 5) on the RBDT.

(b) It is very important to understand what TDWR does NOT DO:

it **DOES NOT** warn of wind shear outside of the alert boxes (on the arrival and departure ends of the runways);

it **DOES NOT** detect wind shear that is NOT a microburst or a gust front;

it **DOES NOT** detect gusty or cross wind conditions;

and, it **DOES NOT** detect turbulence.

However, research and development is continuing on these systems. Future improvements may include such areas as storm motion (movement), improved gust front detection, storm growth and decay, microburst prediction, and turbulence detection.

(c) TDWR also provides a geographical situation display (GSD) for supervisors and traffic management specialists for planning purposes. The GSD displays (in color) 6 levels of weather (precipitation), gust fronts and predicted storm movement(s). See FIG 7-1-12 for a sample of what that display looks like. This data is used by the tower supervisor(s), traffic management specialists and controllers to plan for runway changes and arrival/departure route changes in order to both reduce aircraft delays and increase airport capacity.

NCAR GSD

RANGE
[5m] [15m] [30m] [50m]

SCREEN
[1] [2] [3] [4]
[5] [6] [7] [8]

MAPS
☑ Vortac & fixes
☑ ASR rings
☑ Airports
☐ Interstates

PRECIPITATION LEVELS
[Off] [1-6] [3-6] [5-6]

WIND SHIFT:
[Off] [On]

DATE: 08/16/88
TIME: 17:04:24
PDATE: 07/11/88
MTIME: 22:09:00
GTIME: 22:04:01

MB: UP
GF: UP
PRECIP: UP
LLWAS: UP

FIG 7-1-12

4. Weather Systems Processor (WSP)

(a) The WSP provides the controller, supervisor, traffic management specialist, and ultimately the pilot, with the same products as the terminal doppler weather radar (TDWR) at a fraction of the cost of a TDWR. This is accomplished by utilizing new technologies to access the weather channel capabilities of the existing ASR-9 radar located on or near the airport, thus eliminating the requirements for a separate radar location, land acquisition, support facilities and the associated communication landlines and expenses.

(b) The WSP utilizes the same RBDT display as the TDWR and LLWAS, and, just like TDWR, also has a GSD for planning purposes by supervisors, traffic management specialists and controllers. The WSP GSD emulates the TDWR display, i.e., it also depicts 6 levels of precipitation, gust fronts and predicted storm movement, and like the TDWR GSD, is used to plan for runway changes and arrival/departure route changes in order to reduce aircraft delays and to increase airport capacity.

(c) This system is currently under development and is operating in a developmental test status at the Albuquerque, New Mexico, airport. When fielded, the WSP is expected to be installed at 34 airports across the nation, substantially increasing the safety of the American flying public.

5. Operational aspects of LLWAS, TDWR and WSP

To demonstrate how this data is used by both the controller and the pilot, 3 ribbon display examples and their explanations are presented:

(a) MICROBURST ALERTS

EXAMPLE-
This is what the controller sees on his/her ribbon display in the tower cab.

27A MBA 35K- 2MF 250 20

NOTE-
(See FIG 7-1-13 to see how the TDWR/WSP determines the microburst location).

This is what the controller will say when issuing the alert.

PHRASEOLOGY-
RUNWAY 27 ARRIVAL, MICROBURST ALERT, 35 KT LOSS 2 MILE FINAL, THRESHOLD WIND 250 AT 20.

In plain language, the controller is telling the pilot that on approach to runway 27, there is a microburst alert on the approach lane to the runway, and to anticipate or expect a 35 knot loss of airspeed at approximately 2 miles out on final approach (where it will first encounter the phenomena). With that information, the aircrew is forewarned, and should be prepared to apply wind shear/microburst escape procedures should they decide to continue the approach. Additionally, the surface winds at the airport for landing runway 27 are reported as 250 degrees at 20 knots.

NOTE-
Threshold wind is at pilot's request or as deemed appropriate by the controller.

REFERENCE-
FAA ORDER 7110.65, AIR TRAFFIC CONTROL, PARAGRAPH 3-1-8b2(a).

(b) WIND SHEAR ALERTS

EXAMPLE-
This is what the controller sees on his/her ribbon display in the tower cab.

27A WSA 20K- 3MF 200 15

NOTE-
(See FIG 7-1-14 to see how the TDWR/WSP determines the wind shear location).

This is what the controller will say when issuing the alert.

PHRASEOLOGY-
RUNWAY 27 ARRIVAL, WIND SHEAR ALERT, 20 KT LOSS 3 MILE FINAL, THRESHOLD WIND 200 AT 15.

In plain language, the controller is advising the aircraft arriving on runway 27 that at about 3 miles out they can expect to encounter a wind shear condition that will decrease their airspeed by 20 knots and possibly encounter turbulence. Additionally, the airport surface winds for landing runway 27 are reported as 200 degrees at 15 knots.

NOTE-
Threshold wind is at pilot's request or as deemed appropriate by the controller.

REFERENCE-
FAA ORDER 7110.65, AIR TRAFFIC CONTROL, PARAGRAPH 3-1-8b2(a).

MICROBURST ALERT

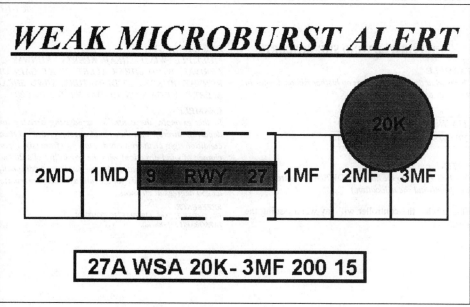

| 2MD | 1MD | 9　RWY　27 | 1MF | 2MF | 3MF |

35K

27A MBA 35K- 2MF 250 20

FIG 7-1-13

WEAK MICROBURST ALERT

| 2MD | 1MD | 9　RWY　27 | 1MF | 2MF | 3MF |

20K

27A WSA 20K- 3MF 200 15

FIG 7-1-14

FIG 7-1-15

(c) MULTIPLE WIND SHEAR ALERTS

EXAMPLE-
This is what the controller sees on his/her ribbon display in the tower cab.

27A WSA 20K+ RWY 250 20
27D WSA 20K+ RWY 250 20

NOTE-
(See FIG 7-1-15 to see how the TDWR/WSP determines the gust front/wind shear location.)

This is what the controller will say when issuing the alert.

PHRASEOLOGY-
MULTIPLE WIND SHEAR ALERTS. RUNWAY 27 ARRIVAL, WIND SHEAR ALERT, 20 KT GAIN ON RUNWAY; RUNWAY 27 DEPARTURE, WIND SHEAR ALERT, 20 KT GAIN ON RUNWAY, WIND 250 AT 20.

EXAMPLE-
In this example, the controller is advising arriving and departing aircraft that they could encounter a wind shear condition right on the runway due to a gust front (significant change of wind direction) with the possibility of a 20 knot gain in airspeed associated with the gust front. Additionally, the airport surface winds (for the runway in use) are reported as 250 degrees at 20 knots.

REFERENCE-
FAA ORDER 7110.65, AIR TRAFFIC CONTROL, PARAGRAPH 3-1-8b2(d).

6. The Terminal Weather Information For Pilots System (TWIP)

(a) With the increase in the quantity and quality of terminal weather information available through TDWR, the next step is to provide this information directly to pilots rather than relying on voice communications from ATC. The National Airspace System has long been in need of a means of delivering terminal weather information to the cockpit more efficiently in terms of both speed and accuracy to enhance pilot awareness of weather hazards and reduce air traffic controller workload. With the TWIP capability, terminal weather information, both alphanumerically and graphically, is now available directly to the cockpit on a test basis at 9 locations.

(b) TWIP products are generated using weather data from the TDWR or the Integrated Terminal Weather System (ITWS) testbed. TWIP products are generated and stored in the form of text and character graphic messages. Software has been developed to allow TDWR or ITWS to format the data and send the TWIP products to a database resident at Aeronautical Radio, Inc. (ARINC). These products can then be accessed by pilots using the ARINC Aircraft Communications Addressing and Reporting System (ACARS) data link services. Airline dispatchers can also access this database and send messages to specific aircraft whenever wind shear activity begins or ends at an airport.

(c) TWIP products include descriptions and character graphics of microburst alerts, wind shear alerts, significant precipitation, convective activity within 30 NM surrounding the terminal area, and expected weather that will impact airport operations. During inclement weather, i.e., whenever a predetermined level of precipitation or wind shear is detected within 15 miles of the terminal area, TWIP products are updated once each minute for text messages and once every five minutes for character graphic messages. During good

weather (below the predetermined precipitation or wind shear parameters) each message is updated every 10 minutes. These products are intended to improve the situational awareness of the pilot/flight crew, and to aid in flight planning prior to arriving or departing the terminal area. It is important to understand that, in the context of TWIP, the predetermined levels for inclement versus good weather has nothing to do with the criteria for VFR/MVFR/IFR/LIFR; it only deals with precipitation, wind shears and microbursts.

7-1-24. PIREP'S RELATING TO VOLCANIC ASH ACTIVITY

a. Volcanic eruptions which send ash into the upper atmosphere occur somewhere around the world several times each year. Flying into a volcanic ash cloud can be extremely dangerous. At least two B747's have lost all power in all four engines after such an encounter. Regardless of the type aircraft, some damage is almost certain to ensue after an encounter with a volcanic ash cloud.

b. While some volcanoes in the United States are monitored, many in remote areas are not. These unmonitored volcanoes may erupt without prior warning to the aviation community. A pilot observing a volcanic eruption who has not had previous notification of it may be the only witness to the eruption. Pilots are strongly encouraged to transmit a PIREP regarding volcanic eruptions and any observed volcanic ash clouds.

c. Pilots should submit PIREP's regarding volcanic activity using the Volcanic Activity Reporting Form (VAR) as illustrated in Appendix 2. If a VAR form is not immediately available, relay enough information to identify the position and type of volcanic activity.

d. Pilots should verbally transmit the data required in items 1 through 8 of the VAR as soon as possible. The data required in items 9 through 16 of the VAR should be relayed after landing if possible.

7-1-25. THUNDERSTORMS

a. Turbulence, hail, rain, snow, lightning, sustained updrafts and downdrafts, icing conditions–all are present in thunderstorms. While there is some evidence that maximum turbulence exists at the middle level of a thunderstorm, recent studies show little variation of turbulence intensity with altitude.

b. There is no useful correlation between the external visual appearance of thunderstorms and the severity or amount of turbulence or hail within them. The visible thunderstorm cloud is only a portion of a turbulent system whose updrafts and downdrafts often extend far beyond the visible storm cloud. Severe turbulence can be expected up to 20 miles from severe thunderstorms. This distance decreases to about 10 miles in less severe storms.

c. Weather radar, airborne or ground based, will normally reflect the areas of moderate to heavy precipitation (radar does not detect turbulence). The frequency and severity of turbulence generally increases with the radar reflectivity which is closely associated with the areas of highest liquid water content of the storm. NO FLIGHT PATH THROUGH AN AREA OF STRONG OR VERY STRONG RADAR ECHOES SEPARATED BY 20-30 MILES OR LESS MAY BE CONSIDERED FREE OF SEVERE TURBULENCE.

d. Turbulence beneath a thunderstorm should not be minimized. This is especially true when the relative humidity is low in any layer between the surface and 15,000 feet. Then the lower altitudes may be characterized by strong out flowing winds and severe turbulence.

e. The probability of lightning strikes occurring to aircraft is greatest when operating at altitudes where temperatures are between minus 5 degrees Celsius and plus 5 degrees Celsius. Lightning can strike aircraft flying in the clear in the vicinity of a thunderstorm.

f. METAR reports do not include a descriptor for severe thunderstorms. However, by understanding severe thunderstorm criteria, i.e., 50 knot winds or $3/4$ inch hail, the information is available in the report to know that one is occurring.

g. NWS radar systems are able to objectively determine radar weather echo intensity levels by use of Video Integrator Processor (VIP) equipment. These thunderstorm intensity levels are on a scale of one to six.

REFERENCE-
PILOT/CONTROLLER GLOSSARY, RADAR WEATHER ECHO INTENSITY LEVELS.

EXAMPLE-
1 *Alert provided by an ATC facility to an aircraft:*
(aircraft identification) level five intense weather echo between ten o'clock and two o'clock, one zero miles, moving east at two zero knots, tops Flight Level three nine zero.
2 *Alert provided by an AFSS/FSS:*
(aircraft identification) level five intense weather echo, two zero miles west of Atlanta V-O-R, two five miles wide, moving east at two zero knots, tops Flight Level three nine zero.

7-1-26. THUNDERSTORM FLYING

a. Above all, remember this: never regard any thunderstorm "lightly" even when radar observers report the echoes are of light intensity. Avoiding thunderstorms is the best policy. Following are some Do's and Don'ts of thunderstorm avoidance:

1. Don't land or takeoff in the face of an approaching thunderstorm. A sudden gust front of low level turbulence could cause loss of control.

2. Don't attempt to fly under a thunderstorm even if you can see through to the other side. Turbulence and wind shear under the storm could be disastrous.

3. Don't fly without airborne radar into a cloud mass containing scattered embedded thunderstorms. Scattered thunderstorms not embedded usually can be visually circumnavigated.

4. Don't trust the visual appearance to be a reliable indicator of the turbulence inside a thunderstorm.

5. Do avoid by at least 20 miles any thunderstorm identified as severe or giving an intense radar echo. This is especially true under the anvil of a large cumulonimbus.

6. Do clear the top of a known or suspected severe thunderstorm by at least 1,000 feet altitude for each 10 knots of wind speed at the cloud top. This should exceed the altitude capability of most aircraft.

7. Do circumnavigate the entire area if the area has $6/10$ thunderstorm coverage.

8. Do remember that vivid and frequent lightning indicates the probability of a strong thunderstorm.

9. Do regard as extremely hazardous any thunderstorm with tops 35,000 feet or higher whether the top is visually sighted or determined by radar.

b. If you cannot avoid penetrating a thunderstorm, following are some Do's before entering the storm:

1. Tighten your safety belt, put on your shoulder harness if you have one and secure all loose objects.

2. Plan and hold your course to take you through the storm in a minimum time.

3. To avoid the most critical icing, establish a penetration altitude below the freezing level or above the level of minus 15 degrees Celsius.

4. Verify that pitot heat is on and turn on carburetor heat or jet engine anti-ice. Icing can be rapid at any altitude and cause almost instantaneous power failure and/or loss of airspeed indication.

5. Establish power settings for turbulence penetration airspeed recommended in your aircraft manual.

6. Turn up cockpit lights to highest intensity to lessen temporary blindness from lightning.

7. If using automatic pilot, disengage altitude hold mode and speed hold mode. The automatic altitude and speed controls will increase maneuvers of the aircraft thus increasing structural stress.

8. If using airborne radar, tilt the antenna up and down occasionally. This will permit you to detect other thunderstorm activity at altitudes other than the one being flown.

c. Following are some Do's and Don'ts during the thunderstorm penetration:

1. Do keep your eyes on your instruments. Looking outside the cockpit can increase danger of temporary blindness from lightning.

2. Don't change power settings; maintain settings for the recommended turbulence penetration airspeed.

3. Do maintain constant attitude; let the aircraft "ride the waves." Maneuvers in trying to maintain constant altitude increase stress on the aircraft.

4. Don't turn back once you are in the thunderstorm. A straight course through the storm most likely will get you out of the hazards most quickly. In addition, turning maneuvers increase stress on the aircraft.

7-1-27. KEY TO AVIATION ROUTINE WEATHER REPORT (METAR) AND AERODROME FORECASTS (TAF)

Key to Aviation Routine Weather Report (METAR) and Aerodrome Forecasts (TAF)

FIG 7-1-16

7-1-28. INTERNATIONAL CIVIL AVIATION ORGANIZATION (ICAO) WEATHER FORMATS

The United States uses the ICAO world standard for aviation weather reporting and forecasting. The utilization of terminal forecasts affirms our commitment to a single global format for aviation weather. The World Meteorological Organization's (WMO) publication No. 782 "Aerodrome Reports and Forecasts" contains the base METAR and TAF code as adopted by the WMO member countries.

a. Although the METAR code is adopted worldwide, each country is allowed to make modifications or exceptions to the code for use in their particular country, e.g., the U.S. will continue to use statute miles for visibility, feet for RVR values, knots for wind speed, and inches of mercury for altimetry. However, temperature and dew point will be reported in degrees Celsius. The U.S. will continue reporting prevailing visibility rather than lowest sector visibility. Most of the current U.S. observing procedures and policies will continue after the METAR conversion date, with the information disseminated in the METAR code and format. The elements in the body of a METAR report are separated with a space. The only exceptions are RVR, temperature and dew point, which are separated with a solidus (/). When an element does not occur, or cannot be observed, the preceding space and that element are omitted from that particular report. A METAR report contains the following sequence of elements in the following order:

1. **Type of Report**

2. **ICAO Station Identifier**

3. **Date and Time of Report**

4. **Modifier (as required)**

5. **Wind**

6. **Visibility**

7. **Runway Visual Range (RVR)**

8. **Weather Phenomena**

9. **Sky Conditions**

10. **Temperature/Dew Point Group**

11. **Altimeter**

12. **Remarks (RMK)**

b. The following paragraphs describe the elements in a METAR report.

1. Type of Report: There are two types of report:

1 Aviation Routine Weather Report (METAR);

2 Nonroutine (special) Aviation Weather Report (SPECI).

The type of report (METAR or SPECI) will always appear as the lead element of the report.

2. ICAO Station Identifier: The METAR code uses ICAO 4-letter station identifiers. In the contiguous 48 States, the 3-letter domestic station identifier is prefixed with a "K;" i.e., the domestic identifier for Seattle is SEA while the ICAO identifier is KSEA. Elsewhere, the first two letters of the ICAO identifier indicate what region of the world and country (or state) the station is in. For Alaska, all station identifiers start with "PA;" for Hawaii, all station identifiers start with "PH." Canadian station identifiers start with "CU," "CW," "CY," and "CZ." Mexican station identifiers start with "MM." The identifier for the western Caribbean is "M" followed by the individual country's letter; i.e., Cuba is "MU;" Dominican Republic "MD;" the Bahamas "MY." The identifier for the eastern Caribbean is "T" followed by the individual country's letter; i.e., Puerto Rico is "TJ." For a complete worldwide listing see ICAO Document 7910, Location Indicators.

3. Date and Time of Report: The date and time the observation is taken are transmitted as a six-digit date/time group appended with Z to denote Coordinated Universal Time (UTC). The first two digits are the date followed with two digits for hour and two digits for minutes.

EXAMPLE-
172345Z (the 17th day of the month at 2345Z)

4. Modifier (As Required): "AUTO" identifies a METAR/SPECI report as an automated weather report with no human intervention. If "AUTO" is shown in the body of the report, the type of sensor equipment used at the station will be encoded in the remarks section of the report. The absence of "AUTO" indicates that a report was made manually by an observer or that an automated report had human augmentation/backup. The modifier "COR" indicates a corrected report that is sent out to replace an earlier report with an error.

NOTE-
There are two types of automated stations, AO1 for auto-
mated weather reporting stations without a precipitation
discriminator, and AO2 for automated stations with a pre-
cipitation discriminator. (A precipitation discriminator
can determine the difference between liquid and frozen/
freezing precipitation). This information appears in the
remarks section of an automated report.

5. **Wind:** The wind is reported as a five digit group
(six digits if speed is over 99 knots). The first three digits are the direction the wind is blowing from, in tens of
degrees referenced to true north, or "VRB" if the direction is variable. The next two digits is the wind speed
in knots, or if over 99 knots, the next three digits. If the
wind is gusty, it is reported as a "G" after the speed followed by the highest gust reported. The abbreviation
"KT" is appended to denote the use of knots for wind
speed.

EXAMPLE-
13008KT - wind from 130 degrees at 8 knots
08032G45KT - wind from 080 degrees at 32 knots with
gusts to 45 knots
VRB04KT - wind variable in direction at 4 knots
00000KT - wind calm
210103G130KT - wind from 210 degrees at 103 knots
with gusts to 130 knots
If the wind direction is variable by 60 degrees or more and
the speed is greater than 6 knots, a variable group consist-
ing of the extremes of the wind direction separated by a
"v" will follow the prevailing wind group.
32012G22KT 280V350

(a) *Peak Wind:* Whenever the peak wind exceeds 25 knots "PK WND" will be included in Remarks, e.g., PK WND 28045/1955 "Peak wind two
eight zero at four five occurred at one niner five five."
If the hour can be inferred from the report time, only the
minutes will be appended, e.g., PK WND 34050/38
"Peak wind three four zero at five zero occurred at three
eight past the hour."

(b) *Wind shift:* Whenever a wind shift occurs,
"WSHFT" will be included in remarks followed by the
time the wind shift began, e.g., WSHFT 30 FROPA
"Wind shift at three zero due to frontal passage."

6. **Visibility:** Prevailing visibility is reported in
statute miles with "SM" appended to it.

EXAMPLE-
7SM - seven statute miles
15SM - fifteen statute miles
$^1/_2$SM - one-half statute mile

(a) **Tower/surface visibility**: If either visibility
(tower or surface) is below four statute miles, the lesser
of the two will be reported in the body of the report; the
greater will be reported in remarks.

(b) **Automated visibility**: Automated visibility
stations will show visibility less than $^1/_4$ statute mile as
"M$^1/_4$SM" and visibility ten or greater than ten miles
as "10SM."

(c) **Variable visibility**: Variable visibility is
shown in remarks (when rapid increase or decrease by
$^1/_2$ statute mile or more and the average prevailing visibility is less than three miles) e.g., VIS 1V2 "visibility
variable between one and two."

(d) **Sector visibility**: Sector visibility is shown
in remarks when it differs from the prevailing visibility,
and either the prevailing or sector visibility is less than
three miles.

EXAMPLE-
VIS N2 - visibility north two

7. **Runway Visual Range (When Reported):**
"R" identifies the group followed by the runway heading (and parallel runway designator, if needed) "/" and
the visual range in feet (meters in other countries) followed with "FT" (feet is not spoken).

(a) *Variability Values:* When RVR varies (by
more than on reportable value), the lowest and highest
values are shown with "V" between them.

(b) *Maximum/Minimum Range:* "P" indicates
an observed RVR is above the maximum value for this
system (spoken as "more than"). "M" indicates an observed RVR is below the minimum value which can be
determined by the system (spoken as "less than").

EXAMPLE-
R32L/1200FT - runway three two left R-V-R one thou-
sand two hundred.
R27R/M1000V4000FT - runway two seven right R-V-R
variable from less than one thousand to four thousand.

8. **Weather Phenomena:** The weather as reported
in the METAR code represents a significant change in
the way weather is currently reported. In METAR,
weather is reported in the format:

Intensity/Proximity/Descriptor/Precipitation/
Obstruction to visibility/Other

NOTE-
The "/" above and in the following descriptions (except as
the separator between the temperature and dew point) are
for separation purposes in this publication and do not
appear in the actual METAR's.

(a) *Intensity:* applies only to the first type of precipitation reported. A "-" denotes light, no symbol denotes moderate, and a "+" denotes heavy.

(b) *Proximity:* applies to and reported only for weather occurring in the vicinity of the airport (between 5 and 10 miles of the point(s) of observation). It is denoted by the letters "VC." (Intensity and "VC" will not appear together in the weather group).

(c) *Descriptor:* these eight descriptors apply to the precipitation or obstructions to visibility:

TS	thunderstorm
DR	low drifting
SH	showers
MI	shallow
FZ	freezing
BC	patches
BL	blowing
PR	partial

NOTE-
*Although "TS" and "SH" are used with precipitation and may be preceded with an intensity symbol, the intensity still applies to the precipitation, **not** the descriptor.*

(d) *Precipitation:* there are nine types of precipitation in the METAR code:

RA	rain
DZ	drizzle
SN	snow
GR	hail ($1/4$" or greater)
GS	small hail/snow pellets
PL	ice pellets
SG	snow grains
IC	ice crystals (diamond dust)
UP	unknown precipitation (automated stations only)

(e) *Obstructions to visibility:* there are eight types of obscuration phenomena in the METAR code (obscurations are any phenomena in the atmosphere, other than precipitation, that reduce horizontal visibility):

FG	fog (vsby less than $5/8$ mile)
HZ	haze
FU	smoke
PY	spray
BR	mist (vsby $5/8$ - 6 miles)
SA	sand
DU	dust
VA	volcanic ash

NOTE-
Fog (FG) is observed or forecast only when the visibility is less than five-eighths of mile, otherwise mist (BR) is observed or forecast.

(f) *Other:* there are five categories of other weather phenomena which are reported when they occur:

SQ	squall
SS	sandstorm
DS	duststorm
PO	dust/sand whirls
FC	funnel cloud
+FC	tornado/waterspout

Examples:

TSRA	thunderstorm with moderate rain
+SN	heavy snow
-RA FG	light rain and fog
BRHZ	mist and haze (visibility $5/8$ mile or greater)
FZDZ	freezing drizzle
VCSH	rain shower in the vicinity
+SHRASNPL	heavy rain showers, snow, ice pellets (intensity indicator refers to the predominant rain)

9. Sky Condition: The sky condition as reported in METAR represents a significant change from the way sky condition is currently reported. In METAR, sky condition is reported in the format:

Amount/Height/(Type) or Indefinite Ceiling/Height

(a) *Amount:* the amount of sky cover is reported in eighths of sky cover, using the contractions:

SKC	clear (no clouds)
FEW	>0 to $2/8$
SCT	scattered ($3/8$'s to $4/8$'s of clouds)
BKN	broken ($5/8$'s to $7/8$'s of clouds)
OVC	overcast ($8/8$'s clouds)
CB	Cumulonimbus when present
TCU	Towering cumulus when present

NOTE-
[1] *"SKC" will be reported at manual stations. "CLR" will be used at automated stations when no clouds below 12,000 feet are reported.*
[2] *A ceiling layer is not designated in the METAR code. For aviation purposes, the ceiling is the lowest broken or overcast layer, or vertical visibility into an obscuration. Also there is no provision for reporting thin layers in the METAR code. When clouds are thin, that layer shall be reported as if it were opaque.*

(b) Height: cloud bases are reported with three digits in hundreds of feet. (Clouds above 12,000 feet cannot be reported by an automated station).

(c) (Type): if Towering Cumulus Clouds (TCU) or Cumulonimbus Clouds (CB) are present, they are reported after the height which represents their base.

EXAMPLE-
(Reported as) SCT025TCU BKN080 BKN250 (spoken as) "TWO THOUSAND FIVE HUNDRED SCATTERED TOWERING CUMULUS, CEILING EIGHT THOUSAND BROKEN, TWO FIVE THOUSAND BROKEN."
(Reported as) SCT008 OVC012CB (spoken as) "EIGHT HUNDRED SCATTERED CEILING ONE THOUSAND TWO HUNDRED OVERCAST CUMULONIMBUS CLOUDS."

(d) Vertical Visibility (indefinite ceiling height): The height into an indefinite ceiling is preceded by "VV" and followed by three digits indicating the vertical visibility in hundreds of feet. This layer indicates <u>total obscuration</u>.

EXAMPLE-
$1/8$ SM FG VV006 - visibility one eighth, fog, indefinite ceiling six hundred.

(e) Obscurations: are reported when the sky is <u>partially obscured</u> by a ground-based phenomena by indicating the amount of obscuration as FEW, SCT, BKN followed by three zeros (000). In remarks, the obscuring phenomenon precedes the amount of obscuration and three zeros.

EXAMPLE-
BKN000 (in body) . . . . "sky partially obscured"
FU BKN000 (in remarks) . . . . "smoke obscuring five- to seven-eighths of the sky"

(f) When sky conditions include a layer aloft, other than clouds, such as smoke or haze the type of phenomena, sky cover and height are shown in remarks.

EXAMPLE-
BKN020 (in body) . . . . . "ceiling two thousand broken"
RMK FU BKN020 . . . . . "broken layer of smoke aloft, based at two thousand"

(g) Variable ceiling. When a ceiling is below three thousand and is variable, the remark "CIG" will be shown followed with the lowest and highest ceiling heights separated by a "V."

EXAMPLE-
CIG 005V010 . . . . "ceiling variable between five hundred and one thousand"

(h) Second site sensor. When an automated station uses meteorological discontinuity sensors, remarks will be shown to identify site specific sky conditions which differ and are lower than conditions reported in the body.

EXAMPLE-
CIG 020 RY11 . . . . . . "ceiling two thousand at runway one one"

(i) Variable cloud layer. When a layer is varying in sky cover, remarks will show the variability range. If there is more than one cloud layer, the variable layer will be identified by including the layer height.

EXAMPLE-
SCT V BKN . . . . "scattered layer variable to broken"
BKN025 V OVC . . . . "broken layer at two thousand five hundred variable to overcast"

(j) Significant clouds. When significant clouds are observed, they are shown in remarks, along with the specified information as shown below:

(1) Cumulonimbus (CB), or Cumulonimbus Mammatus (CBMAM), distance (if known), direction from the station, and direction of movement, if known. If the clouds are beyond 10 miles from the airport, DSNT will indicate distance.

EXAMPLE-
CB W MOV E . . . . "cumulonimbus west moving east"
CBMAM DSNT S . . . . . . "cumulonimbus mammatus distant south"

(2) Towering Cumulus (TCU), location, (if known), or direction from the station.

EXAMPLE-
TCU OHD . . . . "towering cumulus overhead"
TCU W . . . . "towering cumulus west"

(3) Altocumulus Castellanus (ACC), Stratocumulus Standing Lenticular (SCSL), Altocumulus Standing Lenticular (ACSL), Cirrocumulus Standing Lenticular (CCSL) or rotor clouds, describing the clouds (if needed) and the direction from the station.

EXAMPLE-
ACC W . . . . "altocumulus castellanus west"
ACSL SW-S . . . . "standing lenticular altocumulus southwest through south"
APRNT ROTOR CLD S . "apparent rotor cloud south"
CCSL OVR MT E . . . . . . "standing lenticular cirrocumulus over the mountains east"

10. Temperature/Dew Point: Temperature and dew point are reported in two, two-digit groups in degrees Celsius, separated by a solidus ("/"). Temperatures below zero are prefixed with an "M." If the temperature is available but the dew point is missing, the temperature is shown followed by a solidus. If the temperature is missing, the group is omitted from the report.

EXAMPLE-

15/08	. . . .	*"temperature one five, dew point 8"*
00/M02	. . . .	*"temperature zero, dew point minus 2"*
M05/	. . . .	*"temperature minus five, dew point missing"*

11. Altimeter: Altimeter settings are reported in a four-digit format in inches of mercury prefixed with an "A" to denote the units of pressure.

EXAMPLE-

A2995 - "Altimeter two niner niner five"

12. Remarks: Remarks will be included in all observations, when appropriate. The contraction "RMK" denotes the start of the remarks section of a METAR report.

Except for precipitation, phenomena located within 5 statute miles of the point of observation will be reported as at the station. Phenomena between 5 and 10 statute miles will be reported in the vicinity, "VC." Precipitation not occurring at the point of observation but within 10 statute miles is also reported as in the vicinity, "VC." Phenomena beyond 10 statute miles will be shown as distant, "DSNT." Distances are in statute miles except for automated lightning remarks which are in nautical miles. Movement of clouds or weather will be indicated by the direction toward which the phenomena is moving.

    a. There are two categories of remarks:

        1. Automated, manual, and plain language.

        2. Additive and automated maintenance data.

    b. Automated, Manual, and Plain Language.

This group of remarks may be generated from either manual or automated weather reporting stations and generally elaborate on parameters reported in the body of the report. (Plain language remarks are only provided by manual stations).

        1. Volcanic eruptions

        2. Tornado, Funnel Cloud, Waterspout

        3. Station Type (AO1 or AO2)

        4. PK WND

        5. WSHFT (FROPA)

        6. TWR VIS or SFC VIS

        7. VRB VIS

        8. Sector VIS

        9. VIS @ 2nd Site

        10. (freq) LTG (type) (loc)

        11. Beginning/Ending of Precipitation/TSTMS

        12. TSTM Location MVMT

        13. Hailstone Size (GR)

        14. Virga

        15. VRB CIG (height)

        16. Obscuration

        17. VRB Sky Condition

        18. Significant Cloud Types

        19. Ceiling Height 2nd Location

        20. PRESFR PRESRR

        21. Sea-Level Pressure

        22. ACFT Mishap (not transmitted)

        23. NOSPECI

        24. SNINCR

        25. Other SIG Info

    c. Additive and Automated Maintenance Data.

        1. Hourly Precipitation

        2. 3- and 6-Hour Precipitation Amount

        3. 24-Hour Precipitation

        4. Snow Depth on Ground

        5. Water Equivalent of Snow

        6. Cloud Type

        7. Duration of Sunshine

        8. Hourly Temperature/Dew Point (Tenths)

        9. 6-Hour Maximum Temperature

        10. 6-Hour Minimum Temperature

        11. 24-Hour Maximum/Minimum Temperature

        12. Pressure Tendency

13. Sensor Status:
    PWINO
    FZRANO
    TSNO
    RVRNO
    PNO
    VISNO

Examples of METAR reports and explanation:

METAR KBNA 281250Z 33018KT 290V360 1/2SM
R31/2700FT SN BLSN FG VV008 00/M03 A2991
RMK RAE42SNB42

METAR	aviation routine weather report
KBNA	Nashville, TN
281250Z	date 28th, time 1250 UTC
(no modifier)	This is a manually generated report, due to the absence of "AUTO" and "AO1 or AO2" in remarks
33018KT	wind three three zero at one eight
290V360	wind variable between two nine zero and three six zero
1/2SM	visibility one half
R31/2700FT .	Runway three one RVR two thousand seven hundred
SN	moderate snow
BLSN FG ...	visibility obscured by blowing snow and fog
VV008	indefinite ceiling eight hundred
00/M03	temperature zero, dew point minus three
A2991	altimeter two niner niner one
RMK	remarks
RAE42	rain ended at four two
SNB42	snow began at four two

METAR KSFO 041453Z AUTO VRB02KT 3SM BR
CLR 15/12 A3012 RMK AO2

METAR	aviation routine weather report
KSFO	San Francisco, CA
041453Z	date 4th, time 1453 UTC
AUTO	fully automated; no human intervention
VRB02KT ...	wind variable at two
3SM	visibility three
BR	visibility obscured by mist
CLR	no clouds below one two thousand

15/12	temperature one five, dew point one two
A3012	altimeter three zero one two
RMK	remarks
AO2	this automated station has a weather discriminator (for precipitation)

SPECI KCVG 152224Z 28024G36KT 3/4SM +TSRA
BKN008 OVC020CB 28/23 A3000 RMK TSRAB24
TS W MOV E

SPECI	(nonroutine) aviation special weather report
KCVG	Cincinnati, OH
152228Z	date 15th, time 2228 UTC
(no modifier)	This is a manually generated report due to the absence of "AUTO" and "AO1 or AO2" in remarks
28024G36KT	wind two eight zero at two four gusts three six
3/4SM	visibility three fourths
+TSRA	thunderstorms, heavy rain
BKN008	ceiling eight hundred broken
OVC020CB .	two thousand overcast cumulonimbus clouds
28/23	temperature two eight, dew point two three
A3000	altimeter three zero zero zero
RMK	remarks
TSRAB24 ...	thunderstorm and rain began at two four
TS W MOV E	thunderstorm west moving east

Aerodrome Forecast (TAF): a concise statement of the expected meteorological conditions at an airport during a specified period (usually 24 hours). TAF's use the same codes as METAR weather reports. They are scheduled four times daily for 24-hour periods beginning at 0000Z, 0600Z, 1200Z, and 1800Z. TAF's are issued in the following format:

TYPE OF REPORT/ICAO STATION IDENTIFIER/
DATE AND TIME OF ORIGIN/VALID PERIOD
DATE AND TIME/FORECAST METEOROLOG-
ICAL CONDITIONS

NOTE-
The "/" above and in the following descriptions are for separation purposes in this publication and do not appear in the actual TAF's.

TAF
KOKC 051130Z 051212 14008KT 5SM BR BKN030
TEMPO 1316 1 $^1/_2$SM BR
   FM1600 16010KT P6SM SKC
   FM2300 20013G20KT 4SM SHRA OVC020
PROB40 0006 2SM TSRA OVC008CB BECMG 0608
21015KT P6SM NSW SCT040

TAF format observed in the above example:

TAF = type of report

KOKC = ICAO station identifier

051130Z = date and time of origin

051212 = valid period date and times

14008KT 5SM BR BKN030 = forecast meteorological conditions

Explanation of TAF elements:

1. Type of report: There are two types of TAF issuances, a routine forecast issuance (TAF) and an amended forecast (TAF AMD). An amended TAF is issued when the current TAF no longer adequately describes the on-going weather or the forecaster feels the TAF is not representative of the current or expected weather. Corrected (COR) or delayed (RTD) TAF's are identified only in the communications header which precedes the actual forecasts.

2. ICAO Station Identifier: The TAF code uses ICAO 4-letter location identifiers as described in the METAR section.

3. Date and Time of Origin: This element is the date and time the forecast is actually prepared. The format is a two-digit date and four-digit time followed, without a space, by the letter "Z."

4. Valid Period Date and Time: The UTC valid period of the forecast is a two-digit date followed by the two-digit beginning hour and two-digit ending hour. In the case of an amended forecast, or a forecast which is corrected or delayed, the valid period may be for less than 24 hours. Where an airport or terminal operates on a part-time basis (less than 24 hours/day), the TAF's issued for those locations will have the abbreviated statement "NIL AMD SKED AFT (closing time) Z" added to the end of the forecasts. For the TAF's issued while these locations are closed, the word "NIL" will appear in place of the forecast text. A delayed (RTD) forecast will then be issued for these locations after two complete observations are received.

5. Forecast Meteorological Conditions: This is the body of the TAF. The basic format is:

WIND/VISIBILITY/WEATHER/SKY CONDITION/
OPTIONAL DATA (WIND SHEAR)

The wind, visibility, and sky condition elements are always included in the initial time group of the forecast. Weather is included only if significant to aviation. If a significant, lasting change in any of the elements is expected during the valid period, a new time period with the changes is included. It should be noted that with the exception of a "FM" group the new time period will include only those elements which are expected to change, i.e., if a lowering of the visibility is expected but the wind is expected to remain the same, the new time period reflecting the lower visibility would not include a forecast wind. The forecast wind would remain the same as in the previous time period.

Any temporary conditions expected during a specific time period are included with that time period. The following describes the elements in the above format.

(a) *Wind:* This five (or six) digit group includes the expected wind direction (first 3 digits) and speed (last 2 digits or 3 digits if 100 knots or greater). The contraction "KT" follows to denote the units of wind speed. Wind gusts are noted by the letter "G" appended to the wind speed followed by the highest expected gust.

A variable wind direction is noted by "VRB" where the three digit direction usually appears. A calm wind (3 knots or less) is forecast as "00000KT."

EXAMPLE-
18010KT ..... *wind one eight zero at one zero (wind is blowing from 180).*
35012G20KT .. *wind three five zero at one two gust two zero.*

(b) *Visibility:* The expected prevailing visibility up to and including 6 miles is forecast in statute miles, including fractions of miles, followed by "SM" to note the units of measure. Expected visibilities greater than 6 miles are forecast as P6SM (plus six statute miles).

EXAMPLE-
$^1/_2$SM - visibility one-half
4SM - visibility four
P6SM - visibility more than six

(c) *Weather Phenomena:* The expected weather phenomena is coded in TAF reports using the same format, qualifiers, and phenomena contractions as METAR reports (except UP).

Obscurations to vision will be forecast whenever the prevailing visibility is forecast to be 6 statute miles or less.

If no significant weather is expected to occur during a specific time period in the forecast, the weather phenomena group is omitted for that time period. If, after a time period in which significant weather phenomena has been forecast, a change to a forecast of no significant weather phenomena occurs, the contraction NSW (No Significant Weather) will appear as the weather group in the new time period. (NSW is included only in BECMG or TEMPO groups).

NOTE-
It is very important that pilots understand that NSW only refers to weather phenomena, i.e., rain, snow, drizzle, etc. Omitted conditions, such as sky conditions, visibility, winds, etc., are carried over from the previous time group.

(d) *Sky Condition:* TAF sky condition forecasts use the METAR format described in the METAR section. Cumulonimbus clouds (CB) are the only cloud type forecast in TAF's.

When clear skies are forecast, the contraction "SKC" will always be used. The contraction "CLR" is never used in the aerodrome forecast (TAF).

When the sky is obscured due to a surface-based phenomenon, vertical visibility (VV) into the obscuration is forecast. The format for vertical visibility is "VV" followed by a three-digit height in hundreds of feet.

NOTE-
As in METAR, ceiling layers are not designated in the TAF code. For aviation purposes, the ceiling is the lowest broken or overcast layer or vertical visibility into a complete obscuration.

SKC . . . . "sky clear"
SCT005 BKN025CB . . . "five hundred scattered, ceiling two thousand five hundred broken cumulonimbus clouds"
VV008 . . . . "indefinite ceiling eight hundred"

(e) *Optional Data (Wind Shear):* Wind shear is the forecast of nonconvective low level winds (up to 2,000 feet). The forecast includes the letters "WS" followed by the height of the wind shear, the wind direction and wind speed at the indicated height and the ending letters "KT" (knots). Height is given in hundreds of feet (AGL) up to and including 2,000 feet. Wind

shear is encoded with the contraction "WS," followed by a three-digit height, slant character "/," and winds at the height indicated in the same format as surface winds. The wind shear element is omitted if not expected to occur.

WS010/18040KT - "LOW LEVEL WIND SHEAR AT ONE THOUSAND, WIND ONE EIGHT ZERO AT FOUR ZERO"

d. Probability Forecast: The probability or chance of thunderstorms or other precipitation events occurring, along with associated weather conditions (wind, visibility, and sky conditions).

The PROB30 group is used when the occurrence of thunderstorms or precipitation is 30-39% and the PROB40 group is used when the occurrence of thunderstorms or precipitation is 40-49%. This is followed by a four-digit group giving the beginning hour and ending hour of the time period during which the thunderstorms or precipitation are expected.

NOTE-
Neither PROB30 nor PROB40 will be shown during the first six hours of a forecast.

EXAMPLE-
PROB40 2102 ¹/₂SM +TSRA . . . . "chance between 2100Z and 0200Z of visibility one-half statute mile in thunderstorms and heavy rain."
PROB30 1014 1SM RASN . . . . . . "chance between 1000Z and 1400Z of visibility one statute mile in mixed rain and snow."

e. Forecast Change Indicators: The following change indicators are used when either a rapid, gradual, or temporary change is expected in some or all of the forecast meteorological conditions. Each change indicator marks a time group within the TAF report.

1. From (FM) group: The FM group is used when a rapid change, usually occurring in less than one hour, in prevailing conditions is expected. Typically, a rapid change of prevailing conditions to more or less a completely new set of prevailing conditions is associated with a synoptic feature passing through the terminal area (cold or warm frontal passage). Appended to the "FM" indicator is the four-digit hour and minute the change is expected to begin and continues until the next change group or until the end of the current forecast.

A "FM" group will mark the beginning of a new line in a TAF report (indented 5 spaces). Each "FM" group contains all the required elements-wind, visibility, weather, and sky condition. Weather will be omitted in "FM" groups when it is not significant to aviation. FM groups will not include the contraction NSW.

EXAMPLE-

FM0100 14010KT P6SM SKC - "after 0100Z, wind one four zero at one zero, visibility more than six, sky clear."

2. Becoming (BECMG) group: The BECMG group is used when a gradual change in conditions is expected over a longer time period, usually two hours. The time period when the change is expected is a four-digit group with the beginning hour and ending hour of the change period which follows the BECMG indicator. The gradual change will occur at an unspecified time within this time period. Only the changing forecast meteorological conditions are included in BECMG groups. The omitted conditions are carried over from the previous time group.

EXAMPLE-

OVC012 BECMG 1416 BKN020 - "ceiling one thousand two hundred overcast. Then a gradual change to ceiling two thousand broken between 1400Z and 1600Z."

3. Temporary (TEMPO) group: The TEMPO group is used for any conditions in wind, visibility, weather, or sky condition which are expected to last for generally less than an hour at a time (occasional), and are expected to occur during less than half the time period. The TEMPO indicator is followed by a four-digit group giving the beginning hour and ending hour of the time period during which the temporary conditions are expected. Only the changing forecast meteorological conditions are included in TEMPO groups. The omitted conditions are carried over from the previous time group.

EXAMPLE-

[1] *SCT030 TEMPO 1923 BKN030 - "three thousand scattered with occasional ceilings three thousand broken between 1900Z and 2300Z."*

[2] *4SM HZ TEMPO 0006 2SM BR HZ - "visibility four in haze with occasional visibility two in mist and haze between 0000Z and 0600Z."*

Section 2. ALTIMETER SETTING PROCEDURES

7-2-1. GENERAL

a. The accuracy of aircraft altimeters is subject to the following factors:

1. Nonstandard temperatures of the atmosphere.

2. Nonstandard atmospheric pressure.

3. Aircraft static pressure systems (position error), and

4. Instrument error.

b. EXTREME CAUTION SHOULD BE EXERCISED WHEN FLYING IN PROXIMITY TO OBSTRUCTIONS OR TERRAIN IN LOW TEMPERATURES AND PRESSURES. This is especially true in extremely cold temperatures that cause a large differential between the Standard Day temperature and actual temperature. This circumstance can cause serious errors that result in the aircraft being significantly lower than the indicated altitude.

NOTE–
Standard temperature at sea level is 15 degrees celsius (59 degrees fahrenheit). The temperature gradient from sea level is minus 2 degrees celsius (3.6 degrees fahrenheit) per 1,000 feet. Pilots should apply corrections for static pressure systems and/or instruments, if appreciable errors exist.

c. The adoption of a standard altimeter setting at the higher altitudes eliminates station barometer errors, some altimeter instrument errors, and errors caused by altimeter settings derived from different geographical sources.

7-2-2. PROCEDURES

The cruising altitude or flight level of aircraft shall be maintained by reference to an altimeter which shall be set, when operating:

a. Below 18,000 feet MSL:

1. *When the barometric pressure is 31.00 inches Hg. or less:* to the current reported altimeter setting of a station along the route and within 100 NM of the aircraft, or if there is no station within this area, the current reported altimeter setting of an appropriate available station. When an aircraft is en route on an instrument flight plan, air traffic controllers will furnish this information to the pilot at least once while the aircraft is in the controllers area of jurisdiction. In the case of an aircraft not equipped with a radio, set to the elevation of the departure airport or use an appropriate altimeter setting available prior to departure.

2. *When the barometric pressure exceeds 31.00 inches Hg.:* the following procedures will be placed in effect by NOTAM defining the geographic area affected:

(a) *For all aircraft:* Set 31.00 inches for en route operations below 18,000 feet MSL. Maintain this setting until beyond the affected area or until reaching final approach segment. At the beginning of the final approach segment, the current altimeter setting will be set, if possible. If not possible, 31.00 inches will remain set throughout the approach. Aircraft on departure or missed approach will set 31.00 inches prior to reaching any mandatory/crossing altitude or 1,500 feet AGL, whichever is lower. (Air traffic control will issue actual altimeter settings and advise pilots to set 31.00 inches in their altimeters for en route operations below 18,000 feet MSL in affected areas.)

(b) During preflight, barometric altimeters shall be checked for normal operation to the extent possible.

(c) For aircraft with the capability of setting the current altimeter setting and operating into airports with the capability of measuring the current altimeter setting, no additional restrictions apply.

(d) For aircraft operating VFR, there are no additional restrictions, however, extra diligence in flight planning and in operating in these conditions is essential.

(e) Airports unable to accurately measure barometric pressures above 31.00 inches of Hg. will report the barometric pressure as "missing" or "in excess of 31.00 inches of Hg." Flight operations to and from those airports are restricted to VFR weather conditions.

(f) For aircraft operating IFR and unable to set the current altimeter setting, the following restrictions apply:

(1) To determine the suitability of departure alternate airports, destination airports, and destination alternate airports, increase ceiling requirements by 100 feet and visibility requirements by $1/4$ statute mile for each $1/10$ of an inch of Hg., or any portion thereof, over 31.00 inches. These adjusted values are then applied in accordance with the requirements of the applicable operating regulations and operations specifications.

EXAMPLE–
Destination altimeter is 31.28 inches, ILS DH 250 feet (200–^{1}/$_2$). When flight planning, add 300–^{3}/$_4$ to the weather requirements which would become 500–1^1/$_4$.

(2) On approach, 31.00 inches will remain set. Decision height or minimum descent altitude shall be deemed to have been reached when the published altitude is displayed on the altimeter.

NOTE–
Although visibility is normally the limiting factor on an approach, pilots should be aware that when reaching DH the aircraft will be higher than indicated. Using the example above the aircraft would be approximately 300 feet higher.

(3) These restrictions do not apply to authorized Category II and III ILS operations nor do they apply to certificate holders using approved QFE altimetry systems.

(g) The FAA Regional Flight Standards Division Manager of the affected area is authorized to approve temporary waivers to permit emergency resupply or emergency medical service operation.

b. **At or above 18,000 feet MSL:** to 29.92 inches of mercury (standard setting). The lowest usable flight level is determined by the atmospheric pressure in the area of operation as shown in TBL 7–2–1.

Lowest Usable Flight Level

Altimeter Setting (Current Reported)	Lowest Usable Flight Level
29.92 or higher	180
29.91 to 29.42	185
29.41 to 28.92	190
28.91 to 28.42	195
28.41 to 27.92	200

TBL 7–2–1

c. Where the minimum altitude, as prescribed in FAR Part 91.159 and FAR Part 91.177, is above 18,000 feet MSL, the lowest usable flight level shall be the flight level equivalent of the minimum altitude plus the number of feet specified in TBL 7–2–2.

Lowest Flight Level Correction Factor

Altimeter Setting	Correction Factor
29.92 or higher	none
29.91 to 29.42	500 feet
29.41 to 28.92	1000 feet
28.91 to 28.42	1500 feet
28.41 to 27.92	2000 feet
27.91 to 27.42	2500 feet

TBL 7–2–2

EXAMPLE–
The minimum safe altitude of a route is 19,000 feet MSL and the altimeter setting is reported between 29.92 and 29.42 inches of mercury, the lowest usable flight level will be 195, which is the flight level equivalent of 19,500 feet MSL (minimum altitude plus 500 feet).

7–2–3. ALTIMETER ERRORS

a. Most pressure altimeters are subject to mechanical, elastic, temperature, and installation errors. (Detailed information regarding the use of pressure altimeters is found in the Instrument Flying Handbook, Chapter IV.) Although manufacturing and installation specifications, as well as the periodic test and inspections required by regulations (FAR Part 43, Appendix E), act to reduce these errors, any scale error may be observed in the following manner:

1. Set the current reported altimeter setting on the altimeter setting scale.

2. Altimeter should now read field elevation if you are located on the same reference level used to establish the altimeter setting.

3. Note the variation between the known field elevation and the altimeter indication. If this variation is in the order of plus or minus 75 feet, the accuracy of the altimeter is questionable and the problem should be referred to an appropriately rated repair station for evaluation and possible correction.

b. Once in flight, it is very important to obtain frequently current altimeter settings en route. If you do not reset your altimeter when flying *from* an area of high pressure into an area of low pressure, *your aircraft will be closer to the surface than your altimeter indicates.* An inch error in the altimeter setting equals 1,000 feet of altitude. To quote an old saying: ***"GOING FROM A HIGH TO A LOW, LOOK OUT BELOW."***

c. Temperature also has an effect on the accuracy of altimeters and your altitude. The crucial values to consider are standard temperature versus the ambient (at altitude) temperature. It is this "difference" that causes the error in indicated altitude. When the air is warmer than standard, you are higher than your altimeter indicates. Subsequently, when the air is colder than standard you are lower than indicated. It is the magnitude of this "difference" that determines the magnitude of the error. When flying into a cooler air mass while maintaining a constant indicated altitude, you are losing true altitude. However, flying into a cooler air mass does not necessarily mean you will be lower than indicated if the *difference* is still on the plus side. For example, while flying at 10,000 feet (where **STANDARD** temperature is 5 degrees Celsius (C)), the outside air temperature cools from +5 degrees C to 0 degrees C, the temperature error will nevertheless cause the aircraft to be **HIGHER** than indicated. It is the extreme "cold" difference that normally would be of concern to the pilot. Also, when flying in cold conditions over mountainous country, the pilot should exercise caution in flight planning both in regard to route and altitude to ensure adequate en route terrain clearance.

d. The possible results of the above situations is obvious, particularly if operating at the minimum altitude or when conducting an instrument approach. If the altimeter is in error, you may still be on instruments when reaching the minimum altitude (as indicated on the altimeter), whereas you might have been in the clear and able to complete the approach if the altimeter setting was correct.

7-2-4. HIGH BAROMETRIC PRESSURE

a. Cold, dry air masses may produce barometric pressures in excess of 31.00 inches of Mercury, and many altimeters do not have an accurate means of being adjusted for settings of these levels. When the altimeter cannot be set to the higher pressure setting, the aircraft actual altitude will be higher than the altimeter indicates.

REFERENCE-
AIM, ALTIMETER ERRORS, PARAGRAPH 7-2-3.

b. When the barometric pressure exceeds 31.00 inches, air traffic controllers will issue the actual altimeter setting, and:

1. *En Route/Arrivals:* Advise pilots to remain set on 31.00 inches until reaching the final approach segment.

2. *Departures:* Advise pilots to set 31.00 inches prior to reaching any mandatory/crossing altitude or 1,500 feet, whichever is lower.

c. The altimeter error caused by the high pressure will be in the opposite direction to the error caused by the cold temperature.

7-2-5. LOW BAROMETRIC PRESSURE

When abnormally low barometric pressure conditions occur (below 28.00), flight operations by aircraft unable to set the actual altimeter setting are not recommended.

NOTE-
*The true altitude of the aircraft is **lower** than the indicated altitude if the pilot is unable to set the actual altimeter setting.*

Section 3. WAKE TURBULENCE

7-3-1. GENERAL

a. Every aircraft generates a wake while in flight. Initially, when pilots encountered this wake in flight, the disturbance was attributed to "prop wash." It is known, however, that this disturbance is caused by a pair of counter rotating vortices trailing from the wing tips. The vortices from larger aircraft pose problems to encountering aircraft. For instance, the wake of these aircraft can impose rolling moments exceeding the roll-control authority of the encountering aircraft. Further, turbulence generated within the vortices can damage aircraft components and equipment if encountered at close range. The pilot must learn to envision the location of the vortex wake generated by larger (transport category) aircraft and adjust the flight path accordingly.

b. During ground operations and during takeoff, jet engine blast (thrust stream turbulence) can cause damage and upsets if encountered at close range. Exhaust velocity versus distance studies at various thrust levels have shown a need for light aircraft to maintain an adequate separation behind large turbojet aircraft. Pilots of larger aircraft should be particularly careful to consider the effects of their "jet blast" on other aircraft, vehicles, and maintenance equipment during ground operations.

7-3-2. VORTEX GENERATION

Wake Vortex Generation

FIG 7-3-1

Lift is generated by the creation of a pressure differential over the wing surface. The lowest pressure occurs over the upper wing surface and the highest pressure

under the wing. This pressure differential triggers the roll up of the airflow aft of the wing resulting in swirling air masses trailing downstream of the wing tips. After the roll up is completed, the wake consists of two counter rotating cylindrical vortices. (See FIG 7-3-1.) Most of the energy is within a few feet of the center of each vortex, but pilots should avoid a region within about 100 feet of the vortex core.

7-3-3. VORTEX STRENGTH

a. The strength of the vortex is governed by the weight, speed, and shape of the wing of the generating aircraft. The vortex characteristics of any given aircraft can also be changed by extension of flaps or other wing configuring devices as well as by change in speed. However, as the basic factor is weight, the vortex strength increases proportionately. Peak vortex tangential speeds exceeding 300 feet per second have been recorded. The greatest vortex strength occurs when the generating aircraft is HEAVY, CLEAN, and SLOW.

b. INDUCED ROLL

Wake Encounter Counter Control

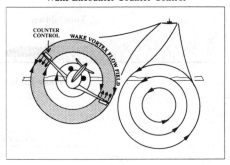

FIG 7-3-2

1. In rare instances a wake encounter could cause inflight structural damage of catastrophic proportions. However, the usual hazard is associated with induced rolling moments which can exceed the roll-control authority of the encountering aircraft. In flight experiments, aircraft have been intentionally flown directly up trailing vortex cores of larger aircraft. It was shown that the capability of an aircraft to counteract the roll imposed by the wake vortex primarily depends on the wingspan and counter-control responsiveness of the encountering aircraft.

2. Counter control is usually effective and induced roll minimal in cases where the wingspan and ailerons of the encountering aircraft extend beyond the rotational flow field of the vortex. It is more difficult for aircraft with short wingspan (relative to the generating aircraft) to counter the imposed roll induced by vortex flow. Pilots of short span aircraft, even of the high performance type, must be especially alert to vortex encounters. (See FIG 7–3–2.)

3. The wake of larger aircraft requires the respect of all pilots.

7–3–4. VORTEX BEHAVIOR

a. Trailing vortices have certain behavioral characteristics which can help a pilot visualize the wake location and thereby take avoidance precautions.

1. Vortices are generated from the moment aircraft leave the ground, since trailing vortices are a by-product of wing lift. Prior to takeoff or touchdown pilots should note the rotation or touchdown point of the preceding aircraft. (See FIG 7–3–3.)

2. The vortex circulation is outward, upward and around the wing tips when viewed from either ahead or behind the aircraft. Tests with large aircraft have shown that the vortices remain spaced a bit less than a wingspan apart, drifting with the wind, at altitudes greater than a wingspan from the ground. In view of this, if persistent vortex turbulence is encountered, a slight change of altitude and lateral position (preferably upwind) will provide a flight path clear of the turbulence.

3. Flight tests have shown that the vortices from larger (transport category) aircraft sink at a rate of several hundred feet per minute, slowing their descent and diminishing in strength with time and distance behind the generating aircraft. Atmospheric turbulence hastens breakup. Pilots should fly at or above the preceding aircraft's flight path, altering course as necessary to avoid the area behind and below the generating aircraft. (See FIG 7–3–4.) However vertical separation of 1,000 feet may be considered safe.

Wake Ends/Wake Begins

Touchdown

Rotation

Wake Ends

Wake Begins

FIG 7–3–3

Vortex Flow Field

AVOID

Nominally 500-1000 Ft.

**Sink Rate
Several Hundred Ft./Min.**

FIG 7–3–4

4. When the vortices of larger aircraft sink close to the ground (within 100 to 200 feet), they tend to move laterally over the ground at a speed of 2 or 3 knots. (See FIG 7–3–5.)

Vortex Movement Near Ground – No Wind

FIG 7–3–5

Vortex Movement Near Ground – with Cross Winds

FIG 7–3–6

b. A crosswind will decrease the lateral movement of the upwind vortex and increase the movement of the downwind vortex. Thus a light wind with a cross runway component of 1 to 5 knots could result in the upwind vortex remaining in the touchdown zone for a period of time and hasten the drift of the downwind vortex toward another runway. (See FIG 7–3–6.) Similarly, a tailwind condition can move the vortices of the preceding aircraft forward into the touchdown zone. THE LIGHT QUARTERING TAILWIND REQUIRES MAXIMUM CAUTION. Pilots should be alert to large aircraft upwind from their approach and takeoff flight paths. (See FIG 7–3–7.)

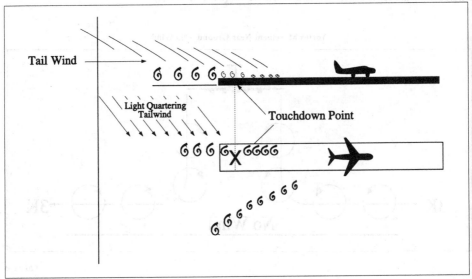

FIG 7-3-7

7-3-5. OPERATIONS PROBLEM AREAS

a. A wake encounter can be catastrophic. In 1972 at Fort Worth a DC-9 got too close to a DC-10 (two miles back), rolled, caught a wingtip, and cartwheeled coming to rest in an inverted position on the runway. All aboard were killed. Serious and even fatal GA accidents induced by wake vortices are not uncommon. However, a wake encounter is not necessarily hazardous. It can be one or more jolts with varying severity depending upon the direction of the encounter, weight of the generating aircraft, size of the encountering aircraft, distance from the generating aircraft, and point of vortex encounter. The probability of induced roll increases when the encountering aircraft's heading is generally aligned with the flight path of the generating aircraft.

b. AVOID THE AREA BELOW AND BEHIND THE GENERATING AIRCRAFT, ESPECIALLY AT LOW ALTITUDE WHERE EVEN A MOMENTARY WAKE ENCOUNTER COULD BE HAZARDOUS. This is not easy to do. Some accidents have occurred even though the pilot of the trailing aircraft had carefully noted that the aircraft in front was at a considerably lower altitude. Unfortunately, this does not ensure that the flight path of the lead aircraft will be below that of the trailing aircraft.

c. Pilots should be particularly alert in calm wind conditions and situations where the vortices could:

1. Remain in the touchdown area.

2. Drift from aircraft operating on a nearby runway.

3. Sink into the takeoff or landing path from a crossing runway.

4. Sink into the traffic pattern from other airport operations.

5. Sink into the flight path of VFR aircraft operating on the hemispheric altitude 500 feet below.

d. Pilots of all aircraft should visualize the location of the vortex trail behind larger aircraft and use proper vortex avoidance procedures to achieve safe operation. It is equally important that pilots of larger aircraft plan or adjust their flight paths to minimize vortex exposure to other aircraft.

7-3-6. VORTEX AVOIDANCE PROCEDURES

a. Under certain conditions, airport traffic controllers apply procedures for separating IFR aircraft. The controllers will also provide to VFR aircraft, with whom they are in communication and which in the tower's opinion may be adversely affected by wake turbulence from a larger aircraft, the position, altitude and direction of flight of larger aircraft followed by the phrase "CAUTION – WAKE TURBULENCE." WHETHER OR NOT A WARNING HAS BEEN GIVEN, PILOTS ARE EXPECTED TO ADJUST THEIR OPERATIONS AND FLIGHT PATH(S) AS NECESSARY TO PRECLUDE SERIOUS WAKE ENCOUNTERS.

b. The following vortex avoidance procedures are recommended for the various situations:

1. Landing behind a larger aircraft– same runway: Stay at or above the larger aircraft's final approach flight path-note its touchdown point-land beyond it.

2. Landing behind a larger aircraft– when parallel runway is closer than 2,500 feet: Consider possible drift to your runway. Stay at or above the larger aircraft's final approach flight path– note its touchdown point.

3. Landing behind a larger aircraft– crossing runway: Cross above the larger aircraft's flight path.

4. Landing behind a departing larger aircraft– same runway: Note the larger aircraft's rotation point– and well prior to rotation point.

5. Landing behind a departing larger aircraft– crossing runway: Note the larger aircraft's rotation point– if past the intersection– continue the approach– and prior to the intersection. If larger aircraft rotates prior to the intersection, avoid flight below the larger aircraft's flight path. Abandon the approach unless a landing is ensured well before reaching the intersection.

6. Departing behind a larger aircraft: Note the larger aircraft's rotation point and rotate prior to the larger aircraft's rotation point. Continue climbing above the larger aircraft's climb path until turning clear of the larger aircraft's wake. Avoid subsequent headings which will cross below and behind a larger aircraft. Be alert for any critical takeoff situation which could lead to a vortex encounter.

7. Intersection takeoffs– same runway: Be alert to adjacent larger aircraft operations, particularly upwind of your runway. If intersection takeoff clearance is received, avoid subsequent heading which will cross below a larger aircraft's path.

8. Departing or landing after a larger aircraft executing a low approach, missed approach or touch-and-go landing: Because vortices settle and move laterally near the ground, the vortex hazard may exist along the runway and in your flight path after a larger aircraft has executed a low approach, missed approach or a touch-and-go landing, particular in light quartering wind conditions. You should ensure that an interval of at least 2 minutes has elapsed before your takeoff or landing.

9. En route VFR (thousand-foot altitude plus 500 feet): Avoid flight below and behind a large aircraft's path. If a larger aircraft is observed above on the same track (meeting or overtaking) adjust your position laterally, preferably upwind.

7-3-7. HELICOPTERS

In a slow hover taxi or stationary hover near the surface, helicopter main rotor(s) generate downwash producing high velocity outwash vortices to a distance approximately three times the diameter of the rotor. When rotor downwash hits the surface, the resulting outwash vortices have behavioral characteristics similar to wing tip vortices produced by fixed wing aircraft. However, the vortex circulation is outward, upward, around, and away from the main rotor(s) in all directions. Pilots of small aircraft should avoid operating within three rotor diameters of any helicopter in a slow hover taxi or stationary hover. In forward flight, departing or landing helicopters produce a pair of strong, high-speed trailing vortices similar to wing tip vortices of larger fixed wing aircraft. Pilots of small aircraft should use caution when operating behind or crossing behind landing and departing helicopters.

7-3-8. PILOT RESPONSIBILITY

a. Government and industry groups are making concerted efforts to minimize or eliminate the hazards of trailing vortices. However, the flight disciplines necessary to ensure vortex avoidance during VFR operations must be exercised by the pilot. Vortex visualization and avoidance procedures should be exercised by the pilot using the same degree of concern as in collision avoidance.

b. Wake turbulence may be encountered by aircraft in flight as well as when operating on the airport movement area.

REFERENCE-
PILOT/CONTROLLER GLOSSARY TERM - WAKE TURBULENCE.

c. Pilots are reminded that in operations conducted behind all aircraft, acceptance of instructions from ATC in the following situations is an acknowledgment that the pilot will ensure safe takeoff and landing intervals and accepts the responsibility for providing wake turbulence separation.

1. Traffic information,

2. Instructions to follow an aircraft, and

3. The acceptance of a visual approach clearance.

d. For operations conducted behind **heavy** aircraft, ATC will specify the word "**heavy**" when this information is known. Pilots of **heavy** aircraft should always use the word "**heavy**" in radio communications.

e. Heavy and large jet aircraft operators should use the following procedures during an approach to landing. These procedures establish a dependable baseline from which pilots of in-trail, lighter aircraft may reasonably expect to make effective flight path adjustments to avoid serious wake vortex turbulence.

1. Pilots of aircraft that produce strong wake vortices should make every attempt to fly on the established glidepath, not above it; or, if glidepath guidance is not available, to fly as closely as possible to a "3-1" glidepath, not above it.

EXAMPLE-
Fly 3,000 feet at 10 miles from touchdown, 1,500 feet at 5 miles, 1,200 feet at 4 miles, and so on to touchdown.

2. Pilots of aircraft that produce strong wake vortices should fly as closely as possible to the approach course centerline or to the extended centerline of the runway of intended landing as appropriate to conditions.

f. Pilots operating lighter aircraft on visual approaches in-trail to aircraft producing strong wake vortices should use the following procedures to assist in avoiding wake turbulence. These procedures apply only to those aircraft that are on visual approaches.

1. Pilots of lighter aircraft should fly on or above the glidepath. Glidepath reference may be furnished by an ILS, by a visual approach slope system, by other ground-based approach slope guidance systems, or by other means. In the absence of visible glidepath guid-

ance, pilots may very nearly duplicate a 3-degree glideslope by adhering to the "3 to 1" glidepath principle.

EXAMPLE-
Fly 3,000 feet at 10 miles from touchdown, 1,500 feet at 5 miles, 1,200 feet at 4 miles, and so on to touchdown.

2. If the pilot of the lighter following aircraft has visual contact with the preceding heavier aircraft and also with the runway, the pilot may further adjust for possible wake vortex turbulence by the following practices:

(a) Pick a point of landing no less than 1,000 feet from the arrival end of the runway.

(b) Establish a line-of-sight to that landing point that is above and in front of the heavier preceding aircraft.

(c) When possible, note the point of landing of the heavier preceding aircraft and adjust point of intended landing as necessary.

EXAMPLE-
A puff of smoke may appear at the 1,000-foot markings of the runway, showing that touchdown was that point; therefore, adjust point of intended landing to the 1,500-foot markings.

(d) Maintain the line-of-sight to the point of intended landing above and ahead of the heavier preceding aircraft; maintain it to touchdown.

(e) Land beyond the point of landing of the preceding heavier aircraft.

3. During visual approaches pilots may ask ATC for updates on separation and groundspeed with respect to heavier preceding aircraft, especially when there is any question of safe separation from wake turbulence.

7-3-9. AIR TRAFFIC WAKE TURBULENCE SEPARATIONS

a. Because of the possible effects of wake turbulence, controllers are required to apply no less than specified minimum separation for aircraft operating behind a **heavy** jet and, in certain instances, behind large **nonheavy** aircraft (i.e., B757 aircraft).

1. Separation is applied to aircraft operating directly behind a **heavy/B757** jet at the same altitude or less than 1,000 feet below:

(a) Heavy jet behind **heavy** jet-4 miles.

(b) Large/heavy behind **B757** - 4 miles.

(c) Small behind **B757** - 5 miles.

(d) **Small/large** aircraft behind **heavy** jet - 5 miles.

2. Also, separation, measured at the time the preceding aircraft is over the landing threshold, is provided to small aircraft:

(a) **Small** aircraft landing behind **heavy** jet- 6 miles.

(b) **Small** aircraft landing behind **B757** - 5 miles.

(c) **Small** aircraft landing behind **large** aircraft- 4 miles.

REFERENCE-
PILOT/CONTROLLER GLOSSARY TERM- AIRCRAFT CLASSES.

3. Additionally, appropriate time or distance intervals are provided to departing aircraft:

(a) Two minutes or the appropriate 4 or 5 mile radar separation when takeoff behind a **heavy/B757** jet will be:

(1) from the same threshold;

(2) on a crossing runway and projected flight paths will cross;

(3) from the threshold of a parallel runway when staggered ahead of that of the adjacent runway by less than 500 feet and when the runways are separated by less than 2,500 feet.

NOTE-
Controllers may not reduce or waive these intervals.

b. A 3-minute interval will be provided when a **small** aircraft will takeoff:

1. From an intersection on the same runway (same or opposite direction) behind a departing **large** aircraft,

2. In the opposite direction on the same runway behind a large aircraft takeoff or low/missed approach.

NOTE-
This 3-minute interval may be waived upon specific pilot request.

c. A 3-minute interval will be provided for all aircraft taking off when the operations are as described in subparagraph b.1. and 2. above, the preceding aircraft is a **heavy/B757** jet, and the operations are on either the same runway or parallel runways separated by less than 2,500 feet. Controllers may not reduce or waive this interval.

d. Pilots may request additional separation i.e., 2 minutes instead of 4 or 5 miles for wake turbulence avoidance. This request should be made as soon as practical on ground control and at least before taxiing onto the runway.

NOTE-
14 CFR Section 91.3(a) states: "The pilot in command of an aircraft is directly responsible for and is the final authority as to the operation of that aircraft."

e. Controllers may anticipate separation and need not withhold a takeoff clearance for an aircraft departing behind a **large/heavy** aircraft if there is reasonable assurance the required separation will exist when the departing aircraft starts takeoff roll.

Section 4. BIRD HAZARDS AND FLIGHT OVER NATIONAL REFUGES, PARKS, AND FORESTS

-4-1. MIGRATORY BIRD ACTIVITY

a. Bird strike risk increases because of bird migration uring the months of March through April, and August hrough November.

b. The altitudes of migrating birds vary with winds loft, weather fronts, terrain elevations, cloud condi- ions, and other environmental variables. While over 90 ercent of the reported bird strikes occur at or below ,000 feet AGL, strikes at higher altitudes are common uring migration. Ducks and geese are frequently ob- erved up to 7,000 feet AGL and pilots are cautioned to ninimize en route flying at lower altitudes during nigration.

c. Considered the greatest potential hazard to aircraft ecause of their size, abundance, or habit of flying in ense flocks are gulls, waterfowl, vultures, hawks, wls, egrets, blackbirds, and starlings. Four major mi- ratory flyways exist in the United States. The Atlantic lyway parallels the Atlantic Coast. The Mississippi lyway stretches from Canada through the Great Lakes nd follows the Mississippi River. The Central Flyway epresents a broad area east of the Rockies, stretching rom Canada through Central America. The Pacific Fly- ay follows the west coast and overflies major parts of Vashington, Oregon, and California. There are also nu- nerous smaller flyways which cross these major north- outh migratory routes.

-4-2. REDUCING BIRD STRIKE RISKS

a. The most serious strikes are those involving ngestion into an engine (turboprops and turbine jet ngines) or windshield strikes. These strikes can result n emergency situations requiring prompt action by the ilot.

b. Engine ingestions may result in sudden loss of ower or engine failure. Review engine out procedures, specially when operating from airports with known ird hazards or when operating near high bird con- entrations.

c. Windshield strikes have resulted in pilots experi- ncing confusion, disorientation, loss of communica- ions, and aircraft control problems. Pilots are encour- ged to review their emergency procedures before lying in these areas.

d. When encountering birds en route, climb to avoid collision, because birds in flocks generally distribute themselves downward, with lead birds being at the highest altitude.

e. Avoid overflight of known areas of bird concentra- tion and flying at low altitudes during bird migration. Charted wildlife refuges and other natural areas contain unusually high local concentration of birds which may create a hazard to aircraft.

7-4-3. REPORTING BIRD STRIKES

Pilots are urged to report any bird or other wildlife strike using FAA Form 5200-7, Bird Strike Incident/Inges- tion Report (Appendix 1). Additional forms are avail- able at any FSS or at any FAA Regional Office. The data derived from these reports are used to develop standards to cope with this potential hazard to aircraft and for doc- umentation of necessary habitat control on airports.

7-4-4. REPORTING BIRD AND OTHER WILDLIFE ACTIVITIES

If you observe birds or other animals on or near the runway, request airport management to disperse the wildlife before taking off. Also contact the nearest FAA ARTCC, FSS, or tower (including non-Federal towers) regarding large flocks of birds and report the:

1. Geographic location;

2. Bird type (geese, ducks, gulls, etc.);

3. Approximate numbers;

4. Altitude;

5. Direction of bird flight path.

7-4-5. PILOT ADVISORIES ON BIRD AND OTHER WILDLIFE HAZARDS

Many airports advise pilots of other wildlife hazards caused by large animals on the runway through the A/FD and the NOTAM system. Collisions of landing and departing aircraft and animals on the runway are increasing and are not limited to rural airports. These accidents have also occurred at several major airports. Pilots should exercise extreme caution when warned of the presence of wildlife on and in the vicinity of airports. If you observe deer or other large animals in close proximity to movement areas, advise the FSS, tower, or airport management.

7-4-6. FLIGHTS OVER CHARTED U.S. WILDLIFE REFUGES, PARKS, AND FOREST SERVICE AREAS

a. The landing of aircraft is prohibited on lands or waters administered by the National Park Service, U.S. Fish and Wildlife Service, or U.S. Forest Service without authorization from the respective agency. Exceptions, including

1. when forced to land due to an emergency beyond the control of the operator,

2. at officially designated landing sites, or

3. an approved official business of the Federal Government.

b. Pilots are requested to maintain a minimum altitude of 2,000 feet above the surface of the following: National Parks, Monuments, Seashores, Lakeshores, Recreation Areas and Scenic Riverways administered by the National Park Service, National Wildlife Refuges, Big Game Refuges, Game Ranges and Wildlife Ranges administered by the U.S. Fish and Wildlife Service, and Wilderness and Primitive areas administered by the U.S. Forest Service.

NOTE-
FAA Advisory Circular AC 91-36, Visual Flight Rules (VFR Flight Near Noise-Sensitive Areas, defines the surface of national park area (including parks, forests, primitive areas wilderness areas, recreational areas, national seashores national monuments, national lakeshores, and nationa wildlife refuge and range areas) as: the highest terrai within 2,000 feet laterally of the route of flight, or th upper-most rim of a canyon or valley.

c. Federal statutes prohibit certain types of flight ac tivity and/or provide altitude restrictions over desig nated U.S. Wildlife Refuges, Parks, and Forest Servic Areas. These designated areas, for example: Boundar Waters Canoe Wilderness Areas, Minnesota; Haleakal National Park, Hawaii; Yosemite National Park California; and Grand Canyon National Park, Arizon are charted on Sectional Charts.

d. Federal regulations also prohibit airdrops by para chute or other means of persons, cargo, or objects from aircraft on lands administered by the three agencie without authorization from the respective agency. Ex ceptions include:

1. emergencies involving the safety of human life or

2. threat of serious property loss.

Section 5. POTENTIAL FLIGHT HAZARDS

7-5-1. ACCIDENT CAUSE FACTORS

a. The 10 most frequent cause factors for General Aviation Accidents that involve the pilot-in-command are:

1. Inadequate preflight preparation and/or planning.

2. Failure to obtain and/or maintain flying speed.

3. Failure to maintain direction control.

4. Improper level off.

5. Failure to see and avoid objects or obstructions.

6. Mismanagement of fuel.

7. Improper inflight decisions or planning.

8. Misjudgment of distance and speed.

9. Selection of unsuitable terrain.

10. Improper operation of flight controls.

b. This list remains relatively stable and points out the need for continued refresher training to establish a higher level of flight proficiency for all pilots. A part of the FAA's continuing effort to promote increased aviation safety is the Aviation Safety Program. For information on Aviation Safety Program activities contact your nearest Flight Standards District Office.

c. Alertness: Be alert at all times, especially when the weather is good. Most pilots pay attention to business when they are operating in full IFR weather conditions, but strangely, air collisions almost invariably have occurred under ideal weather conditions. Unlimited visibility appears to encourage a sense of security which is not at all justified. Considerable information of value may be obtained by listening to advisories being issued in the terminal area, even though controller workload may prevent a pilot from obtaining individual service.

d. Giving Way: If you think another aircraft is too close to you, give way instead of waiting for the other pilot to respect the right-of-way to which you may be entitled. It is a lot safer to pursue the right-of-way angle after you have completed your flight.

7-5-2. VFR IN CONGESTED AREAS

A high percentage of near midair collisions occur below 8,000 feet AGL and within 30 miles of an airport. When operating VFR in these highly congested areas, whether you intend to land at an airport within the area or are just flying through, it is recommended that extra vigilance be maintained and that you monitor an appropriate control frequency. Normally the appropriate frequency is an approach control frequency. By such monitoring action you can "get the picture" of the traffic in your area. When the approach controller has radar, radar traffic advisories may be given to VFR pilots upon request.

REFERENCE-
AIM, RADAR TRAFFIC INFORMATION SERVICE,
PARAGRAPH 4-1-14.

7-5-3. OBSTRUCTIONS TO FLIGHT

a. General:

Many structures exist that could significantly affect the safety of your flight when operating below 500 feet AGL, and particularly below 200 feet AGL. While FAR Part 91.119 allows flight below 500 AGL when over sparsely populated areas or open water, such operations are very dangerous. At and below 200 feet AGL there are numerous power lines, antenna towers, etc., that are not marked and lighted as obstructions and therefore may not be seen in time to avoid a collision. Notices to Airmen (NOTAM's) are issued on those lighted structures experiencing temporary light outages. However, some time may pass before the FAA is notified of these outages, and the NOTAM issued, thus pilot vigilance is imperative.

b. Antenna Towers:

Extreme caution should be exercised when flying less than 2,000 feet AGL because of numerous skeletal structures, such as radio and television antenna towers, that exceed 1,000 feet AGL with some extending higher than 2,000 feet AGL. Most skeletal structures are supported by guy wires which are very difficult to see in good weather and can be invisible at dusk or during periods of reduced visibility. These wires can extend about 1,500 feet horizontally from a structure; therefore, all skeletal structures should be avoided horizontally by at least 2,000 feet. Additionally, new towers may not be on your current chart because the information was not received prior to the printing of the chart.

c. Overhead Wires:

Overhead transmission and utility lines often span approaches to runways, natural flyways such as lakes, rivers, gorges, and canyons, and cross other landmarks pilots frequently follow such as highways, railroad tracks, etc. As with antenna towers, these high voltage/power lines or the supporting structures of these lines may not always be readily visible and the wires may be virtually impossible to see under certain conditions. In some locations, the supporting structures of overhead transmission lines are equipped with unique sequence flashing white strobe light systems to indicate that there are wires between the structures. However, many power lines do not require notice to the FAA and, therefore, are not marked and/or lighted. Many of those that do require notice do not exceed 200 feet AGL or meet the Obstruction Standard of FAR Part 77 and, therefore, are not marked and/or lighted. All pilots are cautioned to remain extremely vigilant for these power lines or their supporting structures when following natural flyways or during the approach and landing phase. This is particularly important for seaplane and/or float equipped aircraft when landing on, or departing from, unfamiliar lakes or rivers.

d. Other Objects/Structures:

There are other objects or structures that could adversely affect your flight such as construction cranes near an airport, newly constructed buildings, new towers, etc. Many of these structures do not meet charting requirements or may not yet be charted because of the charting cycle. Some structures do not require obstruction marking and/or lighting and some may not be marked and lighted even though the FAA recommended it.

7-5-4. AVOID FLIGHT BENEATH UNMANNED BALLOONS

a. The majority of unmanned free balloons currently being operated have, extending below them, either a suspension device to which the payload or instrument package is attached, or a trailing wire antenna, or both. In many instances these balloon subsystems may be invisible to the pilot until the aircraft is close to the balloon, thereby creating a potentially dangerous situation. Therefore, good judgment on the part of the pilot dictates that aircraft should remain well clear of all unmanned free balloons and flight below them should be avoided at all times.

b. Pilots are urged to report any unmanned free balloons sighted to the nearest FAA ground facility with which communication is established. Such information will assist FAA ATC facilities to identify and flight follow unmanned free balloons operating in the airspace.

7-5-5. MOUNTAIN FLYING

a. Your first experience of flying over mountainous terrain (particularly if most of your flight time has been over the flatlands of the midwest) could be a *never-to-be-forgotten nightmare* if proper planning is not done and if you are not aware of the potential hazards awaiting. Those familiar section lines are not present in the mountains; those flat, level fields for forced landings are practically nonexistent; abrupt changes in wind direction and velocity occur; severe updrafts and downdrafts are common, particularly near or above abrupt changes of terrain such as cliffs or rugged areas; even the clouds look different and can build up with startling rapidity. Mountain flying need not be hazardous if you follow the recommendations below:

b. **File a flight plan:** Plan your route to avoid topography which would prevent a safe forced landing. The route should be over populated areas and well known mountain passes. Sufficient altitude should be maintained to permit gliding to a safe landing in the event of engine failure.

c. Don't fly a light aircraft when the winds aloft, at your proposed altitude, exceed 35 miles per hour. Expect the winds to be of much greater velocity over mountain passes than reported a few miles from them. Approach mountain passes with as much altitude as possible. Downdrafts of from 1,500 to 2,000 feet per minute are not uncommon on the leeward side.

d. Don't fly near or above abrupt changes in terrain. Severe turbulence can be expected, especially in high wind conditions.

e. Some canyons run into a dead end. Don't fly so far up a canyon that you get trapped. ALWAYS BE ABLE TO MAKE A 180 DEGREE TURN!

f. VFR flight operations may be conducted at night in mountainous terrain with the application of sound judgment and common sense. Proper pre-flight planning, giving ample consideration to winds and weather, knowledge of the terrain and pilot experience in mountain flying are prerequisites for safety of flight. Continuous visual contact with the surface and obstructions is a major concern and flight operations under an overcast or in the vicinity of clouds should be approached with extreme caution.

g. When landing at a high altitude field, the same indicated airspeed should be used as at low elevation fields. *Remember:* that due to the less dense air at altitude, this same indicated airspeed actually results in higher true airspeed, a faster landing speed, and more important, a longer landing distance. During gusty wind conditions which often prevail at high altitude fields, a power approach and power landing is recommended. Additionally, due to the faster groundspeed, your takeoff distance will increase considerably over that required at low altitudes.

h. Effects of Density Altitude: Performance figures in the aircraft owner's handbook for length of takeoff run, horsepower, rate of climb, etc., are generally based on standard atmosphere conditions (59 degrees Fahrenheit (15 degrees Celsius), pressure 29.92 inches of mercury) at sea level. However, inexperienced pilots, as well as experienced pilots, may run into trouble when they encounter an altogether different set of conditions. This is particularly true in hot weather and at higher elevations. Aircraft operations at altitudes above sea level and at higher than standard temperatures are commonplace in mountainous areas. Such operations quite often result in a drastic reduction of aircraft performance capabilities because of the changing air density. Density altitude is a measure of air density. It is not to be confused with pressure altitude, true altitude or absolute altitude. It is not to be used as a height reference, but as a determining criteria in the performance capability of an aircraft. Air density decreases with altitude. As air density decreases, density altitude increases. The further effects of high temperature and high humidity are cumulative, resulting in an increasing high density altitude condition. High density altitude reduces all aircraft performance parameters. To the pilot, this means that the normal horsepower output is reduced, propeller efficiency is reduced and a higher true airspeed is required to sustain the aircraft throughout its operating parameters. It means an increase in runway length requirements for takeoff and landings, and decreased rate of climb. An average small airplane, for example, requiring 1,000 feet for takeoff at sea level under standard atmospheric conditions will require a takeoff run of approximately 2,000 feet at an operational altitude of 5,000 feet.

NOTE-
A turbo-charged aircraft engine provides some slight advantage in that it provides sea level horsepower up to a specified altitude above sea level.

1. Density Altitude Advisories: at airports with elevations of 2,000 feet and higher, control towers and FSS's will broadcast the advisory "Check Density Altitude" when the temperature reaches a predetermined level. These advisories will be broadcast on appropriate tower frequencies or, where available, ATIS. FSS's will broadcast these advisories as a part of Local Airport Advisory, and on TWEB.

2. These advisories are provided by air traffic facilities, as a reminder to pilots that high temperatures and high field elevations will cause significant changes in aircraft characteristics. The pilot retains the responsibility to compute density altitude, when appropriate, as a part of preflight duties.

NOTE-
All FSS's will compute the current density altitude upon request.

i. Mountain Wave: Many pilots go all their lives without understanding what a mountain wave is. Quite a few have lost their lives because of this lack of understanding. One need not be a licensed meteorologist to understand the mountain wave phenomenon.

1. Mountain waves occur when air is being blown over a mountain range or even the ridge of a sharp bluff area. As the air hits the upwind side of the range, it starts to climb, thus creating what is generally a smooth updraft which turns into a turbulent downdraft as the air passes the crest of the ridge. From this point, for many miles downwind, there will be a series of downdrafts and updrafts. Satellite photos of the Rockies have shown mountain waves extending as far as 700 miles downwind of the range. Along the east coast area, such photos of the Appalachian chain have picked up the mountain wave phenomenon over a hundred miles eastward. All it takes to form a mountain wave is wind blowing across the range at 15 knots or better at an intersection angle of not less than 30 degrees.

2. Pilots from flatland areas should understand a few things about mountain waves in order to stay out of trouble. When approaching a mountain range from the upwind side (generally the west), there will usually be a smooth updraft; therefore, it is not quite as dangerous an area as the lee of the range. From the leeward side, it is always a good idea to add an extra thousand feet or so of altitude because downdrafts can exceed the climb capability of the aircraft. Never expect an updraft when approaching a mountain chain from the leeward. Always be prepared to cope with a downdraft and turbulence.

3. When approaching a mountain ridge from the downwind side, it is recommended that the ridge be approached at approximately a 45 degree angle to the horizontal direction of the ridge. This permits a safer retreat from the ridge with less stress on the aircraft should severe turbulence and downdraft be experienced. If severe turbulence is encountered, simultaneously reduce power and adjust pitch until aircraft approaches maneuvering speed, then adjust power and trim to maintain maneuvering speed and fly away from the turbulent area.

7-5-6. USE OF RUNWAY HALF-WAY SIGNS AT UNIMPROVED AIRPORTS

When installed, runway half-way signs provide the pilot with a reference point to judge takeoff acceleration trends. Assuming that the runway length is appropriate for takeoff (considering runway condition and slope, elevation, aircraft weight, wind, and temperature), typical takeoff acceleration should allow the airplane to reach 70% of lift-off airspeed by the midpoint of the runway. The "rule of thumb" is that should airplane acceleration not allow the airspeed to reach this value by the midpoint, the takeoff should be aborted, as it may not be possible to liftoff in the remaining runway.

Several points are important when considering using this "rule of thumb":

a. Airspeed indicators in small airplanes are not required to be evaluated at speeds below stalling, and may not be usable at 70% of liftoff airspeed.

b. This "rule of thumb" is based on a uniform surface condition. Puddles, soft spots, areas of tall and/or wet grass, loose gravel, etc., may impede acceleration or even cause deceleration. Even if the airplane achieves 70% of liftoff airspeed by the midpoint, the condition of the remainder of the runway may not allow further acceleration. The entire length of the runway should be inspected prior to takeoff to ensure a usable surface.

c. This "rule of thumb" applies only to runway required for actual liftoff. In the event that obstacles affect the takeoff climb path, appropriate distance must be available after liftoff to accelerate to best angle of climb speed and to clear the obstacles. This will, in effect, require the airplane to accelerate to a higher speed by midpoint, particularly if the obstacles are close

to the end of the runway. In addition, this technique does not take into account the effects of upslope or tailwinds on takeoff performance. These factors will also require greater acceleration than normal and, under some circumstances, prevent takeoff entirely.

d. Use of this "rule of thumb" does not alleviate the pilot's responsibility to comply with applicable Federal Aviation Regulations, the limitations and performance data provided in the FAA approved Airplane Flight Manual (AFM), or, in the absence of an FAA approved AFM, other data provided by the aircraft manufacturer.

In addition to their use during takeoff, runway half-way signs offer the pilot increased awareness of his or her position along the runway during landing operations.

7-5-7. SEAPLANE SAFETY

a. Acquiring a seaplane class rating affords access to many areas not available to landplane pilots. Adding a seaplane class rating to your pilot certificate can be relatively uncomplicated and inexpensive. However, more effort is required to become a safe, efficient, competent "bush" pilot. The natural hazards of the backwoods have given way to modern man-made hazards. Except for the far north, the available bodies of water are no longer the exclusive domain of the airman. Seaplane pilots must be vigilant for hazards such as electric power lines, power, sail and rowboats, rafts, mooring lines, water skiers, swimmers, etc.

b. Seaplane pilots must have a thorough understanding of the right-of-way rules as they apply to aircraft versus other vessels. Seaplane pilots are expected to know and adhere to both the United States Coast Guard's (USCG) Navigation Rules, International-Inland, and 14 CFR Section 91.115, Right-of-Way Rules; Water Operations. The navigation rules of the road are a set of collision avoidance rules as they apply to aircraft on the water. A seaplane is considered a vessel when on the water for the purposes of these collision avoidance rules. In general, a seaplane on the water shall keep well clear of all vessels and avoid impeding their navigation. The CFR requires, in part, that aircraft operating on the water ". . . shall, insofar as possible, keep clear of all vessels and avoid impeding their navigation, and shall give way to any vessel or other aircraft that is given the right-of-way . . . ." This means that a seaplane should avoid boats and commercial shipping when on the water. If on a collision course, the seaplane should slow, stop, or maneuver to the right, away from the bow of the oncoming vessel. Also, while on the surface with an engine running, an aircraft must give way to all nonpowered vessels. Since a seaplane in the water may not be as maneuverable as one in the air, the aircraft on the water has right-of-way over one in the air, and one taking off has right-of-way over one landing. A seaplane is exempt from the USCG safety equipment requirements, including the requirements for Personal Flotation Devices (PFD). Requiring seaplanes on the water to comply with USCG equipment requirements in addition to the FAA equipment requirements would be an unnecessary burden on seaplane owners and operators.

c. Unless they are under Federal jurisdiction, navigable bodies of water are under the jurisdiction of the state, or in a few cases, privately owned. Unless they are specifically restricted, aircraft have as much right to operate on these bodies of water as other vessels. To avoid problems, check with Federal or local officials in advance of operating on unfamiliar waters. In addition to the agencies listed in TBL 7-5-1, the nearest Flight Standards District Office can usually offer some practical suggestions as well as regulatory information. If you land on a restricted body of water because of an inflight emergency, or in ignorance of the restrictions you have violated, report as quickly as practical to the nearest local official having jurisdiction and explain your situation.

d. When operating a seaplane over or into remote areas, appropriate attention should be given to survival gear. Minimum kits are recommended for summer and winter, and are required by law for flight into sparsely settled areas of Canada and Alaska. Alaska State Department of Transportation and Canadian Ministry of Transport officials can provide specific information on survival gear requirements. The kit should be assembled in one container and be easily reachable and preferably floatable.

e. The FAA recommends that each seaplane owner or operator provide flotation gear for occupants any time a seaplane operates on or near water. 14 CFR Section 91.205(b)(12) requires approved flotation gear for aircraft operated for hire over water and beyond power-off gliding distance from shore. FAA-approved gear differs from that required for navigable waterways under USCG rules. FAA-approved life vests are inflatable designs as compared to the USCG's noninflatable PFD's that may consist of solid, bulky material. Such USCG PFD's are impractical for seaplanes and other aircraft because they may block passage through the relatively narrow exits available to pilots and passengers. Life vests approved under Technical Standard Order (TSO) C13E contain fully inflatable compartments. The wearer inflates the compartments (AFTER exiting the aircraft) primarily by independent CO_2 cartridges, with an oral inflation tube as a backup. The flotation gear also contains a water-activated, self-illuminating signal light. The fact that pilots and passengers can easily don and wear inflatable life vests (when not inflated) provides maximum effectiveness and allows for unrestricted movement. It is imperative that passengers are briefed on the location and proper use of available PFD's prior to leaving the dock.

Jurisdictions Controlling Navigable Bodies of Water

AUTHORITY TO CONSULT FOR USE OF A BODY OF WATER		
Location	*Authority*	*Contact*
Wilderness Area	U.S. Department of Agriculture, Forest Service	Local forest ranger
National Forest	USDA Forest Service	Local forest ranger
National Park	U.S. Department of the Interior, National Park Service	Local park ranger
Indian Reservation	USDI, Bureau of Indian Affairs	Local Bureau office
State Park	State government or state forestry or park service	Local state aviation office for further information
Canadian National and Provincial Parks	Supervised and restricted on an individual basis from province to province and by different departments of the Canadian government; consult Canadian Flight Information Manual and/or Water Aerodrome Supplement	Park Superintendent in an emergency

TBL 7-5-1

f. The FAA recommends that seaplane owners and operators obtain Advisory Circular (AC) 91-69, Seaplane Safety for FAR Part 91 Operations, free from the U.S. Department of Transportation, Subsequent Distribution Office, SVC-121.23, Ardmore East Business Center, 3341 Q 75th Avenue, Landover, MD 20785; fax: (301) 386-5394. The USCG Navigation Rules International-Inland (COMDTINSTM 16672.2B) is available for a fee from the Government Printing Office by facsimile request to (202) 512-2250, and can be ordered using Mastercard or Visa.

AIM

■ 7-5-8. FLIGHT OPERATIONS IN VOLCANIC ASH

a. Severe volcanic eruptions which send ash into the upper atmosphere occur somewhere around the world several times each year. Flying into a volcanic ash cloud can be exceedingly dangerous. A B747-200 lost all four engines after such an encounter and a B747-400 had the same nearly catastrophic experience. Piston-powered aircraft are less likely to lose power but severe damage is almost certain to ensue after an encounter with a volcanic ash cloud which is only a few hours old.

b. Most important is to avoid any encounter with volcanic ash. The ash plume may not be visible, especially in instrument conditions or at night; and even if visible, it is difficult to distinguish visually between an ash cloud and an ordinary weather cloud. Volcanic ash clouds are not displayed on airborne or ATC radar. The pilot must rely on reports from air traffic controllers and other pilots to determine the location of the ash cloud and use that information to remain well clear of the area. Every attempt should be made to remain on the upwind side of the volcano.

c. It is recommended that pilots encountering an ash cloud should immediately reduce thrust to idle (altitude permitting), and reverse course in order to escape from the cloud. Ash clouds may extend for hundreds of miles and pilots should not attempt to fly through or climb out of the cloud. In addition, the following procedures are recommended:

1. Disengage the autothrottle if engaged. This will prevent the autothrottle from increasing engine thrust;

2. Turn on continuous ignition;

3. Turn on all accessory airbleeds including all air conditioning packs, nacelles, and wing anti-ice. This will provide an additional engine stall margin by reducing engine pressure.

d. The following has been reported by flightcrews who have experienced encounters with volcanic dust clouds:

1. Smoke or dust appearing in the cockpit;

2. An acrid odor similar to electrical smoke;

3. Multiple engine malfunctions, such as compressor stalls, increasing EGT, torching from tailpipe, and flameouts;

4. At night, St. Elmo's fire or other static discharges accompanied by a bright orange glow in the engine inlets;

5. A fire warning in the forward cargo area.

e. It may become necessary to shut down and then restart engines to prevent exceeding EGT limits. Volcanic ash may block the pitot system and result in unreliable airspeed indications.

f. If you see a volcanic eruption and have not been previously notified of it, you may have been the first person to observe it. In this case, immediately contact ATC and alert them to the existence of the eruption. If possible, use the Volcanic Activity Reporting form (VAR) depicted in Appendix 2 of this manual. Items 1 through 8 of the VAR should be transmitted immediately. The information requested in items 9 through 16 should be passed after landing. If a VAR form is not immediately available, relay enough information to identify the position and nature of the volcanic activity. Do not become unnecessarily alarmed if there is merely steam or very low-level eruptions of ash.

g. When landing at airports where volcanic ash has been deposited on the runway be aware that even a thin layer of dry ash can be detrimental to braking action. Wet ash on the runway may also reduce effectiveness of braking. It is recommended that reverse thrust be limited to minimum practical to reduce the possibility of reduced visibility and engine ingestion of airborne ash.

h. When departing from airports where volcanic ash has been deposited it is recommended that pilots avoid operating in visible airborne ash. Allow ash to settle before initiating takeoff roll. It is also recommended that flap extension be delayed until initiating the before takeoff checklist and that a rolling takeoff be executed to avoid blowing ash back into the air.

7-5-9. EMERGENCY AIRBORNE INSPECTION OF OTHER AIRCRAFT

a. Providing airborne assistance to another aircraft may involve flying in very close proximity to that aircraft. Most pilots receive little, if any, formal training or instruction in this type of flying activity. Close proximity flying without sufficient time to plan (i.e., in an emergency situation), coupled with the stress involved in a perceived emergency can be hazardous.

b. The pilot in the best position to assess the situation should take the responsibility of coordinating the airborne intercept and inspection, and take into account the unique flight characteristics and differences of the category(s) of aircraft involved.

c. Some of the safety considerations are:

1. Area, direction and speed of the intercept;

2. Aerodynamic effects (i.e., rotorcraft down-wash);

3. Minimum safe separation distances;

4. Communications requirements, lost communications procedures, coordination with ATC;

5. Suitability of diverting the distressed aircraft to the nearest safe airport; and

6. Emergency actions to terminate the intercept.

d. Close proximity, inflight inspection of another aircraft is uniquely hazardous. The pilot in command of the aircraft experiencing the problem/emergency must not relinquish control of the situation and/or jeopardize the safety of their aircraft. The maneuver must be accomplished with minimum risk to both aircraft.

7-5-10. PRECIPITATION STATIC

a. Precipitation static is caused by aircraft in flight coming in contact with uncharged particles. These particles can be rain, snow, fog, sleet, hail, volcanic ash, dust; any solid or liquid particles. When the aircraft strikes these neutral particles the positive element of the particle is reflected away from the aircraft and the negative particle adheres to the skin of the aircraft. In a very short period of time a substantial negative charge will develop on the skin of the aircraft. If the aircraft is not equipped with static dischargers, or has an ineffective static discharger system, when a sufficient negative voltage level is reached, the aircraft may go into "CORONA." That is, it will discharge the static electricity from the extremities of the aircraft, such as the wing tips, horizontal stabilizer, vertical stabilizer, antenna, propeller tips, etc.. This discharge of static electricity is what you will hear in your headphones and is what we call P-static.

b. A review of pilot reports often shows different symptoms with each problem that is encountered. The following list of problems is a summary of many pilot reports from many different aircraft. Each problem was caused by P-static:

1. Complete loss of VHF communications;

2. Erroneous magnetic compass readings (30% in error);

3. High pitched squeal on audio;

4. Motor boat sound on audio;

5. Loss of all avionics in clouds;

6. VLF navigation system inoperative most of the time;

7. Erratic instrument readouts;

8. Weak transmissions and poor receptivity of radios;

9. "St. Elmo's Fire" on windshield.

c. Each of these symptoms is caused by one general problem on the airframe. This problem is the inability of the accumulated charge to flow easily to the wing tips and tail of the airframe, and properly discharge to the airstream.

d. Static dischargers work on the principal of creating a relatively easy path for discharging negative charges that develop on the aircraft by using a discharger with fine metal points, carbon coated rods, or carbon wicks rather than wait until a large charge is developed and discharged off the trailing edges of the aircraft that will interfere with avionics equipment. This process offers approximately 50 decibels (dB) static noise reduction which is adequate in most cases to be below the threshold of noise that would cause interference in avionics equipment.

e. It is important to remember that precipitation static problems can only be corrected with the proper number of quality static dischargers, properly installed on a properly bonded aircraft. P-static is indeed a problem in the all weather operation of the aircraft, but there are effective ways to combat it. All possible methods of reducing the effects of P-static should be considered so as to provide the best possible performance in the flight environment.

f. A wide variety of discharger designs is available on the commercial market. The inclusion of well-designed dischargers may be expected to improve airframe noise in P-static conditions by as much as 50 dB. Essentially, the discharger provides a path by which accumulated charge may leave the airframe quietly. This is generally accomplished by providing a group of tiny corona points to permit onset of corona-current flow at a low aircraft potential. Additionally, aerodynamic design of dischargers to permit corona to occur at the lowest possible atmospheric pressure also lowers the corona threshold. In addition to permitting a low-potential discharge, the discharger will minimize the radiation of radio frequency (RF) energy which accompanies the corona discharge, in order to minimize effects of RF components at communications and navigation frequencies on avionics performance. These effects are reduced through resistive attachment of the corona point(s) to the airframe, preserving direct current connection but attenuating the higher-frequency components of the discharge.

g. Each manufacturer of static dischargers offers information concerning appropriate discharger location on specific airframes. Such locations emphasize the trailing outboard surfaces of wings and horizontal tail surfaces, plus the tip of the vertical stabilizer, where charge tends to accumulate on the airframe. Sufficient dischargers must be provided to allow for current-carrying capacity which will maintain airframe potential below the corona threshold of the trailing edges.

h. In order to achieve full performance of avionic equipment, the static discharge system will require periodic maintenance. A pilot knowledgeable of P-static causes and effects is an important element in assuring optimum performance by early recognition of these types of problems.

7-5-11. LIGHT AMPLIFICATION BY STIMULATED EMISSION OF RADIATION (LASER) OPERATIONS

a. Lasers have many applications. Of concern to users of the National Airspace System are those laser events that may affect pilots, e.g., outdoor laser light shows or demonstrations for entertainment and advertisements at special events and theme parks. Generally,

the beams from these events appear as bright blue-green in color; however, they may be red, yellow, or white. However, some laser systems produce light which is invisible to the human eye.

b. Currently, there are no FAA regulations that specifically address the above-mentioned laser activities. However, FAA regulations prohibit the disruption of aviation activity by any person on the ground or in the air. The FAA and the Food and Drug Administration (the Federal agency that has the responsibility to enforce compliance with Federal requirements for laser systems and laser light show products) are working together to ensure that operators of these devices do not pose a hazard to aircraft operators.

c. Pilots should be aware that illumination from these laser operations are able to create temporary vision impairment miles from the actual location. In addition, these operations can produce permanent eye damage. Pilots should make themselves aware of where these activities are being conducted and avoid these areas if possible.

d. When these activities become known to the FAA, Notices to Airmen (NOTAM's) are issued to inform the aviation community of the events. Pilots should consult NOTAM's or the Special Notices section of the Airport/Facility Directory for information regarding these activities.

Section 6. SAFETY, ACCIDENT, AND HAZARD REPORTS

7-6-1. AVIATION SAFETY REPORTING PROGRAM

a. The FAA has established a voluntary Aviation Safety Reporting Program designed to stimulate the free and unrestricted flow of information concerning deficiencies and discrepancies in the aviation system. This is a positive program intended to ensure the safest possible system by identifying and correcting unsafe conditions before they lead to accidents. The primary objective of the program is to obtain information to evaluate and enhance the safety and efficiency of the present system.

b. This cooperative safety reporting program invites pilots, controllers, flight attendants, maintenance personnel and other users of the airspace system, or any other person, to file written reports of actual or potential discrepancies and deficiencies involving the safety of aviation operations. The operations covered by the program include departure, en route, approach, and landing operations and procedures, air traffic control procedures and equipment, crew and air traffic control communications, aircraft cabin operations, aircraft movement on the airport, near midair collisions, aircraft maintenance and record keeping and airport conditions or services.

c. The report should give the date, time, location, persons and aircraft involved (if applicable), nature of the event, and all pertinent details.

d. To ensure receipt of this information, the program provides for the waiver of certain disciplinary actions against persons, including pilots and air traffic controllers, who file timely written reports concerning potentially unsafe incidents. To be considered timely, reports must be delivered or postmarked within 10 days of the incident unless that period is extended for good cause. Reports should be submitted on NASA ARC Forms 277, which are available free of charge, postage prepaid, at FAA Flight Standards District Offices and Flight Service Stations, and from NASA, ASRS, PO Box 189, Moffet Field, CA 94035.

e. The FAA utilizes the National Aeronautics and Space Administration (NASA) to act as an independent third party to receive and analyze reports submitted under the program. This program is described in AC 00–46, Aviation Safety Reporting Program.

7-6-2. AIRCRAFT ACCIDENT AND INCIDENT REPORTING

a. Occurrences Requiring Notification: The operator of an aircraft shall immediately, and by the most expeditious means available, notify the nearest National Transportation Safety Board (NTSB) Field Office when:

1. An aircraft accident or any of the following listed incidents occur:

(a) Flight control system malfunction or failure;

(b) Inability of any required flight crew member to perform their normal flight duties as a result of injury or illness;

(c) Failure of structural components of a turbine engine excluding compressor and turbine blades and vanes;

(d) Inflight fire;

(e) Aircraft collide in flight;

(f) Damage to property, other than the aircraft, estimated to exceed $25,000 for repair (including materials and labor) or fair market value in the event of total loss, whichever is less.

(g) For large multi-engine aircraft (more than 12,500 pounds maximum certificated takeoff weight):

(1) Inflight failure of electrical systems which requires the sustained use of an emergency bus powered by a back-up source such as a battery, auxiliary power unit, or air-driven generator to retain flight control or essential instruments;

(2) Inflight failure of hydraulic systems that results in sustained reliance on the sole remaining hydraulic or mechanical system for movement of flight control surfaces;

(3) Sustained loss of the power or thrust produced by two or more engines; and

(4) An evacuation of aircraft in which an emergency egress system is utilized.

2. An aircraft is overdue and is believed to have been involved in an accident.

AIM

b. Manner of Notification:

1. The most expeditious method of notification to the NTSB by the operator will be determined by the circumstances existing at that time. The NTSB has advised that any of the following would be considered examples of the type of notification that would be acceptable:

(a) Direct telephone notification;

(b) Telegraphic notification;

(c) Notification to the FAA who would in turn notify the NTSB by direct communication; i.e., dispatch or telephone.

c. Items To Be Notified: The notification required above shall contain the following information, if available:

1. Type, nationality, and registration marks of the aircraft;

2. Name of owner and operator of the aircraft;

3. Name of the pilot-in-command;

4. Date and time of the accident, or incident;

5. Last point of departure, and point of intended landing of the aircraft;

6. Position of the aircraft with reference to some easily defined geographical point;

7. Number of persons aboard, number killed, and number seriously injured;

8. Nature of the accident, or incident, the weather, and the extent of damage to the aircraft so far as is known; and

9. A description of any explosives, radioactive materials, or other dangerous articles carried.

d. Follow–up Reports:

1. The operator shall file a report on NTSB Form 6120.1 or 6120.2, available from NTSB Field Offices or from the NTSB, Washington, DC, 20594:

(a) Within 10 days after an accident;

(b) When, after 7 days, an overdue aircraft is still missing;

(c) A report on an incident for which notification is required as described in subparagraph a(1) shall be filed only as requested by an authorized representative of the NTSB.

2. Each crewmember, if physically able at the time the report is submitted, shall attach a statement setting forth the facts, conditions and circumstances relating to the accident or incident as they appeared. If the crewmember is incapacitated, a statement shall be submitted as soon as physically possible.

e. Where To File the Reports:

1. The operator of an aircraft shall file with the NTSB Field Office nearest the accident or incident any report required by this section.

2. The NTSB Field Offices are listed under U.S. Government in the telephone directories in the following cities: Anchorage, AK; Atlanta, GA; Chicago, IL; Denver, CO; Forth Worth, TX; Los Angeles, CA; Miami, FL; Parsippany, NJ; Seattle, WA.

7–6–3. NEAR MIDAIR COLLISION REPORTING

a. Purpose and Data Uses: The primary purpose of the Near Midair Collision (NMAC) Reporting Program is to provide information for use in enhancing the safety and efficiency of the National Airspace System. Data obtained from NMAC reports are used by the FAA to improve the quality of FAA services to users and to develop programs, policies, and procedures aimed at the reduction of NMAC occurrences. All NMAC reports are thoroughly investigated by Flight Standards Facilities in coordination with Air Traffic Facilities. Data from these investigations are transmitted to FAA Headquarters in Washington, DC, where they are compiled and analyzed, and where safety programs and recommendations are developed.

b. Definition: A near midair collision is defined as an incident associated with the operation of an aircraft in which a possibility of collision occurs as a result of proximity of less than 500 feet to another aircraft, or a report is received from a pilot or a flight crew member stating that a collision hazard existed between two or more aircraft.

c. Reporting Responsibility: It is the responsibility of the pilot and/or flight crew to determine whether a near midair collision did actually occur and, if so, to initiate a NMAC report. Be specific, as ATC will not interpret a casual remark to mean that a NMAC is being reported. The pilot should state "I wish to report a near midair collision."

d. Where To File Reports: Pilots and/or flight crew members involved in NMAC occurrences are urged to report each incident immediately:

1. By radio or telephone to the nearest FAA ATC facility or FSS.

2. In writing, in lieu of the above, to the nearest Flight Standards District Office (FSDO).

e. Items To Be Reported:

1. Date and time (UTC) of incident.

2. Location of incident and altitude.

3. Identification and type of reporting aircraft, aircrew destination, name and home base of pilot.

4. Identification and type of other aircraft, aircrew destination, name and home base of pilot.

5. Type of flight plans; station altimeter setting used.

6. Detailed weather conditions at altitude or flight level.

7. Approximate courses of both aircraft: indicate if one or both aircraft were climbing or descending.

8. Reported separation in distance at first sighting, proximity at closest point horizontally and vertically, and length of time in sight prior to evasive action.

9. Degree of evasive action taken, if any (from both aircraft, if possible).

10. Injuries, if any.

f. Investigation: The FSDO in whose area the incident occurred is responsible for the investigation and reporting of NMAC's.

g. Existing radar, communication, and weather data will be examined in the conduct of the investigation. When possible, all cockpit crew members will be interviewed regarding factors involving the NMAC incident. Air traffic controllers will be interviewed in cases where one or more of the involved aircraft was provided ATC service. Both flight and ATC procedures will be evaluated. When the investigation reveals a violation of an FAA regulation, enforcement action will be pursued.

Chapter 8. MEDICAL FACTS FOR PILOTS

Section 1. FITNESS FOR FLIGHT

8-1-1. FITNESS FOR FLIGHT

a. **Medical Certification:**

1. All pilots except those flying gliders and free air balloons must possess valid medical certificates in order to exercise the privileges of their airman certificates. The periodic medical examinations required for medical certification are conducted by designated Aviation Medical Examiners, who are physicians with a special interest in aviation safety and training in aviation medicine.

2. The standards for medical certification are contained in FAR Part 67. Pilots who have a history of certain medical conditions described in these standards are mandatorily disqualified from flying. These medical conditions include a personality disorder manifested by overt acts, a psychosis, alcoholism, drug dependence, epilepsy, an unexplained disturbance of consciousness, myocardial infarction, angina pectoris and diabetes requiring medication for its control. Other medical conditions may be temporarily disqualifying, such as acute infections, anemia, and peptic ulcer. Pilots who do not meet medical standards may still be qualified under special issuance provisions or the exemption process. This may require that either additional medical information be provided or practical flight tests be conducted.

3. Student pilots should visit an Aviation Medical Examiner as soon as possible in their flight training in order to avoid unnecessary training expenses should they not meet the medical standards. For the same reason, the student pilot who plans to enter commercial aviation should apply for the highest class of medical certificate that might be necessary in the pilot's career.

CAUTION–
The FAR's prohibit a pilot who possesses a current medical certificate from performing crewmember duties while the pilot has a known medical condition or increase of a known medical condition that would make the pilot unable to meet the standards for the medical certificate.

b. **Illness:**

1. Even a minor illness suffered in day-to-day living can seriously degrade performance of many piloting tasks vital to safe flight. Illness can produce fever and distracting symptoms that can impair judgment, memory, alertness, and the ability to make calculations.

Although symptoms from an illness may be under adequate control with a medication, the medication itself may decrease pilot performance.

2. The safest rule is not to fly while suffering from any illness. If this rule is considered too stringent for a particular illness, the pilot should contact an Aviation Medical Examiner for advice.

c. **Medication:**

1. Pilot performance can be seriously degraded by both prescribed and over-the-counter medications, as well as by the medical conditions for which they are taken. Many medications, such as tranquilizers, sedatives, strong pain relievers, and cough-suppressant preparations, have primary effects that may impair judgment, memory, alertness, coordination, vision, and the ability to make calculations. Others, such as antihistamines, blood pressure drugs, muscle relaxants, and agents to control diarrhea and motion sickness, have side effects that may impair the same critical functions. Any medication that depresses the nervous system, such as a sedative, tranquilizer or antihistamine, can make a pilot much more susceptible to hypoxia.

2. The FAR's prohibit pilots from performing crewmember duties while using any medication that affects the faculties in any way contrary to safety. The safest rule is not to fly as a crewmember while taking any medication, unless approved to do so by the FAA.

d. **Alcohol:**

1. Extensive research has provided a number of facts about the hazards of alcohol consumption and flying. As little as one ounce of liquor, one bottle of beer or four ounces of wine can impair flying skills, with the alcohol consumed in these drinks being detectable in the breath and blood for at least 3 hours. Even after the body completely destroys a moderate amount of alcohol, a pilot can still be severely impaired for many hours by hangover. There is simply no way of increasing the destruction of alcohol or alleviating a hangover. Alcohol also renders a pilot much more susceptible to disorientation and hypoxia.

2. A consistently high alcohol related fatal aircraft accident rate serves to emphasize that alcohol and flying are a potentially lethal combination. The FAR's prohibit pilots from performing crewmember duties within 8 hours after drinking any alcoholic beverage or while

under the influence of alcohol. However, due to the slow destruction of alcohol, a pilot may still be under influence 8 hours after drinking a moderate amount of alcohol. Therefore, an excellent rule is to allow at least 12 to 24 hours between "bottle and throttle," depending on the amount of alcoholic beverage consumed.

e. Fatigue:

1. Fatigue continues to be one of the most treacherous hazards to flight safety, as it may not be apparent to a pilot until serious errors are made. Fatigue is best described as either acute (short-term) or chronic (long-term).

2. A normal occurrence of everyday living, acute fatigue is the tiredness felt after long periods of physical and mental strain, including strenuous muscular effort, immobility, heavy mental workload, strong emotional pressure, monotony, and lack of sleep. Consequently, coordination and alertness, so vital to safe pilot performance, can be reduced. Acute fatigue is prevented by adequate rest and sleep, as well as by regular exercise and proper nutrition.

3. Chronic fatigue occurs when there is not enough time for full recovery between episodes of acute fatigue. Performance continues to fall off, and judgment becomes impaired so that unwarranted risks may be taken. Recovery from chronic fatigue requires a prolonged period of rest.

f. Stress:

1. Stress from the pressures of everyday living can impair pilot performance, often in very subtle ways. Difficulties, particularly at work, can occupy thought processes enough to markedly decrease alertness. Distraction can so interfere with judgment that unwarranted risks are taken, such as flying into deteriorating weather conditions to keep on schedule. Stress and fatigue (see above) can be an extremely hazardous combination.

2. Most pilots do not leave stress "on the ground." Therefore, when more than usual difficulties are being experienced, a pilot should consider delaying flight until these difficulties are satisfactorily resolved.

g. Emotion:

Certain emotionally upsetting events, including a serious argument, death of a family member, separation or divorce, loss of job, and financial catastrophe, can render a pilot unable to fly an aircraft safely. The emotions of anger, depression, and anxiety from such

events not only decrease alertness but also may lead t taking risks that border on self-destruction. Any pilo who experiences an emotionally upsetting event shoul not fly until satisfactorily recovered from it.

h. Personal Checklist: Aircraft accident statistic show that pilots should be conducting preflight check lists on themselves as well as their aircraft for pilot im pairment contributes to many more accidents than fail ures of aircraft systems. A personal checklist, whic includes all of the categories of pilot impairment as dis cussed in this section, that can be easily committed t memory is being distributed by the FAA in the form o a wallet-sized card.

i. PERSONAL CHECKLIST: *I'm physically and mentally safe to fly; not being impaired by:*

Illness

Medication

Stress

Alcohol

Fatigue

Emotion

8-1-2. EFFECTS OF ALTITUDE

a. Hypoxia:

1. Hypoxia is a state of oxygen deficiency in the body sufficient to impair functions of the brain and other organs. Hypoxia from exposure to altitude is due only to the reduced barometric pressures encountered at altitude, for the concentration of oxygen in the atmosphere remains about 21 percent from the ground out to space.

2. Although a deterioration in night vision occurs at a cabin pressure altitude as low as 5,000 feet, other significant effects of altitude hypoxia usually do not occur in the normal healthy pilot below 12,000 feet. From 12,000 to 15,000 feet of altitude, judgment, memory, alertness, coordination and ability to make calculations are impaired, and headache, drowsiness, dizziness and either a sense of well-being (euphoria) or belligerence occur. The effects appear following increasingly shorte periods of exposure to increasing altitude. In fact, pilot performance can seriously deteriorate within 15 minutes at 15,000 feet.

3. At cabin pressure altitudes above 15,000 feet, the periphery of the visual field grays out to a point where only central vision remains (tunnel vision). A blue coloration (cyanosis) of the fingernails and lips develops. The ability to take corrective and protective action is lost in 20 to 30 minutes at 18,000 feet and 5 to 12 minutes at 20,000 feet, followed soon thereafter by unconsciousness.

4. The altitude at which significant effects of hypoxia occur can be lowered by a number of factors. Carbon monoxide inhaled in smoking or from exhaust fumes, lowered hemoglobin (anemia), and certain medications can reduce the oxygen-carrying capacity of the blood to the degree that the amount of oxygen provided to body tissues will already be equivalent to the oxygen provided to the tissues when exposed to a cabin pressure altitude of several thousand feet. Small amounts of alcohol and low doses of certain drugs, such as antihistamines, tranquilizers, sedatives and analgesics can, through their depressant action, render the brain much more susceptible to hypoxia. Extreme heat and cold, fever, and anxiety increase the body's demand for oxygen, and hence its susceptibility to hypoxia.

5. The effects of hypoxia are usually quite difficult to recognize, especially when they occur gradually. Since symptoms of hypoxia do not vary in an individual, the ability to recognize hypoxia can be greatly improved by experiencing and witnessing the effects of hypoxia during an altitude chamber "flight." The FAA provides this opportunity through aviation physiology training, which is conducted at the FAA Civil Aeromedical Institute and at many military facilities across the United States, to attend the Physiological Training Program at the Civil Aeromedical Institute, Mike Monroney Aeronautical Center, Oklahoma City, OK, contact by telephone (405) 954–6212, or by writing Airmen Education Program Branch, AAM–420, CAMI, Mike Monroney Aeronautical Center, P.O. Box 25082, Oklahoma City, OK 73125.

NOTE-
To attend the physiological training program at one of the military installations having the training capability, an application form and a fee must be submitted. Full particulars about location, fees, scheduling procedures, course content, individual requirements, etc., are contained in the physiological training application, form number AC 3150–7, which is obtained by contacting the accident prevention specialist or the office forms manager in the nearest FAA office.

6. Hypoxia is prevented by heeding factors that reduce tolerance to altitude, by enriching the inspired air with oxygen from an appropriate oxygen system, and by maintaining a comfortable, safe cabin pressure altitude. For optimum protection, pilots are encouraged to use supplemental oxygen above 10,000 feet during the day, and above 5,000 feet at night. The FAR's require that at the minimum, flight crew be provided with and use supplemental oxygen after 30 minutes of exposure to cabin pressure altitudes between 12,500 and 14,000 feet and immediately on exposure to cabin pressure altitudes above 14,000 feet. Every occupant of the aircraft must be provided with supplemental oxygen at cabin pressure altitudes above 15,000 feet.

b. Ear Block:

1. As the aircraft cabin pressure decreases during ascent, the expanding air in the middle ear pushes the eustachian tube open, and by escaping down it to the nasal passages, equalizes in pressure with the cabin pressure. But during descent, the pilot must periodically open the eustachian tube to equalize pressure. This can be accomplished by swallowing, yawning, tensing muscles in the throat, or if these do not work, by a combination of closing the mouth, pinching the nose closed, and attempting to blow through the nostrils (Valsalva maneuver).

2. Either an upper respiratory infection, such as a cold or sore throat, or a nasal allergic condition can produce enough congestion around the eustachian tube to make equalization difficult. Consequently, the difference in pressure between the middle ear and aircraft cabin can build up to a level that will hold the eustachian tube closed, making equalization difficult if not impossible. The problem is commonly referred to as an "ear block."

3. An ear block produces severe ear pain and loss of hearing that can last from several hours to several days. Rupture of the ear drum can occur in flight or after landing. Fluid can accumulate in the middle ear and become infected.

4. An ear block is prevented by not flying with an upper respiratory infection or nasal allergic condition. Adequate protection is usually not provided by decongestant sprays or drops to reduce congestion around the eustachian tubes. Oral decongestants have side effects that can significantly impair pilot performance.

5. If an ear block does not clear shortly after landing, a physician should be consulted.

c. Sinus Block:

1. During ascent and descent, air pressure in the sinuses equalizes with the aircraft cabin pressure through small openings that connect the sinuses to the nasal passages. Either an upper respiratory infection, such as a cold or sinusitis, or a nasal allergic condition can produce enough congestion around an opening to slow equalization, and as the difference in pressure between the sinus and cabin mounts, eventually plug the opening. This "sinus block" occurs most frequently during descent.

2. A sinus block can occur in the frontal sinuses, located above each eyebrow, or in the maxillary sinuses, located in each upper cheek. It will usually produce excruciating pain over the sinus area. A maxillary sinus block can also make the upper teeth ache. Bloody mucus may discharge from the nasal passages.

3. A sinus block is prevented by not flying with an upper respiratory infection or nasal allergic condition. Adequate protection is usually not provided by decongestant sprays or drops to reduce congestion around the sinus openings. Oral decongestants have side effects that can impair pilot performance.

4. If a sinus block does not clear shortly after landing, a physician should be consulted.

d. Decompression Sickness After Scuba Diving:

1. A pilot or passenger who intends to fly after scuba diving should allow the body sufficient time to rid itself of excess nitrogen absorbed during diving. If not, decompression sickness due to evolved gas can occur during exposure to low altitude and create a serious inflight emergency.

2. The recommended waiting time before going to flight altitudes of up to 8,000 feet is at least 12 hours after diving which has not required controlled ascent (nondecompression stop diving), and at least 24 hours after diving which has required controlled ascent (decompression stop diving). The waiting time before going to flight altitudes above 8,000 feet should be at least 24 hours after any SCUBA dive. These recommended altitudes are actual flight altitudes above mean sea level (AMSL) and not pressurized cabin altitudes. This takes into consideration the risk of decompression of the aircraft during flight.

8-1-3. HYPERVENTILATION IN FLIGHT

a. Hyperventilation, or an abnormal increase in the volume of air breathed in and out of the lungs, can occur subconsciously when a stressful situation is encountered in flight. As hyperventilation "blows off" excessive carbon dioxide from the body, a pilot can experience symptoms of lightheadedness, suffocation, drowsiness, tingling in the extremities, and coolness and react to them with even greater hyperventilation. Incapacitation can eventually result from incoordination disorientation, and painful muscle spasms. Finally, unconsciousness can occur.

b. The symptoms of hyperventilation subside within a few minutes after the rate and depth of breathing are consciously brought back under control. The buildup of carbon dioxide in the body can be hastened by controlled breathing in and out of a paper bag held over the nose and mouth.

c. Early symptoms of hyperventilation and hypoxia are similar. Moreover, hyperventilation and hypoxia can occur at the same time. Therefore, if a pilot is using an oxygen system when symptoms are experienced, the oxygen regulator should immediately be set to deliver 100 percent oxygen, and then the system checked to assure that it has been functioning effectively before giving attention to rate and depth of breathing.

8-1-4. CARBON MONOXIDE POISONING IN FLIGHT

a. Carbon monoxide is a colorless, odorless, and tasteless gas contained in exhaust fumes. When breathed even in minute quantities over a period of time, it can significantly reduce the ability of the blood to carry oxygen. Consequently, effects of hypoxia occur.

b. Most heaters in light aircraft work by air flowing over the manifold. Use of these heaters while exhaust fumes are escaping through manifold cracks and seals is responsible every year for several nonfatal and fatal aircraft accidents from carbon monoxide poisoning.

c. A pilot who detects the odor of exhaust or experiences symptoms of headache, drowsiness, or dizziness while using the heater should suspect carbon monoxide poisoning, and immediately shut off the heater and open air vents. If symptoms are severe or continue after landing, medical treatment should be sought.

8–1–5. ILLUSIONS IN FLIGHT

a. Introduction: Many different illusions can be experienced in flight. Some can lead to spatial disorientation. Others can lead to landing errors. Illusions rank among the most common factors cited as contributing to fatal aircraft accidents.

b. Illusions Leading to Spatial Disorientation:

1. Various complex motions and forces and certain visual scenes encountered in flight can create illusions of motion and position. Spatial disorientation from these illusions can be prevented only by visual reference to reliable, fixed points on the ground or to flight instruments.

2. *The leans:* An abrupt correction of a banked attitude, which has been entered too slowly to stimulate the motion sensing system in the inner ear, can create the illusion of banking in the opposite direction. The disoriented pilot will roll the aircraft back into its original dangerous attitude, or if level flight is maintained, will feel compelled to lean in the perceived vertical plane until this illusion subsides.

(a) *Coriolis illusion:* An abrupt head movement in a prolonged constant-rate turn that has ceased stimulating the motion sensing system can create the illusion of rotation or movement in an entirely different axis. The disoriented pilot will maneuver the aircraft into a dangerous attitude in an attempt to stop rotation. This most overwhelming of all illusions in flight may be prevented by not making sudden, extreme head movements, particularly while making prolonged constant-rate turns under IFR conditions.

(b) *Graveyard spin:* A proper recovery from a spin that has ceased stimulating the motion sensing system can create the illusion of spinning in the opposite direction. The disoriented pilot will return the aircraft to its original spin.

(c) *Graveyard spiral:* An observed loss of altitude during a coordinated constant-rate turn that has ceased stimulating the motion sensing system can create the illusion of being in a descent with the wings level. The disoriented pilot will pull back on the controls, tightening the spiral and increasing the loss of altitude.

(d) *Somatogravic illusion:* A rapid acceleration during takeoff can create the illusion of being in a nose up attitude. The disoriented pilot will push the aircraft into a nose low, or dive attitude. A rapid deceleration by a quick reduction of the throttles can have the opposite effect, with the disoriented pilot pulling the aircraft into a nose up, or stall attitude.

(e) *Inversion illusion:* An abrupt change from climb to straight and level flight can create the illusion of tumbling backwards. The disoriented pilot will push the aircraft abruptly into a nose low attitude, possibly intensifying this illusion.

(f) *Elevator illusion:* An abrupt upward vertical acceleration, usually by an updraft, can create the illusion of being in a climb. The disoriented pilot will push the aircraft into a nose low attitude. An abrupt downward vertical acceleration, usually by a downdraft, has the opposite effect, with the disoriented pilot pulling the aircraft into a nose up attitude.

(g) *False horizon:* Sloping cloud formations, an obscured horizon, a dark scene spread with ground lights and stars, and certain geometric patterns of ground light can create illusions of not being aligned correctly with the actual horizon. The disoriented pilot will place the aircraft in a dangerous attitude.

(h) *Autokinesis:* In the dark, a static light will appear to move about when stared at for many seconds. The disoriented pilot will lose control of the aircraft in attempting to align it with the light.

3. *Illusions Leading to Landing Errors:*

(a) Various surface features and atmospheric conditions encountered in landing can create illusions of incorrect height above and distance from the runway threshold. Landing errors from these illusions can be prevented by anticipating them during approaches, aerial visual inspection of unfamiliar airports before landing, using electronic glide slope or VASI systems when available, and maintaining optimum proficiency in landing procedures.

(b) *Runway width illusion:*
A narrower-than-usual runway can create the illusion that the aircraft is at a higher altitude than it actually is. The pilot who does not recognize this illusion will fly a lower approach, with the risk of striking objects along the approach path or landing short. A wider-than-usual runway can have the opposite effect, with the risk of leveling out high and landing hard or overshooting the runway.

(c) *Runway and terrain slopes illusion:* An upsloping runway, upsloping terrain, or both, can create the illusion that the aircraft is at a higher altitude than it actually is. The pilot who does not recognize this illusion will fly a lower approach. A downsloping runway, downsloping approach terrain, or both, can have the opposite effect.

(d) *Featureless terrain illusion:* An absence of ground features, as when landing over water, darkened areas, and terrain made featureless by snow, can create the illusion that the aircraft is at a higher altitude than it actually is. The pilot who does not recognize this illusion will fly a lower approach

(e) *Atmospheric illusions:* Rain on the windscreen can create the illusion of greater height, and atmospheric haze the illusion of being at a greater distance from the runway. The pilot who does not recognize these illusions will fly a lower approach. Penetration of fog can create the illusion of pitching up. The pilot who does not recognize this illusion will steepen the approach, often quite abruptly.

(f) *Ground lighting illusions:* Lights along a straight path, such as a road, and even lights on moving trains can be mistaken for runway and approach lights. Bright runway and approach lighting systems, especially where few lights illuminate the surrounding terrain, may create the illusion of less distance to the runway. The pilot who does not recognize this illusion will fly a higher approach. Conversely, the pilot overflying terrain which has few lights to provide height cues may make a lower than normal approach.

8-1-6. VISION IN FLIGHT

a. Introduction: Of the body senses, vision is the most important for safe flight. Major factors that determine how effectively vision can be used are the level of illumination and the technique of scanning the sky for other aircraft.

b. Vision Under Dim and Bright Illumination:

1. Under conditions of dim illumination, small print and colors on aeronautical charts and aircraft instruments become unreadable unless adequate cockpit lighting is available. Moreover, another aircraft must be much closer to be seen unless its navigation lights are on.

2. In darkness, vision becomes more sensitive to light, a process called dark adaptation. Although exposure to total darkness for at least 30 minutes is required for complete dark adaptation, a pilot can achieve a moderate degree of dark adaptation within 20 minutes under dim red cockpit lighting. Since red light severely distorts colors, especially on aeronautical charts, and can cause serious difficulty in focusing the eyes on objects

inside the aircraft, its use is advisable only where optimum outside night vision capability is necessary. Even so, white cockpit lighting must be available when needed for map and instrument reading, especially under IFR conditions. Dark adaptation is impaired by exposure to cabin pressure altitudes above 5,000 feet, carbon monoxide inhaled in smoking and from exhaust fumes, deficiency of Vitamin A in the diet, and by prolonged exposure to bright sunlight. Since any degree of dark adaptation is lost within a few seconds of viewing a bright light, a pilot should close one eye when using a light to preserve some degree of night vision.

3. Excessive illumination, especially from light reflected off the canopy, surfaces inside the aircraft, clouds, water, snow, and desert terrain, can produce glare, with uncomfortable squinting, watering of the eyes, and even temporary blindness. Sunglasses for protection from glare should absorb at least 85 percent of visible light (15 percent transmittance) and all colors equally (neutral transmittance), with negligible image distortion from refractive and prismatic errors.

c. Scanning for Other Aircraft:

1. Scanning the sky for other aircraft is a key factor in collision avoidance. It should be used continuously by the pilot and copilot (or right seat passenger) to cover all areas of the sky visible from the cockpit. Although pilots must meet specific visual acuity requirements, the ability to read an eye chart does not ensure that one will be able to efficiently spot other aircraft. Pilots must develop an effective scanning technique which maximizes one's visual capabilities. The probability of spotting a potential collision threat obviously increases with the time spent looking outside the cockpit. Thus, one must use timesharing techniques to efficiently scan the surrounding airspace while monitoring instruments as well.

2. While the eyes can observe an approximate 200 degree arc of the horizon at one glance, only a very small center area called the fovea, in the rear of the eye, has the ability to send clear, sharply focused messages to the brain. All other visual information that is not processed directly through the fovea will be of less detail. An aircraft at a distance of 7 miles which appears in sharp focus within the foveal center of vision would have to be as close as $7/10$ of a mile in order to be recognized if it were outside of foveal vision. Because the eyes can focus only on this narrow viewing area, effective scanning is accomplished with a series of short, regularly spaced eye movements that bring successive areas of the sky into the central visual field. Each movement should not exceed 10 degrees, and each area should be observed for at least 1 second to enable detection. Although horizontal back-and-forth eye movements seem preferred by most pilots, each pilot should develop a scanning pattern that is most comfortable and then adhere to it to assure optimum scanning.

3. Studies show that the time a pilot spends on visual tasks inside the cabin should represent no more that $1/4$ to $1/3$ of the scan time outside, or no more than 4 to 5 seconds on the instrument panel for every 16 seconds outside. Since the brain is already trained to process sight information that is presented from left to right, one may find it easier to start scanning over the left shoulder and proceed across the windshield to the right.

4. Pilots should realize that their eyes may require several seconds to refocus when switching views between items in the cockpit and distant objects. The eyes will also tire more quickly when forced to adjust to distances immediately after close-up focus, as required for scanning the instrument panel. Eye fatigue can be reduced by looking from the instrument panel to the left wing past the wing tip to the center of the first scan quadrant when beginning the exterior scan. After having scanned from left to right, allow the eyes to return to the cabin along the right wing from its tip inward. Once back inside, one should automatically commence the panel scan.

5. Effective scanning also helps avoid "empty-field myopia." This condition usually occurs when flying above the clouds or in a haze layer that provides nothing specific to focus on outside the aircraft. This causes the eyes to relax and seek a comfortable focal distance which may range from 10 to 30 feet. For the pilot, this means looking without seeing, which is dangerous.

8-1-7. AEROBATIC FLIGHT

a. Pilots planning to engage in aerobatics should be aware of the physiological stresses associated with accelerative forces during aerobatic maneuvers. Many prospective aerobatic trainees enthusiastically enter aerobatic instruction but find their first experiences with G forces to be unanticipated and very uncomfortable. To minimize or avoid potential adverse effects, the aerobatic instructor and trainee must have a basic understanding of the physiology of G force adaptation.

b. Forces experienced with a rapid push-over maneuver result in the blood and body organs being displaced toward the head. Depending on forces involved and individual tolerance, a pilot may experience discomfort, headache, "red-out," and even unconsciousness.

c. Forces experienced with a rapid pull-up maneuver result in the blood and body organ displacement toward the lower part of the body away from the head. Since the brain requires continuous blood circulation for an adequate oxygen supply, there is a physiologic limit to the time the pilot can tolerate higher forces before losing consciousness. As the blood circulation to the brain decreases as a result of forces involved, a pilot will experience "narrowing" of visual fields, "gray-out," "black-out," and unconsciousness. Even a brief loss of consciousness in a maneuver can lead to improper control movement causing structural failure of the aircraft or collision with another object or terrain.

d. In steep turns, the centrifugal forces tend to push the pilot into the seat, thereby resulting in blood and body organ displacement toward the lower part of the body as in the case of rapid pull-up maneuvers and with the same physiologic effects and symptoms.

e. Physiologically, humans progressively adapt to imposed strains and stress, and with practice, any maneuver will have decreasing effect. Tolerance to G forces is dependent on human physiology and the individual pilot. These factors include the skeletal anatomy, the cardiovascular architecture, the nervous system, the quality of the blood, the general physical state, and experience and recency of exposure. The pilot should consult an Aviation Medical Examiner prior to aerobatic training and be aware that poor physical condition can reduce tolerance to accelerative forces.

f. The above information provides pilots with a brief summary of the physiologic effects of G forces. It does not address methods of "counteracting" these effects. There are numerous references on the subject of G forces during aerobatics available to pilots. Among these are "G Effects on the Pilot During Aerobatics," FAA–AM–72–28, and "G Incapacitation in Aerobatic Pilots: A Flight Hazard" FAA–AM–82–13. These are available from the National Technical Information Service, Springfield, Virginia 22161.

REFERENCE–
FAA AC 91-61, A HAZARD IN AEROBATICS: EFFECTS OF G-FORCES ON PILOTS.

8-1-8. JUDGMENT ASPECTS OF COLLISION AVOIDANCE

a. Introduction: The most important aspects of vision and the techniques to scan for other aircraft are described in paragraph 8-1-6, Vision in Flight. Pilots should also be familiar with the following information to reduce the possibility of mid-air collisions.

b. Determining Relative Altitude: Use the horizon as a reference point. If the other aircraft is above the horizon, it is probably on a higher flight path. If the aircraft appears to be below the horizon, it is probably flying at a lower altitude.

c. Taking Appropriate Action: Pilots should be familiar with rules on right-of-way, so if an aircraft is on an obvious collision course, one can take immediate evasive action, preferably in compliance with applicable Federal Aviation Regulations.

d. Consider Multiple Threats: The decision to climb, descend, or turn is a matter of personal judgment, but one should anticipate that the other pilot may also be making a quick maneuver. Watch the other aircraft during the maneuver and begin your scanning again immediately since there may be other aircraft in the area.

e. Collision Course Targets: Any aircraft that appears to have no relative motion and stays in one scan quadrant is likely to be on a collision course. Also, if a target shows no lateral or vertical motion, but increases in size, *take evasive action.*

f. Recognize High Hazard Areas:

1. Airways, especially near VOR's, and Class B, Class C, Class D, and Class E surface areas are places where aircraft tend to cluster.

2. Remember, most collisions occur during days when the weather is good. Being in a "radar environment" still requires vigilance to avoid collisions.

g. Cockpit Management: Studying maps, checklists, and manuals before flight, with other proper preflight planning; e.g., noting necessary radio frequencies and organizing cockpit materials, can reduce the amount of time required to look at these items during flight, permitting more scan time.

h. Windshield Conditions: Dirty or bug-smeared windshields can greatly reduce the ability of pilots to see other aircraft. Keep a clean windshield.

i. Visibility Conditions: Smoke, haze, dust, rain, and flying towards the sun can also greatly reduce the ability to detect targets.

j. Visual Obstructions in the Cockpit:

1. Pilots need to move their heads to see around blind spots caused by fixed aircraft structures, such as door posts, wings, etc. It will be necessary at times to maneuver the aircraft; e.g., lift a wing, to facilitate seeing.

2. Pilots must insure curtains and other cockpit objects; e.g., maps on glare shield, are removed and stowed during flight.

k. Lights On:

1. Day or night, use of exterior lights can greatly increase the conspicuity of any aircraft.

2. Keep interior lights low at night.

l. ATC support: ATC facilities often provide radar traffic advisories on a workload-permitting basis. Flight through Class C and Class D airspace requires communication with ATC. Use this support whenever possible or when required.

Chapter 9. AERONAUTICAL CHARTS AND RELATED PUBLICATIONS

Section 1. TYPES OF CHARTS AVAILABLE

9-1-1. GENERAL

Civil aeronautical charts for the U.S. and its territories, and possessions are produced by the National Ocean Service (NOS), which is a part of the National Oceanic and Atmospheric Administration (NOAA). Aeronautical data is furnished by the FAA.

9-1-2. OBTAINING AERONAUTICAL CHARTS

a. Most charts and publications described in this Chapter can be obtained by subscription or one-time sales from:

NOAA Distribution Division, N/ACC3
National Ocean Service
Riverdale, MD 20737-1199
Telephone: 1-800-638-8972 (Toll free within U.S.)
         301-436-8301/6990
         301-436-6829 (FAX)

b. Public sales of charts and publications are also available through a network of NOAA/NOS chart agents primarily located at or near major civil airports. A listing of products and agents is printed in the free NOS catalog, *Aeronautical Charts and Related Products.* (NOS Stock No. ACATSET). A free quarterly bulletin, *Dates of Latest Editions, VFR Aeronautical Charts* (NOS Stock No. 5318), is also available from NOS.

9-1-3. SELECTED CHARTS AND PRODUCTS AVAILABLE

VFR Navigation Charts
IFR Navigation Charts
Planning Charts
Supplementary Charts and Publications
Digital Products

9-1-4. GENERAL DESCRIPTION OF EACH CHART SERIES

a. VFR Navigation Charts.

1. Sectional Aeronautical Charts: Sectional Charts are designed for visual navigation of slow to medium speed aircraft. The topographic information consists of contour lines, shaded relief, drainage patterns, and an extensive selection of visual checkpoints and landmarks used for flight under VFR. Cultural features include cities and towns, roads, railroads, and other distinct landmarks. The aeronautical information includes visual and radio aids to navigation, airports, controlled airspace, special-use airspace, obstructions, and related data. Scale 1 inch = 6.86nm/1:500,000. 60 x 20 inches folded to 5 x 10 inches. Revised semiannually, except most Alaskan charts are revised annually.
(See FIG 9-1-1 and FIG 9-1-11.)

2. VFR Terminal Area Charts (TAC): TAC's depict the airspace designated as Class B airspace. While similar to sectional charts, TAC's have more detail because the scale is larger. The TAC should be used by pilots intending to operate to or from airfields within or near Class B or Class C airspace. Areas with TAC coverage are indicated by a • on the Sectional Chart indexes. Scale 1 inch = 3.43nm/1:250,000. Charts are revised semiannually, except Puerto Rico–Virgin Islands revised annually.
(See FIG 9-1-1 and FIG 9-1-11.)

3. World Aeronautical Charts (WAC): WAC's cover land areas for navigation by moderate speed aircraft operating at high altitudes. Included are city tints, principal roads, railroads, distinctive landmarks, drainage patterns, and relief. Aeronautical information includes visual and radio aids to navigation, airports, airways, special-use airspace, and obstructions. Because of a smaller scale, WAC's do not show as much detail as sectional or TAC's, and therefore are not recommended for exclusive use by pilots of low speed, low altitude aircraft. Scale 1 inch = 13.7nm/1:1,000,000. 60 x 20 inches folded to 5 x 10 inches. WAC's are revised annually, except for a few in Alaska and the Caribbean, which are revised biennially.
(See FIG 9-1-12 and FIG 9-1-13.)

4. U.S. Gulf Coast VFR Aeronautical Chart: The Gulf Coast Chart is designed primarily for helicopter operation in the Gulf of Mexico area. Information depicted includes offshore mineral leasing areas and blocks, oil drilling platforms, and high density helicopter activity areas. Scale 1 inch = 13.7nm/1:1,000,000. 55 x 27 inches folded to 5 x 10 inches. Revised annually.

Sectional and VFR Terminal Area Charts for the Conterminous U.S., Hawaii, Puerto Rico, and Virgin Islands

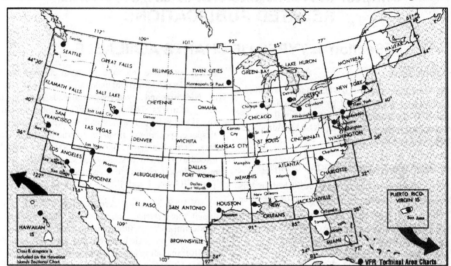

FIG 9–1–1

5. Grand Canyon VFR Aeronautical Chart: Covers the Grand Canyon National Park area and is designed to promote aviation safety, flight free zones, and facilitate VFR navigation in this popular area. The chart contains aeronautical information for general aviation VFR pilots on one side and commercial VFR air tour operators on the other side.

6. Helicopter Route Charts: A three–color chart series which shows current aeronautical information useful to helicopter pilots navigating in areas with high concentrations of helicopter activity. Information depicted includes helicopter routes, four classes of heliports with associated frequency and lighting capabilities, NAVAID's, and obstructions. In addition, pictorial symbols, roads, and easily identified geographical features are portrayed. Helicopter charts have a longer life span than other chart products and may be current for several years. All new editions of these charts are printed on a durable plastic material. Helicopter Route Charts are updated as requested by the FAA. Scale 1 inch = 1.71nm/1:125,000. 34 x 30 inches folded to 5 x 10 inches.

b. IFR Navigation Charts.

1. IFR Enroute Low Altitude Charts (Conterminous U.S. and Alaska): Enroute low altitude charts provide aeronautical information for navigation under IFR conditions below 18,000 feet MSL. This four–color chart series includes airways; limits of controlled air space; VHF NAVAID's with frequency, identification, channel, geographic coordinates; airports with terminal air/ground communications; minimum en route and obstruction clearance altitudes; airway distances; reporting points; special use airspace; and military training routes. Scales vary from 1 inch = 5nm to 1 inch = 20nm. 50 x 20 inches folded to 5 x 10 inches. Charts revised every 56 days. *Area charts* show congested terminal areas at a large scale. They are included with subscriptions to any conterminous U.S. Set Low (Full set, East or West sets). (See FIG 9–1–2 and FIG 9–1–4.)

2. IFR Enroute High Altitude Charts (Conterminous U.S. and Alaska): Enroute high altitude charts are designed for navigation at or above 18,000 feet MSL. This four–color chart series includes the jet route structure; VHF NAVAID's with frequency, identification, channel, geographic coordinates; selected airports; reporting points. Scales vary from 1 inch = 45nm to 1 inch = 18nm. 55 x 20 inches folded to 5 x 10 inches. Revised every 56 days.
(See FIG 9–1–3 and FIG 9–1–5.)

Enroute Low Altitude Instrument Charts for the Conterminous U.S. (Includes Area Charts)

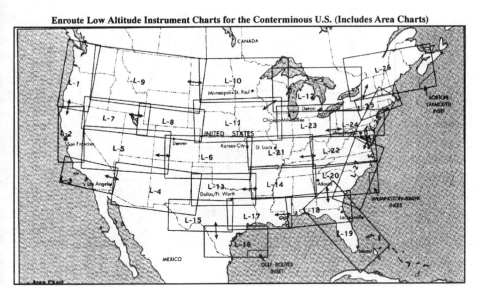

FIG 9–1–2

Enroute High Altitude Charts for the Conterminous U.S.

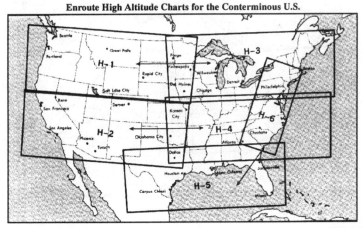

FIG 9–1–3

Alaska Enroute Low Altitude Chart

FIG 9-1-4

Alaskan Enroute High Altitude Chart

FIG 9-1-5

3. U.S. Terminal Procedures Publication (TPP): TPP's are published in 20 loose-leaf or perfect bound volumes covering the conterminous U.S., Puerto Rico and the Virgin Islands. A Change Notice is published at the midpoint between revisions in bound volume format. (See FIG 9-1-9.) The TPP's include:

(a) Instrument Approach Procedure (IAP) Charts: IAP charts portray the aeronautical data that is required to execute instrument approaches to airports. Each chart depicts the IAP, all related navigation data, communications information, and an airport sketch. Each procedure is designated for use with a specific electronic navigational aid, such as ILS, VOR, NDB, RNAV, etc.

(b) Instrument Departure Procedure (DP) Charts: DP charts are designed to expedite clearance delivery and to facilitate transition between takeoff and en route operations. They furnish pilots' departure routing clearance information in graphic and textual form.

(c) Standard Terminal Arrival (STAR) Charts: STAR charts are designed to expedite ATC arrival procedures and to facilitate transition between en route and instrument approach operations. They depict preplanned IFR ATC arrival procedures in graphic and textual form. Each STAR procedure is presented as a separate chart and may serve either a single airport or more than one airport in a given geographic area.

(d) Airport Diagrams: Full page airport diagrams are designed to assist in the movement of ground traffic at locations with complex runway/taxiway configurations and provide information for updating geodetic position navigational systems aboard aircraft.

4. Alaska Terminal Procedures Publication: This publication contains all terminal flight procedures for civil and military aviation in Alaska. Included are IAP charts, DP charts, STAR charts, airport diagrams, radar minimums, and supplementary support data such as IFR alternate minimums, take-off minimums, rate of descent tables, rate of climb tables and inoperative components tables. Volume is 5-3/8 x 8-1/4 inch top bound. Publication revised every 56 days with provisions for a Terminal Change Notice, as required.

c. Planning Charts.

1. U.S. IFR/VFR Low Altitude Planning Chart: This chart is designed for prefight and en route flight planning for IFR/VFR flights. Depiction includes low altitude airways and mileage, NAVAID's, airports, special use airspace, cities, times zones, major drainage, a

directory of airports with their airspace classification, and a mileage table showing great circle distances between major airports. Scale 1 inch = 47nm/1:3,400,000. Chart revised annually, and is available either folded or unfolded for wall mounting. (See FIG 9-1-6.)

2. Gulf of Mexico and Caribbean Planning Chart: This is a VFR planning chart on the reverse side of the *Puerto Rico - Virgin Islands VFR Terminal Area Chart.* Information shown includes mileage between airports of entry, a selection of special use airspace and a directory of airports with their available services. Scale 1 inch = 85nm/1:6,192,178. 60 x 20 inches folded to 5 x 10 inches. Chart revised annually. (See FIG 9-1-6.)

Planning Charts

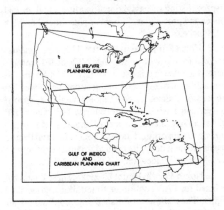

FIG 9-1-6

3. Charted VFR Flyway Planning Charts: This chart is printed on the reverse side of selected TAC charts. The coverage is the same as the associated TAC. Flyway planning charts depict flight paths and altitudes recommended for use to bypass high traffic areas. Ground references are provided as a guide for visual orientation. Flyway planning charts are designed for use in conjunction with TAC's and sectional charts and are not to be used for navigation. Chart scale 1 inch = 3.43nm/1:250,000.

d. Supplementary Charts and Publications.

1. Airport/Facility Directory (AFD): This 7-volume booklet series contains data on airports, seaplane bases, heliports, NAVAID's, communications data, weather data sources, airspace, special notices,

and operational procedures. Coverage includes the conterminous United States, Puerto Rico, and the Virgin Islands. The AFD shows data that cannot be readily depicted in graphic form; e.g. airport hours of operations,
types of fuel available, runway widths, lighting codes,
etc. The AFD also provides a means for pilots to update
visual charts between edition dates (AFD is published
every 56 days while sectional and Terminal Area Charts
are generally revised every six months). Volumes are
side-bound 5-3/8 x 8-1/4 inches.
(See FIG 9-1-10.)

2. Supplement Alaska: This is a civil/military
flight information publication issued by NOAA every
56 days. It is a single volume booklet designed for use
with appropriate IFR or VFR charts. The Supplement
Alaska contains an airport/facility directory, airport
sketches, communications data, weather data sources,
airspace, listing of navigational facilities, and special
notices and procedures. Volume is side-bound 5-3/8 x
8-1/4 inches.

3. Chart Supplement Pacific: This supplement is
designed for use with appropriate VFR or IFR enroute
charts. Included in this one-volume booklet are the air-
port/facility directory, communications data, weather
data sources, airspace, navigational facilities, special
notices, and Pacific area procedures. IAP charts, DP
charts, STAR charts, airport diagrams, radar minimums, and supporting data for the Hawaiian and Pacific
Islands are included. The manual is published every 56
days. Volume is side-bound 5-3/8 x 8-1/4 inches.

4. North Pacific Route Charts: These charts are
designed for FAA controllers to monitor transoceanic
flights. They show established intercontinental air
routes, including reporting points with geographic
positions. Composite Chart: Scale 1 inch =
164nm/1:12,000,000. 48 x 41-1/2 inches. Area Charts:
Scale 1 inch = 95.9nm/1:7,000,000. 52 x 40-1/2 inches.
All charts shipped unfolded. Charts revised every 56
days. (See FIG 9-1-8.)

5. North Atlantic Route Chart: Designed for
FAA controllers to monitor transatlantic flights, this
5-color chart shows oceanic control areas, coastal
navigation aids, oceanic reporting points, and NAVAID
geographic coordinates. Full Size Chart: Scale 1 inch =
113.1nm/1:8,250,000. Chart is shipped flat only. Half
Size Chart: Scale 1 inch = 150.8nm/1:11,000,000.
Chart is 29-3/4 x 20-1/2 inches, shipped folded to 5 x
10 inches only. Chart revised every 56 weeks.
(See FIG 9-1-7.)

North Atlantic Route Charts

FIG 9-1-7

North Pacific Oceanic Route Charts

FIG 9-1-8

6. Airport Obstruction Charts (OC): The OC is a 1:12,000 scale graphic depicting 14 CFR Part 77, *Objects Affecting Navigable Airspace,* surfaces, a representation of objects that penetrate these surfaces, aircraft movement and apron areas, navigational aids, prominent airport buildings, and a selection of roads and other planimetric detail in the airport vicinity. Also included are tabulations of runway and other operational data.

7. NOAA Aeronautical Chart User's Guide: A booklet designed to be used as a teaching aid and reference document. It describes the substantial amount of information provided on NOAA's aeronautical charts and publications. It includes explanations and illustrations of chart terms and symbols organized by chart type.

e. Digital Products

1. The NAVAID Digital Data File: This file contains a current listing of NAVAID's that is compatible with the National Airspace System. Updated every 56 days, the file contains all NAVAID's including ILS and its components, in the U.S., Puerto Rico, and the Virgin Islands plus bordering facilities in Canada, Mexico, and the Atlantic and Pacific areas. The file is available by subscription only, on 3.5-inch, 1.4 megabyte diskette.

2. The Digital Obstacle File: This file describes all obstacles of interest to aviation users in the U.S., with limited coverage of the Pacific, Caribbean, Canada, and Mexico. The obstacles are assigned unique numerical identifiers, accuracy codes, and listed in order of ascending latitude within each state or area. The file is updated every 56 days. File is available on 3.5-inch, 1.4 megabyte diskettes.

3. The Digital Aeronautical Chart Supplement (DACS): The DACS is a subset of the data NOAA provides to FAA controllers every 56 days. It reflects digitally what is shown on the enroute high and low charts. The DACS is designed to be used with aeronautical charts for flight planning purposes only. It should not be used as a substitute for a chart. The DACS is available on two 3.5-inch diskettes, compressed format. The supplement is divided into nine individual sections.

Section 1: High altitude airways, conterminous U.S.
Section 2: Low altitude airways, conterminous U.S.
Section 3: Selected instrument approach procedure NAVAID and fix data
Section 4: Military training routes
Section 5: Alaska, Hawaii, Puerto Rico, Bahamas and selected oceanic routes
Section 6: STAR's - Standard Terminal Arrivals
Section 7: DP's - Instrument Departure Procedures
Section 8: Preferred IFR routes (low and high altitude)
Section 9: Air route and airport surveillance radar facilities

U.S. Terminal Publication Volumes

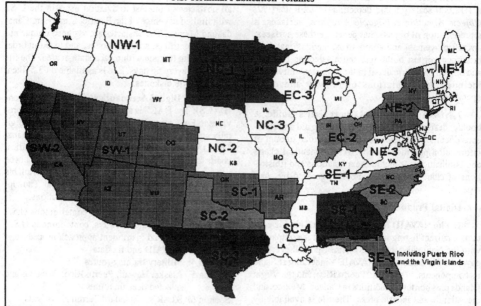

Including Puerto Rico and the Virgin Islands

FIG 9-1-9

Airport/Facility Directory Geographic Areas

FIG 9-1-10

Sectional and VFR Terminal Area Charts for Alaska

FIG 9–1–11

World Aeronautical Charts for Alaska

FIG 9-1-12

World Aeronautical Charts for the Conterminous U.S.
Mexico, and the Caribbean Areas

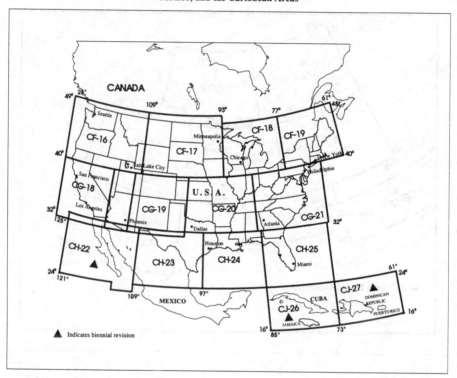

FIG 9-1-13

9-1-5. WHERE AND HOW TO GET CHARTS OF FOREIGN AREAS

a. **National Imagery and Mapping Agency (NIMA) Products:** A National Ocean Service (NOS) catalog of *NIMA Public Sale Aeronautical Charts and Publications* (NOS Stock No. DMAACATSET), is available from the NOAA Distribution Division. The catalog describes available charts and publications primarily covering areas outside the U.S. A free quarterly bulletin, *Dates of Latest Editions – NIMA Aeronautical Charts and Publications* (NOS Stock No. DADOLE), is also available from NOS.

1. **Flight Information Publication (FLIP) Planning Documents**

General Planning (GP)
Area Planning

Area Planning – Special Use Airspace –
  Planning Charts

2. **FLIP Enroute Charts and Chart Supplements**

Pacific, Australasia, and Antarctica
United States – IFR and VFR Supplements
Flight Information Handbook
Caribbean and South America – Low Altitude
Caribbean and South America – High Altitude
Europe, North Africa, and Middle East –
  Low Altitude
Europe, North Africa, and Middle East –
  High Altitude
Africa
Eastern Europe and Asia
Area Arrival Charts

3. FLIP Instrument Approach Procedures (IAP's)

Africa
Canada and North Atlantic
Caribbean and South America
Eastern Europe and Asia
Europe, North Africa, and Middle East
Pacific, Australasia, and Antarctica
VFR Arrival/Departure Routes - Europe and Korea
United States

4. Miscellaneous DoD Charts and Products

Aeronautical Chart Updating Manual (CHUM)
DoD Weather Plotting Charts (WPC)
Tactical Pilotage Charts (TPC)
Operational Navigation Charts (ONC)
Global Navigation and Planning Charts (GNC)
Global LORAN-C Navigation Charts (GLCC)
LORAN-C Coastal Navigation Charts (LCNC)
Jet Navigation Charts (JNC) and Universal Jet
   Navigation Charts (JNU)
Jet Navigation Charts (JNCA)
Aerospace Planning Charts (ASC)
Oceanic Planning Charts (OPC)
Joint Operations Graphics - Air (JOG-A)
Standard Index Charts (SIC)
Universal Plotting Sheet (VP-OS)
Sight Reduction Tables for Air Navigation (PUB249)
Plotting Sheets (VP-30)
Dial-Up Electronic CHUM

b. Canadian Charts: Information on available Canadian charts and publications may be obtained from designated NOAA/NOS chart agents or by contacting the:

Canada Map Office
Department of Natural Resources
130 Bentley Ave
Nepean, Ontario
K1A 0E9, Canada
Telephone: (613) 952-7000 or
                      1-800-465-6277
Fax: (613) 957-8861 or
          1-800-661-6277

c. Mexican Charts: Information on available Mexican charts and publications may be obtained by contacting:

Dirección General de Aeronaútical Civil (DGAC)
Departamento de Recursos Financieros
Calle de Nueva York No. 115, 4to. piso
Col. Napoles
C.P. 03810 Mexico, D.F.
Telephone: (52) (5) 682-1076 or 682-1077
Fax: (52) (5) 687-7325 or 523-8310

d. International Civil Aviation Organization (ICAO): A free *ICAO Publications and Audio-Visual Training Aids Catalogue* is available from:

International Civil Aviation Organization
ATTN: Document Sales Unit
999 University Street
Montreal, Quebec
H3C 5H7, Canada
Telephone: (514) 954-8022
Fax: (514) 954-6769
E-mail: sales_unit@icao.org
Internet:
http://www.icao.org/cgi/goto.pl?icao/en/sales.htm
Sitatex: YULCAYA
Telex: 05-24513

Appendix 1.

Bird Strike Incident/Ingestion Report

Form Approved
OMB No. 2120-0045

BIRD STRIKE INCIDENT/INGESTION REPORT
Other Wildlife Species May Be Described Here
Operation Cost and Engine Damage Information

US Department of Transportation
Federal Aviation Administration

1. Name of Operator	2. Aircraft Make/Model	3. Engine Make/Model

4. Aircraft Registration | 5. Date of Incident (DD, MM, YY) | 6. Local Time of Incident
☐ Dawn ☐ Dusk ☐ Day ☐ Night

7. Aerodrome Name | 8. Runway Used | 9. Location if En Route (Nearest Town/Reference and State)

10. Height (AGL) ___ feet | 11. Speed (IAS) ___ knots

12. Phase of Flight
☐ A. Parked
☐ B. Taxi
☐ C. Take-off
☐ D. Climb
☐ E. En Route
☐ F. Descent
☐ G. Approach
☐ H. Landing Roll

13. Part(s) of Aircraft Struck or Damaged

	Struck	Damaged		Struck	Damaged
A. Radome	☐	☐	H. Propeller	☐	☐
B. Windshield	☐	☐	I. Wing/Rotor	☐	☐
C. Nose	☐	☐	J. Fuselage	☐	☐
D. Engine No. 1	☐	☐	K. Landing Gear	☐	☐
E. Engine No. 2	☐	☐	L. Tail	☐	☐
F. Engine No. 3	☐	☐	M. Lights	☐	☐
G. Engine No. 4	☐	☐	N. Other (specify)	☐	☐

14. Effect on Flight
☐ None
☐ Aborted Take-Off
☐ Precautionary Landing
☐ Engines Shut Down
☐ Other (specify)

15. Sky Condition
☐ No Cloud
☐ Some Cloud
☐ Overcast

16. Precipitation
☐ Fog
☐ Rain
☐ Snow

17. Bird Species

18. Number of birds seen and/or struck

Number of Birds	Seen	Struck
1	☐	☐
2-10	☐	☐
11-100	☐	☐
more than 100	☐	☐

19. Size of Bird(s)
☐ Small
☐ Medium
☐ Large

20. Pilot Warned of Birds ☐ Yes ☐ No

21. Remarks (describe damage, injuries and other pertinent information).

ENGINE DAMAGE COST INFORMATION

22. Aircraft time out of service: ___ hours | 23. Estimated cost of repairs or replacement ($ U.S. in thousands): $ | 24. Estimated other cost ($ U.S. thousands) (e.g. loss of revenue, fuel, hotels): $

Reported by (Optional) | Title | Date

FAA Form 5200-7 (6-95) Supersedes Previous Edition

NSN. 0052-00-651-9004

BIRD STRIKE INCIDENT/INGESTION REPORT (Continued)

SPECIAL INFORMATION ON ENGINE DAMAGE STRIKES

Reason for failure/shutdown	Engine 1	Engine 2	Engine 3	Engine 4	Comments
Unconditional Failure	☐	☐	☐	☐	
Fire	☐	☐	☐	☐	
Shutdown — Vibration	☐	☐	☐	☐	
Shutdown — Temperature	☐	☐	☐	☐	
Shutdown — Fire warning	☐	☐	☐	☐	
Shutdown — Other (specify)	☐	☐	☐	☐	
Shutdown — Unknown	☐	☐	☐	☐	
	☐	☐	☐	☐	
Estimated percentage of thrust loss*					
Estimated number of birds ingested					

*These may be difficult to determine but even estimates are useful.

FAA Form 5200-7 (6-95) Supersedes Previous Edition   NSN: 0052-00-651-9004

Agency Display of Estimated Burden: The FAA estimates that the average burden for this report form is 5 minutes per response. You may submit any comments concerning the accuracy of this burden estimate or any suggestions for reducing the burden to the Office of Management and Budget. You may also send comments to the Federal Aviation Administration, Program Support Branch, ARP-11, 800 Independence Avenue, SW. Washington, DC 20591. Attention: OMB number 2120-0045.

*U.S. Government Printing Office: 1995 — 623-192/83121

U.S. Department
of Transportation

**Federal Aviation
Administration**

800 Independence Ave., S.W.
Washington, D.C. 20591

NO POSTAGE
NECESSARY
IF MAILED
IN THE
UNITED STATES

BUSINESS REPLY MAIL
FIRST CLASS   PERMIT NO. 12438   WASHINGTON, D.C.

POSTAGE WILL BE PAID BY FEDERAL AVIATION ADMINISTRATION

Official Business
Penalty for
Private Use $300

Federal Aviation Administration
Office of Airport Safety and Standards, AAS-310
800 Independence Avenue, SW
Washington, DC 20591

Appendix 2.

Volcanic Activity Reporting Form (VAR)

Date _____

SECTION 1 - Transmit to ATC via radio

1. Aircraft Identification	
2. Position	
3. Time (UTC)	
4. Flight level or altitude	
5. Position/location of volcanic activity or ash cloud	
6. Air temperature	
7. Wind	
8. Supplementary Information (Brief description of activity including vertical and lateral extent of the ash cloud, horizontal movement. rate of growth, etc., as available.)	

SECTION 2 - Complete and forward as directed

Mark the appropriate box(s)

9. *Density of ash cloud*	☐ wispy	☐ moderately dense	☐ very dense
10. *Color of ash*	☐ white ☐ black	☐ light gray	☐ dark gray
11. *Eruption*	☐ continuous	☐ intermittent	☐ not visible
12. *Position of activity*	☐ summit ☐ multiple	☐ side ☐ not observed	☐ single
13. *Other observed features of eruption*	☐ lightning ☐ ash fallout	☐ glow ☐ mushroom cloud	☐ large rocks ☐ none
14. *Effect on aircraft*	☐ communications ☐ pitot static ☐ none	☐ navigation system ☐ windscreen	☐ engines ☐ other windows
15. *Other effects*	☐ turbulence ☐ ash deposits	☐ St. Elmo's fire	☐ fumes
16. *Other information deemed useful*			

Forward completed form via mail to:
Global Volcanism Program
NHB-119
Smithsonian Institution
Washington, DC 20560

Or Fax to:
Global Volcanism Program
(202) 357-2476

PILOT/CONTROLLER GLOSSARY

This Glossary was compiled to promote a common understanding of the terms used in the Air Traffic Control system. It includes those terms which are intended for pilot/controller communications. Those terms most frequently used in pilot/controller communications are printed in *bold italics*. The definitions are primarily defined in an operational sense applicable to both users and operators of the National Airspace System. Use of the Glossary will preclude any misunderstandings concerning the system's design, function, and purpose.

Because of the international nature of flying, terms used in the Lexicon, published by the International Civil Aviation Organization (ICAO), are included when they differ from FAA definitions. These terms are followed by "[ICAO]." For the reader's convenience, there are also cross references to related terms in other parts of the Glossary and to other documents, such as the Federal Aviation Regulations (FAR's) and the Aeronautical Information Manual (AIM).

This Glossary will be revised, as necessary, to maintain a common understanding of the system.

P/C

A

AAI- (See ARRIVAL AIRCRAFT INTERVAL.)

AAR- (See AIRPORT ACCEPTANCE RATE.)

ABBREVIATED IFR FLIGHT PLANS- An authorization by ATC requiring pilots to submit only that information needed for the purpose of ATC. It includes only a small portion of the usual IFR flight plan information. In certain instances, this may be only aircraft identification, location, and pilot request. Other information may be requested if needed by ATC for separation/control purposes. It is frequently used by aircraft which are airborne and desire an instrument approach or by aircraft which are on the ground and desire a climb to VFR-on-top.

(See VFR-ON-TOP.)

(Refer to AIM.)

ABEAM- An aircraft is "abeam" a fix, point, or object when that fix, point, or object is approximately 90 degrees to the right or left of the aircraft track. Abeam indicates a general position rather than a precise point.

ABORT- To terminate a preplanned aircraft maneuver; e.g., an aborted takeoff.

ACC [ICAO]- (See AREA CONTROL CENTER.)

ACCELERATE-STOP DISTANCE AVAILABLE- The runway plus stopway length declared available and suitable for the acceleration and deceleration of an airplane aborting a takeoff.

ACCELERATE-STOP DISTANCE AVAILABLE [ICAO]- The length of the take-off run available plus the length of the stopway if provided.

ACDO- (See AIR CARRIER DISTRICT OFFICE.)

ACKNOWLEDGE- Let me know that you have received my message.

(See ICAO term ACKNOWLEDGE.)

ACKNOWLEDGE [ICAO]- Let me know that you have received and understood this message.

ACLS- (See AUTOMATIC CARRIER LANDING SYSTEM.)

ACLT- (See ACTUAL CALCULATED LANDING TIME.)

ACROBATIC FLIGHT- An intentional maneuver involving an abrupt change in an aircraft's attitude, an abnormal attitude, or abnormal acceleration not necessary for normal flight.

(Refer to Part 91.)

(See ICAO term ACROBATIC FLIGHT.)

ACROBATIC FLIGHT [ICAO]- Maneuvers intentionally performed by an aircraft involving an abrupt change in its attitude, an abnormal attitude, or an abnormal variation in speed.

ACTIVE RUNWAY- (See RUNWAY IN USE/ACTIVE RUNWAY/DUTY RUNWAY.)

ACTUAL CALCULATED LANDING TIME- ACLT is a flight's frozen calculated landing time. An actual time determined at freeze calculated landing time (FCLT) or meter list display interval (MLDI) for the adapted vertex for each arrival aircraft based upon runway configuration, airport acceptance rate, airport arrival delay period, and other metered arrival aircraft. This time is either the vertex time of arrival (VTA) of the aircraft or the tentative calculated landing time (TCLT)/ACLT of the previous aircraft plus the arrival aircraft interval (AAI), whichever is later. This time will not be updated in response to the aircraft's progress.

ADDITIONAL SERVICES- Advisory information provided by ATC which includes but is not limited to the following:

a. Traffic advisories.

b. Vectors, when requested by the pilot, to assist aircraft receiving traffic advisories to avoid observed traffic.

c. Altitude deviation information of 300 feet or more from an assigned altitude as observed on a verified (reading correctly) automatic altitude readout (Mode C.)

d. Advisories that traffic is no longer a factor.

e. Weather and chaff information.

f. Weather assistance.

g. Bird activity information.

h. Holding pattern surveillance. Additional services are provided to the extent possible contingent only upon the controller's capability to fit them into the performance of higher priority duties and on the basis of limitations of the radar, volume of traffic, frequency congestion, and controller workload. The controller has complete discretion for determining if he/she is able to provide or continue to provide a service in a particular case. The controller's reason not to provide or continue to provide a service in a particular case is not subject to question by the pilot and need not be made known to him/her.

(See TRAFFIC ADVISORIES.)

(Refer to AIM.)

ADF- (See AUTOMATIC DIRECTION FINDER.)

ADIZ- (See AIR DEFENSE IDENTIFICATION ZONE.)

ADLY- (See ARRIVAL DELAY.)

ADMINISTRATOR- The Federal Aviation Administrator or any person to whom he/she has delegated his/her authority in the matter concerned.

P/C

ADVISE INTENTIONS- Tell me what you plan to do.

ADVISORY- Advice and information provided to assist pilots in the safe conduct of flight and aircraft movement.

(See ADVISORY SERVICE.)

ADVISORY FREQUENCY- The appropriate frequency to be used for Airport Advisory Service.

(See LOCAL AIRPORT ADVISORY.)

(See UNICOM.)

(Refer to ADVISORY CIRCULAR NO. 90-42.)

(Refer to AIM.)

ADVISORY SERVICE- Advice and information provided by a facility to assist pilots in the safe conduct of flight and aircraft movement.

(See LOCAL AIRPORT ADVISORY.)

(See TRAFFIC ADVISORIES.)

(See SAFETY ALERT.)

(See ADDITIONAL SERVICES.)

(See RADAR ADVISORY.)

(See EN ROUTE FLIGHT ADVISORY SERVICE.)

(Refer to AIM.)

AERIAL REFUELING- A procedure used by the military to transfer fuel from one aircraft to another during flight.

(Refer to VFR/IFR Wall Planning Charts.)

AERODROME- A defined area on land or water (including any buildings, installations and equipment) intended to be used either wholly or in part for the arrival, departure, and movement of aircraft.

AERODROME BEACON [ICAO]- Aeronautical beacon used to indicate the location of an aerodrome from the air.

AERODROME CONTROL SERVICE [ICAO]- Air traffic control service for aerodrome traffic.

AERODROME CONTROL TOWER [ICAO]- A unit established to provide air traffic control service to aerodrome traffic.

AERODROME ELEVATION [ICAO]- The elevation of the highest point of the landing area.

AERODROME TRAFFIC CIRCUIT [ICAO]- The specified path to be flown by aircraft operating in the vicinity of an aerodrome.

AERONAUTICAL BEACON- A visual NAVAID displaying flashes of white and/or colored light to indicate the location of an airport, a heliport, a landmark, a certain point of a Federal airway in mountainous terrain, or an obstruction.

(See AIRPORT ROTATING BEACON.)

(Refer to AIM.)

AERONAUTICAL CHART- A map used in air navigation containing all or part of the following: topographic features, hazards and obstructions, navigation aids, navigation routes, designated airspace, and airports. Commonly used aeronautical charts are:

a. Sectional Aeronautical Charts (1:500,000)- Designed for visual navigation of slow or medium speed aircraft. Topographic information on these charts features the portrayal of relief and a judicious selection of visual check points for VFR flight. Aeronautical information includes visual and radio aids to navigation, airports, controlled airspace, restricted areas, obstructions, and related data.

b. VFR Terminal Area Charts (1:250,000)- Depict Class B airspace which provides for the control or segregation of all the aircraft within Class B airspace. The chart depicts topographic information and aeronautical information which includes visual and radio aids to navigation, airports, controlled airspace, restricted areas, obstructions, and related data.

c. World Aeronautical Charts (WAC) (1:1,000,000)- Provide a standard series of aeronautical charts covering land areas of the world at a size and scale convenient for navigation by moderate speed aircraft. Topographic information includes cities and towns, principal roads, railroads, distinctive landmarks, drainage, and relief. Aeronautical information includes visual and radio aids to navigation, airports, airways, restricted areas, obstructions, and other pertinent data.

d. En Route Low Altitude Charts- Provide aeronautical information for en route instrument navigation (IFR) in the low altitude stratum. Information includes the portrayal of airways, limits of controlled airspace, position identification and frequencies of radio aids, selected airports, minimum en route and minimum obstruction clearance altitudes, airway distances, reporting points, restricted areas, and related data. Area charts, which are a part of this series, furnish terminal data at a larger scale in congested areas.

e. En Route High Altitude Charts- Provide aeronautical information for en route instrument navigation (IFR) in the high altitude stratum. Information includes the portrayal of jet routes, identification and frequencies of radio aids, selected airports, distances, time zones, special use airspace, and related information.

f. Instrument Approach Procedures (IAP) Charts- Portray the aeronautical data which is required to execute an instrument approach to an airport. These charts depict the procedures, including all related data, and the airport diagram. Each procedure is designated for use with a specific type of electronic navigation system including NDB, TACAN, VOR, ILS/MLS, and RNAV. These charts are identified by the type of navigational aid(s) which provide final approach guidance.

g. Instrument Departure Procedure (DP) Charts- Designed to expedite clearance delivery and to facilitate transition between takeoff and en route operations. Each DP is presented as a separate chart and may serve a single airport or more than one airport in a given geographical location.

h. Standard Terminal Arrival (STAR) Charts– Designed to expedite air traffic control arrival procedures and to facilitate transition between en route and instrument approach operations. Each STAR procedure is presented as a separate chart and may serve a single airport or more than one airport in a given geographical location.

i. Airport Taxi Charts– Designed to expedite the efficient and safe flow of ground traffic at an airport. These charts are identified by the official airport name; e.g., Washington National Airport.

(See ICAO term AERONAUTICAL CHART.)

AERONAUTICAL CHART [ICAO]– A representation of a portion of the earth, its culture and relief, specifically designated to meet the requirements of air navigation.

AERONAUTICAL INFORMATION MANUAL– A primary FAA publication whose purpose is to instruct airmen about operating in the National Airspace System of the U.S. It provides basic flight information, ATC Procedures and general instructional information concerning health, medical facts, factors affecting flight safety, accident and hazard reporting, and types of aeronautical charts and their use.

AERONAUTICAL INFORMATION PUBLICATION [AIP] [ICAO]– A publication issued by or with the authority of a State and containing aeronautical information of a lasting character essential to air navigation.

A/FD– (See AIRPORT/FACILITY DIRECTORY.)

AFFIRMATIVE– Yes.

AIM– (See AERONAUTICAL INFORMATION MANUAL.)

AIP [ICAO]– (See AERONAUTICAL INFORMATION PUBLICATION.)

AIRBORNE DELAY– Amount of delay to be encountered in airborne holding.

AIR CARRIER DISTRICT OFFICE– An FAA field office serving an assigned geographical area, staffed with Flight Standards personnel serving the aviation industry and the general public on matters related to the certification and operation of scheduled air carriers and other large aircraft operations.

AIRCRAFT– Device(s) that are used or intended to be used for flight in the air, and when used in air traffic control terminology, may include the flight crew.

(See ICAO term AIRCRAFT.)

AIRCRAFT [ICAO]– Any machine that can derive support in the atmosphere from the reactions of the air other than the reactions of the air against the earth's surface.

AIRCRAFT APPROACH CATEGORY– A grouping of aircraft based on a speed of 1.3 times the stall speed in the landing configuration at maximum gross landing weight. An aircraft shall fit in only one category. If it is necessary to maneuver at speeds in excess of the upper limit of a speed range for a category, the minimums for the next higher category should be used. For example, an aircraft which falls in Category A, but is circling to land at a speed in excess of 91 knots, should use the approach Category B minimums when circling to land. The categories are as follows:

a. Category A– Speed less than 91 knots.

b. Category B– Speed 91 knots or more but less than 121 knots.

c. Category C– Speed 121 knots or more but less than 141 knots.

d. Category D– Speed 141 knots or more but less than 166 knots.

e. Category E– Speed 166 knots or more.

(Refer to Part 97.)

AIRCRAFT CLASSES– For the purposes of Wake Turbulence Separation Minima, ATC classifies aircraft as Heavy, Large, and Small as follows:

a. Heavy– Aircraft capable of takeoff weights of more than 255,000 pounds whether or not they are operating at this weight during a particular phase of flight.

b. Large– Aircraft of more than 41,000 pounds, maximum certificated takeoff weight, up to 255,000 pounds.

c. Small– Aircraft of 41,000 pounds or less maximum certificated takeoff weight.

(Refer to AIM.)

AIRCRAFT SITUATION DISPLAY– ASD is a computer system that receives radar track data from all 20 CONUS ARTCC's, organizes this data into a mosaic display, and presents it on a computer screen. The display allows the traffic management coordinator multiple methods of selection and highlighting of individual aircraft or groups of aircraft. The user has the option of superimposing these aircraft positions over any number of background displays. These background options include ARTCC boundaries, any stratum of en route sector boundaries, fixes, airways, military and other special use airspace, airports, and geopolitical boundaries. By using the ASD, a coordinator can monitor any number of traffic situations or the entire systemwide traffic flows.

AIRCRAFT SURGE LAUNCH AND RECOVERY– Procedures used at USAF bases to provide increased launch and recovery rates in instrument flight rules conditions. ASLAR is based on:

a. Reduced separation between aircraft which is based on time or distance. Standard arrival separation applies between participants including multiple flights until the DRAG point. The DRAG point is a published location on an ASLAR approach where aircraft landing second in a formation slows to a predetermined airspeed. The DRAG point is the reference point at which MARSA applies as expanding elements effect separation within a flight or between subsequent participating flights.

P/C

b. ASLAR procedures shall be covered in a Letter of Agreement between the responsible USAF military ATC facility and the concerned Federal Aviation Administration facility. Initial Approach Fix spacing requirements are normally addressed as a minimum.

AIR DEFENSE EMERGENCY– A military emergency condition declared by a designated authority. This condition exists when an attack upon the continental U.S., Alaska, Canada, or U.S. installations in Greenland by hostile aircraft or missiles is considered probable, is imminent, or is taking place.

(Refer to AIM.)

AIR DEFENSE IDENTIFICATION ZONE– The area of airspace over land or water, extending upward from the surface, within which the ready identification, the location, and the control of aircraft are required in the interest of national security.

a. Domestic Air Defense Identification Zone. An ADIZ within the United States along an international boundary of the United States.

b. Coastal Air Defense Identification Zone. An ADIZ over the coastal waters of the United States.

c. Distant Early Warning Identification Zone (DEWIZ.) An ADIZ over the coastal waters of the State of Alaska.

ADIZ locations and operating and flight plan requirements for civil aircraft operations are specified in FAR Part 99.

(Refer to AIM.)

AIRMAN'S METEOROLOGICAL INFORMATION– (See AIRMET.)

AIRMET– In-flight weather advisories issued only to amend the area forecast concerning weather phenomena which are of operational interest to all aircraft and potentially hazardous to aircraft having limited capability because of lack of equipment, instrumentation, or pilot qualifications. AIRMET's concern weather of less severity than that covered by SIGMET's or Convective SIGMET's. AIRMET's cover moderate icing, moderate turbulence, sustained winds of 30 knots or more at the surface, widespread areas of ceilings less than 1,000 feet and/or visibility less than 3 miles, and extensive mountain obscurement.

(See AWW.)
(See SIGMET.)
(See CONVECTIVE SIGMET.)
(See CWA.)
(Refer to AIM.)

AIR NAVIGATION FACILITY– Any facility used in, available for use in, or designed for use in, aid of air navigation, including landing areas, lights, any apparatus or equipment for disseminating weather information, for signaling, for radio-directional finding, or for radio or other electrical communication, and any other structure or mechanism having a similar purpose for guiding or controlling flight in the air or the landing and take-off of aircraft.

(See NAVIGATIONAL AID.)

AIRPORT– An area on land or water that is used or intended to be used for the landing and takeoff of aircraft and includes its buildings and facilities, if any.

AIRPORT ACCEPTANCE RATE– A dynamic input parameter specifying the number of arriving aircraft which an airport or airspace can accept from the ARTCC per hour. The AAR is used to calculate the desired interval between successive arrival aircraft.

AIRPORT ADVISORY AREA– The area within ten miles of an airport without a control tower or where the tower is not in operation, and on which a Flight Service Station is located.

(See LOCAL AIRPORT ADVISORY.)
(Refer to AIM.)

AIRPORT ELEVATION– The highest point of an airport's usable runways measured in feet from mean sea level.

(See TOUCHDOWN ZONE ELEVATION.)
(See ICAO term AERODROME ELEVATION.)

AIRPORT/FACILITY DIRECTORY– A publication designed primarily as a pilot's operational manual containing all airports, seaplane bases, and heliports open to the public including communications data, navigational facilities, and certain special notices and procedures. This publication is issued in seven volumes according to geographical area.

AIRPORT INFORMATION AID– (See AIRPORT INFORMATION DESK.)

AIRPORT INFORMATION DESK– An airport unmanned facility designed for pilot self-service briefing, flight planning, and filing of flight plans.

(Refer to AIM.)

AIRPORT LIGHTING– Various lighting aids that may be installed on an airport. Types of airport lighting include:

a. Approach Light System (ALS)– An airport lighting facility which provides visual guidance to landing aircraft by radiating light beams in a directional pattern by which the pilot aligns the aircraft with the extended centerline of the runway on his final approach for landing. Condenser-Discharge Sequential Flashing Lights/Sequenced Flashing Lights may be installed in conjunction with the ALS at some airports. Types of Approach Light Systems are:

1. ALSF-1– Approach Light System with Sequenced Flashing Lights in ILS Cat-I configuration.

2. ALSF-2– Approach Light System with Sequenced Flashing Lights in ILS Cat-II configuration. The ALSF-2 may operate as an SSALR when weather conditions permit.

3. SSALF– Simplified Short Approach Light System with Sequenced Flashing Lights.

4. SSALR– Simplified Short Approach Light System with Runway Alignment Indicator Lights.

5. MALSF– Medium Intensity Approach Light System with Sequenced Flashing Lights.

6. MALSR– Medium Intensity Approach Light System with Runway Alignment Indicator Lights.

7. LDIN– Lead-in-light system– Consists of one or more series of flashing lights installed at or near ground level that provides positive visual guidance along an approach path, either curving or straight, where special problems exist with hazardous terrain, obstructions, or noise abatement procedures.

8. RAIL– Runway Alignment Indicator Lights– Sequenced Flashing Lights which are installed only in combination with other light systems.

9. ODALS– Omnidirectional Approach Lighting System consists of seven omnidirectional flashing lights located in the approach area of a nonprecision runway. Five lights are located on the runway centerline extended with the first light located 300 feet from the threshold and extending at equal intervals up to 1,500 feet from the threshold. The other two lights are located, one on each side of the runway threshold, at a lateral distance of 40 feet from the runway edge, or 75 feet from the runway edge when installed on a runway equipped with a VASI.

*(Refer to FAA Order 6850.2, VISUAL GUID-
ANCE LIGHTING SYSTEMS.)*

b. Runway Lights/Runway Edge Lights– Lights having a prescribed angle of emission used to define the lateral limits of a runway. Runway lights are uniformly spaced at intervals of approximately 200 feet, and the intensity may be controlled or preset.

c. Touchdown Zone Lighting– Two rows of transverse light bars located symmetrically about the runway centerline normally at 100 foot intervals. The basic system extends 3,000 feet along the runway.

d. Runway Centerline Lighting– Flush centerline lights spaced at 50-foot intervals beginning 75 feet from the landing threshold and extending to within 75 feet of the opposite end of the runway.

e. Threshold Lights– Fixed green lights arranged symmetrically left and right of the runway centerline, identifying the runway threshold.

f. Runway End Identifier Lights (REIL)– Two synchronized flashing lights, one on each side of the runway threshold, which provide rapid and positive identification of the approach end of a particular runway.

g. Visual Approach Slope Indicator (VASI)– An airport lighting facility providing vertical visual approach slope guidance to aircraft during approach to landing by radiating a directional pattern of high intensity red and white focused light beams which indicate to the pilot that he is "on path" if he sees red/white, "above path" if white/white, and "below path" if red/red. Some airports serving large aircraft have three-bar VASI's which provide two visual glide paths to the same runway.

h. Boundary Lights– Lights defining the perimeter of an airport or landing area.

(Refer to AIM.)

AIRPORT MARKING AIDS– Markings used on runway and taxiway surfaces to identify a specific runway, a runway threshold, a centerline, a hold line, etc. A runway should be marked in accordance with its present usage such as:

a. Visual.

b. Nonprecision instrument.

c. Precision instrument.

(Refer to AIM.)

AIRPORT REFERENCE POINT (ARP) – The approximate geometric center of all usable runway surfaces.

AIRPORT RESERVATION OFFICE– Office responsible for monitoring the operation of the high density rule. Receives and processes requests for IFR operations at high density traffic airports.

AIRPORT ROTATING BEACON– A visual NAVAID operated at many airports. At civil airports, alternating white and green flashes indicate the location of the airport. At military airports, the beacons flash alternately white and green, but are differentiated from civil beacons by dualpeaked (two quick) white flashes between the green flashes.

(See SPECIAL VFR OPERATIONS.)
(See INSTRUMENT FLIGHT RULES.)
(Refer to AIM.)
(See ICAO term AERODROME BEACON.)

AIRPORT SURFACE DETECTION EQUIPMENT– Radar equipment specifically designed to detect all principal features on the surface of an airport, including aircraft and vehicular traffic, and to present the entire image on a radar indicator console in the control tower. Used to augment visual observation by tower personnel of aircraft and/or vehicular movements on runways and taxiways.

AIRPORT SURVEILLANCE RADAR– Approach control radar used to detect and display an aircraft's position in the terminal area. ASR provides range and azimuth information but does not provide elevation data. Coverage of the ASR can extend up to 60 miles.

AIRPORT TAXI CHARTS– (See AERONAUTICAL CHART.)

AIRPORT TRAFFIC CONTROL SERVICE– A service provided by a control tower for aircraft operating on the movement area and in the vicinity of an airport.

(See MOVEMENT AREA.)
(See TOWER.)
*(See ICAO term AERODROME CONTROL
SERVICE.)*

AIRPORT TRAFFIC CONTROL TOWER– (See TOWER.)

AIR ROUTE SURVEILLANCE RADAR– Air route traffic control center (ARTCC) radar used primarily to detect and display an aircraft's position while en route between terminal areas. The ARSR enables controllers to provide radar air traffic control service when aircraft are within the ARSR coverage. In some instances, ARSR may enable an ARTCC to provide terminal radar services similar to but usually more limited than those provided by a radar approach control.

AIR ROUTE TRAFFIC CONTROL CENTER– A facility established to provide air traffic control service to aircraft operating on IFR flight plans within controlled airspace and principally during the en route phase of flight. When equipment capabilities and controller workload permit, certain advisory/assistance services may be provided to VFR aircraft.

(See NAS STAGE A.)

(See EN ROUTE AIR TRAFFIC CONTROL SERVICES.)

(Refer to AIM.)

AIRSPACE HIERARCHY– Within the airspace classes, there is a hierarchy and, in the event of an overlap of airspace: Class A preempts Class B, Class B preempts Class C, Class C preempts Class D, Class D preempts Class E, and Class E preempts Class G.

AIRSPEED– The speed of an aircraft relative to its surrounding air mass. The unqualified term "airspeed" means one of the following:

a. Indicated Airspeed– The speed shown on the aircraft airspeed indicator. This is the speed used in pilot/controller communications under the general term "airspeed."

(Refer to FAR Part 1.)

b. True Airspeed– The airspeed of an aircraft relative to undisturbed air. Used primarily in flight planning and en route portion of flight. When used in pilot/controller communications, it is referred to as "true airspeed" and not shortened to "airspeed."

AIRSTART– The starting of an aircraft engine while the aircraft is airborne, preceded by engine shutdown during training flights or by actual engine failure.

AIR TAXI– Used to describe a helicopter/VTOL aircraft movement conducted above the surface but normally not above 100 feet AGL. The aircraft may proceed either via hover taxi or flight at speeds more than 20 knots. The pilot is solely responsible for selecting a safe airspeed/altitude for the operation being conducted.

(See HOVER TAXI.)

(Refer to AIM.)

AIR TRAFFIC– Aircraft operating in the air or on an airport surface, exclusive of loading ramps and parking areas.

(See ICAO term AIR TRAFFIC.)

AIR TRAFFIC [ICAO]– All aircraft in flight or operating on the manoeuvring area of an aerodrome.

AIR TRAFFIC CLEARANCE– An authorization by air traffic control for the purpose of preventing collision between known aircraft, for an aircraft to proceed under specified traffic conditions within controlled airspace. The pilot-in-command of an aircraft may not deviate from the provisions of a visual flight rules (VFR) or instrument flight rules (IFR) air traffic clearance except in an emergency or unless an amended clearance has been obtained. Additionally, the pilot may request a different clearance from that which has been issued by air traffic control (ATC) if information available to the pilot makes another course of action more practicable or if aircraft equipment limitations or company procedures forbid compliance with the clearance issued. Pilots may also request clarification or amendment, as appropriate, any time a clearance is not fully understood, or considered unacceptable because of safety of flight. Controllers should, in such instances and to the extent of operational practicality and safety, honor the pilot's request. FAR Part 91.3(a) states: "The pilot in command of an aircraft is directly responsible for, and is the final authority as to, the operation of that aircraft." THE PILOT IS RESPONSIBLE TO REQUEST AN AMENDED CLEARANCE if ATC issues a clearance that would cause a pilot to deviate from a rule or regulation, or in the pilot's opinion, would place the aircraft in jeopardy.

(See ATC INSTRUCTIONS.)

(See ICAO term AIR TRAFFIC CONTROL CLEARANCE.)

AIR TRAFFIC CONTROL– A service operated by appropriate authority to promote the safe, orderly and expeditious flow of air traffic.

(See ICAO term AIR TRAFFIC CONTROL SERVICE.)

AIR TRAFFIC CONTROL CLEARANCE [ICAO]– Authorization for an aircraft to proceed under conditions specified by an air traffic control unit.

Note 1: For convenience, the term air traffic control clearance is frequently abbreviated to clearance when used in appropriate contexts.

Note 2: The abbreviated term clearance may be prefixed by the words taxi, takeoff, departure, en route, approach or landing to indicate the particular portion of flight to which the air traffic control clearance relates.

AIR TRAFFIC CONTROL SERVICE– (See AIR TRAFFIC CONTROL.)

AIR TRAFFIC CONTROL SERVICE [ICAO]– A service provided for the purpose of:

a. Preventing collisions:

1. Between aircraft; and

2. On the manoeuvring area between aircraft and obstructions; and

b. Expediting and maintaining an orderly flow of air traffic.

AIR TRAFFIC CONTROL SPECIALIST– A person authorized to provide air traffic control service.

(See AIR TRAFFIC CONTROL.)

(See FLIGHT SERVICE STATION.)

(See ICAO term CONTROLLER.)

AIR TRAFFIC CONTROL SYSTEM COMMAND CENTER– An Air Traffic Operations Service facility consisting of four operational units.

a. Central Flow Control Function (CFCF). Responsible for coordination and approval of all major intercenter flow control restrictions on a system basis in order to obtain maximum utilization of the airspace.

(See QUOTA FLOW CONTROL.)

b. Central Altitude Reservation Function (CARF). Responsible for coordinating, planning, and approving special user requirements under the Altitude Reservation (ALTRV) concept.

(See ALTITUDE RESERVATION.)

c. Airport Reservation Office (ARO). Responsible for approving IFR flights at designated high density traffic airports (John F. Kennedy, LaGuardia, O'Hare, and Washington National) during specified hours.

(Refer to FAR Part 93 and AIRPORT/FACIL-ITY DIRECTORY.)

d. ATC Contingency Command Post. A facility which enables the FAA to manage the ATC system when significant portions of the system's capabilities have been lost or are threatened.

AIR TRAFFIC SERVICE– A generic term meaning:

a. Flight Information Service:

b. Alerting Service:

c. Air Traffic Advisory Service:

d. Air Traffic Control Service:

    1. Area Control Service,

    2. Approach Control Service, or

    3. Airport Control Service.

AIRWAY– A Class E airspace area established in the form of a corridor, the centerline of which is defined by radio navigational aids.

(See FEDERAL AIRWAYS.)

(Refer to FAR Part 71.)

(Refer to AIM.)

(See ICAO term AIRWAY.)

AIRWAY [ICAO]– A control area or portion thereof established in the form of corridor equipped with radio navigational aids.

AIRWAY BEACON– Used to mark airway segments in remote mountain areas. The light flashes Morse Code to identify the beacon site.

(Refer to AIM.)

AIT– (See AUTOMATED INFORMATION TRANSFER.)

ALERFA (Alert Phase) [ICAO]– A situation wherein apprehension exists as to the safety of an aircraft and its occupants.

ALERT AREA– (See SPECIAL USE AIRSPACE.)

ALERT NOTICE– A request originated by a flight service station (FSS) or an air route traffic control center (ARTCC) for an extensive communication search for overdue, unreported, or missing aircraft.

ALERTING SERVICE– A service provided to notify appropriate organizations regarding aircraft in need of search and rescue aid and assist such organizations as required.

ALNOT– (See ALERT NOTICE.)

ALONG TRACK DISTANCE (LTD) – The distance measured from a point–in–space by systems using area navigation reference capabilities that are not subject to slant range errors.

ALPHANUMERIC DISPLAY– Letters and numerals used to show identification, altitude, beacon code, and other information concerning a target on a radar display.

(See AUTOMATED RADAR TERMINAL SYSTEMS.)

(See NAS STAGE A.)

ALTERNATE AERODROME [ICAO]– An aerodrome to which an aircraft may proceed when it becomes either impossible or inadvisable to proceed to or to land at the aerodrome of intended landing.

Note: The aerodrome from which a flight departs may also be an en-route or a destination alternate aerodrome for the flight.

ALTERNATE AIRPORT– An airport at which an aircraft may land if a landing at the intended airport becomes inadvisable.

(See ICAO term ALTERNATE AERODROME.)

ALTIMETER SETTING– The barometric pressure reading used to adjust a pressure altimeter for variations in existing atmospheric pressure or to the standard altimeter setting (29.92.)

(Refer to FAR Part 91.)

(Refer to AIM.)

ALTITUDE– The height of a level, point, or object measured in feet Above Ground Level (AGL) or from Mean Sea Level (MSL.)

(See FLIGHT LEVEL.)

a. MSL Altitude– Altitude expressed in feet measured from mean sea level.

b. AGL Altitude– Altitude expressed in feet measured above ground level.

P/C

c. Indicated Altitude– The altitude as shown by an altimeter. On a pressure or barometric altimeter it is altitude as shown uncorrected for instrument error and uncompensated for variation from standard atmospheric conditions.

(See ICAO term ALTITUDE.)

ALTITUDE [ICAO]– The vertical distance of a level, a point or an object considered as a point, measured from mean sea level (MSL.)

ALTITUDE READOUT– An aircraft's altitude, transmitted via the Mode C transponder feature, that is visually displayed in 100-foot increments on a radar scope having readout capability.

(See AUTOMATED RADAR TERMINAL SYSTEMS.)

(See NAS STAGE A.)

(See ALPHANUMERIC DISPLAY.)

(Refer to AIM.)

ALTITUDE RESERVATION– Airspace utilization under prescribed conditions normally employed for the mass movement of aircraft or other special user requirements which cannot otherwise be accomplished. ALTRV's are approved by the appropriate FAA facility.

(See AIR TRAFFIC CONTROL SYSTEM COMMAND CENTER.)

ALTITUDE RESTRICTION– An altitude or altitudes, stated in the order flown, which are to be maintained until reaching a specific point or time. Altitude restrictions may be issued by ATC due to traffic, terrain, or other airspace considerations.

ALTITUDE RESTRICTIONS ARE CANCELED– Adherence to previously imposed altitude restrictions is no longer required during a climb or descent.

ALTRV– (See ALTITUDE RESERVATION.)

AMVER– (See AUTOMATED MUTUAL-ASSISTANCE VESSEL RESCUE SYSTEM

APPROACH CLEARANCE– Authorization by ATC for a pilot to conduct an instrument approach. The type of instrument approach for which a clearance and other pertinent information is provided in the approach clearance when required.

(See INSTRUMENT APPROACH PROCEDURE.)

(See CLEARED APPROACH.)

(Refer to AIM and FAR Part 91.)

APPROACH CONTROL FACILITY– A terminal ATC facility that provides approach control service in a terminal area.

(See APPROACH CONTROL SERVICE.)

(See RADAR APPROACH CONTROL FACILITY.)

APPROACH CONTROL SERVICE– Air traffic control service provided by an approach control facility for arriving and departing VFR/IFR aircraft and, on occasion, en route aircraft. At some airports not served by an approach control facility, the ARTCC provides limited approach control service.

(Refer to AIM.)

(See ICAO term APPROACH CONTROL SERVICE.)

APPROACH CONTROL SERVICE [ICAO]– Air traffic control service for arriving or departing controlled flights.

APPROACH GATE– An imaginary point used within ATC as a basis for vectoring aircraft to the final approach course. The gate will be established along the final approach course 1 mile from the outer marker (or the fix used in lieu of the outer marker) on the side away from the airport for precision approaches and 1 mile from the final approach fix on the side away from the airport for nonprecision approaches. In either case when measured along the final approach course, the gate will be no closer than 5 miles from the landing threshold.

APPROACH LIGHT SYSTEM– (See AIRPORT LIGHTING.)

APPROACH SEQUENCE– The order in which aircraft are positioned while on approach or awaiting approach clearance.

(See LANDING SEQUENCE.)

(See ICAO term APPROACH SEQUENCE.)

APPROACH SEQUENCE [ICAO]– The order in which two or more aircraft are cleared to approach to land at the aerodrome.

APPROACH SPEED– The recommended speed contained in aircraft manuals used by pilots when making an approach to landing. This speed will vary for different segments of an approach as well as for aircraft weight and configuration.

APPROPRIATE ATS AUTHORITY [ICAO]– The relevant authority designated by the State responsible for providing air traffic services in the airspace concerned. In the United States, the "appropriate ATS authority" is the Program Director for Air Traffic Operations, ATO-1.

APPROPRIATE AUTHORITY–

a. Regarding flight over the high seas: the relevant authority is the State of Registry.

b. Regarding flight over other than the high seas: the relevant authority is the State having sovereignty over the territory being overflown.

APPROPRIATE OBSTACLE CLEARANCE MINIMUM ALTITUDE- Any of the following:

(See Minimum IFR Altitude- MIA.)

(See Minimum En Route Altitude- MEA.)

(See Minimum Obstruction Clearance Altitude- MOCA.)

(See Minimum Vectoring Altitude- MVA.)

APPROPRIATE TERRAIN CLEARANCE MINIMUM ALTITUDE- Any of the following:

(See Minimum IFR Altitude- MIA.)

(See Minimum En Route Altitude- MEA.)

(See Minimum Obstruction Clearance Altitude- MOCA.)

(See Minimum Vectoring Altitude- MVA.)

APRON- A defined area on an airport or heliport intended to accommodate aircraft for purposes of loading or unloading passengers or cargo, refueling, parking, or maintenance. With regard to seaplanes, a ramp is used for access to the apron from the water.

(See ICAO term APRON.)

APRON [ICAO]- A defined area, on a land aerodrome, intended to accommodate aircraft for purposes of loading or unloading passengers, mail or cargo, refueling, parking or maintenance.

ARC- The track over the ground of an aircraft flying at a constant distance from a navigational aid by reference to distance measuring equipment (DME).

AREA CONTROL CENTER [ICAO]- An ICAO term for an air traffic control facility primarily responsible for ATC services being provided IFR aircraft during the en route phase of flight. The U.S. equivalent facility is an air route traffic control center (ARTCC).

AREA NAVIGATION- A method of navigation that permits aircraft operation on any desired course within the coverage of station-referenced navigation signals or within the limits of a self-contained system capability. Random area navigation routes are direct routes, based on area navigation capability, between waypoints defined in terms of latitude/longitude coordinates, degree/distance fixes, or offsets from published or established routes/airways at a specified distance and direction. The major types of equipment are:

a. VORTAC referenced or Course Line Computer (CLC) systems, which account for the greatest number of RNAV units in use. To function, the CLC must be within the service range of a VORTAC.

b. OMEGA/VLF, although two separate systems, can be considered as one operationally. A long-range navigation

system based upon Very Low Frequency radio signals transmitted from a total of 17 stations worldwide.

c. Inertial (INS) systems, which are totally self-contained and require no information from external references. They provide aircraft position and navigation information in response to signals resulting from inertial effects on components within the system.

d. MLS Area Navigation (MLS/RNAV), which provides area navigation with reference to an MLS ground facility.

e. LORAN-C is a long-range radio navigation system that uses ground waves transmitted at low frequency to provide user position information at ranges of up to 600 to 1,200 nautical miles at both en route and approach altitudes. The usable signal coverage areas are determined by the signal-to-noise ratio, the envelope-to-cycle difference, and the geometric relationship between the positions of the user and the transmitting stations.

f. GPS-is a space-base radio positioning, navigation, and time-transfer system. The system provides highly accurate position and velocity information, and precise time, on a continuous global basis, to an unlimited number of properly equipped users. The system is unaffected by weather, and provides a worldwide common grid reference system.

(See ICAO term AREA NAVIGATION.)

AREA NAVIGATION [ICAO]- A method of navigation which permits aircraft operation on any desired flight path within the coverage of station-referenced navigation aids or within the limits of the capability of self-contained aids, or a combination of these.

AREA NAVIGATION (RNAV) APPROACH CONFIGURATION:

a. STANDARD T- An RNAV approach whose design allows direct flight to any one of three initial approach fixes (IAF) and eliminates the need for procedure turns. The standard design is to align the procedure on the extended centerline with the missed approach point (MAP) at the runway threshold, the final approach fix (FAF), and the initial approach/intermediate fix (IAF/IF). The other two IAF's will be established perpendicular to the IF.

b. MODIFIED T- An RNAV approach design for single or multiple runways where terrain or operational constraints do not allow for the standard T. The "T" may be modified by increasing or decreasing the angle from the corner IAF(s) to the IF or by eliminating one or both corner IAF's.

c. STANDARD I- An RNAV approach design for a single runway with both corner IAF's eliminated. Course reversal or radar vectoring may be required at busy terminals with multiple runways.

d. TERMINAL ARRIVAL AREA (TAA)- The TAA is controlled airspace established in conjunction with the Standard or Modified T and I RNAV approach configurations. In the standard TAA, there are three areas: straight-in, left base, and right base. The arc boundaries of the three areas

P/C

of the TAA are published portions of the approach and allow aircraft to transition from the en route structure direct to the nearest IAF. TAA's will also eliminate or reduce feeder routes, departure extensions, and procedure turns or course reversal.

    1. STRAIGHT-IN AREA- A 30NM arc centered on the IF bounded by a straight line extending through the IF perpendicular to the intermediate course.

    2. LEFT BASE AREA- A 30NM arc centered on the right corner IAF. The area shares a boundary with the straight-in area except that it extends out for 30NM from the IAF and is bounded on the other side by a line extending from the IF through the FAF to the arc.

    3. RIGHT BASE AREA- A 30NM arc centered on the left corner IAF. The area shares a boundary with the straight-in area except that it extends out for 30NM from the IAF and is bounded on the other side by a line extending from the IF through the FAF to the arc.

ARINC- An acronym for Aeronautical Radio, Inc., a corporation largely owned by a group of airlines. ARINC is licensed by the FCC as an aeronautical station and contracted by the FAA to provide communications support for air traffic control and meteorological services in portions of international airspace.

ARMY AVIATION FLIGHT INFORMATION BULLE-TIN- A bulletin that provides air operation data covering Army, National Guard, and Army Reserve aviation activities.

ARO- (See AIRPORT RESERVATION OFFICE.)

ARRESTING SYSTEM- A safety device consisting of two major components, namely, engaging or catching devices and energy absorption devices for the purpose of arresting both tailhook and/or nontailhook-equipped aircraft. It is used to prevent aircraft from overrunning runways when the aircraft cannot be stopped after landing or during aborted takeoff. Arresting systems have various names; e.g., arresting gear, hook device, wire barrier cable.

    (See ABORT.)

    (Refer to AIM.)

ARRIVAL AIRCRAFT INTERVAL- An internally generated program in hundredths of minutes based upon the AAR. AAI is the desired optimum interval between successive arrival aircraft over the vertex.

ARRIVAL CENTER- The ARTCC having jurisdiction for the impacted airport.

ARRIVAL DELAY- A parameter which specifies a period of time in which no aircraft will be metered for arrival at the specified airport.

ARRIVAL SECTOR- An operational control sector containing one or more meter fixes.

ARRIVAL SECTOR ADVISORY LIST- An ordered list of data on arrivals displayed at the PVD/MDM of the sector which controls the meter fix.

ARRIVAL SEQUENCING PROGRAM- The automated program designed to assist in sequencing aircraft destined for the same airport.

ARRIVAL TIME- The time an aircraft touches down on arrival.

ARSR- (See AIR ROUTE SURVEILLANCE RADAR.)

ARTCC- (See AIR ROUTE TRAFFIC CONTROL CENTER.)

ARTS- (See AUTOMATED RADAR TERMINAL SYSTEMS.)

ASD- (See AIRCRAFT SITUATION DISPLAY.)

ASDA- (See ACCELERATE-STOP DISTANCE AVAILABLE.)

ASDA [ICAO]- (See ICAO Term ACCELERATE-STOP DISTANCE AVAILABLE.)

ASDE- (See AIRPORT SURFACE DETECTION EQUIPMENT.)

ASLAR- (See AIRCRAFT SURGE LAUNCH AND RECOVERY.)

ASP- (See ARRIVAL SEQUENCING PROGRAM.)

ASR- (See AIRPORT SURVEILLANCE RADAR.)

ASR APPROACH- (See SURVEILLANCE APPROACH.)

ATC- (See AIR TRAFFIC CONTROL.)

ATCAA- (See ATC ASSIGNED AIRSPACE.)

ATC ADVISES- Used to prefix a message of noncontrol information when it is relayed to an aircraft by other than an air traffic controller.

    (See ADVISORY.)

ATC ASSIGNED AIRSPACE- Airspace of defined vertical/lateral limits, assigned by ATC, for the purpose of providing air traffic segregation between the specified activities being conducted within the assigned airspace and other IFR air traffic.

    (See SPECIAL USE AIRSPACE.)

ATC CLEARANCE- (See AIR TRAFFIC CLEARANCE.)

ATC CLEARS- Used to prefix an ATC clearance when it is relayed to an aircraft by other than an air traffic controller.

ATC INSTRUCTIONS- Directives issued by air traffic control for the purpose of requiring a pilot to take specific actions; e.g., "Turn left heading two five zero," "Go around," "Clear the runway."

    (Refer to FAR Part 91.)

ATCRBS- (See RADAR.)

ATC REQUESTS- Used to prefix an ATC request when it is relayed to an aircraft by other than an air traffic controller.

ATCSCC– (See AIR TRAFFIC CONTROL SYSTEM COMMAND CENTER.)

ATCSCC DELAY FACTOR– The amount of delay calculated to be assigned prior to departure.

ATCT– (See TOWER.)

ATIS– (See AUTOMATIC TERMINAL INFORMATION SERVICE.)

ATIS [ICAO]– (See ICAO Term AUTOMATIC TERMINAL INFORMATION SERVICE.)

ATS Route [ICAO]– A specified route designed for channelling the flow of traffic as necessary for the provision of air traffic services.

Note: The term "ATS Route" is used to mean variously, airway, advisory route, controlled or uncontrolled route, arrival or departure, etc.

AUTOLAND APPROACH– An autoland approach is a precision instrument approach to touchdown and, in some cases, through the landing rollout. An autoland approach is performed by the aircraft autopilot which is receiving position information and/or steering commands from onboard navigation equipment (See COUPLED APPROACH.)

Note: Autoland and coupled approaches are flown in VFR and IFR. It is common for carriers to require their crews to fly coupled approaches and autoland approaches (if certified) when the weather conditions are less than approximately 4,000 RVR.

AUTOMATED INFORMATION TRANSFER– A precoordinated process, specifically defined in facility directives, during which a transfer of altitude control and/or radar identification is accomplished without verbal coordination between controllers using information communicated in a full data block.

AUTOMATED MUTUAL-ASSISTANCE VESSEL RESCUE SYSTEM– A facility which can deliver, in a matter of minutes, a surface picture (SURPIC) of vessels in the area of a potential or actual search and rescue incident, including their predicted positions and their characteristics.

(See FAA Order 7110.65, paragraph 10–7–4, IN-FLIGHT CONTINGENCIES.)

AUTOMATED RADAR TERMINAL SYSTEMS– The generic term for the ultimate in functional capability afforded by several automation systems. Each differs in functional capabilities and equipment. ARTS plus a suffix roman numeral denotes a specific system. A following letter indicates a major modification to that system. In general, an ARTS displays for the terminal controller aircraft identification, flight plan data, other flight associated information; e.g., altitude, speed, and aircraft position symbols in conjunction with his radar presentation. Normal radar co-exists with the alphanumeric display. In addition to enhancing visualization of the air traffic situation, ARTS facilitate intra/inter-facility transfer and coordination of flight information. These capabilities are enabled by specially designed computers and subsystems tailored to the radar and communications equipments and operational requirements of each automated facility. Modular design permits adoption of improvements in computer software and electronic technologies as they become available while retaining the characteristics unique to each system.

a. ARTS II. A programmable nontracking, computer-aided display subsystem capable of modular expansion. ARTS II systems provide a level of automated air traffic control capability at terminals having low to medium activity. Flight identification and altitude may be associated with the display of secondary radar targets. The system has the capability of communicating with ARTCC's and other ARTS II, IIA, III, and IIIA facilities.

b. ARTS IIA. A programmable radar-tracking computer subsystem capable of modular expansion. The ARTS IIA detects, tracks, and predicts secondary radar targets. The targets are displayed by means of computer-generated symbols, ground speed, and flight plan data. Although it does not track primary radar targets, they are displayed coincident with the secondary radar as well as the symbols and alphanumerics. The system has the capability of communicating with ARTCC's and other ARTS II, IIA, III, and IIIA facilities.

c. ARTS III. The Beacon Tracking Level of the modular programmable automated radar terminal system in use at medium to high activity terminals. ARTS III detects, tracks, and predicts secondary radar-derived aircraft targets. These are displayed by means of computer-generated symbols and alphanumeric characters depicting flight identification, aircraft altitude, ground speed, and flight plan data. Although it does not track primary targets, they are displayed coincident with the secondary radar as well as the symbols and alphanumerics. The system has the capability of communicating with ARTCC's and other ARTS III facilities.

d. ARTS IIIA. The Radar Tracking and Beacon Tracking Level (RT&BTL) of the modular, programmable automated radar terminal system. ARTS IIIA detects, tracks, and predicts primary as well as secondary radar-derived aircraft targets. This more sophisticated computer-driven system upgrades the existing ARTS III system by providing improved tracking, continuous data recording, and fail-soft capabilities.

AUTOMATIC ALTITUDE REPORT– (See ALTITUDE READOUT.)

AUTOMATIC ALTITUDE REPORTING– That function of a transponder which responds to Mode C interrogations by transmitting the aircraft's altitude in 100-foot increments.

AUTOMATIC CARRIER LANDING SYSTEM– U.S. Navy final approach equipment consisting of precision tracking radar coupled to a computer data link to provide continuous information to the aircraft, monitoring capability to the pilot, and a backup approach system.

P/C

AUTOMATIC DIRECTION FINDER– An aircraft radio navigation system which senses and indicates the direction to a L/MF nondirectional radio beacon (NDB) ground transmitter. Direction is indicated to the pilot as a magnetic bearing or as a relative bearing to the longitudinal axis of the aircraft depending on the type of indicator installed in the aircraft. In certain applications, such as military, ADF operations may be based on airborne and ground transmitters in the VHF/UHF frequency spectrum.

(See BEARING.)

(See NONDIRECTIONAL BEACON.)

AUTOMATIC TERMINAL INFORMATION SERVICE– The continuous broadcast of recorded noncontrol information in selected terminal areas. Its purpose is to improve controller effectiveness and to relieve frequency congestion by automating the repetitive transmission of essential but routine information; e.g., "Los Angeles information Alfa. One three zero zero Coordinated Universal Time. Weather, measured ceiling two thousand overcast, visibility three, haze, smoke, temperature seven one, dew point five seven, wind two five zero at five, altimeter two niner niner six. I-L-S Runway Two Five Left approach in use, Runway Two Five Right closed, advise you have Alfa."

(Refer to AIM.)

(See ICAO term AUTOMATIC TERMINAL INFORMATION SERVICE.)

AUTOMATIC TERMINAL INFORMATION SERVICE [ICAO]– The provision of current, routine information to arriving and departing aircraft by means of continuous and repetitive broadcasts throughout the day or a specified portion of the day.

AUTOROTATION– A rotorcraft flight condition in which the lifting rotor is driven entirely by action of the air when the rotorcraft is in motion.

a. Autorotative Landing/Touchdown Autorotation. Used by a pilot to indicate that the landing will be made without applying power to the rotor.

b. Low Level Autorotation. Commences at an altitude well below the traffic pattern, usually below 100 feet AGL and is used primarily for tactical military training.

c. 180 degrees Autorotation. Initiated from a downwind heading and is commenced well inside the normal traffic pattern. "Go around" may not be possible during the latter part of this maneuver.

AVAILABLE LANDING DISTANCE (ALD)– The portion of a runway available for landing and roll–out for aircraft cleared for LAHSO. This distance is measured from the landing threshold to the hold–short point.

AVIATION WEATHER SERVICE– A service provided by the National Weather Service (NWS) and FAA which collects and disseminates pertinent weather information for pilots, aircraft operators, and ATC. Available aviation weather reports and forecasts are displayed at each NWS office and FAA FSS.

(See EN ROUTE FLIGHT ADVISORY SERVICE.)

(See TRANSCRIBED WEATHER BROADCAST.)

(See WEATHER ADVISORY.)

(See PILOTS AUTOMATIC TELEPHONE WEATHER ANSWERING SERVICE.)

(Refer to AIM.)

AWW– (See SEVERE WEATHER FORECAST ALERTS.)

AZIMUTH (MLS)– A magnetic bearing extending from an MLS navigation facility.

Note: azimuth bearings are described as magnetic and are referred to as "azimuth" in radio telephone communications.

B

BACK–TAXI– A term used by air traffic controllers to taxi an aircraft on the runway opposite to the traffic flow. The aircraft may be instructed to back–taxi to the beginning of the runway or at some point before reaching the runway end for the purpose of departure or to exit the runway.

BASE LEG– (See TRAFFIC PATTERN.)

BEACON– (See RADAR.)

(See NONDIRECTIONAL BEACON.)

(See MARKER BEACON.)

(See AIRPORT ROTATING BEACON.)

(See AERONAUTICAL BEACON.)

(See AIRWAY BEACON.)

BEARING– The horizontal direction to or from any point, usually measured clockwise from true north, magnetic north, or some other reference point through 360 degrees.

(See NONDIRECTIONAL BEACON.)

BELOW MINIMUMS– Weather conditions below the minimums prescribed by regulation for the particular action involved; e.g., landing minimums, takeoff minimums.

BLAST FENCE– A barrier that is used to divert or dissipate jet or propeller blast.

BLIND SPEED– The rate of departure or closing of a target relative to the radar antenna at which cancellation of the primary radar target by moving target indicator (MTI) circuits in the radar equipment causes a reduction or complete loss of signal.

(See ICAO term BLIND VELOCITY.)

BLIND SPOT– An area from which radio transmissions and/or radar echoes cannot be received. The term is also used to describe portions of the airport not visible from the control tower.

BLIND TRANSMISSION– (See TRANSMITTING IN THE BLIND.)

BLIND VELOCITY [ICAO]– The radial velocity of a moving target such that the target is not seen on primary radars fitted with certain forms of fixed echo suppression.

BLIND ZONE– (See BLIND SPOT.)

BLOCKED– Phraseology used to indicate that a radio transmission has been distorted or interrupted due to multiple simultaneous radio transmissions.

BOUNDARY LIGHTS– (See AIRPORT LIGHTING.)

BRAKING ACTION (GOOD, FAIR, POOR, OR NIL)– A report of conditions on the airport movement area providing a pilot with a degree/quality of braking that he might expect. Braking action is reported in terms of good, fair, poor, or nil.

(See RUNWAY CONDITION READING.)

BRAKING ACTION ADVISORIES– When tower controllers have received runway braking action reports which include the terms "poor" or "nil," or whenever weather conditions are conducive to deteriorating or rapidly changing runway braking conditions, the tower will include on the ATIS broadcast the statement, "BRAKING ACTION ADVISORIES ARE IN EFFECT." During the time Braking Action Advisories are in effect, ATC will issue the latest braking action report for the runway in use to each arriving and departing aircraft. Pilots should be prepared for deteriorating braking conditions and should request current runway condition information if not volunteered by controllers. Pilots should also be prepared to provide a descriptive runway condition report to controllers after landing.

BREAKOUT– A technique to direct aircraft out of the approach stream. In the context of close parallel operations, a breakout is used to direct threatened aircraft away from a deviating aircraft.

BROADCAST– Transmission of information for which an acknowledgement is not expected.

(See ICAO term BROADCAST.)

BROADCAST [ICAO]– A transmission of information relating to air navigation that is not addressed to a specific station or stations.

P/C

C

CALCULATED LANDING TIME- A term that may be used in place of tentative or actual calculated landing time, whichever applies.

CALL UP- Initial voice contact between a facility and an aircraft, using the identification of the unit being called and the unit initiating the call.

(Refer to AIM.)

CALL FOR RELEASE- Wherein the overlying ARTCC requires a terminal facility to initiate verbal coordination to secure ARTCC approval for release of a departure into the en route environment.

CANADIAN MINIMUM NAVIGATION PERFORMANCE SPECIFICATION AIRSPACE- That portion of Canadian domestic airspace within which MNPS separation may be applied.

CARDINAL ALTITUDES- "Odd" or "Even" thousand-foot altitudes or flight levels; e.g., 5,000, 6,000, 7,000, FL 250, FL 260, FL 270.

(See ALTITUDE.)

(See FLIGHT LEVEL.)

CARDINAL FLIGHT LEVELS- (See CARDINAL ALTITUDES.)

CAT- (See CLEAR-AIR TURBULENCE.)

CDT PROGRAMS- (See CONTROLLED DEPARTURE TIME PROGRAMS.)

CEILING- The heights above the earth's surface of the lowest layer of clouds or obscuring phenomena that is reported as "broken," "overcast," or "obscuration," and not classified as "thin" or "partial."

(See ICAO term CEILING.)

CEILING [ICAO]- The height above the ground or water of the base of the lowest layer of cloud below 6,000 meters (20,000 feet) covering more than half the sky.

CENRAP- (See CENTER RADAR ARTS PRESENTATION/PROCESSING.)

CENRAP-PLUS- (See CENTER RADAR ARTS PRESENTATION/PROCESSING-PLUS.)

CENTER- (See AIR ROUTE TRAFFIC CONTROL CENTER.)

CENTER'S AREA- The specified airspace within which an air route traffic control center (ARTCC) provides air traffic control and advisory service.

(See AIR ROUTE TRAFFIC CONTROL CENTER.)

(Refer to AIM.)

CENTER RADAR ARTS PRESENTATION/PROCESSING- A computer program developed to provide a back-up system for airport surveillance radar in the event of a failure or malfunction. The program uses air route traffic control center radar for the processing and presentation of data on the ARTS IIA or IIIA displays.

CENTER RADAR ARTS PRESENTATION/PROCESSING-PLUS- A computer program developed to provide a back-up system for airport surveillance radar in the event of a terminal secondary radar system failure. The program uses a combination of Air Route Traffic Control Center Radar and terminal airport surveillance radar primary targets displayed simultaneously for the processing and presentation of data on the ARTS IIA or IIIA displays.

CENTER WEATHER ADVISORY- An unscheduled weather advisory issued by Center Weather Service Unit meteorologists for ATC use to alert pilots of existing or anticipated adverse weather conditions within the next 2 hours. A CWA may modify or redefine a SIGMET.

(See AWW.)

(See SIGMET.)

(See CONVECTIVE SIGMET.)

(See AIRMET.)

(Refer to AIM.)

CENTRAL EAST PACIFIC- An organized route system between the U.S. West Coast and Hawaii.

CEP- (See CENTRAL EAST PACIFIC.)

CERAP- (See COMBINED CENTER-RAPCON.)

CFR- (See CALL FOR RELEASE.)

CHAFF- Thin, narrow metallic reflectors of various lengths and frequency responses, used to reflect radar energy. These reflectors when dropped from aircraft and allowed to drift downward result in large targets on the radar display.

CHARTED VFR FLYWAYS- Charted VFR Flyways are flight paths recommended for use to bypass areas heavily traversed by large turbine-powered aircraft. Pilot compliance with recommended flyways and associated altitudes is strictly voluntary. VFR Flyway Planning charts are published on the back of existing VFR Terminal Area charts.

CHARTED VISUAL FLIGHT PROCEDURE APPROACH- An approach conducted while operating on an instrument flight rules (IFR) flight plan which authorizes the pilot of an aircraft to proceed visually and clear of clouds to the airport via visual landmarks and other information depicted on a charted visual flight procedure. This approach must be authorized and under the control of the appropriate air traffic control facility. Weather minimums required are depicted on the chart.

P/C

CHASE- An aircraft flown in proximity to another aircraft normally to observe its performance during training or testing.

CHASE AIRCRAFT- (See CHASE.)

CIRCLE-TO-LAND MANEUVER- A maneuver initiated by the pilot to align the aircraft with a runway for landing when a straight-in landing from an instrument approach is not possible or is not desirable. This maneuver is made only after ATC authorization has been obtained and the pilot has established required visual reference to the airport.

> *(See CIRCLE TO RUNWAY.)*
> *(See LANDING MINIMUMS.)*
> *(Refer to AIM.)*

CIRCLE TO RUNWAY (RUNWAY NUMBER)- Used by ATC to inform the pilot that he must circle to land because the runway in use is other than the runway aligned with the instrument approach procedure. When the direction of the circling maneuver in relation to the airport/runway is required, the controller will state the direction (eight cardinal compass points) and specify a left or right downwind or base leg as appropriate; e.g., "Cleared VOR Runway Three Six Approach circle to Runway Two Two," or "Circle northwest of the airport for a right downwind to Runway Two Two."

> *(See CIRCLE-TO-LAND MANEUVER.)*
> *(See LANDING MINIMUMS.)*
> *(Refer to AIM.)*

CIRCLING APPROACH- (See CIRCLE-TO-LAND MANEUVER.)

CIRCLING MANEUVER- (See CIRCLE-TO-LAND MANEUVER.)

CIRCLING MINIMA- (See LANDING MINIMUMS.)

CLASS A AIRSPACE- (SEE CONTROLLED AIRSPACE)

CLASS B AIRSPACE- (SEE CONTROLLED AIRSPACE)

CLASS C AIRSPACE- (SEE CONTROLLED AIRSPACE)

CLASS D AIRSPACE- (SEE CONTROLLED AIRSPACE)

CLASS E AIRSPACE- (SEE CONTROLLED AIRSPACE)

CLASS G AIRSPACE- That airspace not designated as Class A, B, C, D or E.

CLEAR-AIR TURBULENCE- Turbulence encountered in air where no clouds are present. This term is commonly applied to high-level turbulence associated with wind shear. CAT is often encountered in the vicinity of the jet stream.

> *(See WIND SHEAR.)*
> *(See JET STREAM.)*

CLEAR OF THE RUNWAY-

a. A taxiing aircraft, which is approaching a runway, is clear of the runway when all parts of the aircraft are held short of the applicable holding position marking.

b. A pilot or controller may consider an aircraft, which is exiting or crossing a runway, to be clear of the runway when all parts of the aircraft are beyond the runway edge and there is no ATC restriction to its continued movement beyond the applicable holding position marking.

c. Pilots and controllers shall exercise good judgement to ensure that adequate separation exists between all aircraft on runways and taxiways at airports with inadequate runway edge lines or holding position markings.

CLEARANCE- (See AIR TRAFFIC CLEARANCE.)

CLEARANCE LIMIT- The fix, point, or location to which an aircraft is cleared when issued an air traffic clearance.

> *(See ICAO term CLEARANCE LIMIT.)*

CLEARANCE LIMIT [ICAO]- The point of which an aircraft is granted an air traffic control clearance.

CLEARANCE VOID IF NOT OFF BY (TIME)- Used by ATC to advise an aircraft that the departure clearance is automatically canceled if takeoff is not made prior to a specified time. The pilot must obtain a new clearance or cancel his IFR flight plan if not off by the specified time.

> *(See ICAO term CLEARANCE VOID TIME.)*

CLEARANCE VOID TIME [ICAO]- A time specified by an air traffic control unit at which a clearance ceases to be valid unless the aircraft concerned has already taken action to comply therewith.

CLEARED AS FILED- Means the aircraft is cleared to proceed in accordance with the route of flight filed in the flight plan. This clearance does not include the altitude, DP, or DP Transition.

> *(See REQUEST FULL ROUTE CLEARANCE.)*
> *(Refer to AIM.)*

CLEARED (Type Of) APPROACH- ATC authorization for an aircraft to execute a specific instrument approach procedure to an airport; e.g., "Cleared ILS Runway Three Six Approach."

> *(See INSTRUMENT APPROACH PROCEDURE.)*
> *(See APPROACH CLEARANCE.)*
> *(Refer to AIM.)*
> *(Refer to FAR Part 91.)*

CLEARED APPROACH- ATC authorization for an aircraft to execute any standard or special instrument approach procedure for that airport. Normally, an aircraft will be cleared for a specific instrument approach procedure.

> *(See INSTRUMENT APPROACH PROCEDURE.)*
> *(See CLEARED (TYPE OF) APPROACH.)*
> *(Refer to AIM.)*
> *(Refer to Part 91.)*

CLEARED FOR TAKEOFF– ATC authorization for an aircraft to depart. It is predicated on known traffic and known physical airport conditions.

CLEARED FOR THE OPTION– ATC authorization for an aircraft to make a touch-and-go, low approach, missed approach, stop and go, or full stop landing at the discretion of the pilot. It is normally used in training so that an instructor can evaluate a student's performance under changing situations.

(See OPTION APPROACH.)

(Refer to AIM.)

CLEARED THROUGH– ATC authorization for an aircraft to make intermediate stops at specified airports without refiling a flight plan while en route to the clearance limit.

CLEARED TO LAND– ATC authorization for an aircraft to land. It is predicated on known traffic and known physical airport conditions.

CLEARWAY– An area beyond the takeoff runway under the control of airport authorities within which terrain or fixed obstacles may not extend above specified limits. These areas may be required for certain turbine-powered operations and the size and upward slope of the clearway will differ depending on when the aircraft was certificated.

(Refer to FAR Part 1.)

CLIMBOUT– That portion of flight operation between takeoff and the initial cruising altitude.

CLIMB TO VFR– ATC authorization for an aircraft to climb to VFR conditions within Class B, C, D, and E surface areas when the only weather limitation is restricted visibility. The aircraft must remain clear of clouds while climbing to VFR.

(See SPECIAL VFR.)

(Refer to AIM.)

CLOSE PARALLEL RUNWAYS– Two parallel runways whose extended centerlines are separated by less than 4,300 feet, having a Precision Runway Monitoring (PRM) system that permits simultaneous independent ILS approaches.

CLOSED RUNWAY– A runway that is unusable for aircraft operations. Only the airport management/military operations office can close a runway.

CLOSED TRAFFIC– Successive operations involving takeoffs and landings or low approaches where the aircraft does not exit the traffic pattern.

CLT– (See CALCULATED LANDING TIME.)

CLUTTER– In radar operations, clutter refers to the reception and visual display of radar returns caused by precipitation, chaff, terrain, numerous aircraft targets, or other phenomena. Such returns may limit or preclude ATC from providing services based on radar.

(See GROUND CLUTTER.)

(See CHAFF.)

(See PRECIPITATION.)

(See TARGET.)

(See ICAO term Radar Clutter.)

CMNPS– (See CANADIAN MINIMUM NAVIGATION PERFORMANCE SPECIFICATION AIRSPACE.)

COASTAL FIX– A navigation aid or intersection where an aircraft transitions between the domestic route structure and the oceanic route structure.

CODES– The number assigned to a particular multiple pulse reply signal transmitted by a transponder.

(See DISCRETE CODE.)

COMBINED CENTER-RAPCON– An air traffic facility which combines the functions of an ARTCC and a radar approach control facility.

(See AIR ROUTE TRAFFIC CONTROL CENTER.)

(See RADAR APPROACH CONTROL FACILITY.)

COMMON POINT– A significant point over which two or more aircraft will report passing or have reported passing before proceeding on the same or diverging tracks. To establish/maintain longitudinal separation, a controller may determine a common point not originally in the aircraft's flight plan and then clear the aircraft to fly over the point. (See SIGNIFICANT POINT.)

COMMON PORTION– (See COMMON ROUTE.)

COMMON ROUTE– That segment of a North American Route between the inland navigation facility and the coastal fix.

COMMON TRAFFIC ADVISORY FREQUENCY (CTAF)– A frequency designed for the purpose of carrying out airport advisory practices while operating to or from an airport without an operating control tower. The CTAF may be a UNICOM, Multicom, FSS, or tower frequency and is identified in appropriate aeronautical publications.

(Refer to AC 90-42, Traffic Advisory Practices at Airports Without Operating Control Towers.)

COMPASS LOCATOR– A low power, low or medium frequency (L/MF) radio beacon installed at the site of the outer or middle marker of an instrument landing system (ILS). It can be used for navigation at distances of approximately 15 miles or as authorized in the approach procedure.

a. Outer Compass Locator (LOM)– A compass locator installed at the site of the outer marker of an instrument landing system.

(See OUTER MARKER.)

b. Middle Compass Locator (LMM)– A compass locator installed at the site of the middle marker of an instrument landing system.

(See MIDDLE MARKER.)

(See ICAO term LOCATOR.)

COMPASS ROSE– A circle, graduated in degrees, printed on some charts or marked on the ground at an airport. It is used as a reference to either true or magnetic direction.

COMPOSITE FLIGHT PLAN– A flight plan which specifies VFR operation for one portion of flight and IFR for another portion. It is used primarily in military operations.

(Refer to AIM.)

COMPOSITE ROUTE SYSTEM– An organized oceanic route structure, incorporating reduced lateral spacing between routes, in which composite separation is authorized.

COMPOSITE SEPARATION– A method of separating aircraft in a composite route system where, by management of route and altitude assignments, a combination of half the lateral minimum specified for the area concerned and half the vertical minimum is applied.

COMPULSORY REPORTING POINTS– Reporting points which must be reported to ATC. They are designated on aeronautical charts by solid triangles or filed in a flight plan as fixes selected to define direct routes. These points are geographical locations which are defined by navigation aids/fixes. Pilots should discontinue position reporting over compulsory reporting points when informed by ATC that their aircraft is in "radar contact."

CONFLICT ALERT– A function of certain air traffic control automated systems designed to alert radar controllers to existing or pending situations between tracked targets (known IFR or VFR aircraft) that require his/her immediate attention/action.

(See MODE C INTRUDER ALERT.)

CONFLICT RESOLUTION– The resolution of potential conflicts between aircraft that are radar identified and in communication with ATC by ensuring that radar targets do not touch. Pertinent traffic advisories shall be issued when this procedure is applied.

Note: This procedure shall not be provided utilizing mosaic radar systems.

CONSOLAN– A low frequency, long-distance NAVAID used principally for transoceanic navigations.

CONTACT–

a. Establish communication with (followed by the name of the facility and, if appropriate, the frequency to be used).

b. A flight condition wherein the pilot ascertains the attitude of his aircraft and navigates by visual reference to the surface.

(See CONTACT APPROACH.)

(See RADAR CONTACT.)

CONTACT APPROACH– An approach wherein an aircraft on an IFR flight plan, having an air traffic control authorization, operating clear of clouds with at least 1 mile flight visibility and a reasonable expectation of continuing to the destination airport in those conditions, may deviate from the instrument approach procedure and proceed to the destination airport by visual reference to the surface. This approach will only be authorized when requested by the pilot and the reported ground visibility at the destination airport is at least 1 statute mile.

(Refer to AIM.)

CONTAMINATED RUNWAY– A runway is considered contaminated whenever standing water, ice, snow, slush, frost in any form, heavy rubber, or other substances are present. A runway is contaminated with respect to rubber deposits or other friction–degrading substances when the average friction value for any 500–foot segment of the runway within the ALD falls below the recommended minimum friction level and the average friction value in the adjacent 500–foot segments falls below the maintenance planning friction level.

CONTERMINOUS U.S.– The 48 adjoining States and the District of Columbia.

CONTINENTAL UNITED STATES– The 49 States located on the continent of North America and the District of Columbia.

CONTROL AREA [ICAO]– A controlled airspace extending upwards from a specified limit above the earth.

CONTROLLED AIRSPACE– An airspace of defined dimensions within which air traffic control service is provided to IFR flights and to VFR flights in accordance with the airspace classification.

a. Controlled airspace is a generic term that covers Class A, Class B, Class C, Class D, and Class E airspace.

b. Controlled airspace is also that airspace within which all aircraft operators are subject to certain pilot qualifications, operating rules, and equipment requirements in FAR Part 91 (for specific operating requirements, please refer to FAR Part 91). For IFR operations in any class of controlled airspace, a pilot must file an IFR flight plan and receive an appropriate ATC clearance. Each Class B, Class C, and Class D airspace area designated for an airport contains at least one primary airport around which the airspace is designated (for specific designations and descriptions of the airspace classes, please refer to FAR Part 71).

c. Controlled airspace in the United States is designated as follows:

1. CLASS A–Generally, that airspace from 18,000 feet MSL up to and including FL 600, including the airspace overlying the waters within 12 nautical miles of the coast of the 48 contiguous States and Alaska. Unless otherwise authorized, all persons must operate their aircraft under IFR.

2. CLASS B–Generally, that airspace from the surface to 10,000 feet MSL surrounding the nation's busiest airports in terms of airport operations or passenger enplanements. The configuration of each Class B airspace area is individually tailored and consists of a surface area and two or more layers (some Class B airspaces areas resemble upside-down wedding cakes), and is designed to contain all published instrument procedures once an aircraft enters the airspace. An ATC clearance is required for all aircraft to operate in the area, and all aircraft that are so cleared receive separation services within the airspace. The cloud clearance requirement for VFR operations is "clear of clouds."

3. CLASS C–Generally, that airspace from the surface to 4,000 feet above the airport elevation (charted in MSL) surrounding those airports that have an operational control tower, are serviced by a radar approach control, and that have a certain number of IFR operations or passenger enplanements. Although the configuration of each Class C area is individually tailored, the airspace usually consists of a surface area with a 5 nautical mile (NM) radius, an outer circle with a 10NM radius that extends from 1,200 feet to 4,000 feet above the airport elevation and an outer area. Each person must establish two-way radio communications with the ATC facility providing air traffic services prior to entering the airspace and thereafter maintain those communications while within the airspace. VFR aircraft are only separated from IFR aircraft within the airspace. (See OUTER AREA)

4. CLASS D–Generally, that airspace from the surface to 2,500 feet above the airport elevation (charted in MSL) surrounding those airports that have an operational control tower. The configuration of each Class D airspace area is individually tailored and when instrument procedures are published, the airspace will normally be designed to contain the procedures. Arrival extensions for instrument approach procedures may be Class D or Class E airspace. Unless otherwise authorized, each person must establish two-way radio communications with the ATC facility providing air traffic services prior to entering the airspace and thereafter maintain those communications while in the airspace. No separation services are provided to VFR aircraft.

5. CLASS E– Generally, if the airspace is not Class A, Class B, Class C, or Class D, and it is controlled airspace, it is Class E airspace. Class E airspace extends upward from either the surface or a designated altitude to the overlying or adjacent controlled airspace. When designated as a surface area, the airspace will be configured to contain all instrument procedures. Also in this class are Federal airways, airspace beginning at either 700 or 1,200 feet AGL used to tran-

sition to/from the terminal or en route environment, en route domestic, and offshore airspace areas designated below 18,000 feet MSL. Unless designated at a lower altitude, Class E airspace begins at 14,500 MSL over the United States, including that airspace overlying the waters within 12 nautical miles of the coast of the 48 contiguous States and Alaska, up to, but not including 18,000 feet MSL, and the airspace above FL 600.

CONTROLLED AIRSPACE [ICAO]– An airspace of defined dimensions within which air traffic control service is provided to IFR flights and to VFR flights in accordance with the airspace classification.

(Note: Controlled airspace is a generic term which covers ATS airspace Classes A, B, C, D, and E.)

CONTROLLED DEPARTURE TIME PROGRAMS– These programs are the flow control process whereby aircraft are held on the ground at the departure airport when delays are projected to occur in either the en route system or the terminal of intended landing. The purpose of these programs is to reduce congestion in the air traffic system or to limit the duration of airborne holding in the arrival center or terminal area. A CDT is a specific departure slot shown on the flight plan as an expected departure clearance time (EDCT).

CONTROLLED TIME OF ARRIVAL– The original estimated time of arrival adjusted by the ATCSCC ground delay factor.

CONTROLLER– (See AIR TRAFFIC CONTROL SPECIALIST.)

CONTROLLER [ICAO]– A person authorized to provide air traffic control services.

CONTROL SECTOR– An airspace area of defined horizontal and vertical dimensions for which a controller or group of controllers has air traffic control responsibility, normally within an air route traffic control center or an approach control facility. Sectors are established based on predominant traffic flows, altitude strata, and controller workload. Pilot-communications during operations within a sector are normally maintained on discrete frequencies assigned to the sector.

(See DISCRETE FREQUENCY.)

CONTROL SLASH– A radar beacon slash representing the actual position of the associated aircraft. Normally, the control slash is the one closest to the interrogating radar beacon site. When ARTCC radar is operating in narrowband (digitized) mode, the control slash is converted to a target symbol.

CONVECTIVE SIGMET– A weather advisory concerning convective weather significant to the safety of all aircraft. Convective SIGMET's are issued for tornadoes, lines of thunderstorms, embedded thunderstorms of any intensity level, areas of thunderstorms greater than or equal to VIP

P/C

level 4 with an area coverage of $^4/_{10}$ (40%) or more, and hail $^3/_4$ inch or greater.

(See AWW.)
(See SIGMET.)
(See CWA.)
(See AIRMET.)
(Refer to AIM.)

CONVECTIVE SIGNIFICANT METEOROLOGICAL INFORMATION– (See CONVECTIVE SIGMET.)

COORDINATES– The intersection of lines of reference, usually expressed in degrees/minutes/seconds of latitude and longitude, used to determine position or location.

COORDINATION FIX– The fix in relation to which facilities will handoff, transfer control of an aircraft, or coordinate flight progress data. For terminal facilities, it may also serve as a clearance for arriving aircraft.

COPTER– (See HELICOPTER.)

CORRECTION– An error has been made in the transmission and the correct version follows.

COUPLED APPROACH– A coupled approach is an instrument approach performed by the aircraft autopilot which is receiving position information and/or steering commands from onboard navigation equipment. In general, coupled nonprecision approaches must be discontinued and flown manually at altitudes lower than 50 feet below the minimum descent altitude, and coupled precision approaches must be flown manually below 50 feet AGL.

(See AUTOLAND APPROACH.)

Note: Coupled and autoland approaches are flown in VFR and IFR. It is common for carriers to require their crews to fly coupled approaches and autoland approaches (if certified) when the weather conditions are less than approximately 4,000 RVR.

COURSE–

a. The intended direction of flight in the horizontal plane measured in degrees from north.

b. The ILS localizer signal pattern usually specified as the front course or the back course.

c. The intended track along a straight, curved, or segmented MLS path.

(See BEARING.)
(See RADIAL.)
(See INSTRUMENT LANDING SYSTEM.)
(See MICROWAVE LANDING SYSTEM.)

CPL [ICAO]– (See CURRENT FLIGHT PLAN)

CRITICAL ENGINE– The engine which, upon failure, would most adversely affect the performance or handling qualities of an aircraft.

CROSS (FIX) AT (ALTITUDE)– Used by ATC when a specific altitude restriction at a specified fix is required.

CROSS (FIX) AT OR ABOVE (ALTITUDE)– Used by ATC when an altitude restriction at a specified fix is required. It does not prohibit the aircraft from crossing the fix at a higher altitude than specified; however, the higher altitude may not be one that will violate a succeeding altitude restriction or altitude assignment.

(See ALTITUDE RESTRICTION.)
(Refer to AIM.)

CROSS (FIX) AT OR BELOW (ALTITUDE)– Used by ATC when a maximum crossing altitude at a specific fix is required. It does not prohibit the aircraft from crossing the fix at a lower altitude; however, it must be at or above the minimum IFR altitude.

(See MINIMUM IFR ALTITUDES.)
(See ALTITUDE RESTRICTION.)
(Refer to FAR Part 91.)

CROSSWIND–

a. When used concerning the traffic pattern, the word means "crosswind leg."

(See TRAFFIC PATTERN.)

b. When used concerning wind conditions, the word means a wind not parallel to the runway or the path of an aircraft.

(See CROSSWIND COMPONENT.)

CROSSWIND COMPONENT– The wind component measured in knots at 90 degrees to the longitudinal axis of the runway.

CRUISE– Used in an ATC clearance to authorize a pilot to conduct flight at any altitude from the minimum IFR altitude up to and including the altitude specified in the clearance. The pilot may level off at any intermediate altitude within this block of airspace. Climb/descent within the block is to be made at the discretion of the pilot. However, once the pilot starts descent and verbally reports leaving an altitude in the block, he may not return to that altitude without additional ATC clearance. Further, it is approval for the pilot to proceed to and make an approach at destination airport and can be used in conjunction with:

a. An airport clearance limit at locations with a standard/special instrument approach procedure. The FAR's require that if an instrument letdown to an airport is necessary, the pilot shall make the letdown in accordance with a standard/special instrument approach procedure for that airport, or

b. An airport clearance limit at locations that are within/below/outside controlled airspace and without a standard/special instrument approach procedure. Such a clearance is NOT AUTHORIZATION for the pilot to descend under IFR conditions below the applicable minimum IFR altitude nor does it imply that ATC is exercising control over aircraft in Class G airspace; however, it provides a means for the aircraft to proceed to destination airport, descend, and land in accordance with applicable FAR's governing VFR flight operations. Also, this provides search and rescue protection until such time as the IFR flight plan is closed.

(See INSTRUMENT APPROACH
PROCEDURE.)

CRUISING ALTITUDE– An altitude or flight level maintained during en route level flight. This is a constant altitude and should not be confused with a cruise clearance.

(See ALTITUDE.)
(See ICAO term CRUISING LEVEL.)

CRUISING LEVEL [ICAO]– A level maintained during a significant portion of a flight.

CRUISE CLIMB– A climb technique employed by aircraft, usually at a constant power setting, resulting in an increase of altitude as the aircraft weight decreases.

CRUISING LEVEL– (See CRUISING ALTITUDE.)

CT MESSAGE– An EDCT time generated by the ATCSCC to regulate traffic at arrival airports. Normally, a CT message is automatically transferred from the Traffic Management System computer to the NAS en route computer and appears as an EDCT. In the event of a communication failure between the TMS and the NAS, the CT message can be manually entered by the TMC at the en route facility.

CTA– (See CONTROLLED TIME OF ARRIVAL.)

CTA– (See CONTROL AREA [ICAO].)

CTAF– (See COMMON TRAFFIC ADVISORY FREQUENCY.)

CURRENT FLIGHT PLAN [ICAO]– The flight plan, including changes, if any, brought about by subsequent clearances.

CVFP APPROACH– (See CHARTED VISUAL FLIGHT PROCEDURE APPROACH.)

CWA– (See CENTER WEATHER ADVISORY and *WEATHER ADVISORY.)*

P/C

D

DA [ICAO]– (See ICAO Term DECISION ALTITUDE/DE-CISION HEIGHT.)

DAIR– (See DIRECT ALTITUDE AND IDENTITY READOUT.)

DANGER AREA [ICAO]– An airspace of defined dimensions within which activities dangerous to the flight of aircraft may exist at specified times.

Note: The term "Danger Area" is not used in reference to areas within the United States or any of its possessions or territories.

DATA BLOCK– (See ALPHANUMERIC DISPLAY.)

DEAD RECKONING– Dead reckoning, as applied to flying, is the navigation of an airplane solely by means of computations based on airspeed, course, heading, wind direction, and speed, groundspeed, and elapsed time.

DECISION ALTITUDE/DECISION HEIGHT [ICAO]–
A specified altitude or height (A/H) in the precision approach at which a missed approach must be initiated if the required visual reference to continue the approach has not been established.

Note 1: Decision altitude [DA] is referenced to mean sea level [MSL] and decision height [DH] is referenced to the threshold elevation.

Note 2: The required visual reference means that section of the visual aids or of the approach area which should have been in view for sufficient time for the pilot to have made an assessment of the aircraft position and rate of change of position, in relation to the desired flight path.

DECISION HEIGHT– With respect to the operation of aircraft, means the height at which a decision must be made during an ILS, MLS, or PAR instrument approach to either continue the approach or to execute a missed approach.

(See ICAO term DECISION ALTITUDE/ DECISION HEIGHT.)

DECODER– The device used to decipher signals received from ATCRBS transponders to effect their display as select codes.

(See CODES.)

(See RADAR.)

DEFENSE VISUAL FLIGHT RULES– Rules applicable to flights within an ADIZ conducted under the visual flight rules in FAR Part 91.

(See AIR DEFENSE IDENTIFICATION ZONE.)

(Refer to FAR Part 91.)

(Refer to FAR Part 99.)

DELAY INDEFINITE (REASON IF KNOWN) EXPECT FURTHER CLEARANCE (TIME)– Used by ATC to inform a pilot when an accurate estimate of the delay time and the reason for the delay cannot immediately be determined; e.g., a disabled aircraft on the runway, terminal or center area saturation, weather below landing minimums, etc.

(See EXPECT FURTHER CLEARANCE (TIME).)

DELAY TIME– The amount of time that the arrival must lose to cross the meter fix at the assigned meter fix time. This is the difference between ACLT and VTA.

DEPARTURE CENTER– The ARTCC having jurisdiction for the airspace that generates a flight to the impacted airport.

DEPARTURE CONTROL– A function of an approach control facility providing air traffic control service for departing IFR and, under certain conditions, VFR aircraft.

(See APPROACH CONTROL FACILITY.)

(Refer to AIM.)

DEPARTURE SEQUENCING PROGRAM– A program designed to assist in achieving a specified interval over a common point for departures.

DEPARTURE TIME– The time an aircraft becomes airborne.

DESCENT SPEED ADJUSTMENTS– Speed deceleration calculations made to determine an accurate VTA. These calculations start at the transition point and use arrival speed segments to the vertex.

DESIRED COURSE–

a. True– A predetermined desired course direction to be followed (measured in degrees from true north).

b. Magnetic– A predetermined desired course direction to be followed (measured in degrees from local magnetic north).

DESIRED TRACK– The planned or intended track between two waypoints. It is measured in degrees from either magnetic or true north. The instantaneous angle may change from point to point along the great circle track between waypoints.

DETRESFA (DISTRESS PHASE) [ICAO]– The code word used to designate an emergency phase wherein there is reasonable certainty that an aircraft and its occupants are threatened by grave and imminent danger or require immediate assistance.

DEVIATIONS–

a. A departure from a current clearance, such as an off course maneuver to avoid weather or turbulence.

b. Where specifically authorized in the FAR's and requested by the pilot, ATC may permit pilots to deviate from certain regulations.

(Refer to AIM.)

DF– (See DIRECTION FINDER.)

DF APPROACH PROCEDURE– Used under emergency conditions where another instrument approach procedure cannot be executed. DF guidance for an instrument approach is given by ATC facilities with DF capability.

(See DF GUIDANCE.)

(See DIRECTION FINDER.)

(Refer to AIM.)

DF FIX– The geographical location of an aircraft obtained by one or more direction finders.

(See DIRECTION FINDER.)

DF GUIDANCE– Headings provided to aircraft by facilities equipped with direction finding equipment. These headings, if followed, will lead the aircraft to a predetermined point such as the DF station or an airport. DF guidance is given to aircraft in distress or to other aircraft which request the service. Practice DF guidance is provided when workload permits.

(See DIRECTION FINDER.)

(See DF FIX.)

(Refer to AIM.)

DF STEER– (See DF GUIDANCE.)

DH– (See DECISION HEIGHT.)

DH [ICAO]– (See ICAO Term DECISION ALTITUDE/ DECISION HEIGHT.)

DIRECT– Straight line flight between two navigational aids, fixes, points, or any combination thereof. When used by pilots in describing off-airway routes, points defining direct route segments become compulsory reporting points unless the aircraft is under radar contact.

DIRECT ALTITUDE AND IDENTITY READOUT– The DAIR System is a modification to the AN/TPX-42 Interrogator System. The Navy has two adaptations of the DAIR System-Carrier Air Traffic Control Direct Altitude and Identification Readout System for Aircraft Carriers and Radar Air Traffic Control Facility Direct Altitude and Identity Readout System for land-based terminal operations. The

DAIR detects, tracks, and predicts secondary radar aircraft targets. Targets are displayed by means of computer-generated symbols and alphanumeric characters depicting flight identification, altitude, ground speed, and flight plan data. The DAIR System is capable of interfacing with ARTCC's.

DIRECTION FINDER– A radio receiver equipped with a directional sensing antenna used to take bearings on a radio transmitter. Specialized radio direction finders are used in aircraft as air navigation aids. Others are ground-based, primarily to obtain a "fix" on a pilot requesting orientation assistance or to locate downed aircraft. A location "fix" is established by the intersection of two or more bearing lines plotted on a navigational chart using either two separately located Direction Finders to obtain a fix on an aircraft or by a pilot plotting the bearing indications of his DF on two separately located ground-based transmitters, both of which can be identified on his chart. UDF's receive signals in the ultra high frequency radio broadcast band; VDF's in the very high frequency band; and UVDF's in both bands. ATC provides DF service at those air traffic control towers and flight service stations listed in the Airport/Facility Directory and the DOD FLIP IFR En Route Supplement.

(See DF GUIDANCE.)

(See DF FIX.)

DISCRETE BEACON CODE– (See DISCRETE CODE.)

DISCRETE CODE– As used in the Air Traffic Control Radar Beacon System (ATCRBS), any one of the 4096 selectable Mode 3/A aircraft transponder codes except those ending in zero zero; e.g., discrete codes: 0010, 1201, 2317, 7777; nondiscrete codes: 0100, 1200, 7700. Nondiscrete codes are normally reserved for radar facilities that are not equipped with discrete decoding capability and for other purposes such as emergencies (7700), VFR aircraft (1200), etc.

(See RADAR.)

(Refer to AIM.)

DISCRETE FREQUENCY– A separate radio frequency for use in direct pilot-controller communications in air traffic control which reduces frequency congestion by controlling the number of aircraft operating on a particular frequency at one time. Discrete frequencies are normally designated for each control sector in en route/terminal ATC facilities. Discrete frequencies are listed in the Airport/Facility Directory and the DOD FLIP IFR En Route Supplement.

(See CONTROL SECTOR.)

DISPLACED THRESHOLD– A threshold that is located at a point on the runway other than the designated beginning of the runway.

(See THRESHOLD.)

(Refer to AIM.)

DISTANCE MEASURING EQUIPMENT– Equipment (airborne and ground) used to measure, in nautical miles, the slant range distance of an aircraft from the DME navigational aid.

(See TACAN.)

(See VORTAC.)

(See MICROWAVE LANDING SYSTEM.)

DISTRESS– A condition of being threatened by serious and/or imminent danger and of requiring immediate assistance.

DIVE BRAKES– (See SPEED BRAKES.)

DIVERSE VECTOR AREA– In a radar environment, that area in which a prescribed departure route is not required as the only suitable route to avoid obstacles. The area in which random radar vectors below the MVA/MIA, established in accordance with the TERPS criteria for diverse departures, obstacles and terrain avoidance, may be issued to departing aircraft.

DME– (See DISTANCE MEASURING EQUIPMENT.)

DME FIX– A geographical position determined by reference to a navigational aid which provides distance and azimuth information. It is defined by a specific distance in nautical miles and a radial, azimuth, or course (i.e., localizer) in degrees magnetic from that aid.

(See DISTANCE MEASURING EQUIPMENT.)

(See FIX.)

(See MICROWAVE LANDING SYSTEM.)

DME SEPARATION– Spacing of aircraft in terms of distances (nautical miles) determined by reference to distance measuring equipment (DME).

(See DISTANCE MEASURING EQUIPMENT.)

DOD FLIP– Department of Defense Flight Information Publications used for flight planning, en route, and terminal operations. FLIP is produced by the National Imagery and Mapping Agency (NIMA) for world-wide use. United States Government Flight Information Publications (en route charts and instrument approach procedure charts) are incorporated in DOD FLIP for use in the National Airspace System (NAS).

DOMESTIC AIRSPACE– Airspace which overlies the continental land mass of the United States plus Hawaii and U.S. possessions. Domestic airspace extends to 12 miles offshore.

DOWNBURST– A strong downdraft which induces an outburst of damaging winds on or near the ground. Damaging winds, either straight or curved, are highly divergent. The sizes of downbursts vary from 1/2 mile or less to more than 10 miles. An intense downburst often causes widespread damage. Damaging winds, lasting 5 to 30 minutes, could reach speeds as high as 120 knots.

DOWNWIND LEG– (See TRAFFIC PATTERN.)

DRAG CHUTE– A parachute device installed on certain aircraft which is deployed on landing roll to assist in deceleration of the aircraft.

DSP– (See DEPARTURE SEQUENCING PROGRAM.)

DT– (See DELAY TIME.)

DUE REGARD– A phase of flight wherein an aircraft commander of a State-operated aircraft assumes responsibility to separate his aircraft from all other aircraft.

(See also FAA Order 7110.65,
paragraph 1–2–1, WORD MEANINGS.)

DUTY RUNWAY– (See RUNWAY IN USE/ACTIVE RUNWAY/DUTY RUNWAY.)

DVA– (See DIVERSE VECTOR AREA.)

DVFR– (See DEFENSE VISUAL FLIGHT RULES.)

DVFR FLIGHT PLAN– A flight plan filed for a VFR aircraft which intends to operate in airspace within which the ready identification, location, and control of aircraft are required in the interest of national security.

DYNAMIC– Continuous review, evaluation, and change to meet demands.

DYNAMIC RESTRICTIONS– Those restrictions imposed by the local facility on an "as needed" basis to manage unpredictable fluctuations in traffic demands.

P/C

E

EARTS– (See EN ROUTE AUTOMATED RADAR TRACKING SYSTEM.)

EDCT– (See EXPECTED DEPARTURE CLEARANCE TIME.)

EFC– (See EXPECT FURTHER CLEARANCE (TIME).)

ELT– (See EMERGENCY LOCATOR TRANSMITTER.)

EMERGENCY– A distress or an urgency condition.

EMERGENCY LOCATOR TRANSMITTER– A radio transmitter attached to the aircraft structure which operates from its own power source on 121.5 MHz and 243.0 MHz. It aids in locating downed aircraft by radiating a downward sweeping audio tone, 2-4 times per second. It is designed to function without human action after an accident.

(Refer to FAR Part 91.)

(Refer to AIM.)

E-MSAW– (See EN ROUTE MINIMUM SAFE ALTITUDE WARNING.)

ENGINEERED PERFORMANCE STANDARDS– A mathematically derived runway capacity standard. EPS's are calculated for each airport on an individual basis and reflect that airport's aircraft mix, operating procedures, runway layout, and specific weather conditions. EPS's do not give consideration to staffing, experience levels, equipment outages, and in-trail restrictions as does the AAR.

EN ROUTE AIR TRAFFIC CONTROL SERVICES– Air traffic control service provided aircraft on IFR flight plans, generally by centers, when these aircraft are operating between departure and destination terminal areas. When equipment, capabilities, and controller workload permit, certain advisory/assistance services may be provided to VFR aircraft.

(See NAS STAGE A.)

(See AIR ROUTE TRAFFIC CONTROL CENTER.)

(Refer to AIM.)

EN ROUTE AUTOMATED RADAR TRACKING SYSTEM– An automated radar and radar beacon tracking system. Its functional capabilities and design are essentially the same as the terminal ARTS IIIA system except for the EARTS capability of employing both short-range (ASR) and long-range (ARSR) radars, use of full digital radar displays, and fail-safe design.

(See AUTOMATED RADAR TERMINAL SYSTEMS.)

EN ROUTE CHARTS– (See AERONAUTICAL CHART.)

EN ROUTE DESCENT– Descent from the en route cruising altitude which takes place along the route of flight.

EN ROUTE FLIGHT ADVISORY SERVICE– A service specifically designed to provide, upon pilot request, timely weather information pertinent to his type of flight, intended route of flight, and altitude. The FSS's providing this service are listed in the Airport/Facility Directory.

(See FLIGHT WATCH.)

(Refer to AIM.)

EN ROUTE HIGH ALTITUDE CHARTS– (See AERONAUTICAL CHART.)

EN ROUTE LOW ALTITUDE CHARTS– (See AERONAUTICAL CHART.)

EN ROUTE MINIMUM SAFE ALTITUDE WARNING– A function of the NAS Stage A en route computer that aids the controller by alerting him when a tracked aircraft is below or predicted by the computer to go below a predetermined minimum IFR altitude (MIA).

EN ROUTE SPACING PROGRAM– A program designed to assist the exit sector in achieving the required in-trail spacing.

EPS– (See ENGINEERED PERFORMANCE STANDARDS.)

ESP– (See EN ROUTE SPACING PROGRAM.)

ESTABLISHED– To be stable or fixed on a route, route segment, altitude, heading, etc.

ESTIMATED ELAPSED TIME [ICAO]– The estimated time required to proceed from one significant point to another.

(See ICAO Term TOTAL ESTIMATED ELAPSED TIME.)

ESTIMATED OFF-BLOCK TIME [ICAO]– The estimated time at which the aircraft will commence movement associated with departure.

ESTIMATED TIME OF ARRIVAL– The time the flight is estimated to arrive at the gate (scheduled operators) or the actual runway on times for nonscheduled operators.

ESTIMATED TIME EN ROUTE– The estimated flying time from departure point to destination (lift-off to touchdown).

ETA– (See ESTIMATED TIME OF ARRIVAL.)

ETE– (See ESTIMATED TIME EN ROUTE.)

EXECUTE MISSED APPROACH– Instructions issued to a pilot making an instrument approach which means continue inbound to the missed approach point and execute the missed approach procedure as described on the Instrument Approach Procedure Chart or as previously assigned by ATC. The pilot may climb immediately to the altitude specified in the missed approach procedure upon making a missed

P/C

approach. No turns should be initiated prior to reaching the missed approach point. When conducting an ASR or PAR approach, execute the assigned missed approach procedure immediately upon receiving instructions to "execute missed approach."

(Refer to AIM.)

EXPECT (ALTITUDE) AT (TIME) or (FIX)– Used under certain conditions to provide a pilot with an altitude to be used in the event of two-way communications failure. It also provides altitude information to assist the pilot in planning.

(Refer to AIM.)

EXPECTED DEPARTURE CLEARANCE TIME– The runway release time assigned to an aircraft in a controlled departure time program and shown on the flight progress strip as an EDCT.

EXPECT FURTHER CLEARANCE (TIME)– The time a pilot can expect to receive clearance beyond a clearance limit.

EXPECT FURTHER CLEARANCE VIA (AIRWAYS, ROUTES OR FIXES)– Used to inform a pilot of the routing he can expect if any part of the route beyond a short range clearance limit differs from that filed.

EXPEDITE– Used by ATC when prompt compliance is required to avoid the development of an imminent situation.

F

FAF– (See FINAL APPROACH FIX.)

FAST FILE– A system whereby a pilot files a flight plan via telephone that is tape recorded and then transcribed for transmission to the appropriate air traffic facility. Locations having a fast file capability are contained in the Airport/Facility Directory.

(Refer to AIM.)

FAWP– Final Approach Waypoint

FCLT– (See FREEZE CALCULATED LANDING TIME.)

FEATHERED PROPELLER– A propeller whose blades have been rotated so that the leading and trailing edges are nearly parallel with the aircraft flight path to stop or minimize drag and engine rotation. Normally used to indicate shutdown of a reciprocating or turboprop engine due to malfunction.

FEDERAL AIRWAYS– (See LOW ALTITUDE AIRWAY STRUCTURE.)

FEEDER FIX– The fix depicted on Instrument Approach Procedure Charts which establishes the starting point of the feeder route.

FEEDER ROUTE– A route depicted on instrument approach procedure charts to designate routes for aircraft to proceed from the en route structure to the initial approach fix (IAF).

(See INSTRUMENT APPROACH PROCEDURE.)

FERRY FLIGHT– A flight for the purpose of:

a. Returning an aircraft to base.

b. Delivering an aircraft from one location to another.

c. Moving an aircraft to and from a maintenance base.– Ferry flights, under certain conditions, may be conducted under terms of a special flight permit.

FIELD ELEVATION– (See AIRPORT ELEVATION.)

FILED– Normally used in conjunction with flight plans, meaning a flight plan has been submitted to ATC.

FILED EN ROUTE DELAY– Any of the following preplanned delays at points/areas along the route of flight which require special flight plan filing and handling techniques.

a. Terminal Area Delay. A delay within a terminal area for touch-and-go, low approach, or other terminal area activity.

b. Special Use Airspace Delay. A delay within a Military Operations Area, Restricted Area, Warning Area, or ATC Assigned Airspace.

c. Aerial Refueling Delay. A delay within an Aerial Refueling Track or Anchor.

FILED FLIGHT PLAN– The flight plan as filed with an ATS unit by the pilot or his designated representative without any subsequent changes or clearances.

FINAL– Commonly used to mean that an aircraft is on the final approach course or is aligned with a landing area.

(See FINAL APPROACH COURSE.)

(See FINAL APPROACH-IFR.)

(See SEGMENTS OF AN INSTRUMENT APPROACH PROCEDURE.)

FINAL APPROACH [ICAO]– That part of an instrument approach procedure which commences at the specified final approach fix or point, or where such a fix or point is not specified,

a. At the end of the last procedure turn, base turn or inbound turn of a racetrack procedure, if specified; or

b. At the point of interception of the last track specified in the approach procedure; and ends at a point in the vicinity of an aerodrome from which:

1. A landing can be made; or

2. A missed approach procedure is initiated.

FINAL APPROACH COURSE– A bearing/radial/track of an instrument approach leading to a runway or an extended runway centerline all without regard to distance.

FINAL APPROACH FIX– The fix from which the final approach (IFR) to an airport is executed and which identifies the beginning of the final approach segment. It is designated on Government charts by the Maltese Cross symbol for non-precision approaches and the lightning bolt symbol for precision approaches; or when ATC directs a lower-than-published glideslope/path intercept altitude, it is the resultant actual point of the glideslope/path intercept.

(See FINAL APPROACH POINT.)

(See GLIDESLOPE INTERCEPT ALTITUDE.)

(See SEGMENTS OF AN INSTRUMENT APPROACH PROCEDURE.)

FINAL APPROACH-IFR– The flight path of an aircraft which is inbound to an airport on a final instrument approach course, beginning at the final approach fix or point and extending to the airport or the point where a circle-to-land maneuver or a missed approach is executed.

(See SEGMENTS OF AN INSTRUMENT APPROACH PROCEDURE.)

(See FINAL APPROACH FIX.)

(See FINAL APPROACH COURSE.)

(See FINAL APPROACH POINT.)

(See ICAO term FINAL APPROACH.)

FINAL APPROACH POINT- The point, applicable only to a nonprecision approach with no depicted FAF (such as an on airport VOR), where the aircraft is established inbound on the final approach course from the procedure turn and where the final approach descent may be commenced. The FAP serves as the FAF and identifies the beginning of the final approach segment.

(See FINAL APPROACH FIX.)

(See SEGMENTS OF AN INSTRUMENT APPROACH PROCEDURE.)

FINAL APPROACH SEGMENT- (See SEGMENTS OF AN INSTRUMENT APPROACH PROCEDURE.)

FINAL APPROACH SEGMENT [ICAO]- That segment of an instrument approach procedure in which alignment and descent for landing are accomplished.

FINAL CONTROLLER- The controller providing information and final approach guidance during PAR and ASR approaches utilizing radar equipment.

(See RADAR APPROACH.)

FINAL MONITOR AID- A high resolution color display that is equipped with the controller alert system hardware/software which is used in the precision runway monitor (PRM) system. The display includes alert algorithms providing the target predictors, a color change alert when a target penetrates or is predicted to penetrate the no transgression zone (NTZ), a color change alert if the aircraft transponder becomes inoperative, synthesized voice alerts, digital mapping, and like features contained in the PRM system.

(See RADAR APPROACH.)

FINAL MONITOR CONTROLLER- Air Traffic Control Specialist assigned to radar monitor the flight path of aircraft during simultaneous parallel and simultaneous close parallel ILS approach operations. Each runway is assigned a final monitor controller during simultaneous parallel and simultaneous close parallel ILS approaches. Final monitor controllers shall utilize the Precision Runway Monitor (PRM) system during simultaneous close parallel ILS approaches.

FIR- (See FLIGHT INFORMATION REGION.)

FIRST TIER CENTER- The ARTCC immediately adjacent to the impacted center.

FIX- A geographical position determined by visual reference to the surface, by reference to one or more radio NAVAID's, by celestial plotting, or by another navigational device.

FIX BALANCING- A process whereby aircraft are evenly distributed over several available arrival fixes reducing delays and controller workload.

FLAG- A warning device incorporated in certain airborne navigation and flight instruments indicating that:

a. Instruments are inoperative or otherwise not operating satisfactorily, or

b. Signal strength or quality of the received signal falls below acceptable values.

FLAG ALARM- (See FLAG.)

FLAMEOUT- An emergency condition caused by a loss of engine power.

FLAMEOUT PATTERN –An approach normally conducted by a single–engine military aircraft experiencing loss or anticipating loss of engine power or control. The standard overhead approach starts at a relatively high altitude over a runway ("high key") followed by a continuous 180 degree turn to a high, wide position ("low key") followed by a continuous 180 degree turn final. The standard straight–in pattern starts at a point that results in a straight–in approach with a high rate of descent to the runway. Flameout approaches terminate in the type approach requested by the pilot (normally fullstop).

FLIGHT CHECK- A call-sign prefix used by FAA aircraft engaged in flight inspection/certification of navigational aids and flight procedures. The word "recorded" may be added as a suffix; e.g., "Flight Check 320 recorded" to indicate that an automated flight inspection is in progress in terminal areas.

(See FLIGHT INSPECTION.)

(Refer to AIM.)

FLIGHT FOLLOWING- (See TRAFFIC ADVISORIES.)

FLIGHT INFORMATION REGION- An airspace of defined dimensions within which Flight Information Service and Alerting Service are provided.

a. Flight Information Service. A service provided for the purpose of giving advice and information useful for the safe and efficient conduct of flights.

b. Alerting Service. A service provided to notify appropriate organizations regarding aircraft in need of search and rescue aid and to assist such organizations as required.

FLIGHT INFORMATION SERVICE- A service provided for the purpose of giving advice and information useful for the safe and efficient conduct of flights.

FLIGHT INSPECTION- Inflight investigation and evaluation of a navigational aid to determine whether it meets established tolerances.

(See NAVIGATIONAL AID.)

(See FLIGHT CHECK.)

FLIGHT LEVEL –A level of constant atmospheric pressure related to a reference datum of 29.92 inches of mercury. Each is stated in three digits that represent hundreds of feet. For example, flight level (FL) 250 represents a barometric altimeter indication of 25,000 feet; FL 255, an indication of 25,500 feet.

(See ICAO term FLIGHT LEVEL.)

FLIGHT LEVEL [ICAO]– A surface of constant atmospheric pressure which is related to a specific pressure datum, 013.2 hPa (1013.2 mb), and is separated from other such surfaces by specific pressure intervals.

Note 1: A pressure type altimeter calibrated in accordance with the standard atmosphere:

a. When set to a QNH altimeter setting, will indicate altitude;

b. When set to a QFE altimeter setting, will indicate height above the QFE reference datum; and

c. When set to a pressure of 1013.2 hPa (1013.2 mb), may be used to indicate flight levels.

Note 2: The terms 'height' and 'altitude,' used in Note 1 above, indicate altimetric rather than geometric heights and altitudes.

FLIGHT LINE– A term used to describe the precise movement of a civil photogrammetric aircraft along a predetermined course(s) at a predetermined altitude during the actual photographic run.

FLIGHT MANAGEMENT SYSTEMS– A computer system that uses a large data base to allow routes to be preprogrammed and fed into the system by means of a data loader. The system is constantly updated with respect to position accuracy by reference to conventional navigation aids. The sophisticated program and its associated data base insures that the most appropriate aids are automatically selected during the information update cycle.

FLIGHT MANAGEMENT SYSTEM PROCEDURE– An arrival, departure, or approach procedure developed for use by aircraft with a slant (/) E or slant (/) F equipment suffix.

FLIGHT PATH– A line, course, or track along which an aircraft is flying or intended to be flown.

(See TRACK.)
(See COURSE.)

FLIGHT PLAN– Specified information relating to the intended flight of an aircraft that is filed orally or in writing with an FSS or an ATC facility.

(See FAST FILE.)
(See FILED.)
(Refer to AIM.)

FLIGHT PLAN AREA– The geographical area assigned by regional air traffic divisions to a flight service station for the purpose of search and rescue for VFR aircraft, issuance of NOTAMs, pilot briefing, in-flight services, broadcast, emergency services, flight data processing, international operations, and aviation weather services. Three letter identifiers are assigned to every flight service station and are annotated in AFD's and FAA Order 7350.6, LOCATION IDENTIFIERS, as tie-in-facilities.

(See FAST FILE.)
(See FILED.)
(Refer to AIM.)

FLIGHT RECORDER– A general term applied to any instrument or device that records information about the performance of an aircraft in flight or about conditions encountered in flight. Flight recorders may make records of airspeed, outside air temperature, vertical acceleration, engine RPM, manifold pressure, and other pertinent variables for a given flight.

(See ICAO term FLIGHT RECORDER.)

FLIGHT RECORDER [ICAO]– Any type of recorder installed in the aircraft for the purpose of complementing accident/incident investigation.

Note: See Annex 6 Part I, for specifications relating to flight recorders.

FLIGHT SERVICE STATION– Air traffic facilities which provide pilot briefing, en route communications and VFR search and rescue services, assist lost aircraft and aircraft in emergency situations, relay ATC clearances, originate Notices to Airmen, broadcast aviation weather and NAS information, receive and process IFR flight plans, and monitor NAVAID's. In addition, at selected locations, FSS's provide En Route Flight Advisory Service (Flight Watch), take weather observations, issue airport advisories, and advise Customs and Immigration of transborder flights.

(Refer to AIM.)

FLIGHT STANDARDS DISTRICT OFFICE– An FAA field office serving an assigned geographical area and staffed with Flight Standards personnel who serve the aviation industry and the general public on matters relating to the certification and operation of air carrier and general aviation aircraft. Activities include general surveillance of operational safety, certification of airmen and aircraft, accident prevention, investigation, enforcement, etc.

FLIGHT TEST– A flight for the purpose of:

a. Investigating the operation/flight characteristics of an aircraft or aircraft component.

b. Evaluating an applicant for a pilot certificate or rating.

FLIGHT VISIBILITY– (See VISIBILITY.)

FLIGHT WATCH– A shortened term for use in air-ground contacts to identify the flight service station providing En Route Flight Advisory Service; e.g., "Oakland Flight Watch."

(See EN ROUTE FLIGHT ADVISORY SERVICE.)

FLIP– (See DOD FLIP.)

FLOW CONTROL– Measures designed to adjust the flow of traffic into a given airspace, along a given route, or bound for a given aerodrome (airport) so as to ensure the most effective utilization of the airspace.

(See QUOTA FLOW CONTROL.)

(Refer to AIRPORT/FACILITY DIRECTORY.)

FLY–BY WAYPOINT– A fly–by waypoint requires the use of turn anticipation to avoid overshoot of the next flight segment.

FLY HEADING (DEGREES)– Informs the pilot of the heading he should fly. The pilot may have to turn to, or continue on, a specific compass direction in order to comply with the instructions. The pilot is expected to turn in the shorter direction to the heading unless otherwise instructed by ATC.

FLY–OVER WAYPOINT– A fly–over waypoint precludes any turn until the waypoint is overflown and is followed by an intercept maneuver of the next flight segment.

FMA– (See FINAL MONITOR AID.)

FMS– (See FLIGHT MANAGEMENT SYSTEM.)

FMSP– (See FLIGHT MANAGEMENT SYSTEM PROCEDURE.)

FORMATION FLIGHT– More than one aircraft which, by prior arrangement between the pilots, operate as a single aircraft with regard to navigation and position reporting. Separation between aircraft within the formation is the responsibility of the flight leader and the pilots of the other aircraft in the flight. This includes transition periods when aircraft within the formation are maneuvering to attain separation from each other to effect individual control and during join-up and breakaway.

a. A standard formation is one in which a proximity of no more than 1 mile laterally or longitudinally and within 100 feet vertically from the flight leader is maintained by each wingman.

b. Nonstandard formations are those operating under any of the following conditions:

1. When the flight leader has requested and ATC has approved other than standard formation dimensions.

2. When operating within an authorized altitude reservation (ALTRV) or under the provisions of a letter of agreement.

3. When the operations are conducted in airspace specifically designed for a special activity.

(See ALTITUDE RESERVATION.)

(Refer to FAR Part 91.)

FRC– (See REQUEST FULL ROUTE CLEARANCE.)

FREEZE/FROZEN– Terms used in referring to arrival which have been assigned ACLT's and to the lists in which they are displayed.

FREEZE CALCULATED LANDING TIME– A dynamic parameter number of minutes prior to the meter fix calculated time of arrival for each aircraft when the TCLT is frozen and becomes an ACLT (i.e., the VTA is updated and consequently the TCLT is modified as appropriate until FCLT minutes prior to meter fix calculated time of arrival, at which time updating is suspended and an ACLT and a frozen meter fix crossing time (MFT) is assigned).

FREEZE SPEED PARAMETER– A speed adapted for each aircraft to determine fast and slow aircraft. Fast aircraft freeze on parameter FCLT and slow aircraft freeze on parameter MLDI.

FRICTION MEASUREMENT– A measurement of the friction characteristics of the runway pavement surface using continuous self–watering friction measurement equipment in accordance with the specifications, procedures and schedules contained in AC 150/5320–12, Measurement, Construction, and Maintenance of Skid Resistant Airport Pavement Surfaces.

FSDO– (See FLIGHT STANDARDS DISTRICT OFFICE.)

FSPD– (See FREEZE SPEED PARAMETER.)

FSS– (See FLIGHT SERVICE STATION.)

FUEL DUMPING– Airborne release of usable fuel. This does not include the dropping of fuel tanks.

(See JETTISONING OF EXTERNAL STORES.)

FUEL REMAINING– A phrase used by either pilots or controllers when relating to the fuel remaining on board until actual fuel exhaustion. When transmitting such information in response to either a controller question or pilot initiated cautionary advisory to air traffic control, pilots will state the APPROXIMATE NUMBER OF MINUTES the flight can continue with the fuel remaining. All reserve fuel SHOULD BE INCLUDED in the time stated, as should an allowance for established fuel gauge system error.

FUEL SIPHONING– Unintentional release of fuel caused by overflow, puncture, loose cap, etc.

FUEL VENTING– (See FUEL SIPHONING.)

G

GATE HOLD PROCEDURES- Procedures at selected airports to hold aircraft at the gate or other ground location whenever departure delays exceed or are anticipated to exceed 15 minutes. The sequence for departure will be maintained in accordance with initial call-up unless modified by flow control restrictions. Pilots should monitor the ground control/clearance delivery frequency for engine start/taxi advisories or new proposed start/taxi time if the delay changes.

(See FLOW CONTROL.)

GCA- (See GROUND CONTROLLED APPROACH.)

GENERAL AVIATION- That portion of civil aviation which encompasses all facets of aviation except air carriers holding a certificate of public convenience and necessity from the Civil Aeronautics Board and large aircraft commercial operators.

(See ICAO term GENERAL AVIATION.)

GENERAL AVIATION [ICAO]- All civil aviation operations other than scheduled air services and nonscheduled air transport operations for remuneration or hire.

GEO MAP- The digitized map markings associated with the ASR-9 Radar System.

GLIDEPATH- (See GLIDESLOPE.)

GLIDEPATH INTERCEPT ALTITUDE- (See GLIDESLOPE INTERCEPT ALTITUDE.)

GLIDESLOPE- Provides vertical guidance for aircraft during approach and landing. The glideslope/glidepath is based on the following:

a. Electronic components emitting signals which provide vertical guidance by reference to airborne instruments during instrument approaches such as ILS/MLS, or

b. Visual ground aids, such as VASI, which provide vertical guidance for a VFR approach or for the visual portion of an instrument approach and landing.

c. PAR. Used by ATC to inform an aircraft making a PAR approach of its vertical position (elevation) relative to the descent profile.

(See ICAO term GLIDEPATH.)

GLIDEPATH [ICAO]- A descent profile determined for vertical guidance during a final approach.

GLIDESLOPE INTERCEPT ALTITUDE- The minimum altitude to intercept the glideslope/path on a precision ap-

proach. The intersection of the published intercept altitude with the glideslope/path, designated on Government charts by the lightning bolt symbol, is the precision FAF; however, when ATC directs a lower altitude, the resultant lower intercept position is then the FAF.

(See FINAL APPROACH FIX.)

(See SEGMENTS OF AN INSTRUMENT APPROACH PROCEDURE.)

GLOBAL POSITIONING SYSTEM (GPS)- A space-base radio positioning, navigation, and time-transfer system. The system provides highly accurate position and velocity information, and precise time, on a continuous global basis, to an unlimited number of properly equipped users. The system is unaffected by weather, and provides a worldwide common grid reference system. The GPS concept is predicated upon accurate and continuous knowledge of the spatial position of each satellite in the system with respect to time and distance from a transmitting satellite to the user. The GPS receiver automatically selects appropriate signals from the satellites in view and translates these into three-dimensional position, velocity, and time. System accuracy for civil users is normally 100 meters horizontally.

GO AHEAD- Proceed with your message. Not to be used for any other purpose.

GO AROUND- Instructions for a pilot to abandon his approach to landing. Additional instructions may follow. Unless otherwise advised by ATC, a VFR aircraft or an aircraft conducting visual approach should overfly the runway while climbing to traffic pattern altitude and enter the traffic pattern via the crosswind leg. A pilot on an IFR flight plan making an instrument approach should execute the published missed approach procedure or proceed as instructed by ATC; e.g., "Go around" (additional instructions if required).

(See LOW APPROACH.)

(See MISSED APPROACH.)

GPS- (See Global Positioning System.)

GROUND CLUTTER- A pattern produced on the radar scope by ground returns which may degrade other radar returns in the affected area. The effect of ground clutter is minimized by the use of moving target indicator (MTI) circuits in the radar equipment resulting in a radar presentation which displays only targets which are in motion.

(See CLUTTER.)

GROUND COMMUNICATION OUTLET (GCO)- An unstaffed, remotely controlled, ground/ground communications facility. Pilots at uncontrolled airports may contact ATC and FSS via VHF to a telephone connection to obtain an instrument clearance or close a VFR or IFR flight plan. They may also get an updated weather briefing prior to takeoff. Pilots will use four "key clicks" on the VHF radio to contact the appropriate ATC facility or six "key clicks " to contact the FSS. The GCO system is intended to be used only on the ground.

GROUND CONTROLLED APPROACH- A radar approach system operated from the ground by air traffic control personnel transmitting instructions to the pilot by radio. The approach may be conducted with surveillance radar (ASR) only or with both surveillance and precision approach radar (PAR). Usage of the term "GCA" by pilots is discouraged except when referring to a GCA facility. Pilots should specifically request a "PAR" approach when a precision radar approach is desired or request an "ASR" or "surveillance" approach when a nonprecision radar approach is desired.

(See RADAR APPROACH.)

GROUND DELAY- The amount of delay attributed to ATC, encountered prior to departure, usually associated with a CDT program.

GROUND SPEED- The speed of an aircraft relative to the surface of the earth.

GROUND STOP- Normally, the last initiative to be utilized; this method mandates that the terminal facility will not allow any departures to enter the ARTCC airspace until further notified.

GROUND VISIBILITY- (See VISIBILITY.)

H

HAA- (See HEIGHT ABOVE AIRPORT.)

HAL- (See HEIGHT ABOVE LANDING.)

HANDOFF- An action taken to transfer the radar identification of an aircraft from one controller to another if the aircraft will enter the receiving controller's airspace and radio communications with the aircraft will be transferred.

HAT- (See HEIGHT ABOVE TOUCHDOWN.)

HAVE NUMBERS- Used by pilots to inform ATC that they have received runway, wind, and altimeter information only.

HAZARDOUS INFLIGHT WEATHER ADVISORY SERVICE- Continuous recorded hazardous inflight weather forecasts broadcasted to airborne pilots over selected VOR outlets defined as an HIWAS BROADCAST AREA.

HAZARDOUS WEATHER INFORMATION- Summary of significant meteorological information (SIGMET/WS), convective significant meteorological information (convective SIGMET/WST), urgent pilot weather reports (urgent PIREP/UUA), center weather advisories (CWA), airmen's meteorological information (AIRMET/WA) and any other weather such as isolated thunderstorms that are rapidly developing and increasing in intensity, or low ceilings and visibilities that are becoming widespread which is considered significant and are not included in a current hazardous weather advisory.

HEAVY (AIRCRAFT)- (See AIRCRAFT CLASSES.)

HEIGHT ABOVE AIRPORT- The height of the Minimum Descent Altitude above the published airport elevation. This is published in conjunction with circling minimums.

(See MINIMUM DESCENT ALTITUDE.)

HEIGHT ABOVE LANDING- The height above a designated helicopter landing area used for helicopter instrument approach procedures.

(Refer to FAR Part 97.)

HEIGHT ABOVE TOUCHDOWN- The height of the Decision Height or Minimum Descent Altitude above the highest runway elevation in the touchdown zone (first 3,000 feet of the runway). HAT is published on instrument approach charts in conjunction with all straight-in minimums.

(See DECISION HEIGHT.)
(See MINIMUM DESCENT ALTITUDE.)

HELICOPTER- Rotorcraft that, for its horizontal motion, depends principally on its engine-driven rotors.

(See ICAO term HELICOPTER.)

HELICOPTER [ICAO]- A heavier-than-air aircraft supported in flight chiefly by the reactions of the air on one or more power-driven rotors on substantially vertical axes.

HELIPAD- A small, designated area, usually with a prepared surface, on a heliport, airport, landing/takeoff area, apron/ramp, or movement area used for takeoff, landing, or parking of helicopters.

HELIPORT- An area of land, water, or structure used or intended to be used for the landing and takeoff of helicopters and includes its buildings and facilities if any.

HELIPORT REFERENCE POINT (HRP)- The geographic center of a heliport.

HERTZ- The standard radio equivalent of frequency in cycles per second of an electromagnetic wave. Kilohertz (kHz) is a frequency of one thousand cycles per second. Megahertz (MHz) is a frequency of one million cycles per second.

HF- (See HIGH FREQUENCY.)

HF COMMUNICATIONS- (See HIGH FREQUENCY COMMUNICATIONS.)

HIGH FREQUENCY- The frequency band between 3 and 30 MHz.

(See HIGH FREQUENCY COMMUNICATIONS.)

HIGH FREQUENCY COMMUNICATIONS- High radio frequencies (HF) between 3 and 30 MHz used for air-to-ground voice communication in overseas operations.

HIGH SPEED EXIT- (See HIGH SPEED TAXIWAY.)

HIGH SPEED TAXIWAY- A long radius taxiway designed and provided with lighting or marking to define the path of aircraft, traveling at high speed (up to 60 knots), from the runway center to a point on the center of a taxiway. Also referred to as long radius exit or turn-off taxiway. The high speed taxiway is designed to expedite aircraft turning off the runway after landing, thus reducing runway occupancy time.

HIGH SPEED TURNOFF- (See HIGH SPEED TAXIWAY.)

HIWAS- (See HAZARDOUS INFLIGHT WEATHER ADVISORY SERVICE.)

HIWAS AREA- (See HAZARDOUS INFLIGHT WEATHER ADVISORY SERVICE.)

HIWAS BROADCAST AREA- A geographical area of responsibility including one or more HIWAS outlet areas assigned to an AFSS/FSS for hazardous weather advisory broadcasting.

HIWAS OUTLET AREA- An area defined as a 150 NM radius of a HIWAS outlet, expanded as necessary to provide coverage.

HOLDING PROCEDURE- (See HOLD PROCEDURE.)

HOLD PROCEDURE– A predetermined maneuver which keeps aircraft within a specified airspace while awaiting further clearance from air traffic control. Also used during ground operations to keep aircraft within a specified area or at a specified point while awaiting further clearance from air traffic control.

(See HOLDING FIX.)

(Refer to AIM.)

HOLD–SHORT POINT– A point on the runway beyond which a landing aircraft with a LAHSO clearance is not authorized to proceed. This point may be located prior to an intersecting runway, taxiway, predetermined point, or approach/departure flight path.

HOLDING FIX– A specified fix identifiable to a pilot by NAVAID's or visual reference to the ground used as a reference point in establishing and maintaining the position of an aircraft while holding.

(See FIX.)

(See VISUAL HOLDING.)

(Refer to AIM.)

HOLDING POINT [ICAO]– A specified location, identified by visual or other means, in the vicinity of which the position of an aircraft in flight is maintained in accordance with air traffic control clearances.

HOLD FOR RELEASE– Used by ATC to delay an aircraft for traffic management reasons; i.e., weather, traffic volume, etc. Hold for release instructions (including departure delay information) are used to inform a pilot or a controller (either directly or through an authorized relay) that an IFR departure clearance is not valid until a release time or additional instructions have been received.

(See ICAO term HOLDING POINT.)

HOLD–SHORT POSITION MARKING– The painted runway marking located at the hold–short point on all LAHSO runways.

HOLD–SHORT POSITION LIGHTS– Flashing in–pavement white lights located at specified hold–short points.

HOLD–SHORT POSITION SIGNS– Red and white holding position signs located alongside the hold–short point.

HOMING – Flight toward a NAVAID, without correcting for wind, by adjusting the aircraft heading to maintain a relative bearing of zero degrees.

(See BEARING.)

(See ICAO term HOMING.)

HOMING [ICAO]– The procedure of using the direction finding equipment of one radio station with the emission of another radio station, where at least one of the stations is mobile, and whereby the mobile station proceeds continuously towards the other station.

HOVER CHECK– Used to describe when a helicopter/VTOL aircraft requires a stabilized hover to conduct a performance/power check prior to hover taxi, air taxi, or takeoff. Altitude of the hover will vary based on the purpose of the check.

HOVER TAXI– Used to describe a helicopter/VTOL aircraft movement conducted above the surface and in ground effect at airspeeds less than approximately 20 knots. The actual height may vary, and some helicopters may require hover taxi above 25 feet AGL to reduce ground effect turbulence or provide clearance for cargo slingloads.

(See AIR TAXI.)

(See HOVER CHECK.)

(Refer to AIM.)

HOW DO YOU HEAR ME? – A question relating to the quality of the transmission or to determine how well the transmission is being received.

HZ– (See HERTZ.)

I

IAF- (See INITIAL APPROACH FIX.)

IAP- (See INSTRUMENT APPROACH PROCEDURE.)

IAWP- Initial Approach Waypoint

ICAO- (See INTERNATIONAL CIVIL AVIATION ORGANIZATION.)

ICAO [ICAO]- (See ICAO Term INTERNATIONAL CIVIL AVIATION ORGANIZATION.)

ICING- The accumulation of airframe ice.

Types of icing are:

    a. Rime Ice- Rough, milky, opaque ice formed by the instantaneous freezing of small supercooled water droplets.

    b. Clear Ice- A glossy, clear, or translucent ice formed by the relatively slow freezing or large supercooled water droplets.

    c. Mixed- A mixture of clear ice and rime ice.

Intensity of icing:

    a. Trace- Ice becomes perceptible. Rate of accumulation is slightly greater than the rate of sublimation. It is not hazardous even though deicing\anti-icing equipment is not utilized unless encountered for an extended period of time (over 1 hour).

    b. Light- The rate of accumulation may create a problem if flight is prolonged in this environment (over 1 hour). Occasional use of deicing\anti-icing equipment removes\prevents accumulation. It does not present a problem if the deicing\anti-icing equipment is used.

    c. Moderate- The rate of accumulation is such that even short encounters become potentially hazardous and use of deicing\anti-icing equipment or flight diversion is necessary.

    d. Severe- The rate of accumulation is such that deicing\anti-icing equipment fails to reduce or control the hazard. Immediate flight diversion is necessary.

IDENT- A request for a pilot to activate the aircraft transponder identification feature. This will help the controller to confirm an aircraft identity or to identify an aircraft.

    (Refer to AIM.)

IDENT FEATURE- The special feature in the Air Traffic Control Radar Beacon System (ATCRBS) equipment. It is used to immediately distinguish one displayed beacon target from other beacon targets.

    (See IDENT.)

IF- (See INTERMEDIATE FIX.)

IFIM- (See INTERNATIONAL FLIGHT INFORMATION MANUAL.)

IF NO TRANSMISSION RECEIVED FOR (TIME)- Used by ATC in radar approaches to prefix procedures which should be followed by the pilot in event of lost communications.

    (See LOST COMMUNICATIONS.)

IFR- (See INSTRUMENT FLIGHT RULES.)

IFR AIRCRAFT- An aircraft conducting flight in accordance with instrument flight rules.

IFR CONDITIONS- Weather conditions below the minimum for flight under visual flight rules.

    (See INSTRUMENT METEOROLOGICAL CONDITIONS.)

IFR DEPARTURE PROCEDURE- (See IFR TAKEOFF MINIMUMS AND DEPARTURE PROCEDURES.)

    (Refer to AIM.)

IFR FLIGHT- (See IFR AIRCRAFT.)

IFR LANDING MINIMUMS- (See LANDING MINIMUMS.)

IFR MILITARY TRAINING ROUTES (IR)- Routes used by the Department of Defense and associated Reserve and Air Guard units for the purpose of conducting low-altitude navigation and tactical training in both IFR and VFR weather conditions below 10,000 feet MSL at airspeeds in excess of 250 knots IAS.

IFR TAKEOFF MINIMUMS AND DEPARTURE PROCEDURES- Federal Aviation Regulations, Part 91, prescribes standard takeoff rules for certain civil users. At some airports, obstructions or other factors require the establishment of nonstandard takeoff minimums, departure procedures, or both to assist pilots in avoiding obstacles during climb to the minimum en route altitude. Those airports are listed in NOS/DOD Instrument Approach Charts (IAP's) under a section entitled "IFR Takeoff Minimums and Departure Procedures." The NOS/DOD IAP chart legend illustrates the symbol used to alert the pilot to nonstandard takeoff minimums and departure procedures. When departing IFR from such airports or from any airports where there are no departure procedures, DP's, or ATC facilities available, pilots should advise ATC of any departure limitations. Controllers may query a pilot to determine acceptable departure directions, turns, or headings after takeoff. Pilots should be familiar with the departure procedures and must assure that their aircraft can meet or exceed any specified climb gradients.

IF/IAWP- Intermediate Fix/Initial Approach Waypoint. The waypoint where the final approach course of a T approach meets the crossbar of the T. When designated (in conjunction with a TAA) this waypoint will be used as an IAWP when approaching the airport from certain directions, and as an IFWP when beginning the approach from another IAWP.

P/C

■ IFWP- Intermediate Fix Waypoint

ILS- (See INSTRUMENT LANDING SYSTEM.)

ILS CATEGORIES- 1. ILS Category I. An ILS approach procedure which provides for approach to a height above touchdown of not less than 200 feet and with runway visual range of not less than 1,800 feet.- 2. ILS Category II. An ILS approach procedure which provides for approach to a height above touchdown of not less than 100 feet and with runway visual range of not less than 1,200 feet.- 3. ILS Category III:

a. IIIA.-An ILS approach procedure which provides for approach without a decision height minimum and with runway visual range of not less than 700 feet.

b. IIIB.-An ILS approach procedure which provides for approach without a decision height minimum and with runway visual range of not less than 150 feet.

c. IIIC.-An ILS approach procedure which provides for approach without a decision height minimum and without runway visual range minimum.

ILS PRM APPROACH- An instrument landing system (ILS) approach conducted to parallel runways whose extended centerlines are separated by less than 4,300 feet and the parallel runways have a Precision Runway Monitoring (PRM) system that permits simultaneous independent ILS approaches.

IM- (See INNER MARKER.)

IMC- (See INSTRUMENT METEOROLOGICAL CONDITIONS.)

IMMEDIATELY- Used by ATC when such action compliance is required to avoid an imminent situation.

INCERFA Uncertainty Phase) [ICAO]- A situation wherein uncertainty exists as to the safety of an aircraft and its occupants.

INCREASE SPEED TO (SPEED)- (See SPEED ADJUSTMENT.)

INERTIAL NAVIGATION SYSTEM- An RNAV system which is a form of self-contained navigation.

(See Area Navigation/RNAV.)

INFLIGHT REFUELING- (See AERIAL REFUELING.)

INFLIGHT WEATHER ADVISORY- (See WEATHER ADVISORY.)

INFORMATION REQUEST- A request originated by an FSS for information concerning an overdue VFR aircraft.

INITIAL APPROACH FIX- The fixes depicted on instrument approach procedure charts that identify the beginning of the initial approach segment(s).

(See FIX.)

(See SEGMENTS OF AN INSTRUMENT APPROACH PROCEDURE.)

INITIAL APPROACH SEGMENT- (See SEGMENTS OF AN INSTRUMENT APPROACH PROCEDURE.)

INITIAL APPROACH SEGMENT [ICAO]- That segment of an instrument approach procedure between the initial approach fix and the intermediate approach fix or, where applicable, the final approach fix or point.

INLAND NAVIGATION FACILITY- A navigation aid on a North American Route at which the common route and/or the noncommon route begins or ends.

INNER MARKER- A marker beacon used with an ILS (CAT II) precision approach located between the middle marker and the end of the ILS runway, transmitting a radiation pattern keyed at six dots per second and indicating to the pilot, both aurally and visually, that he is at the designated decision height (DH), normally 100 feet above the touchdown zone elevation, on the ILS CAT II approach. It also marks progress during a CAT III approach.

(See INSTRUMENT LANDING SYSTEM.)

(Refer to AIM.)

INNER MARKER BEACON- (See INNER MARKER.)

INREQ- (See INFORMATION REQUEST.)

INS- (See INERTIAL NAVIGATION SYSTEM.)

INSTRUMENT APPROACH- (See INSTRUMENT APPROACH PROCEDURE.)

INSTRUMENT APPROACH PROCEDURE- A series of predetermined maneuvers for the orderly transfer of an aircraft under instrument flight conditions from the beginning of the initial approach to a landing or to a point from which a landing may be made visually. It is prescribed and approved for a specific airport by competent authority.

(See SEGMENTS OF AN INSTRUMENT APPROACH PROCEDURE.)

(Refer to FAR Part 91.)

(See AIM.)

a. U.S. civil standard instrument approach procedures are approved by the FAA as prescribed under Part 97 and are available for public use.

b. U.S. military standard instrument approach procedures are approved and published by the Department of Defense.

c. Special instrument approach procedures are approved by the FAA for individual operators but are not published in Part 97 for public use.

(See ICAO term INSTRUMENT APPROACH PROCEDURE.)

INSTRUMENT APPROACH PROCEDURE [ICAO]- A series of predetermined maneuvers by reference to flight instruments with specified protection from obstacles from the initial approach fix, or where applicable, from the beginning of a defined arrival route to a point from which a landing can be completed and thereafter, if a landing is not completed, to a position at which holding or en route obstacle clearance criteria apply.

INSTRUMENT APPROACH PROCEDURES CHARTS- (See AERONAUTICAL CHART.)

INSTRUMENT DEPARTURE PROCEDURE (DP)- A pre-anned instrument flight rule (IFR) air traffic control depar-re procedure printed for pilot use in graphic and/or textual rm. DP's provide transition from the terminal to the ap-opriate en route structure.

(See IFR TAKEOFF MINIMUMS AND DEPARTURE PROCEDURES.)

(Refer to AIM.)

INSTRUMENT DEPARTURE PROCEDURE (DP) HARTS-

(See AERONAUTICAL CHART.)

INSTRUMENT FLIGHT RULES- Rules governing the rocedures for conducting instrument flight. Also a term sed by pilots and controllers to indicate type of flight plan.

(See VISUAL FLIGHT RULES.)

(See INSTRUMENT METEOROLOGICAL CONDITIONS.)

(See VISUAL METEOROLOGICAL CONDITIONS.)

(Refer to AIM.)

(See ICAO term INSTRUMENT FLIGHT RULES.)

INSTRUMENT FLIGHT RULES [ICAO]- A set of rules overning the conduct of flight under instrument meteoro-ogical conditions.

INSTRUMENT LANDING SYSTEM- A precision instru-nent approach system which normally consists of the fol-owing electronic components and visual aids:

a. Localizer.

(See LOCALIZER.)

b. Glideslope.

(See GLIDESLOPE.)

c. Outer Marker.

(See OUTER MARKER.)

d. Middle Marker.

(See MIDDLE MARKER.)

e. Approach Lights.

(See AIRPORT LIGHTING.)

(Refer to FAR Part 91.)

(See AIM.)

INSTRUMENT METEOROLOGICAL CONDITIONS- Meteorological conditions expressed in terms of visibility, distance from cloud, and ceiling less than the minima speci-fied for visual meteorological conditions.

(See VISUAL METEOROLOGICAL CONDITIONS.)

(See INSTRUMENT FLIGHT RULES.)

(See VISUAL FLIGHT RULES.)

INSTRUMENT RUNWAY- A runway equipped with elec-tronic and visual navigation aids for which a precision or nonprecision approach procedure having straight-in landing minimums has been approved.

(See ICAO term INSTRUMENT RUNWAY.)

INSTRUMENT RUNWAY [ICAO]- One of the following types of runways intended for the operation of aircraft using instrument approach procedures:

a. Nonprecision Approach Runway-An instrument run-way served by visual aids and a nonvisual aid providing at least directional guidance adequate for a straight-in ap-proach.

b. Precision Approach Runway, Category I-An instru-ment runway served by ILS and visual aids intended for op-erations down to 60 m (200 feet) decision height and down to an RVR of the order of 800 m.

c. Precision Approach Runway, Category II-An instru-ment runway served by ILS and visual aids intended for op-erations down to 30 m (100 feet) decision height and down to an RVR of the order of 400 m.

d. Precision Approach Runway, Category III-An instru-ment runway served by ILS to and along the surface of the runway and:

1. Intended for operations down to an RVR of the or-der of 200 m (no decision height being applicable) using visual aids during the final phase of landing;

2. Intended for operations down to an RVR of the or-der of 50 m (no decision height being applicable) using visual aids for taxiing;

3. Intended for operations without reliance on visual reference for landing or taxiing.

Note 1: See Annex 10 Volume I, Part I, Chapter 3, for related ILS specifications.

Note 2: Visual aids need not necessarily be matched to the scale of nonvisual aids pro-vided. The criterion for the selection of visual aids is the conditions in which operations are intended to be conducted.

INTEGRITY- The ability of a system to provide timely warnings to users when the system should not be used for navigation.

INTERMEDIATE APPROACH SEGMENT- (See SEGMENTS OF AN INSTRUMENT APPROACH PROCEDURE.)

INTERMEDIATE APPROACH SEGMENT [ICAO]- That segment of an instrument approach procedure between ei-ther the intermediate approach fix and the final approach fix or point, or between the end of a reversal, race track or dead reckoning track procedure and the final approach fix or point, as appropriate.

P/C

INTERMEDIATE FIX- The fix that identifies the beginning of the intermediate approach segment of an instrument approach procedure. The fix is not normally identified on the instrument approach chart as an intermediate fix (IF).

(See SEGMENTS OF AN INSTRUMENT APPROACH PROCEDURE.)

INTERMEDIATE LANDING- On the rare occasion that this option is requested, it should be approved. The departure center, however, must advise the ATCSCC so that the appropriate delay is carried over and assigned at the intermediate airport. An intermediate landing airport within the arrival center will not be accepted without coordination with and the approval of the ATCSCC.

INTERNATIONAL AIRPORT- Relating to international flight, it means:

a. An airport of entry which has been designated by the Secretary of Treasury or Commissioner of Customs as an international airport for customs service.

b. A landing rights airport at which specific permission to land must be obtained from customs authorities in advance of contemplated use.

c. Airports designated under the Convention on International Civil Aviation as an airport for use by international commercial air transport and/or international general aviation.

(Refer to AIRPORT/FACILITY DIRECTORY.)

(Refer to IFIM.)

(See ICAO term INTERNATIONAL AIRPORT.)

INTERNATIONAL AIRPORT [ICAO]- Any airport designated by the Contracting State in whose territory it is situated as an airport of entry and departure for international air traffic, where the formalities incident to customs, immigration, public health, animal and plant quarantine and similar procedures are carried out.

INTERNATIONAL CIVIL AVIATION ORGANIZATION [ICAO]- A specialized agency of the United Nations whose objective is to develop the principles and techniques of international air navigation and to foster planning and development of international civil air transport.

a. Regions include:

1. African-Indian Ocean Region

2. Caribbean Region

3. European Region

4. Middle East/Asia Region

5. North American Region

6. North Atlantic Region

7. Pacific Region

8. South American Region

INTERNATIONAL FLIGHT INFORMATION MANUAL A publication designed primarily as a pilot's preflight planning guide for flights into foreign airspace and for flights returning to the U.S. from foreign locations.

INTERROGATOR- The ground-based surveillance radar beacon transmitter-receiver, which normally scans in synchronism with a primary radar, transmitting discrete radar signals which repetitiously request all transponders on the mode being used to reply. The replies received are mixed with the primary radar returns and displayed on the same plan position indicator (radar scope). Also, applied to the airborne element of the TACAN/DME system.

(See TRANSPONDER.)

(Refer to AIM.)

INTERSECTING RUNWAYS- Two or more runways which cross or meet within their lengths.

(See INTERSECTION.)

INTERSECTION-

a. A point defined by any combination of courses, radial or bearings of two or more navigational aids.

b. Used to describe the point where two runways, a runway and a taxiway, or two taxiways cross or meet.

INTERSECTION DEPARTURE- A departure from an runway intersection except the end of the runway.

(See INTERSECTION.)

INTERSECTION TAKEOFF- (See INTERSECTION DEPARTURE.)

IR- (See IFR MILITARY TRAINING ROUTES.)

I SAY AGAIN- The message will be repeated.

J

JAMMING– Electronic or mechanical interference which may disrupt the display of aircraft on radar or the transmission / reception of radio communications / navigation.

JET BLAST– Jet engine exhaust (thrust stream turbulence).

(See WAKE TURBULENCE.)

JET ROUTE– A route designed to serve aircraft operations from 18,000 feet MSL up to and including flight level 450. The routes are referred to as "J" routes with numbering to identify the designated route; e.g., J105.

(See Class A AIRSPACE.)
(Refer to FAR Part 71.)

JET STREAM– A migrating stream of high-speed winds present at high altitudes.

JETTISONING OF EXTERNAL STORES– Airborne release of external stores; e.g., tiptanks, ordnance.

(See FUEL DUMPING.)
(Refer to FAR Part 91.)

JOINT USE RESTRICTED AREA– (See RESTRICTED AREA.)

K

KNOWN TRAFFIC− With respect to ATC clearances, means aircraft whose altitude, position, and intentions are known to ATC.

L

LAA– (See LOCAL AIRPORT ADVISORY.)

LAAS– (See LOW ALTITUDE ALERT SYSTEM.)

LAHSO– An acronym for "Land and Hold Short Operation." These operations include landing and holding short of an intersecting runway, a taxiway, a predetermined point, or an approach/departure flightpath.

LAHSO–DRY– Land and hold short operations on runways that are dry.

LAHSO–WET– Land and hold short operations on runways that are wet (but not contaminated).

LAND AND HOLD SHORT OPERATIONS– Operations which include simultaneous takeoffs and landings and/or simultaneous landings when a landing aircraft is able and is instructed by the controller to hold–short of the intersecting runway/taxiway or designated hold–short point. Pilots are expected to promptly inform the controller if the hold short clearance cannot be accepted.

    (See PARALLEL RUNWAYS.)

    (Refer to AIM.)

LANDING AREA– Any locality either on land, water, or structures, including airports/heliports and intermediate landing fields, which is used, or intended to be used, for the landing and takeoff of aircraft whether or not facilities are provided for the shelter, servicing, or for receiving or discharging passengers or cargo.

    (See ICAO term LANDING AREA.)

LANDING AREA [ICAO]– That part of a movement area intended for the landing or takeoff of aircraft.

LANDING DIRECTION INDICATOR– A device which visually indicates the direction in which landings and takeoffs should be made.

    (See TETRAHEDRON.)

    (Refer to AIM.)

LANDING DISTANCE AVAILABLE [ICAO]– The length of runway which is declared available and suitable for the ground run of an aeroplane landing.

LANDING MINIMUMS– The minimum visibility prescribed for landing a civil aircraft while using an instrument approach procedure. The minimum applies with other limitations set forth in FAR Part 91 with respect to the Minimum Descent Altitude (MDA) or Decision Height (DH) prescribed in the instrument approach procedures as follows:

    a. Straight-in landing minimums. A statement of MDA and visibility, or DH and visibility, required for a straight – in landing on a specified runway, or

    b. Circling minimums. A statement of MDA and visibility required for the circle-to-land maneuver.

    Note: Descent below the established MDA or DH is not authorized during an approach unless the aircraft is in a position from which a normal approach to the runway of intended landing can be made and adequate visual reference to required visual cues is maintained.

    (See STRAIGHT-IN LANDING.)

    (See CIRCLE-TO-LAND MANEUVER.)

    (See DECISION HEIGHT.)

    (See MINIMUM DESCENT ALTITUDE.)

    (See VISIBILITY.)

    (See INSTRUMENT APPROACH PROCEDURE.)

    (Refer to FAR Part 91.)

LANDING ROLL– The distance from the point of touchdown to the point where the aircraft can be brought to a stop or exit the runway.

LANDING SEQUENCE– The order in which aircraft are positioned for landing.

    (See APPROACH SEQUENCE.)

LAST ASSIGNED ALTITUDE– The last altitude/flight level assigned by ATC and acknowledged by the pilot.

    (See MAINTAIN.)

    (Refer to FAR Part 91.)

LATERAL SEPARATION– The lateral spacing of aircraft at the same altitude by requiring operation on different routes or in different geographical locations.

    (See SEPARATION.)

LDA– (See LOCALIZER TYPE DIRECTIONAL AID.)

LDA [ICAO]– (See ICAO Term LANDING DISTANCE AVAILABLE.)

LF– (See LOW FREQUENCY.)

LIGHTED AIRPORT– An airport where runway and obstruction lighting is available.

    (See AIRPORT LIGHTING.)

    (Refer to AIM.)

LIGHT GUN– A handheld directional light signaling device which emits a brilliant narrow beam of white, green, or red light as selected by the tower controller. The color and type of light transmitted can be used to approve or disapprove anticipated pilot actions where radio communication is not available. The light gun is used for controlling traffic operating in the vicinity of the airport and on the airport movement area.

    (Refer to AIM.)

LOCALIZER– The component of an ILS which provides course guidance to the runway.

(See INSTRUMENT LANDING SYSTEM.)

(Refer to AIM.)

(See ICAO term LOCALIZER COURSE.)

LOCALIZER COURSE [ICAO]– The locus of points, in any given horizontal plane, at which the DDM (difference in depth of modulation) is zero.

LOCALIZER OFFSET– An angular offset of the localizer from the runway extended centerline in a direction away from the no transgression zone (NTZ) that increases the normal operating zone (NOZ) width. An offset requires a 50 foot increase in DH and is not authorized for CAT II and CAT III approaches.

LOCALIZER TYPE DIRECTIONAL AID– A NAVAID used for nonprecision instrument approaches with utility and accuracy comparable to a localizer but which is not a part of a complete ILS and is not aligned with the runway.

(Refer to AIM.)

LOCALIZER USABLE DISTANCE– The maximum distance from the localizer transmitter at a specified altitude, as verified by flight inspection, at which reliable course information is continuously received.

(Refer to AIM.)

LOCAL AIRPORT ADVISORY [LAA]– A service provided by flight service stations or the military at airports not serviced by an operating control tower. This service consists of providing information to arriving and departing aircraft concerning wind direction and speed, favored runway, altimeter setting, pertinent known traffic, pertinent known field conditions, airport taxi routes and traffic patterns, and authorized instrument approach procedures. This information is advisory in nature and does not constitute an ATC clearance.

(See AIRPORT ADVISORY AREA.)

LOCAL TRAFFIC– Aircraft operating in the traffic pattern or within sight of the tower, or aircraft known to be departing or arriving from flight in local practice areas, or aircraft executing practice instrument approaches at the airport.

(See TRAFFIC PATTERN.)

LOCATOR [ICAO]– An LM/MF NDB used as an aid to final approach.

Note: A locator usually has an average radius of rated coverage of between 18.5 and 46.3 km (10 and 25 NM).

LONGITUDINAL SEPARATION– The longitudinal spacing of aircraft at the same altitude by a minimum distance expressed in units of time or miles.

(See SEPARATION.)

(Refer to AIM.)

LONG RANGE NAVIGATION– (See LORAN.)

LORAN– An electronic navigational system by which hyperbolic lines of position are determined by measuring the difference in the time of reception of synchronized pulse signals from two fixed transmitters. Loran A operates in the 1750-1950 kHz frequency band. Loran C and D operate in the 100-110 kHz frequency band.

(Refer to AIM.)

LOST COMMUNICATIONS– Loss of the ability to communicate by radio. Aircraft are sometimes referred to as NORDO (No Radio). Standard pilot procedures are specified in Part 91. Radar controllers issue procedures for pilots to follow in the event of lost communications during a radar approach when weather reports indicate that an aircraft will likely encounter IFR weather conditions during the approach.

(Refer to FAR Part 91.)

(Refer AIM.)

LOW ALTITUDE AIRWAY STRUCTURE– The network of airways serving aircraft operations up to but not including 18,000 feet MSL.

(See AIRWAY.)

(Refer to AIM.)

LOW ALTITUDE ALERT, CHECK YOUR ALTITUDE IMMEDIATELY– (See SAFETY ALERT.)

LOW ALTITUDE ALERT SYSTEM– An automated function of the TPX-42 that alerts the controller when a Mode C transponder – equipped aircraft on an IFR flight plan is below a predetermined minimum safe altitude. If requested by the pilot, LAAS monitoring is also available to VFR Mode C transponder – equipped aircraft.

LOW APPROACH– An approach over an airport or runway following an instrument approach or a VFR approach including the go – around maneuver where the pilot intentionally does not make contact with the runway.

(Refer to AIM.)

LOW FREQUENCY– The frequency band between 30 and 300 kHz.

(Refer to AIM.)

M

MAA- (See MAXIMUM AUTHORIZED ALTITUDE.)

MACH NUMBER- The ratio of true airspeed to the speed of sound; e.g., MACH .82, MACH 1.6. (See AIRSPEED.)

MACH TECHNIQUE [ICAO]- Describes a control technique used by air traffic control whereby turbojet aircraft operating successively along suitable routes are cleared to maintain appropriate MACH numbers for a relevant portion of the en route phase of flight. The principle objective is to achieve improved utilization of the airspace and to ensure that separation between successive aircraft does not decrease below the established minima.

MAHWP- Missed Approach Holding Waypoint

MAINTAIN-

a. Concerning altitude/flight level, the term means to remain at the altitude/flight level specified. The phrase "climb and" or "descend and" normally precedes "maintain" and the altitude assignment; e.g., "descend and maintain 5,000."

b. Concerning other ATC instructions, the term is used in its literal sense; e.g., maintain VFR.

MAINTENANCE PLANNING FRICTION LEVEL- The friction level specified in AC 150/5320-12, Measurement, Construction, and Maintenance of Skid Resistant Airport Pavement Surfaces, which represents the friction value below which the runway pavement surface remains acceptable for any category or class of aircraft operations but which is beginning to show signs of deterioration. This value will vary depending on the particular friction measurement equipment used.

MAKE SHORT APPROACH- Used by ATC to inform a pilot to alter his traffic pattern so as to make a short final approach.

(See TRAFFIC PATTERN.)

MANDATORY ALTITUDE- An altitude depicted on an instrument Approach Procedure Chart requiring the aircraft to maintain altitude at the depicted value.

MAP- (See MISSED APPROACH POINT.)

MARKER BEACON- An electronic navigation facility transmitting a 75 mHz vertical fan or boneshaped radiation pattern. Marker beacons are identified by their modulation frequency and keying code, and when received by compatible airborne equipment, indicate to the pilot, both aurally and visually, that he is passing over the facility.

(See OUTER MARKER.)
(See MIDDLE MARKER.)
(See INNER MARKER.)
(Refer to AIM.)

MARSA- (See MILITARY AUTHORITY ASSUMES RESPONSIBILITY FOR SEPARATION OF AIRCRAFT.)

MAWP- Missed Approach Waypoint

MAXIMUM AUTHORIZED ALTITUDE- A published altitude representing the maximum usable altitude or flight level for an airspace structure or route segment. It is the highest altitude on a Federal airway, jet route, area navigation low or high route, or other direct route for which an MEA is designated in Part 95 at which adequate reception of navigation aid signals is assured.

MAYDAY- The international radiotelephony distress signal. When repeated three times, it indicates imminent and grave danger and that immediate assistance is requested.

(See PAN-PAN-PAN.)
(Refer to AIM.)

MCA- (See MINIMUM CROSSING ALTITUDE.)

MDA- (See MINIMUM DESCENT ALTITUDE.)

MEA- (See MINIMUM EN ROUTE IFR ALTITUDE.)

METEOROLOGICAL IMPACT STATEMENT- An unscheduled planning forecast describing conditions expected to begin within 4 to 12 hours which may impact the flow of air traffic in a specific center's (ARTCC) area.

METER FIX TIME/SLOT TIME- A calculated time to depart the meter fix in order to cross the vertex at the ACLT. This time reflects descent speed adjustment and any applicable time that must be absorbed prior to crossing the meter fix.

METER LIST DISPLAY INTERVAL- A dynamic parameter which controls the number of minutes prior to the flight plan calculated time of arrival at the meter fix for each aircraft, at which time the TCLT is frozen and becomes an ACLT; i.e., the VTA is updated and consequently the TCLT modified as appropriate until frozen at which time updating is suspended and an ACLT is assigned. When frozen, the flight entry is inserted into the arrival sector's meter list for display on the sector PVD/MDM. MLDI is used if filed true airspeed is less than or equal to freeze speed parameters (FSPD).

METERING- A method of time-regulating arrival traffic flow into a terminal area so as not to exceed a predetermined terminal acceptance rate.

METERING AIRPORTS- Airports adapted for metering and for which optimum flight paths are defined. A maximum of 15 airports may be adapted.

METERING FIX- A fix along an established route from over which aircraft will be metered prior to entering terminal airspace. Normally, this fix should be established at a distance from the airport which will facilitate a profile descent 10,000 feet above airport elevation [AAE] or above.

P/C

METERING POSITION(S)- Adapted PVD's/MDM's and associated "D" positions eligible for display of a metering position list. A maximum of four PVD's/MDM's may be adapted.

METERING POSITION LIST- An ordered list of data on arrivals for a selected metering airport displayed on a metering position PVD/MDM.

MFT- (See METER FIX TIME/SLOT TIME.)

MHA- (See MINIMUM HOLDING ALTITUDE.)

MIA- (See MINIMUM IFR ALTITUDES.)

MICROBURST- A small downburst with outbursts of damaging winds extending 2.5 miles or less. In spite of its small horizontal scale, an intense microburst could induce wind speeds as high as 150 knots

(Refer to AIM.)

MICROWAVE LANDING SYSTEM- A precision instrument approach system operating in the microwave spectrum which normally consists of the following components:

a. Azimuth Station.

b. Elevation Station.

c. Precision Distance Measuring Equipment.

(See MLS CATEGORIES.)

MIDDLE COMPASS LOCATOR- (See COMPASS LOCATOR.)

MIDDLE MARKER- A marker beacon that defines a point along the glideslope of an ILS normally located at or near the point of decision height (ILS Category I). It is keyed to transmit alternate dots and dashes, with the alternate dots and dashes keyed at the rate of 95 dot/dash combinations per minute on a 1300 Hz tone, which is received aurally and visually by compatible airborne equipment.

(See MARKER BEACON.)

(See INSTRUMENT LANDING SYSTEM.)

(Refer to AIM.)

MID RVR- (See VISIBILITY.)

MILES-IN-TRAIL- A specified distance between aircraft, normally, in the same stratum associated with the same destination or route of flight.

MILITARY AUTHORITY ASSUMES RESPONSIBILITY FOR SEPARATION OF AIRCRAFT- A condition whereby the military services involved assume responsibility for separation between participating military aircraft in the ATC system. It is used only for required IFR operations which are specified in letters of agreement or other appropriate FAA or military documents.

MILITARY OPERATIONS AREA- (See SPECIAL USE AIRSPACE.)

MILITARY TRAINING ROUTES- Airspace of defined vertical and lateral dimensions established for the conduct of military flight training at airspeeds in excess of 250 knots IAS.

(See IFR MILITARY TRAINING ROUTES.)

(See VFR MILITARY TRAINING ROUTES.)

MINIMA- (See MINIMUMS.)

MINIMUM CROSSING ALTITUDE- The lowest altitude at certain fixes at which an aircraft must cross when proceeding in the direction of a higher minimum en route IFR altitude (MEA).

(See MINIMUM EN ROUTE IFR ALTITUDE.)

MINIMUM DESCENT ALTITUDE- The lowest altitude, expressed in feet above mean sea level, to which descent is authorized on final approach or during circle-to-land maneuvering in execution of a standard instrument approach procedure where no electronic glideslope is provided.

(See NONPRECISION APPROACH PROCEDURE.)

MINIMUM EN ROUTE IFR ALTITUDE- The lowest published altitude between radio fixes which assures acceptable navigational signal coverage and meets obstacle clearance requirements between those fixes. The MEA prescribed for a Federal airway or segment thereof, area navigation low or high route, or other direct route applies to the entire width of the airway, segment, or route between the radio fixes defining the airway, segment, or route.

(Refer to Part 91.)

(Refer to Part 95.)

(Refer to AIM.)

MINIMUM FRICTION LEVEL- The friction level specified in AC 150/5320-12, Measurement, Construction, and Maintenance of Skid Resistant Airport Pavement Surfaces, that represents the minimum recommended wet pavement surface friction value for any turbojet aircraft engaged in LAHSO. This value will vary with the particular friction measurement equipment used.

MINIMUM FUEL- Indicates that an aircraft's fuel supply has reached a state where, upon reaching the destination, it can accept little or no delay. This is not an emergency situation but merely indicates an emergency situation is possible should any undue delay occur.

(Refer to AIM.)

MINIMUM HOLDING ALTITUDE- The lowest altitude prescribed for a holding pattern which assures navigational signal coverage, communications, and meets obstacle clearance requirements.

MINIMUM IFR ALTITUDES- Minimum altitudes for IFR operations as prescribed in Part 91. These altitudes are published on aeronautical charts and prescribed in Part 95 for airways and routes, and in Part 97 for standard instrument approach procedures. If no applicable minimum altitude is prescribed in FAR 95 or FAR 97, the following minimum IFR altitude applies:

a. In designated mountainous areas, 2,000 feet above the highest obstacle within a horizontal distance of 4 nautical miles from the course to be flown; or

b. Other than mountainous areas, 1,000 feet above the highest obstacle within a horizontal distance of 4 nautical miles from the course to be flown; or

c. As otherwise authorized by the Administrator or assigned by ATC.

(See MINIMUM EN ROUTE IFR ALTITUDE.)

(See MINIMUM OBSTRUCTION CLEARANCE ALTITUDE.)

(See MINIMUM CROSSING ALTITUDE.)

(See MINIMUM SAFE ALTITUDE.)

(See MINIMUM VECTORING ALTITUDE.)

(Refer to Part 91.)

MINIMUM NAVIGATION PERFORMANCE SPECIFICATION- A set of standards which require aircraft to have a minimum navigation performance capability in order to operate in MNPS designated airspace. In addition, aircraft must be certified by their State of Registry for MNPS operation.

MINIMUM NAVIGATION PERFORMANCE SPECIFICATION AIRSPACE- Designated airspace in which MNPS procedures are applied between MNPS certified and equipped aircraft. Under certain conditions, non-MNPS aircraft can operate in MNPSA. However, standard oceanic separation minima is provided between the non-MNPS aircraft and other traffic. Currently, the only designated MNPSA is described as follows:

a. Between FL 285 and FL 420;

b. Between latitudes 27°N and the North Pole;

c. In the east, the eastern boundaries of the CTA's Santa Maria Oceanic, Shanwick Oceanic, and Reykjavik;

d. In the west, the western boundaries of CTA's Reykjavik and Gander Oceanic and New York Oceanic excluding the area west of 60°W and south of 38°30'N.

MINIMUM OBSTRUCTION CLEARANCE ALTITUDE- The lowest published altitude in effect between radio fixes on VOR airways, off-airway routes, or route segments which meets obstacle clearance requirements for the entire route segment and which assures acceptable navigational signal coverage only within 25 statute (22 nautical) miles of a VOR.

(Refer to Part 91.)

(Refer to Part 95.)

MINIMUM RECEPTION ALTITUDE- The lowest altitude at which an intersection can be determined.

(Refer to Part 95.)

MINIMUM SAFE ALTITUDE-

a. The minimum altitude specified in Part 91 for various aircraft operations.

b. Altitudes depicted on approach charts which provide at least 1,000 feet of obstacle clearance for emergency use within a specified distance from the navigation facility upon which a procedure is predicated. These altitudes will be identified as Minimum Sector Altitudes or Emergency Safe Altitudes and are established as follows:

1. Minimum Sector Altitudes. Altitudes depicted on approach charts which provide at least 1,000 feet of obstacle clearance within a 25-mile radius of the navigation facility upon which the procedure is predicated. Sectors depicted on approach charts must be at least 90 degrees in scope. These altitudes are for emergency use only and do not necessarily assure acceptable navigational signal coverage.

(See ICAO term Minimum Sector Altitude.)

2. Emergency Safe Altitudes. Altitudes depicted on approach charts which provide at least 1,000 feet of obstacle clearance in nonmountainous areas and 2,000 feet of obstacle clearance in designated mountainous areas within a 100-mile radius of the navigation facility upon which the procedure is predicated and normally used only in military procedures. These altitudes are identified on published procedures as "Emergency Safe Altitudes."

MINIMUM SAFE ALTITUDE WARNING- A function of the ARTS III computer that aids the controller by alerting him when a tracked Mode C- equipped aircraft is below or is predicted by the computer to go below a predetermined minimum safe altitude.

(Refer to AIM.)

MINIMUM SECTOR ALTITUDE [ICAO]- The lowest altitude which may be used under emergency conditions which will provide a minimum clearance of 300 m (1,000 feet) above all obstacles located in an area contained within a sector of a circle of 46 km (25 NM) radius centered on a radio aid to navigation.

MINIMUMS- Weather condition requirements established for a particular operation or type of operation; e.g., IFR takeoff or landing, alternate airport for IFR flight plans, VFR flight, etc.

(See LANDING MINIMUMS.)

(See IFR TAKEOFF MINIMUMS AND DEPARTURE PROCEDURES.)

(See VFR CONDITIONS.)

(See IFR CONDITIONS.)

(Refer to Part 91.)

(Refer to AIM.)

MINIMUM VECTORING ALTITUDE- The lowest MSL altitude at which an IFR aircraft will be vectored by a radar controller, except as otherwise authorized for radar approaches, departures, and missed approaches. The altitude

P/C

meets IFR obstacle clearance criteria. It may be lower than the published MEA along an airway or J-route segment. It may be utilized for radar vectoring only upon the controller's determination that an adequate radar return is being received from the aircraft being controlled. Charts depicting minimum vectoring altitudes are normally available only to the controllers and not to pilots.

(Refer to AIM.)

MINUTES-IN-TRAIL- A specified interval between aircraft expressed in time. This method would more likely be utilized regardless of altitude.

MIS- (See METEOROLOGICAL IMPACT STATEMENT.)

MISSED APPROACH-

a. A maneuver conducted by a pilot when an instrument approach cannot be completed to a landing. The route of flight and altitude are shown on instrument approach procedure charts. A pilot executing a missed approach prior to the Missed Approach Point (MAP) must continue along the final approach to the MAP. The pilot may climb immediately to the altitude specified in the missed approach procedure.

b. A term used by the pilot to inform ATC that he is executing the missed approach.

c. At locations where ATC radar service is provided, the pilot should conform to radar vectors when provided by ATC in lieu of the published missed approach procedure.

(See MISSED APPROACH POINT.)

(Refer to AIM.)

MISSED APPROACH POINT- A point prescribed in each instrument approach procedure at which a missed approach procedure shall be executed if the required visual reference does not exist.

(See MISSED APPROACH.)

(See SEGMENTS OF AN INSTRUMENT AP-PROACH PROCEDURE.)

MISSED APPROACH PROCEDURE [ICAO]- The procedure to be followed if the approach cannot be continued.

MISSED APPROACH SEGMENT- (See SEGMENTS OF AN INSTRUMENT APPROACH PROCEDURE.)

MLDI- (See METER LIST DISPLAY INTERVAL.)

MLS- (See MICROWAVE LANDING SYSTEM.)

MLS CATEGORIES-

a. MLS Category I. An MLS approach procedure which provides for an approach to a height above touchdown of not less than 200 feet and a runway visual range of not less than 1,800 feet.

b. MLS Category II. Undefined until data gathering/analysis completion.

c. MLS Category III. Undefined until data gathering/analysis completion.

MM- (See MIDDLE MARKER.)

MNPS- (See MINIMUM NAVIGATION PERFORMANCE SPECIFICATION.)

MNPSA- (See MINIMUM NAVIGATION PERFORMANCE SPECIFICATION AIRSPACE.)

MOA- (See MILITARY OPERATIONS AREA.)

MOCA- (See MINIMUM OBSTRUCTION CLEARANCE ALTITUDE.)

MODE- The letter or number assigned to a specific pulse spacing of radio signals transmitted or received by ground interrogator or airborne transponder components of the Air Traffic Control Radar Beacon System (ATCRBS). Mode A (military Mode 3) and Mode C (altitude reporting) are used in air traffic control.

(See TRANSPONDER.)

(See INTERROGATOR.)

(See RADAR.)

(Refer to AIM.)

(See ICAO term MODE.)

MODE (SSR MODE) [ICAO]- The letter or number assigned to a specific pulse spacing of the interrogation signals transmitted by an interrogator. There are 4 modes, A, B, C and D specified in Annex 10, corresponding to four different interrogation pulse spacings.

MODE C INTRUDER ALERT- A function of certain air traffic control automated systems designed to alert radar controllers to existing or pending situations between a tracked target (known IFR or VFR aircraft) and an untracked target (unknown IFR or VFR aircraft) that requires immediate attention/action.

(See CONFLICT ALERT.)

MONITOR- (When used with communication transfer) listen on a specific frequency and stand by for instructions. Under normal circumstances do not establish communications.

MONITOR ALERT (MA)- A function of the ETMS that provides traffic management personnel with a tool for predicting potential capacity problems in individual operational sectors. The MA is an indication that traffic management personnel need to analyze a particular sector for actual activity and to determine the required action(s), if any, needed to control the demand.

MONITOR ALERT PARAMETER (MAP)- The number designated for use in monitor alert processing by the ETMS. The MAP is designated for each operational sector for increments of 15 minutes.

MOVEMENT AREA– The runways, taxiways, and other areas of an airport/heliport which are utilized for taxiing/hover taxiing, air taxiing, takeoff, and landing of aircraft, exclusive of loading ramps and parking areas. At those airports/heliports with a tower, specific approval for entry onto the movement area must be obtained from ATC.

(See ICAO term MOVEMENT AREA.)

MOVEMENT AREA [ICAO]– That part of an aerodrome to be used for the takeoff, landing and taxiing of aircraft, consisting of the maneuvering area and the apron(s).

MOVING TARGET INDICATOR– An electronic device which will permit radar scope presentation only from targets which are in motion. A partial remedy for ground clutter.

MRA– (See MINIMUM RECEPTION ALTITUDE.)

MSA– (See MINIMUM SAFE ALTITUDE.)

MSAW– (See MINIMUM SAFE ALTITUDE WARNING.)

MTI– (See MOVING TARGET INDICATOR.)

MTR– (See MILITARY TRAINING ROUTES.)

MULTICOM– A mobile service not open to public correspondence used to provide communications essential to conduct the activities being performed by or directed from private aircraft.

MULTIPLE RUNWAYS– The utilization of a dedicated arrival runway(s) for departures and a dedicated departure runway(s) for arrivals when feasible to reduce delays and enhance capacity.

MVA– (See MINIMUM VECTORING ALTITUDE.)

P/C

N

NAS- (See NATIONAL AIRSPACE SYSTEM.)

NAS STAGE A- The en route ATC system's radar, computers and computer programs, controller plan view displays (PVD's/Radar Scopes), input/output devices, and the related communications equipment which are integrated to form the heart of the automated IFR air traffic control system. This equipment performs Flight Data Processing (FDP) and Radar Data Processing (RDP). It interfaces with automated terminal systems and is used in the control of en route IFR aircraft.

(Refer to AIM.)

NATIONAL AIRSPACE SYSTEM- The common network of U.S. airspace; air navigation facilities, equipment and services, airports or landing areas; aeronautical charts, information and services; rules, regulations and procedures, technical information, and manpower and material. Included are system components shared jointly with the military.

NATIONAL BEACON CODE ALLOCATION PLAN AIRSPACE- Airspace over United States territory located within the North American continent between Canada and Mexico, including adjacent territorial waters outward to about boundaries of oceanic control areas (CTA)/Flight Information Regions (FIR).

(See FLIGHT INFORMATION REGION.)

NATIONAL FLIGHT DATA CENTER- A facility in Washington D.C., established by FAA to operate a central aeronautical information service for the collection, validation, and dissemination of aeronautical data in support of the activities of government, industry, and the aviation community. The information is published in the National Flight Data Digest.

(See NATIONAL FLIGHT DATA DIGEST.)

NATIONAL FLIGHT DATA DIGEST- A daily (except weekends and Federal holidays) publication of flight information appropriate to aeronautical charts, aeronautical publications, Notices to Airmen, or other media serving the purpose of providing operational flight data essential to safe and efficient aircraft operations.

NATIONAL ROUTE PROGRAM (NRP)- The NRP is a set of rules and procedures which are designed to increase the flexibility of user flight planning within published guidelines.

NATIONAL SEARCH AND RESCUE PLAN- An interagency agreement which provides for the effective utilization of all available facilities in all types of search and rescue missions.

NAVAID- (See NAVIGATIONAL AID.)

NAVAID CLASSES- VOR, VORTAC, and TACAN aids are classed according to their operational use. The three classes of NAVAID's are:

a. T- Terminal.

b. L- Low altitude.

c. H- High altitude.

Note: The normal service range for T, L, and H class aids is found in the AIM. Certain operational requirements make it necessary to use some of these aids at greater service ranges than specified. Extended range is made possible through flight inspection determinations. Some aids also have lesser service range due to location, terrain, frequency protection, etc. Restrictions to service range are listed in Airport/Facility Directory.

NAVIGABLE AIRSPACE- Airspace at and above the minimum flight altitudes prescribed in the FAR's including airspace needed for safe takeoff and landing.

(Refer to FAR Part 91.)

NAVIGATIONAL AID- Any visual or electronic device airborne or on the surface which provides point-to-point guidance information or position data to aircraft in flight.

(See AIR NAVIGATION FACILITY.)

NBCAP AIRSPACE- (See NATIONAL BEACON CODE ALLOCATION PLAN AIRSPACE.)

NDB- (See NONDIRECTIONAL BEACON.)

NEGATIVE- "No," or "permission not granted," or "that is not correct."

NEGATIVE CONTACT- Used by pilots to inform ATC that:

a. Previously issued traffic is not in sight. It may be followed by the pilot's request for the controller to provide assistance in avoiding the traffic.

b. They were unable to contact ATC on a particular frequency.

NFDC- (See NATIONAL FLIGHT DATA CENTER.)

NFDD- (See NATIONAL FLIGHT DATA DIGEST.)

NIGHT- The time between the end of evening civil twilight and the beginning of morning civil twilight, as published in the American Air Almanac, converted to local time.

(See ICAO term NIGHT.)

P/C

NIGHT [ICAO]– The hours between the end of evening civil twilight and the beginning of morning civil twilight or such other period between sunset and sunrise as may be specified by the appropriate authority.

> *Note. Civil twilight ends in the evening when the center of the sun's disk is 6 degrees below the horizon and begins in the morning when the center of the sun's disk is 6 degrees below the horizon.*

NO GYRO APPROACH– A radar approach/vector provided in case of a malfunctioning gyro-compass or directional gyro. Instead of providing the pilot with headings to be flown, the controller observes the radar track and issues control instructions "turn right/left" or "stop turn" as appropriate.

> *(Refer to AIM.)*

NO GYRO VECTOR– (See NO GYRO APPROACH.)

NO TRANSGRESSION ZONE (NTZ)– The NTZ is a 2,000 foot wide zone, located equidistant between parallel runway final approach courses in which flight is not allowed.

NONAPPROACH CONTROL TOWER– Authorizes aircraft to land or takeoff at the airport controlled by the tower or to transit the Class D airspace. The primary function of a nonapproach control tower is the sequencing of aircraft in the traffic pattern and on the landing area. Nonapproach control towers also separate aircraft operating under instrument flight rules clearances from approach controls and centers. They provide ground control services to aircraft, vehicles, personnel, and equipment on the airport movement area.

NONCOMMON ROUTE/PORTION– That segment of a North American Route between the inland navigation facility and a designated North American terminal.

NONCOMPOSITE SEPARATION– Separation in accordance with minima other than the composite separation minimum specified for the area concerned.

NONDIRECTIONAL BEACON– An L/MF or UHF radio beacon transmitting nondirectional signals whereby the pilot of an aircraft equipped with direction finding equipment can determine his bearing to or from the radio beacon and "home" on or track to or from the station. When the radio beacon is installed in conjunction with the Instrument Landing System marker, it is normally called a Compass Locator.

> *(See COMPASS LOCATOR.)*
> *(See AUTOMATIC DIRECTION FINDER.)*

NONMOVEMENT AREAS– Taxiways and apron (ramp) areas not under the control of air traffic.

NONPRECISION APPROACH– (See NONPRECISION APPROACH PROCEDURE.)

NONPRECISION APPROACH PROCEDURE– A standard instrument approach procedure in which no electronic gli-

deslope is provided; e.g., VOR, TACAN, NDB, LOC, ASR, LDA, or SDF approaches.

NONRADAR– Precedes other terms and generally means without the use of radar, such as:

a. Nonradar Approach. Used to describe instrument approaches for which course guidance on final approach is not provided by ground-based precision or surveillance radar. Radar vectors to the final approach course may or may not be provided by ATC. Examples of nonradar approaches are VOR, NDB, TACAN, and ILS/MLS approaches.

> *(See FINAL APPROACH-IFR.)*
> *(See FINAL APPROACH COURSE.)*
> *(See RADAR APPROACH.)*
> *(See INSTRUMENT APPROACH PROCEDURE.)*

b. Nonradar Approach Control. An ATC facility providing approach control service without the use of radar.

> *(See APPROACH CONTROL FACILITY.)*
> *(See APPROACH CONTROL SERVICE.)*

c. Nonradar Arrival. An aircraft arriving at an airport without radar service or at an airport served by a radar facility and radar contact has not been established or has been terminated due to a lack of radar service to the airport.

> *(See RADAR ARRIVAL.)*
> *(See RADAR SERVICE.)*

d. Nonradar Route. A flight path or route over which the pilot is performing his own navigation. The pilot may be receiving radar separation, radar monitoring, or other ATC services while on a nonradar route.

> *(See RADAR ROUTE.)*

e. Nonradar Separation. The spacing of aircraft in accordance with established minima without the use of radar; e.g., vertical, lateral, or longitudinal separation.

> *(See RADAR SEPARATION.)*
> *(See ICAO term NONRADAR SEPARATION.)*

NONRADAR SEPARATION [ICAO]– The separation used when aircraft position information is derived from sources other than radar.

NOPAC– (See NORTH PACIFIC.)

NORDO– (See LOST COMMUNICATIONS.)

NORMAL OPERATING ZONE (NOZ)– The NOZ is the operating zone within which aircraft flight remains during normal independent simultaneous parallel ILS approaches.

NORTH AMERICAN ROUTE– A numerically coded route preplanned over existing airway and route systems to and from specific coastal fixes serving the North Atlantic. North American Routes consist of the following:

a. Common Route/Portion. That segment of a North American Route between the inland navigation facility and the coastal fix.

b. Noncommon Route/Portion. That segment of a North American Route between the inland navigation facility and a designated North American terminal.

c. Inland Navigation Facility. A navigation aid on a North American Route at which the common route and/or the noncommon route begins or ends.

d. Coastal Fix. A navigation aid or intersection where an aircraft transitions between the domestic route structure and the oceanic route structure.

NORTH MARK– A beacon data block sent by the host computer to be displayed by the ARTS on a 360 degree bearing at a locally selected radar azimuth and distance. The North Mark is used to ensure correct range/azimuth orientation during periods of CENRAP.

NORTH PACIFIC– An organized route system between the Alaskan west coast and Japan.

NOTAM– (See NOTICE TO AIRMEN.)

NOTICE TO AIRMEN– A notice containing information (not known sufficiently in advance to publicize by other means) concerning the establishment, condition, or change in any component (facility, service, or procedure of, or hazard in the National Airspace System) the timely knowledge of which is essential to personnel concerned with flight operations.

a. NOTAM(D)– A NOTAM given (in addition to local dissemination) distant dissemination beyond the area of responsibility of the Flight Service Station. These NOTAM's will be stored and available until canceled.

b. NOTAM(L)– A NOTAM given local dissemination by voice and other means, such as telautograph and telephone, to satisfy local user requirements.

c. FDC NOTAM– A NOTAM regulatory in nature, transmitted by USNOF and given system wide dissemination.

(See ICAO term NOTAM.)

NOTAM [ICAO]– A notice containing information concerning the establishment, condition or change in any aeronautical facility, service, procedure or hazard, the timely knowledge of which is essential to personnel concerned with flight operations.

a. I Distribution– Distribution by means of telecommunication.

b. II Distribution– Distribution by means other than telecommunications.

NOTICES TO AIRMEN PUBLICATION– A publication issued every 28 days, designed primarily for the pilot, which contains current NOTAM information considered essential to the safety of flight as well as supplemental data to other aeronautical publications. The contraction NTAP is used in NOTAM text.

(See NOTICE TO AIRMEN.)

NTAP– (See NOTICES TO AIRMEN PUBLICATION.)

NUMEROUS TARGETS VICINITY (LOCATION)– A traffic advisory issued by ATC to advise pilots that targets on the radar scope are too numerous to issue individually.

(See TRAFFIC ADVISORIES.)

O

OBSTACLE– An existing object, object of natural growth, or terrain at a fixed geographical location or which may be expected at a fixed location within a prescribed area with reference to which vertical clearance is or must be provided during flight operation.

OBSTACLE FREE ZONE– The OFZ is a three dimensional volume of airspace which protects for the transition of aircraft to and from the runway. The OFZ clearing standard precludes taxiing and parked airplanes and object penetrations, except for frangible NAVAID locations that are fixed by function. Additionally, vehicles, equipment, and personnel may be authorized by air traffic control to enter the area using the provisions of FAA Order 7110.65, *paragraph 3–1–5, VEHICLES/EQUIPMENT/PERSONNEL ON RUNWAYS.* The runway OFZ and when applicable, the inner-approach OFZ, and the inner-transitional OFZ, comprise the OFZ.

   a. Runway OFZ. The runway OFZ is a defined volume of airspace centered above the runway. The runway OFZ is the airspace above a surface whose elevation at any point is the same as the elevation of the nearest point on the runway centerline. The runway OFZ extends 200 feet beyond each end of the runway. The width is as follows:

   1. For runways serving large airplanes, the greater of:

   (a) 400 feet, or

   (b) 180 feet, plus the wingspan of the most demanding airplane, plus 20 feet per 1,000 feet of airport elevation.

   2. For runways serving only small airplanes:

   (a) 300 feet for precision instrument runways.

   (b) 250 feet for other runways serving small airplanes with approach speeds of 50 knots, or more.

   (c) 120 feet for other runways serving small airplanes with approach speeds of less than 50 knots.

   b. Inner-approach OFZ. The inner-approach OFZ is a defined volume of airspace centered on the approach area. The inner-approach OFZ applies only to runways with an approach lighting system. The inner-approach OFZ begins 200 feet from the runway threshold at the same elevation as the runway threshold and extends 200 feet beyond the last light unit in the approach lighting system. The width of the inner-approach OFZ is the same as the runway OFZ and rises at a slope of 50 (horizontal) to 1 (vertical) from the beginning.

   c. Inner-transitional OFZ. The inner transitional surface OFZ is a defined volume of airspace along the sides of the runway and inner-approach OFZ and applies only to precision instrument runways. The inner-transitional surface OFZ slopes 3 (horizontal) to 1 (vertical) out from the edges of the runway OFZ and inner-approach OFZ to a height of 150 feet above the established airport elevation.
   (Refer to AC 150/5300-13, Chapter 3 and FAA Order 7110.65, paragraph 3–1–5, VEHICLES/EQUIPMENT/PERSONNEL ON RUNWAYS.)

OBSTRUCTION– Any object/obstacle exceeding the obstruction standards specified by FAR Part 77, Subpart C.

OBSTRUCTION LIGHT– A light or one of a group of lights, usually red or white, frequently mounted on a surface structure or natural terrain to warn pilots of the presence of an obstruction.

OCEANIC AIRSPACE– Airspace over the oceans of the world, considered international airspace, where oceanic separation and procedures per the International Civil Aviation Organization are applied. Responsibility for the provisions of air traffic control service in this airspace is delegated to various countries, based generally upon geographic proximity and the availability of the required resources.

OCEANIC DISPLAY AND PLANNING SYSTEM– An automated digital display system which provides flight data processing, conflict probe, and situation display for oceanic air traffic control.

OCEANIC NAVIGATIONAL ERROR REPORT– A report filed when an aircraft exiting oceanic airspace has been observed by radar to be off course. ONER reporting parameters and procedures are contained in FAA Order 7110.82, Monitoring of Navigational Performance In Oceanic Areas.

OCEANIC PUBLISHED ROUTE– A route established in international airspace and charted or described in flight information publications, such as Route Charts, DOD Enroute Charts, Chart Supplements, NOTAM's, and Track Messages.

OCEANIC TRANSITION ROUTE– An ATS route established for the purpose of transitioning aircraft to/from an organized track system.

ODAPS– (See OCEANIC DISPLAY AND PLANNING SYSTEM.)

OFF COURSE– A term used to describe a situation where an aircraft has reported a position fix or is observed on radar at a point not on the ATC-approved route of flight.

OFFSHORE CONTROL AREA– That portion of airspace between the U.S. 12-mile limit and the oceanic CTA/FIR boundary within which air traffic control is exercised. These areas are established to permit the application of domestic procedures in the provision of air traffic control services. Offshore control area is generally synonymous with Federal Aviation Regulations, FAR Part 71, Subpart E, "Control Areas and Control Area Extensions."

OFF-ROUTE VECTOR– A vector by ATC which takes an aircraft off a previously assigned route. Altitudes assigned by ATC during such vectors provide required obstacle clearance.

OFFSET PARALLEL RUNWAYS– Staggered runways having centerlines which are parallel.

OFT– (See OUTER FIX TIME.)

OM– (See OUTER MARKER.)

OMEGA– An RNAV system designed for long-range navigation based upon ground-based electronic navigational aid signals.

ONE–MINUTE WEATHER– The most recent one minute updated weather broadcast received by a pilot from an uncontrolled airport ASOS/AWOS.

ONER– (See OCEANIC NAVIGATIONAL ERROR REPORT.)

OPERATIONAL– (See DUE REGARD.)

ON COURSE-

a. Used to indicate that an aircraft is established on the route centerline.

b. Used by ATC to advise a pilot making a radar approach that his aircraft is lined up on the final approach course.

(See ON-COURSE INDICATION-COURSE INDICATION.)

ON-COURSE INDICATION– An indication on an instrument, which provides the pilot a visual means of determining that the aircraft is located on the centerline of a given navigational track, or an indication on a radar scope that an aircraft is on a given track.

OPPOSITE DIRECTION AIRCRAFT– Aircraft are operating in opposite directions when:

a. They are following the same track in reciprocal directions; or

b. Their tracks are parallel and the aircraft are flying in reciprocal directions; or

c. Their tracks intersect at an angle of more than 135°.

OPTION APPROACH– An approach requested and conducted by a pilot which will result in either a touch-and-go, missed approach, low approach, stop-and-go, or full stop landing.

(See CLEARED FOR THE OPTION.)

(Refer to AIM.)

ORGANIZED TRACK SYSTEM– A movable system of oceanic tracks that traverses the North Atlantic between Europe and North America the physical position of which is determined twice daily taking the best advantage of the winds aloft.

ORGANIZED TRACK SYSTEM– A series of ATS routes which are fixed and charted; i.e., CEP, NOPAC, or flexible and described by NOTAM; i.e., NAT TRACK MESSAGE.

OROCA– An off-route altitude which provides obstruction clearance with a 1,000 foot buffer in nonmountainous terrain areas and a 2,000 foot buffer in designated mountainous areas within the United States. This altitude may not provide signal coverage from ground-based navigational aids, air traffic control radar, or communications coverage.

OTR– (See OCEANIC TRANSITION ROUTE.)

OTS– (See ORGANIZED TRACK SYSTEM.)

OUT- The conversation is ended and no response is expected.

OUTER AREA (associated with Class C airspace)– Nonregulatory airspace surrounding designated Class C airspace airports wherein ATC provides radar vectoring and sequencing on a full-time basis for all IFR and participating VFR aircraft. The service provided in the outer area is called Class C service which includes: IFR/IFR-standard IFR separation; IFR/VFR-traffic advisories and conflict resolution; and VFR/VFR-traffic advisories and, as appropriate, safety alerts. The normal radius will be 20 nautical miles with some variations based on site-specific requirements. The outer area extends outward from the primary Class C airspace airport and extends from the lower limits of radar/radio coverage up to the ceiling of the approach control's delegated airspace excluding the Class C charted area and other airspace as appropriate.

(See CONTROLLED AIRSPACE.)

(See CONFLICT RESOLUTION.)

OUTER COMPASS LOCATOR– (See COMPASS LOCATOR.)

OUTER FIX– A general term used within ATC to describe fixes in the terminal area, other than the final approach fix. Aircraft are normally cleared to these fixes by an Air Route Traffic Control Center or an Approach Control Facility. Aircraft are normally cleared from these fixes to the final approach fix or final approach course.

OUTER FIX– An adapted fix along the converted route of flight, prior to the meter fix, for which crossing times are calculated and displayed in the metering position list.

OUTER FIX TIME– A calculated time to depart the outer fix in order to cross the vertex at the ACLT. The time reflects descent speed adjustments and any applicable delay time that must be absorbed prior to crossing the meter fix.

OUTER MARKER– A marker beacon at or near the glideslope intercept altitude of an ILS approach. It is keyed to transmit two dashes per second on a 400 Hz tone, which is received aurally and visually by compatible airborne equipment. The OM is normally located four to seven miles from

Pilot/Controller Glossary

the runway threshold on the extended centerline of the runway.

(See MARKER BEACON.)

(See INSTRUMENT LANDING SYSTEM.)

(Refer to AIM.)

OVER– My transmission is ended; I expect a response.

OVERHEAD MANEUVER– A series of predetermined maneuvers prescribed for aircraft (often in formation) for entry into the visual flight rules (VFR) traffic pattern and to proceed to a landing. An overhead maneuver is not an instrument flight rules (IFR) approach procedure. An aircraft executing an overhead maneuver is considered VFR and the IFR flight plan is cancelled when the aircraft reaches the "initial point" on the initial approach portion of the maneuver. The pattern usually specifies the following:

a. The radio contact required of the pilot.

b. The speed to be maintained.

c. An initial approach 3 to 5 miles in length.

d. An elliptical pattern consisting of two 180 degree turns.

e. A break point at which the first 180 degree turn is started.

f. The direction of turns.

g. Altitude (at least 500 feet above the conventional pattern).

h. A "Roll-out" on final approach not less than 1/4 mile from the landing threshold and not less than 300 feet above the ground.

OVERLYING CENTER– The ARTCC facility that is responsible for arrival/departure operations at a specific terminal.

P

P TIME-
(See PROPOSED DEPARTURE TIME.)

PAN-PAN- The international radio-telephony urgency signal. When repeated three times, indicates uncertainty or alert followed by the nature of the urgency.

(See MAYDAY.)

(Refer to AIM.)

PAR-
(See PRECISION APPROACH RADAR.)

PAR [ICAO]-
(See ICAO Term PRECISION APPROACH RADAR.)

PARALLEL ILS APPROACHES- Approaches to parallel runways by IFR aircraft which, when established inbound toward the airport on the adjacent final approach courses, are radar-separated by at least 2 miles.

(See FINAL APPROACH COURSE.)

(See SIMULTANEOUS ILS APPROACHES.)

PARALLEL MLS APPROACHES-
(See PARALLEL ILS APPROACHES.)

PARALLEL OFFSET ROUTE- A parallel track to the left or right of the designated or established airway/route. Normally associated with Area Navigation (RNAV) operations.

(See AREA NAVIGATION.)

PARALLEL RUNWAYS- Two or more runways at the same airport whose centerlines are parallel. In addition to runway number, parallel runways are designated as L (left) and R (right) or, if three parallel runways exist, L (left), C (center), and R (right).

PATWAS-
(See PILOTS AUTOMATIC TELEPHONE WEATHER ANSWERING SERVICE.)

PBCT-
(See PROPOSED BOUNDARY CROSSING TIME.)

PERMANENT ECHO- Radar signals reflected from fixed objects on the earth's surface; e.g., buildings, towers, terrain. Permanent echoes are distinguished from "ground clutter" by being definable locations rather than large areas. Under certain conditions they may be used to check radar alignment.

PHOTO RECONNAISSANCE- Military activity that requires locating individual photo targets and navigating to the targets at a preplanned angle and altitude. The activity normally requires a lateral route width of 16 NM and altitude range of 1,500 feet to 10,000 feet AGL.

PIDP-
(See PROGRAMMABLE INDICATOR DATA PROCESSOR.)

PILOT BRIEFING- A service provided by the FSS to assist pilots in flight planning. Briefing items may include weather information, NOTAMS, military activities, flow control information, and other items as requested.

(Refer to AIM.)

PILOT IN COMMAND- The pilot responsible for the operation and safety of an aircraft during flight time.

(Refer to FAR Part 91.)

PILOTS AUTOMATIC TELEPHONE WEATHER ANSWERING SERVICE- A continuous telephone recording containing current and forecast weather information for pilots.

(See FLIGHT SERVICE STATION.)

(Refer to AIM.)

PILOT'S DISCRETION- When used in conjunction with altitude assignments, means that ATC has offered the pilot the option of starting climb or descent whenever he wishes and conducting the climb or descent at any rate he wishes. He may temporarily level off at any intermediate altitude. However, once he has vacated an altitude, he may not return to that altitude.

PILOT WEATHER REPORT- A report of meteorological phenomena encountered by aircraft in flight.

(Refer to AIM.)

PIREP-
(See PILOT WEATHER REPORT.)

POINT OUT-
(See RADAR POINT OUT.)

POLAR TRACK STRUCTURE- A system of organized routes between Iceland and Alaska which overlie Canadian MNPS Airspace.

POSITION REPORT- A report over a known location as transmitted by an aircraft to ATC.

(Refer to AIM.)

POSITION SYMBOL- A computer-generated indication shown on a radar display to indicate the mode of tracking.

POSITIVE CONTROL- The separation of all air traffic within designated airspace by air traffic control.

PRACTICE INSTRUMENT APPROACH- An instrument approach procedure conducted by a VFR or an IFR aircraft for the purpose of pilot training or proficiency demonstrations.

PREARRANGED COORDINATION- A standardized procedure which permits an air traffic controller to enter the airspace assigned to another air traffic controller without verbal coordination. The procedures are defined in a facility directive which ensures standard separation between aircraft.

PRECIPITATION- Any or all forms of water particles (rain, sleet, hail, or snow) that fall from the atmosphere and reach the surface.

PRECISION APPROACH-
(See PRECISION APPROACH PROCEDURE.)

PRECISION APPROACH PROCEDURE- A standard instrument approach procedure in which an electronic glideslope/glidepath is provided; e.g., ILS/MLS and PAR.

(See INSTRUMENT LANDING SYSTEM.)

(See MICROWAVE LANDING SYSTEM.)

(See PRECISION APPROACH RADAR.)

PRECISION APPROACH RADAR- Radar equipment in some ATC facilities operated by the FAA and/or the military services at joint-use civil/military locations and separate military installations to detect and display azimuth, elevation, and range of aircraft on the final approach course to a runway. This equipment may be used to monitor certain nonradar approaches, but is primarily used to conduct a precision instrument approach (PAR) wherein the controller issues guidance instructions to the pilot based on the aircraft's position in relation to the final approach course (azimuth), the glidepath (elevation), and the distance (range) from the touchdown point on the runway as displayed on the radar scope.

(Note: The abbreviation "PAR" is also used to denote preferential arrival routes in ARTCC computers).

(See GLIDEPATH.)

(See PAR.)

(See PREFERENTIAL ROUTES.)

(See ICAO term PRECISION APPROACH RADAR.)

(Refer to AIM.)

PRECISION APPROACH RADAR [ICAO]- Primary radar equipment used to determine the position of an aircraft during final approach, in terms of lateral and vertical deviations relative to a nominal approach path, and in range relative to touchdown.

Note: Precision approach radars are designed to enable pilots of aircraft to be given guidance by radio communication during the final stages of the approach to land.

PRECISION RUNWAY MONITOR (PRM)- Provides air traffic controllers with high precision secondary surveillance data for aircraft on final approach to parallel runways that have extended centerlines separated by less than 4,300 feet. High resolution color monitoring displays (FMA) are required to present surveillance track data to controllers along with detailed maps depicting approaches and no transgression zone.

PREFERENTIAL ROUTES- Preferential routes (PDR's, PAR's, and PDAR's) are adapted in ARTCC computers to accomplish inter/intrafacility controller coordination and to assure that flight data is posted at the proper control positions. Locations having a need for these specific inbound and outbound routes normally publish such routes in local facility bulletins, and their use by pilots minimizes flight plan route amendments. When the workload or traffic situation permits, controllers normally provide radar vectors or assign requested routes to minimize circuitous routing. Preferential routes are usually confined to one ARTCC's area and are referred to by the following names or acronyms:

a. Preferential Departure Route (PDR). A specific departure route from an airport or terminal area to an en route point where there is no further need for flow control. It may be included in an Instrument Departure Procedure (DP) or a Preferred IFR Route.

b. Preferential Arrival Route (PAR). A specific arrival route from an appropriate en route point to an airport or terminal area. It may be included in a Standard Terminal Arrival (STAR) or a Preferred IFR Route. The abbreviation "PAR" is used primarily within the ARTCC and should not be confused with the abbreviation for Precision Approach Radar.

c. Preferential Departure and Arrival Route (PDAR). A route between two terminals which are within or immediately adjacent to one ARTCC's area. PDAR's are not synonymous with Preferred IFR Routes but may be listed as such as they do accomplish essentially the same purpose.

(See PREFERRED IFR ROUTES.)

(See NAS STAGE A.)

PREFERRED IFR ROUTES- Routes established between busier airports to increase system efficiency and capacity. They normally extend through one or more ARTCC areas and are designed to achieve balanced traffic flows among high density terminals. IFR clearances are issued on the basis of these routes except when severe weather avoidance procedures or other factors dictate otherwise. Preferred IFR Routes are listed in the Airport/Facility Directory. If a flight is planned to or from an area having such routes but the departure or arrival point is not listed in the Airport/Facility Directory, pilots may use that part of a Preferred IFR Route which is appropriate for the departure or arrival point that is listed. Preferred IFR Routes are correlated with DP's and STAR's and may be defined by airways, jet routes, direct routes between NAVAID's, Waypoints, NAVAID radials/DME, or any combinations thereof.

(See INSTRUMENT DEPARTURE PROCEDURE.)

(See STANDARD TERMINAL ARRIVAL.)

(See PREFERENTIAL ROUTES.)

(See CENTER'S AREA.)

(Refer to AIRPORT/FACILITY DIRECTORY.)

(Refer to NOTICES TO AIRMEN PUBLICATION.)

PRE-FLIGHT PILOT BRIEFING-
(See PILOT BRIEFING.)

PREVAILING VISIBILITY-
(See VISIBILITY.)

PRM-
(See ILS PRM APPROACH and PRECISION RUNWAY MONITOR.)

PROCEDURE TURN- The maneuver prescribed when it is necessary to reverse direction to establish an aircraft on the intermediate approach segment or final approach course. The outbound course, direction of turn, distance within which the turn must be completed, and minimum altitude are specified in the procedure. However, unless otherwise restricted, the point at which the turn may be commenced and the type and rate of turn are left to the discretion of the pilot.

(See ICAO term PROCEDURE TURN.)

PROCEDURE TURN [ICAO]- A manoeuvre in which a turn is made away from a designated track followed by a turn in the opposite direction to permit the aircraft to intercept and proceed along the reciprocal of the designated track.

Note 1: Procedure turns are designated "left" or "right" according to the direction of the initial turn.

Note 2: Procedure turns may be designated as being made either in level flight or while descending, according to the circumstances of each individual approach procedure.

PROCEDURE TURN INBOUND- That point of a procedure turn maneuver where course reversal has been completed and an aircraft is established inbound on the intermediate approach segment or final approach course. A report of "procedure turn inbound" is normally used by ATC as a position report for separation purposes.

(See FINAL APPROACH COURSE.)

(See PROCEDURE TURN.)

(See SEGMENTS OF AN INSTRUMENT APPROACH PROCEDURE.)

PROFILE DESCENT- An uninterrupted descent (except where level flight is required for speed adjustment; e.g., 250 knots at 10,000 feet MSL) from cruising altitude/level to interception of a glideslope or to a minimum altitude specified for the initial or intermediate approach segment of a nonprecision instrument approach. The profile descent normally terminates at the approach gate or where the glideslope or other appropriate minimum altitude is intercepted.

PROGRAMMABLE INDICATOR DATA PROCESSOR- The PIDP is a modification to the AN/TPX-42 interrogator system currently installed in fixed RAPCON's. The PIDP detects, tracks, and predicts secondary radar aircraft targets. These are displayed by means of computer-generated symbols and alphanumeric characters depicting flight identification, aircraft altitude, ground speed, and flight plan data. Although primary radar targets are not tracked, they are displayed coincident with the secondary radar targets as well as with the other symbols and alphanumerics. The system has the capability of interfacing with ARTCC's.

PROGRESS REPORT-
(See POSITION REPORT.)

PROGRESSIVE TAXI- Precise taxi instructions given to a pilot unfamiliar with the airport or issued in stages as the aircraft proceeds along the taxi route.

PROHIBITED AREA-
(See SPECIAL USE AIRSPACE.)

(See ICAO term PROHIBITED AREA.)

PROHIBITED AREA [ICAO]- An airspace of defined dimensions, above the land areas or territorial waters of a State, within which the flight of aircraft is prohibited.

PROPOSED BOUNDARY CROSSING TIME- Each center has a PBCT parameter for each internal airport. Proposed internal flight plans are transmitted to the adjacent center if the flight time along the proposed route from the departure airport to the center boundary is less than or equal to the value of PBCT or if airport adaptation specifies transmission regardless of PBCT.

PROPOSED DEPARTURE TIME- The time a scheduled flight will depart the gate (scheduled operators) or the actual runway off time for nonscheduled operators. For EDCT purposes, the ATCSCC adjusts the "P" time for scheduled operators to reflect the runway off times.

PROTECTED AIRSPACE- The airspace on either side of an oceanic route/track that is equal to one-half the lateral separation minimum except where reduction of protected airspace has been authorized.

PT-
(See PROCEDURE TURN.)

PTS-
(See POLAR TRACK STRUCTURE.)

PUBLISHED ROUTE- A route for which an IFR altitude has been established and published; e.g., Federal Airways, Jet Routes, Area Navigation Routes, Specified Direct Routes.

P/C

Q

QUEUING– (See STAGING/QUEUING.)

QNE– The barometric pressure used for the standard altimeter setting (29.92 inches Hg.).

QNH– The barometric pressure as reported by a particular station.

QUADRANT– A quarter part of a circle, centered on a NAVAID, oriented clockwise from magnetic north as follows: NE quadrant 000-089, SE quadrant 090-179, SW quadrant 180-269, NW quadrant 270-359.

QUICK LOOK– A feature of NAS Stage A and ARTS which provides the controller the capability to display full data blocks of tracked aircraft from other control positions.

QUOTA FLOW CONTROL– A flow control procedure by which the Central Flow Control Function (CFCF) restricts traffic to the ARTC Center area having an impacted airport, thereby avoiding sector/area saturation.

(See AIR TRAFFIC CONTROL SYSTEM COMMAND CENTER.)

(Refer to AIRPORT/FACILITY DIRECTORY.)

P/C

R

RADAR– A device which, by measuring the time interval between transmission and reception of radio pulses and correlating the angular orientation of the radiated antenna beam or beams in azimuth and/or elevation, provides information on range, azimuth, and/or elevation of objects in the path of the transmitted pulses.

   a. Primary Radar– A radar system in which a minute portion of a radio pulse transmitted from a site is reflected by an object and then received back at that site for processing and display at an air traffic control facility.

   b. Secondary Radar/Radar Beacon (ATCRBS)– A radar system in which the object to be detected is fitted with cooperative equipment in the form of a radio receiver/transmitter (transponder). Radar pulses transmitted from the searching transmitter/receiver (interrogator) site are received in the cooperative equipment and used to trigger a distinctive transmission from the transponder. This reply transmission, rather than a reflected signal, is then received back at the transmitter/receiver site for processing and display at an air traffic control facility.

   (See INTERROGATOR.)

   (See TRANSPONDER.)

   (See ICAO term PRIMARY RADAR.)

   (See ICAO term RADAR.)

   (See ICAO term SECONDARY RADAR.)

   (Refer to AIM.)

RADAR [ICAO]– A radio detection device which provides information on range, azimuth and/or elevation of objects.

   a. Primary Radar– Radar system which uses reflected radio signals.

   b. Secondary Radar– Radar system wherein a radio signal transmitted from a radar station initiates the transmission of a radio signal from another station.

RADAR ADVISORY– The provision of advice and information based on radar observations.

   (See ADVISORY SERVICE.)

RADAR ALTIMETER– (See RADIO ALTIMETER.)

RADAR APPROACH– An instrument approach procedure which utilizes Precision Approach Radar (PAR) or Airport Surveillance Radar (ASR).

   (See AIRPORT SURVEILLANCE RADAR.)

   (See INSTRUMENT APPROACH PROCEDURE.)

   (See PRECISION APPROACH RADAR.)

   (See SURVEILLANCE APPROACH.)

   (See ICAO term RADAR APPROACH.)

   (Refer to AIM.)

RADAR APPROACH [ICAO]– An approach, executed by an aircraft, under the direction of a radar controller.

RADAR APPROACH CONTROL FACILITY– A terminal ATC facility that uses radar and nonradar capabilities to provide approach control services to aircraft arriving, departing, or transiting airspace controlled by the facility

   (See APPROACH CONTROL SERVICE.)

   a. Provides radar ATC services to aircraft operating in the vicinity of one or more civil and/or military airports in a terminal area. The facility may provide services of a ground controlled approach (GCA); i.e., ASR and PAR approaches. A radar approach control facility may be operated by FAA, USAF, US Army, USN, USMC, or jointly by FAA and a military service. Specific facility nomenclatures are used for administrative purposes only and are related to the physical location of the facility and the operating service generally as follows:

   1. Army Radar Approach Control (ARAC) (Army).

   2. Radar Air Traffic Control Facility (RATCF) (Navy/FAA).

   3. Radar Approach Control (RAPCON) (Air Force/FAA).

   4. Terminal Radar Approach Control (TRACON) (FAA).

   5. Air Traffic Control Tower (ATCT) (FAA). (Only those towers delegated approach control authority.).

RADAR ARRIVAL– An aircraft arriving at an airport served by a radar facility and in radar contact with the facility.

   (See NONRADAR.)

RADAR BEACON– (See RADAR.)

P/C

RADAR CONTACT-

a. Used by ATC to inform an aircraft that it is identified on the radar display and radar flight following will be provided until radar identification is terminated. Radar service may also be provided within the limits of necessity and capability. When a pilot is informed of "radar contact," he automatically discontinues reporting over compulsory reporting points.

(See RADAR CONTACT LOST.)

(See RADAR FLIGHT FOLLOWING.)

(See RADAR SERVICE.)

(See RADAR SERVICE TERMINATED.)

(Refer to AIM.)

b. The term used to inform the controller that the aircraft is identified and approval is granted for the aircraft to enter the receiving controllers airspace.

(See ICAO term RADAR CONTACT.)

RADAR CONTACT LOST- Used by ATC to inform a pilot that radar data used to determine the aircraft's position is no longer being received, or is no longer reliable and radar service is no longer being provided. The loss may be attributed to several factors including the aircraft merging with weather or ground clutter, the aircraft operating below radar line of sight coverage, the aircraft entering an area of poor radar return, failure of the aircraft transponder, or failure of the ground radar equipment.

(See CLUTTER.)

(See RADAR CONTACT.)

RADAR CLUTTER [ICAO]- The visual indication on a radar display of unwanted signals.

RADAR CONTACT [ICAO]- The situation which exists when the radar blip or radar position symbol of a particular aircraft is seen and identified on a radar display.

RADAR ENVIRONMENT- An area in which radar service may be provided.

(See ADDITIONAL SERVICES.)

(See RADAR CONTACT.)

(See RADAR SERVICE.)

(See TRAFFIC ADVISORIES.)

RADAR FLIGHT FOLLOWING- The observation of the progress of radar identified aircraft, whose primary navigation is being provided by the pilot, wherein the controller retains and correlates the aircraft identity with the appropriate target or target symbol displayed on the radar scope.

(See RADAR CONTACT.)

(See RADAR SERVICE.)

(Refer to AIM.)

RADAR IDENTIFICATION- The process of ascertaining that an observed radar target is the radar return from a particular aircraft.

(See RADAR CONTACT.)

(See RADAR SERVICE.)

(See ICAO term RADAR IDENTIFICATION.)

RADAR IDENTIFICATION [ICAO]- The process of correlating a particular radar blip or radar position symbol with a specific aircraft.

RADAR IDENTIFIED AIRCRAFT- An aircraft, the position of which has been correlated with an observed target or symbol on the radar display.

(See RADAR CONTACT.)

(See RADAR CONTACT LOST.)

RADAR MONITORING- (See RADAR SERVICE.)

RADAR NAVIGATIONAL GUIDANCE- (See RADAR SERVICE.)

RADAR POINT OUT- An action taken by a controller to transfer the radar identification of an aircraft to another controller if the aircraft will or may enter the airspace or protected airspace of another controller and radio communications will not be transferred.

RADAR REQUIRED- A term displayed on charts and approach plates and included in FDC NOTAM's to alert pilots that segments of either an instrument approach procedure or a route are not navigable because of either the absence or unusability of a NAVAID. The pilot can expect to be provided radar navigational guidance while transiting segments labeled with this term.

(See RADAR ROUTE.)

(See RADAR SERVICE.)

RADAR ROUTE- A flight path or route over which an aircraft is vectored. Navigational guidance and altitude assignments are provided by ATC.

(See FLIGHT PATH.)

(See ROUTE.)

RADAR SEPARATION- (See RADAR SERVICE.)

RADAR SERVICE- A term which encompasses one or more of the following services based on the use of radar which can be provided by a controller to a pilot of a radar identified aircraft.

a. Radar Monitoring- The radar flight-following of aircraft, whose primary navigation is being performed by the pilot, to observe and note deviations from its authorized flight path, airway, or route. When being applied specifically to radar monitoring of instrument approaches; i.e., with precision approach radar (PAR) or radar monitoring of simultaneous ILS/MLS approaches, it includes advice and instructions whenever an aircraft nears or exceeds the prescribed PAR safety limit or simultaneous ILS/MLS no transgression zone.

(See ADDITIONAL SERVICES.)

(See TRAFFIC ADVISORIES.)

b. Radar Navigational Guidance– Vectoring aircraft to provide course guidance.

c. Radar Separation– Radar spacing of aircraft in accordance with established minima.

(See ICAO term RADAR SERVICE.)

RADAR SERVICE [ICAO]– Term used to indicate a service provided directly by means of radar.

a. Monitoring– The use of radar for the purpose of providing aircraft with information and advice relative to significant deviations from nominal flight path.

b. Separation– The separation used when aircraft position information is derived from radar sources.

RADAR SERVICE TERMINATED– Used by ATC to inform a pilot that he will no longer be provided any of the services that could be received while in radar contact. Radar service is automatically terminated, and the pilot is not advised in the following cases:

a. An aircraft cancels its IFR flight plan, except within Class B airspace, Class C airspace, a TRSA, or where Basic Radar service is provided.

b. An aircraft conducting an instrument, visual, or contact approach has landed or has been instructed to change to advisory frequency.

c. An arriving VFR aircraft, receiving radar service to a tower-controlled airport within Class B airspace, Class C airspace, a TRSA, or where sequencing service is provided, has landed; or to all other airports, is instructed to change to tower or advisory frequency.

d. An aircraft completes a radar approach.

RADAR SURVEILLANCE– The radar observation of a given geographical area for the purpose of performing some radar function.

RADAR TRAFFIC ADVISORIES– Advisories issued to alert pilots to known or observed radar traffic which may affect the intended route of flight of their aircraft.

(See TRAFFIC ADVISORIES.)

RADAR TRAFFIC INFORMATION SERVICE– (See TRAFFIC ADVISORIES.)

RADAR VECTORING [ICAO]– Provision of navigational guidance to aircraft in the form of specific headings, based on the use of radar.

RADAR WEATHER ECHO INTENSITY LEVELS– Existing radar systems cannot detect turbulence. However, there is a direct correlation between the degree of turbulence and other weather features associated with thunderstorms and the radar weather echo intensity. The National Weather Service has categorized radar weather echo intensity for precipitation into six levels. These levels are sometimes expressed during communications as "VIP LEVEL" 1 through 6 (derived from the component of the radar that produces the information-Video Integrator and Processor). The following

list gives the "VIP LEVELS" in relation to the precipitation intensity within a thunderstorm:

a. Level 1. WEAK

b. Level 2. MODERATE

c. Level 3. STRONG

d. Level 4. VERY STRONG

e. Level 5. INTENSE

f. Level 6. EXTREME

(See AC 00-45, Aviation Weather Services.)

RADIAL– A magnetic bearing extending from a VOR/ VORTAC/TACAN navigation facility.

RADIO–

a. A device used for communication.

b. Used to refer to a flight service station; e.g., "Seattle Radio" is used to call Seattle FSS.

RADIO ALTIMETER– Aircraft equipment which makes use of the reflection of radio waves from the ground to determine the height of the aircraft above the surface.

RADIO BEACON– (See NONDIRECTIONAL BEACON.)

RADIO DETECTION AND RANGING– (See RADAR.)

RADIO MAGNETIC INDICATOR– An aircraft navigational instrument coupled with a gyro compass or similar compass that indicates the direction of a selected NAVAID and indicates bearing with respect to the heading of the aircraft.

RAMP– (See APRON.)

RANDOM ALTITUDE– An altitude inappropriate for direction of flight and/or not in accordance with FAA Order 7110.65, paragraph 4-5-1, VERTICAL SEPARATION MINIMA.

RANDOM ROUTE– Any route not established or charted/ published or not otherwise available to all users.

RC– (See ROAD RECONNAISSANCE.)

RCAG– (See REMOTE COMMUNICATIONS AIR/ GROUND FACILITY.)

RCC– (See RESCUE COORDINATION CENTER.)

RCO– (See REMOTE COMMUNICATIONS OUTLET.)

RCR– (See RUNWAY CONDITION READING.)

READ BACK– Repeat my message back to me.

RECEIVER AUTONOMOUS INTEGRITY MONITORING (RAIM)– A technique whereby a civil GNSS receiver/ processor determines the integrity of the GNSS navigation signals without reference to sensors or non–DoD integrity systems other than the receiver itself. This determination is achieved by a consistency check among redundant pseudo-range measurements.

RECEIVING CONTROLLER– A controller/facility receiving control of an aircraft from another controller/facility.

RECEIVING FACILITY– (See RECEIVING CONTROLLER.)

P/C

REDUCE SPEED TO (SPEED)- (See SPEED ADJUST-MENT.)

REIL- (See RUNWAY END IDENTIFIER LIGHTS.)

RELEASE TIME- A departure time restriction issued to a pilot by ATC (either directly or through an authorized relay) when necessary to separate a departing aircraft from other traffic.

(See ICAO term RELEASE TIME.)

RELEASE TIME [ICAO]- Time prior to which an aircraft should be given further clearance or prior to which it should not proceed in case of radio failure.

REMOTE COMMUNICATIONS AIR/GROUND FACIL-ITY- An unmanned VHF/UHF transmitter/receiver facility which is used to expand ARTCC air/ground communications coverage and to facilitate direct contact between pilots and controllers. RCAG facilities are sometimes not equipped with emergency frequencies 121.5 MHz and 243.0 MHz.

(Refer to AIM.)

REMOTE COMMUNICATIONS OUTLET- An unmanned communications facility remotely controlled by air traffic personnel. RCO's serve FSS's. RTR's serve terminal ATC facilities. An RCO or RTR may be UHF or VHF and will extend the communication range of the air traffic facility. There are several classes of RCO's and RTR's. The class is determined by the number of transmitters or receivers. Classes A through G are used primarily for air/ground purposes. RCO and RTR class O facilities are nonprotected outlets subject to undetected and prolonged outages. RCO (O's) and RTR (O's) were established for the express purpose of providing ground-to-ground communications between air traffic control specialists and pilots located at a satellite airport for delivering en route clearances, issuing departure authorizations, and acknowledging instrument flight rules cancellations or departure/landing times. As a secondary function, they may be used for advisory purposes whenever the aircraft is below the coverage of the primary air/ground frequency.

REMOTE TRANSMITTER/RECEIVER- (See REMOTE COMMUNICATIONS OUTLET.)

REPORT- Used to instruct pilots to advise ATC of specified information; e.g., "Report passing Hamilton VOR."

REPORTING POINT- A geographical location in relation to which the position of an aircraft is reported.

(See COMPULSORY REPORTING POINTS.)

(See ICAO term REPORTING POINT.)

(Refer to AIM.)

REPORTING POINT [ICAO]- A specified geographical location in relation to which the position of an aircraft can be reported.

REQUEST FULL ROUTE CLEARANCE- Used by pilots to request that the entire route of flight be read verbatim in an ATC clearance. Such request should be made to preclude receiving an ATC clearance based on the original filed flight plan when a filed IFR flight plan has been revised by the pilot, company, or operations prior to departure.

RESCUE COORDINATION CENTER- A search and rescue (SAR) facility equipped and manned to coordinate and control SAR operations in an area designated by the SAR plan. The U.S. Coast Guard and the U.S. Air Force have responsibility for the operation of RCC's.

(See ICAO term RESCUE CO-ORDINATION CENTRE.)

RESCUE CO-ORDINATION CENTRE [ICAO]- A unit responsible for promoting efficient organization of search and rescue service and for coordinating the conduct of search and rescue operations within a search and rescue region.

RESOLUTION ADVISORY-A display indication given to the pilot by the traffic alert and collision avoidance systems (TCAS II) recommending a maneuver to increase vertical separation relative to an intruding aircraft. Positive, negative, and vertical speed limit (VSL) advisories constitute the resolution advisories. A resolution advisory is also classified as corrective or preventive

RESTRICTED AREA- (See SPECIAL USE AIRSPACE.)

(See ICAO term RESTRICTED AREA.)

RESTRICTED AREA [ICAO]- An airspace of defined dimensions, above the land areas or territorial waters of a State, within which the flight of aircraft is restricted in accordance with certain specified conditions.

RESUME OWN NAVIGATION- Used by ATC to advise a pilot to resume his own navigational responsibility. It is issued after completion of a radar vector or when radar contact is lost while the aircraft is being radar vectored.

(See RADAR CONTACT LOST.)

(See RADAR SERVICE TERMINATED.)

RESUME NORMAL SPEED- Used by ATC to advise a pilot that previously issued speed control restrictions are deleted. An instruction to "resume normal speed" does not delete speed restrictions that are applicable to published procedures of upcoming segments of flight, unless specifically stated by ATC. This does not relieve the pilot of those speed restrictions which are applicable to FAR 91.117.

RMI- (See RADIO MAGNETIC INDICATOR.)

RNAV- (See AREA NAVIGATION.)

RNAV [ICAO]- (See ICAO Term AREA NAVIGATION.)

RNAV APPROACH- An instrument approach procedure which relies on aircraft area navigation equipment for navigational guidance.

(See AREA NAVIGATION.)

(See INSTRUMENT APPROACH PROCEDURE.)

ROAD RECONNAISSANCE- Military activity requiring navigation along roads, railroads, and rivers. Reconnaissance route/route segments are seldom along a straight line and normally require a lateral route width of 10 NM to 30 NM and an altitude range of 500 feet to 10,000 feet AGL.

ROGER- I have received all of your last transmission. It should not be used to answer a question requiring a yes or a no answer.

(See AFFIRMATIVE.)

(See NEGATIVE.)

ROLLOUT RVR- (See VISIBILITY.)

ROUTE- A defined path, consisting of one or more courses in a horizontal plane, which aircraft traverse over the surface of the earth.

(See AIRWAY.)

(See JET ROUTE.)

(See PUBLISHED ROUTE.)

(See UNPUBLISHED ROUTE.)

ROUTE SEGMENT- As used in Air Traffic Control, a part of a route that can be defined by two navigational fixes, two NAVAID's, or a fix and a NAVAID.

(See FIX.)

(See ROUTE.)

(See ICAO term ROUTE SEGMENT.)

ROUTE SEGMENT [ICAO]- A portion of a route to be flown, as defined by two consecutive significant points specified in a flight plan.

RSA- (See RUNWAY SAFETY AREA.)

RTR- (See REMOTE TRANSMITTER/RECEIVER.)

RUNWAY- A defined rectangular area on a land airport prepared for the landing and takeoff run of aircraft along its length. Runways are normally numbered in relation to their magnetic direction rounded off to the nearest 10 degrees; e.g., Runway 1, Runway 25.

(See PARALLEL RUNWAYS.)

(See ICAO term RUNWAY.)

RUNWAY [ICAO]- A defined rectangular area on a land aerodrome prepared for the landing and takeoff of aircraft.

RUNWAY CENTERLINE LIGHTING- (See AIRPORT LIGHTING.)

RUNWAY CONDITION READING- Numerical decelerometer readings relayed by air traffic controllers at USAF and certain civil bases for use by the pilot in determining runway braking action. These readings are routinely relayed only to USAF and Air National Guard Aircraft.

(See BRAKING ACTION.)

RUNWAY END IDENTIFIER LIGHTS- (See AIRPORT LIGHTING.)

RUNWAY GRADIENT- The average slope, measured in percent, between two ends or points on a runway. Runway gradient is depicted on Government aerodrome sketches when total runway gradient exceeds 0.3%.

RUNWAY HEADING- The magnetic direction that corresponds with the runway centerline extended, not the painted runway number. When cleared to "fly or maintain runway heading," pilots are expected to fly or maintain the heading that corresponds with the extended centerline of the departure runway. Drift correction shall not be applied; e.g., Runway 4, actual magnetic heading of the runway centerline 044, fly 044.

RUNWAY IN USE/ACTIVE RUNWAY/DUTY RUNWAY- Any runway or runways currently being used for takeoff or landing. When multiple runways are used, they are all considered active runways. In the metering sense, a selectable adapted item which specifies the landing runway configuration or direction of traffic flow. The adapted optimum flight plan from each transition fix to the vertex is determined by the runway configuration for arrival metering processing purposes.

RUNWAY LIGHTS- (See AIRPORT LIGHTING.)

RUNWAY MARKINGS- (See AIRPORT MARKING AIDS.)

RUNWAY OVERRUN- In military aviation exclusively, a stabilized or paved area beyond the end of a runway, of the same width as the runway plus shoulders, centered on the extended runway centerline.

RUNWAY PROFILE DESCENT- An instrument flight rules (IFR) air traffic control arrival procedure to a runway published for pilot use in graphic and/or textual form and may be associated with a STAR. Runway Profile Descents provide routing and may depict crossing altitudes, speed restrictions, and headings to be flown from the en route structure to the point where the pilot will receive clearance for and execute an instrument approach procedure. A Runway Profile Descent may apply to more than one runway if so stated on the chart.

(Refer to AIM.)

RUNWAY SAFETY AREA- A defined surface surrounding the runway prepared, or suitable, for reducing the risk of damage to airplanes in the event of an undershoot, overshoot, or excursion from the runway. The dimensions of the RSA vary and can be determined by using the criteria contained within AC 150/5300-13, Airport Design, Chapter 3. Figure 3-1 in AC 150/5300-13 depicts the RSA. The design standards dictate that the RSA shall be:

a. Cleared, graded, and have no potentially hazardous ruts, humps, depressions, or other surface variations;

b. Drained by grading or storm sewers to prevent water accumulation;

P/C

c. Capable, under dry conditions, of supporting snow removal equipment, aircraft rescue and firefighting equipment, and the occasional passage of aircraft without causing structural damage to the aircraft; and,

d. Free of objects, except for objects that need to be located in the runway safety area because of their function. These objects shall be constructed on low impact resistant supports (frangible mounted structures) to the lowest practical height with the frangible point no higher than 3 inches above grade.

(Refer to AC 150/5300-13, Airport Design, Chapter 3.)

RUNWAY USE PROGRAM- A noise abatement runway selection plan designed to enhance noise abatement efforts with regard to airport communities for arriving and departing aircraft. These plans are developed into runway use programs and apply to all turbojet aircraft 12,500 pounds or heavier; turbojet aircraft less than 12,500 pounds are included only if the airport proprietor determines that the aircraft creates a noise problem. Runway use programs are coordinated with FAA offices, and safety criteria used in these programs are developed by the Office of Flight Operations. Runway use programs are administered by the Air Traffic Service as "Formal" or "Informal" programs.

a. Formal Runway Use Program- An approved noise abatement program which is defined and acknowledged in a Letter of Understanding between Flight Operations, Air Traffic Service, the airport proprietor, and the users. Once established, participation in the program is mandatory for aircraft operators and pilots as provided for in FAR Part 91.129.

b. Informal Runway Use Program- An approved noise abatement program which does not require a Letter of Understanding, and participation in the program is voluntary for aircraft operators/pilots.

RUNWAY VISIBILITY VALUE- (See VISIBILITY.)

RUNWAY VISUAL RANGE- (See VISIBILITY.)

S

SAFETY ALERT– A safety alert issued by ATC to aircraft under their control if ATC is aware the aircraft is at an altitude which, in the controller's judgment, places the aircraft in unsafe proximity to terrain, obstructions, or other aircraft. The controller may discontinue the issuance of further alerts if the pilot advises he is taking action to correct the situation or has the other aircraft in sight.

   a. Terrain/Obstruction Alert– A safety alert issued by ATC to aircraft under their control if ATC is aware the aircraft is at an altitude which, in the controller's judgment, places the aircraft in unsafe proximity to terrain/obstructions; e.g., "Low Altitude Alert, check your altitude immediately."

   b. Aircraft Conflict Alert– A safety alert issued by ATC to aircraft under their control if ATC is aware of an aircraft that is not under their control at an altitude which, in the controller's judgment, places both aircraft in unsafe proximity to each other. With the alert, ATC will offer the pilot an alternate course of action when feasible; e.g., "Traffic Alert, advise you turn right heading zero niner zero or climb to eight thousand immediately."

   The issuance of a safety alert is contingent upon the capability of the controller to have an awareness of an unsafe condition. The course of action provided will be predicated on other traffic under ATC control. Once the alert is issued, it is solely the pilot's prerogative to determine what course of action, if any, he will take.

SAIL BACK– A maneuver during high wind conditions (usually with power off) where float plane movement is controlled by water rudders/opening and closing cabin doors.

SAME DIRECTION AIRCRAFT– Aircraft are operating in the same direction when:

   a. They are following the same track in the same direction; or

   b. Their tracks are parallel and the aircraft are flying in the same direction; or

   c. Their tracks intersect at an angle of less than 45 degrees.

SAR–
   (*See* SEARCH AND RESCUE.)

SAY AGAIN– Used to request a repeat of the last transmission. Usually specifies transmission or portion thereof not understood or received; e.g., "Say again all after ABRAM VOR."

SAY ALTITUDE– Used by ATC to ascertain an aircraft's specific altitude/flight level. When the aircraft is climbing or descending, the pilot should state the indicated altitude rounded to the nearest 100 feet.

SAY HEADING– Used by ATC to request an aircraft heading. The pilot should state the actual heading of the aircraft.

SDF–
   (*See* SIMPLIFIED DIRECTIONAL FACILITY.)

SEA LANE– A designated portion of water outlined by visual surface markers for and intended to be used by aircraft designed to operate on water.

SEARCH AND RESCUE– A service which seeks missing aircraft and assists those found to be in need of assistance. It is a cooperative effort using the facilities and services of available Federal, state and local agencies. The U.S. Coast Guard is responsible for coordination of search and rescue for the Maritime Region, and the U.S. Air Force is responsible for search and rescue for the Inland Region. Information pertinent to search and rescue should be passed through any air traffic facility or be transmitted directly to the Rescue Coordination Center by telephone.
   (*See* FLIGHT SERVICE STATION.)
   (*See* RESCUE COORDINATION CENTER.)
   (*Refer to* AIM.)

SEARCH AND RESCUE FACILITY– A facility responsible for maintaining and operating a search and rescue (SAR) service to render aid to persons and property in distress. It is any SAR unit, station, NET, or other operational activity which can be usefully employed during an SAR Mission; e.g., a Civil Air Patrol Wing, or a Coast Guard Station.
   (*See* SEARCH AND RESCUE.)

SECTIONAL AERONAUTICAL CHARTS–
   (*See* AERONAUTICAL CHART.)

SECTOR LIST DROP INTERVAL– A parameter number of minutes after the meter fix time when arrival aircraft will be deleted from the arrival sector list.

SEE AND AVOID– When weather conditions permit, pilots operating IFR or VFR are required to observe and maneuver to avoid other aircraft. Right-of-way rules are contained in FAR Part 91.

SEGMENTED CIRCLE– A system of visual indicators designed to provide traffic pattern information at airports without operating control towers.
   (*Refer to* AIM.)

SEGMENTS OF AN INSTRUMENT APPROACH PROCEDURE– An instrument approach procedure may have as many as four separate segments depending on how the approach procedure is structured.

P/C

a. Initial Approach– The segment between the initial approach fix and the intermediate fix or the point where the aircraft is established on the intermediate course or final approach course.

(See ICAO term INITIAL APPROACH SEGMENT.)

b. Intermediate Approach– The segment between the intermediate fix or point and the final approach fix.

(See ICAO term INTERMEDIATE APPROACH SEGMENT.)

c. Final Approach– The segment between the final approach fix or point and the runway, airport, or missed approach point.

(See ICAO term FINAL APPROACH SEGMENT.)

d. Missed Approach– The segment between the missed approach point or the point of arrival at decision height and the missed approach fix at the prescribed altitude.

(Refer to FAR Part 97.)

(See ICAO term MISSED APPROACH PROCEDURE.)

SELECTED GROUND DELAYS– A traffic management procedure whereby selected flights are issued ground delays to better regulate traffic flows over a particular fix or area.

SEPARATION– In air traffic control, the spacing of aircraft to achieve their safe and orderly movement in flight and while landing and taking off.

(See SEPARATION MINIMA.)

(See ICAO term SEPARATION.)

SEPARATION [ICAO]– Spacing between aircraft, levels or tracks.

SEPARATION MINIMA– The minimum longitudinal, lateral, or vertical distances by which aircraft are spaced through the application of air traffic control procedures.

(See SEPARATION.)

SERVICE– A generic term that designates functions or assistance available from or rendered by air traffic control. For example, Class C service would denote the ATC services provided within a Class C airspace area.

SEVERE WEATHER AVOIDANCE PLAN– An approved plan to minimize the affect of severe weather on traffic flows in impacted terminal and/or ARTCC areas. SWAP is normally implemented to provide the least disruption to the ATC system when flight through portions of airspace is difficult or impossible due to severe weather.

SEVERE WEATHER FORECAST ALERTS– Preliminary messages issued in order to alert users that a Severe Weather Watch Bulletin (WW) is being issued. These messages define areas of possible severe thunderstorms or tornado activity. The messages are unscheduled and issued as required by the National Severe Storm Forecast Center at Kansas City, Missouri.

(See AIRMET.)

(See SIGMET.)

(See CONVECTIVE SIGMET.)

(See CWA.)

SFA–

(See SINGLE FREQUENCY APPROACH.)

SFO–

(See SIMULATED FLAMEOUT.)

SHF–

(See SUPER HIGH FREQUENCY.)

SHORT RANGE CLEARANCE– A clearance issued to a departing IFR flight which authorizes IFR flight to a specific fix short of the destination while air traffic control facilities are coordinating and obtaining the complete clearance.

SHORT TAKEOFF AND LANDING AIRCRAFT AIRCRAFT– An aircraft which, at some weight within its approved operating weight, is capable of operating from a STOL runway in compliance with the applicable STOL characteristics, airworthiness, operations, noise, and pollution standards.

(See VERTICAL TAKEOFF AND LANDING AIRCRAFT.)

SIAP–

(See STANDARD INSTRUMENT APPROACH PROCEDURE.)

SIDESTEP MANEUVER– A visual maneuver accomplished by a pilot at the completion of an instrument approach to permit a straight-in landing on a parallel runway not more than 1,200 feet to either side of the runway to which the instrument approach was conducted.

(Refer to AIM.)

SIGMET– A weather advisory issued concerning weather significant to the safety of all aircraft. SIGMET advisories cover severe and extreme turbulence, severe icing, and widespread dust or sandstorms that reduce visibility to less than 3 miles.

(See AIRMET.)

(See AWW.)

(See CONVECTIVE SIGMET.)

(See CWA.)

(See ICAO term SIGMET INFORMATION.)

(Refer to AIM.)

SIGMET INFORMATION [ICAO]- Information issued by a meteorological watch office concerning the occurrence or expected occurrence of specified en-route weather phenomena which may affect the safety of aircraft operations.

SIGNIFICANT METEOROLOGICAL INFORMATION-

   (*See* SIGMET.)

SIGNIFICANT POINT- A point, whether a named intersection, a NAVAID, a fix derived from a NAVAID(s), or geographical coordinate expressed in degrees of latitude and longitude, which is established for the purpose of providing separation, as a reporting point, or to delineate a route of flight.

SIMPLIFIED DIRECTIONAL FACILITY- A NAVAID used for nonprecision instrument approaches. The final approach course is similar to that of an ILS localizer except that the SDF course may be offset from the runway, generally not more than 3 degrees, and the course may be wider than the localizer, resulting in a lower degree of accuracy.

   (*Refer to AIM.*)

SIMULATED FLAMEOUT- A practice approach by a jet aircraft (normally military) at idle thrust to a runway. The approach may start at a runway (high key) and may continue on a relatively high and wide downwind leg with a continuous turn to final. It terminates in landing or low approach. The purpose of this approach is to simulate a flameout.

   (*See* FLAMEOUT.)

SIMULTANEOUS ILS APPROACHES- An approach system permitting simultaneous ILS/MLS approaches to airports having parallel runways separated by at least 4,300 feet between centerlines. Integral parts of a total system are ILS/MLS, radar, communications, ATC procedures, and appropriate airborne equipment.

   (*See PARALLEL RUNWAYS.*)

   (*Refer to AIM.*)

SIMULTANEOUS MLS APPROACHES-

   (*See* SIMULTANEOUS ILS APPROACHES.)

SINGLE DIRECTION ROUTES- Preferred IFR Routes which are sometimes depicted on high altitude en route charts and which are normally flown in one direction only.

   (*See PREFERRED IFR ROUTES.*)

   (*Refer to AIRPORT/FACILITY DIRECTORY.*)

SINGLE FREQUENCY APPROACH- A service provided under a letter of agreement to military single-piloted turbojet aircraft which permits use of a single UHF frequency during approach for landing. Pilots will not normally be required to change frequency from the beginning of the approach to touchdown except that pilots conducting an en route descent are required to change frequency when control is transferred from the air route traffic control center to the terminal facility. The abbreviation "SFA" in the DOD FLIP IFR Supplement under "Communications" indicates this service is available at an aerodrome.

SINGLE-PILOTED AIRCRAFT- A military turbojet aircraft possessing one set of flight controls, tandem cockpits, or two sets of flight controls but operated by one pilot is considered single-piloted by ATC when determining the appropriate air traffic service to be applied.

   (*See SINGLE FREQUENCY APPROACH.*)

SLASH- A radar beacon reply displayed as an elongated target.

SLDI-

   (*See* SECTOR LIST DROP INTERVAL.)

SLOT TIME-

   (*See* METER FIX TIME/SLOT TIME.)

SLOW TAXI- To taxi a float plane at low power or low RPM.

SN-

   (*See* SYSTEM STRATEGIC NAVIGATION.)

SPEAK SLOWER- Used in verbal communications as a request to reduce speech rate.

SPECIAL EMERGENCY- A condition of air piracy or other hostile act by a person(s) aboard an aircraft which threatens the safety of the aircraft or its passengers.

SPECIAL INSTRUMENT APPROACH PROCEDURE-

   (*See* INSTRUMENT APPROACH
   PROCEDURE.)

SPECIAL USE AIRSPACE- Airspace of defined dimensions identified by an area on the surface of the earth wherein activities must be confined because of their nature and/or wherein limitations may be imposed upon aircraft operations that are not a part of those activities. Types of special use airspace are:

   a. Alert Area- Airspace which may contain a high volume of pilot training activities or an unusual type of aerial activity, neither of which is hazardous to aircraft. Alert Areas are depicted on aeronautical charts for the information of nonparticipating pilots. All activities within an Alert Area are conducted in accordance with Federal Aviation Regulations, and pilots of participating aircraft as well as pilots transiting the area are equally responsible for collision avoidance.

b. Controlled Firing Area- Airspace wherein activities are conducted under conditions so controlled as to eliminate hazards to nonparticipating aircraft and to ensure the safety of persons and property on the ground.

c. Military Operations Area (MOA)- A MOA is airspace established outside of Class A airspace area to separate or segregate certain nonhazardous military activities from IFR traffic and to identify for VFR traffic where these activities are conducted.

(Refer to AIM.)

d. Prohibited Area- Airspace designated under part 73 within which no person may operate an aircraft without the permission of the using agency.

(Refer to En Route Charts, AIM.)

e. Restricted Area- Airspace designated under FAR Part 73, within which the flight of aircraft, while not wholly prohibited, is subject to restriction. Most restricted areas are designated joint use and IFR/VFR operations in the area may be authorized by the controlling ATC facility when it is not being utilized by the using agency. Restricted areas are depicted on en route charts. Where joint use is authorized, the name of the ATC controlling facility is also shown.

(Refer to FAR Part 73.)

(Refer to AIM.)

f. Warning Area- A warning area is airspace of defined dimensions extending from 3 nautical miles outward from the coast of the United States, that contains activity that may be hazardous to nonparticipating aircraft. The purpose of such warning area is to warn nonparticipating pilots of the potential danger. A warning area may be located over domestic or international waters or both.

SPECIAL VFR CONDITIONS- Meteorological conditions that are less than those required for basic VFR flight in Class B, C, D, or E surface areas and in which some aircraft are permitted flight under visual flight rules.

(See SPECIAL VFR OPERATIONS.)

(Refer to FAR Part 91.)

SPECIAL VFR FLIGHT [ICAO]- A VFR flight cleared by air traffic control to operate within Class B, C, D, and E surface areas in metrological conditions below VMC.

SPECIAL VFR OPERATIONS- Aircraft operating in accordance with clearances within Class B, C, D, and E surface areas in weather conditions less than the basic VFR weather minima. Such operations must be requested by the pilot and approved by ATC.

(See SPECIAL VFR CONDITIONS.)

(See ICAO term SPECIAL VFR FLIGHT.)

SPEED- *(See AIRSPEED.)*

(See GROUND SPEED.)

SPEED ADJUSTMENT- An ATC procedure used to request pilots to adjust aircraft speed to a specific value for the purpose of providing desired spacing. Pilots are expected to maintain a speed of plus or minus 10 knots or 0.02 Mach number of the specified speed.

Examples of speed adjustments are:

1. "Increase/reduce speed to Mach point (number.)"

2. "Increase/reduce speed to (speed in knots)" or "Increase/reduce speed (number of knots) knots."

SPEED BRAKES- Moveable aerodynamic devices on aircraft that reduce airspeed during descent and landing.

SPEED SEGMENTS- Portions of the arrival route between the transition point and the vertex along the optimum flight path for which speeds and altitudes are specified. There is one set of arrival speed segments adapted from each transition point to each vertex. Each set may contain up to six segments.

SQUAWK (Mode, Code, Function)- Activate specific modes/codes/functions on the aircraft transponder; e.g., "Squawk three/alpha, two one zero five, low."

(See TRANSPONDER.)

STAGING/QUEUING- The placement, integration, and segregation of departure aircraft in designated movement areas of an airport by departure fix, EDCT, and/or restriction.

STANDARD INSTRUMENT APPROACH PROCEDURE-

(See INSTRUMENT APPROACH PROCEDURE.)

STANDARD RATE TURN- A turn of three degrees per second.

STANDARD TERMINAL ARRIVAL- A preplanned instrument flight rule (IFR) air traffic control arrival procedure published for pilot use in graphic and/or textual form. STAR's provide transition from the en route structure to an outer fix or an instrument approach fix/arrival waypoint in the terminal area.

STANDARD TERMINAL ARRIVAL CHARTS-

(See AERONAUTICAL CHART.)

STAND BY- Means the controller or pilot must pause for a few seconds, usually to attend to other duties of a higher priority. Also means to wait as in "stand by for clearance." The caller should reestablish contact if a delay is lengthy. "Stand by" is not an approval or denial.

STAR-

(See STANDARD TERMINAL ARRIVAL.)

STATE AIRCRAFT- Aircraft used in military, customs and police service, in the exclusive service of any government, or of any political subdivision, thereof including the government of any state, territory, or possession of the United States or the District of Columbia, but not including any government-owned aircraft engaged in carrying persons or property for commercial purposes.

STATIC RESTRICTIONS- Those restrictions that are usually not subject to change, fixed, in place, and/or published.

STATIONARY RESERVATIONS- Altitude reservations which encompass activities in a fixed area. Stationary reservations may include activities, such as special tests of weapons systems or equipment, certain U.S. Navy carrier, fleet, and anti-submarine operations, rocket, missile and drone operations, and certain aerial refueling or similar operations.

STEPDOWN FIX- A fix permitting additional descent within a segment of an instrument approach procedure by identifying a point at which a controlling obstacle has been safely overflown.

STEP TAXI- To taxi a float plane at full power or high RPM.

STEP TURN- A maneuver used to put a float plane in a planing configuration prior to entering an active sea lane for takeoff. The STEP TURN maneuver should only be used upon pilot request.

STEREO ROUTE- A routinely used route of flight established by users and ARTCC's identified by a coded name; e.g., ALPHA 2. These routes minimize flight plan handling and communications.

STOL AIRCRAFT-

    (See SHORT TAKEOFF AND LANDING AIRCRAFT.)

STOP ALTITUDE SQUAWK- Used by ATC to inform an aircraft to turn-off the automatic altitude reporting feature of its transponder. It is issued when the verbally reported altitude varies 300 feet or more from the automatic altitude report.

    (See ALTITUDE READOUT.)

    (See TRANSPONDER.)

STOP AND GO- A procedure wherein an aircraft will land, make a complete stop on the runway, and then commence a takeoff from that point.

    (See LOW APPROACH.)

    (See OPTION APPROACH.)

STOP BURST-

    (See STOP STREAM.)

STOP BUZZER-

    (See STOP STREAM.)

STOPOVER FLIGHT PLAN- A flight plan format which permits in a single submission the filing of a sequence of flight plans through interim full-stop destinations to a final destination.

STOP SQUAWK (Mode or Code)- Used by ATC to tell the pilot to turn specified functions of the aircraft transponder off.

    (See STOP ALTITUDE SQUAWK.)

    (See TRANSPONDER.)

STOP STREAM- Used by ATC to request a pilot to suspend electronic countermeasure activity.

    (See JAMMING.)

STOPWAY- An area beyond the takeoff runway no less wide than the runway and centered upon the extended centerline of the runway, able to support the airplane during an aborted takeoff, without causing structural damage to the airplane, and designated by the airport authorities for use in decelerating the airplane during an aborted takeoff.

STRAIGHT-IN APPROACH IFR- An instrument approach wherein final approach is begun without first having executed a procedure turn, not necessarily completed with a straight-in landing or made to straight-in landing minimums.

    (See STRAIGHT-IN LANDING.)

    (See LANDING MINIMUMS.)

    (See STRAIGHT-IN APPROACH VFR.)

STRAIGHT-IN APPROACH VFR- Entry into the traffic pattern by interception of the extended runway centerline (final approach course) without executing any other portion of the traffic pattern.

    (See TRAFFIC PATTERN.)

STRAIGHT-IN LANDING- A landing made on a runway aligned within 30° of the final approach course following completion of an instrument approach.

    (See STRAIGHT-IN APPROACH-IFR.)

STRAIGHT-IN LANDING MINIMUMS-

    (See LANDING MINIMUMS.)

STRAIGHT-IN MINIMUMS-

    (See STRAIGHT-IN LANDING MINIMUMS.)

SUBSTITUTIONS- Users are permitted to exchange CTA's. Normally, the airline dispatcher will contact the ATCSCC with this request. The ATCSCC shall forward approved substitutions to the TMU's who will notify the appropriate terminals. Permissible swapping must not change the traffic load for any given hour of an EQF program.

SUBSTITUTE ROUTE- A route assigned to pilots when any part of an airway or route is unusable because of NAVAID status. These routes consist of:

    a. Substitute routes which are shown on U.S. Government charts.

P/C

b. Routes defined by ATC as specific NAVAID radials or courses.

c. Routes defined by ATC as direct to or between NAVAID's.

SUNSET AND SUNRISE- The mean solar times of sunset and sunrise as published in the Nautical Almanac, converted to local standard time for the locality concerned. Within Alaska, the end of evening civil twilight and the beginning of morning civil twilight, as defined for each locality.

SUPER HIGH FREQUENCY- The frequency band between 3 and 30 gigahertz (GHz). The elevation and azimuth stations of the microwave landing system operate from 5031 MHz to 5091 MHz in this spectrum.

SUPPLEMENTAL WEATHER SERVICE LOCATION- Airport facilities staffed with contract personnel who take weather observations and provide current local weather to pilots via telephone or radio. (All other services are provided by the parent FSS).

SUPPS- Refers to ICAO Document 7030 Regional Supplementary Procedures. SUPPS contain procedures for each ICAO Region which are unique to that Region and are not covered in the worldwide provisions identified in the ICAO Air Navigation Plan. Procedures contained in chapter 8 are based in part on those published in SUPPS.

SURFACE AREA- The airspace contained by the lateral boundary of the Class B, C, D, or E airspace designated for an airport that begins at the surface and extends upward.

SURPIC- A description of surface vessels in the area of a Search and Rescue incident including their predicted positions and their characteristics.

(See FAA Order 7110.65, paragraph 10-6-4, INFLIGHT CONTINGENCIES.)

SURVEILLANCE APPROACH- An instrument approach wherein the air traffic controller issues instructions, for pilot compliance, based on aircraft position in relation to the final approach course (azimuth), and the distance (range) from the end of the runway as displayed on the controller's radar scope. The controller will provide recommended altitudes on final approach if requested by the pilot.

(Refer to AIM.)

SWAP- *(See* SEVERE WEATHER AVOIDANCE PLAN.)

SWSL- *(See* SUPPLEMENTAL WEATHER SERVICE LOCATION.)

SYSTEM STRATEGIC NAVIGATION- Military activity accomplished by navigating along a preplanned route using internal aircraft systems to maintain a desired track. This activity normally requires a lateral route width of 10 NM and altitude range of 1,000 feet to 6,000 feet AGL with some route segments that permit terrain following.

T

TACAN-

    (See TACTICAL AIR NAVIGATION.)

TACAN-ONLY AIRCRAFT- An aircraft, normally military, possessing TACAN with DME but no VOR navigational system capability. Clearances must specify TACAN or VORTAC fixes and approaches.

TACTICAL AIR NAVIGATION- An ultra-high frequency electronic rho-theta air navigation aid which provides suitably equipped aircraft a continuous indication of bearing and distance to the TACAN station.

    (See VORTAC.)

    (Refer to AIM.)

TAILWIND- Any wind more than 90 degrees to the longitudinal axis of the runway. The magnetic direction of the runway shall be used as the basis for determining the longitudinal axis.

TAKEOFF AREA-

    (See LANDING AREA.)

TAKE-OFF DISTANCE AVAILABLE [ICAO]- The length of the take-off run available plus the length of the clearway, if provided.

TAKE-OFF RUN AVAILABLE [ICAO]- The length of runway declared available and suitable for the ground run of an aeroplane take-off.

TARGET- The indication shown on a radar display resulting from a primary radar return or a radar beacon reply.

    (See RADAR.)

    (See TARGET SYMBOL.)

    (See ICAO term TARGET.)

TARGET [ICAO]- In radar:

    a. Generally, any discrete object which reflects or retransmits energy back to the radar equipment.

    b. Specifically, an object of radar search or surveillance.

TARGET RESOLUTION- A process to ensure that correlated radar targets do not touch. Target resolution shall be applied as follows:

    a. Between the edges of two primary targets or the edges of the ASR-9 primary target symbol.

    b. Between the end of the beacon control slash and the edge of a primary target.

    c. Between the ends of two beacon control slashes.

    MANDATORY TRAFFIC ADVISORIES AND SAFETY ALERTS SHALL BE ISSUED WHEN THIS PROCEDURE IS USED.

    Note: This procedure shall not be provided utilizing mosaic radar systems.

TARGET SYMBOL- A computer-generated indication shown on a radar display resulting from a primary radar return or a radar beacon reply.

TAXI- The movement of an airplane under its own power on the surface of an airport (FAR Part 135.100 [Note]). Also, it describes the surface movement of helicopters equipped with wheels.

    (See AIR TAXI.)

    (See HOVER TAXI.)

    (Refer to AIM.)

    (Refer to FAR Part 135.100.)

TAXI INTO POSITION AND HOLD- Used by ATC to inform a pilot to taxi onto the departure runway in takeoff position and hold. It is not authorization for takeoff. It is used when takeoff clearance cannot immediately be issued because of traffic or other reasons.

    (See CLEARED FOR TAKEOFF.)

TAXI PATTERNS- Patterns established to illustrate the desired flow of ground traffic for the different runways or airport areas available for use.

TCAS-

    (See TRAFFIC ALERT AND COLLISION AVOIDANCE SYSTEM.)

TCH-

    (See THRESHOLD CROSSING HEIGHT.)

TCLT-

    (See TENTATIVE CALCULATED LANDING TIME.)

TDZE-

    (See TOUCHDOWN ZONE ELEVATION.)

TELEPHONE INFORMATION BRIEFING SERVICE- A continuous telephone recording of meteorological and/or aeronautical information.

    (Refer to AIM.)

TENTATIVE CALCULATED LANDING TIME- A projected time calculated for adapted vertex for each arrival aircraft based upon runway configuration, airport acceptance rate, airport arrival delay period, and other metered arrival aircraft. This time is either the VTA of the aircraft or the TCLT/ACLT of the previous aircraft plus the AAI, whichever is later. This time will be updated in response to an aircraft's progress and its current relationship to other arrivals.

TERMINAL AREA- A general term used to describe airspace in which approach control service or airport traffic control service is provided.

TERMINAL AREA FACILITY- A facility providing air traffic control service for arriving and departing IFR, VFR, Special VFR, and on occasion en route aircraft.

(See APPROACH CONTROL FACILITY.)

(See TOWER.)

TERMINAL RADAR SERVICE AREA- Airspace surrounding designated airports wherein ATC provides radar vectoring, sequencing, and separation on a full-time basis for all IFR and participating VFR aircraft. The AIM contains an explanation of TRSA. TRSA's are depicted on VFR aeronautical charts. Pilot participation is urged but is not mandatory.

TERMINAL VFR RADAR SERVICE- A national program instituted to extend the terminal radar services provided instrument flight rules (IFR) aircraft to visual flight rules (VFR) aircraft. The program is divided into four types service referred to as basic radar service, terminal radar service area (TRSA) service, Class B service and Class C service. The type of service provided at a particular location is contained in the Airport/Facility Directory.

a. Basic Radar Service- These services are provided for VFR aircraft by all commissioned terminal radar facilities. Basic radar service includes safety alerts, traffic advisories, limited radar vectoring when requested by the pilot, and sequencing at locations where procedures have been established for this purpose and/or when covered by a letter of agreement. The purpose of this service is to adjust the flow of arriving IFR and VFR aircraft into the traffic pattern in a safe and orderly manner and to provide traffic advisories to departing VFR aircraft.

b. TRSA Service- This service provides, in addition to basic radar service, sequencing of all IFR and participating VFR aircraft to the primary airport and separation between all participating VFR aircraft. The purpose of this service is to provide separation between all participating VFR aircraft and all IFR aircraft operating within the area defined as a TRSA.

c. Class C Service- This service provides, in addition to basic radar service, approved separation between IFR and VFR aircraft, and sequencing of VFR aircraft, and sequencing of VFR arrivals to the primary airport.

d. Class B Service- This service provides, in addition to basic radar service, approved separation of aircraft based on

IFR, VFR, and/or weight, and sequencing of VFR arrivals to the primary airport(s).

(See CONTROLLED AIRSPACE.)
(See TERMINAL RADAR SERVICE AREA.)
(Refer to AIM.)
(Refer to AIRPORT/FACILITY DIRECTORY.)
(See TERMINAL RADAR PROGRAM.)
(Refer to AIM.)
(Refer to AIRPORT/FACILITY DIRECTORY.)

TERMINAL-VERY HIGH FREQUENCY OMNIDIRECTIONAL RANGE STATION- A very high frequency terminal omnirange station located on or near an airport and used as an approach aid.

(See NAVIGATIONAL AID.)
(See VOR.)

TERRAIN FOLLOWING- The flight of a military aircraft maintaining a constant AGL altitude above the terrain or the highest obstruction. The altitude of the aircraft will constantly change with the varying terrain and/or obstruction.

TETRAHEDRON- A device normally located on uncontrolled airports and used as a landing direction indicator. The small end of a tetrahedron points in the direction of landing. At controlled airports, the tetrahedron, if installed, should be disregarded because tower instructions supersede the indicator.

(See SEGMENTED CIRCLE.)
(Refer to AIM.)

TF-

(See TERRAIN FOLLOWING.)

THAT IS CORRECT- The understanding you have is right.

360 OVERHEAD-

(See OVERHEAD APPROACH.)

THRESHOLD- The beginning of that portion of the runway usable for landing.

(See AIRPORT LIGHTING.)
(See DISPLACED THRESHOLD.)

THRESHOLD CROSSING HEIGHT- The theoretical height above the runway threshold at which the aircraft's glideslope antenna would be if the aircraft maintains the trajectory established by the mean ILS glideslope or MLS glidepath.

(See GLIDESLOPE.)
(See THRESHOLD.)

THRESHOLD LIGHTS-

(See AIRPORT LIGHTING.)

TIBS-

(See TELEPHONE INFORMATION BRIEFING SERVICE.)

TIME GROUP- Four digits representing the hour and minutes from the Coordinated Universal Time (UTC) clock. FAA uses UTC for all operations. The term "ZULU" may be used to denote UTC. The word "local" or the time zone equivalent shall be used to denote local when local time is given during radio and telephone communications. When written, a time zone designator is used to indicate local time; e.g. "0205M" (Mountain). The local time may be based on the 24-hour clock system. The day begins at 0000 and ends at 2359.

TMPA-

    (See TRAFFIC MANAGEMENT
    PROGRAM ALERT.)

TMU-

    (See TRAFFIC MANAGEMENT UNIT.)

TODA [ICAO]-

    (See ICAO Term TAKE-OFF DISTANCE
    AVAILABLE.)

TORA [ICAO]-

    (See ICAO Term TAKE-OFF RUN
    AVAILABLE.)

TORCHING- The burning of fuel at the end of an exhaust pipe or stack of a reciprocating aircraft engine, the result of an excessive richness in the fuel air mixture.

TOTAL ESTIMATED ELAPSED TIME [ICAO]- For IFR flights, the estimated time required from take-off to arrive over that designated point, defined by reference to navigation aids, from which it is intended that an instrument approach procedure will be commenced, or, if no navigation aid is associated with the destination aerodrome, to arrive over the destination aerodrome. For VFR flights, the estimated time required from takeoff to arrive over the destination aerodrome.

    (See ESTIMATED ELAPSED TIME.)

TOUCH-AND-GO- An operation by an aircraft that lands and departs on a runway without stopping or exiting the runway.

TOUCH-AND-GO LANDING-

    (See TOUCH-AND-GO.)

TOUCHDOWN-

    a. The point at which an aircraft first makes contact with the landing surface.

    b. Concerning a precision radar approach (PAR), it is the point where the glide path intercepts the landing surface.

    (See ICAO term TOUCHDOWN.)

TOUCHDOWN [ICAO]- The point where the nominal glide path intercepts the runway.

    Note: *Touchdown as defined above is only a datum and is not necessarily the actual point at which the aircraft will touch the runway.*

TOUCHDOWN RVR-

    (See VISIBILITY.)

TOUCHDOWN ZONE- The first 3,000 feet of the runway beginning at the threshold. The area is used for determination of Touchdown Zone Elevation in the development of straight-in landing minimums for instrument approaches.

    (See ICAO term TOUCHDOWN ZONE.)

TOUCHDOWN ZONE [ICAO]- The portion of a runway, beyond the threshold, where it is intended landing aircraft first contact the runway.

TOUCHDOWN ZONE ELEVATION- The highest elevation in the first 3,000 feet of the landing surface. TDZE is indicated on the instrument approach procedure chart when straight-in landing minimums are authorized.

    (See TOUCHDOWN ZONE.)

TOUCHDOWN ZONE LIGHTING-

    (See AIRPORT LIGHTING.)

TOWER- A terminal facility that uses air/ground communications, visual signaling, and other devices to provide ATC services to aircraft operating in the vicinity of an airport or on the movement area. Authorizes aircraft to land or take-off at the airport controlled by the tower or to transit the Class D airspace area regardless of flight plan or weather conditions (IFR or VFR). A tower may also provide approach control services (radar or nonradar).

    *(See AIRPORT TRAFFIC CONTROL
    SERVICE.)*
    (See APPROACH CONTROL FACILITY.)
    (See APPROACH CONTROL SERVICE.)
    (See MOVEMENT AREA.)
    *(See TOWER EN ROUTE CONTROL
    SERVICE.)*
    (Refer to AIM.)
    *(See ICAO term AERODROME CONTROL
    TOWER.)*

TOWER EN ROUTE CONTROL SERVICE- The control of IFR en route traffic within delegated airspace between two or more adjacent approach control facilities. This service is designed to expedite traffic and reduce control and pilot communication requirements.

TOWER TO TOWER-

    (See TOWER EN ROUTE CONTROL
    SERVICE.)

TPX-42- A numeric beacon decoder equipment/system. It is designed to be added to terminal radar systems for beacon decoding. It provides rapid target identification, reinforcement of the primary radar target, and altitude information from Mode C.

    *(See AUTOMATED RADAR TERMINAL
    SYSTEMS.)*
    (See TRANSPONDER.)

TRACK- The actual flight path of an aircraft over the surface of the earth.

(See COURSE.)

(See ROUTE.)

(See FLIGHT PATH.)

(See ICAO term TRACK.)

TRACK [ICAO]- The projection on the earth's surface of the path of an aircraft, the direction of which path at any point is usually expressed in degrees from North (True, Magnetic, or Grid).

TRAFFIC-

a. A term used by a controller to transfer radar identification of an aircraft to another controller for the purpose of coordinating separation action. Traffic is normally issued:

1. in response to a handoff or point out,

2. in anticipation of a handoff or point out, or

3. in conjunction with a request for control of an aircraft.

b. A term used by ATC to refer to one or more aircraft.

TRAFFIC ADVISORIES- Advisories issued to alert pilots to other known or observed air traffic which may be in such proximity to the position or intended route of flight of their aircraft to warrant their attention. Such advisories may be based on:

a. Visual observation.

b. Observation of radar identified and nonidentified aircraft targets on an ATC radar display, or

c. Verbal reports from pilots or other facilities.

Note 1: The word "traffic" followed by additional information, if known, is used to provide such advisories; e.g., "Traffic, 2 o'clock, one zero miles, southbound, eight thousand."

Note 2: Traffic advisory service will be provided to the extent possible depending on higher priority duties of the controller or other limitations; e.g., radar limitations, volume of traffic, frequency congestion, or controller workload. Radar/nonradar traffic advisories do not relieve the pilot of his responsibility to see and avoid other aircraft. Pilots are cautioned that there are many times when the controller is not able to give traffic advisories concerning all traffic in the aircraft's proximity; in other words, when a pilot requests or is receiving traffic advisories, he should not assume that all traffic will be issued.

(Refer to AIM.)

TRAFFIC ALERT (aircraft call sign), TURN (left/right) IMMEDIATELY, (climb/descend) AND MAINTAIN (altitude).

(See SAFETY ALERT.)

TRAFFIC ALERT AND COLLISION AVOIDANCE SYSTEM- An airborne collision avoidance system based on radar beacon signals which operates independent of ground-based equipment. TCAS-I generates traffic advisories only. TCAS-II generates traffic advisories, and resolution (collision avoidance) advisories in the vertical plane.

TRAFFIC INFORMATION-

(See TRAFFIC ADVISORIES.)

TRAFFIC IN SIGHT- Used by pilots to inform a controller that previously issued traffic is in sight.

(See NEGATIVE CONTACT.)

(See TRAFFIC ADVISORIES.)

TRAFFIC MANAGEMENT PROGRAM ALERT- A term used in a Notice to Airmen (NOTAM) issued in conjunction with a special traffic management program to alert pilots to the existence of the program and to refer them to either the Notices to Airmen publication or a special traffic management program advisory message for program details. The contraction TMPA is used in NOTAM text.

TRAFFIC MANAGEMENT UNIT- The entity in ARTCC's and designated terminals responsible for direct involvement in the active management of facility traffic. Usually under the direct supervision of an assistant manager for traffic management.

TRAFFIC NO FACTOR- Indicates that the traffic described in a previously issued traffic advisory is no factor.

TRAFFIC NO LONGER OBSERVED- Indicates that the traffic described in a previously issued traffic advisory is no longer depicted on radar, but may still be a factor.

TRAFFIC PATTERN- The traffic flow that is prescribed for aircraft landing at, taxiing on, or taking off from an airport. The components of a typical traffic pattern are upwind leg, crosswind leg, downwind leg, base leg, and final approach.

a. Upwind Leg- A flight path parallel to the landing runway in the direction of landing.

b. Crosswind Leg- A flight path at right angles to the landing runway off its upwind end.

c. Downwind Leg- A flight path parallel to the landing runway in the direction opposite to landing. The downwind leg normally extends between the crosswind leg and the base leg.

d. Base Leg- A flight path at right angles to the landing runway off its approach end. The base leg normally extends from the downwind leg to the intersection of the extended runway centerline.

e. Final Approach. A flight path in the direction of landing along the extended runway centerline. The final approach normally extends from the base leg to the runway. An aircraft making a straight-in approach VFR is also considered to be on final approach.

(See STRAIGHT-IN APPROACH VFR.)

(See TAXI PATTERNS.)

(Refer to AIM.)

(Refer to FAR Part 91.)

(See ICAO term AERODROME TRAFFIC CIRCUIT.)

TRANSCRIBED WEATHER BROADCAST- A continuous recording of meteorological and aeronautical information that is broadcast on L/MF and VOR facilities for pilots.

(Refer to AIM.)

TRANSFER OF CONTROL- That action whereby the responsibility for the separation of an aircraft is transferred from one controller to another.

(See ICAO term TRANSFER OF CONTROL.)

TRANSFER OF CONTROL [ICAO]- Transfer of responsibility for providing air traffic control service.

TRANSFERRING CONTROLLER- A controller/facility transferring control of an aircraft to another controller/facility.

(See ICAO term TRANSFERRING UNIT/ CONTROLLER.)

TRANSFERRING FACILITY-

(See TRANSFERRING CONTROLLER.)

TRANSFERRING UNIT/CONTROLLER [ICAO]- Air traffic control unit/air traffic controller in the process of transferring the responsibility for providing air traffic control service to an aircraft to the next air traffic control unit/air traffic controller along the route of flight.

Note: See definition of accepting unit/controller.

TRANSITION-

a. The general term that describes the change from one phase of flight or flight condition to another; e.g., transition from en route flight to the approach or transition from instrument flight to visual flight.

b. A published procedure (DP Transition) used to connect the basic DP to one of several en route airways/jet routes, or a published procedure (STAR Transition) used to connect one of several en route airways/jet routes to the basic STAR.

(Refer to DP/STAR Charts.)

TRANSITIONAL AIRSPACE- That portion of controlled airspace wherein aircraft change from one phase of flight or flight condition to another.

TRANSITION POINT- A point at an adapted number of miles from the vertex at which an arrival aircraft would normally commence descent from its en route altitude. This is the first fix adapted on the arrival speed segments.

TRANSMISSOMETER- An apparatus used to determine visibility by measuring the transmission of light through the atmosphere. It is the measurement source for determining runway visual range (RVR) and runway visibility value (RVV).

(See VISIBILITY.)

TRANSMITTING IN THE BLIND- A transmission from one station to other stations in circumstances where two-way communication cannot be established, but where it is believed that the called stations may be able to receive the transmission.

TRANSPONDER- The airborne radar beacon receiver/transmitter portion of the Air Traffic Control Radar Beacon System (ATCRBS) which automatically receives radio signals from interrogators on the ground, and selectively replies with a specific reply pulse or pulse group only to those interrogations being received on the mode to which it is set to respond.

(See INTERROGATOR.)

(Refer to AIM.)

(See ICAO term TRANSPONDER.)

TRANSPONDER [ICAO]- A receiver/transmitter which will generate a reply signal upon proper interrogation; the interrogation and reply being on different frequencies.

TRANSPONDER CODES-

(See CODES.)

TRSA-

(See TERMINAL RADAR SERVICE AREA.)

TURBOJET AIRCRAFT- An aircraft having a jet engine in which the energy of the jet operates a turbine which in turn operates the air compressor.

TURBOPROP AIRCRAFT- An aircraft having a jet engine in which the energy of the jet operates a turbine which drives the propeller.

TURN ANTICIPATION- (maneuver anticipation).

TVOR-

(See TERMINAL-VERY HIGH FREQUENCY OMNIDIRECTIONAL RANGE STATION.)

TWEB-

(See TRANSCRIBED WEATHER BROADCAST.)

TWO-WAY RADIO COMMUNICATIONS FAILURE-

(See LOST COMMUNICATIONS.)

U

UDF–
   (See DIRECTION FINDER.)

UHF–
   (See ULTRAHIGH FREQUENCY.)

ULTRAHIGH FREQUENCY– The frequency band between 300 and 3,000 mHz. The bank of radio frequencies used for military air/ground voice communications. In some instances this may go as low as 225 mHz and still be referred to as UHF.

ULTRALIGHT VEHICLE– An aeronautical vehicle operated for sport or recreational purposes which does not require FAA registration, an airworthiness certificate, nor pilot certification. They are primarily single occupant vehicles, although some two-place vehicles are authorized for training purposes. Operation of an ultralight vehicle in certain airspace requires authorization from ATC.
   (See FAR Part 103.)

UNABLE– Indicates inability to comply with a specific instruction, request, or clearance.

UNDER THE HOOD– Indicates that the pilot is using a hood to restrict visibility outside the cockpit while simulating instrument flight. An appropriately rated pilot is required in the other control seat while this operation is being conducted.
   (Refer to FAR Part 91.)

UNICOM– A nongovernment communication facility which may provide airport information at certain airports.

Locations and frequencies of UNICOM's are shown on aeronautical charts and publications.
   (See AIRPORT/FACILITY DIRECTORY.)
   (Refer to AIM.)

UNPUBLISHED ROUTE– A route for which no minimum altitude is published or charted for pilot use. It may include a direct route between NAVAID's, a radial, a radar vector, or a final approach course beyond the segments of an instrument approach procedure.
   (See PUBLISHED ROUTE.)
   (See ROUTE.)

UPWIND LEG–
   (See TRAFFIC PATTERN.)

URGENCY– A condition of being concerned about safety and of requiring timely but not immediate assistance; a potential distress condition.
   (See ICAO term URGENCY.)

URGENCY [ICAO]– A condition concerning the safety of an aircraft or other vehicle, or of person on board or in sight, but which does not require immediate assistance.

USAFIB–
   *(See ARMY AVIATION FLIGHT
   INFORMATION BULLETIN.)*

UVDF–
   (See DIRECTION FINDER.)

V

VASI–

    (See VISUAL APPROACH SLOPE INDICATOR.)

VDF–

    (See DIRECTION FINDER.)

VDP–

    (See VISUAL DESCENT POINT.)

VECTOR– A heading issued to an aircraft to provide navigational guidance by radar.

    (See ICAO term RADAR VECTORING.)

***VERIFY*– Request confirmation of information; e.g., "verify assigned altitude."**

***VERIFY SPECIFIC DIRECTION OF TAKEOFF (OR TURNS AFTER TAKEOFF)*– Used by ATC to ascertain an aircraft's direction of takeoff and/or direction of turn after takeoff. It is normally used for IFR departures from an airport not having a control tower. When direct communication with the pilot is not possible, the request and information may be relayed through an FSS, dispatcher, or by other means.**

    (See IFR TAKEOFF MINIMUMS AND DEPARTURE PROCEDURES.)

VERTEX– The last fix adapted on the arrival speed segments. Normally, it will be the outer marker of the runway in use. However, it may be the actual threshold or other suitable common point on the approach path for the particular runway configuration.

VERTEX TIME OF ARRIVAL– A calculated time of aircraft arrival over the adapted vertex for the runway configuration in use. The time is calculated via the optimum flight path using adapted speed segments.

VERTICAL SEPARATION– Separation established by assignment of different altitudes or flight levels.

    (See SEPARATION.)

    (See ICAO term VERTICAL SEPARATION.)

VERTICAL SEPARATION [ICAO]– Separation between aircraft expressed in units of vertical distance.

VERTICAL TAKEOFF AND LANDING AIRCRAFT– Aircraft capable of vertical climbs and/or descents and of using very short runways or small areas for takeoff and landings. These aircraft include, but are not limited to, helicopters.

    (See SHORT TAKEOFF AND LANDING AIRCRAFT.)

VERY HIGH FREQUENCY– The frequency band between 30 and 300 MHz. Portions of this band, 108 to 118 MHz, are used for certain NAVAID's; 118 to 136 MHz are used for civil air/ground voice communications. Other frequencies in this band are used for purposes not related to air traffic control.

VERY HIGH FREQUENCY OMNIDIRECTIONAL RANGE STATION–

    (See VOR.)

VERY LOW FREQUENCY– The frequency band between 3 and 30 kHz.

VFR–

    (See VISUAL FLIGHT RULES.)

VFR AIRCRAFT– An aircraft conducting flight in accordance with visual flight rules.

    (See VISUAL FLIGHT RULES.)

VFR CONDITIONS– Weather conditions equal to or better than the minimum for flight under visual flight rules. The term may be used as an ATC clearance/instruction only when:

    a. An IFR aircraft requests a climb/descent in VFR conditions.

    b. The clearance will result in noise abatement benefits where part of the IFR departure route does not conform to an FAA approved noise abatement route or altitude.

    c. A pilot has requested a practice instrument approach and is not on an IFR flight plan.

    Note: All pilots receiving this authorization must comply with the VFR visibility and distance from cloud criteria in FAR Part 91. Use of the term does not relieve controllers of their responsibility to separate aircraft in Class B and Class C airspace or TRSA's as required by FAA Order 7110.65. When used as an ATC clearance/instruction, the term may be abbreviated "VFR;" e.g., "MAINTAIN VFR," "CLIMB/DESCEND VFR," etc.

VFR FLIGHT–

    (See VFR AIRCRAFT.)

VFR MILITARY TRAINING ROUTES– Routes used by the Department of Defense and associated Reserve and Air Guard units for the purpose of conducting low–altitude navigation and tactical training under VFR below 10,000 feet MSL at airspeeds in excess of 250 knots IAS.

VFR NOT RECOMMENDED– An advisory provided by a flight service station to a pilot during a preflight or inflight weather briefing that flight under visual flight rules is not recommended. To be given when the current and/or forecast weather conditions are at or below VFR minimums. It does not abrogate the pilot's authority to make his own decision.

VFR-ON-TOP- ATC authorization for an IFR aircraft to operate in VFR conditions at any appropriate VFR altitude (as specified in FAR and as restricted by ATC). A pilot receiving this authorization must comply with the VFR visibility, distance from cloud criteria, and the minimum IFR altitudes specified in FAR Part 91. The use of this term does not relieve controllers of their responsibility to separate aircraft in Class B and Class C airspace or TRSA's as required by FAA Order 7110.65.

VFR TERMINAL AREA CHARTS–

(See AERONAUTICAL CHART.)

VHF– (See VERY HIGH FREQUENCY.)

VHF OMNIDIRECTIONAL RANGE/TACTICAL AIR NAVIGATION–

(See VORTAC.)

VIDEO MAP– An electronically displayed map on the radar display that may depict data such as airports, heliports, runway centerline extensions, hospital emergency landing areas, NAVAID's and fixes, reporting points, airway/route centerlines, boundaries, handoff points, special use tracks, obstructions, prominent geographic features, map alignment indicators, range accuracy marks, minimum vectoring altitudes.

VISIBILITY– The ability, as determined by atmospheric conditions and expressed in units of distance, to see and identify prominent unlighted objects by day and prominent lighted objects by night. Visibility is reported as statute miles, hundreds of feet or meters.

(Refer to FAR Part 91.)

(See AIM.)

a. Flight Visibility– The average forward horizontal distance, from the cockpit of an aircraft in flight, at which prominent unlighted objects may be seen and identified by day and prominent lighted objects may be seen and identified by night.

b. Ground Visibility– Prevailing horizontal visibility near the earth's surface as reported by the United States National Weather Service or an accredited observer.

c. Prevailing Visibility– The greatest horizontal visibility equaled or exceeded throughout at least half the horizon circle which need not necessarily be continuous.

d. Runway Visibility Value (RVV)– The visibility determined for a particular runway by a transmissometer. A meter provides a continuous indication of the visibility (reported in miles or fractions of miles) for the runway. RVV is used in lieu of prevailing visibility in determining minimums for a particular runway.

e. Runway Visual Range (RVR)– An instrumentally derived value, based on standard calibrations, that represents the horizontal distance a pilot will see down the runway from the approach end. It is based on the sighting of either high intensity runway lights or on the visual contrast of

other targets whichever yields the greater visual range. RVR in contrast to prevailing or runway visibility, is based on what a pilot in a moving aircraft should see looking down the runway. RVR is horizontal visual range, not slant visual range. It is based on the measurement of a transmissometer made near the touchdown point of the instrument runway and is reported in hundreds of feet. RVR is used in lieu of RVV and/or prevailing visibility in determining minimums for a particular runway.

1. Touchdown RVR– The RVR visibility readout values obtained from RVR equipment serving the runway touchdown zone.

2. Mid–RVR– The RVR readout values obtained from RVR equipment located midfield of the runway.

3. Rollout RVR– The RVR readout values obtained from RVR equipment located nearest the rollout end of the runway.

(See ICAO term VISIBILITY.)

(See ICAO term FLIGHT VISIBILITY.)

(See ICAO term GROUND VISIBILITY.)

(See ICAO term RUNWAY VISUAL RANGE.)

VISIBILITY [ICAO]– The ability, as determined by atmospheric conditions and expressed in units of distance, to see and identify prominent unlighted objects by day and prominent lighted objects by night.

a. Flight Visibility–The visibility forward from the cockpit of an aircraft in flight.

b. Ground Visibility–The visibility at an aerodrome as reported by an accredited observer.

c. Runway Visual Range [RVR]–The range over which the pilot of an aircraft on the centerline of a runway can see the runway surface markings or the lights delineating the runway or identifying its centerline.

VISUAL APPROACH– An approach conducted on an instrument flight rules (IFR) flight plan which authorizes the pilot to proceed visually and clear of clouds to the airport. The pilot must, at all times, have either the airport or the preceding aircraft in sight. This approach must be authorized and under the control of the appropriate air traffic control facility. Reported weather at the airport must be ceiling at or above 1,000 feet and visibility of 3 miles or greater.

(See ICAO term VISUAL APPROACH.)

VISUAL APPROACH [ICAO]– An approach by an IFR flight when either part or all of an instrument approach procedure is not completed and the approach is executed in visual reference to terrain.

VISUAL APPROACH SLOPE INDICATOR–

(See AIRPORT LIGHTING.)

VISUAL DESCENT POINT– A defined point on the final approach course of a nonprecision straight–in approach procedure from which normal descent from the MDA to the runway touchdown point may be commenced, provided the apoach threshold of that runway, or approach lights, or other arkings identifiable with the approach end of that runway e clearly visible to the pilot.

ISUAL FLIGHT RULES– Rules that govern the proceures for conducting flight under visual conditions. The rm "VFR" is also used in the United States to indicate eather conditions that are equal to or greater than minium VFR requirements. In addition, it is used by pilots and ontrollers to indicate type of flight plan.

(See INSTRUMENT FLIGHT RULES.)

(See INSTRUMENT METEOROLOGICAL CONDITIONS.)

(See VISUAL METEOROLOGICAL CONDITIONS.)

(Refer to FAR Part 91.)

(Refer to AIM.)

ISUAL HOLDING– The holding of aircraft at selected, rominent geographical fixes which can be easily recogized from the air.

(See HOLDING FIX.)

ISUAL METEOROLOGICAL CONDITIONS– Meteoroogical conditions expressed in terms of visibility, distance rom cloud, and ceiling equal to or better than specified ninima.

(See INSTRUMENT FLIGHT RULES.)

(See INSTRUMENT METEOROLOGICAL CONDITIONS.)

(See VISUAL FLIGHT RULES.)

VISUAL SEPARATION– A means employed by ATC to eparate aircraft in terminal areas and en route airspace in he NAS. There are two ways to effect this separation:

a. The tower controller sees the aircraft involved and issues instructions, as necessary, to ensure that the aircraft avoid each other.

b. A pilot sees the other aircraft involved and upon instructions from the controller provides his own separation by maneuvering his aircraft as necessary to avoid it. This may involve following another aircraft or keeping it in sight until it is no longer a factor.

(See and Avoid.)

(Refer to FAR Part 91.)

VLF–

(See VERY LOW FREQUENCY.)

VMC–

(See VISUAL METEOROLOGICAL CONDITIONS.)

VOICE SWITCHING AND CONTROL SYSTEM– The VSCS is a computer controlled switching system that provides air traffic controllers with all voice circuits (air to ground and ground to ground) necessary for air traffic control.

(See VOICE SWITCHING AND CONTROL SYSTEM.)

(Refer to AIM.)

VOR– A ground–based electronic navigation aid transmitting very high frequency navigation signals, 360 degrees in azimuth, oriented from magnetic north. Used as the basis for navigation in the National Airspace System. The VOR periodically identifies itself by Morse Code and may have an additional voice identification feature. Voice features may be used by ATC or FSS for transmitting instructions/information to pilots.

(See NAVIGATIONAL AID.)

(Refer to AIM.)

VORTAC– A navigation aid providing VOR azimuth, TACAN azimuth, and TACAN distance measuring equipment (DME) at one site.

(See DISTANCE MEASURING EQUIPMENT.)

(See NAVIGATIONAL AID.)

(See TACAN.)

(See VOR.)

(Refer to AIM.)

VORTICES– Circular patterns of air created by the movement of an airfoil through the air when generating lift. As an airfoil moves through the atmosphere in sustained flight, an area of area of low pressure is created above it. The air flowing from the high pressure area to the low pressure area around and about the tips of the airfoil tends to roll up into two rapidly rotating vortices, cylindrical in shape. These vortices are the most predominant parts of aircraft wake turbulence and their rotational force is dependent upon the wing loading, gross weight, and speed of the generating aircraft. The vortices from medium to heavy aircraft can be of extremely high velocity and hazardous to smaller aircraft.

(See AIRCRAFT CLASSES.)

(See WAKE TURBULENCE.)

(Refer to AIM.)

VOR TEST SIGNAL–

(See VOT.)

VOT– A ground facility which emits a test signal to check VOR receiver accuracy. Some VOT's are available to the user while airborne, and others are limited to ground use only.

(Refer to FAR Part 91.)

(See AIM.)

(See AIRPORT/FACILITY DIRECTORY.)

VR–

(See VFR MILITARY TRAINING ROUTES.)

VSCS–

(See VOICE SWITCHING AND CONTROL SYSTEM.)

P/C

VTA—
(See VERTEX TIME OF ARRIVAL.)
VTOL AIRCRAFT—
(See VERTICAL TAKEOFF AND
LANDING AIRCRAFT.)

W

WA–

    (See AIRMET.)

    (See WEATHER ADVISORY.)

WAKE TURBULENCE– Phenomena resulting from the passage of an aircraft through the atmosphere. The term includes vortices, thrust stream turbulence, jet blast, jet wash, propeller wash, and rotor wash both on the ground and in the air.

    (See AIRCRAFT CLASSES.)

    (See JET BLAST.)

    (See VORTICES.)

    (Refer to AIM.)

WARNING AREA– (See SPECIAL USE AIRSPACE.)

WAYPOINT– A predetermined geographical position used for route/instrument approach definition, or progress reporting purposes, that is defined relative to a VORTAC station or in terms of latitude/longitude coordinates.

WEATHER ADVISORY– In aviation weather forecast practice, an expression of hazardous weather conditions not predicted in the area forecast, as they affect the operation of air traffic and as prepared by the NWS.

    (See SIGMET.)

    (See AIRMET.)

WHEN ABLE– When used in conjunction with ATC instructions, gives the pilot the latitude to delay compliance until a condition or event has been reconciled. Unlike "pilot discretion," when instructions are prefaced "when able," the pilot is expected to seek the first opportunity to comply. Once a maneuver has been initiated, the pilot is expected to continue until the specifications of the instructions have been met. "When able," should not be used when expeditious compliance is required.

***WILCO*–** I have received your message, understand it, and will comply with it.

WIND SHEAR– A change in wind speed and/or wind direction in a short distance resulting in a tearing or shearing effect. It can exist in a horizontal or vertical direction and occasionally in both.

WING TIP VORTICES–

    (See VORTICES.)

***WORDS TWICE*–**

    a. As a request: "Communication is difficult. Please say every phrase twice."

    b. As information: "Since communications are difficult, every phrase in this message will be spoken twice."

WORLD AERONAUTICAL CHARTS–

    (See AERONAUTICAL CHART.)

WS–

    (See SIGMET.)

    (See WEATHER ADVISORY.)

WST–

    (See CONVECTIVE SIGMET.)

    (See WEATHER ADVISORY.)

P/C

INDEX

[References are to page numbers]

[References are to page numbers]

[References are to page numbers]

AIM
INDEX

[References are to page numbers]

[References are to page numbers]

[References are to page numbers]

AIM
INDEX

[References are to page numbers]

[References are to page numbers]

[References are to page numbers]

National Aeronautics and
Space Administration

Ames Research Center
Moffett Field, California 94035

Official Business
Penalty for Private Use $300

FIRST CLASS
AVIATION SAFETY DATA —
DO NOT DELAY

BUSINESS   REPLY   MAIL

FIRST CLASS   PERMIT NO. 12028   WASHINGTON. D.C.

POSTAGE WILL BE PAID BY NASA

NASA Aviation Safety Reporting System
Post Office Box 189
Moffett Field, California 94035

NATIONAL AERONAUTICS AND
SPACE ADMINISTRATION

AVIATION SAFETY
REPORTING SYSTEM

NASA has established an Aviation Safety Reporting System to identify problems in the aviation system which require correction. The program of which this system is a part is described in detail in FAA Advisory Circular 00-46C. Your assistance in informing us about such problems is essential to the success of the program. Please fill out this postage free form as completely as possible, fold it and send it directly to us

The information you provide on the identity strip will be used only if NASA determines that it is necessary to contact you for further information. THE IDENTITY STRIP WILL BE RETURNED DIRECTLY TO YOU. The return of the identity strip assures your anonymity.

Section 91.57 of the Federal Aviation Regulations (14 CFR 91.57) prohibits reports filed with NASA from being used for FAA enforcement purposes. This report will not be made available to the FAA for civil penalty or certificate actions for violations of the Federal Air Regulations. Your identity strip, stamped by NASA, is proof that you have submitted a report to the Aviation Safety Reporting System. We can only return the strip to you, however, if you have provided a mailing address. Equally important, we can often obtain additional useful information if our safety analysts can talk with you directly by telephone. For this reason, we have requested telephone numbers where we may reach you. Thank you for your assistance.

NOTE: AIRCRAFT ACCIDENTS SHOULD NOT BE REPORTED ON THIS FORM SUCH REPORTS SHOULD BE FILED WITH THE NATIONAL TRANSPORTATION SAFETY BOARD AS REQUIRED BY 49CFR830.

---

15. **NARRATIVE DESCRIPTION** (continued): *(Use additional sheets if necessary)*

SECOND FOLD HERE

SECOND FOLD HERE

Note: A full-size version of this form may be downloaded from ASA's website: http://www.asa2fly.com

NASA
FORM

Fold as indicated, fasten with staple or tape, and mail. Thank you for your cooperation.

IDENTIFICATION STRIP: *Please fill in all blanks.* NO RECORD WILL BE KEPT OF YOUR IDENTITY.
This section will be returned to you promptly.

**TELEPHONE NUMBERS where we may reach you for further
details of this occurrence:**

(HOME) Area_____ No. _____ - _____ Hours _____
(WORK) Area_____ No. _____ - _____ Hours _____   (SPACE RESERVED FOR ASRS DATE/TIME STAMP)

NAME _____   TYPE OF EVENT/SITUATION_____
ADDRESS _____
_____   DATE OF OCCURRENCE_____
_____   LOCAL TIME (24 hr. clock)_____

*Except for reports of aircraft accidents and criminal activities — which are not included in the ASRS and should not be
submitted to NASA — all identities contained in this report will be removed to assure complete reporter anonymity.*

PLEASE FILL IN APPROPRIATE SPACES AND CHECK ALL ITEMS WHICH APPLY TO THIS EVENT OR SITUATION.

REPORTER'S ROLE DURING OCCURRENCE
(pilot-flying, radar controller, cabin crew, maintenance, etc.) _____

REPORTER	FLYING TIME	CERTIFICATES/RATINGS		ATC EXPERIENCE	
○ captain/pilot	total _____ hrs.	○ student	○ private	○ FPL	○ developmental
○ first officer	last 90 days _____ hrs.	○ commercial	○ ATP	radar _____ yrs.	
○ other crewmember	in acft type _____ hrs.	○ instrument	○ CFI	non-radar _____ yrs.	
○ controller		○ multiengine	○ F/E	supervisory _____ yrs.	
○		○		military _____ yrs.	

DESCRIBE ONE AIRCRAFT IN THIS SECTION (PILOTS DESCRIBE YOUR OWN) AND ADDITIONAL AIRCRAFT IN THE
"DESCRIBE EVENT/SITUATION" SECTION:

AIRFRAME/ENGINES			OPERATOR	PURPOSE OF FLIGHT	FLIGHT PLAN
○ low fixed wing	○ ultralight	○ reciprocating	○ scheduled carrier	○ passenger	○ VFR ○ IFR
○ high fixed wing	○ wide body	○ turboprop	○ supplemental carrier	○ cargo	○ SVFR ○ none
○ rotary wing	○ small complex	○ turbojet	○ FBO/flying school	○ business	
○ advanced/automated cockpit (e.g., CRT's, FMS, etc.)			○ commuter ○ air taxi		**NAVIGATION IN USE**
○ _____			○ corporate ○ charter	○ training	_____
crew size _____		pax seats _____	○ government ○ private	○ pleasure	_____
gross weight _____		no. of engines _____	○ military (_____)	○ _____	_____
			○		

FIRST FOLD HERE (left margin)   *FIRST FOLD HERE* (right margin)

AIRSPACE/LOCALE		ATC/ADVISORY SERVICE		FLIGHT CONDITIONS		LIGHT AND VISIBILITY	
○ uncontrolled	○ ATA ○ PCA	○ ground	○ approach	○ VMC	○ IMC	○ daylight	○ dawn
○ control zone	○ TRSA ○ TCA	○ local	○ departure	○ mixed	○ marginal	○ dusk	○ night
○ special use airspace	○ ARSA ○ unknown	○ center	○ FSS	○ t'storm	○ rain	ceiling _____ feet	
○ airway/route	○ MTR ○ _____	○ UNICOM	○ CTAF	○ turbulence	○ fog	visibility _____ miles	
ALTITUDE _____ ○ MSL (or) ○ AGL		Name of ATC Facility _____		○ windshear	○ snow	RVR _____ feet	
NEAREST CITY _____ STATE ___				○ ice ○ _____			

SPECIFY LOCATION BY REFERENCE TO AN AIRPORT, NAVAID, OR OTHER FIX (distance, bearing, etc.): _____
_____

AIRCRAFT FLIGHT PHASES AT TIME OF OCCURRENCE (preflight, takeoff, cruise, hover, etc.) _____
IF A CONFLICT: Evasive action? ○ yes ○ no ○ no time ○ unknown. Estimated miss in feet _____ vert'l _____ horiz'l.

DESCRIBE EVENT/SITUATION

Keeping in mind the topics shown below, discuss those which you feel are relevant and anything else you think is important. Include
what you believe really caused the problem, and what can be done to prevent a recurrence, or correct the situation. (CONTINUE ON
THE OTHER SIDE AND USE ADDITIONAL PAPER IF NEEDED).

Note: A full-size version of this form may be downloaded from ASA's website: http://www.asa2fly.com

CHAIN OF EVENTS		HUMAN PERFORMANCE CONSIDERATIONS	
— How the problem arose	— How it was discovered	— Perceptions, judgements, decisions	— Actions or inactions
— Contributing factors	— Corrective actions	— Factors affecting the quality of human performance	

NASA ARC 277(Rev. Oct 84) PREVIOUS EDITIONS ARE OBSOLETE   *U.S. GPO: 1990-785-021/23509

ASA Student Kits:
Complete, comprehensive packages for student training

Built from the best training tools ASA has to offer, these student kits serve as ready-made training packages, or as templates for our ongoing PACKs (Personalized Aviation Custom Kits) program. The contents of each kit ensure that you've met all the regulatory requirements for a successful training program, but because you can substitute listed items for any program's specific needs, they're flexible enough to create the perfect training solution for universities and flight schools.

All kits listed below include what you need: Textbook, Syllabus, Practical Test Standards, Oral Exam Guide, and Flight Training Record. Private kits include Chart Plotter, Logbook, Flight Computer, and Attaché Bag.

Each kit is available from ASA in a Plus Pack that includes a brand-new Test Prep, and a FAR/AIM complete with Midyear Update. The Plus Pack guarantees that every student is completely prepared for both the FAA knowledge exam and checkride.

Pictured above is The Aviator Private Kit featuring Trevor Thom's textbooks.

The Complete Private Kit
Featured textbook: Bob Gardner's *The Complete Private Pilot*, plus a high- or low-wing maneuvers handbook.
#ASA-PPT-KT.............$99.95

Katana Private Pilot Kit
Featured textbook: Bob Gardner's *The Complete Private Pilot* and material customized for Diamond Katana aircraft including the Diamond Katana DA-20 Flight Information Manual, and Katana maneuvers handbook.
#ASA-KIT-KAT.............$99.95

The Aviator Instrument Kit
Featured textbook: Trevor Thom's *Instrument Flying*.
#ASA-PM-KT-I.............$59.95

The Aviator Private Kit
Featured textbooks: Trevor Thom's *Flight Training* and *Private & Commercial*.
#ASA-PM-KT-P.............$124.95

The Aviator Commercial Kit
Featured textbooks: Trevor Thom's *Flight Training* and *Private & Commercial*.
#ASA-PM-KT-C.............$84.95

Price based on U.S. currency.
Subject to change without notice.

Call **1-800-ASA-2-FLY** *for the retailer nearest you.*
1 - 8 0 0 - 2 7 2 - 2 - 3 5 9

Free Update Service
Midyear Update Coupon

00-FR-AM-BK

Mail or fax this completed coupon to ASA to receive the 2000 FAR/AIM Midyear Update. The update will include information from the publication date of this book through May 15, 2000, and will be mailed to you in mid-July. **The update will also be posted on ASA's website in June of 2000.**

Please print clearly. This offer expires October 31, 2000.

Please send me ASA's 2000 FAR/AIM Midyear Update.

Name _____

Address _____

_____

City _____ **State**_____ **Zip**_____

#ASA-00-FR-AM-BK

Does this book satisfy your aviation needs? ❑ Yes ❑ No

If No, please explain: _____

_____

_____

Would you like to see certain regulations *removed*? (List each Part number)

_____

Would you like certain regulations *added*? (List each Part number)

_____

Is there anything else you'd like to see different regarding the book's content or organization?_____

_____

_____

General comments or suggestions: _____

_____

_____

❑ **Please send me an ASA Catalog.**

Mail or fax this coupon to:

Aviation Supplies & Academics, Inc.
7005 132nd Place SE
Newcastle, WA 98059-3153

Fax: (425) 235-0128
Website: http://www.asa2fly.com